WORKS BY THE LATE REV. DR. NEALE.

1. Neale on "Church Difficulties." 6s.; by post, 6s. 6d. This second edition has a Preface by Rev. W. J. E. Bennett, bringing the consideration of the "Difficulties" down to the present time.
2. Sermons on the Apocalypse; on the Name of Jesus; and on the Last Chapter of Proverbs. 5s.; by post, 5s. 4d.
3. Sermons on Passages of the Psalms. 5s.; by post, 5s. 4d.
4. The Song of Songs. A Volume of beautiful Sermons thereon. 6s.; by post, 6s. 4d.
5. Sermons on Blessed Sacrament. Fourth Edition. 2s. 6d.; by post, 2s. 9d.
6. Sermons for Children. Third Edition. 3s. 6d.; by post, 3s. 9d.
7. Catechetical Notes and Class Questions. Literal and Mystical. Second Edition. 5s.; by post 5s. 5d.
8. Original Sequences, Hymns, and Ecclesiastical Verses. 2s. 6d.; by post, 2s. 9d.
9. Stabat Mater Speciosa: Full of Beauty stood the Mother. 1s.; by post, 1s. 2d.
10. Hymns suitable for Invalids. Paper cover, 6d.; by post, 7d.; in cloth, 1s.; by post, 1s. 1d. Fine edition on Toned Paper, cloth, 2s.; by post, 2s. 2d.
11. The Rhythm of Bernard of Morlaix, on the Celestial Country. New Edition, beautifully printed on Toned Paper. 2s. in cloth; by post, 2s. 2d.; in French morocco, 4s. 6d.; by post, 4s. 9d.; in morocco, 7s. 6d.; by post, 7s. 9d. Cheap edition 9d.; by post, 10d.
12. Hymns, chiefly Mediæval, on the Joys and Glories of Paradise. Companion to "Rhythm of Bernard of Morlaix." 1s. 6d.; by post, 1s. 7d.
13. The Revision of the Lectionary. A letter to the late Bishop of Salisbury, 1s.; by post, 1s. 1d.
14. Notes, Ecclesiological and Picturesque, on Dalmatia, Croatia, &c.; with a visit to Montenegro. 6s.; by post, 6s. 4d.
15. The Primitive Liturgies (in Greek) of S. Mark, S. Clement, S. James, S. Chrysostom, and S. Basil. Preface by Dr. Littledale. Second Edition. 6s.; by post 6s. 4d. Calf, 10s. 6d. (for Presents); by post 11s.
16. The Translations of the Primitive Liturgies of SS. Mark, James, Clement Chrysostom and Basil, and the Church of Malabar. By Dr. Neale and Dr. Littledale. 4s.; by post, 4s. 4d.
17. The Hymns of the Eastern Church: Translated by late Rev. J. M. Neale, D.D. 2s. 6d.; by post, 2s. 9d.
18. The Christian Nurse; and her mission in the Sick Room. Translated from the French of Father Gautrelet, by one of the Sisters of S. Margaret's, East Grinsted; Edited by Rev. J. M. Neale. 2s.; by post, 2s. 1d.
19. An Invaluable Sermon Help—The Moral Concordances of S. Antony of Padua Preface by Rev. Dr. Littledale. 3s. 6d.; by post, 3s. 9d.
20. Text Emblems. Twelve beautiful Designs, engraved by Dalziel, illustrating the Mystical Interpretation of as many verses from the Old Testament. By the late Rev. J. M. Neale. Second Edition. 2s.; by post, 2s. 2d.
21. Litanies; to which are added The Way of the Cross, and Hours of the Passion. Translated partly by the late Dr. Neale. Limp cloth, 1s. 6d. Cloth boards, 2s.; postage, 1d.
22. Occasional Sermons. By the Rev. J. M. Neale. 3s. 6d.; by post, 3s. 9d.
23. Sermons on some of the Feast Days. 6s.; postage, 4d.
24. Victories of the Saints. Stories from Church History. 2s.; postage, 2d.
25. Night Hours of the Church. 2 Vols. 15s.
26. The Venerable Sacrament of the Altar. Translated from the Latin of S. Thomas Aquinas. Completed by a Priest of the C. B. S. with Preface by Rev. W. J. E. Bennett. 3s.; postage, 3d.

J. T. HAYES, 17, HENRIETTA STREET, COVENT GARDEN; AND LYALL PLACE, EATON SQUARE.

Notes

ON THE

DIVINE OFFICE.

Notes

ON

THE DIVINE OFFICE,

Historical and Mystical.

From Ancient and Modern Sources.

"That Thou wouldst make the obedience of our service
reasonable:
"We beseech Thee to hear us, good LORD.

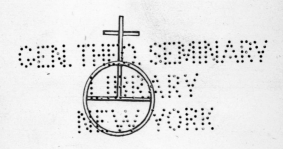

London:

J. T. HAYES:

17, HENRIETTA STREET, COVENT GARDEN; AND
LYALL PLACE, EATON SQUARE.

Pref. 1877

LONDON:
SWIFT AND CO., NEWTON STREET, HIGH HOLBORN, W.C.

PREFACE.

THE revival of Religious Communities in England has naturally led to the restoration, with more or less of alteration, of the ancient Offices of Prayer. These are used more and more widely year by year. They are now recited, according to their English translation, in India on the one hand, in America on the other ; while in England their use is no longer confined to Religious Houses alone, but is found profitable by many private persons.

This little book is an attempt to sketch the history and meaning of the Office, and especially of the old English Use of Sarum. There are great difficulties in the way of such an attempt : —one arises from the extreme indifference which the ancient compilers seem to have felt, regarding the quarries from whence they drew their material. It does not appear to have occurred to them that

any one would ever care to know the sources from
which their works were derived; and these are
generally, therefore, left in extreme obscurity.
Another source of difficulty is, that though several
writers have taken in hand to comment on the
Roman Breviary historically and mystically, no one
ever did the same for the Sarum Portiforium; though
its intricacy and many peculiarities greatly required
something of the kind. The subject is wide and
rich, and hitherto has been little worked; but it is
now beginning to receive the attention of scholars,
whose acquaintance with it is continually growing
more extended and exact. Errors, therefore, will
certainly be found in this book, in spite of the
learned assistance which has very kindly been
afforded to the compilers. But some Companion
to the Office is so much needed, that these few
pages may serve the purpose in some degree, till
some abler pen takes up the subject. Many parts
of the Office, of course, were reproduced in the
Common Prayer Book; and as these are explained
and commented on in many books easy of access,
they are here generally passed over, in order to

avoid needless repetition. In the same manner, those points are mostly omitted, which are fully explained in the General Rubrics of the Breviary.

It was originally intended simply to publish a translation of the fifth book of Durandus, begun many years ago at Dr. Neale's desire; but that idea has now been enlarged upon. A list of authors quoted is placed at the end of the book.

An essay on the mediæval use of the Psalter was published by Dr. Neale in the *Christian Remembrancer*, and partly reproduced in his Commentary on the Psalms. Omitting some portions which do not refer to the subject in hand, it is inserted here for the use of those who are unable to procure that great Commentary; and Mr. A. R. Cooke has been good enough to contribute a learned paper on the Kalendar, which closes the volume.

S. Margaret's, East Grinsted.
1877.

CONTENTS.

CHAPTER I.

Sketch of the Origin and History of the Divine Office.

CHAPTER II.

The Offices, considered generally and particularly.

CHAPTER III.

Some Minor Offices, etc.

CHAPTER IV.

Seasons and Festivals.

CHAPTER V.

CHAPTER VI.

APPENDIX.

" WE find Daniel and the three children, who were strong in faith, and victorious in captivity, to have observed the third, sixth, and ninth hours, in the prayers they offered,—a symbol of the TRINITY, which was to be manifested in the last times. For the first hour passing to the third shews the perfect number of the TRINITY, and in like manner the fourth passing on to the sixth declares another trinity ; and when passing from the seventh hour, the ninth is completed, by the three hours the Perfect TRINITY is numbered. Long ago the worshippers of GOD observed these spaces of time, spiritually fixing them by stated and appointed seasons for prayer. At the third hour, the HOLY SPIRIT descended upon the disciples, fulfilling the grace of the LORD's promise. Also Peter, going up to the top of his roof at the sixth hour, was instructed by a sign, and by the voice of GOD warning him, that he should admit all men to the grace of salvation; whereas he had before doubted about the purification of the Gentiles. And the LORD, being crucified at the sixth hour, washed our sins away in His Blood at the ninth hour, that He might redeem us, and give us life, and then perfected His Victorious Passion.

" But besides the hours anciently observed, to us, beloved brethren, both times and symbols have multiplied. For now we must pray early, that the resurrection of the LORD may be celebrated in morning prayer, which the HOLY SPIRIT denoted of old in the Psalms, saying: 'My KING and my GOD, for unto Thee will I pray, O LORD ; early Thou shalt hear my voice, early will I approach unto Thee, and will contemplate Thee.' And again, the LORD says by the prophet : 'At break of day they will watch unto Me, saying : Let us go and return unto the LORD our GOD.' Also at the going down of the sun, and again at the ending of the day, it is necessary

B

that we should pray. For since CHRIST is the true Sun, and the true Day, when we pray and make request, at the going down of the sun and day of this world, that the light may again shine upon us, we pray for the coming of CHRIST, and the grace of Eternal Light about to be revealed. For the HOLY SPIRIT in the Psalms declares CHRIST to be called the Day. 'The Stone,' He saith, 'which the builders rejected, is become the Head-Stone of the corner. This is the LORD's doing, and it is marvellous in our eyes. This is the Day which the LORD hath made ; we will walk and be glad in it.' In like manner, the prophet Malachi testifies that He is called the Sun, saying: 'But to you that fear My Name shall the Sun of Righteousness arise with healing on His wings.' And if in the Holy Scripture CHRIST is the true Sun and true Day, no hour is excepted by the Christian in which he should not worship GOD, frequently and continually ; that we, who are in CHRIST, that is, in the true Sun and Day, may continue in supplications all day and pray ; and when, according to the laws of the world, through the alternate changes, night in turn succeeds, there cannot be any decrease in our prayers because of the shades of night, for in the night also it is day to the sons of light. For when is he without light, whose light is in his heart ? Or when is there no sun and day to him, whose Sun and Day is CHRIST ?

"Let not us, then, who are in CHRIST, that is, in the Light, cease from prayer even by night. So the widow Anna without ceasing, always praying and watching, persevered in striving to be acceptable to GOD, as it is written in the Gospel: 'She departed not,' it says, 'from the Temple, serving day and night in fastings and prayers.' Both the Gentiles shall see, who are not yet illuminated, and the Jews, who being deserted by the Light, have remained in darkness. Let us, beloved brethren, who are always in the Light of the LORD, who remember and hold fast what we may have begun to have through grace received, count the night as day. Let us believe ourselves to be always walking in the Light; let us not be hindered by the darkness from which we have escaped. Let there be no decrease in the nightly hours of supplication; let there be no slothful or cowardly loss of prayers. Let us, who by the mercy of GOD are spiritually recreated and born again, strive to resemble what we are going to be. Let us, who are to have in the Kingdom one Day without the interruption of night, watch in the night as in the light. Let us, who are going to be always praying and giving thanks, not desist from praying here also and from giving thanks."—*S. Cyprian on the Lord's Prayer*, A.D. 251-2.

NOTES

THE DIVINE OFFICE.

CHAPTER I.

SKETCH OF THE ORIGIN AND HISTORY OF THE DIVINE OFFICE.

IN considering the subject of the Ecclesiastical Office, we naturally begin by inquiring whether, or how far, it has pleased GOD to reveal it as His Will that He should be thus worshipped. Holy Scripture plainly shews two methods whereby He has appointed to be approached in public worship: by act, and by word; by sacrifice, and by vocal prayer.

Very little vocal worship is prescribed in the Mosaic ritual. Almost all is sacrificial. But we find the Choir Office established in Samuel's time. Prophecy, in its primary meaning, signifies recitation of GOD's praises. This, then, was the duty to be performed by the companies of persons called the sons of the prophets; and here also is the first intimation of synagogue worship. In David's time, we find vocal offices united with the sacrificial worship of the Temple. Drawing nearer to the period of the Incarnation, more vivid signs of the Eternal WORD may be expected. On the return of Judah and Benjamin from Babylon, Ezra re-arranged the services; while the ten tribes, scattered through the world, carried their word-worship with them.

This was the state of things at the coming of our LORD. And when Christianity emerged from Judaism, it brought with it both word and act worship: the word-worship modelled to a great extent on the Jewish Offices: the act-worship, (since the institution of the Blessed Sacrament, on Maundy Thursday,) necessarily combined with words. The Jewish Priest sacrificed in silence; the Christian Priest, acting for the Eternal WORD, must speak.

Our present business lies with the vocal or Choir Office alone.

The history of the early Church services is very obscure. Following chiefly the guidance of Archdeacon Freeman, who was the first to examine and prove the kinship and lineal descent of the Jewish, Eastern, and Western Offices, we will endeavour to give a brief, and, if it may be, a clear account of these matters.

The Acts of the Apostles prove very plainly that

the first Christians, although "breaking bread" daily at home or in an upper chamber, also resorted daily to the Temple prayers, and frequented the worship of the Synagogue. (Acts ii. 42, 46; iii. 1; xv. 21.) The prayers of the Jewish Church would therefore naturally serve as a model for those of the primitive Christians, when scattered by persecution beyond the limits of Jerusalem and Judæa.

"The earliest writer who gives us any detailed account of the services of the early Church is S. Basil, in the fourth century. They consisted in his day of Psalmody, with prayers intermingled; the whole ushered in with a profoundly penitential confession. And of these Psalms, as we learn from him, and other writers, the greater part were sung (to all appearance) continuously, and without selection; while others were fixed, and used constantly: as the fifty-first, with which the night service concluded, and the sixty-third, which followed shortly after in the morning office. The mode of singing was in part alternate, in part with a leader; a response being made by the people at the close of each Psalm. Now in all this there is a manifest resemblance of a general kind to the Jewish Temple service, such as we have reason to believe it existed in our LORD's time. For it too consisted entirely of Psalms and prayers, the former making up the bulk of the service; and it commenced with penitential prayer. Moreover, some one Psalm was fixed, only varying with the day of the week; and the singing was alternate, or by way of response or burden.

"Now the existing daily Offices of the Greek Church entirely answer, first of all, to the account given by S. Basil, and others, of the ordinary nocturnal services in their time. They are by name, and in their manifest design, nocturnal and early matutinal Offices. Such at least is by far the greater and the principal portion of them. They still, as in S. Basil's time, present the aspect of a great service of Psalms, with hymns and prayers intermingled. They still commence with a deeply penitential prayer. The Psalms are still sung for the most part continuously, with the addition of certain fixed ones. And among these fixed Psalms are the very same, used in the same part of the service, as in S. Basil's time. The manner of singing is still alternate, or with a response, resembling the Western Antiphon. Thus far, then, the Greek Offices of the present day thoroughly agree with those of the fourth century, and also, like them, exhibit features which tend to connect them with the Jewish services.

"But these Offices, on further examination, betray their origin still more clearly. The most solemn part of the service of the Jewish Synagogue at the present day (called the 'Eighteen Prayers') is believed, on good grounds, to have been in use long before the Christian era. Now the introductory part of the Greek Offices, consisting of invocation, prayer for pardon, invitation to praise, is plainly an epitome, only Christianized, of the first eight of the 'Eighteen Prayers,' as may be seen upon comparison of them.

Part of the 'EIGHTEEN PRAYERS' *of the Synagogue.*

1. Blessed be Thou, O LORD our GOD.

Ans. Blessed art Thou, O LORD, O King, our Helper, our Saviour, Creator and Possessor of the universe, bountifully dispensing benefits.

2. Thou sustainest . . . all that live.

3. Thou art Holy. Thy Name is Holy, for a great King and a Holy art Thou, O GOD. [*Comp.* 2. 'Thou, O LORD, art mighty for ever. . . Thou LORD of might.']

5, 6. Have mercy upon us, O our FATHER.

For we have transgressed; pardon us, for we have sinned.

Commencement of the Eastern Offices.

Blessed be our GOD, now and for ever.

Ans. Amen. Glory be to Thee our GOD, heavenly King, the Comforter, the Spirit of Truth, Who art every where, and fillest all things, Treasury of blessings, and Giver of life; descend and remain on us, O Blessed One, cleanse us from all impurity, and save our souls.

Holy GOD,
Holy and Mighty,
Holy and Immortal,

Have mercy upon us.
Glory be to the FATHER, etc.
O most HOLY TRINITY, have mercy upon us; purify us from our iniquities, and pardon our sins.

7. Look, we beseech Thee, on our afflictions.

Look down upon us, O Holy One.

8. Heal, O LORD . . . our infirmities,

Heal our infirmities.

For Thou art a GOD Who healest.

For Thy Name's sake.

[O LORD, have mercy on us, 6, 16, etc.]

LORD, have mercy (thrice).

'Our FATHER,' 'Merciful FATHER.'

'Our FATHER,' etc., LORD have mercy;' (twelve times.)

18. We will give thanks unto Thee with praise.

O come, let us worship GOD our KING.

LORD, Thou art the LORD our GOD.

O come, etc., and fall down before CHRIST, our King and GOD.

Be Thy Name, O KING, exalted and lifted up on high.

O come, etc. . . . before CHRIST Himself, our KING and GOD."

[Freeman.]

The nocturnal and morning Offices of the Eastern Church are of immense and unfathomable antiquity. The remainder are of later origin, or at least were introduced later into the public service ; but even those are prior to any existing Western Offices.

What these may have been, previous to the sixth century, is entirely uncertain ; but, about that time, there was a great re-organization of old, or importation of new material into the ritual of various European Churches. Simultaneously with this, a new scheme of Monastic Offices was introduced having much affinity with that new ritual, yet containing marked differences : and from internal

testimony, these various offices are proved to have
been brought from the East.

The Offices for the Hours of Prayer, as well as
the number of the Hours themselves, varied greatly
in the Western Churches before the eleventh century. We have traces of six different rites, at
least, in the West, viz., the Roman, the Benedictine, the Ambrosian, the Gallican, the Spanish, and
the Irish rite of Columbanus. Besides this, the
Oriental Church had several peculiar uses, as the
Greek or Oriental, the Egyptian, the Armenian,
and others.

Cassian had a singular work to do for the Church
of GOD. He was a Thracian, born in the latter
part of the fourth century, brought up in S.
Jerome's monastery, at Bethlehem, and ordained
deacon by S. John Chrysostom. As yet it was the
frequent habit of monks to wander about from one
community to another. (S. Benedict, while preventing the practice in his own Order, and, to a great
extent, throughout the West, by the new vow of
stability introduced in his rule, yet also directs that,
if any monk of edifying behaviour happen to visit a
monastery of the Order, he shall be invited to take
up his abode there.) John Cassian, then, wandered
about among the monasteries and lauras and
deserts of Egypt and the East, conversed with their
inmates, learned their habits and their method of
prayer, and in his " Conferences " left a unique ac-

count of the things he saw and heard among those early monks and hermits, when as yet the religious life was in the glow of its first fervour, and the men who practised it meant one only thing, and did it.

After these wanderings, Cassian passed over to Gaul, about A.D. 420, and founded two monasteries near Marseilles, of one of which he became Abbot. He it was who began to introduce a new ritual into that country.

It has been supposed that the much-travelled Cassian, full of monastic and liturgical lore, had, during his residence in Gaul, framed two distinct Offices : that at Pope Leo's desire* he constructed a scheme for the use of the Roman Church, introducing Eastern characteristics into the original Western rite ; and that for his own monasteries and the Churches in his neighbourhood, he compiled a form more exclusively Oriental. Now the south of Gaul was evangelized from Ephesus, and originally received its rite from thence.†

---

* Leo is said to have desired S. Jerome to draw up the Offices. S. Jerome's death in the very year fixed as the date of the Pope's request proves that the work was not performed by his hand ; but it is supposed probable that he handed it over to his disciple Cassian.

† The Offices of the Gallican Church were considerably altered under Charlemagne. "It seems from an account which has been preserved of the Nocturnal Office performed A.D. 499, at Lyons, on the Vigil of S. Justus, during a Conference of Bishops held at that city, that the Service began with lessons from Scripture, of which there were four kinds, viz., from the Law, the Prophets, the Gospels, and the Epistles ; that Psalms were sung between the les-

Towards the middle of the sixth century, the Italian, Gallican, and Spanish Churches completed their scheme of worship; and S. Benedict drew up his monastic office on a plan substantially the same; the divergencies being easily accounted for on a reference to the Eastern office, the common root of all.*

When Gregory the Great sent S. Augustine on his mission for the conversion of England, he, with characteristic large-mindedness, desired him to select from the Churches of Rome, Gaul, and

sons; that the books of Scripture were read consecutively, and that peculiar psalms and lessons were not prescribed for each day; in fine, that there were no hymns or lessons, except from Holy Scriptures, and no reading of the lives or acts of Martyrs or Saints. The Church of Lyons retained so much of this her ancient custom, even after the introduction of Roman rites in the eighth century, that, as we learn from Agobard, her Offices admitted of no lessons except from Holy Scripture, and no hymns of human composition. And Mabillon informs us that in his time (the latter part of the seventeenth century) this ancient Church still adhered so far to her customs, as to use no hymns in her Offices except at Compline—a practice which was also followed by the equally ancient Church of Vienne. There is sufficient evidence that the ancient Gallican Church had Offices only for the Nocturnal, the Matins, and the Evening hours of prayer. We read of the introduction of the lesser intermediate Offices in the sixth century in some parts of Gaul. Sidonius Apollinaris, who wrote in the preceding century, speaks indeed of a Service at the third hour; but his language shows plainly that even in the Church of which he was speaking, there was no Office *between* the Nocturnal Office and that for the third hour, thus proving that Lauds and Prime had not then been instituted."— *Palmer's Origines Liturgicæ.*

* The Benedictine Office shows marks of similarity to the Armenian in several peculiar points.

elsewhere, whatever he found that might be more pleasing to Almighty GOD; and to carry those newly-collected forms into the country, new to the faith, wherein he was about to plant the Church. Mr. Freeman considers that these instructions would be most equably fulfilled by the introduction of the Roman Eucharistic, and the Gallican Choir Offices ; and, as we know, Augustine received consecration from the Gallican Church, and so linked the English Church with that of Ephesus and its founder S. John.

Let us set down a few points of the similarity between the ancient Eastern and the Western Offices.

The repetition of *twelve* Psalms at the Night Office, (and this, again, is manifestly derived from the Jewish ritual, in which the number twelve is strongly emphasized): the introduction of Psalm xxi. in the Sunday Office, (no matter at what apparent inconvenience, as it seems, in some Breviaries): the proceeding in the Psalter, at Matins, no further than Psalm cix. (which was the last daily Eastern morning Psalm).

The Song of Moses, used on Saturday, (both his songs were sung by the Jews on the Sabbath, according to the Talmud: cf. Deut. xxxi. 21): the commencement of the office on the preceding day, with First Vespers (according also to the Jewish custom).

The repetition of the Creed and Lord's Prayer

in silence, according to the Eastern practice of with-holding those precious things from the Catechu-mens.

We will go on presently to note some further points of identity, at the same time observing that in many respects the Eastern Offices do widely differ from any Western rites in manner, matter, and length. Their Matin and Vesper Offices are far longer, and more complex, and between each of the day hours from Prime to Nones, inclusive, is placed a midway hour, which it is well-nigh, if not quite, impossible to find time to recite, by reason of the great length of the other Offices.

Although the earliest English Office is no longer extant in the precise state in which S. Augustine gave it to his converts, the writers of the Saxon period have left us many indications of the manner in which Divine worship was offered in their days. They are thus gathered together by that learned and earnest scholar, Dr. Rock.

" Like the rest of Christendom, then seven times within the day did the Church bell ring, and bid its clerks—from the subdeacon upwards—to come thither and sing GOD's praises, morning, noon, and night; and the parish priest who forgot either of these duties was liable to be punished by a fine. Among those most conspicuous for their learning, or high position in the Church at that period, such men as Beda, Ecgberht and Ælfric, we find telling his country, each in his own time, of this ritual usage, and how it ought to be followed. Beda's notice of the 'hours' in general, or of some particular part in them, is curious; while the Archbishop of York, and the Abbot who was afterwards called to the primatial chair of Canterbury, both lay down the Canon law upon this matter. So thoroughly do those prelates' opinions agree, that Ecgberht's Latin ordinance seems to have been put into Anglo-Saxon by Ælfric, who says : 'Seven canonical hours they (the first four General Councils) appointed for us to sing daily to the praise of our LORD ; as the prophet David in his prophecy: "*Septies in die*," etc. "Seven times, my LORD,' said he, " I have said my praise in one day, for the righteousness of Thy judgments."' The first Canonical song is uht-song, (or matins), with the after-song (lauds), thereunto belonging; prime-song, undern (tierce) song, midday (Sext) song, none-song, evensong, night-song, (Compline). These Seven Canonical Hours ye should sing with great attention to the praise of your LORD, daily in church, always at the hour appointed, and in like manner, celebrate Mass at the appointed time.' That in their general construction and the distribution of their component parts, the Canonical Hours were the same then that they are now, we gather from a variety of documents."

"That these Canonical Hours were, in the main,

the same when Beda lived, we may gather from those notices made on them by chance, and which lie scattered through the writings of our learned and sainted countrymen. While Beda speaks of the Canonical course followed, day and night, as a practice a very long time adopted by the Church, when he wrote, he tells us that the custom of reading a lesson out of the Old or New Testament, at each of these 'hours,' was borrowed from the Jews. To the 'Invitatory' at the beginning of uht-song, or matins, he makes especial reference; and in leading us to understand why it is that the Church has wished the third, sixth, and ninth, rather than the other hours of the day to be more immediately hallowed by her public prayers, this same holy Father lets us know the existence, at the period, of such a rite. Through an observation which Beda dropped by happy chance, we find that the Canticle sung by Moses (Deut. xxxii.) took its place then, as it does now, among the psalms for lauds in Saturday's ferial office.

"In chanting the Canonical Hours, the practice followed by the Anglo-Saxons was the same yet kept in all collegiate churches. Divided into two bodies sitting opposite face to face, in the choir, the clergy on one side sang the verses of the psalms alternately with those seated over against them.

"If wayfaring, or if something unforeseen had hindered him from being with his brethren at public

song-tide in the house of GOD, the devout Anglo-
Saxon clergyman would halt before the first church
upon his road, and though its doors were locked, go
through the unsaid canonical hour at its threshold.

"But the people often joined in the Canonical
Hours. If the church-bells rang, by night as well
as day, to bid priests and clerks to come and sing
their Maker's praises, many too among the Anglo-
Saxon lay folk heard and answered that same call
to prayer, and going to the house of GOD joined
themselves in heart and word with the chanting
choir. Always did our great and glorious King
Alfred carry about with him his book of hours
hidden beneath the folds of his garment, on his
bosom; and while his daily wont was to hear holy
Mass, often likewise did he steal by night away
from his household and bed, and went unknown to
the church to say his prayers, and sing uht-song, or
matins, with the clergy. Though going to hear the
Canonical Hours on weekdays was left to each one's
own devotion, the doing so upon Saturday evening
and Sunday morning amounted to a religious
obligation. Among our Anglo-Saxons the hallow-
ing of the Sunday began with Saturday afternoon's
service; hence all were taught, "It is very fitting
that every Christian man who can accomplish it,
come to Church on Saturday, and bring light with
him and there hear evensong, and, before dawn,
uht-song (matins), and in the morning come with

their offerings to the celebration of the Mass."
—Rock. *Church of our Fathers.*

As the Churches, in the sixth century, seem to
have been simultaneously stirred to re-organize
their ritual, so again in the eleventh, we find
Gregory VII. of Rome, and our own S. Osmund of
Salisbury, engaged about the same time in re-
arranging the Offices of their respective Churches.

The Breviary, properly so called, may be said to
have then taken its present shape in both countries.
Gregory's work assumed that name, as being a
compendium and abbreviation of the services then
in use ; and the title has been extended to all com-
pilations of a like character ; but the Sarum book
was never so designated ; it was styled Portous or
Portiforium.

It is necessary to a clear understanding of our
subject, that we have some idea of the history of
the Roman Breviary and its many vicissitudes.

The work, as arranged by Gregory VII. was
rather a collection of many existing Offices, than, as
its name imported, an abbreviation of them, (breve
orarium=breviary). Its bulk, therefore, naturally
led to subsequent modifications, more and less satisfactory ; and the Breviary arranged by Haymo,
Fourth General of the Minorites, and accepted by
the Church and Pope Nicholas III., about 1278,
continued in general use till the year 1568. This
Franciscan Breviary, however, had been loudly

calling for reform, almost from the time of its
introduction. And the task was entrusted by
Clement VII. to Cardinal Quignon, whose revised
work was first published about 1535, and evidently
exercised no slight influence on the compilers of
our Common Prayer Book. Quignon, however,
deformed almost as much as he reformed ; and reduced the Office to excessive monotony. His book
was never brought into general use. It gave rise to
much discord. The people of Saragossa, for
instance, rose against the clergy, enraged at the
loss of the Tenebræ Office, which the new Breviary
omitted. At last Pius V., himself the latest reviser
of the Roman Breviary, abolished the use of Quignon's in 1568, and published his own reformed book,
which has continued in use to the present day.

In the seventeenth and eighteenth centuries,
various new arrangements of the Breviary were
made in France ; the most beautiful and celebrated
being those of Rouen, Paris, and Amiens. These
have all now been swept away, by the rule which
prohibits national uses, and enforces the Roman
use on all worshippers under the Latin obedience.
Recourse is had, however, to these Office-books in
most preparations of the Breviary for present English use. Their Psalms were arranged on a new
principle ; varying, instead of fixed, Psalms were
assigned to the little hours, and, forsaking the old
numerical order, the Psalms of each day had

reference to some special subject. The hymns were modernized, or replaced by new compositions. These alterations, of at least questionable merit, we are not particularly concerned with; but the strong peculiarity of these Breviaries is their strict rule of admitting no words but those of Scripture into any Antiphons or Responsories. They thus open out a perfect mine of mystical illustration, and, instead of the occasionally tame, cold compositions, which rather dishonour their subject than the reverse, they supply magnificent combinations of Scriptural allusion. Compare the following: (Sarum and Rome). *Ant*: "Rejoice, O Virgin Mary; thou alone hast destroyed all heresies throughout the world," with (Gallican), " I will bless her: and give thee a Son also of her: yea, I will bless her, and she shall be a mother of nations." And so might many passages be contrasted. At the same time, it must be admitted, that these collections of Scripture texts are somewhat incoherent, and far from carrying out the unity of idea which is so beautiful a feature of the more ancient Offices. These late Gallican Breviaries contain very trustworthy histories of the Saints whose festivals they commemorate, and a variety of new Collects; those for Saints' Days being usually a great improvement on their predecessors.

These being precisely the weak points of the Sarum book, its translators have mostly availed

themselves, more or less, of the assistance provided
for them in these later works.

To return to S. Osmund. He, then, the con-
temporary of Gregory VII. perceiving the great
confusion prevalent in England concerning ritual
matters, betook himself to drawing up a Use,
which haply might restore peace and unity.
He thus remoulded the old rite of the South of
England; and his work proved so perfectly successful, that Salisbury became, as it has been said,
precentor to Canterbury; and S. Osmund's book
continued, till 1549, to be the Church text for most
of the Canterbury province and Wales, and much
of Ireland (at least within the Pale during English
occupation). It was also used in some parts of
the Continent; and the Breviary of Aberdeen (the
only existing relic of Scotch Offices) is almost,
though not exactly, identical with it. Various
additions of course were made as time went on,
e.g., the Office for S. Osmund himself, for Trinity
Sunday, Corpus Christi, etc. York, Bangor,
Hereford, Lincoln, etc., had their several uses,
differing but very slightly from that of Sarum; and
the Benedictine Office was of course recited in the
houses of that order. The Roman Breviary was
never introduced into England till about one
hundred and fifty years ago, when it was brought
in by Roman priests, mostly Jesuits, whose rule
required them to use it.

At the Reformation, the Offices of Matins and Evensong in the Common Prayer Book were chiefly compiled from the Sarum Missal* and Breviary: Matins, from Matins, Lauds, and Prime; Evensong, from Vespers and Compline; resuming, however unconsciously, the old Eastern penitential introduction to the service: increasing the Scripture lectionary, and appointing monthly, instead of weekly, recitation of the Psalter.

And as the "sevenfold hours" had not been of late, and could not be, said by the laity in general, the new arrangement proved, on the whole, very widely beneficial; and it is impossible to be too thankful that the Reformers were moved to be so little destructive, and so greatly conservative, in their liturgical labours.† Extraordinary pains were

---

* The Collects, Epistles and Gospels for Sundays and Festivals are principally derived from this source.

† "Nothing is more remarkable in the original Preface to the revised Services, than the utter unconsciousness which it manifests on the part of the Revisers, *of having done anything more than revise.* Certain things taken away,—a certain fusing and consolidation of parts or elements heretofore disjointed and broken up,—certain provisions for securing that the Psalms and Lessons should be really and thoroughly *used*, and not skipped for the most part as in time past,—and the turning of the whole into English;—this was their entire idea of what they had done. They expected the people and Church of the day to accept the Services, as essentially, and for all practical purposes, the same Services, revised;—and, what is more, as such the Church and people manifestly did accept them. So clear were the Revisers on this point, that Cranmer, (as Jeremy Taylor has recorded,) offered to prove that 'the Order of

taken in Edward VI.'s reign, to destroy every old
service book that could be discovered; and it is
rather wonderful to see how many have survived
the devouring flames which so greedily swallowed
Missal, Breviary, Grayle, Antiphoner, etc. Although in the following reign, the printers were
very busy in bringing out fresh editions of such
books, these, in their turn, were zealously destroyed
under Elizabeth. It is but a few years since, that
the English Breviary Offices were spoken of as
absolutely dead and gone, and incapable of
resuscitation; but the revival of the Religious life
in this country naturally led to the recital of fuller
Offices of prayer, and induced a return to the
regular use of the ancient English Church. This
required little alteration; except in the Offices
for Saints, and the lectionary. The latter, on account of the multitude of festivals formerly observed,
had only two sets of lessons for the six days of each
week, as four days out of the six were sure to be
assigned to various Saints; and on Saints' days
the history of the Saints, instead of being confined
to the three lessons of the second nocturn, occupied

the Church of England, set out by authority by Edward VI.
was the *same that had been used in the Church for fifteen
hundred years past.*' Some elements or features, doubtless, they
rejected; others they expanded. *But the exact order of such
elements or parts of the old Services as they retained, they preserved inviolate,* both in the Daily Services and in the Communion
Service; and that without a single exception."—*Principles of
Divine Service,* v. i. p. 8.

all the nine of the three nocturns, and sometimes rather resembled passages from the Arabian Nights than anything fit to form a part of Divine Service. The Roman lectionary had the advantage of being reformed by Pius V. about 1568; and is far superior to the old English one; its Saints' day lessons, though not always trustworthy where the interests of Roman supremacy are concerned, at least contain no "monstrous legends"; and the ferial lessons for the year embody a very large portion of Scripture.

NOTE. "The Service Books among the Anglo-Saxons might easily be drawn up from the chance notices of such codices to be found amid the records of their times. Ælfric says: 'He (the Mass-priest) shall also have for the spiritual work before he be ordained the weapons; that is, these holy books, the Psalter, and Epistle-book, Gospel-book and Mass-book, Song-book (our Breviary), and Hand-book, Numeral and Pastoral, Penitential and Reading-book. These books the Mass-priest should necessarily have,' etc. And among the books bequeathed to the Cathedral of Exeter by its Anglo-Saxon bishop, Leofric, were several such volumes. The whole series of that liturgical service which Austin brought with him from Pope Gregory, for the newly-planted corner of the Church among the Anglo-Saxons, was contained in two great works, the Antiphoner and the Book of the Sacraments. In the Antiphoner was set down not only all the

Canonical Hours both in the nightly and daily
course, but everything that the clergy had to sing
in the choir while the Priest was offering up the
Mass: along, therefore, with the words might be
found the music in which they were chanted. The
Book of the Sacraments contained not only the
ordinary form of the Mass and whatever belonged
to its celebration throughout the year; but besides,
it had in it the forms of the other six Sacraments,
and the rubrics for their administration. As may
be supposed, the Antiphoner and the Sacramentary
were too unwieldy to keep for any length of time
their first size; both of them got broken up, and
each of their constituent parts was made to form
by itself a small and handy liturgical codex. Out
of the Antiphoner, even when it had already been
apportioned into four volumes, came forth the full
song book or whole service for the Canonical Hours,
and which was called in old Catholic England the
" Portous," but now the " Breviary;" the summer
reading book for lessons at Matins, etc., throughout
summer and autumn, and the winter reading book,
the same for winter-tide and spring; the Respon-
sorial, or book of responses; the Antiphoner, strictly
so called, having in it the anthems sung during the
Canonical Hours; the Collectaneum, or Book of the
Collects; the Graduale, having in it the introits,
the graduals, the tracts, etc., sung by the choir at
Mass, (a book the Romans called Cantatorium, the

Anglo-Saxons, " Ad te levavi," because these are the words of the introit for the first Sunday in Advent, with which this codex begins: the English, Grail). The Sacramentary became sub-divided into the full Mass-book, or Missal, properly so named; the Pontifical, or book for those rites which a bishop only may perform; a Blessing-book, containing the blessings bestowed upon the people solemnly at Mass, each Sunday and Festival during the year; the Hand-book, or form for the administration of the priesthood in those sacraments and blessings which they are allowed to give.

" Besides these, there were other liturgical codes in use among the Anglo-Saxon Churchmen. From the sub-deacon upwards, every clerk must have either known by heart, or possess a codex of, the Psalter with its rubrics, to show what psalms were said at Matins, Lauds, and Evensong, each day throughout the year. The Numeral was a calendar or directory which told the variations in the Canonical Hours and Mass, caused by Saints' Days and Festivals. The Penitential, a book only shrift-fathers, or priests who heard shrifts, that is, confessions, might read, contained the penances decreed by the Church for the different kinds of sin. The Pastorale, S. Gregory's work, and the " Regula Canonicorum" were each a looking-glass, as it were, in which the clerk was to behold what manner of man, to be worthy of his calling, he ought to make himself. No sooner was the use of metrical compositions allowed in the several Canonical Hours and at the Holy Sacrifice than the codices wherein they were written became requisites : the Song-books corresponded with the Salisbury Portous and the Roman Breviary; the Hymnal contained the various hymns chanted at Matins, Lauds, Tierce, Sext, and None, Evensong and Compline, all the year round ; and the Troper was a book having in it, besides other things, those verses to be sung along with the Introit, the Kyrie, the Gloria in Excelsis, the Sanctus, and Agnus Dei, on the High Festivals and chief Saints' Days in the Calendar." [Rock. *Church of our Fathers*. Vol. iii.]

CHAPTER II.

THE OFFICES, CONSIDERED GENERALLY AND
PARTICULARLY.

I.—*Of the Offices in General.*

WE must now turn to examine the Breviary Offices
in themselves ; and those more particularly of the
Sarum use. And it may be well to take four points
for consideration : the structure of the Offices,
their derivation, history, and the mystical interpretation given them by mediæval writers. Acquaintance with the antiquity and parentage of these services, increases regard and reverence for them ; and
the key of spiritual interpretation opens a rich store
of devout thought and helpful ideas, quickening the
bare forms with life and love. The historians who
help us most in this part of our subject, are Grancolas, Gavanti, Martene, Neale, and, as before,
Archdeacon Freeman ; the mystical writers are
chiefly Durandus, Sicardus, Rupert of Deutz,
Honorius of Autun, author of the *Gemma
animæ* : and, as regards the structure of the
Offices, the anonymous writer of " The Myrroure
of our Ladye," a rationale of the Office of
the Blessed Virgin, written for the use of the
Sisters of Sion House, at Isleworth, about A.D.

1428. Beautiful and suggestive as are many of their interpretations, it is, however, only fair to state at the outset what we shall sometimes have occasion to repeat : that these ideas were suggested by already existing ceremonies, and did not, as is sometimes supposed, give rise to them. But although the plain matter-of-fact reason for this or that custom may occasionally seem to jar with the pious or poetical construction assigned by the mystical commentators, yet we can but love to follow the guidance of those who saw in every detail some incentive to holiness, or some manifestation of their most dear LORD. And it is a great matter of thankfulness, that our Offices will bear this system of interpretation, which fills them with interest ever varying, ever fresh. We propose, thus, to speak first of the prose, and afterwards of the poetry, connected with the Breviary : premising, however, that we are only attempting a compilation and selection from those authors who have already written on the subject.

The scheme of the Office will be set more intelligibly before the reader, by the following brief synopsis : after which, each Hour shall be taken in detail. The Roman order is indeed that here described (because it seemed better to copy the words of an able scholar, than attempt an original description) : but its main outlines are identical with the Sarum, except in the Office of Compline, and, partly, of Prime. The minor variations will be hereafter noted.

" Each of the volumes of the Breviary consists of six parts." (The Breviary is usually printed in two volumes, one for each half-year, or in four, one for each quarter; when contained in a single volume, it is called a *Totum*.) " 1. The Calendar, Rubrics, and Tables. 2. The Psalms, Versicles, and Responses of the week-day hour, or ferial Office. 3. The *Proprium de tempore :* the collects and lections for the Sundays and weeks in that part of the year which the volume contains. 4. The *Proprium de Sanctis :* the same for the festivals of Saints which occur in that period. 5. The *Commune Sanctorum :* the lections, collects, hymns, etc., common to all those Saints for whom no particular Office is appointed. And to all these we may add—6. The Offices for the Anniversary of a Dedication, for a Departing Soul, of the Dead, the Little Office of S. Mary, etc. ; so that much of the first, and all the second, fifth, and sixth, of these divisions are necessarily repeated in every volume of the Breviary. Matins are preceded by the *Pater Noster*, the *Ave Maria*, and the *Credo ;* as are all Hours except Compline with the *Pater Noster* and *Ave Maria*. This use, however beautiful, is known not to be very ancient.

" The proper commencement of Matins, therefore, is with the Versicles and Responses, " *O* LORD, *open Thou our lips. And our mouth shall shew forth Thy praise. O GOD, make speed to save us. O LORD, make haste to help us;*" the *Gloria*, the *Laus tibi Domine, Rex æternæ gloriæ*, in Septuagesima, or *Alleluia* at other times. The ninety-fifth Psalm is preceded by the Invitatory. The Invitatory is divided into two clauses: both are said before the Psalm, and at the end of the second, seventh, and last verses: the second clause only, at the end of the fourth and ninth verses. The *Gloria* is followed, first, by the second, and then by both clauses.

"The *Venite* is followed by the hymn, either for the day of the week, or proper to the festival, as the case may be. At the conclusion of the hymn, the first nocturn begins. On ordinary days, one Nocturn only is said. This consists of twelve Psalms, recited two and two together, under one Antiphon, and [three] lessons from Holy Scripture; or if it be a simple festival, the second, or the second and third lessons, are of the Saint. On semi-double and double Festivals there are three Nocturns. The first consists of three Psalms, each under its own Antiphon, and three lessons from Scripture; the second also consists of three Psalms, and three lessons from some sermon, generally speaking, on the passage of Scripture which has preceded; the third, of three Psalms, the beginning of the Gospel for the day, and three lessons for a Homily upon it ; and then, under restrictions which we shall afterwards see, the *Te Deum*. But on Sundays, the first Nocturn consists of twelve Psalms, said four and four under one Antiphon ; while on the Festivals of Easter and Pentecost one Nocturn only is said. The Nocturns end with a verse and response. The LORD's Prayer is then said ; and after the ℣. *And lead us not into temptation*, ℟. *But deliver us from evil*," the Priest gives the Absolution.

"We now come to the Lections and the responses following each. To begin with a general outline of the scheme. In a festival that has lections, the three first are from Holy Scripture ; the three next contain the Commentary of some Father on the passage that has been already read : or, in the case of a Saint with proper lessons, containing his Life. The third Nocturn commences with a few lines from the Gospel of the day followed by *Et reliqua* ; then three lections from a Commentary on that. Of course there are exceptions ; and the Tenebræ Service, and Matins of the Dead, are quite anomalous. In a festival of three lections, they are sometimes from Scripture, sometimes from a homily on Scripture. Each lection is closed by, *But Thou, O* LORD, *have mercy upon us*, from the reader ; and *Thanks be to* GOD, as the response. But on the three last days of Holy Week, the first three lections (which are from Jeremiah) are terminated by, *Jerusalem, Jerusalem, return to the* LORD *thy* GOD, without response." In the [Sarum] Breviary, all lessons taken from the Prophets are followed by, *Thus saith the* LORD GOD : *Return unto Me, and ye shall be saved.*

" We have now arrived at one of the most beautiful parts of the Breviary—the responses that follow each lesson. The response is divided into two parts—the beginning, and the reclamation ; which are separated from each other by an asterisk, and of which the reclamation is repeated after the verse ; but, at the last lection of each Nocturn, the *Gloria* is added. The last response of the lections completed, (or, in the Roman use, the last lection,) follows, if it is to be said, *Te Deum.* The Roman rule is this : it is said on all Sundays of the year, except in Septua- gesima and Lent, from Easter to Ascension daily, (except on Rogation Monday,) and on all festivals, whether of three or nine lections, except that of the Holy Innocents.

" *Te Deum* is immediately followed, in the Roman Breviary, by Lauds.

" The usual Sunday Office in the Roman Breviary, which is that of all mediæval Lauds, is this : Psalms 93 and 100, are said : Psalms 63 and 67 under one *Gloria* : *Benedicite* : the three last Psalms under one antiphon and one *Gloria ;* the short chapter, the hymn, the versicle and response,

Benedictus, and the collect for the day. We now proceed to Prime. The Sunday Roman Office is this: After the Pater Noster, etc., and the Hymn, "*Jam lucis orto sidere*," which never alters, three Psalms are said, the 54th, 118th, and the thirty-two first verses of the 119th, under two *Glorias*. After this, when the Office is of the Sunday, the Athanasian Creed; and this is followed by a short chapter, and the versicles and responses. After this follow, if they are to be said, (which they are not on Doubles, nor within Octaves,) the Preces or suffrages, with the *Confiteor*, and the Collect, "Almighty GOD, Who hast safely brought us to the beginning of this day," with which Prime, properly speaking, ends. It is followed by the Office of the Chapter. The Ferial Office is much the same, except that the short lection is different, and that instead of the 118th Psalm, there are said, one on each of the five first days of the week, the 24th, 25th, 26th, 23rd, and 22nd. On Saturday none is substituted for it, and this is the case in all Festivals. The Athanasian Creed is not said."

The Sarum use prescribes the repetition of the Athanasian Creed on all days, festal or ferial, with changed antiphons: Pss. 22-26 inclusive, on all ordinary Sundays, followed by those above set down as the Roman use. On ferias, Pss. 54 and 119 only, are said.

"The three next hours, Tierce, Sexts, and Nones, are arranged on so precisely similar a plan, that they may be all comprehended in a few words. The Office at each consists of the *Pater Noster*, etc., a hymn, (at Tierce, *Nunc Sancte nobis Spiritus ;* at Sexts, *Rector potens verus Deus ;* at Nones, *Rerum Deus tenax vigor :*) three Psalms, *i.e.*, six divisions of the 119th Psalm, under three *Glorias*, the short chapter, varying with the season of the year; verse and response ; and (when the Preces have been said before) the *Kyrie* and short suffrages; the whole concluded by the Proper Collect.*

"We come to Vespers. Five Psalms, each under its own Antiphon, (except in Paschal time, when all are said under *Alleluia*,) then the short chapter, which, on ordinary days, is, *Blessed be* GOD, *even the Father of our* LORD JESUS CHRIST, *the Father of mercies, and* GOD *of all consolation,* etc. ; a beautifully chosen lesson after the fatigues of the day. Then the hymns, varying with the day of the week, the verse and response; the *Magnificat*, with its proper Antiphon ; and the proper Collect. In Advent, Lent, and the Ember Days, the Preces and (in Lent only) the 51st Psalm, are said after the *Magnificat*.

* It ought perhaps to be observed here, that it is more exactly correct to omit the *s* in the words Sexts, and Nones ; but it was very commonly used in the old English times. Compline too was sometimes called *Complines*, and sometimes *Complet*.

"It now only remains to say a word about Compline. This commences with the *Jube Domine, benedicere:* the Benediction, *Almighty* GOD, *grant us a quiet night and a perfect end:* the lection, *Be sober, be vigilant,* etc.: the *Confiteor* and the four Psalms, 4, 31, (vv. 1-6,) 91, 134, under one Antiphon. Then the hymn, *Te Lucis ante terminum,* (which in the English Breviaries varies with the season): the short chapter from Jeremiah, *But Thou art in us, O* LORD, *and Thy Holy Name is called upon us: leave us not, O* LORD *our* GOD: the verse, *Into Thine hands I commend my spirit,* etc.: the Song of Simeon, the Preces, when they are to be said, the beautiful Collect, *Visita quæsumus,* and an Antiphon and Prayer of the Virgin. The Office is concluded with the Lord's Prayer and Belief, that the Church's children may lie down to rest with the faith of their Mother on their lips. By monastic rule, speech was forbidden after Compline."—Neale. *Liturgical Essays.*

Sarum Compline began like the other hours, except that a penitential ℣. and ℟. preceded "O GOD, make speed," etc. The first Roman chapter was omitted. The mutual confession was placed among the Preces instead of being said before the Psalms. The Antiphons, or hymns, or both, varied in no less than twenty-two manners, according to the season; but in the Roman both were invariable.

The mystical interpretation of these hours of prayer, is given diversely by different writers; by none, perhaps, better than by the learned Abbot of Deutz. He begins with Prime.

"At the hour of Prime, praise is due to our Creator before we take any care for our bodies: because at this hour our LORD was spit upon and derided, smitten on the Face, and, loaded with contumely, stood bound before Pilate for our sakes. Moreover, after His Resurrection, He stood at this hour on the shore, when the multitude of fishes were taken, and yet the net was not broken: whereby was signified the Church, such as it shall be in the resurrection of the dead. Because, therefore, we are to seek first the Kingdom of GOD, and all things else shall be added unto us, and because in the law GOD claims the sacrifice of every first fruit, therefore, we offer to our Redeemer the first hour of the day, and seek His Kingdom, Who suffered for our transgressions and rose again for our justification.

"The hour of Tierce is notable for a double reason. For at this hour the LORD JESUS was crowned with thorns and crucified by the tongues of the Jews: according to that, *the children of men, whose teeth are spears and arrows, and their tongue a sharp sword.* And the HOLY GHOST, Who was not given before JESUS was glorified, at this hour was shed forth on the infant Church in tongues of fire.

" At the hour of Sexts CHRIST the LORD was exalted for us upon the Cross, that He might draw all men unto Him; and the light of the Jews was extinguished, whereof the very true Light spake, saying: *Yet a little while, and the world seeth Me no more; but ye see Me: because I live, ye shall live also.* When sensible darkness fell upon the earth, then the true Light passed over to lighten the Gentiles.

" We fitly sound GOD'S praises at the hour of Nones, when, crying with a loud voice, JESUS gave up the ghost; when, by the admission of the thief into Paradise, we perceive the pardon granted to true penitents, however late their repentance; and by the rending of the veil, we understand that, the veil of the Law and the Prophets being removed, we may behold with open face the glory of GOD. Then also from His pierced side flowed blood, whereby to redeem the Church, and water, whereby to cleanse it.

" The Vesper and Matin sacrifices of praise commemorate great mysteries. Under the shadows of the old Law, burnt sacrifices were offered morning and evening; and concerning these it is written: *This shall be a continual burnt offering throughout your generations, for a sweet savour unto the* LORD. At Vesper-tide, the LORD instituted the Sacrament of His Body and Blood, wrote with His own hand a testament for His heirs, chiefly commending humility and love, when He washed the disciples' feet, after which He bade them farewell in a long and solemn discourse. Buried also at Vesper-tide, at Vesper-tide none the less He appeared after His rising, in the form of a pilgrim, and was known in the breaking of bread.

"At Matin-tide Peter, who had thrice denied, was recalled by the crowing of the cock. The LORD looked, and the penitent denier broke into tears. At daybreak also the sorrow of the faithful began to be turned into joy, when the LORD's Resurrection was made known to the holy women by Angels clad in white. They sought the living among the dead; and the Living shewed Himself, and suffered them to touch and worship Him.

"The hour of Compline commemorates that time in the LORD's Passion, when, Judas being already gone to deliver Him up, He began to be sorrowful and very heavy, and, being in an agony, prayed more earnestly, and His sweat was as it were great drops of blood falling down to the ground; for then He trod the winepress alone, and pre-signified the blood of martyrs which should in future times be shed. Moreover, at that time, we celebrate this concerning His Resurrection: that having made peace between GOD and man, He returned as a Messenger to bring good tidings to the faithful, standing in the midst of His disciples, and saying: *Peace be unto you.*"*—Rupert of Deutz.

II.—MATINS.

1.—*Introductory Prayers and Versicles.*

Matins, like other Offices, originally began directly with the Antiphons and Psalms, according to the custom still observed in the latter days of Holy Week, and in the Office for the Dead. The *Pater, Ave,* and *Credo,* were the only prayers of obligation appointed for secular persons; and it was taken for granted that members of religious communities would say them, each person for himself, before coming to Office. S. Ambrose directs that the Apostles' Creed be said daily before dawn. S. Augustine says in one of his sermons: "Ye say it daily when ye rise, and when ye lie down to sleep." And S. Benedict's constitutions,

---

* Dr. Neale remarks, in one of his sermons preached to Sisters: "You know that in the Hours, as the Western Church says them, there is no express or determinate reference to that event of the Passion then celebrated: in the Eastern Church there is. I have heard our Hours called cold and lifeless, because they have no such allusion. But is that fair? or is it not rather that the practice of the Western Church is here, that of the truer love? Because it takes for granted that you *cannot* forget! that you need not, for example, to be reminded at Sexts, that at the Sixth Hour of the Sixth Day CHRIST took away the sins of the world. No, believe me, a Sister's day, so far as her own heart, her own inward real self is concerned, ought to be measured by the Passion, rather than by the clock."

as well as many other ancient writings, direct that
each brother on rising from his bed shall make the
sign of the Cross in invocation of the Holy Trinity,
and say, O LORD, *open Thou my lips*. An ancient
Council adds that he is also to say *Gloria Patri*,
and hasten to the choir repeating the Psalm, *Ad te
levavi*. *Pater* was prefixed to the Offices in the
later Sarum Breviaries, with the additions of *Ave;*
though the first Breviary in which the Angelic
salutation, in its modern form, appears at the beginning of Office, is the Reform of Cardinal Quignon,
1536; Pius V. retained it in the Breviary authorized by himself. The general use of the *Ave
Maria* was first enjoined on the people by Odo of
Solliac, Bishop of Paris, A.D. 1195. The words,
Sancta Maria, *ora pro nobis peccatoribus*, *Amen*,
are found in no formula of prayers till A.D. 1508.
The Franciscans afterwards added *et in hora mortis
nostræ*, in their Breviary of A.D. 1515, and Cardinal
Quignon, being a Franciscan, adopted that form.

The prayer, O GOD, *make speed to save me*, was
introduced into the Office by S. Benedict in imitation
of those monks, who, according to Cassian, were
wont to repeat it in every action of their lives. The
whole Psalm 70, *Haste Thee*, O GOD, *to deliver
me, etc.*, was formerly recited, as now in the Roman
Litany; but later the first verse only was retained,
with *Gloria*, *Amen* and *Alleluia*. The compilers
of our Common Prayer Book do not seem, in trans-

lating this verse and response, to have recognized its source in the Psalter. The origin of the *Gloria Patri* is extremely obscure. The word doxology is derived from the Greek *Doxa*, glory, and *logos*, discourse. *Alleluia, Praise the Lord*, is retained in its original Hebrew.

Of the mystical meaning of this portion of the Service, the "Myrroure" tells us (the spelling and expressions are occasionally modernized in these quotations):

"Men useth in land of war to keep continual watch in cities and castles and walled townes, and when any enemies come nigh, they ring a certain bell, whereby all men are warned to arm them and make them ready, and to go to places of defence to fight and to beat off their enemies. On the same wise, we are closed in this holy monastery as knights in a castle, where we are besieged with great multitudes of fiends, that night and day labour to get entrance and possession in our soules; and often they are most busy in night time, when the wits are oppressed with heaviness of sleep, for to assay to overcome, or at the least to vex and to trouble them of whom they might not have the overhand by day. And therefore when we hear the bell ring to Matins we ought anon, as true GOD's knights, arise quickly and arm us with prayer, and make us ready by dressing up of our intent to GOD with some devout meditation, and haste us to the place of our defence, that is the church, which is fearful to the fiends our enemies : and there we ought to lift up the long spear of fervent desire of our hearts to GOD, and draw out the sharp sword of the word of GOD in His Holy Service, and smite great strokes by devout singing and saying thereof, whereby our enemies shall be rebuked, and we kept in godly praisings, under the banner of His protection. This readiness of coming ought not only to be kept at Matins, but at every hour of the day ; for though we rest sometime from singing or praying with the mouth, our enemies rest not to war against us. And therefore we ought not to cease of keeping of our mind fixed on GOD alway, and in time of prayer to be ready and glad to go thereto, as to a castle of succour, and as to the food and ghostly comfort of our souls. And [ye saye the *Pater*] that is for to stir your hearts to more devotion, or ye begin your service. And therefore it is said in silence. Shewing that GOD is more pleased with the privy devotion of the heart, whereto ye ought principally to intend in all your Service, than with the outward noise with the voice . . . . And forasmuch as our SAVIOUR made this prayer for our health ; it is good that ye intend always to say it to the intent that He made it for and to ask thereby all things that He intended should be asked thereby when He made it."—*Myrroure.*

"At the words, *O* GOD, *make speed to save me*, is

made the sign of the Cross, in order through its virtue to escape all power and cunning of the devil, who greatly feareth the sign of the Cross. Whence Chrysostom : 'Wheresoever the devils see the sign of the Cross, they fly, fearing that staff whereby they received their wound.' . . . . . Therefore doth the Church arm herself with the sign of the Cross on the breast and on the forehead, signifying that this mystery is to be believed with the heart and confessed openly with the lips.* By this sign is confounded the kingdom of Satan, and the Church triumphs, terrible as an army in battle array. The sign of the Cross is expressed by three fingers, because it is made under the invocation of the Trinity. Yet the thumb is uppermost ; for we place all our faith in GOD, One and Trine. But the Jacobites and Eutychians, asserting one only nature in CHRIST, namely the Divine, are said to sign themselves with one finger only. Now some sign themselves from their forehead downwards, (which expresses the mystery wherein GOD bowed the heavens, and came down on earth : He descended, that we might be raised from earth to heaven). And from right to left : first, because eternal things, signified by the right hand, should be preferred to temporal, signified by the left ; secondly, in memory of CHRIST's passing

---

* We sign ourselves thus with the Cross, signifying also that we offer our LORD the thoughts of our head, the love of our heart, and the work of our arms.

from the Jews to the Gentiles; thirdly, because
CHRIST, coming from the Right Hand, *i.e.*, from the
FATHER, destroyed on the Cross the devil, who is
signified by the left: whence, *I came forth from My
Father, and am come into the world*. But others
sign themselves from left to right, for which also
they have this authority: He went forth from the
Father, descended to hell, returned to the throne of
GOD. Secondly, they do thus, to imply that we are to
pass from misery to glory, and from vice, intended
by the left, to virtue, typified by the right; as we
read in the Gospel of S. Matthew: and CHRIST
moreover hath passed from death unto life."—
Durandus.

"The verse *O* LORD, *open Thou my lips*, is only
said at Matins, that is the beginning of GOD's service,
in token that the first opening of your lips or mouth
should be to the praising of GOD, and all the day
after they should abide open and ready to the same,
and be so occupied and filled therewith that nothing
contrary to His praising might enter in nor do
anything any time of the day without His help as
He sayeth Himself in His gospel: *Sine Me nihil
potestes facere*, that is, without Me ye may do right
nought. Therefore, both at Matins, and at beginning of each hour ye ask His help and say, *Deus,
in adjutorium meum intende*, that is, GOD, take heed
unto my help.

"And for as much as he that is in doing of a thing,

and may not bring it about, hath need of hasty
help; therefore feeling your need, ye pray our LORD
to haste Him, and say: *Domine, ad adjuviendum
me festina*, that is, LORD, haste Thee to help me.
And take heed that all this verse, both that part
that is said of one alone, and that that is answered
of all together, are said in the singular number: as
when ye say mine or me, and not our nor us; in
token that ye begin your praising and prayer in the
person of holy Church, which is one, not many.
For though there be many members of holy Church,
as there is many Christian men and women; yet
they make one body, that is holy Church, whereof
CHRIST is the Head. And for that prayer that is
said in the person and unity of holy Church is
never left unsped, therefore, trusting that our LORD
hath heard your prayer, and is come to help you,
ye begin altogether, lowly inclining, to praise the
Blessed Trinity, and say, *Gloria Patri et Filio et
Spiritui Sancto*. Anon, after *Gloria Patri*, ye say
Alleluia, that is a word of joy and praising; and
specially it betokeneth that unspeakable joy that is
in Heaven endlessly in praising and lauding of GOD.
But for it is a word of joy: therefore in time of
penance, that is, from Septuagesima till Easter, it
is left, and instead thereof ye say, *Laus tibi, Domine,
Rex eternæ gloriæ*, that is, *Praise be to Thee, O* LORD,
King of eternal glory. For though penance doing
be praising to GOD, yet it is done in sorrow of heart

and sharpness of body, and not in gladness and joy, namely for sinful people. And, therefore, in time of penance we say, *Laus tibi*, not in joy, but in praising of GOD, and not *Alleluia*, which is a word both of praising and of joy."—*Myrroure*.

2.—*Invitatory*.

At Matins the Invitatory follows the introductory versicles; it directs the worshippers in what light they are at that particular time called on to regard GOD; and stamps its own meaning on the whole series of Psalms.

In the East, the ninety-fifth Psalm itself was not used, but only an Invitatory founded on it. The West uses both: here, as elsewhere, developing the Eastern practice. The present division of the *Venite* is the form in which it was anciently arranged, before the modern distribution of verses. In its recitation, the Psalm is said by the reader alone: the invitatory sentences by the choir.

It was the custom in the time of Amalarius, to say the Invitatory on Sundays only, when the people were wont to come to church; as it was not considered necessary when the brethren only were about to say Office: yet some monks used it as early as the fifth century, according to S. Athanasius.

" But because it suffices not to praise GOD except we invite others to praise Him likewise (as, *Let him that heareth say, Come*, and, *The curtains shall be coupled one to another :*) therefore follow the Invitatory and the Invitatory Psalm, *Venite exultemus,* wherein are rehearsed many reasons why we should praise and exult in GOD ; and the last cause is, lest we be ungrateful like the Jews, who for their ingratitude and wickedness entered not into the promised land.

" After certain verses of the Psalm, the Invitatory is repeated entire, and after others, imperfectly ; because, although all are thereby invited to the praise of GOD, yet some accept this invitation perfectly, and some imperfectly. It is said six times entire, because they receive the invitation entire, who perfectly render praise to GOD. Because six is the first perfect number, being formed of 1, 2, and 3,* therefore it is repeated six times entire.

* A perfect number is one which is equal to the sum of all its factors, or aliquot parts. Six is the first of these : its factors being 1, 2, and 3, which, added together, make six. Each number had also, among mystical writers, its well-defined *spiritual* meaning. "One, the Unity of the Godhead ; two, the two natures of our LORD ; three, the Ever-blessed Trinity ; four, the four Evangelists (hence the preaching of the Gospel) ; five, on the one hand, a full knowledge of Christian mysteries, (the doctrine of the Trinity + that of our Lord's two natures) ; on the other, the state of ordinary sinners who break half and observe half the Law, (compare the five brethren of Dives) ; six, the Passion, from our LORD's being crucified on the sixth hour of the sixth day : also, temptation, from the peculiar reference to that contained in the sixth day of the Creation ; seven, the sevenfold graces of the HOLY GHOST, and later, the seven Sacraments ; eight, regeneration, as being the first number that oversteps seven, the symbol of the Old Creation ; ten, the Law ; eleven, iniquity, as transgressing the law. And not only were simple

E

And it is repeated three times imperfectly, on account of those three sorts of men, who did not accept the invitation to the supper, namely, the covetous, the proud, and the sensual—or by reason of our threefold imperfection, in heart, word, and work."—Durandus.

3.—*Hymn.*

The hymn following the Invitatory may be regarded merely as an expansion or emphasizing of it. The reason assigned for its place at this Office is, that if any souls be yet cold and torpid after the Invitatory has appealed to them, they may by the cheerfulness and jubilation of the hymn be roused to recite their Psalter with due fervour. An analogous reason may be given for the place of the Hymn at the day hours. At Vespers, Compline, and Lauds, the Hymn takes the same place as in

numbers thus explained; compound numbers yielded composite sense. Twelve was the faith preached throughout the world—the doctrine of the Three dispersed into four quarters. Forty, or eighty-eight, the struggle of the regenerate with the old nature; five into eight, or eleven into eight. Sixty-six, the extreme of wickedness; six, in the sense of temptation, into eleven, (and compare this with the number of the beast in the Revelation, the quintessence of all temptation). And even still more remarkably were numbers compounded; as in the one hundred and fifty-three fishes which, in so many sermons, S. Augustine always explains in the same way, of the whole congregation of the elect. Seven stands for the SPIRIT, ten for the Law; seventeen is therefore the fulfilment of the Law by the works of the SPIRIT: sum the progression, $1 + 2 + 3 + 4 \ldots \ldots + 16 + 17$ and you get 153."—Neale. *Commentary on the Psalms.*

the Greek Church: a plea adduced for that position being, that the uninspired should follow the inspired.

There is no evidence of Hymns having been in use among the early monks. The lawfulness of using them at all in Divine service has been questioned. They were forbidden by the Councils of Laodicæa, Chalcedon, and Braga, on the ground that nothing ought to be inserted in the public prayers except passages drawn from Scripture, and thus all human compositions, poetical or other, must be excluded. But at a very early period, some of the greatest writers of the Church turned their attention to hymnology, and their productions were soon sung in the public Offices. S. Hilary of Poitiers (✝A.D. 368) is the earliest known Western hymnodist, and S. Ambrose is said to have introduced hymn singing to solace the faithful at Milan under the troubles which lay heavily upon them; and for some time after, Hymns were called Ambrosians. They were first brought into Western monastic use by S. Benedict in Italy, and S.S. Cæsarius and Aurelian in Gaul, and the Eighth Council of Toledo, A.D. 653, repealed the prohibitory Canon past at Braga just a century earlier; but the local Church of Rome continued to exclude them down to the middle of the twelfth century. S. Augustine's definition of a hymn is: "A song in praise of GOD: if it be not addressed to GOD, it is no hymn; nor is it a hymn, except it set forth His praise." The hymns of the

Roman Breviary have been much altered and polished, and have lost much by the process. The hymns of the late Gallican Breviaries are partly new versions, and partly original hymns by writers of the seventeenth and eighteenth centuries, the chief of whom was Jean Baptiste Santeuil, (Santolius Victorinus,) who died in 1697.

The doxology of the Office Hymns varies with the different festivals: Christmas, Epiphany, Easter, Ascension, and Whitsuntide. In the three latter cases, the Sarum Festival Doxology consists of two verses. The prayer for protection from death in the Easter Doxology refers to a pestilence which was devastating Italy about Easter-tide of the year in which it was written. The Christmas Doxology is used for the Feast of the Holy Name, the Blessed Sacrament, and all Festivals of the Blessed Virgin; these being so many commemorations of the Incarnation; just as, very beautifully, in the Sarum use, the Psalms for Vespers on the Feasts of the Blessed Virgin are generally those for Christmas Day. The Matin Hymns for ordinary Sundays vary according to the time of year: the longer hymn *Primo dierum*, being sung only from Epiphany to Lent in the Sarum use: but from the autumnal till the spring equinox in the Roman, etc., because, the nights being then longer, the Matin Office was so likewise, as Lauds were not to be said till daybreak.

4.—*Psalms.*

(*a.*)—*Posture.*

Here then, anciently, began the Office, without any introduction. And first a word as to the posture in which it was said. The worshippers stood throughout the Psalms. Members of religious communities occupied stalls in choir; and the very name, stall, signifies a place for standing in. Sitting during the Divine Service was a thing unheard of, except for the bishop and other clergy, for whom sedilia were provided near the Altar. The naves of our Cathedrals, destitute of any accommodation for sitting, testify to this practice, which, of course, is still in force among the unchanging Easterns. Sharp rebukes were administered even to those who dared to kneel on one knee only, because this was thought to imitate the mockery of the Jews in our LORD's Passion.

Cassian assigns as reasons for standing, that this posture tends to the avoidance of drowsiness and distraction, and denies comfort and ease to the body. Those who were sick or infirm were allowed the indulgence of leaning on staves.

S. Peter Damiani wrote a book "against sitting during the Work of GOD," in which he brings forward the example of the Angels in the Apocalypse, standing at prayer; and "Lo," says he, "where

Seraphim dare not sit, there sitteth a man of clay!"*

But during the lessons, which seem to have been considered as a kind of appendix to the Office proper, it was the custom, even among the desert fathers in Cassian's time, to sit, lowly and very humbly; and, by a rule which they had in common with many later communities of men and women, they were furnished with some work for their hands, which should not distract their minds from attention to the lesson, but should prevent them from dropping asleep.

It was the habit of some, before the Offices took their present forms, to prostrate themselves at the end of each Psalm, and repeat a prayer: and the longer Psalms were broken by two or three such interruptions.

* "The Clerks and Choir ought to stand or be turned towards the Altar at all Choir Services, from the beginning of the Service until the Antiphon on the first Psalm is begun, and always without exception whilst *Gloria Patri* is said. So at the beginning of all Responsories (if any). So at the beginning of all Chapters and Collects, at the conclusion of all the Hymns, of *Magnificat*, *Benedictus*, *Nunc Dimittis*, and of the other Canticles wherein *Gloria Patri* is said, until the end of the Service. So at the end of the last Psalm, until the Responsory or Lesson or Chapter be begun. In particular at Matins the Choir should stand turned towards the Altar until the whole Invitatory and Psalm be finished; so at the beginning of *Te Deum* and *Benedicite* respectively, and whilst the whole of the last verse of each is sung. So in the course of *Te Deum*, whilst 'Holy, Holy, Holy' is said, and during that verse, 'We therefore pray Thee, help Thy servants,'" etc.— Chambers. *Divine Worship in* 13th, 14th, *and* 19th *centuries.*

When the Preces were introduced at the end of the Hours, it was ruled that the choir should kneel from the first *Kyrie* till after the Collect. But during Easter and Christmas-tide, no kneeling, nor prostration was practised throughout the Office.

" In psalmody sometimes ye stand, for ye ought to be ready and strong to do good deeds. And sometimes ye sit; for ye ought to see that all your deeds be done restfully with peace of others as far as in you lieth . . . Though this be true after the spiritual meaning, yet after the letter, the changing that is in GOD's service from one thing to another, is ordained to let and drive away your dulness that ye should not wax tedious and weary, but gladly and joyfully, not in vain joy, but in joy of spiritual devotion, continue in GOD's service. Therefore sometime ye sing, sometime ye read, sometime ye hear, now one alone, now twain together, now all. Sometime ye sit, sometime ye stand, sometime ye incline, sometime ye kneel, now toward the Altar, now toward the choir, now in stalls, now in the midst. And in all this ye middle Hymns with Psalms, and Psalms with Antempnes, and Antempnes with Versicles, and Lessons with Responses, and Responses with Verse, and so forth of many such other. And all to the praising of our LORD JESUS CHRIST and of His most reverent Mother our Lady, and so to exercise the body to quickening of the soul; that therewith all such

bodily observances should not be found without
cause of ghostly understanding, as I said right now
before.   Now join to all this the fruit of that thing
that is sung and read : and thereto the fellowship
of Angels amongst you in time of GOD'S service,
and most of all the miraculous and unspeakable
Presence of GOD Himself, from Whom our Lady is
not far, namely, amongst you that are chosen so
specially to sing her daily praising ; and see
whether it be not nigh another heaven to serve and
praise GOD in the choir."—*Myrroure*.

(b.)—*Manner of Singing.*

In early and fervent times, the Psalms were
chanted after a very simple manner : rather recited
than sung.   Greater sweetness and harmony were
afterwards introduced to warm more chilly hearts.
S. Ephrem Syrus is said to have introduced
modulated chants, in order to foil a sweet-singing
heretic (Harmonicus) with his own weapon.   The
history of Church Music is extremely obscure, as
regards its origin.   Whether derived from the Jewish
worship, as seems most probable, it is not possible
to decide with certainty, because every trace of
ancient Hebrew music has, it is said, long been lost :
though the contrary is affirmed by those who ought
to know something of the subject.*

* Who can willingly relinquish the tradition that the Tonus
Peregrinus was that to which our LORD and His Apostles sang
their " hymn," before they went forth to the Mount of Olives ?

The system is grounded on the classical Greek tones, such gamuts only being selected as satisfied the requirements of a grave and mystic style. A revision of the Church music extant in his time was made by S. Ambrose in the fourth century, and, in the seventh, S. Gregory reformed, revised, compiled, composed, and expunged; and left his great system so firmly established, that all later reforms have only been made for the purpose of removing corruptions which have crept from time to time into the theory and practice of that which has ever since been styled *Gregorian* music. It was believed that S. Gregory accomplished this great work by directly Divine assistance, and it was accepted throughout the Western Church. S. Augustine, when sent to Evangelize England by the same S. Gregory, brought with him this music, and men to teach it; and it was preserved by the English Church in a state of great purity, though marked by national characteristics. The great difference between Gregorian and modern music lies herein : the latter has two scales only, major and minor. The semitones in the major scale occur between the 3rd and 4th, and the 7th and 8th intervals of the scale. Those in the minor, between the 2nd and 3rd, and the 6th and 7th. Whereas, the Gregorian has a variously computed number of scales, in which the semitones occur between various intervals : beginning, it may be said, on different notes of the key of C, and running through an octave without introduction of flats or sharps. This is merely a first rough idea of a subject which deserves, and demands, careful and patient study.

In the time of Cassian, the Psalms were not sung by the whole choir, nor in alternate verses. One monk sang alone, while the others listened: and the singing of the Psalms at each Office was divided among the brethren, a certain number of Psalms being sung consecutively by each, but always so that no more than four should sing, no matter how many were present.

Antiphonal singing is said to have been introduced into the Christian Church by Flavian and Theodosius. These, first, says Theodoret, divided the choir in two parts, and taught the alternate singing of David's Psalms. They began the practice at Antioch, and it gradually became universal. But it had been in use among the Jews, though not exactly in its present manner.

" In a Psalter of the end of the seventh century, at the beginning, in a hand of still older date, is an account ascribed to S. Jerome, of how the Psalms were originally sung among the Jews. King David with his harp and four principal musicians sang the first verse, which was half of ours, and the Seventy and the rest of the people responding, took the strain up, and sung it through, and so on. A number of examples have been collected from the

Fathers, which prove beyond a doubt that one
repeated the verse, and the Choir and people responded. S. Basil divided the singers into two (in
his 63rd Epistle to the Church at Neocæsarea),
'We commit to one person to begin the Psalm,
the rest sing with him.' S. Chrysostom (Homily
36): 'He who chants the Psalms sings alone, the
rest making a great sound in response.' S.
Athanasius, in his apology for his flight: 'I sate
down, and the Deacon read the 135th Psalm, and
at the end of each verse the people responded,
'For His mercy endureth for ever.'

"This mode of Psalmody was undoubtedly followed down to the Reformation, and is now continued over the greater part of Europe—divided
Choirs, half on one side, and half on the other—
being nearly unknown."—Chambers.

(c.)—Recitation of the Psalter.

The recitation of the Psalter, in the early days
of desert monasticism, formed the whole vocal
office, without addition of any kind. Gradually
circled round, as time advanced, by Antiphons, Responsories, and Lessons, varying with the varying
seasons, the repetition of the Psalter continues,
as of old, to be the unchanging substance of the
Office, but reflects perpetually changeful lights and
colours, according to the tone of its surroundings.

One of the first points that strikes us in begin-

ning to use the Breviary, is the division of the
Psalms, the 9th and 10th being treated as one; the
114th and 115th, as one also; while the 116th and
147th are each divided into two. This was the
arrangement of the Septuagint, followed by the
Western Church, prior to the Reformation; but the
compilers of our Common Prayer Book adopted the
ancient Jewish divisions. It would, however, be
more inconvenient than useful to alter the fixed
Psalms in the Breviary to our own more literally
correct use.

" Because the praise of the lips and heart suffice
not, except action follow, (for faith without works
profiteth nothing, but is dead,) therefore, after the
hymn, follow Psalms, which denote good works.
Whence David: *I will sing praises unto Thee
upon a ten-stringed lute*. On such an instrument,
because, on a spiritual psaltery, vivified by faith,
we must sing Psalms to GOD, fulfilling the ten
commandments of the Law.

The Psalms are said alternately, to signify how
saints exhort each other to good works. We say
the Psalms standing, to shew, that standing in good
works we conquer. While the children of Israel
were fighting with Amalek, they prevailed so long as
Moses lifted up his hands; but when he let them
down, they were overcome. Therefore, rising, we
signify the devotion of our minds by the posture of
our bodies,—we shew the affection of our minds,

i.e., our being prepared, whether for the demands of the body, or for the exercise of labour. Moreover, standing, we pray, signifying thereby the joy that shall be hereafter. *Our feet shall stand in thy gates, O Jerusalem.*

"On Sundays and festivals, we say three Nocturns, and represent therein the three epochs, viz., the time before the Law, the time under the Law, and the time of Grace : of which each hath three distinctions. The time before the Law is thus divided : (1) from Adam to Noah ; (2) from Noah to Abraham ; (3) from Abraham to Moses. In the first Nocturn (of Sunday) are said twelve Psalms, and three Antiphons. The LORD glorified Sunday by His Resurrection. Therefore the voice of Sunday calls to our minds the Resurrection of the LORD, and also that of all the faithful, who have been from the beginning, and will be till the end of the world ; because in the Resurrection of the LORD the resurrection of all the elect is signified. The first Nocturn commemorates the time before the Law ; its twelve Psalms refer to the resurrection of all the saints of that time, especially of the twelve patriarchs, by whom GOD'S people were formed into twelve tribes. The quadruple number of the Psalms signifies the four cardinal virtues, namely, prudence, justice, fortitude, and temperance : virtues which we believe the holy patriarchs to have possessed beyond all others in their time ; three

Antiphons signify faith, or delight in the Holy
Trinity.   Four Psalms are said under one *Gloria*,
because the four virtues aforesaid are inseparable,
and who hath one hath all.   And note, that in the
first division of time, before the Law, there watched
Abel, Enos, Enoch and Lamech, as we see in the
first four Psalms; Ps. 1, *Beatus vir*, sings Abel,
who, like a tree planted by the waterside, brought
forth his fruit in due season, till he was slain for
maintaining righteousness.   Ps. 2, *Quam fremu-
erunt*, sings Enos, who served the LORD with fear,
when he called upon the Name of the LORD.   Ps. 3,
Domine, quid multiplicati sunt, sings Enoch, whom
the LORD lifted up, when He translated him to Paradise.   Ps. 6, *Domine ne in furore*, sings Lamech,
whom the LORD heard when He gave him that son,
who saved the human race in the ark.   Here two
Psalms are omitted, Pss. 4 and 5, *Cum invocarem*
and *Verba mea* : the first is always said at Compline,
the second on Monday in Lauds.

   " In the second division of the first time, there
watched Noah, Shem, Eber, and Terah.   Ps. 7,
Domine, Deus meus, sings Noah, whom the LORD
found righteous in his generation, and therefore
saved from the destroying waters.   Ps. 8, *Domine,
Dominus noster*, sings Shem, whom the LORD
crowned with glory and worship, when He made
him higher than his brethren by his father's
blessing.   Pss. 9 10, *Confitebor tibi*, sings Eber, who

spoke of the marvellous works of the LORD, when He destroyed the city of the giants. Ps. 11, *In Domino confido*, sings Terah, who put his trust in the LORD when dwelling in a city of the Chaldees, whose portion was fire and brimstone.

" In the third division of the first time watched Abraham, Isaac, Jacob, and Joseph, as the following Psalms declare. Ps. 12, *Salvum me fac*, sings Abraham, whom the LORD helped when there was not one godly man left, because idolatry was maintained. Ps. 13, *Usque quo*, sings Isaac, whose sacrifice the LORD considered. Ps. 14, *Dixit insipiens*, sings Jacob, who put his trust in the LORD, whence it is there said, *Jacob shall rejoice, and Israel shall be glad*. Ps. 13, *Domine quid habitabit*, sings Joseph, who was uncorrupt, when he refused adultery.

" But the second Nocturn, or the three Psalms, which are now said with three Antiphons, and three *Glorias*, commemorate the resurrection of those who lived under the Mosaic law. And although there were then many saints, yet there were three orders, namely, the Lawgiver with his imitators, the Psalmist with his, and the Prophets. . . . . For these orders we say three Psalms ; and because they served the Trinity with spiritual love, therefore at each we say *Gloria*, etc. with an Antiphon. The reason why all the Psalms of the first Nocturn are sometimes said under one

Antiphon, and all those of the second under three, is that though to them who were under the law of nature very little truth was revealed, yet to those under the law of Moses more was made known; and therefore greater is their exultation, which is signified by the triplication of the Antiphon. In the first division of the time of the Law, watched Priests, as Aaron, by their teaching, which the Psalmist expresses, Psalm 16, *Conserva me;* the LORD was the portion of their inheritance, and of their cup. In the second, Judges, as Gideon, by their judging: which the Psalmist expresses, Psalm 17, *Exaudi Domine justitiam meam:* whose sentence came forth from the Presence of the most High. In the third, Kings, as Solomon, by guarding the people: of whom the Psalmist speaks in Psalm 18, *Diligam te,* whom the LORD made head of the heathen.

" In the third Nocturn we say three Psalms, signifying the resurrection of all those who have lived, do live, (and will live) in the time of grace, under the New Covenant*. . . And because in this time was given the greatest revelation of grace and fulness of truth, therefore these Psalms are frequently sung with the Antiphon *Alleluia,* to signify great joy. This is also the reason why lessons from the New Testament are read in the third Nocturn, and

* " Or," continues Durandus, " the dwellers in the three parts of the world, Europe, Asia, and Africa " !

Te Deum is likewise then said. In the first division of the time of grace, watched the Apostles, as is expressed by the Psalmist, Psalm 19, *Cœli enarrant*, because their sound is gone out into all lands. In the second, Martyrs, as the Psalmist declares, Psalm 20, *Exaudiat te*, because the LORD defended them in the day of trouble. In the third, Confessors, of whom the Psalmist speaks, Psalm 21, *Domine, in virtute*, because they were not denied the request of their lips. . . . . . .

" On ferial days we say twelve Psalms, to shew that we ought to serve GOD in the twelve hours of the night, intending one Psalm for each hour because we cannot attend on the service of GOD without intermission. . . . . The Psalms are said in pairs, to shew that without charity, which must consist between at least two, our praises or our works avail nothing. In some Churches *Gloria*, etc., is interposed between the two Psalms, to signify that CHRIST is the Mediator between GOD and man. In others, two are said under one *Gloria*, to signify that our praises are then accepted by GOD, when we abide in charity . . . . Six Antiphons are said, either for the reason already given, or on account of the six works of mercy, which if we observe, we shall, from the darkness of this night, or death, attain to the true light, and eternal life. And the three lessons which are then said, signify the doctrine of the Elect of the three periods, and the three responses which interpolate them, denote that the things taught by the Elect in the three periods, and done by us in three ages, are referred by us to the Divine Trinity, Which we glorify in faith, hope, and love." —Durandus.

5.—*Antiphons.*

The word *Antiphon* signifies counter or responsive sound, and may therefore be applied to the verses of Psalms sung by alternate choirs, or to the responsories at the Hours: but is generally understood of the verse introduced before and after each Psalm.

Amalarius speaks of it thus: "The Antiphon is begun by one person of one choir, and to its tone the Psalm is sung by the two choirs; and then the Antiphon is sung itself by the two choirs together."

The leader of the singing, who gave the tone to the rest, was called the Precentor: he who sang next after, repeating his chant, was called Succentor. In the Sarum and French use this office was filled by Rulers of the Choir on high days, and by the Hebdomadary on ordinary days. Concerning the singers, more will be said under the head of Vespers. It was sometimes the practice to repeat the Antiphon after every verse of the Psalm. The method in which the 95th Psalm is said with the Invitatory is the only existing relic of this custom in the West. In the Roman use the Antiphons are doubled, (*i.e.*, rehearsed entire both before and after the Psalms at Vespers and Lauds and the Gospel Canticles,) on the Greater Feasts; which are therefore styled *Doubles*. In the Sarum rite, Antiphons to the Psalms were never doubled; and those to the Gospel Canticles, only on Principal and Greater Double Feasts.

The Antiphons were always sung, not merely recited. It is said that in the English use, the organ did not accompany the first words of the Antiphon, sung before the Psalm: though some wind instrument may have been used, to ensure tone and time. But when sung entire after the Psalm, it had organ accompaniment.

"We seem to have the earliest and simplest form of the Antiphon, in the repetition at the end of each Psalm of some verse or other of that Psalm itself. Grancolas, indeed, considers the Western Antiphon to have originated with short prayers said by the Egyptian monks after each Psalm. And it is not improbable that this usage may have influenced the form of the more fully constructed Antiphons, taken from other parts of Scripture than the Psalms, or composed on purpose, and often taking the form of a short hymn. But in its proper nature, the Antiphon would seem to be some part of the Psalm itself, so selected as to express, as far as may be, the leading character, or some salient feature of it.

" The Western Church has, however, developed with great beauty and power the simple Antiphon idea of the East. Following this hint, she has devised a vast variety of Antiphons, according to the season or day; by means of which the key-note of the season, etc., was sounded, or intended to be so, at intervals during the Psalmody. This was unquestionably a powerful instrument for imparting distinctness of expression to the Psalms. It reminded the worshipper, from time to time, what colour his devotions might fitly derive from the associations of particular seasons; it taught him what kind of instruction to be then more especially on the watch for in the Psalms."—Freeman.

The Antiphon, then, in its later stage, is not always chosen from the current Psalm, nor necessarily from Scripture at all. The compilers of the Sarum book chose freely elsewhere. Those, for instance, on the Octave of Epiphany, are drawn from S. Cyril of Alexandria; some of those on the Conversion of S. Paul, from a sermon of S. Bernard's on that Festival: and in the Offices of Saints, the Antiphons, as well as the ℞℞., are often taken from the acts of their martyrdoms. Here, however, we notice one curious point of the Sarum Breviary. For, though by far the greater proportion of its Antiphons are very

beautiful and noble, in some the old English love
of the grotesque and of doggrel rhyme is
apparent. The charms of alliteration seem to have
been irresistible. Take, for example, these: for
the Feast of S. Chad, at Lauds:

" Claustri clausus carcere cedda monachatur:
  ut divinis libere vacans his utatur.
  Cujus fama claruit quod pontificatur,
  lucerna quæ latuit, ne plus abscondatur.
  Pastor pavit populum pabulo doctrine,
  reddens receptaculum regule divine."

But fortunately such lines as these mostly occur in
Offices which are not now needed for practical use.

" The Antiphon refers to the following Psalm,
as the Responsory refers to the preceding Lesson.
It is begun before the Psalm, signifying action;
and this sets forth the bond of charity, or mutual
love, without which labour avails not, and whereby
labour hath its merit. Rightly therefore, according
to its melody, is formed the tone of the Psalms;
because love shapes our works. So the Psalm is
intoned according to the melody of the Antiphon,
and the hand works according to that which the
spark of love hath excited. Moreover, the Psalms
are intermingled with the Antiphons, because *faith
worketh by love*. And the Antiphon is said imperfectly before, and perfectly after, the Psalm, because
charity, in the way, is imperfect: here it is begun;
but in our Country it is perfected by good works,

which flow from love. According to that of Isaiah, *The* LORD, *Whose fire is in Sion, and His furnace in Jerusalem.* Yet in the greater of our Feasts, the Antiphon is said entire before the Psalm also, to wit, that in those times we should shew ourselves more perfect in good works. It is begun by one of one choir, and ended by many of both choirs, first, because love begins from One, that is CHRIST, and is consummated in His members, through Himself; as He saith in S. John's Gospel: *A new commandment I give unto you, that ye love one another ;* GOD first loved us, and therefore we must correspond in common to His love. Moreover, the Antiphons after the Psalms are sung by all in common, because from common love arises joy. The song is of two choirs alternately, to signify mutual love ; or charity, which cannot exist among fewer than two. Thus the Antiphon joins the two choirs, as love joins two brothers by good works. Isidore saith, that the Greek word *antiphonos* signifies a reciprocal voice, because two choirs answering each other, alternate the song of the melody, as the two Seraphim and the two Testaments call one to another. Wherefore clerks, singing Antiphons, turn not towards the Altar, but towards each other : which manner of singing was introduced by the Greeks, and is from them derived.

" Furthermore, in certain churches joy is expressed by *neuma* * at the end of the Antiphon; for, *Blessed are the people that can rejoice in Thee.* For neuma signifies ineffable joy, or the exultation of mind which Heaven knows. Therefore on days of fasting and affliction, it is not to be used; as, in time of mourning, the harp is laid aside; and it is made on one, and that the last, letter of the Antiphon, to mark that the praise of GOD is ineffable, and incomprehensible. Ineffable joy is signified by neuma, because it is foretasted here, but cannot be fully expressed, nor left entirely unexpressed. Neumatizing, therefore, more expressly than words, saith what are the joys of Heaven, where words cease, and men know all."—Durandus.

" What is it to sing with jubilation? To be unable to understand, to express in words, what is being sung in the heart. For singers, either in the harvest, or in the vineyard, or in any other busy work, after they have begun in the words of their hymns to exult and rejoice, being, as it were, filled with so great joy that they cannot express it in words, then proceed to sounds of jubilation. Thus jubilee is a sound signifying that the heart laboureth with that which it cannot utter. And whom beseemeth that jubilation but the ineffable GOD? For He is ineffable Whom thou canst not speak;

---

* This refers to the practice of lengthening out the last syllable, and singing twenty, thirty, or more notes upon it: which was called *neuma*.

and if thou canst not speak Him, and oughtest not
to keep Him silent, what remaineth to thee but
jubilation; that the heart may rejoice without
words, and the boundless extent of joy may have
no limits of syllables? 'Sing skilfully unto Him
with jubilation.'"—*S. Augustine on Ps.* xxxiii.

6.—*The Versicles, etc., preceding the Lessons.*

After the Psalms, according to the later practice,
follow a versicle and response, the LORD's Prayer,
prayer for blessing, Benediction and Absolution.

None of these were anciently in use. Amalarius
says, that in his time it was not customary at
Rome even to say *Pater* after the nocturnal Psalms,
as was done in France. The Offices for the Dead,
and for the three days before Easter, which retain
more of the ancient form than any others, have
only a versicle and response, and *Pater*.

A Versicle is a short prayer addressed to GOD,
and derives its name from *versus* = turned, because
it was to be said turning towards the Altar. It is
sung by one person alone, and the whole choir
joins in the response.

The LORD's Prayer was said, as forming the
conclusion of the Office: and the Absolution likewise was a concluding prayer. For *Absolution* in
this place means conclusion, and has nothing at
all to do with remission of sins. *Absolutio* means
accomplishment, as well as loosing, or acquittal.

But this Absolution finds no place in the Sarum rite. The Benediction was only the blessing at the end of the Office; like *Bless we the* LORD, etc., at the close of other hours.

Here then the ancient Nocturn Office ended, as we learn from Cassian, and from the rules of all primitive Orders. Lessons were subsequently added.

"There has been much doubt as to the origin of the words: *Jube domine benedicere,* and also as to their meaning. Grancolas takes it to mean a request that his superior would bless him. It is variously rendered: *Pray, Sir, a blessing:* or *Sir, pray for a blessing.* Its origin, however, appears to be Eastern. The question is, whether it is addressed by the reader to GOD, or to the priest. In the Roman use, it is said in the former sense, in private recitation of the service; in the latter, in public. The English use apparently knew of no such distinction;—it was taken, as the passage in the Greek Office seems to prove it ought, for a request to the priest that he would desire a blessing. The *Jube* is only a recognition, in a somewhat strong form, of the priestly *power* or commission to invoke a blessing. The formula is best rendered, 'Sir, desire GOD to bless us.' But it is singular that in the East the priest acceded to the request by blessing GOD; in the West, by blessing himself and the congregation. This is somewhat characteristic;

for it is much more usual in the Eastern forms than in the Western, for man to lose himself in the thought of GOD, and in the pure joy of jubilant praise."*—Freeman.

"Versicles are said, that if perchance our minds have wandered during the work of the Psalms, they may, on hearing the versicle, be turned towards the east, *i.e.*, to CHRIST, Who is our East: according to the signification of the word verse, which is derived from *reversio*, a word signifying to turn: and, therefore, while ye say the versicle, that is to say, a little turning, ye turn to the east, or to the Altar, (for ye turn you from psalmody to reading and hearing,) in token that all is intended to the worship of GOD, and also to ask forgiveness of Him if ye have offended Him by any negligence in your Psalms, or for to ask help that ye may read here your legend to His pleasance."—*Myrroure*.

"Rightly, therefore, we say with a loud voice the versicle, which signifieth the fruit of good works: to excite the slothful who are torpid in praising GOD, and understanding things divine, that they may turn again to their hearts, that is, that hearing

* S. Peter Damiani wrote a little book in answer to some scrupulous hermits, who doubted whether to use this phrase and some other analogous expressions, when saying Office entirely alone. He rules that solitary Office is to be said as in common; for he who recites it, does so in the name of the whole Church: otherwise all expressions of the plural number must be altered whenever they occur: as in, *O come let us worship*, etc. A Christian cannot pray alone: he speaks for and with all his brethren.

the verse, they may call back all thoughts which have wandered abroad to gaze on temporal things......

" But it is asked why the versicles of the Nocturns are said before the lessons, and in the other hours, after the chapter? I answer that, by reason of the length and magnitude of the nocturnal lessons, we are wont to sit. Lest, therefore, by long sitting, we forget the doctrine of the LORD, which is signified by the lessons, therefore the preceding versicle incites us to the hearing of the lessons; but in the other hours, because the lessons are neither so many, nor so long, it is not necessary to sit down, nor to preface them with versicles. They are said in the other hours after the lessons, to signify that, in the intervals of the hours, the LORD's doctrine is not to be neglected. And the versicles are often sung by children, to show that service offered in innocence is pleasing to GOD......

" After the verse before the lessons, in which we receive doctrine, is said the LORD's Prayer. First, to signify that he who lacketh wisdom and understanding of doctrine, is to ask it of GOD, Who, according to blessed James, *giveth to all men liberally and upbraideth not.* Also to repel thereby the temptations of the devil. For he, hearing us read lessons, wherein the victories of the Saints over himself are set forth, seeks to attack us more keenly, wherefore we protect ourselves by that Prayer."

"Lessons are preceded by prayer, because we ought to pray the LORD of the harvest that He would send forth labourers into His harvest, and that He may open our hearts to His law and commandments; lest the seed of GOD's word which we are about to hear, be devoured of birds, or choked of thorns, or hindered of taking root by reason of the hardness of our hearts."—Durandus.

"Then cometh the reader, and asketh leave of GOD Almighty, and help of your prayer, that she may read to our LORD's worship, and sayeth *Jube domine benedicere*, ' LORD, bid me say well.' As if she said, ' LORD, give me leave, and bid me say or read, for else I dare not presume to open my mouth to these holy words; and give me strength and grace to read and say well, and so well that Thou be pleased and the hearers edified, and my soul unhurt.' And though these words be said thus principally to GOD, yet they are said also to her that giveth the blessing, which therein occupieth GOD's stead. For by blessing is understood giving of leave, wherefore she sayeth *Jube domine benedicere*, that is, ' LORD, bid her bless.' And this is done to shew that none ought in holy Church to read and speak and preach openly the Word of GOD, but if he be specially licensed thereto."— *Myrroure.*

7.—*Lessons.*

The Synagogue practice of reading and expounding the Scriptures every Sabbath Day, was adopted from the very earliest times in the Christian Church. In the Liturgy, *i.e.*, the celebration of the Holy Eucharist, the holy books were read and expounded; but nothing of the kind took place in the night or day Offices. In the Eastern Church, at the present day, Lessons are read only on Sundays, Festivals, and Vigils; the Synagogue pattern being thus, in its measure, followed. But the Western system of Lessons seems to have been drawn from the Eastern use of odes (also called lections by some monks of S. Basil, in Italy). These were sung in three groups, each containing three odes; except during the time between Septuagesima and Easter, when one group of three, only, was used: and they answer to the responsories sung after each of the Western Lessons. The Council of Laodicæa (circ. 360), enjoins that reading be alternated with singing. Although little trace of the practice is found in Eastern antiquity, yet the Church of Lyons, which derived its ritual from Ephesus, in the exarchate of which Laodicæa was situated, had, at least as early as 499, a scheme of Lessons in accordance with that Canon; and the Roman and English use may have, at least partly, resulted from combining the Lyonnese model with the Eastern ode scheme.

When Lessons were first introduced into the Roman Office, Scripture alone was read, as is still the practice on ordinary ferias. But when the number of nocturns was increased, homilies were read for the sake of variety. The Lessons of the second nocturn are intended as an explanation, by one or other of the Fathers of the Church, of the Scripture Lessons read in the first nocturn ; while the Lessons of the third nocturn expound the Gospel for the day, which is to be read at the following Mass, and of which the first verse only, for brevity's sake, is read at the beginning of the third nocturn Lessons. This threefold manner of Lessons is only observed on Sundays and Festivals. According to old usage, Scripture alone is used on ferial days, except when they have proper Gospels, as in Lent, etc. On such occasions, the homily of the Gospel is read. Originally, the length of the lessons was not fixed, but was left optional. This accounts for their having been in early times so long as to involve the possibility of drowsiness, and for their having been cut down to such very small proportions as we find in most books of the late pre-reformation type.

The Sarum lectionary was similar to the Roman, as to the sequence of books : beginning Advent with Isaiah, reading S. Paul after Epiphany, Genesis at

Septuagesima, Exodus in Lent, Jeremiah in Passion-tide, Samuel and Kings after Pentecost; and then proceeding to the books of Solomon, some parts of the Apocrypha, and the Prophets, exclusive of Isaiah and Jeremiah. But two sets of Lessons only were set down for the ferial office in any one week; because the great number of Saints' days then observed rendered a larger supply needless. And on festivals, all nine lessons, or the six first, were wont to consist of a homily on the occasion, or of the legend of the Saint commemorated: sometimes very lovely, but sometimes also exceedingly apocryphal. It ought to be remembered, however, that the selection of homilies in the Sarum book is in no wise to be despised. Some of them are wonderfully beautiful; full of life and unction.

"The first three lessons on Sundays were read (in England) by boys of the lowest form on each side alternately: the two next by deacons or sub-deacons on alternate sides; the sixth by some clerk of the higher form: the last three, by higher dignitaries, ending with the highest on the choir side. The reader stood facing the choir: on Festivals and Sundays of the first class, he read in the pulpit, but on other days from the reading desk in the choir, or, for convenience' sake, from the west end of the choir. The reader bowed to the Altar and to the choir, and then turned to the officiating priest, and asked his blessing."—Chambers.

At the close of each lesson (or rather, originally, to give notice that enough had been read, the Officiant said, " But Thou ;" and the reader continued, " O LORD, have mercy upon us." If, however, the lesson was from one of the prophets, the officiant said, " Thus saith the LORD ;" and the reader answered, " Turn ye unto Me, and be ye saved."

" Thanks be to GOD," was then responded by the choir; but in England, this was not said aloud at Matins.

" Some say that Scripture Lessons were not introduced till the time of S. Gregory ; and those on the passions of the Saints were not generally read till that of Pope Adrian I. The histories of the Saints, as now read in the Roman Breviary, were recognized and approved by Baronius and Bellarmine, at the command of Clement VIII.

" Lections are said at every hour of night and day. And they are called lections, because they are not sung, but read. The lections of Nocturns are our instruction, because by them we are taught to offer our works to GOD. But the reader, approaching the book, ascendeth a step, because the teacher ought to surpass the crowd in perfection of life."—Durandus.

8.—*Responsories.*

Responsories are prayers used after the Lessons, as it were responsively : having some reference to that which has been read : sad answering to sad, joyful to joyful. The Responsories were called Histories in the Sarum use, and often are in fact an epitome of the history read in the Lessons.

Allusion has already been made to the rich veil of Scripture imagery which the compilers of the late Gallican Breviaries cast over the subject of the office, adorning it, yet half hiding it from the unskilled eye. The earlier writers, wisely considerate, took some great fact or doctrine connected with the day, and, with a noble unity and sequence of idea, pressed it home again and again to the understanding of all—or at least, of all to whom the Latin language was intelligible, (and those who understood it not, were in those days taught by the eye).

S. Benedict introduced *Gloria Patri* into the last R̷. of each Nocturn, and this practice was afterwards adopted elsewhere. The present Roman Breviary cuts off the R̷. after the ninth lesson, substituting *Te Deum*. This was wont to be sung after the ninth R̷. and is so set down in the Sarum book. Much cutting down and polishing have left on the Roman book their usual result ; it is beautiful, but cold and hard ; and has lost much energy and vividness.

The Responsories were always intended to be sung, and the music for them is very elaborate.

" The lection being finished, the reader saith,

But Thou, O LORD, *have mercy upon us,* which is not of the lection, nor doth it continue it ; but he, directing his speech to GOD, excuseth himself, as if he said, ' LORD, I have sinned peradventure in my reading, desiring the praise or favour of men, and perchance the hearers have likewise sinned by entertaining vain thoughts, or averting their minds from the Lesson : but Thou, O LORD, have mercy upon us.' Where all respond, *Thanks be to* GOD —this refers to the Lesson ; not to, *But Thou, O* LORD, etc. This is the voice of the Church rendering thanks to GOD, as if she said : GOD hath given us the words of salvation, which are the food of the soul, and for that blessing we humbly pay our thanks to GOD."—*Myrroure.*

" In the day hours is not said, *Thou, O* LORD, etc., as in the night hours, because the priest ought to be perfect, and one who yieldeth not easily to the suggestions of the devil ; and because in a short lection and among his familiars, he can hardly be caught by the wind of human favour. But yet the response is then given, *Thanks be to* GOD, for the same reason as at Matins. . . . . .

" The Responsory is added after the Lessons ; by the Responsory is signified the good works, and doctrine is signified by the Lessons ; therefore the Responses are subjoined to the Lessons, because by good works we must respond to doctrine, that we may not be cast into outer darkness with the slothful servant who hid his lord's money.

"The Responses of Nocturns are, as it were, spiritual songs; for those things are called songs which are sung; and they are spiritual because they proceed from the jubilation of the spiritual mind. But they are sung, that in the recitation of the Lessons our minds may be lifted up to the heavenly Country, and therefore *Gloria* is inserted. The Responsory is begun by one, to be joined in by others, whereby we understand the mutual exhortation of brethren to serve GOD. The Response is repeated imperfectly after the verse, to signify that those who cannot attain to the mountain, that is, to the state of perfection, may yet be saved in Zoar, that is, in another way, and in a state of imperfection. It is also repeated imperfectly, to signify that what we do while living in this world is imperfect; . . . . . but on Festivals it is again repeated perfectly, to signify the joy and perfection of the Saints."—Durandus.

"Three things are needful to the common health of man. The first is, that the understanding be lightened with knowledge of truth to know what is good and what is evil. And, for this knowledge is had by reading and hearing of wholesome doctrine, therefore it is understood by the Lessons. The second is, good use of the free will, that the will assent to that that is known good, and hate that that is

known evil. And for the will answereth thus to
the knowledge, therefore it is to be understood by the
Response, that is as much as to say as answer:
for it answereth in sentence to the Lesson as it is
before said. The third is work, so that the thing
that the understanding knoweth good, and that the
will, ruled by grace, loveth, be done in deed. And
this is understood by the verse, that is as much as to
say as a turning, for the knowledge and will ought
thus to be turned into deed. And after the verse a
part of the Response is sung again. For as a
good will causeth good deeds, so good deeds help
to steady and to strengthen the good will.

"The Lessons are heard and the Responses are
sung sitting, for knowledge of truth and right ruling
of the will may not be but in a restful soul. But
the verse is sung standing, for good deeds may not
be done without labour.

"The Response is sung of all, for every man may
have a good will, that is understood by the
Response. But the verse is sung but of few, for all
folk may not fulfil their good wills in deed, that is
understood by the verse, so much as the holy
Apostle Saint Paul said that he might not do the
good that he would. The Lesson is read of one
and heard of all, in token that each congregation
ought to live under one governour that shall teach
them and rule them after GOD's law. For each
man, namely religious, ought not to do after his

own wit or knowledge, but after the obedience and teaching of Holy Church."—*Myrroure*.

9.—*Te Deum*.

This canticle closes the Sunday and Festival Matin Office, except in Lent, when (as well as on Sundays in Advent) it is replaced in the Roman use by a ninth responsory. The Sarum use, which always keeps its ninth response when three Nocturns are said, omits *Te Deum* on all days in Advent as well as in Lent. Its authorship or origin has never yet been settled; its germ, however, may be found in a very ancient Eastern hymn, and, indeed, in a part of the Song of the Three Children. (vv. 29·33, 66). Some of the verses are extracted from S. Cyprian on Mortality, where he dwells on the subject of eternal life—" The glorious choir of the Apostles," etc., etc. It was called by some the Dominical hymn, on account of its being reserved for Sundays.

The English Prayer Book retains the Sarum orthography, *Cherubin* and *Seraphin*, instead of adopting the more usual ending. This is according to the Aramaic, the dialect of Syriac spoken by our LORD Himself; the termination in *im*, is according to the original Hebrew.—Leslie.

The Sacerdotal verse, which has now been removed from the Roman book, but was always retained in the Sarum, was said after the *Te Deum*, or the last responsory; and was thus called, in order to be distinguished from the other versicles which were sung by boys, or younger clerics, whereas this was said by the Priest officiating.

"The nocturns being ended, the bells are rung, and *Te Deum* is sung with a loud voice, to shew how openly and gloriously the Church praises GOD in the time of grace, and to signify that if by good works we correspond well to holy teaching, we shall attain to the heavenly praises together with the Angels."—Durandus.

II.—LAUDS.

LAUDS were anciently said at daybreak, and were therefore called *laudes matutinæ*, morning Lauds. Some space of time therefore intervened between the close of Matins and the beginning of this service; but they are now almost always said consecutively. The Office takes its name from the three psalms, (counted as one,) which form an invariable part of it.

"Lauds is so called, as being an Office of praise to Him Who hath brought us out of darkness into His marvellous light. We sing Lauds in the morning, and Vespers in the evening, as offering frequent sacrifice to the LORD. And morning and evening sacrifice was offered under the Law; yet the Jews say that the evening sacrifice was worthier and fatter than the morning. Now by the Office

of Lauds we understand the Law, and by Vespers
the Passion of the SAVIOUR, Who, at the eventide
of the world, that is, in the sixth age, offered Himself to GOD the FATHER for us. And as those
two sacrifices were each like unto each, so are
Lauds and Vespers. For in both, the Psalms
are divided by five *Glorias*; in both, hymn,
lesson, and versicle follow according to the same
order: in this is sung the Song of Zacharias, in
that, the Song of Mary. Nevertheless, the Vesper
Office is the worthier of the two, by reason of the
worthier thing which it signifies; therefore, on the
greater Festivals, Vespers are sung more solemnly
than Lauds, and the Responsory is inserted."—
Durandus.

1.—*Psalms and Canticles.*

The number of Psalms recited at this Office is
differently calculated, but, counting the Gospel
Canticle as one, we have six, the Eastern number.
They are more usually, however, counted as five,
and that Canticle is not commonly enumerated
with them.

Durandus is exceedingly full in his comments
on this Office, and it may, perhaps, be better to
quote him too largely than too scantily; because
those who daily recite the same words, will gladly
take them, now in one sense, now in another, so
as to avoid the coldness of routine.

"Five Psalms are said at Lauds, to signify reparation for the five senses, and for five conditions in the Church. The first Psalm at Sunday Lauds is Ps. 93, *Dominus regnavit*, wherein GOD is praised, Who made the round world fast, that is to say, in faith, and by the Resurrection; therefore this Psalm belongs to the kingdom of CHRIST. The second is Ps. 100, *Jubilate*, which belongs to Confessors, whence it is there said, *Go ye into His gates with confession*," (Vulgate: *confessio* signifying both the confession of sin, and the act of praise,) "and it rightly begins with joyfulness, because confession is greatly pleasing to GOD. The third is Ps. 63, *Deus, Deus meus*; which signifies the state of Martyrs who thirst for the LORD, whence it is there said, *My soul thirsteth*; and because all our thirst and intent ought to be in and for the Trinity, therefore follows Ps. 67, *Deus misereatur*, wherein the whole Trinity is mentioned, for it is said: GOD, *even our GOD, shall give us His blessing*: GOD *shall bless us*: GOD being named thrice, as being FATHER, SON, and HOLY GHOST. The fourth is the Song of the Three Children, *Benedicite*, signifying the time of Antichrist, and at the end of that Psalm we do not say *Gloria*, because the last verse of the Canticle is identical with that ascription of praise. The fifth is Ps. 148, *Laudate Dominum*, in which the time is signified, when, after the death of Antichrist, the Jews will be con-

verted. . . . . It might be said that eight Psalms are
recited at Lauds ; for that Office mystically represents the state of the Church from the beginning
of Apostolical stability, till the perfection of the
elect : under which state are to be found the eight
orders of the Church, or elect in the Church saved
by baptism ; as in the ark of Noah, eight souls,
signifying these, were saved thereby. For by the
flood is denoted Baptism, and by the ark, the
Church. The first order was the primitive Church,
having its conversation amongst the Jews, which
was formed and edified by the preaching of CHRIST,
as is shewn in the first Psalm, *Dominus regnavit*,
and in the first verse, where the SAVIOUR's kingdom
and power are set forth. The second verse deals
with the foundation of the Church, which then
began to be set on that foundation, which is
CHRIST. . . . .

"The second order was the primitive Church
entering among the Gentiles by the preaching of
the LORD and His Apostles, and summoning all
the earth to praise the LORD ; as is shewn by the
second Psalm, *Jubilate Deo omnis terra*. The
third order was that of the believing Gentiles, and
the third Psalm, *Deus, Deus meus*, sets forth their
praise and goodwill for the Apostles' call. The
fourth will be the returning Jewish people converted
by Enoch and Elias, and the fourth Psalm, *Deus
misereatur*, shews them, after their return, praying

GOD for His mercy, and then they will rejoice to know the way of the LORD, which they perceive to exist among the Gentiles. The fifth will be those that live in the future times of Antichrist; (of whom Nebuchadnezzar was a type;) but although he shall trouble the Saints of both peoples, yet they will not cease praising GOD, like the three children in the fire; and therefore *Benedicite* rightly follows; and on account of the tribulation, the Antiphon has no *Alleluia*, and it is said without *Gloria*. This same hymn also has three divisions: in the first, supernal creatures are invited to praise GOD: those in the heaven and the air. In the second are invited to His praise, creatures on earth, and those that move in the waters. In the third are invited all spirits and souls; that we may praise GOD with all creatures; because, as the three children escaped Nebuchadnezzar, and the fiery furnace, so we, the devil, and the fire of hell.*

---

* This idea has been worked out very elaborately in a Sermon by the Rev. O. S. Prescott. The following is a brief analysis:—

The hymn consists of four parts:

1st division contains 5 verses: subdivided into 1 verse and a series of 4 verses.

2nd   „   12   „   a series of 4 triplets of verses.
3rd   „   9   „   a series of 3 triplets.
4th   „   6   „   a series of 2 triplets.

The first part contains the 1 of unity, and the 4 of fundamental completeness.

The 1st verse, a general invitatory.

"And this hymn well befits Sundays and festivals: because on the first day GOD created all things, and by His Resurrection He afterwards renewed them. And therefore the same Lauds are said on

The 4 verses following invoke *all heavenly powers*: 4 primary orders of spiritual intelligence.

(Waters above the heavens=living spirits of glory. 4=foundation.)

The second part contains 12 verses: the heavens have 12 signs, Church has 12 foundations: material heaven=shadow of Church.

A series of 4 triplets, each complete=invocation of material heavens.

1. Sun and moon: stars of heaven: showers and dew.
2. Winds: fire and heat: seasons.
3. Dews and frost: frost and cold: ice and snow.
4. Nights and days: light and darkness: lightnings and clouds.

The 3rd part comprises 9 verses: including all things of earth: 9, a number of judgment: and the earth is to be judged.

A series of 3 triplets: things beneath the firmament.

1. Earth: mountains and hills: green things.
2. Wells: seas and floods: all that move in waters.
3. Fowls of the air: beasts and cattle: children of men.

The 4th part contains 6 verses: 6=temporary completeness: 2 triplets: Church militant and expectant.

1. Israel: priests of the LORD: servants of the LORD=Church militant.
2. Spirits and souls of the righteous=Saints, holy and humble: innocent and penitent, faithful departed.
3. Ananias, Azarias, and Misael=those in whom GOD hath specially glorified His Name, and who have glorified Him in the fire.

In the hymn, 50 objects or classes invoked: 50=release, jubilee, beatitude.

It has 32 verses: 8 of salvation × 4 of completeness=heavenly and earthly completeness and bliss.

Every part but the first, which tells of heaven, and may not be divided, subdivided into series of 3: 3=the Triune GOD, in Whose honour the hymn is sung.

Sundays and Saints' days, and in Easter-tide, because they represent the joy of CHRIST's Resurrection, and of our own. The sixth, seventh, and eighth will be those who are to be converted and brought together out of all parts of the world, and, after the persecution of Antichrist, and his death, will enjoy greater peace than the Church hath now, till the Day of Judgment : in which time of quietness the praise of GOD, as contained in the three last Psalms at Lauds, will be sung by the three orders of the righteous, namely, the married, the continent, and the virgins, (which are typified by Job, Noah, and Daniel,) and by all Saints in general . . . . . .

"It is asked why these three Psalms are said under one Antiphon and one *Gloria ?* Because the firstfruits of the elect, gathered out of all the world, will be together without any interval, and will give glory together. Also these three Psalms celebrate the triumph over the world, the flesh, and the devil ; and because one is not to be had without the other, therefore they are duly joined together. It is also asked why the two Psalms, *Deus, Deus meus*, and *Deus misereatur*, are joined in like manner? First, because Psalm 63 signifies thirst for GOD, and in Psalm 67 the Trinity is pointed out. This is so done, therefore, to signify continual thirst and desire for GOD. Secondly, to signify that before the persecution of Antichrist the people of the believing Gentiles, who are signified by Psalm

63 and the Jewish people, signified by Psalm 67 shall be one in faith, and after they are joined together shall come the tribulation of Antichrist. Thirdly, because the first of these Psalms signifies the love of GOD, wherefore it is said therein: *My soul thirsteth for Thee.* But the second, the love of our neighbour, whereas it is said: *That Thy saving health may be known among all nations.* And these two graces are so joined together, that one cannot consist without the other in Christian profession. Moreover, at the end of the sixty-third Psalm is not said *Gloria*, because it deals with the misery of human kind, where it saith *My soul thirsteth ....* But to the following Psalm is joined *Gloria*, because it treats of the mercy of GOD, whereby human-kind receives good things, and is delivered from evil. The aforesaid two Psalms, and three last, Ps. 148, etc., are never changed, to signify that Christians ought never to be without faith in, and desire for, the Trinity, which is expressed by the two united Psalms, and without praise to GOD, which is signified by the Psalm *Laudate* ... The first Sunday Psalm, Ps. 93, which is a Psalm of joy, is changed on ferias to Ps. 51, which is penitential.

"The second Sunday Psalm, *Jubilate*, is changed on the six ferial days for six other Psalms, whereby the same preaching of the Church is set forth. In Septuagesima, Ps. 118, *Confitemini*, takes the place of *Jubilate* on Sunday.

"On Monday is said Psalm 5, *Verba mea*, which is the voice of the Church called into the heritage of GOD. . . . On Tuesday, Ps. 43, *Judica me, Deus*, which commemorates the time when the primitive Church entered in to the Gentiles; on Wednesday, Ps. 65, *Te decet*, which is sung in a figure of the Gentiles who turned from idols to GOD; on Thursday, Ps. 90, *Domine refugium*, which is entitled, 'A prayer of Moses, the man of GOD,' and is suitable to the return of the Jews; on Friday, Ps. 143, *Domine exaudi*, which David sang when his son persecuted him; signifying the persecution of Antichrist; on Saturday, Ps. 92, *Bonum est*, which is entitled a Psalm for the Sabbath Day, that is, the day of quiet, wherein the Saints shall rest and praise GOD, after the persecution of Antichrist. The afore-mentioned six Psalms are arranged in this order also, that in them may be noted the order of Christian conversion.

"Instead of *Benedicite*, six Canticles are said on the six ferial days, because as that contains the thanksgiving of the Three Children, so these contain the thanksgiving of the elect. There is such difference between Canticles and Psalms, as between good works and giving of thanks. *Canticle* signifies the act of the human voice; *Psalm* that which is sung to the Psaltery. . . . . .

"On every ferial day throughout the week the

second and fifth Psalms vary. But the Psalms
Deus, Deus meus and *Laudate* are never omitted,
nor prætermitted, because there never was, nor
will there ever be, a time when the souls of the
righteous thirst not for GOD, the fountain of living
water, and praise not GOD in the height. . . . . .

" The six varying Psalms and Canticles fit one
another, and may aptly be assigned to the various
periods of the time of grace. On Monday is commemorated the state of the Primitive Church,
which received the inheritance by the preaching of
the Saints ; wherefore in the Psalm, *Verba mea*,
the Church prays for the eternal inheritance which
it receives through CHRIST. . . . But in the Canticle
she gives thanks, saying, *O* LORD, *I will praise
Thee ; though Thou wast angry with me, Thine
anger is turned away, and Thou comfortedst me.*
For the anger of GOD remained until the Passion
of the SAVIOUR, but then His wrath being turned
away, He comforted the Church, opening to her
the gates of the kingdom of Heaven. Also, in
the Psalm, the Church, setting forth its solitude,
saith, *Early in the morning will I direct my prayer
unto Thee, and will look up.* But in the Canticle,
shewing her confidence, she says, *The* LORD JE-
HOVAH *is my strength and my song ;* that is, It is He
through Whom I am strong, and Whom I am
bound to praise. The Psalm *Verba mea* belongs,
indeed, to the whole Church, but especially to the

Primitive, whereunto, first, by the Apostles was given the promise of the eternal inheritance, and then the banner of the Cross began to be lifted up on the nations. To which time also pertains the Canticle, as is apparent by the passages preceding it in the book of Isaiah. For it is said in that book a little before : *In that day there shall be a root of Jesse, which shall stand for an ensign of the people ; to it shall the Gentiles seek : and His rest shall be glorious.* And a little after that : *He shall set up an ensign for the nations, and shall assemble the outcasts of Israel.* . . . . .

"On Tuesday we commemorate that time when the Church suffered persecution from the wicked ; first from the Jews, and afterwards from divers Roman emperors, beginning at the time of Nero, till the time of the Emperors Diocletian and Maximian. What things the Church then suffered are noted by the Psalm, *Give sentence with me, O* GOD, *and defend my cause against the ungodly people ;* and she showeth her sadness when she saith : *Why go I so heavily, while the enemy oppresseth me ?* But, because she was delivered from that persecution, she sings the Canticle *Ego dixi*, which was sung by Hezekiah, after his deliverance from Sennacherib, and after the illness which fell upon him, either that his heart might not be lifted up in pride, or because it was lifted up in consequence of his unexpected triumph over the army of Sennacherib. For as he, being delivered, gave glory to God, so though at first, the Church as it were despairing, says: *Mine age is departed, and is removed from me as a shepherd's tent: I have cut off like a weaver my life: He will cut me off with pining sickness; from day even to night wilt Thou make an end of me:* yet she continueth hopefully: *The living,* now in Thy protection, *the living,* hereafter in future quiet, *he shall praise Thee as I do this day,* delivered from enemies, and I deal like a good *father,* who *makes known* to his *children* the truth.

"On Wednesday is commemorated the time when the Church began to be exalted over her enemies, peace being restored to her by the Emperor Constantine; wherefore she sings: *Thou, O God, art praised in Sion.* Sion, by interpretation, is speculation or contemplation; because in the time of quiet the Church could occupy herself in contemplation . . . . . For this deliverance she sings the song of Hannah, the mother of Samuel, who sang it when delivered from the persecution of her rival Peninnah; namely, *My heart rejoiceth in the* Lord, etc. For when the affairs of State began to be administered by holy men and Christian emperors, the *mouth* of the Church might be *enlarged over* her *enemies,* namely, the Jews, Pagans, and heretics.

" That same peace which is enjoyed by the con-

verted Gentiles, converted Jews may also enjoy
Wherefore, in the person of the Jewish people, we
sing, on Thursday, Psalm 90, LORD, *Thou hast
been our Refuge.* That this psalm belongs to the
Jews, is shewn by its title, *A prayer of Moses the
man of* GOD. To the same also pertains the
Canticle of Moses: *I will sing unto the* LORD.
For as the Jews rejoiced at the destruction of
Pharaoh and his host, so Christians now rejoice at
the overthrow of divers emperors who persecuted
the Church for hatred of the Name of CHRIST.

"On Friday is made commemoration of the
Passion of the LORD. Therefore is sung that
psalm: *Hear my prayer, O* LORD, whereof the title
is; *A psalm of David, when he was persecuted by
his son Absalom;* for as David had many sons,
but was persecuted by one of them, namely,
Absalom, so likewise our LORD hath many sons,
of whom He now saith: *Can the children of the
bridechamber mourn, as long as the Bridegroom is
with them?* But He was persecuted by one of
them, namely, Judas, who is called Absalom, or
Abassalom, which is, by interpretation, the 'peace
of the father," by reason of the kiss he gave to our
LORD, which is the sign of peace. To the same
matter belongs the Canticle of Habakkuk: *O*
LORD, *I have heard Thy speech:* wherein it is said :
*He had horns coming out of His hand, and there
was the hiding of His power; before Him went*

the pestilence. By horns, we understand kingdoms. Horns in His hand signify kingdoms in His power; but this power He merited to take to Himself, (or rather, He made known that it was given to Him,) by His Passion: whereof He Himself saith: *All power is given unto Me in Heaven and in earth.* But in the second place may be understood the two horns of the Cross: whence it might appear that it would be more fitting to say, that His Hands were in the horns, than the horns in His hand. But the Prophet chose to express himself thus, to shew that He was crucified of His Own power and will, as He Himself said: *No man taketh My Life from Me: I have power to lay it down, and I have power to take it again.* Here, in the Cross, His power was hidden at that time, because He was esteemed as smitten of GOD and afflicted: *And before Him went the pestilence,* (*before His face went death,* Vulg.,) because death was destroyed by His Death.

" On Saturday is made a commemoration of the victory of the Jewish people; which shall be joined to the Church of GOD at the end of the world, and with the Church shall sing the Psalm, *It is a good thing to give thanks unto the* LORD: *to tell of Thy lovingkindness early in the morning,* that is, in prosperity, *and of Thy truth in the night-season,* that is, in adversity. That this Psalm pertains to the Jewish people is shewn by that verse: *Upon*

an instrument of ten strings. The instrument ⟨
ten strings signifies the Law and its ten comman⟨
ments. . . . . The Canticle of Moses: *Give ear, ⟨
ye heavens,* belongs to the sabbath day, and to th⟨
Jewish people; according to the words of Bed⟨
who saith in his commentary on S. Luke, that o⟨
the sabbath day the Jews crowded to the syn⟨
gogues to meditate on the commandments of th⟨
divine law, laying aside the business of th⟨
world. . . . In memory, therefore, of the pristin⟨
religion, is sung on the Saturday this same Car⟨
ticle, wherein is described the state of that peopl⟨
according as they had offended or had appease⟨
the wrath of GOD."—Durandus.

2.—*Chapter and Gospel Canticles.*

The Chapter at Lauds was to be read by th⟨
Officiant; such was the rule when one lesso⟨
only occurred in the Office. At Matins, the lesson⟨
being many, the last alone, taken from the Gospe⟨
was reserved to be read by the worthiest presen⟨
No request for a blessing preceded the Chapt⟨
at the hours, for this reason: that it was abou⟨
to be read by the person of highest dignit⟨
present, who therefore could not ask blessing ⟨
the lesser.

"A Chapter is as much to say as a little hea⟨
(capitula): it is called little for shortness. And ⟨
is called a head, for it is always taken of Hol⟨

Scripture, and often of the Epistle that is read in the Mass the same day. And Holy Scripture is chief above all other scriptures, as the head is above all other members of the body. And the Chapters are read at other hours instead of lessons in way of doctrine and teaching, as lessons are at Matins. And therefore in other hours after the Chapter followeth a response with a verse, which meaneth the same understanding as doth the lessons and response and verse at Matins."— *Myrroure.*

"In the Chapter is made an exhortation that we faint not in the way. After the Chapter the choir, assenting to the exhortation, sings a hymn. After the hymn follows the versicle, *Because Thou hast been my Helper,* etc. Because the promises are set down in the song of Zacharias, which immediately follows, and we are slow to believe the promises, therefore the versicle is said previously with a loud voice, that we may be excited to believe the promises of God. . . . .

"The Psalm *Benedictus* is said in this place, because it deals with the forerunner of Him Who came in the sixth age of the world. And this is the sixth Psalm at Lauds. And note, that because this Canticle and the Song of Mary, *Magnificat,* are Gospels, therefore we sing them standing. Moreover, these two Canticles are not sung in Church in the order in which they were composed

For the Song of *Zacharias* is sung first, and yet it was made second; because therein we read, *And hath raised up a mighty salvation for us*, which came to pass in the Resurrection, and because the child is addressed who was as daybreak to the sun, therefore it is sung at Lauds.

"But the song of the Virgin is sung at Vespers, *i.e.*, at the sixth day-office, because therein we read, *He hath regarded the lowliness of His handmaiden*, the Church, or Mary herself, because made in the sixth age; and it deals with the Incarnation in that place, *He hath holpen His servant Israel.*

"The third Canticle, that of Simeon, is sung at the seventh Office, *i.e.*, Compline, because he prays to depart in peace, and the seventh age will be the time of rest.

"Again at three hours, we say three Gospels: at dawn, *Benedictus;* because therein the True Light is announced. At Vespers, *Magnificat*, because in the end of the world, according as it is there said, GOD *shall scatter the proud, and exalt the humble.*

"At Compline, *Nunc Dimittis;* because after the Judgment the Saints shall reign in peace.

"The Canticle being finished, the Antiphon which signifies the love or devotion which we ought to have in praising GOD is repeated. But while the verse is said before the Canticle, incense is offered to signify devotion issuing forth from the fire of

charity, which ought to exist in all praises. And
let not that happen to us, which befell Zacharias,
who disbelieved the Angel appearing to him with
promise of a son, and was therefore struck dumb.
Let us believe in the promises of GOD, lest we be
silenced from His praise."—Durandus.

3.—*Preces.*

The Preces intervening between the *Benedictus*
and the collect at ferial Lauds, were built up
gradually. They at first consisted simply in the
repetition of the *Kyrie.* In some uses it was said
thrice. S. Aurelian ruled that it was to be said
twelve times at every day hour. The Sarum use and
the modern Roman have the nine-fold repetition,
which the compilers of our Prayer Book evidently
had in mind when arranging the beginning of the
Communion Service. The Carthusians now also
say it nine times at Lauds. (This was called Litany,
and was the earliest Western form of that kind of
prayer.) S. Benedict added the *Pater,* as crown and
conclusion of the Office; further additions were
subsequently made up of short sentences from the
Psalms; (of which we hear in the sixth century;)
and still later the whole of Ps. 51. was introduced.
These ferial Preces were prescribed in England by
the Council of Cloveshoo, in the eighth century.

The Preces always began in the Greek language :
Kyrie eleison, Christe eleison (just as *Alleluia* was

always retained in its original Hebrew). The
Lord's Prayer, which followed, was, and is, said
in silence. After this are said the ℣. and ℞.
'And lead us not into temptation. But deliver us
from evil.' This seems to represent the *embolismus*,
or prayer against temptation, which follows the
Lord's Prayer in the Eastern Liturgy.

The Roman Office prescribes that the two first
words, and two last petitions of the Lord's Prayer
be said aloud: the Sarum is careful to point out
that such is not *its* rule; and that 'the whole is
always said in silence, *according to the use of the
Church of Sarum*.' The two petitions are then
repeated afterwards.

" After your *Pater Noster* and *Ave Maria* " (this
referred to the Office of the Blessed Virgin said by
the Brigittines) " which ye say in silence for to
gather the more restfully your mind together, ye
say again two petitions of your *Pater Noster* all
aloud, that is *Et ne nos*, and *Sed libera nos*, asking
to be delivered from the malice of the fiend that he
overcome you not by any temptation in time of
reading and hearing. And this is done to shew
the need that ye have to be mindful of the two
petitions, that causeth them here to be asked
twice, first privily and after openly, for both she that
readeth openly hath need to be kept from vanity,
and they that hear it in stillness have need to be
kept from dulness and distraction."—*Myrroure*.

The Sarum book always retained the fifty-first Psalm among the ferial Preces through the year at every hour, except in Easter-tide. It was introduced toward A.D. 1000, when men generally believed that the world was coming to an end, and additional acts of penitence were deemed needful. After that expectation had proved groundless, the psalm was removed from the Preces of other Breviaries, except for Lenten use; the English, rather characteristically, retained it. And also in the English use, one of the penitential psalms was added to Ps. 51 on ferias in Lent, at every hour except Sexts, when Ps. 67 was said instead of, not in addition to, it. At Nones on Saturday, and on the eves of double feasts, in Lent, the three last penitential psalms were said consecutively, in order that their recitation might not be cut short by the first Vespers of the festival. According to the present Roman use, the seven psalms are only recited on Fridays in Lent, after Nones, with Litany.

4.—*Collect.*

Collects were not said at Office, according to any of the ancient rules. They were gradually introduced, at first on Sundays only; the Missal Collect for the day being, of course, used.

" The Collect form, as we have it, is Western in every feature, in unity of sentiment and severity of style : in its Roman brevity and majestic con-

ciseness, its freedom from all luxurious ornament
and all inflation of phraseology. It has a truly
illustrious Roman parentage; its inventor, Mr.
Freeman says, was S. Leo, emphatically and justly
called the Great, who held the first See of Christendom from 440 to 461. Of him it may be said, even
by those who cannot shut their eyes to his ambition
and love of domination, that although by human
weakness he was led to grasp at excessive authority,
and so far left an evil example to his successors,
yet by faith he confronted Attila and Genseric with
a dignity which compelled their reverence; by
faith he so proclaimed the One CHRIST in two
Natures, as well nigh to justify the famous accla-
mation, ' Peter hath spoken by Leo;' by faith he
stood forth as the first great Roman preacher, in
sermons full of CHRIST; by faith he maintained
religion, on the throne of Rome alone, of all the
greater sees, in its majesty, its sanctity, its piety."
—Bright, *Ancient Collects.*

S. Gelasius, Bishop of Rome from A.D. 492 to
496, is believed to have re-arranged the Eucharistic
Collects, etc., adding much original matter. S.
Gregory the Great, Bishop of Rome from A.D. 590 to
604, amongst his multitudinous labours, arranged
a famous Sacramentary, in which the three books
of Gelasius were condensed into one volume, many
things being withdrawn, some altered, and some
added.

"The derivation of the word [Collect] is uncertain. It may be because the substance of the prayer is *collected* from the Epistle and Gospel which it accompanies; or, much more probably, because into that prayer the priest *collects* the wishes and supplications of the bystanding faithful. This much better agrees with the Greek synonym, *Synapte*.

"A Collect then is (1) a liturgical prayer; (2) must be short; (3) embraces but one main petition; (4) consists but of one sentence; (5) asks through the merits of our LORD; (6) ends properly with an ascription of praise to the Blessed Trinity. It is a composition belonging to the Western Church; for, as is well known, the Eastern Church has nothing resembling it. In the East, (1) There is no varying Collect for Sundays and Festivals; (2) the prayers are almost all lengthy; (3) they form various sentences, and embrace a variety of particulars; and (4) they do not, in so many words, base their request on our LORD's merits."—Neale.

"Orisons [Collects] are said in the end of each hour; for the Apostles, whenever they were together, they kneeled down on their knees and prayed ere they departed asunder. And she that sayeth the orison standeth turned to the East, for Paradise, from whence we are exiled, is in the East; and therefore thinking what we have lost and where we are and whither we desire to return, we

pray turned towards the East. Orison is as much
as to say prayer; it is also called a Collect, that is
as much as to say a gathering together; for before
this prayer ye address you to GOD, and gather you
in unity to pray in the person of Holy Church that
ye should be the sooner heard. Ye end all your
orisons by our LORD JESUS CHRIST and in His
Blessed Name, because He said in His gospel
that whatever ye ask the Father in My Name He
shall give it you."—*Myrroure*.

5.—*Memorials*.

After the Collect is said ℣. *Bless we the* LORD,
and ℞. *Thanks be to* GOD; which is followed at
Lauds and Vespers by the memorials for the season,
and, if there be such, for the day. The Memorials
(or Commemorations, as the Roman use calls
them,) are prayers in commemoration of certain
subjects. Originally, one Collect only was said at
Mass, and the same practice was observed at Office.
Consequently, when Collects were multiplied in the
former service, they were multiplied also in the
latter. Certain Memorials were fixed for repetition
during certain seasons, and in addition to these,
commemoration was made of any Saint whose
Office fell on a day already occupied by an Office
of superior dignity. The ferias of Advent and
Lent were also to be noticed on all feasts which
fell during those seasons. Memorials, according

to the Sarum use, were to be said in the following sequence: (1) Memorial of any Saint. (2)
Of the Octave (if one be current). (3) Of the
feria (in Advent and Lent). (4) Of S. Mary or
other Memorials, according to the season, in
order as set down in the Psalter. The present
Roman use differs from this. Common Memorials
of S. Mary, the Apostles, the Patron of the place,
and the peace of the Church, are said from the
Octave of Epiphany to Passion Sunday, exclusive of
both those days, and from the Octave of Pentecost
till Advent Sunday, also exclusively: on Sundays,
ferias, and simple feasts. A Memorial of the Cross
precedes these on ferias, and in Easter time no
Memorial is made, except only of the Cross; this
being, however, different from that used throughout the year.

Memorials are always composed of Antiphon, ℣.
and ℞., and Collect. The reason of this is, that
formerly, when a Saint was to be commemorated
on another festival, Lauds or Vespers of that
festival being ended, the Antiphon of the Saint was
sung with *Benedictus* or *Magnificat*, as the case
might be, ℣. and ℞., and Collect. As time went
on, all Memorials were furnished with Antiphons,
but the repetition of the Canticles was considered
wearisome, and was therefore forborne.

The number of Collects said at any Office must
never exceed seven, that being the number of the

petitions in the LORD's Prayer. More than six Memorials, therefore, cannot be said.

According to the present Roman use, the first and last Collect only have their proper endings; the others have none, and *Amen* is said to the first and last only. The ℣. *The* LORD *be with you.* ℞. *And with thy spirit*, is said to the first alone; before each of the others is only said, *Let us pray.* In the Sarum use, all Memorials retained their proper endings, except those terminating *Through* etc.; *Amen* immediately following the word LORD: the rest of the conclusion, only, being omitted. The Sarum Memorials were much more numerous and varied than the Roman.

After the last Memorial, in both uses, is repeated, ℣. *The* LORD *be with you.* ℞. *And with thy spirit.* ℣. *Bless we the* LORD. ℞. *Thanks be to* GOD. And so the Office ends: except that in the Roman use at every hour but Compline, and in the Sarum at Compline only, is said in the last place, with the sign of the Cross: *May the souls of the faithful, through the mercy of* GOD, *rest in peace.* *Pater* and *Ave* were said in silence after the end of the Office, as at the beginning: in the modern Roman use, *Pater* only, except at Compline, when *Pater*, *Ave*, and *Credo* follow the final Collect.

" After the Collect is said, *Bless we the* LORD . . . It is said sometimes by children, imperfect of age, to signify the imperfection of all our works, and to mark how childish and imperfect is all our praise, in comparison with Him to Whom we offer it . . . . Again, after the suffrage is said another Collect, which signifies the mercy of GOD preventing and following man in good works. Again is said, *Bless we the* LORD, and *Thanks be to* GOD, because, as the LORD twice after His Resurrection saluted His disciples and blessed them, and they, returning thanks, adored Him, so the priest, or some other, the Collect being said, repeats, *Bless we the* LORD, meaning, Whose members we are, and in Whom we bless, and Who blesses. Then the Choir says, *Thanks be to* GOD, whereby is signified that we must preserve innocence to the end of our lives, and bless GOD, returning thanks to Him for His benefits."—Durandus.

III.—PRIME.

Prime was wont to be said at sunrise: the Church transferred to the Sun of Righteousness that worship which Gentiles had been wont to pay to the rising sun, and as they, like the heathen, but for a better cause, worshipped toward the east, and built their temples in that direction, they were accused by the Pagans of worshipping the sun.

"The Hours, from first to ninth, and Compline, were the growth of the private and household devotions of the earlier ages in the East; probably those of the very first ages. That, as private forms, these services are of immense, and perhaps primitive antiquity, is indicated by the Psalms used in them, which are in most cases so singularly adapted to the time of day for which they are prescribed, that it is inconceivable but that they would have been adopted as part of the public daily services from the beginning, had they not already been allotted to private use."—Freeman.

Cassian speaks of Prime as having first been used in S. Jerome's monastery at Bethlehem, of which he himself had been a member. Its then contents were Pss. 5, 90, 101, with Pss. 119, vv. 133-135, Ps. 71, v. 7, and some short hymns. The "mid-way hour" attached to it, contains two prayers of S. Basil. In the English Office are a prayer framed from Ps. 71, v. 7, and a literal translation of one of S. Basil's prayers for use on Doubles. The prayer for ordinary Sundays and ferias, identical with the Roman, (and retained as one of the post-communion collects in the Common Prayer Book,) is an amplification of this. That which forms the third collect for morning prayer in the Prayer Book, and is found both in the Sarum and Roman Prime, is framed on both prayers of S. Basil.

Sarum Prime and Compline, as before observed, differed more than any other Hours from the present Roman form. Anciently the two uses were nearly identical, as far as we can judge. On ordinary Sundays, a much larger number of Psalms was recited. After the Pater, versicles, and hymn *Jam Lucis*, were said in remembrance of the Passion, Pss. 22-26, inclusive, followed by Pss. 54, 118, 119, (two portions of sixteen verses each, 1-32); on ordinary week-days and in Easter-tide, the Passion Psalms, and Ps. 118, were omitted; but we need not enter into more minute details. The Athanasian Creed was said daily, except in Christmas and Easter-tides. (This is still the use of the Carthusians.) After this came varying Chapter and Responsory, Preces, Collect, and Chapter Office.

The Roman Sunday Office has Pss. 54, 118., 119, vv. 1-32, Athanasian Creed, fixed Chapter, varying Responsory, Preces, Collect, and Chapter Office. The week-day Office replaces Ps. 118, by one Passion Psalm on each day except Saturday. The Athanasian Creed is not said on week-days. There is one fixed week-day Chapter, and one for Sundays and Festivals. The Preces are not said in the Roman use on Doubles, or within Octaves; in the Sarum they are always said except from Maundy Thursday to Low Sunday inclusive.

The form of Confession at Prime and Compline, from which that in our Communion Service is derived, is not sacramental in character. It is a mutual acknowledgment of sin, and prayer for

I

pardon; and was originally said after Prime, and before Ps. 51, which was also then said after that Office.

Durandus deals first with the ferial Office, as follows. The Roman use in his day evidently resembled the Sarum. "The hymn at Prime is invariable, as at Compline, because on every day we require deliverance . . . After the Antiphon follow the Psalms; and they plainly appear to carry on the idea of the preceding Hymn; because the first Psalm is Ps. 54, *Deus in nomine tuo*, wherein the Church prays to be delivered from danger and enemies. Then she arms herself against her foes, first with the girdle of chastity, saying Ps. 119, *Beati immaculati;* secondly, with the helmet of salvation, *i.e.*, Hope, saying, *Retribue servo tuo*. Thirdly, with the shield of Faith, saying, *Quicunque vult*, in which Creed is contained our faith, which is our shield, our defence, and victory against the world, the flesh, and the devil, and all their temptations; whence Peter: *Whom resist stedfast in the faith*, etc. Fourthly, she assumes the sword of the Spirit, which is the word of God, and she says a chapter or lesson, which pertains to doctrine. Good works, which are signified by Psalms, are to go first, and then follows the teaching of spiritual and more secret things; according to that: Jesus *began both to do and teach*. And because faith is the foundation of the commandments and the victory which overcometh the world, therefore follows the Creed, *Quicunque vult*.

"On Sundays when the history (responsory) is changed, are said at Prime five Psalms, continuing from the end of the Nocturns of Sunday; beginning, that is, at Ps. 22, *Deus, Deus meus*. But in certain churches they are only said from Septuagesima till Easter; in which season is also said at Prime Ps. 118, *Confitemini Domino*, lest any part of the Psalter be omitted (for the whole ought to be said in the course of the week); that verse, *This is the day which the* LORD *hath made*, speaks of the Resurrection, to which Sunday pertains. For this reason also are said at Prime on Sunday nine Psalms : that with the nine orders of the Angels we may praise the Trinity in the joy of the Resurrection. In the first five, namely, Ps. 22, *Deus, Deus meus*, and those which follow, CHRIST's Passion is sung; then, in Ps. 118, *Confitemini*, and the three daily Psalms, we are taught how, in the four quarters of the world, we are to praise the doctrine of the four Evangelists. In Ps. 54, *Deus in nomine tuo*, we pray for the putting down of error; in Ps. 118., *Confitemini*, we exhort to the yielding of praise; in Ps. 119, *Beati immaculati*, to the works of praise; in *Retribue servo tuo*, to the keeping of the commandments. But because faith is the foundation of the commandments, and the victory which overcometh the world : because moreover, without faith, they are made void, here is subjoined the Creed, *Quicunque vult*. And note, that in this Creed there are two principal parts, namely, of the Trinity, and of the Incarnation of the Word ; but as touching free-will is premised the introduction, *Whosoever will*, etc.*

"Afterwards follows the Chapter, in which the shepherd comforts his sheep, and the householder his labourers, lest they faint in the heat and toil. . . . . After the Chapter follows the Responsory : JESU CHRIST, *Son of the Living* GOD, *have mercy upon us*, that the Church may shew herself to understand and rejoice in those things said in the Chapter; but nevertheless, she also prays for herself. Wherefore is added the Versicle, O LORD, *arise*, that is, make us arise. For to arise from vices is nothing else than to return to the LORD. . . . . After this follow petitions, which are said for three reasons : (1) To cut off superfluous thoughts ; (2) to obtain mercy for wandering sheep, and negligent labourers ; (3) to ask help against temptation, that in the LORD's Prayer we may more safely call upon the FATHER. And they are said on this wise. The LORD's Prayer is first said, wherein are seven petitions, in order to the obtaining of the

---

* "Holy Church hath ordained that it should be sung each day openly at Prime, both in token that faith is the first beginning of health, and also for people use that time most to come to church."
—*Myrroure.*

seven gifts of the HOLY GHOST. But because dying flies destroy the sweetness of ointment (Vulg.), it is preceded by *Kyrie Eleison*. It is fitting that this should go first, to repel inane thoughts from the mind; so that in saying the LORD's Prayer, the soul which speaks invisible things, should think invisible things alone. . . . . The LORD's Prayer is said silently, in order to signify the devotion and humility of the prayer. Also, because therein we speak to GOD, Who searcheth out not so much the words as the reins and the heart. The end of the prayer is pronounced aloud, that it may be confirmed by all, and all that are present answer, *Amen*, because, as Augustine has it, it is impossible that a multitude be not heard. The beginning also is pronounced aloud, in order to invite those present to pray. The LORD's Prayer is said to obtain spiritual life for the soul; wherefore, so soon as it is finished, the words follow: *O let my soul live, and it shall praise Thee.* . . . . He cannot live in GOD who confesseth Him not. Therefore follows the Apostles' Creed, wherein is contained our faith, without which it is impossible to please GOD, and whereby those who are purified by the LORD's Prayer, are armed against all adverse things. And it is said softly, but ended aloud, to point out that *with the heart man believeth unto righteousness, and with the mouth confession is made unto salvation.* . . . . Then follow many petitions, wherein the Church pleads, prays, postulates, and gives thanks, according to the teaching of the Apostle to Timothy. (1 Tim. ii. 1.)

" Pleading, properly speaking, is prayer with adjuration ; as, *By Thy Passion, deliver us, O* LORD. Prayer is made when good things are asked, as, *Create in me a clean heart, O* GOD, *and renew a right spirit within me.* Postulation desires the removal of evils ; as here, *Vouchsafe, O* LORD, *to keep us this day without sin.* Thanksgiving is made for blessings received ; as, *Praise the* LORD, *O my soul.* . . . .

" While the Priest makes these petitions, he kneels on the ground, in order to excite greater devotion in himself and others ; but, having finished the Psalm *Miserere,* while the rest remain kneeling, he rises, and says the Collect standing ; as holding the place of that Priest Who is in heaven, and daily maketh intercession for us. In the first place he prays kneeling amongst the others, as the LORD, Whose vicar he is, before His Resurrection had His conversation with sinners, and was laid on the Cross ; afterwards, he says the Collect standing, to commemorate the rising again of Him Whose office he fills. On Sundays, and in Easter-tide, there is no kneeling, but we pray standing ; by reason of the Resurrection joy, which we then celebrate—and so likewise, on other festivals, on account of the joy of those festivals. . . . . But, standing on those days, we ought to pray with our heads bowed down, like the devout women at the Sepulchre."—Durandus.

IV.—Chapter.

Chapter signifies the assembling of the members of religious houses, for the purpose of reading the Martyrology, Necrology, and Rule ; and for correction of faults, injunctions, and distribution of tasks. It perhaps derived its name from the chapter of the rule, daily read at this meeting, and that title was extended from the office to the place where the office was held, and which, originally, seems to have been the eastern cloister of the monastery. Peter of Blois mentions various parts of the cloister as set apart for special uses. The western was for "the subjection of scholars ;" the part next the church, for moral reading ; (the church itself, for spiritual meditation ;) and the eastern cloister for chapter. Hither the brethren or sisters betook themselves in procession, after Prime, or, in some cases, after Tierce ; and having saluted the Cross, and bowed to each other, they sat down to hear the reading of the Martyrology.

The origin of this lection is easily traceable to the primitive Church. Commemorations of the Saints were daily made at the Altar ; and, on the previous day, were recited the names of those who were to be remembered at the morrow's Mass ;

hence the Martyrology, or Discourse of Martyrs. Great pains were taken by the early Church to collect the true acts of those who suffered for CHRIST. S. Clement appointed notaries for the purpose. The African Church did likewise, as we learn from S. Cyprian. S. Asterius Amasenus, who lived in the fourth century, under Julian the Apostate, clearly implies that a manuscript then existed, and was daily read, which contained a catalogue of Martyrs for the year. But when the number of Martyrs and Confessors had greatly increased, the narration of their acts became too lengthy; and Gregory the Great was the first to introduce a Martyrology, containing merely the name of each Martyr, with the place and date of his passion. In 1584, Baronius, Bellarmine, and six other learned men, produced an amended edition (open, however, to the same objection as their Breviary lessons : exaggeration of Roman claims, etc.). This was authorized by Urban VIII., and is still in use.

The Martyrology was followed by the ℣. and ℟. *Pretiosa* (*Right dear,*) etc., (whence the whole Office was often called *Pretiosa,*) at which all stood ; and was alluded to originally in the ensuing prayer, which ran simply thus : *May they* (*i.e.,* those now commemorated) *and all Saints intercede for us,* etc. As finally developed, it stood in the Sarum book : " May holy Mary, Mother of our LORD GOD JESUS

CHRIST, and all the Saints, righteous, and elect of GOD pray for us: that we may attain help and salvation of Him Who in perfect Trinity liveth and reigneth GOD, to all ages of ages. Amen." The modern Roman form is shorter. The mention of the Blessed Virgin was a late addition, and was inserted for her greater veneration, but, in this instance, with more devoutness than suitability.

The second act of the Chapter was a prayer for Divine assistance in all the actions of the day. The ℣. *O* GOD, *make speed*, etc., was the sign for cessation of the nocturnal silence, which had lasted since Compline on the previous evening. After the versicles and collect for grace and guidance, the community, having knelt down at the first *Kyrie*, again seated themselves to hear the reading of a chapter of the Rule, and exposition on the same, given by the Superior. But on Sundays and Festivals, instead of the Rule, was read a homily from one of the Fathers. In either case, next followed the Necrology; that is, a list of persons departed: those, the anniversary of whose death occurred on that day; and, also, the members, friends, and benefactors of the community for whom it was fitting to make daily prayer. When the anniversary of a simple monk was thus mentioned, it was merely stated that he had died: but the death of the abbot was recorded as his *deposition*. After Chapter in some places (and S. Dunstan

mentions the custom) five psalms were sung for
the dead, (Pss. 5, 6, 116, parts 1 and 2, 130).
Next after the Necrology, was made commemoration of living benefactors, with prayer; and this
was followed by distribution of tasks and offices,
daily or weekly, as the case might be. Lastly, at
Chapter was made confession of sins: and not
merely of faults against the external rule. The
framers of the ancient rules were very strict on this
point of open confession among the brethren. S.
Basil directs that every one shall carefully search
his conscience at the close of each day, that if he
find himself to have done or said or thought anything unfitting, he may not hide his sin, but declare
it openly, that by the prayers of the brethren his
disease may be purged: S. Benedict is severe as
to the punishments of those who abstain from confession at Chapter. These Saints both prescribed
that it should be made daily: but in some orders it
was made thrice a week. Novices, lay brethren, and
guests were first dismissed. Then, if any brother
felt guilty in his conscience, he prostrated himself on
the ground, confessing his sin; and received
penance, then and there, of sharp castigation: or
of fasting and prayer to be subsequently accomplished. After this, in some orders, those who
were cognizant of hidden faults in others proclaimed them. But everything done in Chapter
is Confession, says the Book of the uses of Bec:

and ought to be shielded by silence like Confession.

Honorius thus prettily expounds this office. " Shepherds are wont to change their places, and lead their flocks to fresh pastures. So the Superior leads his flock out of the church into the chapter-house. There (as other shepherds give their sheep salt to lick) salt is given to GOD's flock when they hear the reading of the Martyrology. The shepherd lays, as it were, food before them, when he magnifies the patience of the Saints by the verse: *Right dear in the sight of the* LORD. Then he calls thrice on the LORD to help, that His flock may escape spiritual dangers. Next, as it were, he blesses the sheepfold, praying for direction and governance in GOD's law. And, the reading being ended, each is sent to his work, like labourers to the vineyard."

V.—TIERCE, SEXTS, AND NONES.

These three hours were, as we know from Scripture, observed as times of prayer among the Jews; and they naturally, therefore, were kept among the primitive Christians. At the risk of repeating what is too well known, a few words must be said here as to the Eastern distribution of time. The night was divided into four watches, each of equal duration: the day into twelve hours. *" Are there not twelve hours in the day ?"* said our LORD. But the first hour began at sunrise, and the last ended at sunset; so that in summer each hour was longer than in winter: although in a semi-tropical latitude the variations are naturally less than in our northern countries. The third hour, then, was *about* 9 a.m.; the sixth, *at* noon, the meridian: the ninth, *about* 3 p.m.; and hence the names, Tierce, Sexts, and Nones.

Cassian says that the Eastern monks recited these Hours whilst occupied in their various works, apart, and only assembled for their recitation on Sunday. The Eastern, like the Western Church, has three psalms for each of these hours; but the psalms are not identical. Grancolas says, but incorrectly, that the distribution of Ps. 119, through the three hours, is peculiar to the Roman use, and is found in no monastic Breviary. S. Benedict prescribed the introductory ℣. O GOD, *make speed*, etc., and the hymn before the psalms. The Eastern use, of course, had no lessons: S. Benedict prescribed one; but S. Isidore, and some others, ordered the reading of two, one from the Old Testament, the other from the New.

The Sarum Breviary directs that on every week-day in Lent, after Tierce, the fifteen Gradual Psalms be sung "for the whole Church of GOD,"*

---

* The "Ancren Riwle" (for solitary recluses) directs thus: "Those fifteen psalms sing about undern time: for about such time as men sing Mass in all holy religions, our Lord tholed pain on the rood, ye ought to be especially in prayer and supplication."

and followed by the Litany. On both these subjects we have more to say hereafter.

The mystical interpretation of these hours is rather laboured : however, such as it is, here it follows. The 119th Psalm, nevertheless, being so constantly recited, requires to be further dwelt upon : and it shall have a section to itself.

" At Tierce, the promised SPIRIT was given to the Apostles, and they spake the wondrous works of GOD. Therefore is said the hymn : *Nunc Sancte nobis Spiritus.* We also say the Psalm (119) *Legem pone,* because then the new law was given to the Apostles. Because, by the law of GOD, man is healed from the sickness of sin, therefore the Chapter is *Heal me, O* LORD, etc., and the Responsory, *Heal my soul,* etc. And because it profiteth not that he be healed, except he be preserved, therefore follows the ℣. *Thou hast been my succour,* etc., as much as to say, Although I stand free and healed, in Thy way, yet I am not sufficient without Thy help to attain to that noon, whereof it is said, *Tell me where Thou feedest, where Thou makest Thy flock to lie down at noon.*

" At the sixth hour CHRIST was crucified for us, therefore the Church duly gives praise to GOD at that hour ; rendering thanks to Him, because He vouchsafed to suffer for her ; for which cause also she loves Him vehemently ; therefore she now says the Psalm (119) *Deficit anima, My soul hath longed,* continues the ℣., *I will always give thanks unto the* LORD, because He vouchsafed to suffer for me.

" The Office of Sexts corresponds to the time of day, like the Offices of the other hours. For at the first hour is beginning; in the third, progress; in the sixth, consummation: just as the sun at Prime begins to shine, at Tierce gives greater heat, and at Sexts is in its full glow; as is pointed out by the words of the hymns used in these hours, and also at Nones. To beginnings correspond the words which are said at Prime, in Ps. 54, *Save me, O* GOD, *for Thy Name's sake, and deliver me in Thy strength;* that is, save me from the Ziphites.* For at the beginning of our conversion, we begin to be parted from evil. . . To this also belongs that word in the second psalm, *O that my ways were made so direct:* and that in the third, *O do well unto Thy servant . . . that I may live;* because, having been dead through sin, he prays to be justified by grace. That belongs to progress which is said at the beginning of Tierce, *Teach me, O* LORD, *the way of Thy statutes, and I shall keep it unto the end.* He who is set in the right way desires that the law of correction be given to him. That pertains to consummation which is said at the beginning of Sexts: *My soul hath longed for Thy salvation;* that is, my soul, looking to Thy salvation, fails (*deficit*) with regard to

* See title of Ps. 54.

earthly things. For the more one longs after GOD, the more one withdraws from earthly things, and sickens, as it were, with great desire, according to that in the Canticles: *Stay me with flagons* [*flowers*, Vulg.] *comfort me with apples, for I am sick of love.* By flowers we understand a beginning of good works, and by apples their perfection, which bring some degree of consolation; nevertheless, such comfort is not entire, but the soul rather is sorrowful through love. Whence it follows: *Mine eyes long sore for Thy word: saying, O when wilt Thou comfort me?* And in the second part: LORD, *what love have I unto Thy law!* And in the third: *Mine eyes are wasted away with looking for Thy health, and for the word of Thy righteousness.* To this perfection belongs the responsory: *I will alway give thanks unto the* LORD. Then follows the versicle: *The* LORD *is my Shepherd, therefore shall I lack nothing;* for he who knows that GOD has set him in the place of pasture, where the faithful are more fulfilled with faith, looks to receive all spiritual support from GOD.

" At the hour of Nones, CHRIST cried with a loud voice, and gave up the ghost; . . . at the same hour the soldier opened the Side of CHRIST with a spear, and drew forth two sacraments of our salvation, namely, the water of Baptism, and the Blood of our redemption; and the vail of the temple was rent, and the graves were opened. At the same hour, descending into Hell, He broke the bonds of the Saints, and restored them to Paradise . . . therefore, for all these blessings, the Church duly praises GOD at this hour, saying Ps. 119, *Mirabilia*, and the responsory, *O deliver me,* etc., praying for her redemption, that it may be evident she does not forget that at that hour she was redeemed.

" It is to be considered that at the ninth hour the sun is declining from the zenith. Therefore the season of the day signifies that state wherein through temptation the soul is cooled from the heat it once possessed. For as saith blessed Gregory : ' Let vices tempt us, let virtues humble us.' For when the perfect man is tempted from the height of internal joys, he descends to consider his own frailty, and to see how easy it is to fall ; as it appears in the case of the Apostle, who said : *Lest I should be exalted above measure through the abundance of the revelations.* Paul rejoiced in the revelation ; he sorrowed for the temptation. Wherefore himself saith : *For this thing I besought the* LORD *thrice,* etc. But unless the temptation had been painful, he would not have prayed for its removal. Yet it was not removed, because strength is made perfect in weakness. These tribulations and troubles are expressed by some verses of the psalm of Nones, as in the first part : *Trouble and heaviness have taken hold upon me ;* and in the second: *Many are they that trouble me and perse-cute me;* and in the third: *I have gone astray like a sheep that is lost.* From these things we pray to be delivered in the responsory: *O deliver me, and be merciful unto me;* that is, grant that in my tribulations I may feel the effect of the redemption which was wrought by Thy Blood. And so, in the versicle, *O cleanse Thou me from my secret faults.* . . . And note that the Sunday responsory at the three Hours, namely, Tierce, Sexts, and Nones, corresponds to the ferial responsories. For in the ferial responsory of Tierce, *Heal my soul,* etc., prayer is made for the healing of those wounds which were made by past sins; and in the Sunday responsory, *Incline my heart,* etc., and the ver-sicle, *Turn away mine eyes,* etc., prayer is made for safeguard against future sins, which is obtained by fulfilment of the divine commandments. In the ferial responsory at Sexts: *I will alway give thanks,* etc., a promise is made of continually praising GOD; in the Sunday responsory, *O LORD, Thy word,* etc., the promise is fulfilled. In the ferial responsory at Nones, *O deliver me,* etc., prayer is made for the effect of redemption, whereby the energy of the soul, namely, love, may be directed to GOD. And in the Sunday re-sponsory *I call with my whole heart,* the effect is shewn by the cry of the heart addressed to GOD.

K

VI.—VESPERS.

The Office of Vespers has always been performed with more solemnity than any other. It corresponds to the evening sacrifice of the Jews. Incense was offered in that service, as also at Vespers : just as it was likewise offered at Lauds, and at the Jewish morning sacrifice. But chiefly the Church at Vesper-time makes solemn commemoration of that Sacrifice made for all, and of the institution of the Holy Eucharist, which took place about this hour. So says S. Isidore ; as also, that the Office takes its name from the Vesper star, which rises about sunset. It was also called the Office of Lights, on account of the tapers and lamps which were kindled by reason of the darkness. It was, moreover, called the Twelfth Hour, because recited at the twelfth hour of the day, as Prime, at the first. S. Ambrose calls it the Hour of Incense.

Certain prayers were wont to be made at the lighting of the lamps before Vespers. The Mozarabic office begins with such, thus : *Kyrie, Christe, Kyrie ; Pater ;* and then : In the Name of our LORD JESUS CHRIST, Light and Peace ; Amen : this light is offered. R̶. Thanks be to GOD.

In imitation of the Jews, whose feasts began at eventide, and lasted till the evening of the day following, the Church begins her vigils at Vesper-time. The more solemn feasts thus have two

Vespers, one on the eve, one on the day itself; simple feasts have but one, and that, the first Vespers. That is, according to the present Roman use; for of feasts called simple in Sarum, some had two Vespers, as elsewhere set forth.

Now comes the occasion for trying to explain with some clearness, how Sarum Vespers used to be sung with their elaborate ritual, and by the various officiators.

The choir was fitted up with three rows of seats: the uppermost being stalls for the higher dignitaries, and these were returned: that is, they did not merely run from east to west, like the two rows of forms below, but were turned round at the west end, so as to afford places for the highest dignitaries of all, facing the east. On the second form sat clerics of lower rank, and choirmen, etc.; on the first, or lowest, the choirboys. On a platform towards the west end of the choir, were placed the Ruler or Rulers of the choir for the day: four on Double Feasts, two on Sundays and Simple Feasts. Each of these wore a cap, and a silk cope, and carried a staff.

The whole choir of singers (representing the congregation) responded to the officiant: who was always on the opposite side. To divide the work of officiating equally among the clergy, the singing men and boys (*chorus cantorum*) moved from one side of the choir to the other every week. Singing

the Psalms, etc., in alternate verses by semi-choirs
is of late introduction as a general practice, and in
the last century was considered a novelty in
France; but the custom was certainly observed by
Religious Houses, as we gather from the *Myrroure*
and other like books.

Mr. Chambers describes the work of the Rulers,
and the method of singing at Vespers, with great
minuteness, as follows:

"The Antiphon should indicate the tone in
which the succeeding Psalm should be sung; and
especial rubrical directions are given that it should
always be sung before the Psalm, far enough to
indicate what this tone should be. The mode of
singing both Antiphons and Psalms should be
this: the choirmaster, or principal ruler on the
decanal side, whose duty it is to lead the Psalmody,
should (with his fellow on the same side, if it be a
feast with four rulers), staff in hand, and his cap
on his head, go to the precentor, or sub-precentor
in his stall, and learn of him what is the tone in
which the Antiphon is to be sung, and which of
the clerks is to sing it. Being so instructed, he
or they should then walk up to this clerk, to whom
bowing, and each taking off his cap, he or they
should intone the three or four first words of the
Antiphon or Psalm, whereupon the clerk taking
off his cap, and standing turned towards the
choir, should sing out the three or four first words

of this Antiphon or Psalm. Let him then turn towards the Altar and bow, and afterwards turn again towards the choir. He should always sing out the Antiphon or Psalm far enough to indicate clearly what the tone of the succeeding Psalm should be. The ruler or rulers being now returned to their places should next begin, sing out and pursue the first verse of the Psalm, together with the clerk aforesaid and the whole choir. The second verse should not be sung by the full choir, but by the secondary ruler on the west, or opposite side, and by such clerk or clerks as may be there. The third verse by the aforesaid ruler or rulers, together with the aforesaid clerk and the whole choir, and so on to the end of the Psalm, when *Gloria Patri* and *Sicut erat* should be sung by the rulers and whole choir, turning to the Altar and bowing. Then let the clerk who had originally begun the Antiphon begin it again, and sing it throughout, along with the rulers and all the choir and people together."—*Divine Worship*, etc.

Other customs observed at Vespers in England, are thus described:

"On Sundays and lower holidays, each canon had on his cassock, surplice, black choir-cope, and furred amice; the boys, their surplices; the rulers of the choir were the only individuals who walked from the vestry arrayed in silken embroidered

copes; all, including the officiating priest, sat in
the choir. After the third Psalm had been chanted,
the boys, at the bidding of the first ruler of the
choir, went into the vestry to change their surplices
for amices and girdled albs; two of them to serve
as acolytes, and bear the candles; the third, the
thurible. The officiating priest stopped at his
stall, but turned himself, clad merely in his cancn's
dress, towards the Altar, while he read the little
chapter. Two canons now put on silken copes,
and sang the response at the foot of the steps
leading from the choir up to the presbytery." (Or
rather, to lead the responsory, which was taken up
by the full choir after the two or three first words,
and to sing the intervening verse and *Gloria*; the
full choir singing the repetition of the response.)
" Towards the end of the hymn, the priest came
down from his stall, and had put on him a silken
cope; and the acolytes with their lighted candles,
and the thurifer, came forth to meet him at the
foot of the presbytery steps, where he blessed the
incense; and, going thence up to the high Altar,
made his genuflection. He then incensed the Altar,
the image of the Blessed Virgin Mary, which always
stood on the north side, and the shrine; or, where
there was none, the relics. Having bowed to the
Altar, and with the acolytes and their candles going
before him, he went to the easternmost of the
sedilia, or canopied seats, in the south wall of the

presbytery, and was there incensed by the thurifer, who afterwards incensed the rulers of the choir, then the dean and all the higher canons on the same side, and then the precentor, and all on his side, and after the minor canons on both sides; making, as he did so, a bow to each one.   In the meanwhile was sung the *Magnificat;* and as its Antiphon had also been chanted again at the end, the priest, accompanied by the acolytes, came down to the steps, took his book from the boy who had to carry it, and sang the prayer for the day. After the first *Benedicamus,* a procession of the whole choir went through some part of the Church, —at Easter-time to visit the newly-hallowed waters of the baptismal font,—at other seasons, to make commemoration of the Saint whose eve it was, at his Altar.   Both in going and coming back they chanted anthems : one, on their return, in honour of the Blessed Virgin Mary.   On reaching the west door of the choir, or chancel, they stopped ; that is, held a station there below the rood, to sing versicle, and antiphon, and collect, in reverence of the Cross.

"Upon the higher festivals, the incensing at Evensong was much more solemn.   As soon as the hymn was begun, there were brought to the Celebrant two silken copes, of which he put on one, and sent the second to whomsoever among the priests he liked ; and thus arrayed, and followed by two thurifers, both walked up together and incensed the high Altar. This done, they separated: one going to incense all the Altars at the eastern, the other at the western part of the church, and meeting again by the south door of the presbytery, incensed the bishop, and then one another."—Rock.

It was the practice according to Sarum, to sing a responsory after the Chapter at Vespers, always during Advent and Lent; and on festivals and Sundays, in some cases at both Vespers, in some, at first Vespers only. It was usually selected from the R̥.R̥. at Matins. Amalarius alludes to the custom as existing in some churches at his day; and Durandus refers to it; but it has long ceased to be a Roman usage.

The Eastern Church daily repeated *Magnificat*, besides *Benedictus*, at Lauds. The Armenian Church used it likewise at Compline, and so, perhaps, it made its way into Western Vespers, where it has always held the position of honour which *Benedictus* takes in Western Lauds.

"The points in which the Western Evening Office has taken the Eastern as its model, are for the most part sufficiently obvious. There is the same acknowledgment of this as being the second great Office in point of importance in the twenty-four hours, answering to the conjoint Nocturns and Lauds. Like Nocturns, it has a fixed number of Psalms, said continuously, and in about the

Eastern proportion to those of Nocturns. Like
Lauds, again, it has a Canticle, Collect, and Preces.
The number of Psalms said continuously was in
general *five;* in S. Benedict's scheme, *four.* But
the capital feature of this resemblance lies in this:
that as the Morning Office leads up through a
finely varied series of plaintive and jubilant
psalmody to the natural dawn, considered as the
memorial of the Creation, and of CHRIST's Resurrection; so does the Evening Office, through a
similar progression, to the beginning of artificial
light at the close of day; the type and the remembrancer of the coming in of the True Light, 'not of
this world,' in the world's eventide, and of His
giving Himself, also at the evening hour, for its
salvation."—Freeman.

The Eastern Vespers contain much else that is
exceedingly grand; and they have a direct relation
to the Eucharistic Office. On one point we must
dwell, viz., the *Prokeimenon,* or summary of the
Epistle, which is supposed to have furnished
the example for the Chapter in Western Vespers
(subsequently introduced also into the other
hours).

" It does not seem difficult to discern how it was
that the *Epistle* more particularly came to us thus
projected upon the ordinary weekly Offices of the
Church, probably even in primitive times. The
Epistles were from the first, and by the express

tenor of some of them, designed to be recited in
the Churches. And they would in the first instance
be read, not exactly as Scripture, but as the living
voice of Apostolic authority and teaching. It is
probable that as such they obtained a place in the
Communion Office at an earlier period than the
Gospels did ; which may be the reason of the
Epistles universally taking the precedence in that
service.

"It is an interesting circumstance, that the fixed
weekly Capitulum at Vespers in the English
Church was 2 Thess. iii. 4 : ' The LORD direct your
hearts into the love of GOD, and into the patient
waiting for CHRIST ;' for, as is generally admitted,
the Epistles to the Thessalonians were the earliest
written of any, and they were specially ordered to
be read in the Church. (1 Thess. v. 2, 7 ; cf.
2 Thess. iii. 17.) And it is at least conceivable
that the habit, as at first formed, of thus com-
memoratively fulfilling the Apostolic injunction at
the ordinary Offices, passed over from S. Paul's
favourite Church of Ephesus to Gaul, and so
reached our shores."—Freeman.

"The Church in this hour says five Psalms : first,
on account of the five wounds of CHRIST, Who
offered His Sacrifice for us at the Vesper-tide of
the world. Secondly, because we pray for forgiveness of those sins which in the course of the day
we have committed through the five senses of our

body. Thirdly, by these five Psalms the Church mans herself against nocturnal tribulations. For this hour brings to mind the weeping of those on whom the Sun of righteousness hath set, and who therefore are in darkness. The Psalms are sung according to the subject of the day, as, for instance, on the seventh day, *i.e.*, the Sabbath, we speak of victory, and of the praise of GOD, on account of the Resurrection which follows."— Durandus.

Durandus proceeds with Saturday Vespers. "The first Psalm (144), *Benedictus Dominus*, literally speaks of the victory of David over Goliath, but spiritually of our victory whereby we overcome Satan. Because, therefore, after victory, nothing remains but to praise the LORD, by Whom we obtain victory, there follow four Psalms, which are of praise : for in the first, the Church begins her praise, Ps. 145, *Exaltabo te Deus* ; in the second she incites herself to it, Ps. 146, *Lauda anima mea* in the third she invites others, Ps. 147, *Laudate Dominum*. In the fourth she congratulates the heavenly Jerusalem, saying, Ps. 147. 10, *Lauda Hierusalem* ; and so with other ferias and Psalms."

" In like manner Monday Vespers follow the Nativity ; Tuesday, the Epiphany ; Wednesday, The Betrayal ; Thursday, the Institution of the Blessed Eucharist ; Friday, the Passion."—Neale.

" It is in fitting order that the Hymn should follow

the Psalms ; because the first thing needful is love
in the heart, which is signified by Antiphons.
Then follow good works, denoted by Psalms ; and
afterwards, exultation of the mind, which is represented by the Hymn.

"But because exultation often engenders negligence, the Chapter comes in to call man back to his
own heart. . . . . After the Hymn follows the ℣.
*Let my prayer be set forth in Thy sight as the
incense ;* and it is customary, whilst it is said, that
the Priest cense the Altar for the acceptance of
the sacrifice, as was done under the law, (and the
censing is done at Vespers and Lauds,) after the
Psalms and lesson, while the verse is said ; to
signify that no man can offer sweet savour to GOD,
nor give a good example to others by his work,
except first his service be wrought, and he himself
instruct others, in GOD.

"*Magnificat* is repeated daily, in order that the
frequent mention of our LORD's Incarnation may
kindle the souls of the faithful to devotion in the
works they have begun.

"The song of the Blessed Virgin Mary is rather
sung at Vespers than at other Offices ; because
hereby we make constant commemoration of the
Incarnation, which took place at the Vesper-tide
of the world. Moreover, it is sung in the sixth
office of praise, because our LORD came in the
sixth age of the world. As the Song of Simeon is

sung in the seventh, by reason of the seventh age, that is, rest.

"To represent the rejoicing expressed in this Canticle, lights are kindled at Vespers; either because the Canticle is of the Gospel, or that we, being of the number of the wise virgins, may run with the lamps of good works in the odour of the ointment of the Blessed Virgin; entering with her into the joy of our LORD.

"And because our works are not radiant in lamps, except they be moulded by love, therefore the Canticle closes with the Antiphon, whereby love is signified."—Durandus.

That it is a fitting and holy custom to offer incense at time of *Magnificat*, the Canticle of the Incarnation, Origen very finely sets forth as follows:

"Behold how our High Priest standeth and offereth Himself, to separate the living from the dead. Rise to the loftier heights of this Word, and behold how the Very High Priest, JESUS CHRIST, having assumed the censer of human flesh, and set therein the fire of the Altar, that is, the glorious soul wherewith He was born according to His human nature, and adding thereunto the incense, which is His immaculate Spirit, stood between the living and the dead, and suffered death to rule us no longer."

VII.—COMPLINE.

Compline is so called, because it completes the day's service of prayer. It is said by Grancolas to have originated with S. Benedict, that is, in the West, and was instituted as a form of prayer to be recited before going to rest : after which silence was kept until the next day, no food taken, and no work done.

The Roman Compline began with a Lesson. This is in imitation of those monastic uses in which, as a lesson was read at Chapter, before going to work, so another was read at night, when work was over. The latter was read in the Chapter-house, or cloister, like the former; at its close, the Prior said, *Our help is in the Name of the* LORD, and the Community departed into church; where, having searched their consciences, at a sign from the Prior, they made the mutual Confession.

There is no trace of this practice in the Sarum Book. Compline begins with the ℣. *Turn us, O* GOD, *our* SAVIOUR, and then, after the usual introductory versicles, proceeds to the four psalms which are never changed : Ps. 91 being omitted, however, during the three days before Easter, and the week following. The hymn and Antiphons, unlike the Roman, vary with the seasons. Some of the Antiphons are of wonderful beauty : one, for the third and fourth weeks in Lent, is drawn from that famous early Notkerian sequence, "In the midst of life we are in death."

The fuller form of Eastern Compline is immensely long; and the chief materials of our own Service are to be found in it: Pss. 4, 31, 91, a hymn of three stanzas, returning thanks for preservation, and asking protection, many prayers, versicles and responses, mutual Confession and Absolution, etc.

The varying hymns in the English Office are said to be manifestly translated and condensed from parts of the Great Eastern Compline. The prayer, "Lighten our darkness," appears to be founded on a long hymn similar in character to that now so well known through Dr. Neale's translation:

> "The day is past and over,
>   All thanks, O LORD, to Thee!
> I pray Thee that offenceless
>   The hours of dark may be.
>   *   *   *   *
> O JESU! make their darkness light,
> And save me through the coming night!"

"This Office begins contrary to the manner of the other Offices; for because we have been, as it were, singing psalms all day, and it is well-nigh impossible but that we should have contracted some dust of pride, therefore we humble ourselves, saying, *Turn us, O* GOD, *our* SAVIOUR, for, *if we say we have no sin, we deceive ourselves.* . . . Then

we proceed to call on the Divine help, saying: *O
GOD, make speed*, etc.

"*Turn us*, etc., refers to the taking away of past
evils. *O GOD, make speed*, etc., to the doing of
future good works; because without the help of
GOD we can do no good thing.

"And because all is to be done in praise of the
Trinity, therefore follows *Gloria*. Four psalms are
said, to obtain remission of the sins which we commit whilst we are in this body formed out of the
four elements and four humours or temperaments.*
... And the Church begins by the voice of perfection,
saying (Ps. 4), *Cum invocarem*, for this is to be said
of the perfect. But because the perfect must hold
themselves as imperfect, there follows in the same
Psalm, *Have mercy upon me, and hearken unto my
prayer*, which is the speech of the imperfect. After
other admonitions to good, is made in the same
Psalm mention of eternal peace: *in peace, in the
very same*, [Vulg.] i.e., which is invariable, because
we are always to have that peace in our minds;
and specially while the body is to rest in its bed,
the mind must rest in GOD, and must *also rest in
hope*, wherefore follows the second Psalm (31,) *In
Te Domine speravi*.

"But because hope without fear is not true hope,
but rather presumption, therefore follows the third

* According to the old theories: bilious, sanguine, lymphatic,
and melancholic.

Psalm, concerning temptation, namely, Ps. 91, *Qui habitat*, wherein GOD promises to deliver the Church. This Psalm is said in order that we may be delivered from four temptations, namely, the terror by night, the arrow flying by day, the *Thing* [Vulg.] that walketh in darkness, and the sickness that destroyeth in the noon-day. The first is slight and hidden: the second slight and manifest; the third great and hidden; the fourth great and manifest. In the fourth Psalm, namely, Ps. 134, *Ecce nunc*, the Church blesses GOD for deliverance from nightly temptations, saying, *Lift up your hands in the sanctuary, and praise the* LORD.*

"Concerning this Psalm, Augustine saith, 'Night is sad, day is joyful. Therefore by night is understood adversity, by day, prosperity.'

"The LORD is to be praised in adversity, as in prosperity, according to the example of Job. Therefore we now say, *Bless ye the* LORD."—Durandus.

"The common use of the Church is to say four Psalms at Compline, but S. Benet setteth in his rule but three Psalms to be said at Compline. And thereto accordeth your service,† [Brigittine] that hath at Compline but three Psalms, which are these: *Memento Domine, Ecce quam bonum,*

* "The fourth Psalm is the Psalm of charity. Thus, then, you offer these four psalms for the four graces—peace, hope, godly fear, and unity."—Neale.

† The Office of the Blessed Virgin is that referred to in this extract, and the Psalms are the last three Graduals.

L

Ecce nunc. In the first Psalm, that is, *Memento,*
ye promise that ye will neither go to bed, nor sleep,
till ye have found in yourself a resting-place to our
LORD GOD. And how that shall be, the other two
Psalms teach; for the one, that is *Ecce quam bonum,*
telleth of the love and unity that each one ought to
have with the other; and the other, that is, *Ecce
nunc,* speaketh of the praising and joy that ought
to be had in our LORD GOD. And in what soul
ever these two things are, that is, unity and peace
with all others, and love and joy in GOD, there liketh
our LORD to rest and to abide. And therefore, if
ye say well your Compline, ye shall not be without
these two. And if ye feel these two in you verily,
then bless you, and go to bed, and sleep restfully
and safely, for our LORD Himself resteth in you,
and He will keep you while ye sleep."—*Myrroure.*

"But it is asked why six verses only are said of
that Psalm, *In Te Domine speravi.* The answer
is: because the LORD laid down His Life on the
sixth day, in the sixth age of the world, and in the
act of saying this sixth verse, namely, *Into Thy
Hands, O LORD, I commend My Spirit.* Therefore
we rightly conclude that Psalm at the sixth verse
at Compline, in order that in this sixth age, wherein
by Him we have been redeemed, (as the last verse
ends, *Thou hast redeemed us, O LORD, Thou GOD
of Truth,*) our sleep may be conformable to His;
our body resting, and our heart watching, like as

His Flesh rested in the Sepulchre, and His Godhead watched. The Chapter is not omitted, because exhortation is always useful for perseverance in good things. Then follows the hymn, *Te lucis*, wherein we pray to be protected in the troubles of the night. After the hymn, comes the versicle, *Keep us, O* Lord, which marks the idea of the whole Office. For it prays the Lord to guard us against the dangers of the night.

"After this, having called to remembrance the in-effable joys which shall be the reward of our labours, we sing the Song of Simeon: *Nunc Dimittis*. First, in order that, finding peace after his example, we may attain to the true Light, which is Christ ; secondly, because as holy Simeon said these words, desiring to pass from this life to another, so, when we are about to sleep, it is as though we were to die ; for sleep is the image of death, and by the singing of this hymn, we commend ourselves to the Lord. Thirdly, for a cause mentioned under the head of Vespers. It is, moreover, to be considered that while the other Hours consist of seven parts : namely, Verse and Gloria, Hymn, Psalms, Lessons, Canticle (or Responsory), Preces, and Collect, yet in three Hours, namely, Lauds, Vespers, and Compline, is added an eighth, namely, the Evangelical Canticle ; because these three Hours belong to the Octave, namely, to the Resurrection of the Lord. For He rose early in the morning, at Vespers shewed Himself to the disciples, and at Compline said unto them, " Peace be unto you ;" and therefore at these three Hours, the Hymn, which is an example of joy, is followed by the Canticle, that we may continue in the grace of the Gospel. The Gospel of grace in this Office is the Song of Simeon, wherein we ask for eternal grace, that, as Simeon, desiring to pass away after he had seen CHRIST, prayed to be let depart, so may we, after the light of faith, attain to the glory of hope, wherein shall be peace eternal. The LORD's Prayer and Petitions are said afterwards, in order to guard us against nightly phantasies. The Creed, containing the profession of our faith, is added, in order that if we be overtaken by death, we may die in the confession of faith. In certain Churches confession is made as at Prime, according to that Scripture, *Confess your faults one to another*. In order that we give no rest to our temples until we have found out a place for the Temple of the LORD, Petitions and Collect complete this Office, according to that of the Apostle : *Pray one for another, that ye may be healed*. Again, Petitions mystically signify humility ; which ought to find its place in the end, even as it was necessary in the beginning. . . The Apostles' Creed is said at Prime and at Compline, because we begin and end all our works in Him in Whose Name we believe. . . In the last place it is to be noted, that in every Day Office the Psalms are invariable, but in the Night Offices they are variable. For by night is understood this world, which is changeable; but by day, that eternal world which is changeless. . . This Office also in certain Churches is invariable as to the Hymn, and also the Psalms, the Lesson, Petitions, and Collect; because it deals with peace, and especially with that peace for which we long, and which is changeless.

"But why, when the five Psalms, beginning with the twenty-second, *Deus, Deus meus,* are said at Prime, is the Psalm *In Te Domine,* down to the verse, *Into Thy Hands I commend My Spirit,* said at Compline, rather than at any other hour? I answer: we read that CHRIST, Who is the Beginning and the End, and to Whom in these hours we sing, began on the Cross the Psalm, *My GOD, My GOD,* and continued to repeat all those Psalms following, till the above-named verse; and there He ended and gave up the ghost. Therefore it was fitting that we, who are undergoing the sufferings of this world, should be directed to the imitation of His at the Hour of Prime, which is the beginning of the Hours of the day; and at Compline, which in some points of view may be considered as the close, or the last, of these Hours of the day, this verse ought to be said."— Durandus.

VII.—Comparison of Eastern and Western Offices.

" It will not be uninteresting to endeavour briefly to discriminate in this place the genius of the East and of the West, as exhibited in their respective forms of ordinary worship which we have now passed under review ; more especially as our present Offices (in the Common Prayer Book) combine, in a measure, the temper and characteristics of both.

" The East, then, if we leave out of the account those enrichments which her ordinary Offices derive from the Eucharist on Sundays and Festivals, and take her, so to speak, in her every-day dress, is more uniform and unchanging ; the West more multiform and variable. Witness the single changeless Invitatory and Benediction of the one Church, and their endless varieties in the other. While the West rings countless changes, according to the season, on the same essential idea, the East prolongs it in one unvaried and majestic toll, from the beginning to the end of the year. The East, again, is more rapt, the West more intellectual. The East loves rather to meditate on GOD as He is, and on the facts of Christian doctrine as they stand in the Creed ; the West contemplates more practically the great phenomena of Christian psychology, and the relations of man to GOD. The East has had its Athanasius and its Andrew of Crete ; the West its Augustine and Leo. Hence Psalms and hymns in more profuse abundance characterise the Eastern ; larger use and more elaborate adaptations of Scripture, the Western Offices. The East, by making the Psalms all her meditation, seems to declare her mind that praise is the only way to knowledge ; the West, by her combined Psalm and lection system, that knowledge is the proper fuel of praise. While the East, again, soars to GOD in exclamations of angelic self-forgetfulness, the West comprehends all the spiritual needs of man in Collects of matchless profundity ; reminding us of the alleged distinction between the Seraphim, who love most, and the Cherubim, who know most. Thus the East praises, the West pleads ; the one has fixed her eye more intently on the Glory-throne of CHRIST, the other on His Cross. Both alike have been dazzled and led astray by the wondrous accidents of the Incarnation. Finally, the East has been more inquisitive and inventive in the departments both of knowledge and praise ; the West, more constructive, has wrought up, out of scattered Eastern materials, her exhaustive Athanasian Creed, and her matchless *Te Deum*."—Freeman.

CHAPTER III.

SOME MINOR OFFICES, ETC.

I.—*Office of the Blessed Virgin.*

SIDE by side with the great Divine Office, which we have now been considering, we find a lesser Office of similar construction : that of the Blessed Virgin. Its history is very obscure. S. John Damascene, in the eighth century, is said to have used, or composed it ; and in the same century, the Benedictine monks of Monte Cassino appear to have been bound to say the Hours of this Office after, and those of the Office of S. Benedict before, every day and night hour of the Divine Office. The use of the Little Office of the Blessed Virgin, much shorter than that just mentioned, was promoted about the eleventh century, by S. Peter Damiani, and the Cistercians accepted it in the twelfth ; never omitting its recitation at any time, except for the solemnity of Easter. Pius V. confirmed the decree. The Office was to be omitted on double feasts, Christmas Eve, etc., and on Saturday, when the Office of the Blessed Virgin is said on that day. In 1096, Urban II. ordered all clerics to say it daily : and it became customary, though not perhaps, as an universal law.

Salisbury Cathedral is dedicated to the Blessed Virgin. The devotion to her, which was so marked a feature in mediæval England, was sure therefore to find full expression in the Sarum use.

Daily throughout the year were said Vespers and Matins of her Office, either in choir or in the chapter-house; except on Double Feasts, and in the time from Christmas Eve to the Octave of S. Stephen, on the Vigil of Epiphany, from Maundy Thursday to Low Sunday, and in Whitsun week. The Vesper Psalms, said under one Antiphon, were 122-126, inclusive, except on Tuesday, when they had been already said in the Divine Office, and therefore were replaced by those of the second Vespers of Christmas Day. The Vesper hymn was always *Ave maris stella;* Antiphons, Chapters, Collects, and Hymns at other hours, varied according as the season was that of Advent, the time between Christmas and Candlemas, Eastertide, or the time between Candlemas and Advent, exclusive of Easter: the Collects were chosen out of those in the Divine Office, and were those for Christmas Eve, and for the memorials of our Lady in Advent, Eastertide, and through the year.

No ferial petitions were said at any hour: but the Collect was immediately followed at Vespers and Lauds by memorials of the HOLY GHOST, the Patron of the Church, the Saints whose relics were kept in it, All Saints, and Peace.

The Psalms at Compline were 13, 26, 129, 131, followed by *Nunc Dimittis* and Collect.

At Matins, the Invitatory was, *Hail, Mary, full of grace: the* LORD *is with thee:* the hymn *Quem terra*. Three Psalms were said under one Antiphon: on Sunday and Monday, 8, 19, 24; on Tuesday, 45, 46, 87; on Wednesday, 96, 97, 98. On Thursday and Saturday, unless full service of our Lady was held, the order of Psalms and Antiphons was as on preceding ferias. Three lessons and responses followed, and *Te Deum*, except when forbidden by the season.

At Lauds, Sunday psalms were said under one Antiphon: Hymn, *O Gloriosa fœmina*, or *Enixa est puerpera: Benedictus*, and Collect.

At Prime, the Psalms were 54, 117, 118 (no Athanasian Creed); at Tierce, 120, 121, 122; at Sexts, 123, 124, 125; at Nones, 126, 127, 128. According to the present Roman use, when said in Choir, Matins and Vespers of this Office precede the Office of the day; but the other hours follow it. The full Office of the Blessed Virgin, with three Nocturns, is now said in the Roman Church by those bound to recite the Divine Office, on Saturday, instead of the regular Saturday Office; and there are not wanting those who attribute this substitution to indolence; the Office of nine lessons, with nine short psalms, being much shorter than the

ommon Saturday Office with twelve, some of
which are very long.

At the present time, most active orders in the
Roman Church, and some contemplative, say the
Little Office of our Lady only.

The Antiphons of the Blessed Virgin now said
at the end of the Roman Compline, do not form
part of the Office, and were originally said simply
as private and voluntary devotions. They were first
placed in the Breviary by Cardinal Quignon, whose
example was followed in this instance by Pius V.

II.—*Office of the Faithful Departed.*

It was a primitive custom in the Church, that
the Priest at Mass should always offer the Sacrifice for dead as well as for living: reciting the
names of the departed, as inscribed on diptychs;
which were double tablets, made to close like a
book, on one side of which were set the names of
the dead, and, on the other, those of living persons
of note. Afterwards a special Office for the Dead
was instituted, and was said after the Canonical
Hours. The original author is unknown; but it
is very ancient. Its composition has been attri-
buted to Origen, and also to S. Augustine. The
Responsories are ascribed to Maurice, Bishop of
Paris, who died in 1196. Of the Collects, those
beginning, GOD, *Who among Apostolic Priests*, and
GOD, *the Creator and Redeemer of all the faithful,*

are from the Sacramentary of S. Gregory. Pius V
added three: for burial, anniversary, and parents.
That for burial is from the Sacramentary. Clement
VIII. added other two: one, for man or woman,
being taken from the Sacramentary. No later
change has been made. The Sarum use was like
the Roman, but more ancient in its form. The
rule in the Sarum book was to say one Nocturn
of the Office every night after ordinary Matins,
except on occasion of a feast of nine lessons, and
in Christmas and Easter-tide, etc., and to endeavour to go through the three Nocturns once in every
week. The Office began with the Antiphon to the
Psalms at Matins, as well as at Vespers and
Lauds; the Invitatory being omitted. The verse
"*Eternal rest grant unto them, O* Lord: *and
light perpetual shine upon them,*" was the Antiphon under which all the Psalms at Vespers were
said, and was not used, as in the modern Roman
Office, to replace *Gloria* at the end of each Psalm,
and in the last response of each Nocturn. The
Psalms and Lessons are identical with the Roman:
the Responsory and Collects have some characteristic and beautiful variations.

Mass for the dead was also said daily in the
Chapter House of Salisbury Cathedral. The
ancient form of this Office, resembling that for
the three days before Easter, is accounted for
by some as being in imitation of Christ's obse-

quies; but the true reason appears to be that, in this case, modern innovations have not been introduced. The Invitatory is omitted in the Roman use, unless three Nocturns are said; because more are to be called to that longer and more solemn service. The Office for the Dead has only first Vespers, Matins, and Lauds. Gavanti supposes the absence of Second Vespers to arise from the lesser dignity of the solemnity: like a simple feast which has first Vespers only. Others say, the Office will have its close when the soul, now commended to the memory of GOD, enters on perfect beatitude. In reference to the incomplete blessedness of the faithful departed, also, the coffin is censed at the top and two sides, but not all round. The third, seventh, and thirtieth days after a death, are noted for special commemoration. The third day, because as CHRIST'S Resurrection on the third day renewed our life, so we pray for the happier state of the departed, and hope for their blessed resurrection. The seventh, because the seventh day of the week is the Sabbath; and we pray the LORD of the Sabbath to give eternal rest to the souls of the faithful departed. The thirtieth day, or month's mind, is kept according to Old Testament examples (Num. 20; Deut. 34: the thirty days' weeping for Moses and Aaron). The year's mind, or anniversary, is commemorated "lest the soul prayed for be not yet released: for it is better

to pray more than enough, rather than too little.'
It was hardly necessary to adduce such a reason as
that.

The Office is said (in the Roman use) on the
first feria of the week, in Advent and Lent, in order
to lose no time in praying for the dead. Monday
is also said to be the fittest day for this Office,
because on that day were made the heavens, to
which the Church prays that the faithful souls may
be admitted. The Office in old time was said
daily as in England : but Pius V. confined it to one
day in the week, in Advent and Lent ; and in other
seasons, to the first day, unhindered, in every
month : always excepting Easter-tide, during which
it is omitted.

III.—*Psalm* 119.

"The 119th Psalm, daily recited in the Church's
Office, is called pre-eminently the 'Psalm of
Saints.' It was composed after the return from
Babylon : when the Jews had at last put idolatry
away for ever, and some among them began to
realize more fully the spiritual character of their
Law. Almost every verse contains some reference
to the Law under one or other of ten names.
These have been classified as follows : '*Law* is
the generic phrase, including all the others, and
taken for the whole scope of Divine revelation :
Testimonies, are such precepts as are prohibitory

attesting GOD's holiness, *protesting* against man's sinfulness ; *Statutes*, are positive enactments, ceremonial ordinances, and the like ; *Commandments*, moral enactments ; *Judgments*, formal decisions of duties as laid down in the Law ; *Precepts*, are counsels recommended to individuals for their guidance and profit ; *Word*, is any verbal revelation of GOD's will ; *Saying*, or rather *promise*, the declaration of blessings to follow on obedience ; *Way*, the prescribed rule of conduct ; *Faithfulness*, the abiding character and permanence of the Law.'

" ' This Psalm,' says the *Gloss*, ' is the teacher of the faithful, a paradise of all fruits, the storehouse of the HOLY GHOST ; and just in proportion as it seems easier on the surface, so is it deeper in the abyss of its mysteries. Other Psalms shine a little, as lesser stars, but this one like the sun, glowing with the noonday heat of his full blaze ; and it glows with every kind of moral sweetness. And it has been compared to a tree of two and twenty branches, each with eight boughs, from which drops of sweetness continually fall. They observe further that the alphabetical arrangement, as noting the very rudiments of knowledge, implies that moral teaching in the first principles of life which the perfect need to give the unlearned, that they may attain the palm of blessedness at last. And the grouping into octonaries of verses signifies on

the one hand this blessedness, summed up in the
eight beatitudes, while the day of the new creation
is itself counted as the eighth, coming as it does
after the recurring seven days of this present
world.' "—Littledale.—*Commentary on the Psalms.*

IV.—*Penitential Psalms.*

These Psalms, as Dr. Neale says, are the seven
weapons wherewith to oppose the seven deadly
sins: the seven prayers inspired by the sevenfold
SPIRIT to the repenting sinner: the seven guardians
for the seven days of the week: the seven companions for the seven Canonical Hours of the
day.

They were in use under their present name, in
the time of S. Augustine. Innocent III. ordered
their recitation in Lent: and they were originally
said daily during that season. So the Sarum book
directed. Pius V. assigned Fridays only for their
use.

Cassiodorus, following Origen, says that they are
seven by reason of the seven ways whereby sins
are remitted: Baptism, martyrdom, almsgiving,
freeing slaves, converting souls, abundant charity,
and penitence.

Cardinal Bona remarks that the ancient canons
imposed seven years' penance for grave offences:
the leper was to be sprinkled seven times; Naaman
was sent to wash seven times in Jordan; in the

seventh year remission was to be made; and the great Jubilee took place after the square of seven years; and other like things: whence he infers, that not without cause is the number of these Psalms fixed at seven; that those cleansed in a sevenfold manner, free from seven plagues, seven devils being cast out, may be brightened by the grace of the sevenfold SPIRIT.

The ladder of repentance, says Bakius, quoted by Dr. Littledale, has seven steps, denoted by the seven Penitential Psalms. The first is fear of punishment, *Rebuke me not*. The next is sorrow for sin, *I will confess my sins unto the* LORD. Thirdly, the hope of pardon, *Thou shalt answer for me, O* LORD *my* GOD. Fourthly, the love of a cleansed soul, *Thou shalt purge me with hyssop, and I shall be clean*. Fifthly, longing for the heavenly Jerusalem, *When the* LORD *shall build up Sion, and when His glory shall appear*. Sixthly, distrust of self, *My soul fleeth unto the* LORD. Seventhly, prayer against final doom, *Enter not into judgment with Thy servant*.

V.—*Gradual Psalms.*

These Psalms, as before observed, were said daily in Lent; and, in the Sarum use, after Tierce, consecutively, without interspersion of prayers, but followed by the great Litany. The present Roman use has them on Wednesday only in Lent,

M

before Matins, and broken into three divisions
of five psalms, with prayers intervening. This
manner of recitation was not unknown in
England, for it is enjoined in the "Ancren
Riwle."

"Ayguan alleges that the fifteen Psalms were
divided by the Jews into three portions of five,
with prayers intercalated, much as the Gregorian
division of Matins into three Nocturns : and that
each of the three grades of advance in the spiritual
life is betokened by each quinary ; the beginners,
the progressors, and the perfect, or, in other terms,
those who are severally in the purgative, the illu-
minative, and the unitive way. And thus it will be
noticed that in Pss. 120—124, there is constant
reference to trouble and danger ; in Pss. 125—129,
to confidence in GOD ; in 130—134, to direct communion with Him in His House. And a late commentator defines the fifteen degrees of going up
out of the valley of weeping to the Presence of
GOD to be (1) affliction, (2) looking to GOD, (3) joy
in communion, (4) invocation, (5) thanksgiving, (6)
confidence, (7) patient waiting for deliverance,
(8) GOD's grace and favour, (9) fear of the LORD,
(10) martyrdom, (11) hatred of sins, (12) humility, (13) desire for the coming of CHRIST, (14)
concord and charity, (15) constant blessing of GOD."
—Littledale.

"Five are the senses of man, whereby he

ascends to the Triune GOD, therefore the Psalms are divided into sets of five.

" Radulphus notes, that as the first five are said for the dead, the second for ourselves and our friends, and the third for all the faithful, from the cleansing of the dead we ascend to the cleansing of ourselves in the second Collect, and to union with GOD in the third ; also that, in the second division, ceasing to do evil, in the third, we may learn to do well ; which includes all righteousness.

" Bellarmine, in his book of the ascent of the soul to GOD, marks fifteen steps in three orders of degrees, which, with a little change, may be very well adapted to these Psalms : in the first five considering corruptible things, earth, water, air, fire, and mingled things ; in the next, heavenly bodies : man, his rational soul, the angelic nature, the Divine essence. In the third, the power of GOD : His mind, wisdom, work, mercy, righteousness. All which is set forth in that golden little book.

" *Gloria* is not said to the first five, because in praying for the dead, we are not so much glorifying the Trinity, as desiring for those that one and eternal rest, after the purification of the five senses whereby they have sinned. But glory is given to GOD by our arising, whether we depart from sin, or do righteousness."—Gavanti.

" The only period of the year in which any long portion of the Psalms is repeated, evening after

evening, in the Eastern Church, is the fifteen weeks
before Christmas Day. And the Psalms repeated
are no other than these ' Pilgrim songs.' The
idea evidently is that the Church is then approaching week by week—a week for each song of degrees
—to the true Tabernacle and Temple, which our
Blessed Lord by His Nativity pitched among men.
These Psalms are also said on week-days in Lent."
—Freeman.

"And these Degrees or Steps are said to be
numbered fifteen in the Psalter, or in Solomon's
temple, to teach that we can rise again to heavenly
things by the septenary of the Law, and the octave
of our Lord's Resurrection; and can in no other
way escape the prince of this world, unless the
repose of the soul after the flesh be granted, as
though in the seventh age, and the resurrection of
the flesh at the end be created, as on the octave.
By reason of these fifteen *degrees*, that is, the knowledge of both Testaments, it is recorded that the
water of the Flood, which rose vastly above the
hollows of the valleys, and the level of the plains,
was fifteen cubits higher than the tops of the loftiest
mountains ; because the faith of the Church, hallowed by the waters of Baptism, not only readily
surpasses the moral code of the Gentiles, but by
its height of virtue exceeds the mightiest intellects
of philosophers, because it knows how to live
rightly in the world, and to believe, hope, and love

the everlasting life of the soul, with the resurrection of the body in the world to come.

"There is some difference of opinion as to the exact meaning of the title, *Songs of Degrees*, or *Gradual Psalms*, prefixed to the fifteen poems which follow the great Song of the Law, and which, from their completeness in themselves, have been aptly styled, 'The Little Psalter.' One ancient Jewish view is that they were intended to be liturgically used in processions to the Temple, one upon each of the fifteen steps leading up from the Court of the women to the great portal of the Inner Court of the men, or 'Court of Israel.' The fact that there was *some* ascent is certain, from the phrase *go up*, used of Hezekiah's visit of thanksgiving; the probability that the steps were *fifteen* in number is inferred from the double mention in Ezekiel of two flights of stairs in the temple of his vision, one of which had seven steps and the other eight. But the most ancient Christian tradition, without being inconsistent with this one, is more probable, that they are originally pilgrim-songs, for *going up* to Jerusalem, and their title is derived from the same root as the verb to denote the *going up* of Israel out of Egypt, and the going up of the Jews with Ezra and Nehemiah out of Babylon to Jerusalem. It is then probable enough that, first written as expressions of longing for a delayed blessing, and perhaps marking a series of events connected with the end of the Captivity, as Origen believes, they came to be used later by the caravans of Hebrew pilgrims going up to Jerusalem at the three yearly festivals. And so explained, a remarkable order is manifest in them. Ps. 120 expresses weariness of heathen companionship and surroundings; 121, the first sight of the mountain girdle of Palestine by the pilgrim, now fairly on his way, and trusting in GOD to keep him safe on the road; 122, the concourse of pilgrims as every cross-road sends its single travellers to swell the great caravan of the main highway; 123, a prayer in peril of an attack by banditti; 124, thanksgiving for deliverance from that danger; 125, the first sight of the mountains round Jerusalem; 126, happy and peaceful talk with sympathising hosts sheltering and feeding their pilgrim countrymen; 127 brings them in sight of the peaceful city itself, and therewith recalls how it was once compassed by war as a punishment for neglecting its Keeper, the true Builder of the glorious House, the one sure Watchman of its formidable walls; 128 is the greeting to the citizens who come out of the houses to meet and welcome the approaching pilgrims; 129 is the thankful expression of security uttered by those who are now safe within the fortifications; 130 brings them in sight of the Temple, and breathes mingled tones of penitence, longing, and hope, uttered from the valley, *out of the deep*, as the pilgrims prepare to ascend Mount Moriah; 131 is the hush of reverence on near approach to GOD's House of Prayer; 132 brings the pilgrims in full view of its pomp and beauty, which causes them to break out into eager words of praise and blessing, recalling the memories of David's zeal for the Tabernacle; 133 is caused by the sight of the anointed priests, visible on the steps and in the outer court; 134 brings the happy pilgrims within the sacred precincts, and is their greeting to the priests whom they had seen at a little distance just before; while the closing words of all, being the priestly benediction uttered upon the travellers, fitly end the pilgrimage, and are the final reply to the first utterance of the series, 'When I was in trouble I called upon the LORD,' answered by, *The LORD that made Heaven and earth, bless thee out of Sion.* Whatever their first occasion and their subsequent employment may have been, at any rate there is no doubt of the religious fitness of the old Jewish comment on this Jacob's ladder of prayer and praise, that each Psalm of the series is a 'Song on the steps on which GOD leads the righteous up to a happy hereafter.' "—Littledale.

IV.—*Litany.*

The word Litany, according to Mr. Palmer, has been used at different times in very different senses. Originally it was applied to all prayers and supplications, public and private. In the fourth century the name was assigned more especially to solemn offices of prayer performed in processions of clergy and people. And when the Arians, being obliged to worship outside the city walls, went forth for the purpose in procession, singing hymns and psalms, S. John Chrysostom instituted still grander processions of a parallel character, to counteract the effect on his people's minds. These were called Litanies.

But the name Litany was sometimes applied to the persons taking part in the procession, as well as to the service then used. Various parts of the Divine Office were called by this name; and especially, in later times, any portion containing the invocation *Kyrie Eleison*.

The Western word Rogation was equivalent to the Eastern Litany; but in process of time the Western service became known by the Eastern name: and the Rogation was taken to signify those three days only, set apart by Mamertus for special prayer at Ascension-tide, as presently to be mentioned. Annual Litanies of this kind were never received by the Eastern Church. In the West, they were used, in some places before, in some, after Ascension Day, and also at other times. Processions were unknown till the fourth century, when first the peace of the Church rendered them possible. The service used in these processions

originally resembled other Offices ; and consisted
of Psalmody, Scripture Lessons, and Prayers.
Such was the Litany of Mamertus.

The later Litanies of the Western Church contain
invocations of many Saints. This use is peculiar to
the West. It is traced back to the eighth century,
but not earlier; and even so is the earliest example
of any such invocation in the public offices of the
Church. The place now filled by these addresses,
was probably occupied originally by frequent repe-
tions of *Kyrie*. Gregory of Tours, speaking of the
Litany instituted at Rome by S. Gregory, says:
"*Kyrie Eleison* was sung through the streets of the
city." According to the very ancient Roman
Ritual, " They say one hundred times *Kyrie
Eleison*, one hundred times *Christe Eleison*, one
hundred times again *Kyrie Eleison* :" and Walafrid
Strabo observes that Litanies are rather invocations
of Divine mercy than invocations of the Saints.
But we find the later practice mentioned by Victor
Vitensis, who says that in public calamities and
Vandal persecutions, it was the custom to call on
all Saints, thus: " Pray, ye holy Patriarchs, holy
Prophets, holy Apostles, be ye our advocates,
especially thou blessed Peter . . . . . thou blessed
Paul . . . . . ye holy ones, let your groans for us
rise up together."

The form of Litany prayers begun by the officiant
and responded to by the people, is copied from an

Eastern model: the Ectene, recited in every Liturgy, and familiar to many English readers through its reproduction in Bishop Andrewes' Devotions.

The Antiphonary of Gregory the Great appoints a large number of anthems to be sung during processions; and one of these is the very Litany which, according to Venerable Bede, was sung by S. Augustine and his company as they approached Canterbury for the first time.

VII.—*Dignity of Festivals.*

Something must be said on the Dignity of Festivals: an intricate and perplexing subject, with which the use of the Breviary brings us in contact. Without attempting a dissertation which would require learning and research, it may be possible to put a few puzzling things in a clearer light.

All days, then, are divided under the two heads of *ferias*, and *feasts* or *festivals*. Feria, in the ecclesiastical sense of the word, means an ordinary week-day. In classical Latin, it means, on the contrary, a holy day. And the reason given, whether rightly or not, for this change of application is, that in the Christian Church all days become holy.

The days of the week, then, if we begin with Monday, are styled *feria secunda*, *feria tertia*, etc., till Saturday and Sunday, which are respectively *dies sabbato* and *dies dominica*. The ecclesiastical Kalendar retains the ancient Latin arrangement of Kalends, (whence the name Kalendar,) Ides, and Nones.

Festivals were variously arranged according to the diverse Uses, and herein lay their chief diversity. For practical purposes, it is only needful here to consider the orders of the Sarum and Roman books.

There are in both, two great divisions: into Double and Simple Feasts.

The classification of Double Feasts is as follows:—

In the Sarum use:	In the Roman:
Principal ⎫	Doubles of the First Class,
Greater ⎬ Doubles.	Doubles of the Second Class,
Lesser ⎪	Greater Doubles,
Inferior ⎭	Semi-Doubles (that is, having two Vespers, but not doubling the Antiphons). Days in Octaves fall under this head.

None of these terms are strictly interchangeable ; that is, for instance, although *Principal Double* in the Sarum answers to the dignity of *Double of the first class* in the Roman, we find placed under that head in the Roman Kalendar not only all the Principal Doubles of the Sarum, but some of its Greater and Lesser Doubles also.

The Sundays of the year are also divided according to their dignity :

Sarum :		Roman :
Principal privileged		Greater Sundays of
Greater privileged		the first class,
Lesser privileged	Sundays.	Greater Sundays of
Inferior privileged		the second class,
Ordinary		Ordinary Sundays.

A simple feast in the Roman Kalendar is one, the celebration of which begins at the Chapter of the first Vespers ; having one Nocturn only at Matins, and ending after Nones, without second Vespers. This is the rule of the Roman Simple, and it has no exception.

The Simples of Sarum are very much more elaborate, and are many more in number. There are several divisions, of sorts rather than of degree : Simples of nine and of three Lessons ; with and without rulers ; with Triple and Double Invitatories. The Simples of nine Lessons nearly correspond to the Roman Semi-Doubles, have two Vespers, and hold the same rank as Sundays of the fourth class. The Simples of three Lessons assimilate to the Roman Simples, and are superseded by all Sundays and by greater Ferias.

The title of Triple or Double Invitatory refers to

the ceremonial only, not to any distinction in the matter of the Office. And thus it was. We have seen that the English Church had Rulers of the Choir, whose duty it was to sing the Antiphons, etc., and to superintend the choristers. A feast was said to have double or triple Invitatories, according as it had two or three Rulers: by whom the Invitatory was sung. Double Feasts had four Rulers.

In addition to all these, there were also Offices of Commemoration, used monthly, weekly, or at other intervals; or when the sets of ferial lessons for any week ran short, and no Saints' day was at hand to fill the gap. These were Offices of the Blessed Virgin, and of the feasts proper to the place (*festi loci*), and never had second Vespers. Nor was any memorial made of them in the place of second Vespers.

Ferias were divided under the name of greater and ordinary ferias: the Sarum use containing, as usual, several sub-divisions. But it is sufficient to say, that among greater ferias, in both uses, were counted the week-days of Advent and Lent, Rogation and Ember days, memorials of which were always to be made, no matter what Feast occurred upon them.

Now all this elaborate classification was made in order to avoid any doubtfulness and confusion on those very frequent occasions when different festivals, moveable or otherwise, clashed with each

other. Or, more correctly speaking, their clashing
was rendered impossible, by the rules laid down
for every possible case.

One festival is said to *occur* with another, or
with a Sunday, if both fall on the same day. One
concurs with another, if it falls on the day following
(so as to raise the question whether to say the second
Vespers of the former, or the first Vespers of the
following). All questions of precedence arising
from occurrence and concurrence are settled by
fixed rules, according to which the festivals are
translated, commemorated, omitted, or celebrated
according to their technical dignity. For instance:
Sundays of the first class (Principal and greater
privileged Sundays) never yield place to any
festival whatever. Any feast occurring on such a
day is, according to its dignity, transferred, or, for
the current year, omitted. All this arrangement is
made perfectly clear in modern Breviaries by the
Tables of Occurrence and Concurrence. But this
convenience was entirely unknown to our fore-
fathers: therefore that well-known complaint in
the Preface of the Common Prayer Book:
"Moreover, the number and hardness of the
rules called the *Pie*, and the manifold chang-
ings of the service, was the cause, that to
turn the book only, was so hard and intricate
a matter, that many times there was more business to find out what should be read, than to

read it when it was found out."* Nor was there formerly to be found any such arrangements of General Rubrics, full, clear, and conveniently placed, as that which renders the use of the modern books so much easier. In the Sarum books, the rubrics are indeed plentiful : but they are scattered here, there, and everywhere ; and sometimes, unfortunately, are to be found no-where.

---

* By way of example, here are are some few lines from the Pie, or Pica, which was its Latin name, *said* to have been derived from the piebald appearance of the red and black words. It is a list of every possible combination of commemorations that could take place under every Sunday Letter. (This first extract gives the rule for the occurrence of S. Andrew's day on Advent Sunday.)

Littera do. E. pridie kalen. decembri tota cantetur hysto. et solen. memo. de sancta maria : et fes. apostoli differatur in crastino : licet fes. loci fuerit : secunde vespere erunt de apostolo cum oratione *Maiestatem* et memo. de domi. et de sancta maria solenniter cum an. *Ave maria.* Feria 2. de apostolo. Feria 3. 4. et 6. commemo. Feria 5. de sancto Osmundo. ix. lec. omnia de communi.

That was made out clearly, because it was on the first page : but take this for Rogation-tide, by which time greater skill in decipher-ing is evidently expected.

4.G. Do. 5. post pas. de do. In lau. oe. ae. dnr. Fe. 2. et 4. de fe. in. 2. fe. dnr. R̶. de. 4. fe. et in. 4. fe. dnr. R̶. de. 2. fe. cu. R̶. *Dicant nunc.* Fe. 5. de ascen. ad 2. vespe. fiat memo. de sanctis sub silen. Feria. 3. de sancta maria.

CHAPTER IV.

SEASONS AND FESTIVALS.

" THE great year of this present life, extending from the beginning to the ending of the world, is divided into four parts: first, the time of erring, from Adam to Moses; wherein all men departed from the worship of GOD. Second, the time of recall: from Moses to CHRIST; wherein men were recalled by the law and the prophets. Third, the time of reconciliation: from the birth of CHRIST to the Ascension; wherein human things were reconciled to Divine. Fourth, the time of pilgrimage: from the Ascension to the end of the world. These seasons of the great year of the world are commemorated by the Church in her own various seasons. For in Advent, she celebrates the time of recall; from Septuagesima till Low Sunday, the time of error; in Easter-tide, the time of reconciliation; from Trinity to Advent, the time of pilgrimage. And the Church begins the offices of her spiritual warfare at that season which figures recall, not following the natural order; for it was not fitting that she should begin by the time of wandering astray, who desired to avoid error, and find the physician."—Sicardus.

I.— ADVENT.

Advent is an old name for Christmas. The Mozarabic Missal, and Lanfranc's Statutes, mentioning the Sundays before Christmas, call them the Sundays before Advent. It appears always to have been the practice to set apart some time in preparation for Christmas, though no certain mention of the period is found in the records of the first five centuries. The first distinct notice we have of its observance is in Gaul, whence it appears to have passed into Italy. S. Gregory of Tours says that Perpetuus, bishop also of Tours, prescribed fasts in his diocese, on three days in the week, from Martinmas to Christmas. The ancient monks caused their Advent preparation to consist chiefly in three things: prayer, fasting, and withdrawal from the conversation of men. In S. Gregory's Sacramentary are set down five Sundays before Christmas; the first being that of the five loaves; (the Gospel still read on the Sunday next before Advent, and fifth from the Nativity, when, after five ages, CHRIST, coming in the sixth age of the world, satisfied the faithful with heavenly food.)

" The Advent of the LORD is well said to have taken place (albeit He is everywhere always present by His Divine Majesty) when, assuming that which is visible to us, He manifested Himself to eyes of flesh. Which came to pass, when the Word—by

N

Whom all things were made, Who was in the world, and the world was made by Him, and the world knew Him not—when the Word was made flesh, that He might dwell among men : and again, it is future ; when He Who now sitteth at the right hand of God, and yet is with us till the end of the world, shall appear to us in that same form which He assumed at His first coming. Therefore the time preceding Christmas is called Advent, because it commemorates His comings, both past and future. The first Sunday, treating of the first Advent as though yet future, speaks in the person of the ancient Church. The second and third Sundays, setting the second Advent before expectant and longing souls as now nigh at hand, sounds the warning trumpet of the prophets and apostles. The fourth Sunday looks to the time immediately preceding the Lord's Nativity, when His Divinity shod Itself with our nature."—Rupert of Deutz.

Sicardus enters into detailed expositions of various parts of the offices for each Sunday and festival; but it will be sufficient for us to confine our notices to those passages which are of most importance, or of least obvious meaning.

The first Responsory at Matins on Advent Sunday was sung with great pomp. The words, " Go ye forth to meet Him," were accompanied by instrumental symphonies, and in the Churches at Paris and elsewhere, the largest bell was tolled at

the same time, as a sign to the people to go forth
to meet Him. This is the only response which
has three versicles; and the exposition of it is very
elaborate. "Its subject is the first Advent, and
it is sung in the person of John Baptist, or of the
Bride, saying, *Beholding from afar*, namely, from
earth to heaven, *lo, I see the glory* [power] *of* GOD.
Although Power be properly assigned to the
FATHER, Wisdom to the SON, and Love to the
HOLY GHOST, the word here signifieth the SON of
GOD, to Whom all power is given in heaven and
earth. He came, when He shewed Himself visibly,
with *a cloud covering the whole earth*. This cloud
is the mercy of GOD. Hereinto Moses entered
when he went to receive the Law. This led the
people in the wilderness. This is the power of the
Most Highest, which overshadowed the Virgin,
and which covers the whole earth, because the
earth is full of the mercy of the LORD. *Go forth to
meet Him and say, Tell us if Thou art He that
shall reign over Thy people Israel.* Thus John said
to his disciples, *Prepare ye the way of the* LORD;
and, through his disciples to CHRIST, *Art Thou He
that should come, or look we for another?* Or,
they are the words of the Bride to the virgins: Go
forth to meet the Bridegroom. This response has
three versicles and one Gloria, signifying the four-
fold Advent of CHRIST: (1) His Nativity; (2) His
entrance into the faithful soul; (3) the hour of

each man's death ; (4) the last Judgment. Or, the
four ages ; before the law, under the law, under the
prophets, and under grace. The Church, addressing
all men who lived before the law, few of whom
followed the One GOD, saith in the first versicle,
*All ye people, and all that dwell in the world, rich
and poor, one with another,* (that is, all of you, bad
and good,) *go forth to meet Him.* In the second
versicle, speaking in the person of those men who
lived under the law, she addresses their Lawgiver :
Hear, O Thou Shepherd of Israel, as if to say, Thou
That rulest the people of Israel in Thy law, and
leadest them as a shepherd doth his sheep, *Tell us
if Thou art He that shall reign over Thy people
Israel.* In the third versicle, being certified by the
prophets of the SAVIOUR'S Advent, she cries out
with desire : *Lift up your heads, O ye gates, and
the King of Glory shall come in.* In the fourth,
rendering thanks to the SAVIOUR, and to the whole
Trinity, for the Advent, she says, *Glory be,* etc.
The response is repeated from the beginning,
because the LORD'S Advent is again expected by
the faithful."—Sicardus.

The mention of the ox and ass in the first lesson
at these Matins, referring to the stupidity of the
Jews, led to their introduction in pictures of the
Nativity ; there is no ancient tradition as to their
being present at that time.

The Gospel for the first Sunday in Advent was

in Sarum, as in the modern English use, of the entry into Jerusalem.   The ass tied, with the colt, being typical of human nature, which CHRIST unbound at His coming.

" The Office of the second Sunday is an Office to rejoice the heart of him who hath accepted the LORD's first Advent, and, justified by faith, and having peace with GOD, desires in the second Advent to behold His glorious kingdom.

" That of the third Sunday is an Office of consolation, especially for the rulers of the Church.

" The fourth Sunday sets forth the mystery of the Incarnation.   *Over Edom will I cast out My shoe*, signifies, To the Gentiles I will make known My Incarnation.   *Whose shoe's latchet I am not worthy to unloose*, is, in other words, I am not worthy to unfold the mystery of the Incarnation."   Or, it refers to the Jewish law, whereby he who refused to redeem, had his shoe's latchet loosed.

Ember days are not mentioned before the time of S. Leo, who refers to them in his homily read on Advent Sunday.   He perhaps adopted them from the four yearly Jewish fasts.

" In the third week of Advent are the winter Ember days.   Wednesday and Friday are chosen from among the other days of the week, because they are more particularly marked with the memory of the LORD's Passion ; for on Wednesday He was betrayed, and on Friday crucified.   As the body is

formed of four elements, and the year divided into
four parts, each consisting of three months, so,
four times a year we fast for three days: the three
days refer to three months; one day is offered to
the LORD for each month, that He may grant us a
peaceful and healthy life, and that fasting may
chasten our bodies; or again, in order to lay before
GOD the firstfruits of our days. In this week are
begun the great Antiphons, sung, each one on its
proper day, until Christmas Eve; and in the second
tone, because they are addressed to CHRIST, the
'Giant of twofold substance.'"—Sicardus.

These Great O's are mentioned in the life of
Alcuin. They were sung either at Lauds or Vespers,
or at both. They are preferably sung at Vespers,
on account of our LORD's being expected at the
vespertide of the world; and are repeated, to represent the repeated yearnings of the faithful for the
first Advent of CHRIST. These Antiphons were
doubled, according to the Roman use; but in the
Paris rite they were sung thrice, once before the
beginning of the canticle, once at its close, and
once after the *Gloria Patri*: and to sing them
thus was called *triumphare*. And, a practice
which led to much abuse, portions of good wine
were served out in the refectory, and these Antiphons were sung there the while; to typify the
good gifts and the joy which CHRIST's coming
brought to men. *O Virgo Virginum*, the eighth

Antiphon in the Sarum book, was abolished by Pius V. In 1680 the Parisian Breviary replaced *O Virgo Virginum* by *O Sancte Sanctorum*, and *O Thome*, the Antiphon for S. Thomas's Day, by *O Pastor Israel;* always reciting nine as a ninefold preparation for Christmas.

"In these Antiphons the Church sets forth her manifold sicknesses, and prays for their healing. For, before the coming of CHRIST, we were ignorant and blind, given over to eternal punishment; servants of Satan, bound by the evil habits of sin, seated in darkness, exiles and expelled from our country.

"Therefore we need a Teacher, Redeemer, Deliverer, Enlightener, and SAVIOUR. In the first Antiphon we cry, *O Wisdom*, etc. Ecclus. xxiv. 3; Wisd. viii. 1; ix. 10; Isa. xi. 2. But because it would profit little, if we were taught and yet not redeemed, in the second Antiphon we ask redemption, saying: *O* LORD *and Ruler*, etc., Exod. vi. 3; iii. 2; xix. 20; xiv. 13-21. But since it would avail nothing to be taught and redeemed, if, after redemption, we were still held captive, therefore, in the third, we pray for deliverance: *O Root of Jesse*, etc., Isa. xi. 10; lii. 15. But what would it profit captives to be redeemed and delivered, and yet not loosed from all bonds, (continuing, that is, bound under sin,) and unable to go where they would? Therefore, in the fourth, we ask to be delivered from all sin: *O Key of David*, etc. Rev.

iii. 7; Isa. xlii. 7; S. Luke i. 79. Moreover, because they who have been long in prison are dim-eyed, so that they cannot see clearly, therefore, having been loosed from our chains, it remains that we be enlightened to see whither we should go; and we pray for this in the fifth Antiphon: *O Orient*, etc., Zech. vi. 12; Wisd. vii. 26; Mal. iv. 2; S. Luke i. 79. But, if taught, and fully delivered from enemies, and enlightened, it would avail us nothing, except we were brought to the Kingdom and saved therein; therefore in the two following Antiphons we ask salvation: *O King of the Gentiles*, Hag. ii. 7; 1 S. Pet. ii. 6; Eph. ii. 14; Gen. iii. 19: wherein we ask for the salvation of the Gentiles; and *O Emmanuel*, Isa. vii. 14; S. Matt. i. 23; Gen. iii. 15; Isa. xxxiii. 22: wherein we pray for the salvation of the Jews."—Durandus.

Honorius of Autun refers the order of these seven Antiphons to the seven gifts of the HOLY GHOST, brought us by CHRIST in His Incarnation. *O Wisdom*, referring, of course, to *wisdom*: *O LORD and Ruler*, to *understanding* (concerning the law given by Moses); *O Root of Jesse*, to the *counsel* of GOD for our redemption; *O Key of David*, to the *might* which closed hell and opened heaven; *O Orient*, to light, truth, and *knowledge*; *O King of the Gentiles*, to *piety*, that is, lovingkindness, whereby He was moved to save the Gentiles; *O*

Emmanuel, to filial *fear*, which He rouses in our hearts, that we may love GOD.

Those who only used seven Antiphons did so on the principle of devoting a week to pleading that our LORD might come; by the example of the Church of Toledo, which, according to a Council held A.D. 656, celebrated the Feast of the Annunciation eight days before Christmas, rather than in Lent: and kept up the observance of the Festival during the six days next following. After the Annunciation was finally fixed for March, a Festival of the Blessed Virgin was still, in Spain and elsewhere, kept on Dec. 18th, and was called The Expectation. "Two added to seven," says Durandus, "make up the number nine; in some Churches two Antiphons were added to the seven" [and so it was in the Sarum use]; "in honour of the Blessed Virgin Mary, and of S. Thomas, whose feast falls at this time. These numbers signify that by the sevenfold gift of the HOLY GHOST we attain to the nine orders of the Angels, who earnestly desired the Nativity of CHRIST, that by its means the places of the fallen Angels might be supplied."

The Advent Sacerdotal Verse and Response at Lauds, *Send, O* LORD, *the Lamb*, etc., was sung solemnly in some churches by the whole choir kneeling, as longing for their promised salvation.

In the Sarum use a memorial of All Saints was

said on ferias, but not on Sundays, in Advent.
Elsewhere it was omitted altogether, because the
Office was devoted to the expectation of the Chief
and Crown of all Saints. Elsewhere, again, it was
used to signify the great joy and benefit received by
the Saints at CHRIST's coming. A memorial of S.
Mary was said daily, to set forth more clearly the
great truth, that GOD, by her means, vouchsafed to
give us His SON. But no memorial of the Cross
was made, because, at this time, our LORD's Birth
was to be considered rather than His Passion.

Te Deum and *Gloria in Excelsis* were not omitted
in Advent at Rome till the twelfth century; at
which time also violet vestments came into use
there. But elsewhere they were omitted as early
as the time of Lanfranc, and earlier. "*Gloria in
Excelsis* is not sung during Advent, in order that on
the night of the Nativity it may be used with greater
devotion and eagerness: for on that night it was
first sung by the Angels. Nor is *Te Deum* sung;
because He is not yet present Whom we look for;
and we are wont to sing this hymn only to One
Who is present. But why is not *Alleluia* hushed
at this time? for it is the sound of joy, but Advent
is a time of fasting. Because this fast partaketh
both of joy and sadness: joy, by reason of our
LORD's first Advent; and sadness, by reason of
His second coming to judge the world. Therefore
we sing a song of joy for His Advent of mercy,

and we fast for His Advent of justice. All Antiphons at Sunday Lauds end with *Alleluia*, setting
forth joy in the certainty of that Advent, which,
having been, as it were, prophesied in the Matin
Office, may well be exulted in at Lauds."—
Durandus.

II.—Christmas.

1.—*Christmas Eve.*

The fast of Christmas Eve is very ancient. S.
Augustine deposed a priest for breaking it. The
Antiphons and Responsory refer chiefly to the
miraculous help given by God to His people under
Jehoshaphat (2 Chron. xx.), and to the gift of
manna in the wilderness. " The Invitatory is : *Ye
shall know this day that the* Lord *will come ; and
in the morning then shall ye see His glory*. This is
slightly altered from Exodus, where the Lord said
to the children of Israel, *At even, then shall ye know
that the* Lord *hath brought you out from the land
of Egypt : and in the morning, then ye shall see the
glory of the* Lord. This pertains partly to the
Nativity, and partly to the Resurrection; thus: *Today*, that is, in this present life, *ye shall know that
the* Lord *shall come*, namely, the Living Bread from
heaven : *and in the morning*, that is, in the glory
of the Resurrection, *ye shall see*, not only the
humanity, but also the *glory* of His Divinity.

"At Lauds the first Antiphon is, *O Judah and Jerusalem*, that is, ye who confess and desire peace, *fear not ; to-morrow*, that is, presently, *go ye forth, for the* LORD *will be with you ;* like unto you : He will dwell in you."—Sicardus.

After Prime, the martyrology was wont to be read with greater pomp than usual, all standing : and all except the reader, who was vested in a cope, and the cerifers, who attended on him, as if at the solemn reading of the Gospel, fell on their knees at the words, *In Bethlehem of Judæa,* after which the reader continued in the solemn tone used in reading the Passion, *The Nativity of our* LORD JESUS CHRIST *according to the flesh.* A similar ceremony took place at reading the Martyrology on the eve of the Annunciation of our LORD.

2.—*Christmas Day.*

The festival of the Nativity, as apart from the Epiphany, was not kept in the East till the time of S. Chrysostom, and the Armenian Church still keeps this feast combined with that of the Epiphany. But in the West, Christmas was kept, from a very early period, on December 25th. Some suppose that day to have been fixed by Pope Julius, A.D. 336, to stop the heathen worship paid to the new-born sun, after the winter solstice ; and it is now considered very probable that the Nativity took place about the time of the feast of tabernacles. But the

Roman Church, says Grancolas, had full opportunity of ascertaining the correct time, because the acts of the census of Quirinus, under Augustus, which occasioned the Blessed Virgin's journey to Bethlehem, were carefully kept at Rome. This feast, then, is fixed, not moveable, like those which are derived from the Jews.

" The LORD willed to be born at the end of the year, to shew that He came in the last age of the world : to be conceived on the sixth day, born on the first, crucified on the sixth, risen on the first : that He Who had lost His creature, man, on the sixth day, might on the sixth day deliver him : and that He Who on the first day said, *Let there be light*, might, coming on the first day, the Dayspring from on high, bestow on us heavenly light. And He was born by night, to signify His hiding of Himself in flesh, and His coming to lighten our darkness."—Durandus.

The days grow longer after His Birth, because they that believe on Him are called to the unending light of eternity.

Two sets of Matins were formerly said at Rome, on this and other great festivals. Mass was said on Christmas night after the first set, and the second was then sung with greater dignity. Afterwards, the first set of these festival Matins was transferred to the Vigil, which thus came to have an Office of its own. But in this case, Christmas

Eve having already its proper Office, the first set of Christmas Matins was transferred to the Octave, the feast of the Circumcision.

"Concerning the Night-office, it is to be known that the Invitatory, *Christ is born to us*, is sung in the person of the Angels, calling on the shepherds, or rather, on all people, to worship the new-born LORD. Nine Psalms are said in the three nocturns, signifying that all the holy fathers, who lived in the three ages, before the law, under the law, and under grace, are joined, by CHRIST's coming, to the nine orders of Angels, to rejoice with them."—Durandus.

"The first subject is the ineffable and eternal generation of CHRIST; the second, His Incarnation; the third, the praises of the Bridegroom and the Bride. And witness is borne hereunto by the three lessons of Isaiah, which describe the Incarnation of CHRIST, not so much prophetically as evangelically; and we rejoice with the Angels in the three ℟℟., which represent all things in heaven and earth restored by the Nativity of CHRIST. In the first, "*The armies of the Angels rejoice*, etc., the restoration of heavenly things is sung; in the second, where *true peace came down from heaven*, is sung the reparation of things earthly; in the third, where is said, *He hath appeared upon earth*, is commemorated the deliverance of them that dwelt in the shadow of death."—Sicardus.

The lessons from Isaiah are read without title ; and this was formerly the general use, except when the beginning of any book was to be read. But the mystical reason assigned to the custom on this occasion is, that GOD speaketh not now by prophets, but by His SON.

"In the second nocturn are read lessons from expositions ; and, singing, we rejoice with the shepherds, commemorating their devotion. In the third nocturn *Alleluia* is frequently used ; because in the third age, the time of grace, joy came to the world. In this nocturn are read three Gospels : two deal with the temporal Nativity ; the third sets forth the Giant of twofold substance."—Sicardus.

It was sometimes the case, when an emperor happened to be present at these Matins, that he would read the seventh lesson, bareheaded : on account of its beginning, *There went out a decree from Cæsar Augustus.* It was done by Charles IV. and Frederic III. ; so that directions, in case of such an occurrence, were set down in the Roman Ritual.

The first Christmas Mass is said after Matins, and before Lauds : mystically, because it pertains to the night, but Lauds to the day : and also because it refers to the eternal generation of CHRIST, which was, before any creature existed that could praise GOD. Pope Telesphorus is said to have ordered three Masses for this day, to shew that the

Nativity of CHRIST saved the fathers of the three ages above mentioned. We perceive from the lesson of the second nocturn, that three Masses were celebrated on Christmas Day in the time of S. Gregory. The custom of repeating Masses on solemn festivals arose from the desire of affording opportunity for all the faithful to communicate. The first Christmas Mass was said at midnight, at the first cockcrow. The second, at daybreak, immediately after Lauds and before Prime. The third, in broad daylight; and this, says Gavanti, is fitly sung after Tierce, because Mass should not be celebrated till after some canonical Hour has prepared the choir for it.

It may be said that, as the first Mass is of the eternal generation, so the second is of our LORD's Birth in time, and the third, of His Birth in the hearts of the faithful.

In some Churches, as Rouen, Rheims, and Tours, there was, after Matins and the first Mass, a rite called *Office of the Shepherds*. A manger having been prepared behind the Altar, with figures of the Virgin and Child, the choir betook themselves thither. A young chorister, representing an angel, sang *Gloria* to the clergy: the canons, as shepherds, saluted the Virgin, and worshipped the Child: after which they returned to their places; whereupon the Celebrant, who had not left the Altar, turning to the clergy, said: *Whom saw ye,*

O shepherds? say ye, tell us, Who hath appeared upon earth? And they who had represented the shepherds made answer: *We have seen the Child.* These words continue to be used at the beginning of Lauds.

It was particularly ruled that, when Christmas Day fell on Friday, meat was to be eaten. S. Epiphanius mentions this. Matthew Paris, in his history of England, speaking of A.D. 1255, says: "That year Christmas Day fell on Friday, and they ate meat out of reverence to the LORD." S. Leo wrote against the Manichæans, and others, who fasted at Christmas and Easter, not believing our LORD truly to have assumed human flesh.

The week following Christmas was kept as festal before the sixth century. During this time the Office was sung more solemnly, and with *Alleluia ;* and there was no kneeling. Before the Roman Breviary inserted the feasts of S. Thomas of Canterbury and S. Sylvester, it repeated the Office of Christmas Day on the three last days of the year ; and this was probably the case in the Sarum use also.

3.—*S. Stephen's Day.*

The feast of S. Stephen is mentioned by S. Gregory Nyssen, in the fourth century. In some Churches, it was formerly the practice at Vespers for the cantor to lay down his rod, which was taken up by a deacon, who proceeded to rule the choir, and upon the deacons all the Office of that Feast then devolved. In Salisbury Cathedral, there was on S. Stephen's Day a procession of deacons, as on S. John's Day of priests, and on Holy Innocents' of choir boys, with the boy-bishop.

The Nazarenes, referred to by S. Jerome in the ninth lesson at Matins, were a sect of Judaizing Christians, who observed circumcision, and the ceremonies of the old law; they had a peculiar Gospel, written in Hebrew; which is often quoted by S. Jerome, but never was acknowledged by the Church.

4.—*S. John's Day.*

S. Gregory Nyssen says, that in his time, immediately after Christmas Day (that is, after January 6th, for he wrote of Eastern uses,) were kept the feasts of SS. Stephen, Peter, James, John, Paul, and Basil. The Western Church fixed the feast of SS. Peter and Paul for the day of their martyrdom (June 29), and gave the morrow of S. Stephen to SS. James and John, as we find it in some ancient books. But after the translation of S. James's relics on July 25th, that day was assigned to him, and the Christmas festival was left to S. John alone. The Responses alluding to the Apostle's virginity, are from S. Jerome.

5.—*Holy Innocents', or Childermas, Day.*

This feast does not date earlier than the eighth century. Some say that it originated in Africa. The office is now doleful, but, according to Amalarius, was not so originally. At Cluny, and elsewhere, the monks were taught to keep to the old custom, and sing *Alleluia* and *Gloria in Excelsis* at Mass, and *Te Deum* at Matins. S. Gregory's Sacramentary omits the two former, and after the twelfth century a rubric was made, forbidding the use of *Te Deum* when those were forborne. Gavanti says that *Te Deum* is omitted, because Paradise was not opened to the Innocents at the time of their death; but that on the Octave, (and on the feast itself, if it fall on Sunday,) that canticle is used, because on Sunday the joy of the Resurrection rises above all tears; and the Octave signifies eternal beatitude. It has also been said that the reason for the sadness of the Office is, that the children died instead of CHRIST, and therefore that the service is, as it were, in commemoration of His own death.

In some Churches, the cantor's rod, being laid down at Vespers on S. John's Day, was taken up by the youngest chorister, who ruled the choir from thenceforth till the end of the next day's Office. One of the boys was dressed as a bishop, with mitre, vestments, and crozier, and gave the blessing

in episcopal fashion. Others were dressed as kings
and princes, and in course of time much merry
making prevailed, with dancing and laughter. This
Feast of Fools was severely reprehended by councils
and preachers.

6.—*S. Thomas of Canterbury's Day.*

This Saint was not placed in the Roman Breviary
till after the Reformation, by Pope Pius V. But
his Office had been kept long before in England.
He died on Christmas Day, 1170, and was canon-
ized in 1173 by Alexander III., who commanded
that his feast should everywhere be kept after
Childermas, and it was counted as a festival of the
first class by the Council of Exeter, A.D. 1287.
This festival, with those of Corpus Christi and
the Assumption, was arbitrarily removed from the
English Kalendar by Henry VIII., without the
consent of the Church.

7.—*Festival of the Circumcision.*

This day, in very early times, was kept with
fasting, in reparation for the sinful customs prevalent on the kalends of January, at the festival of
Janus. It is not known when the fast was changed
to a feast. " On Christmas Day we commemorate
CHRIST's coming to us: on the Octave, we commemorate man's coming to CHRIST; for He came
to us that we might go to Him. And this is

lainly denoted by the antiphons. Then it was said, *A maiden hath borne the King:* now, *O wonderful exchange,* etc.: and the word exchange shews that one thing is given and another received. CHRIST gave us His Divinity, and received our humanity; what He gave is celebrated on Christmas Day: what He received, on the Octave. Thus also is the Octave of Epiphany kept: on the feast is sung, *To-day the* LORD *was baptized in Jordan;* on the Octave is recited the cause of His Baptism: namely, that we ourselves should be baptized."—Durandus.

III.—EPIPHANY.

This feast was originally kept in the East as that of CHRIST's Nativity; the Western custom of celebrating Christmas on December 25th, not being introduced till about the time of S. John Chrysostom. It was called by the Easterns, the Holy Light, on account of the commemoration of our LORD's Baptism: which Sacrament went by the name of *illumination.* The word Epiphany is generally understood to refer, as our Prayer Book implies, to the Manifestation of CHRIST to the Gentiles, in the persons of the wise men: but the Breviary includes the manifesting of His Divinity in His Baptism, and in the miracle of water made wine. And it has been supposed that these three Epiphanies of CHRIST were celebrated by the Church in one festival, to blot out the memory of a

feast held at the same time of year in honour of
Augustus Cæsar, and his closing the gates of the
temple of Janus, after his threefold triumph over
Egypt, Parthia, and Media. Yet the Adoration of
the Magi has always been the chief subject-matter
of this festival. The idea of their being kings is
supposed to have been derived from the verse, *The
kings of Tharsis*, etc., said at the beginning of
Lauds, and elsewhere.

The Night Office of Epiphany was always celebrated with great dignity. Vigil was kept all
night, as at Christmas. At Milan, the people
flocked in crowds to Matins, as they did on Christmas night ; and in the Ambrosian rite, those are the
only two Matin Offices which have three nocturns :
and each of these nocturns contains seven psalms.

The antiquity of the Matin Office appears in its
construction. It begins straightway with the first
antiphon and first Psalm, like the Offices for the
Dead, and for the latter days of Holy Week.
When the practice was introduced of prefacing
Matins with introductory versicles, and the ninety-
fifth Psalm, the Epiphany Office was left untouched,
because that Psalm did already occur in the third
nocturn. Mystically, we are told that the absence
of versicles represents the promptitude of the
Gentiles, who came at once to worship the LORD,
as soon as they saw the star : that there is no
invitatory, because the kings came uninvited ; and

because we would mark our abhorrence of Herod's treacherous invitations. But the Psalm *Venite* is said in the third nocturn, under the seventh antiphon, to shew that in the third age, namely, the time of grace, the Church of the Gentiles hath been sufficiently invited, and hath not wherewith to excuse herself; for *their sound is gone out into all lands.* The two following Psalms shew the commotion of the Gentiles at the Apostles' preaching, the subversion of idolatry, and the conversion of the faithful.

It was an ancient practice, at this festival, to give notice of the day on which Easter would fall in the current year; and this day, as also Easter Monday, was chosen for the consecration of virgins.

The Octave of Epiphany deals altogether with our LORD's Baptism, and is supplementary to the feast itself; for, as on Epiphany we call to mind how CHRIST was baptized, so on the Octave, the antiphons set forth the reason why He was baptized. They are partly taken from S. Cyril's Catechetical Lectures (unless, contrariwise, S. Cyril quotes from them). And the Office of the LORD's Baptism is well deferred to the Octave, because Baptism takes the place of circumcision, which was performed on the eighth day.

On the Sundays after Epiphany, following the Octave, is sung at first Vespers in the Sarum use, the antiphon to Magnificat, *My sins, O* LORD, *are stuck fast in me like arrows.* Here the first shadow of the coming Lent begins to fall upon us, and the Responsory at Matins is of the same character.

Almost all the Sunday Responses used in this season till Septuagesima, are taken from the Sunday Psalms, those of Monday from the Monday Psalms, and so with the rest. S. Paul's epistles are read; first, (the mystical interpreters say,) because he, more than others, speaks of faith, whereby, as by a star, CHRIST is known. Moreover, as the prophets, especially Isaiah, foretold the LORD's birth, (and therefore Isaiah is read before Christmas,) so the Apostles preached the LORD Who had been born: and their epistles are read after Christmas.

IV.—SEPTUAGESIMA.

The three weeks preceding Lent form a penitential preparation for that season. The custom of thus observing them began in the East. As Quadragesima was the title given to the forty days of Lent, so the three Sundays next preceding respectively received the names, (using round numbers,) of Quinquagesima, Sexagesima, and Septuagesima: and each name has its mystical rendering. "Septuagesima recalls the seventy years' captivity. But 70 × 10 = 7000. Here is the 7000 years' captivity of GOD's people in the Babylon of this world, under the power of Satan, the antitype of Nebuchadnezzar, and exiled from Jerusalem, the place of paradise. Sexagesima, in the number 60, refers to the 10 commandments × the 6 works of mercy, (they were formerly counted as six, not seven). Quinquagesima speaks of penitence and the 50th [51st] psalm."—*Gemma animæ*.

Alleluia is omitted from this time till Easter, and in its stead is said at the beginning of Office, *Praise be to Thee*, O LORD, *King of eternal glory*: and at the end of antiphons, (as in the Offices of Saints) its place is supplied in the Sarum use by the words, *For evermore*: probably chosen as containing the same number of syllables, and therefore available for the same music. Alexander II., about A.D. 1073, prescribed the use of *Praise be*, etc., at times when *Alleluia* was to be omitted. The two phrases are similar in meaning; but, it was said, *Alleluia* is the very language of angels, and should be laid aside while we lament our human frailty. The words substituted for it have the same meaning, but are mere human language, not angelic.

" The laying aside of this gladdest and brightest of our Church Anthems, was formerly made the subject of far greater ceremony than it obtains in any part of the Church now. In the old Spanish Church, *Alleluia* was personified ; was regarded and addressed as a living being, for whose sweet com-

panionship earth, in the days of her Lent, was too
sad and dreary ; who, during that time of penitence,
must seek the throne of GOD, and the choirs of the
Angels ; but who, after the winter of our humiliation, would return and gladden us at Easter."
The custom of repeating it frequently on the
Saturday before Septuagesima, as if by way of
farewell is found in more than one ritual. Thus it
runs in the Mozarabic rite. "After the hymn,
Alleluia Perenne, the Capitula are as follows :
Alleluia in heaven and in earth : it is perpetuated
in heaven, it is sung in earth. There it resounds
everlastingly : here sweetly. There happily : here
concordantly. There ineffably : here earnestly.
There without syllables : here in musical numbers.
There from the Angels : here from the people.
Which at the birth of CHRIST the LORD, not only
in heaven, but on earth, did the Angels sing ;
while they proclaimed, ' Glory to GOD in the
highest, and on earth peace to men of goodwill.'
The Benediction : ' Let that Alleluia which is
ineffably sung in heaven, be more efficaciously declared in your praises. *Amen.* Unceasingly sung
by Angels, let it here be uttered brokenly by all
faithful peoples. *Amen.* That it, as it is called
the praise of GOD, and as it imitates you in that
praise, may cause you to be enrolled as denizens
of the eternal mansion. *Amen.*' *The Lauda :*
' Thou shalt go, O Alleluia ; thou shalt have a

prosperous journey, O Alleluia. Ȓ. And again with joy thou shalt return to us, O Alleluia. V̑. For in their hands they shall bear thee up : lest thou hurt thy foot against a stone. Ȓ. And again with joy thou shalt return to us, O Alleluia.'"
—Neale.

Te Deum at Sunday Matins is also omitted henceforth till Easter, and in its stead is said on Sundays in the Roman use a ninth Response. Formerly, it was the practice always to sing a ninth Response, which then was followed by *Te Deum* at the seasons appointed for its use. This was always the custom of the Sarum Church. *Gloria in excelsis* is of course omitted at Mass.

" Now the psalms of joy are laid aside. We now commemorate the state of the Church not yet redeemed (the season henceforth till Easter being that of *devagation*, or wandering astray). We now lament our exile, and it is fitting to lay by what especially denotes the Church's glory. *Alleluia* signifies CHRIST, without Whom the human race is now represented as existing, by reason of Adam's sin, which is chiefly set forth at Septuagesima. Yet we cease not from the *Song of the Three Children*, nor from *Gloria Patri ;* for never was there any time wherein some worshippers of the true GOD were not to be found. Now also, two psalms are changed at Sunday Lauds. Ps. 51, *Miserere*, a penitential Psalm, is said in place of

Ps. 93, *Dominus regnavit*, a psalm of joy. Ps. 118, *Confitemini*, is said in place of Ps. 100, *Jubilate*. And for this reason: because by penitence we come to the setting forth of praise; and by fear to hope. For whoso is in pilgrimage, (which state is signified by Septuagesima,) is subjected to fear and hope."—Durandus.

The Antiphons to *Benedictus* and *Magnificat* for these weeks, as also at some other times, are taken from the Sunday Gospels, in order to impress their teaching more strongly on the mind.

" The books of Moses are now begun, wherein are set forth the degrees of penitence. The first, Genesis, instructs us in the beginnings of penitence, namely, faith, hope, and fear: for through these repentance is conceived. It instructs us in faith, as in the Creed. As in the latter we hear of *things visible and invisible*, so here we are told, *In the beginning* GOD *created the heavens and the earth*. As the Creed speaks of the Persons of the FATHER and the SON, so here, *in the Beginning*, that is, in the SON, GOD, that is, the FATHER, *created the heavens and the earth*. The Person of the HOLY GHOST, too, is mentioned, in the words, *The* SPIRIT *of* GOD, that is, the HOLY GHOST Which created and governs all things, *moved upon the face of the waters*. We are instructed in the faith of the Incarnation and Passion, and to believe that CHRIST suffered according to His Manhood, and not according to His Godhead, by the type of Isaac, instead of whom a ram was offered. Again, we are taught that CHRIST was given by grace and not by merit; for so was His type Isaac bestowed upon his parents. We are taught to believe in the Resurrection, Ascension, and sending of the HOLY GHOST, by the history of Joseph, who, having been sold, was carried up into Egypt, and distributed corn through the whole country: as CHRIST, after being sold, was lifted up from the earth, and distributed the corn of the Word by His preachers throughout the world. There is a further reason for reading Genesis at Septuagesima: we now call to mind the misery we have incurred through the sin of our first parents. Concerning which also we sing the Response, *In the sweat of thy brow*, etc., and that, *Behold, Adam is become like unto Us*, etc. And, to make this great misery the more striking, we first read and sing of the dignity of man: how he was made in the image and likeness of GOD, and placed in a paradise, with an help meet for him; and how he could neither die nor suffer anything, but by his own fault."—Durandus.

V.—LENT.

1.—*Ash Wednesday.*

It was not anciently the practice to begin the Lenten fast till the first Monday in Lent. This is evidently the reason why the Ferial Office remains unaltered up to that day. But in process of time, a scruple arose as to the imperfect keeping of a forty days' fast, when in fact Lent contained only thirty-six days, exclusive of Sundays, which were never fasted ; and the four week-days immediately preceding were added to Lent, and called the Head of the Fast.

Ash Wednesday, as the solemn beginning of Lent, yields place to no other solemnity which can possibly fall on the same day.

The sprinkling of ashes, though a rite not included in the Breviary Office, must not be left unmentioned here. The custom, derived from the Jews, is spoken of by S. Isidore of Seville ; who says that in his time sinners were wont to sprinkle ashes on their heads, to remind themselves that they were but dust and ashes, and should turn their thoughts to that death which they had deserved.

When the sprinkling of ashes became a public ceremony of the Church, notorious sinners alone, who desired to manifest their penitence, were so sprinkled at the church door : and, after divers prayers said, were cast forth from the church, as Adam from Paradise, not to re-enter it again till Maundy Thursday. This was the godly discipline referred to in the Prayer Book Commination Service.

After the twelfth century, the custom became common to all the faithful. First, pious persons put ashes on their own heads, in token of humiliation. Next, voluntary penitents who were not egregious sinners, offered themselves to receive ashes: and at last it became the rule that all persons should do so.

The ashes were to be made from the palms used on the foregoing Palm Sunday, and were sometimes placed in an earthen vessel, for the sake of further symbolism. The ceremonies attendant on the sprinkling were and are various.

Confessions were to be made during the week preceding Lent, (whence our name Shrove Tuesday,) and also in the earlier part of the season itself; and those who then placed themselves in the rank of penitents, were, as aforesaid, solemnly reconciled to the Church on Maundy Thursday.

They who returned from captivity, say the mystical expounders, built the LORD's temple. " And we, being delivered from Satan's captivity, are bound in these days to build the temple of GOD, which is ourselves. On Ash Wednesday we lay the foundation ; for this is the fourth day of the week, and Solomon built the temple in the fourth age of the world. The temple of the Body was forty-six years in building :* forty-six days

* S. Augustine says (on S. John ii. 20), The first letters of the words North, South, East, and West, in Greek, form the word

after Ash Wednesday, namely, on Easter Day, CHRIST raised up the temple of His Body."—Rupert.

"By the putting ashes on our heads, we commemorate the day of our expulsion from Paradise, when it was said, *Dust thou art, and unto dust shalt thou return.* That we may attain to re-enter that blessed place, we do penance in sackcloth and ashes. And because we struggle to return to our country, and know that enemies are in our way, therefore we put on the armour of humiliation, prayer, and affliction, so to fight against spiritual wickedness."—Durandus.

2.—*Lent.*

S. Jerome speaks of Lent as an apostolic tradition. The examples of Moses, Elijah, and much more, of our LORD Himself, naturally led Christians from the earliest times to keep one, or more than one, forty days' fast in the course of the year. This was at first a matter of voluntary and private devotion: but the spring (=lenten) fast soon became the general rule of the Church. The bodily fast consisted in entire abstinence from flesh, and in fasting from all food till nightfall; for, says Venerable Bede, dining and fasting are contradictory terms. Mass was said after Nones, and

Adam. Adam is therefore the type of all nations. But these Greek letters being taken according to the value of their number. make 46: $\alpha = 1 + \delta = 4 + \alpha = 1 + \mu = 40 = 46$. Our LORD did of Adam receive a body; and He did in three days raise it up.

Vespers at the end of Mass, as still directed in the Breviary for Maundy Thursday and Easter Eve; and this is the reason why the post-communion Collect for the day is the Collect at Vespers on all ferias in Lent. Mass and Vespers ended under one and the same Collect. Therefore the frequent reference to *the heavenly gift*, in the Vesper Collects; and therefore also no proper Collect is given for Sunday Vespers, Mass never being said with Vespers on that day; nor for Saturday, as being the first Vespers of Sunday. As, with time, discipline grew more lax, eating was permitted earlier in the day; and this gave rise to the innovation of anticipating the Hours, till Vespers came to be said in the morning, (as is still the Roman use in Lent,) that men might break their fast at noon, and yet be able to declare that they had not eaten till after Vespers!

Each day in Lent having its proper Collect, Epistle, and Gospel, that Collect is used at each Hour till Vespers, and the Gospel generally furnishes the antiphons for *Benedictus* and *Magnificat*. The reading of the Pentateuch was formerly continued on the ferias in Lent. Pius V. ruled that every day having proper Gospel at Mass should have proper Homily at Matins.

On Sunday in Lent, (as in Advent, and after Septuagesima, with some little variation,) the Epistle read at Mass is divided into short chapters

P

for use at Office : the reading of which is begun at Saturday Vespers.

Offices were multiplied and lengthened in Lent. The Sarum Breviary directs that the fifteen Gradual Psalms be said daily after Tierce, with the great Litany, "for the whole Church of GOD"; and one of the Penitential Psalms was added to Ps. 51, in the petitions at each Hour, except Sexts, when Ps. 67 was said instead. The present Roman practice is, to say the Graduals on Wednesday, and the Penitentials on Friday, only. This was ruled by Pius V.

It was formerly the custom in the Western Church to keep no feasts at all in Lent; therefore the Annunciation was removed to Advent, as a more fitting season, or postponed till after Easter. The images in churches were covered, because the sight of gold and jewels was considered unsuitable for penitents. A veil was hung before the Altar on the first Monday in Lent, and undrawn only on Sundays and festivals, and at the time of Consecration at the daily Mass, till Wednesday in Holy Week, at the reading of those words in the Passion, *The veil of the temple was rent ;* and then it was removed.

In the first Nocturn at Sunday Matins, the course of Genesis is now broken off, and lessons are read, more fitting to urge man to penitence. The Responses are full of the same spirit : and as

Amalarius mentions them, and also the Lauds
Antiphons, and the frequent use of parts of Ps. 91,
the antiquity of these portions of the Office becomes evident.

"It is to be noted, that at the beginning of the
fast, the order of the Responses is interrupted.
For as we have been singing of Adam, Noah, and
Abraham, now we first treat of the fruits of
penitence, and not till afterwards of Jacob, Joseph,
and Moses. On the first Sunday in Lent, in the
Epistle, which is read likewise in portions as
Chapters at the Hours, the Church arms her
soldiers with the four cardinal virtues; first, with
fortitude, saying, *Behold, now is the accepted time,
now is the day of salvation:* and so with the rest.

"On the second Sunday, the first Response at
Matins treats of the increase of grace. Isaac saith
unto his son, *Take now thy weapons, thy quiver and
thy bow.* The weapons of preachers are Holy Scripture, called a quiver, because it furnishes arrows
to smite the devil. Jacob, that is, the true preacher,
makes assault on man, and brings away spoil, by
the bow which also is Scripture. He slays beasts,
that is, vices and sins, and then Isaac sups with
him: namely, the LORD, Who delighteth in such
spoils. And because His delight is to sup thus,
the second Response is, *Behold, the smell of my
son is as the smell of a field which the* LORD *hath
blessed.* And the Versicle follows, *Cursed be every*

P 2

one that curseth thee ; for all who curse the younger,
that is, the Christian people, are accursed.

"On the third Sunday is made mention of the
Passion of the LORD, typified in the history of
Joseph. For CHRIST, through humility, was delivered from the plots of His brethren the Jews,
and exalted over all Egypt, that is, throughout all
the world. And as Joseph was sold by his
brethren, and fed them in time of dearth, so CHRIST,
being crucified by the Jews, through His death redeemed mankind, and delivered them from the
power of the devil, as is read in the gospel for
this day.

"On the fourth Sunday we read Exodus, wherein
GOD speaks of seeing the affliction of His people,
and also delivers them through plagues sent upon
Pharaoh, like as He delivers us from the hand of
Satan, who will not let us go, no, not save by a
mighty hand. By faith we depart from Egypt, and
by baptism, typified by the Red Sea, and keeping
the commandments of GOD, and the faith of the
four Gospels, we become the tabernacle of GOD,
and pass through the wilderness of this world, to
the heavenly Canaan.

"After Exodus follows [in order, though not now
read,] the Book of Leviticus, concerning the tribe
of Levi, and the sacrifices offered to GOD. For a
man who fulfils the commandments, and becomes
GOD's tabernacle, must needs make offerings to

Him. He must bring salt with every sacrifice, because all things are to be done discreetly. And whereas he ought to be pure from all sin, and offer to the LORD a clean oblation, holy, and undefiled, there follows in Leviticus the law for cleansing the leper, and the manifold repetition of the command, *Be ye holy, for I am holy.*

" Quadragesima, the name of Lent, shews the number forty, the spiritual number of penitence, when the Church fasts and repents of her sins.* The forty days of Lent represent the years of the Israelite wanderings, and the space of our lives in this world. Moses delivered the Israelites from Pharaoh and Egypt : CHRIST delivers us from Satan and the world. They were nourished with food from heaven and drank water from the rock : we receive the Body and Blood of CHRIST. Thus they were brought by Jesus the son of Nun, to the land flowing with milk and honey, after forty-two stations in the wilderness, and kept the Passover in the promised land. JESUS the SON of the Highest brings us after forty-two days (=six

---

* S. Augustine (on S. John v.) says that forty signifies the fulfilling of the law : the Ten Commandments, preached through the four quarters of the world = forty : in Law, Prophets, and Gospel, forty is a number of fasting. But fasting, taken largely, is abstinence from sin. And, in another place, he says that we fast forty days, in order that, as our LORD descended to us through forty generations, according to S. Matthew, so we may rise to Him by the fortyfold number of our fast.

weeks) to the Feast of Easter, and the joy of risen life."—Durandus.

" Six weekdays we fast, because in the six ages of this world we sin : and we now haste to make what satisfaction we may by the six Gospel works of mercy. And, being CHRIST'S members, we must begin by ourselves : our souls, hungering for the bread of life, must be refreshed with the food of charity ; thirsting for righteousness, they must drink of the stream of Scripture ; naked of holiness, be clothed with virtue ; wandering in vices and errors, be received in the hostel of holy conversation ; sick with sin, be visited by confession ; in the prison of evil habits, be redeemed by penitence."—Rupert.

" The whole time of this life is signified by Lent, the season of affliction ; as joyful Easter-tide signifies the future life of happiness. The six weeks of Lent may represent the six ages.

" The first Sunday sets forth the first age : the time of Paradise. The second Sunday, the second age : wherein the servants of GOD rejoiced in their deliverance by means of the Ark. The third Sunday, the third age : when the children of Israel exulted in their salvation under Joseph, while others were perishing of hunger. The fourth Sunday, the fourth age : when GOD'S people enjoyed great rest under Solomon. The fifth Sunday, the fifth age : when the people returned from Babylon to Jerusalem. The sixth Sunday, the sixth age: from the coming of CHRIST to the Ascension: when the faithful rejoiced in the Presence of the Bridegroom."—Durandus.

The missions of Joseph, Moses, and Jeremiah, are read in evident reference to Him Whose mission to save lost man the Church is immediately to celebrate.

3.—*Passion-tide*.

We are bound, in a spiritual sense, to commemorate the LORD's Passion during the two weeks before Easter; first, because He suffered for and through two peoples, Jews and Gentiles, and next, because two weeks express the two Testaments, of which one prophesies, and the other narrates His sufferings. In S. Augustine's time, Good Friday alone seems to have received the name of Passion-season; but afterwards the practice became general of devoting the two weeks immediately preceding to a preparation for the better commemoration of the great mystery.

In the Offices of this season, the Church has retained more than usual of her ancient simplicity. The *Gloria Patri* is less frequently said, and in the latter part of Holy Week the preliminary Versicles and Invitatory are omitted. The facts no doubt existed before mystical reasons were assigned for them; but the devout writers who search in every detail for something to touch the soul, say that " we lay aside the *Gloria Patri*, because that verse pertains to the praise of the Trinity, Whose glory was in a certain sense obscured during the LORD's Passion. We now lay it aside in Introits and Ry.Ry., because they treat of the Passion; and also in the Invitatory. But not in psalms and hymns, because psalms represent action. In the three days before Easter it is hushed altogether, because the Divine glory was then most hidden. No memorials of Saints are now said, nor prayer for peace, from this Sunday till the end of Easter-tide. Commemorations of Saints are wont to be made for two reasons: in remembrance of their holiness, and in order to obtain their prayers. But these two things are most perfectly set forth to us in CHRIST our Head, at the time of His Passion and Resurrection; for in His Passion He shewed a most entire pattern of humility and holiness. And after His Resurrection, as John testifies, He became our One Advocate with the FATHER. As then we chiefly desire at this time to magnify the example of His holiness, and to lift our hearts to His one and singular shelter and protection, it is fitting to cease from memorials of the Saints. Hence is also apparent why the prayer for peace is omitted. For CHRIST hath made peace through the Blood of His Cross; and after the Resurrection, He spake peace to His disciples ; and, He Himself being our Peace, held intercourse with them till His Ascension, and then bestowed His peace on them ; and after that, at Pentecost, sent the Comforter."—Sicardus.

In Passion-tide the Lessons of the first Nocturn are read from the Prophet Jeremiah, because he prophesied so manifestly of the LORD'S Passion, and in his own sufferings prefigured those of CHRIST. The first Response on Passion Sunday is proper to the day. By the law of Moses the lamb was to be prepared fourteen days before the Passover. The faithful are now warned afresh to prepare for the Paschal Feast. The rest of the Responses are taken from the Psalms, and are expressive of the Passion.

The great Passion-tide hymns, *Vexilla regis* and *Pange lingua*, were composed by Venantius Fortunatus about the latter part of the sixth century. The former was written at the request of S. Radegund, beforetime queen, but then Abbess of Poitiers, in order to do honour to some relics of the true Cross sent to her and to S. Gregory of Tours.

" It may be objected by some that the Passiontide Offices breathe too great a spirit of fear and apprehension, and that it is not fit to express in our LORD'S Name, as it were, such reiterated prayers for deliverance. But the answer may be, that He, taking our sins upon His head, represents sinners, fearful by consideration of their guilt, and dreading its due punishment, whence they seek to be delivered by penitence."—Grancolas.

" On Saturday in Passion Week our LORD came to Bethany, rested in Simon's house, was served by Martha, and anointed by Mary. Now Simon is, by interpretation, obedience; CHRIST rests in Simon's house, when He rests in an obedient Church. We serve with Martha, when, after the pattern of our great High Priest, we minister to His members, the brethren or the poor. We fill the house with odour of ointment, when we endeavour to fill the Church with the fragrance of virtue."—Rupert of Deutz.

4.—*Palm Sunday.*

The commemoration of this day had its origin in Palestine. We are told, in the life of S. Euthymius, written by one of his disciples, that those monks who went into the desert after Epiphany, to prepare for Easter in solitude, were wont to return to their monasteries to keep the Feast of Palms, on the Sunday of the week before Easter. This Feast seems to have been kept in the East as early as the fifth century.

In the West, we first find mention of it in England, where, according to S. Aldhelm, it was instituted A.D. 709. The procession of Palms was formerly made by the congregations of parish churches and the members of religious communities, who went in a body to the cathedral. This was described in a hymn, seventy-eight verses in length,— the celebrated *Gloria, laus, et honor*, the first verses of which are still sung on this day. The story connected with this hymn is, that it was composed by S. Theodulph while in prison at Metz or Angers, and sung in the emperor's hearing while he and his court passed by the dungeon on their way to the Cathedral. The sweet strain captivated the monarch, and he straightway set the bishop free.

According to some uses the Blessed Sacrament was carried in the procession. Lanfranc ordered this in the constitutions of the Abbey of Bec, and it is one of the first instances of the practice. This was also the custom at S. Alban's Abbey. Matthew Paris speaks of the beautiful vessel kept there, in which the Host was carried on Palm Sunday.

In some churches, the benediction of palms was very simple, consisting only of two or three Collects; but very prolix, according to the Roman and Sarum uses.

"It is notable and admirable to observe how, as it were, in the same order, GOD created and re-created the world. For as He began the Creation on the first day, worked six days, created man on the sixth, and on the Sabbath rested, so He began the re-creation on the first day, entering into Jerusalem: and having entered thereinto on each of the following days, suffered on the Cross for our redemption on the sixth day; and on the Sabbath rested in the grave. As therefore on that first day He said, *Let there be light*, beginning the work of creation by light, so on this first day, by the light or glory of His act, He enters on His saving Passion. . . . . And entering into Jerusalem, He sent two of His disciples, that they might bring Him an ass tied, and a colt with her. Mystically: 'Thou didst march through the land in indignation, Thou didst thresh the heathen in anger. Thou wentest forth for the salvation of Thy people, even for salvation.' (Hab. iii. 12.) Thereby Thou didst signify Thine ascent to the true Mount of Olives, namely, to the Right Hand of the FATHER, Who is the FATHER *of mercies and the* GOD *of all comfort*, sending the Apostles, with power to bind and loose, to absolve from the burden of sin the ass and the colt, that is, the Jewish and Gentile people; and humankind being brought to Thee by faith, Thou shalt sit thereon, (for the seat of GOD is the soul of the righteous, as saith S. Gregory,) and sitting thereon, shalt save it, and bring it in to the heavenly Jerusalem, while the Angels come to meet Thee with palms and olive-branches, (the signs of victory,) and with songs of praise. In representation of that glorious procession, the Church to-day goes forth, carrying flowers and branches of olives and palms.

"When we make the procession, we receive CHRIST Who cometh to us, if we go forth with children; that is, if we preserve innocence. We bear olive branches, if we shew forth works of peace and mercy. We carry palms, if we obtain victory over sins and Satan. We produce blooming flowers and leaves, if we are adorned with virtues. We spread our garments in the way, when we mortify the flesh. We gather branches, following the footsteps of the Saints. The palms are blessed and distributed by the Priest, although we do not read that CHRIST either blessed or distributed them; because CHRIST did not honour them, but was honoured by them; and the Jewish people did that after a corporal manner which we do sacramentally and spiritually. When they carried branches they prefigured the yet incomplete triumph of CHRIST, but the Church thus represents His perfect triumph.

"Concerning the daily Office, it is to be said, that after the Sabbath, whereon was shewn the devotion of Mary, follows the Sunday, wherein is shewn the devotion of the children; we therefore anoint the LORD with Mary, and worship Him with the children."—Sicardus.

5.—*Holy Week.*

In the very early Church, the Friday and Saturday before Easter were the only days set apart for the representation of the Church's mourning over the Death of CHRIST: which mourning consisted in watching for two nights in prayer, and in a fast

of forty hours' duration.   Our LORD's Passion was
thus commemorated during the first two centuries ;
Wednesday was then added to the number of
solemn days, and subsequently the whole week
was dedicated in a like manner ; and S. John
Chrysostom, in his Sermon on Holy Week, well
calls it the Great Week, by reason of the great
mystery wrought by CHRIST during this season.

On Wednesday in Holy Week begins the
omission of all *Glorias* in the Offices.   Matins
open at once with the antiphons and psalms.
The whole order of the Office is described by Amalarius, the most ancient writer on this subject.
There is nothing in the Breviary older than the
Offices of these three days.   They have been said
for more than twelve hundred years in the same
manner as at present.   Ingenious and devout
writers have discovered mystical reasons for every
detail ; helpful to devotion, and, in some instances,
very touching and beautiful; but, as so often, fitted
to Offices already existing.   For many observances
now confined to the three days, were, formerly, not
peculiar to them, and mysterious, but were in
common use : even to the striking of a wooden
clapper instead of a bell, and the styling the night
Office *Tenebræ*.

During Tenebræ, a triangular candlestick is set
before the Altar, bearing many tapers, of which
one is extinguished at the end of each Psalm.

This is a relic of an old custom. For lights were not commonly set upon Altars, but were either hung up, or fixed on frames stretching across the choir, or set on large candlesticks near the Altar. These were lighted for the Night Offices, which, on great solemnities, lasted till daybreak. As dawn advanced, the lights were gradually extinguished, except one, which was hidden within the Altar, for the purpose of kindling the lamp which was to burn before the High Altar; and which was to be lighted without loss of time, in order that the Blessed Sacrament, there reserved, might not be left unhonoured. Hence the present custom at Tenebræ.

In some Eastern monasteries, instead of *Gloria* at the end of the Psalms, was said, *Have mercy upon us, O* Lord, *have mercy upon us.*

The custom of singing the Lessons from Jeremiah, and introducing the letters of the Hebrew alphabet, is very ancient, for Lanfranc forbids it to his monks. The reason of the practice was, that the Lamentations were originally written in verses, each distinguished by a letter, like Ps. 119. At the end of the lesson is said, *Jerusalem, Jerusalem, return to the* Lord *thy* God: " signifying that the fruit of conversion is to be derived from the lessons, which represent the soul under the captivity of sin.

" The Office of Tenebræ begins, *The zeal of*

Thine house hath eaten me up; i.e. vehement love
of the Church was the cause wherefore I suffered.
No Invitatory is said, that by our silence we may
mark our detestation of the pestiferous assembly
of the Jews, when they took counsel together to
bring our LORD to death. No hymn of praise is
said, because He was then made the scorn of men
and the outcast of the people. The end of the
LORD's Prayer, before the Lessons, is said in
silence. CHRIST, Whose is that prayer, being torn
away from his disciples, prayed as it were silently.
Nor do we say at the Lessons, *Pray for a blessing,*
nor *But Thou, O* LORD, etc., by reason of the departure of the Shepherd and Priest, Who should
bless and have mercy on the flock; but because
we have lost Him through sin, we are admonished
to return to Him, in that verse, *Jerusalem, Jerusalem,* etc. which is said at the end of the Lessons,
in order to turn us to penitence. All the Antiphons
are of Passion and Compassion. Moreover, on
these three nights are sung nine Psalms, nine
Lessons, and nine R̷.R̷. : divided into several
Nocturns. The three first Lessons are from the
Lamentations of Jeremiah, weeping over the captivity of his people; and not only the Babylonian
captivity, but also the Roman, which the Jews
incurred in consequence of our LORD's Death.
And as he deplored the death of king Josiah, so
we deplore the Death and Passion of CHRIST our

King. The next three Lessons are from the exposition of the Psalms, treating of the Passion; the three last from the first Epistle of S. Paul to the Corinthians, wherein he teaches how to partake of the Supper of the LORD. From which six Lessons it appears that the Prophets foresaw the death of CHRIST, and the Apostles teach concerning Him as slain.

The gradual extinction of candles and lights in the Offices of the three nights, signifies the darkness of the three hours during which CHRIST hung on the Cross, or the hiding of our true Light for three days and nights in the Sepulchre. Twenty-four candles are sometimes lighted. CHRIST, being the greater light of the day, and the Church being the lesser light of the night, the candles are the Apostles and other Apostolic men. Twenty-four candles point out the verse, *Glory be to the* FATHER, which, if we include the *Te Deum* as an expression of the same thing, is said twenty-four times in the Festival Night Office; but is omitted now, because He, in Whose praise it is said, lies in the Sepulchre. One candle, however, is not extinguished, but hidden away, to be brought out afterwards and to light the Church; this signifies, first the faith which remained in the Blessed Virgin alone, and which afterwards taught and enlightened all the faithful. Secondly, it signifies CHRIST, Who, although dead according to the flesh, yet, according to His hidden Divinity, was living; and afterwards rising again, manifested Himself to His disciples with most clear light. The noise which is made at the Benedictus is in remembrance of the tumultuous onset of the Jews, who came with swords and staves against CHRIST, led by Judas, saying, *Hail Master*. The *Kyries*, etc., signify the lamentation and grief of the women who followed Him from Galilee. In some Churches, *Miserere* and the Collect are said in darkness and silently, as commemorating the fear of the Apostles when they were in hiding. Afterwards a sound is made with the hand or otherwise, before the bringing in of light; which sound represents the terror caused by the tumult of the soldiers, or by the shaking of the earth; in some Churches new fire is struck from a flint, because the HOLY SPIRIT is poured into our hearts through CHRIST our Mediator. From this time till the Octave of Pentecost the Office of S. Mary is omitted in some Churches, in order that we may dwell more ardently on the Passion and Resurrection. And hereby we offer no insult to her whose glory is derived from her Blessed Son. The Office of the Dead is also omitted for the same reason; nor do they thereby suffer; for, being united to us by love, they participate in our blessings, although we cannot make more express prayers for them. Out of choir however, it is useful to say these Offices."—Sicardus.

Bells were not rung from Maundy Thursday till Easter Eve. The Church followed the ancient method for calling the faithful, which was employed before the invention of bells, by wooden clappers, such as are still used in the Eastern Church: this silence is intended to represent the Church's grief. It is nowhere found in ancient books, that a noise should be made at the end of Tenebræ, as is directed in more modern Breviaries. Only the senior person present gave a sign of permission to depart by striking a book or seat.

6.—*Maundy Thursday.*

The rites pertaining to Maundy Thursday were, the public reconciliation of penitents, the blessing of holy oils for use as chrism in the administration of Baptism, Confirmation, Orders and Extreme Unction; and the washing of feet, altars, sacred vessels, and the pavement and walls of churches. Anointing is still the present practice in the sacraments above named throughout most parts of the Western Church. Penitents were reconciled at the beginning of Mass or before the Offertory; the oils were consecrated before Communion.

The Mass of this day was especially solemn before the institution of the Festival of Corpus Christi; and Durandus, writing before that date, says that the feast of this day yields precedence to none, because its object is to commemorate the institution of the Blessed Sacrament.

Vespers were begun immediately after the Celebrant's Communion. After receiving the chalice, he said the first Antiphon, *I will receive the cup*, etc., and Vespers were sung while the people communicated.

Remembering the mystery of this day, it may be said that this feast began with the beginning of the Church, and was kept earlier than any commemoration of the Passion or Resurrection.

" Immediately after Vespers on Maundy Thursday, the Altar is stripped, and so continues till Easter Eve. The stripping signifies, in the first place, the departure of the disciples from our LORD. On the third day it is covered again ; because after the Resurrection the disciples returned to Him ; secondly, the stripping of the Altar signifies the stripping of CHRIST upon the Cross ; thirdly, His being stripped of the glory of Divinity, according to that word, *My* GOD, *My* GOD, *why hast Thou forsaken Me ?* In many places the Altar is washed in wine and water, to signify that the Body of CHRIST, which is the true Altar, was sprinkled with blood and water on the Cross.

" On this day the LORD washed the disciples' feet, (therefore to-day is given the absolution to penitents ; for the washing of feet denotes remission of sins.) By the washing of the disciples' feet, He gave us an example of humility. But mystically, He rose from supper, that is, from the banquet of paternal glory, when He came forth from the throne of the FATHER; He laid aside His garments when He humbled Himself; girded Himself with a towel, when He took upon Himself the form of a servant; poured water into a basin and washed the disciples' feet, when, for the remission of sins, He shed that Blood, whereby He washed our feet, that is, our actions; for though we be washed in Baptism through faith, yet, *if we say we have no sin, we deceive ourselves.* Therefore on this day the pavement of the Church is washed; for this is a symbol of that washing of feet.

" To-day, moreover, the LORD, being at supper with the disciples, after eating the typical lamb, gave them His Body and Blood.

" Now was that accomplished which before was figured, when, as the Jews sought to stone Him, He departed out of the temple, and hid Himself from them. For then He departed, when He forsook their sacrifices; then He hid Himself, when He instituted the rite of a new Sacrifice, wherein carnal eyes could not discern Him. Therefore, because the true High Priest on this day instituted the new and true Sacrifice, being about to die, and wrote the New Testament for His heirs with His own Blood, therefore, like as the sun shines forth between clouds, so the Mass exults between the

sad hours ; for in the midst of sadness, Mass alone is adorned with solemn chanting, and garments of oy, that no beauty be wanting to the celebration of the Holy Sacrifice on the day of its institution."
—Sicardus.

7.—*Good Friday.*

The Night and Day Offices of Good Friday are nearly identical with those of the previous day. Part of the Day Office was said in the morning, part in the evening ; the earlier part of the day was further occupied with lections, prayers, sermons, and veneration of the Cross ; Mass of the Pre-sanctified was said in the evening ; the Blessed Sacrament having been reserved on Maundy Thursday. The Sacrifice was never offered on this day, (nor at Rome, on the Saturday before Easter ;) a relic of the ancient discipline for fasting seasons. The Mass of the Pre-sanctified, used on this day alone in the West, is said in the Greek Church on all week-days in Lent. It has been customary on Good Friday, in the West, since the seventh century. One of the earliest accounts we have of it is in the Ordo Romanum, believed to be of the time of Charlemagne. After the Veneration of the Cross, two priests assisting the Bishop at the Altar, fetched the Body of CHRIST, consecrated the previous day, from the sacristy or other place where It was reserved, and placed It on the

stripped Altar : the celebrant then dipped a particle
of the consecrated Host in the Chalice, wherein
was some wine unconsecrated, and communicated
in silence ; and afterwards the clergy and people
communicated in like manner. The rite of the
Veneration of the Cross began at Jerusalem, and is
mentioned in S. Gregory's Sacramentary, and by
S. Paulinus. Julian reproaches the Christians for
worshipping the wood : S. Ambrose says, "We
worship not the wood, which would be a Gentile
error : but Him Who hung thereon."

The antiphon *We venerate*, etc., is mentioned in
the life of Alcuin, who died A.D. 815. S. Benedict
of Aniane, assisting at his death-bed, gave him the
Cross to kiss, saying, "We venerate Thy Cross,
O LORD, and celebrate Thy glorious Passion.
Thou Who didst suffer for us, have mercy on us."
The *Reproaches* and *Agios O Theos* are to be found
in the Concordia of S. Dunstan, and the Statutes of
Lanfranc. *Agios*, etc., is a very ancient Greek
doxology. S. John Chrysostom says it dates from
the time of Proclus, Patriarch of Constantinople.
It was sung at the Council of Chalcedon. Peter
the Fuller, Patriarch of Antioch, added, *Who wast
crucified for us*, (for which addition his memory is
yearly cursed in the Eastern Church,) and he perhaps made the addition on purpose for Good
Friday use.

It is curious that this very addition found its way

into the Sarum preces for ferial Prime, and kept its place there.

"We defer our rejoicing in so great salvation, in the necessary redemption, in the deliverance·from captivity, in the opening of the gates of Heaven: we defer all this, I say, till the third day, when He arose victorious. But let this day shew forth grief, let each of us go about with head bowed down for consciousness of guilt; let us, with Moses, take our shoes from off our feet, that we may hear the LORD saying from the midst of the bush, *I have surely seen the affliction of My people which are in Egypt, and have heard their cry by reason of their taskmasters; for I know their sorrows. And I am come down to deliver them.* Let us not salute one the other. From the morning till the ninth hour let us keep strict, sad silence, and meditate in solitude, considering the conflict and contumely of the SAVIOUR. For Moses also saith, *The* LORD *shall fight for you, and ye shall hold your peace.* But at the ninth hour when the LORD, about to die, cried, FATHER, *into Thy Hands I commend My Spirit*, and the centurion said, *Surely this was the* SON *of* GOD; and Joseph and Nicodemus took the Body, and wrapped it in a linen cloth with spices; because these and other disciples were then allowed to draw near and begin their funeral lamentations, (the blasphemers having departed, either as satisfied with the sight, or terrified by the earthquake,) at

the ninth hour, I say, it is fitting that we perform the funeral obsequies. But Office is said quietly, and in a low voice, and without its usual beginning, as mentioned before. Upon the Altar, one linen cloth only is laid, which signifies the winding sheet that wrapped the Body of CHRIST."
—Sicardus.

VI.—EASTER.

1.—*Easter Eve.*

The Office of this day is nearly identical with that of Good Friday. The Vigil of Easter night, most solemn of all the Church's vigils, was formerly held to begin after Nones, about sunset, and lasted till daybreak on Easter morning, during all which interval no one was allowed to go out of Church ; a strict fast having been observed since Friday. The whole time was devoted to lessons, prayers, instructions, baptism of catechumens, and the Sacrifice of the Mass, at which those present made their Easter Communion. The Roman, and apparently the English Church, had no Mass of any kind on this day, except the Paschal Mass at night. After discipline was relaxed, as to the hour of saying Vespers, the Church yet kept to the ancient time on this occasion, not anticipating the Office as on other fast days, but reserving it for its proper place in the nocturnal Mass.

"This night is celebrated after the equinox, when day grows longer than night; because, after ignorance, the knowledge of GOD is increased; and where iniquity abounded, there did grace much more abound. This night is celebrated in spring, when, after the harshness of winter, flowers bloom, and birds warble; because the frost of perfidy being driven away, the beauty of nature flourished; and the Apostles' sound went forth throughout all the world. This night concludes the forty days' affliction, and begins the fifty days' absolution, because by the Resurrection we pass from the bondage of captivity, to the joy of liberty.

"The Vespers of Easter Eve are exceedingly short, and indeed are scarcely Vespers; for the Sabbath of eternal rest, which is pre-figured by this Sabbath, has no Vesper-tide; and all this Office, as well as the Offices of the following week, are made short for the sake of the newly-baptized, lest weariness should be engendered by their too great length. And thus the neophytes are invited to the praise of the LORD by Ps. 117, *Praise the* LORD, *all ye people* (gentes), and they respond, saying, as it were every man for himself or for others, *My soul doth magnify the* LORD."—Sicardus.

Laudate, Magnificat, and *Alleluia* are fitly sung at these Vespers. That day shall in no wise be closed by Vesper-tide, wherein GOD shall be praised for ever.

2.—*Easter Day*.

This holy day is the greatest of all feasts; the feast of feasts, and solemnity of solemnities.

It is plain from the Acts of the Apostles, that the first day of the week was kept from the beginning in commemoration of the Resurrection, but the date of the Easter Festival is uncertain, though very ancient, for we find the Council of Arles, A.D. 314, ruling that Easter should be kept everywhere on the same day.

The Night and Day Offices are short; and, although the time of mourning is over, the Church retains much of the same ancient simplicity which characterized the Office of the Passion. No hymns are sung, nor are chapters read.

" Hymns are not sung," says Sicardus, " because in the Resurrection we shall not sing the hymns of men, but in the streets of Jerusalem we shall sing Alleluia, according to that of Tobit; and instead of hymns, Alleluia is sung, by reason of the hope of a glorious resurrection."

One Nocturn only is said at Matins; because the previous services had been so exceedingly long, that day had already broken, and the hour was more fitly that of Lauds. (It was an ancient custom, alluded to by Amalarius, to shorten Matins whenever they were likely to last till dawn, so that Lauds might begin with sunrise.) These brief and simple Hours are said throughout the week, which is counted as one great LORD's Day: and the Alleluias, so long silent, now sound abroad continually. The mystical writers have much to say on the Easter Office. " To signify that by the virtue of the Trinity the Resurrection was wrought, therefore at Matins three lessons are said; and also three psalms are sung with three antiphons. This threefold number is observed for divers reasons. First, in order to spare men worn down by previous fasting. Secondly, lest the neophytes, as aforesaid, be too heavily burdened. Thirdly, by reason of the three days' sepulture of our LORD, which preceded the day of His Resurrection. Three antiphons are sung which signify the patriarchs, prophets, and apostles; three lessons are read, because the law, the psalms, and the prophets, declare the Resurrection of the LORD."—Durandus.

The second Vespers of Easter Day began in the Sarum use, as also in one or more other rituals, with *Kyrie eleison, Christe eleison*, etc., sung nine times at the beginning of Mass. Three psalms only were sung at the second Vespers of Easter Day; namely, Pss. 110, 111, 112, but the other usual Sunday Psalms (Pss. 113, 114-115) were sung in processions to the font and crucifix. Through the week, the five Sunday psalms were sung at Vespers, without procession. The three Vesper psalms are said to fit the Resurrection " by their allusions to *the day of the* LORD's *power;* His sending *redemption to His people;* and the *light risen in darkness.* The two psalms sung at the font signify that by twofold love we attain to eternal life; and these fit baptism: *Praise the* LORD, *ye children* (pueri), and, *What aileth thee, O thou sea, that thou fleddest?*

"The Vesper Office is brightened by the glory of this festivity. It begins not by, *O* GOD, *make speed to save us:* because in that life we shall not need such help; but it begins by, LORD *have mercy.* Baptism having been administered at Vesper-time on Easter Eve, and in the Name of the Trinity, therefore at the same hour throughout the week, in the festive joy of regeneration the Holy Trinity is worshipped. Instead of a hymn is sung *Alleluia,* which is the true hymn of our true city.

"Through the week following three psalms only are sung; and the seven days are called baptismal; because those who have been duly baptized receive the seven gifts of the HOLY SPIRIT which are signified by those seven days; also they receive the three virtues, Faith, Hope, and Charity; therefore we sing three psalms, to recognize the reception of those three, but under one antiphon, because from One alone all these things come. And moreover, as all this week is, so to speak, one LORD's Day, therefore through its course we sing the psalms of the Sunday Nocturn; but in the following weeks the psalms are multiplied, because they signify good habits, whereby that glory is attained which is figured by the whole of Easter tide. In certain churches however, three psalms only are said until Pentecost, and this order is set forth by Alcuin. But it is not well to do so at the present time, for the original reason of this institution has now ceased. Those who say that all things should be made easy during this time for the neophytes, extend ease too far. For there are only two weeks for neophytes : namely, Easter and Whitsun weeks."—Durandus.

The Gradual of the Mass for the day was sung in the place of chapter or hymn at Vespers on Easter Day, and through the week till the first Vespers of Low Sunday. "The Gradual and Alleluia are sung through Easter week, because in the six ages of life between baptism and the last resurrection, men are to labour in active and contemplative life. But this labour shall be turned into joy : therefore the Gradual is followed by Alleluia."

On the Saturday before the octave are sung two Alleluias, "denoting the twofold glory of body and soul in the life to come ; on the previous Saturday one alone is sung, because the soul, parted from the body, rejoices alone.

"As before the Resurrection we read the Law and the Prophets ; so afterwards we read the Apocalypse and the Canonical Epistles. For the Law and Prophets foretold the Passion and Resurrection of CHRIST: but the Apostles bore witness to these as having taken place. It is reasonable also now to read the Apocalypse, and its visions of CHRIST and discourses of Angels. For in that life which is signified by Easter-tide, our souls will be rejoiced by the vision of GOD."—Durandus.

The Sunday after Easter was called *Dominica in albis*, or *in albis deponendis*, because, after the first Vespers, the neophytes laid aside the white baptismal robes which they had worn at the Church services during the week.

" The verse, *This is the day which the* LORD *hath made*, etc., is said during this week, at Prime and the other hours instead of a Chapter, because we now figure that life wherein no teaching shall be necessary, but all, having been taught, shall be glad and rejoice. The Athanasian Creed is not said in Easter week: because that pertains to faith, but this time signifies the eighth age, wherein faith shall have passed away. For the same purpose the Apostles' Creed is omitted at Prime, according to that of S. Paul: *For when that which is perfect is come, that which is in part shall be done away.* Also the petitions are forborne, because when there shall be no misery, no mercy shall be asked ; where no temptation, there shall not be said, *Deliver us from evil.*"—Sicardus.

3.—*Easter-tide.*

This season extends from the first Vespers of
Easter Day to Nones on the Saturday in Whitsun
week inclusive, and is not confined to the Great
Forty Days between Easter and the Ascension.
After the Octave of Easter, the Offices return to
their usual festal form; no ferial petitions being
said till after Trinity. *Alleluia* is added to every
Antiphon and Responsory. The Roman use
appends it to almost all Versicles and Responses;
the Sarum, to Responses, but not to Versicles.
After the Octave of Easter, the present Roman
Breviary returns to the usual three Nocturns on
Sunday, and one Nocturn of twelve Psalms on
ferias; but in the Sarum book, the Sunday Office
till Ascension was nearly as on Easter Day, and three
Psalms only were said on ferias: the twelve Psalms
for each day being divided into clusters of three, in
consecutive order, one of which was used on its
own day in each week; so, for instance, if on the
first Monday after Low Sunday were said Pss. 27,
28, 29, the following Monday would have Pss. 30,
31, 32 : and so forth. According to this use also,
festivals always had one Nocturn only in Easter-
tide, and the Matin Psalms were those of the feria.
An Antiphon greatly used on festivals in Easter-
tide, for Apostles, Martyrs, and Confessors, was :
" Daughters of Jerusalem, come and behold the

Martyr with the crown wherewith the LORD crowned Him in the day of solemnity and gladness. Alleluia. Alleluia :" and a rubric noted that the word *martyr* was not to be changed for the plural on a feast of many Saints, because the word referred to CHRIST crucified. Memorials of the Resurrection were used on every day between Low Sunday and Ascension, except on the feast of the Invention of the Cross. The Office was saturated with Easter joy.

" It is noteworthy also that from Easter to Whitsuntide we do not kneel, but pray standing : as if to profit by the liberty won for us by our LORD's rising. And we omit the petitions, (preces,) because there shall be no deprecation of the miserable, but only the praise of the blessed : as is the usual custom on Sundays and other festivals, whereon are represented our resurrection and the society of the Angels.

" But as this solemnity signifies that Octave which shall follow the septennate of this life, why hath it Octaves, whereby its celebration is protracted, not only for eight days, but even till Whitsun Day ? It is answered : because that future resurrection is signified by circumcision, which was commanded for the eighth day ; eight are the blessings of true circumcision ; and the eighth returns to the first, as if on the LORD's harp, whereof is said, *Awake up, My glory, awake, lute and harp*, to sound the

heavenly diapason ; and therefore, to represent the
beatitudes, we solemnly celebrate for eight days
the Octave of the LORD's Resurrection, which is
the cause and sign of our own future rising. Which
beatitudes, Augustine in his book of *Christian
Doctrine*, combines with the gifts of the SPIRIT,
omitting the last, because it returns to the first.
Fear, saith he, causeth poverty, that is, humility ;
for when we fear eternal death, we nail the motions
of pride to the wood of the Cross ; godliness be-
getteth meekness ; for when we worship GOD, we
grow meek, and subject ourselves to the Divine
Scriptures ; knowledge, mourning : for whoso puts
on knowledge puts on mourning ; might, endurance
in adversity ; that we may always hunger and thirst
after righteousness. Counsel causes mercy, for he
is merciful to another, who desires that mercy
should be shewn to himself. Understanding
purges the eye of the soul, that the pure in heart
may see GOD ; wisdom gives peace to the bosom,
that the peace of eternity may be attained. Here,
as by a ladder, we attain from fear to wisdom.
Wherefore : *The fear of the* LORD *is the beginning
of wisdom*. Therefore, for seven days, the baptismal Offices are celebrated. The Offices of each
day fit those gifts and blessings.

" The Office of the Resurrection of the LORD pertains to fear, for we fear the terrible office of the
Judge. The spirit of fear is set as a foundation for

a firm building; and is the first of the seven steps whereby to ascend to the eastern gate, spoken of by Ezekiel. But it may be asked why we begin by fear and end by wisdom, while Isaiah begins by wisdom and descends to fear? Isaiah thus speaking described the SAVIOUR, and so came downwards from the highest. But we are beginning to rise from earthly to heavenly things; and therefore we must count the steps as ascending, so that by fear we may attain to wisdom."—Sicardus.

4.—*Rogation Days.*

The days of the Rogation, or supplication preceding Ascension Day, originated in France. Before the time of S. Mamertus, Bishop of Vienne, who put fresh vigour into their observance, they were kept in a vague, uncertain manner, with little fasting, and at various times; and chiefly for prayer concerning the fruits of the earth. In consequence of earthquakes and other calamities, especially a great fire which took place on Easter night, A.D. 469, S. Mamertus, then bishop, sought to appease the wrath of GOD by fervent prayers, and to this end set apart the three days preceding the Ascension. The practice soon spread, and had become general by the time of S. Cæsarius of Arles. The days were kept variously; as days of fasting, though in Easter-tide; or at least, of abstinence from flesh: because their intention was to avert

GOD's anger, and stay His punishing hand. The great Litany, sung in procession on this day, is said to have been instituted by Gregory the Great, on occasion of a pestilence in Rome, A.D. 590. He prescribed its recitation on S. Mark's Day; and it came to be adopted for the Rogation days likewise.

5.—ASCENSION DAY.

The Feast of the Ascension has often been included among those said to have been instituted by the Apostles, and its date is at least very ancient. S. Augustine speaks of its general observance, which he attributes to Apostolic institution, or the order of some great Council.

"*Where the Body is, there shall the eagles be gathered together.* They who gaze on the true Sun and love His glory, follow Him, soaring on spiritual wings towards heavenly places. For that Body, on which alone such eagle souls feed, is in heaven: namely, CHRIST, in Whom dwelleth the fulness of the Godhead bodily, Who is the food of Angels and the support and life of all rational creatures. Therefore this day's Office is one of great joy."— Rupert of Deutz.

It was anciently the custom at Rome to keep this Feast thirteen days, more than an octave, even till Whitsun Day.

The Office has almost always and everywhere

been much the same as at the present day. Vene
rable Bede repeated the Vesper Antiphon : *O King
of glory*, etc., on his deathbed, and expired when
he came to the words, *leave us not orphans*.

According to some Rituals, Nones was said with
great solemnity, because it is supposed that CHRIST
ascended at that hour.

The Sunday within the Octave of Ascension was
formerly called at Rome Rose Sunday ; because
roses begin to bloom about that time, and were
scattered in the church where the station of that
day was held.

6.—*Whitsun Eve.*

The eve of Whitsun Day was kept as solemnly
as that of Easter : the Saturday was fasted, and
watching and prayers continued through the night,
" For then," as S. Ambrose says, " we receive the
SAVIOUR rising from hell : now we look for the
HOLY GHOST descending from heaven."

The Office is as it were a continuation of the
Octave of the Ascension, and rather fitted for the
last day of the baptismal preparation, than for the
Vigil of Pentecost.

Amalarius says that Vespers began on this day
at the ninth hour, in memory of Cornelius, who was
praying at that time, in preparation for receiving
the HOLY GHOST.

The ceremonial was similar to that of Easter

Eve, except that the blessing of the taper was omitted.

Easter and Whitsun-tide were solemn times of baptism from the first days of the Church, as Tertullian witnesses.

7.—WHITSUN DAY.

This is the Feast of the nativity, foundation and dedication of the Church. Eusebius did not fear to call it the greatest of all feasts. For herein we celebrate the consummation of all the mysteries of our religion, which all concur to bestow on us the HOLY SPIRIT. We find it celebrated at Jerusalem in the time of S. Cyril. The Office of Whitsun Day is similar to that of Easter.

Two sets of Matins were formerly said on Whitsun night: the first, without Invitatory, and containing four Psalms: the second, with Invitatory, and one only Nocturn, containing Pss. 1, 2, and 3. The brevity of the Night Office is due to the long Offices of the Vigil; nor was it thought unfitting to continue the short Office through the week, both in honour of the feast, the solemnity whereof continues during that period, and also in order not to fatigue the newly baptized.

The hymn *Veni Creator Spiritus* is sung at Tierce on Whitsun Day, and the three days next following; its greater length and fulness rendering it more suitable than the ordinary Office hymn, for

the solemn celebration of that hour when the HOLY
GHOST came down on the Apostles.   The practice
is said to have been introduced by S. Hugh of
Cluny.   In some places, the whole of Tierce was
sung, all the Altar candles being lighted, and all
the clergy present.   The celebrant intoned the
hymn, in amice, alb, stole, and cope.   At the Abbey
of Corby it was the custom to throw down fire and
water from the bell-tower while this hymn was
being sung in the choir.

8.—*Whitsun Ember Days, etc.*

Whitsun Day, from the beginning, was counted
as the close of Easter-tide, the period of which was
fifty days ; but, on account of the newly-baptized,
who were brought to Office daily during the week
ensuing, as at Easter, an Octave was assigned to
this feast in the West, but never in the East.

Easter-tide is now considered to end at Nones
on Saturday in Whitsun week, and the following
Sunday is not kept as the Octave of Whitsun Day.
It was formerly the practice so to keep it in some
places.   But S. Dunstan, in his Concordia, says
that Pentecost is seven days in length, to honour
the seven gifts of the HOLY GHOST ; and has no
Octave day.   Traces of such a day are, however,
to be met with elsewhere.

The fast in Whitsun week has been kept from
very early times, though not always as an Ember

fast. S. Isidore of Seville says that a fast should be kept after Pentecost, in fulfilment of our LORD's words, that the children of the bridechamber should fast when the Bridegroom was taken away from them. The *Micrologus* asserts that Gregory VII. fixed the June Ember-tide for Whitsun week; and goes on to say that as the fast was at once solemn and joyful, therefore the Office was festal.

"The Jews celebrated three solemn feasts: the Passover, Pentecost, and Feast of Tabernacles. The Passover, because GOD delivered them from the bondage of Egypt and the destroying Angel; Pentecost, because they then received the Law; Tabernacles, that is, the setting up of tents, in September. Of these feasts we still keep two, viz., the Passover and Pentecost, but for different reasons; for they kept the Passover because they passed out of Egyptian servitude; we keep it because we are redeemed by CHRIST. They celebrated Pentecost because they received the Law; but we, because we received the HOLY GHOST. And Pentecost signifies fiftieth: for the Law was given on Mount Horeb on the fiftieth day after the sacrifice of the Paschal Lamb. And the fiftieth day after the Passover is named Pentecost, because they who labour with their five bodily senses in the vineyard of the LORD, shall be filled with His Spirit, and in the world to come shall receive the penny (denarius) of eternal reward.

" And this number is formed by the multiplication of seven with unity, for there are seven weeks from Easter to this day. And on this day seven-fold grace is given. As by the commandment of the law a sheaf of the first-fruits was offered at Easter, and at Pentecost, two loaves, also of the first-fruits, therefore we, from the day on which the LORD arose and offered His Body as a sheaf of first-fruits, count the fiftieth day, whereon we receive the HOLY GHOST, and we offer two loaves, rendering double thanks for the law then given on tables of stone, and for the grace now shed forth in our hearts. We solemnize the fiftieth day, after seven weeks, representing the time of Jubilee, that after the course of this life we may attain to the year of eternity, wherein we shall not labour, but shall recover the ancient possession we lost through sin."—Sicardus.

VII.—TRINITY.

1.—*Trinity Sunday*.

The feast of the Holy Trinity is not certainly known to have been celebrated previous to the eleventh century, and then only here and there. S. Thomas à Becket is said to have instituted it in England, about A.D. 1162.

Pope Alexander II. declared that no feast ought to be kept in peculiar honour of the Trinity and Unity, because the worship of all Sundays and festivals is directed to that object. It was not formally instituted at Rome till the time of Pope John XXII. Durandus, writing a short time previously, mentions its having been adopted in many churches, and kept at various seasons. It was kept by religious communities before it became otherwise general.

It was not commonly observed till the time of Benedict XIII., A.D. 1405.

" The feast of the FATHER having been celebrated in the Nativity, the feast of the SON in Easter, and the feast of the HOLY GHOST in Whitsuntide, a festival should be kept in honour of the Trinity, and one feast should commemorate the Three Divine Persons, to show that these Three are One. In some churches, to every antiphon at Lauds is prefixed a versicle, which signifies turning and labour, to shew that with all labour and diligence we ought to turn ourselves to the praise of GOD the Holy Trinity."—Sicardus.

2.—Corpus Christi.

Although the Institution of the Blessed Sacrament had been celebrated from primitive times on Maundy Thursday, it seemed good to the Church to set apart another day in its honour; not only because, in Holy Week, the minds of worshippers were almost absorbed in the LORD's Passion, and Maundy Thursday was crowded with other observances, but in order to beat down heresy; or at least to show, in the face of heretics, the faith and reverence which Catholics bore to the most Blessed Sacrament.

In the East, untroubled by heresy on the subject, the Church never instituted any such feast. Its alleged origin is to be found in the history of S. Juliana of Mont Cornillon, near Liège, who was expelled from her convent and died in exile, on account of her persevering endeavours to obtain the institution of this feast, in consequence of a revelation received by her.

For a time, during her life, the feast was kept at S. Martin's in Liège; but was soon put a stop to. When a Canon of Liège became Pope under the name of Urban IV., he carried with him to Rome the remembrance of this festival; and the state of things seeming to call for some public acknowledgment of faith in the doctrine of the Eucharist, then violently assailed by many heretics, he not long after took measures for the institution of a feast in its honour, to be held on the first Thursday after Trinity Sunday.

The story goes that S. Thomas Aquinas and S. Bonaventura were each required by the Pope to write an Office for this day, and that S. Bonaventura, on reading the composition of S. Thomas Aquinas, felt its superiority so strongly, that he straightway threw his own into the fire. However the truth of this may be, the Pope's direction to S. Thomas was, to set in order the Office ; and as that originally used at Liège, and composed by a monk of that place named John, is not greatly different from that which we now have under the name of S. Thomas, it seems probable that he only revised and altered the then existing Office : inserting especially those glorious hymns which assert his claim to the title of a great sacred poet, no less than to that of the chief of theologians.

The feast was instituted by Urban IV., A.D. 1262, and confirmed by Eugenius IV., A.D. 1433. The Office, as arranged or composed by S. Thomas, is to be found among his works, Opusc. 57. The lessons for the days in the octave were added by Pius V.

3.—*Trinity Season.*

"After Pentecost begins a fourth season of pilgrimage, because we are in the way going to our Country. But because before reaching it we have to fight with enemies, namely, the world, the flesh, and the devil, therefore we read from the Books of Samuel and the Kings, which deal with wars and victories, in order to incite us to fight more strenuously against our foes, so as to gain the victory, as did the Jews over the Philistines : and therefore we say at Vespers, *Blessed be the* LORD *my strength*, etc.

" But because war without discretion is not well

carried on, we afterwards read the Books of
Solomon.   Moreover, because vices will surge up,
against which we have need of patience, the history
of Job follows after.

"Next we read the Book of Tobit, whereby is
figured the human race blinded by original sin,
and healed only by the bitterness of the Passion,
which is signified by the gall, as CHRIST by the
fish.

"The Book of Judith is read to instruct us in
holiness and sobriety by the example of Judith
slaying Holofernes, namely, the devil, who
enervates and slays the world by sensuality; and
we are to cut off his head by holy living; for the
head of the devil is luxury, and hereby he mostly
begins to tempt men.   During four weeks, the
Church reads the Books of the Maccabees, who
suffered many things from Antiochus and the
seven nations, and purified the temple, which had
been polluted by those nations.   Hereby is signified
that the soul, which is the temple of GOD, being
polluted by seven capital sins, needs purification.
After Maccabees, the Church begins to read the
Books of the Prophets: not however Isaiah and
Jeremiah, because we read from the former in
Advent, and from the latter in Passion-tide.
The Book of Ezekiel is first read, because it deals
with the heavenly temple, wherein is the confirmation and the end of all things.   But the twelve

Prophets are read for the foundation of faith, which is always necessary to the perfection of man. It may also be said that, after the return from the captivity, (when Jerusalem was rebuilt, and the temple restored by Ezra,) Zechariah, Haggai, and Malachi, foretold the Advent of the LORD; and therefore in the month of November until Advent the books of those Prophets are read. Their captivity of body signifies our captivity of soul. Return from captivity is remission of sins.

" Four are the conditions of the Church : the first, a state of guilt ; the second, of guilt and penalty ; the third, of penalty and grace ; the fourth, of grace and glory.

The Church represents the first state in Septuagesima, by cutting off *Te Deum* and *Alleluia*, because *praise is not comely in the mouth of sinners ;* and *Gloria in Excelsis*, because *iniquity hath separated between us and our* GOD. The second is represented in Advent, when the aforesaid Canticles are disused, with the exception of *Alleluia*, because the law being given, teaches us to know and praise GOD. The third is represented in summer-time, when we sing these things on festivals by reason of the grace we have received ; but on ferias by reason of penalty we use them not, with the exception of *Alleluia*, which is repeated daily ; because the hope of future resurrection is not weakened.

" The fourth is represented between Easter and

Whitsuntide, when the aforesaid songs of joy are used and multiplied daily. Two *Alleluias* are said on the feasts of Saints, on account of their rest and of their fruition. Be not thou moved because the Church represents things in an irregular order, and sets the last first, and the first last; for the variety of days and of the conditions of men leads to variety of Offices; so that some are celebrated with a Responsory alone, some with *Alleluia* alone, some with *Alleluia* and Responsory; for no acts of men are alike, and by times they weep and labour, and by times they rejoice and do the works of contemplation.''—Sicardus.

[An incorrect statement is made at p. 231, last line. The Sarum use at Prime does follow the practice of applying the epithets, " Holy God, Holy and Mighty, Holy and Immortal" to the Second Person of the Trinity, instead of to all Three Persons; but this is done by adding the response " O Lamb of God," etc., and not the clause introduced by Peter the Fuller.]

CHAPTER V.

APART from its historic interest, and its mystical
beauty, how glorious a thing is the Divine Office
when we look at it in its highest light! It is indeed
Opus Dei, the Work of GOD; and they spoke well
who named it so. Not merely that GOD is served
by us in this work. The signification of the term
goes far deeper. It is true indeed that so He is
served, and that it is a noble privilege bestowed on
His servants thus to have so large a portion of
their waking life devoted to His worship.

But in a sense far more profound this is the
Work of GOD. For the words we use are chiefly
those of the HOLY GHOST Himself; not human,
but Divine. In uttering them, we are but the instruments, lively, reasonable (and may we add
holy!) instruments, whereby Divine worship is
rendered to Divinity. In this, as in all else, we can
only say, *All things are Thine, and of Thine own
have we given Thee*. And as Abbé Gay says very
well, here we repeat the very prayers which CHRIST
our LORD used in His pilgrimage on earth,—which
He uttered on His own behalf and ours, for the

Psalter was His own dear book of prayer. For the support of His mortal weakness, He drew from the Psalms that strength which the God-head had purposely laid up in them beforehand. And with what increase of love and reverence do we recite them, when we remember that they were spoken by His human lips, and expressed the fulness of His human heart; and more still,—that as in some sense He spake them in our name, so now He speaks them by our lips. And if, when we pray, CHRIST speaketh, how shall not the FATHER hear?

(1.) *Devotional exhortations to the right use of Office.*

It would not be doing justice to the mediæval writers who deal with the Divine Office, if we did not set forth, at greater length than in the extracts from the *Myrroure*, the earnest manner in which they pressed the spirit of devotion and reverence on those engaged in its recitation. And such counsels indeed are not limited in their scope to one object, or to one form of life, but are lessons of holiness for all times and all persons.

The first extract is from a "Directory for the Canonical Hours," written by Cisneros, Abbot of Montserrat, in Spain, about A.D. 1500.

"When we have risen from our beds and are dressed, staying awhile in our cell, and standing up

s

where we are wont to pray, we should gather our
thoughts together as best we can, and think thus
within ourselves : what we are going to do, and why
we have risen from our beds ; for whosoever does
not think before acting must needs be careless in
his work.

"And what are we about to do, brethren, at the
time of the Divine Office, unless it is to appear
before the sight of God and His holy Angels, in the
company of our just and holy brethren ? Wherefore
we must diligently bear in mind that we are
going to—

> Adore God,
> Give thanks to God, and
> Pray to Him.

"First, we have to adore God—Three in Persons,
One in Essence—with adoration of highest worship,
for the judgments of His righteousness. By these
judgments or decrees, brethren, we must understand
the Incarnation of His Only-begotten Son our
Saviour, His birth and circumcision, His manifestation to the kings, His presentation in the temple ;
and lastly, His most holy Passion, Resurrection,
and all the other works which our glorious Lord
vouchsafed to work while on earth for our redemption. This, then, is the first thing we must
call to mind with earnestness and devotion as
soon as we have risen from our beds. And for
these judgments the Saints tell us we should

adore, bless, praise, and glorify the LORD, and take them as the object of our worship at the nightly Office.

The second thing to be remembered when we are going to the Divine Office is, that we are about to give thanks to GOD, and to praise Him for His goodness; and

"Thirdly, our mind must be enkindled with some devout feeling, that we may bestir ourselves from our sloth, and sing to GOD with reverence.

"The third preparation, which is called immediate, consists in prayer, for human effort availeth naught unless helped by Divine grace. Therefore, after dwelling on the aforesaid points, let us on our knees humbly beseech the LORD to grant us worthily to adore Him in the judgments of His justice, and devoutly to pay Him the duty of our homage. When, therefore, the sound of the bell hath struck upon our ears, rising from prayer, we should say: This is the sign of the great King; let us go and seek His face, and offer Him gold, incense, and myrrh: the gold of devotion, the incense of devout attention, the myrrh of respectful and manly demeanour. * * * *

"And this is what we had to say concerning the preparation for Matins, which a monk ought to make during a quarter of an hour if he wishes to go onward in the way of the SPIRIT, and that his homage be pleasing to GOD ; and after this he will all day long be devout and cheerful, and in a proper mood for the Divine Office.

" After he has accustomed himself to this, he had best, at the Day Hours, briefly reflect that he is going to place himself in the sight of the LORD, to adore Him, thank Him, and ask favours of Him as we have already said."

The next extract is from Blosius' "Mirror for Monks."

" How we ought to bestow our time from our first rising to Matins in the morning.

" As soon as you are awake and ready to rise to Matins, devoutly arm yourself with the sign of the Cross, and briefly pray to GOD that He will vouchsafe to blot out the stains of sin in you, and be pleased to help you. Then, casting all vain imaginations out of your mind, think upon some other thing that is spiritual, and conceive as much purity of heart as you can, rejoicing in yourself that you are called up to the praise and worship of your Creator. But if frailty of body, if heaviness of sleep, if conturbation of spirit, depress you, be not out of heart, but be comforted, and force yourself; overcoming all impediments with reason and willingness ; for the kingdom of heaven suffereth violence, and the violent take it by force. Certainly,

according to the labour which you undergo for the
love of God, such shall be your recompense and
reward.   Being come off from your bed, commend
and offer yourself, both body and soul, to the Most
High; make haste to the choir, as to a place of
refuge and the garden of spiritual delights.   Until
Divine Office begins, study to keep your mind in
peace and simplicity, free from troubles and the
multiplicity of uncertain thoughts, collecting a
goodly and sweet affection towards your God, by
sincere meditation or prayer.

" In the performance of the Divine Office have a
care to pronounce and hear the holy words reverently, perfectly, thankfully, and attentively, that
you may taste that your Lord is sweet, and may
feel that the Word of God hath incomprehensible
sweetness and power.   For whatsoever the Holy
Ghost hath dictated is indeed the life-procuring
food, and the delightful solace of a chaste, sober,
and humble soul.   Remember, therefore, to be
there faithfully attentive, but avoid too vehement
cogitations and motions of mind, especially if
your head be weak: lest being hurt or wearied,
confounded and, straitened internally, you shut
the sanctuary of God against yourself.   Reject,
likewise, too troublesome care, which commonly
bringeth with it pusillanimity and restlessness,
and persevere with a gentle, quiet, and watchful
spirit in the praises of God, without singularity.

But if you cannot keep your heart from wanderings, be not dejected in mind, but patiently
endeavour, patiently do what lieth in your power,
committing the rest to the Divine will.   Persevere
in your goodly affection towards GOD, and
even your very defects, which you are in no way
able to exclude, will in a manner beget you consolation.

"And what profit do you reap by being impatient?
Do you not heap calamity upon calamity? Do you
not show your want of true humility, and bewray in
yourself a pernicious propriety? As long as you do
reverently assist, and are ready with a prompt
desire of will to attend, you have satisfied GOD;
neither will He impute the inordinateness of this
instability to you, if it be by your negligence you
give not consent unto it, and before the time of
prayer you set a guard over your senses.   If you
cannot offer a perfect dutifulness, offer at least a
good will: offer a right intent in the spirit of
humility; and so the devil shall not find any occasion to cavil against you.   Although you have
nothing else to offer but a readiness, in body and
spirit, to serve our LORD in holy fear, be sure of it
that you shall not lose your reward.   But, woe to
your soul, if you be negligent and remiss, and care
not to give attendance; for it is written, "Cursed
is the man that doth the work of GOD negligently."
Be diligent, that you may perform what you are

able, if you be not able to perform what you desire. Upon this security, be not troubled when impediments happen, and you be not able to perform as much as you would. When, I say, distraction of your senses, dejection of mind, dryness of heart, grief of head, or any other misery or temptation afflicteth you, beware you say not: I am left; our LORD hath cast me away, my duty pleaseth Him not. These are words befitting the children of distrust. Endure, therefore, with a patient and joyful mind all things for His sake that hath called and chosen you, firmly believing that He is near to those that are of a contrite heart. For if you humbly, without murmuring, carry this burden laid on you, not by mortal tongue to be uttered, what a deal of glory you heap up for yourself in the life to come! You may truly say unto GOD: As a beast am I become with Thee. Believe me, brother, if being replete with internal sweetness, and lifted up above yourself, you fly up to the third heaven, and there converse with Angels, you shall not do so great a deed, as if for GOD's sake you shall effectually endure grief and banishment of heart, and be conformable to our SAVIOUR, when in extreme sorrow, anguish, fear, and adversity, crying unto His FATHER—" Let Thy will be done;" Who also, being thrust through His Hands and Feet, hanging on the Cross, had not whereon to lean His Head; Who also most lovingly endured for thee all the griefs and disgraces of His most bitter Passion. Therefore, in holy longanimity, contain yourself, and expect in silence until it shall please the Most High to dispose otherwise. And certainly in that day it shall not be demanded of you how much internal sweetness you have here felt, but how faithful you have been in the love and service of GOD."

One more passage, and that from an old English book: the Scale of Perfection, by Walter Hilton, who wrote in the latter part of the fifteenth century. The beauty of the extract must plead excuse for its length.

"The soul of a man while it is not touched by special grace, is blunt and dull as regards spiritual work, and can do nought therein. But then cometh the light of grace, and by its touch maketh it sharp and subtle. And how it then prayeth, I shall now tell thee.

"The most special prayer that the soul useth and hath most comfort in, I suppose, is the *Pater Noster*, or else the Psalms of the Psalter. The *Pater Noster* serves for unlearned men, and the Psalms and Hymns and other portions of holy Church suit the learned. And the soul is, as it were, set in the spiritual Presence of Jesus, so that every word and every syllable is sounded softly, sweetly, and delectably, with the full union of mouth and heart. For the soul is then turned all into the fire of love. And there-

fore, every word that it secretly uttereth in prayer
is like a spark rising out of a burning fire.   And
this fire heateth all the powers of the soul, and
turneth them into love, and enlighteneth them so
delightfully, that the soul listeth ever to pray and
to do nothing else.   The more it prayeth the better
and the stronger it becometh.   For grace helpeth
the soul well, and maketh all things light and easy,
so that it delighteth to chant and to sing the praises
of GOD with spiritual mirth in heavenly delight.
This spiritual work is the food of the soul; and
this prayer is of great virtue, for it wasteth and
bringeth to nought all temptations, both secret and
open, of the enemy, and slayeth in the soul all taste
and liking for the world and for fleshy sins.   It
beareth up the body and the soul under the painful
feeling of the wretchedness of this life.   It keepeth
the soul in the keeping of grace and the working of
love, and keepeth it ever fervent, even as wood
nourisheth the fire.   It putteth away all irksome-
ness and heaviness of heart, and preserveth it in
strength and spiritual gladness,   Of this prayer
David speaketh thus : " Dirigatur oratio mea sicut
incensum in conspectu Tuo ;" *Let my prayer be
directed as incense in Thy sight*.   For even as
incense that is cast into the fire maketh a sweet
smell by its smoke rising in the air; so a Psalm
sweetly and softly sung, or said in a burning heart,
giveth forth a fragrant smell before the face of our

LORD JESUS, and before all the Court of Heaven. And as no insect dare rest upon the censer, by reason of the fire within, even so no fleshy delight can rest upon a pure soul that is all enveloped and warmed with the fire of love, as it glows and teems with its Psalms and prayers to JESUS. This prayer is always heard by JESUS. It yieldeth grace unto JESUS, and receiveth grace again from Him. It maketh the soul familiar, and, as it were, companion with JESUS and all the Angels in Heaven. Use it whosoever can : the work is good and grace-bestowing in itself. And though it be not altogether perfect contemplation in itself, nor the working of love of itself, nevertheless it is in part contemplation. For it cannot be exercised in this manner but by means of plenty of grace, through the opening of the spiritual eye. And therefore, a soul that hath this freedom, and this gracious feeling, in prayer, with spiritual savour and heavenly delight, hath the grace of contemplation after a certain manner.

" This prayer is a rich offering filled with all the fatness of devotion, received by Angels and presented before the face of JESUS. The prayer of other men who are busy in active works, is composed of two words. For they oftentimes form one word in their hearts through thinking of worldly business, and speak with their mouth another word in the Psalm sung or said ; yet, nevertheless, if their intent be true, their prayer is good and acceptable though it lack savour and sweetness.   But the prayer of a contemplative man is made up but of one word ; for as it is formed in the heart, even so doth it sound in the mouth.   And both that which formeth it and that which uttereth it is nothing but one and the same thing.   For the soul is by grace made one and whole in itself.   It is so far separated from sensuality, that it is master of the body ; and then the body is nothing else but an instrument and mouthpiece of the soul, through which the soul soundeth the sweet notes of spiritual prayer to JESUS."

2.—*Intentions.*

When, as in the Roman Church, Office was said in a language unknown to many of those who recited it, the practice naturally arose of assigning intentions to the various Hours, which might make their recitation less like a mere piece of clockwork.

The custom is not needful where the Office is said in the mother tongue.   Yet it is often comfortable and profitable to say an Hour for some particular object that is very near one's heart. Some persons find advantage in fixing intentions for each Hour, as a general rule.

To assist them, it may be useful to give those of F. C. Mayer, (the same writer who is quoted so largely in the " Paradise of the Christian Soul ") and of Drexelius.

" Four ends of Worship.

I. Glorifying GOD.
II. Rendering thanks to Him.
III. Pleasing Him.
IV. Asking things needful for ourselves and the whole Church.

At Office have

I. Voice : distinct.
II. Mind : attentive.
III. Will : hearty.
IV. Body : reverent.

Office may be said as a Prayer throughout Sunday, or only at Matins on any day :

I. For the whole Church ; or,
II. The Clergy ; or,
III. Our own Community ; or,
IV. For an entrance into Heaven.

Throughout Monday, or at Prime daily :

I. For conversion of all infidels ; or,
II. Remission of all sins ; or,
III. A generous, cheerful spirit.

On Tuesday, or at Tierce:

 I. For conversion of misbelievers; or,
 II. True mortification; or,
III. Grace of the HOLY GHOST.

On Wednesday, or at Sexts:

 I. For all in deadly sin; or,
 II. The spread of CHRIST's Kingdom; or,
III. Grace to be faithful.

On Thursday, or at Nones:

 I. For the perseverance of the righteous; or,
 II. Grace to be heavenly-minded; or,
III. Increase of faith in the Blessed Sacrament, and grace to live worthily of It.

On Friday, or at Vespers:

 I. For parents, relations, benefactors, friends and enemies; or,
 II. Grace of prayer; or,
III. Shedding abroad of love to CHRIST; or,
IV. Grace to cleave to the Cross.

On Saturday, or at Compline:

 I. For the faithful departed;
 II. Abundant peace; or,
III. Perfection of love.

AGAIN, *Matins* may be said in commemoration of

    i. Nativity.
    ii. Taking in the garden.
    iii. Judgment. (1 Thess. v. 2.)

Lauds, in commemoration of

The Resurrection.

Prime, in commemoration of the

Leading to Pilate.

Tierce, in commemoration of the

    i. Crowning with thorns.
    ii. Scourging.
    iii. Coming of the HOLY GHOST.

Sexts, in commemoration of the

    i. Fall of Man. (Gen. iii. 8.) (*Vulg.* " in the *heat* of the day.")
    ii. Crucifixion.
    iii. Calling of the Gentiles. (Acts x. 9.)

Nones, in commemoration of the

    i. Death of CHRIST.
    ii. Binding of Satan.

Vespers, in commemoration of the

    i. Burial.

    ii. Ordination of Apostles. (S. John xx. 19, 23.)

Compline, in commemoration of the

    i. Institution of the Eucharist.

    ii. Rest in Paradise.''—

F. Christoph Mayer.

" The intentions may be made at

Matins : in honour of the Most Holy Trinity ; for the conversion of all abiding in mortal sin.

Lauds : in honour of all Holy Angels; for all enemies and persecutors.

Prime : in honour of CHRIST JESUS scourged at the pillar ; for the pardon of my sins, and the attainment of the virtue I most need.

Tierce : in honour of CHRIST JESUS crowned with thorns ; for all Christian kings and rulers.

Sexts : in honour of CHRIST JESUS crucified at that hour : for all especially afflicted at the present time.

Nones : in honour of CHRIST JESUS giving up the ghost at that hour ; for all those dying at the present time.

Vespers: in honour of the Blessed Virgin Mary
receiving the Body of her Son ; for all who
died this day.

Compline: in honour of all Saints ; for perseverance
in good works."—Drexelius.

CHAPTER VI.

[Many years ago, an Essay on the Mystical Interpretation of the Psalms was published by Dr. Neale in the " Christian Remembrancer." It was partly reproduced in two of the dissertations contained in the first volume of his "Commentary on the Psalms." But the price of that great work places it beyond the reach of many persons ; and therefore part of the original essay is here reproduced, with the omission of some portions less immediately bearing on the present subject.]

EXTRACTS FROM AN "ESSAY ON THE MYSTICAL INTERPRETATION OF THE PSALMS." BY THE REV. J. M. NEALE, D.D.

" ' If we keep vigil,' says S. John Chrysostom, ' in the Church, David comes first, last, and midst. If early in the morning we seek for the melody of hymns, first, last, and midst, is David again. If we are occupied with the funeral solemnities of the departed, if virgins sit at home and spin, David is first, last, and midst. O marvellous wonder ! Many who have made but little progress in literature, nay, who shall scarcely even have mastered its first principles, have the whole Psalter by heart. Nor is it in cities and churches alone that, at all times, through every age, David is illustrious ; but in the midst of the forum, in the wilderness and the uninhabitable land, he excites the praises

T

of GOD. In monasteries, amongst those holy choirs of angelic armies, David is first, midst, and last. In the convents of virgins, where are the bands of them that imitate Mary; in the deserts, where are men crucified to this world, and having their conversation with GOD; first, midst, and last, is he. All other men are at night overpowered by natural sleep: David alone is active, and, congregating the servants of GOD into angelic bands, turns earth into heaven, and makes men into angels.' Nothing can more admirably express the feelings of the Church to her κτῆμα ἐς ἀεὶ than these words of the great Doctor of the East. The love, the veneration, the delight, which she has expressed for the Psalter, have almost turned it into a part of her own being. It is not only that, from the beginning till now, the whole Book of Psalms has been weekly recited by many thousand priests: but that the spirit of the Psalter permeates and kindles every other part of the service; that its principal features have received a new and conventional character, have been transfigured from the worship of the synagogue to that of the Church; that, to use the mediæval metaphor, the trumpets of the tabernacle have given place to the psaltery and the New Song of the Christian ritual. We propose to give a brief sketch of the method in which the Church of the Middle Ages adapted the Psalter to her own needs; in which she employed all the luxuriance of her imagination to elicit, to develope,—if you will, to play with,—its meaning. There is—to use the word in a good sense—a perfect treasure of mythology locked up in mediæval Breviaries and commentaries, —a mythology, the beauty of which grows upon the student, till that which at first sight appears strange, unreal, making anything out of anything, perfectly fascinates. If the present writer should seem to be carried away by the richness and love- liness of mediæval allegory, it will not afflict him to plead guilty to the charge. The reader may, if he pleases, view the subject more coolly : it is, at all events, to the advantage of truth, as well as of interest, that any system should be sketched by a warm and loving partisan.

" The first thing that would strike one in the mediæval use of the Psalter, is the large proportion of time which its recital employed out of the whole period disposable by ordinary human strength for the service of GOD. And not its recital only, but its being committed to memory—an ordinary practice of the first twelve centuries.

" And when we say that all the Psalms were weekly recited by every ecclesiastic, we mean, in point of fact, much more than this. For, addition- ally, the 119th Psalm was said daily : three of those in Lauds scarcely ever varied : while the four at Compline remained unchangeable. In the Eastern Church it is well known that were the

Mesoria, as they are called,—the halfway prayers between every two of the Hours,—repeated with the Hours themselves, at only a moderate speed, it would be absolutely impossible to get through the services of the day within the space of the day.

"And this constant and frequent repetition naturally involved the development of a conventional meaning in the Psalms so recited. The same Psalm was said at Christmas, said at Easter, said in Lent, said on the Festival of Martyrs, said in the Office for the Dead : it could not, at all these seasons, be said with the same feelings, in the same frame of mind. Its different emphases required to be brought out : the same sun-ray from the HOLY GHOST rested, indeed, at all times, on the same words, but the prism of the Church separated that colourless light into its component rays—into the violet of penitence, the red of a martyr's festival, the gold of the highest seasons of Christian gladness. Hence arose that wonderful system of antiphons, which, out of twenty different significations, definitely, for the time being, fixed one ; which struck the right key-note, and enabled the worshippers to sing with the spirit, and to sing with the understanding also. * * *

"The first marked point which distinguishes mediæval from modern interpretation of the Psalms is the constant reference to our LORD in which the former delights, and which the latter invariably eschews. Not only each verse is applied to Him, but the very absence of any title is made significative of Him also. 'The first Psalm has no title,' says Venerable Bede, 'because nothing ought to precede the LORD and SAVIOUR, Who is our Head, and of Whom, and Whom only, it is about to speak.' How He did not walk in the counsel of the ungodly, nor stand in the way of sinners; how He exercised Himself in the law of the LORD, in the day of prosperity as well as in the night of adversity; how His fruit was brought forth *in* due season, and not before :—' My time is not yet come, but your time is alway ready ;' —how His leaf—His words, the leaves of the tree which are for the healing of the nations—shall not wither; because ' heaven and earth shall pass away, but My words shall not pass away.'

"What wonderful beauty there is in, ' Let the lifting up of my hands be an evening sacrifice,' when applied to that One Great Sacrifice which was offered up in the evening of the world—in the evening, too, of the Paschal day—by the stretching forth of His hands on the Cross ! in, ' I shall not die but live, and declare the works of the LORD,' when we refer it to the morning of the first Easter Day, and the commission to the Apostles to make disciples of all nations : in, ' I am a stranger upon earth,' when it alludes to Him Who came unto His own and His own received Him not: in the double

answer to the question, ' Who is the King of Glory ?'
the first, ' The LORD mighty in battle,' because our
LORD's first ascension was so soon after His
triumph over death and hell ; the second, ' The LORD
of Hosts,' because His other ascension will be with
the multitude of His redeemed when their warfare
is accomplished ! Again, in such a text as, ' O
think upon Thy servant as concerning Thy Word,
wherein Thou hast caused me to put my trust,'
when we take it of that co-eternal Word, Who is,
indeed, all the salvation and all the trust of His
people ! Or, when we so take, ' Now for the
comfortless troubles' sake of the needy, and because
of the deep sighing of the poor,' as to refer to Him
Who was so needy as to have no place where to lay
His head, and of Whom it is written, ' Neither found
I any to comfort Me.' Indeed, it is remarkable how
much emphasis we may almost always give by taking
THE POOR as applying to our LORD.

" In the same way the so constantly occurring
phrase, ' The righteous,' may be applied with
admirable beauty. * ⁂ But to take some further
examples. To our LORD also we may refer such a
text as, ' While mine enemies are driven back :
they shall fall and perish at Thy Presence :'
understanding it of that speech of His which, when
His enemies had heard, ' They went backward and
fell to the ground.' Or that whole passage, ' The
sorrows of death compassed me, etc., the earth

trembled and quaked;' to those sorrows which did indeed compass our LORD on the Cross, when 'The earth did quake, and the rocks rent;' and when 'He made darkness His secret place,' at the time when there was darkness over all the earth from the sixth till the ninth hour. So also, 'When the wicked, even mine enemies and my foes, came upon me to eat up my flesh, they stumbled and fell;' of Judas's fall into final perdition, after the first sacrilegious communion. Or, if we carry on the allusion in, 'False witnesses did rise up; they laid to my charge things which I knew not,' to the next verses, 'Nevertheless, when they were sick,'—the *Salvasti mundum languidum* of the Advent hymn,— 'I put on sackcloth,' that is, the miseries and infirmities of human nature, 'and humbled my soul with fasting,' as in the forty days in the wilderness. Or, to take a curious example of a double sense : 'Blessed is the man that considereth the poor and needy, the LORD shall deliver him in the time of trouble;' which we may either understand of the blessedness of him who fixes his faith and hope on the King Who became poor and needy for our sakes,—or, of the blessing due to His Name Who, 'considering' us, poor and needy as we were, was Himself delivered in the time of His greatest trouble, —was 'preserved' and 'kept alive,' that He might be 'blessed,' not only, as before, in heaven, but also 'upon earth.' * * *

" But to resume our subject. So a glorious prophecy of the Resurrection was seen in that verse, ' As for me, I will sing of Thy power, and will praise Thy mercy betimes in the morning ;'—that morning on which the stone was rolled away so early from the sepulchre. Again, of the Passion : in that, ' Their device is only how to put Him out,' —out of the Synagogue, out of the city, out of the world,—' Whom GOD will exalt '—' to be a Prince and a SAVIOUR, to give repentance and remission of sins :' and in that again, ' But, LORD, I make my prayer unto Thee in an acceptable time :' —the time of that Sacrifice accepted, once and for all, for the sins of the whole world. So again of the Resurrection : ' Yet didst Thou turn and refresh Me ; yea, and broughtest Me from the deep of the earth again :' and yet once more of the Passion, ' He shall refrain the spirit of princes, and is wonderful among the kings of the earth,'—as when He stood in His majesty before Pilate and Herod, and answered not a word, ' insomuch that the governor marvelled greatly.' So,—in a less important event, there is a remarkable coincidence between that verse,—' Thy way is in the sea, and thy paths in the great waters, *and thy footsteps are not known :*' and the passage in S. John's Gospel, where, after our LORD had crossed the sea of Tiberias, ' they also took shipping, and came to Capernaum, seeking for JESUS. And when they had found Him on the other side of the sea, they said unto Him, Rabbi, when camest Thou hither?' So again in, 'Thou hast brought a vine out of Egypt,' those mediæval writers saw a type of the 'True Vine,' —the Son 'called out of Egypt,'—and applied the prophecy that followed to Him. Especially, according to their interpretation, is that verse noticeable, 'She stretched out her branches unto the sea, and her boughs unto the river;' which, in common with that other passage, 'His dominion shall be also from the one sea to the other, and from the flood unto the world's end:' they referred to the Sea of Baptism at the one end of Christian life, and to the Sea of Glass before the Throne, at the other. And not less strikingly did they see a prophecy of the prayer, 'FATHER, glorify Thy Name,' in that, 'O turn Thee then unto me, and have mercy upon me: give Thy strength unto Thy servant, and help the son of Thine handmaid. Shew some token upon me for good, that they who hate me may see it, and be ashamed: because Thou, LORD, hast holpen me, and comforted me.'

"Again, consider the following, as taken in reference to the Resurrection: 'Up, LORD, why sleepest Thou? awake, and be not absent from us for ever:' or, 'In the multitude of the sorrows that I had in my heart, Thy comforts have refreshed my soul;' compared with the Agony in the garden, when there appeared unto Him an Angel from

heaven, strengthening Him : or, ' Man goeth forth
to his work and to his labour until the evening ;' in
reference to the thirty-three years of our LORD's
work, and the evening in which He said, ' I have
glorified Thee on the earth ; I have finished the work
which Thou gavest me to do.' Consider, once more,
the allusion to the Atonement in those passages, ' So
He said, He would have destroyed them, had not
Moses His chosen stood before Him in the gap :
to turn away His wrathful indignation, lest He
should destroy them ;' and, ' They angered Him
also at the waters of strife : so that He punished
Moses for their sakes :' or, ' At midnight will I rise
to give thanks unto Thee,' with reference to that
glorious midnight, when our LORD burst the bars
of death, because it was not possible that He should
be holden of them : or, ' The plowers plowed upon
my back, and made long furrows,' to His scourging :
or, ' My soul fleeth unto the LORD, before the morning watch, I say, before the morning watch,' to His
rising up a great while before day, on that night
before He left the Apostles.

" Another conventionalism which, from the time
of S. Augustine downwards, directed and influenced
the whole mediæval course of scriptural interpretation, was the appropriation of the name of Jerusalem
—the Vision of Peace—to the Church triumphant ;
that of Sion—expectation—to the Church militant.
It will be found that this rule, with scarcely a

single exception, holds good in the Psalms; and even in those instances which at first sight appear to deviate from the canon, a peculiar beauty is often afforded by following up the clue.* *

"To turn to another subject. Another favourite conventionalism of mediæval writers was to shew how frequently in describing the Christian's enemies, the Psalmist speaks of them, and that in very close juxtaposition, in the singular and the plural number: whence they gather that no trials or afflictions could hurt at all, that they could not be our enemies, unless it were the malice of Satan, the hatred of THE enemy which gave them their venom. And certainly it is remarkable how often this arrangement of words may be observed; so that it has been said, perhaps without much exaggeration, 'It seems to me scarcely to be otherwise.' Take the following examples: 'Lead me, O LORD, in Thy righteousness, because of *mine enemies*; for there is no faithfulness in HIS mouth. Save me from *all them* that persecute me, and deliver me, lest HE devour my soul like a lion.' * * *

"We hardly, perhaps, find so many references to the Cross in the mediæval Psalter as we might, *à priori*, have expected; yet some there are which are not a little quaint and striking. So that verse, 'And now shall He lift up mine head above mine enemies round about me,' is expounded of the lifting up of CHRIST on the Cross; an allusion which naturally bases itself on our LORD'S own words, 'And I, if I be lifted up from the earth, shall draw all men unto Me ;—this spake He, signifying what death He should die.' * * * And in the same sense they also took these other passages :—' I will be *exalted* among the heathen, and I will be exalted in the earth ;' and, 'Now will I arise, saith the LORD, now will *I be exalted :* now will I lift up Myself.' And still more finely, they saw the Cross predicted as the Throne in those verses :—' And *set up Thy Throne* from one generation to another.' ' I have laid help upon One that is mighty, I *have exalted* One chosen out of the people.' ' *His Throne* is as the days of heaven.' So again : ' The green olive-tree in the House of GOD,' and ' the joy of all the trees of the wood before the LORD,' may be taken to point the same way : while that text, ' The LORD shall send the rod of Thy power out of Sion ; be Thou ruler even in the midst among Thine enemies,' is a noble prophecy of the same thing. And yet, once more, it is not difficult to see both the Incarnation and the Atonement predicted in one verse of the 132nd Psalm, when after speaking of the ' habitation for the mighty GOD of Jacob,' the prophet continues, ' Lo, we heard of the same at Ephrata, and found it in the wood ;'—the manger of Bethlehem, and the Cross of Mount Calvary, being thus set forth. So also, ' I stretch forth my hands unto Thee, my soul gaspeth unto thee as a thirsty land,' well expresses the extension of our LORD's arms on the Cross and His cry, that the Scripture might be fulfilled, ' I thirst.'   Or consider, once more, ' The righteous shall flourish like a palm-tree, and shall spread abroad like a cedar in Libanus,' compared with that, ' All the day long have I stretched forth my hands unto a disobedient and gainsaying people.'

" Again, it is remarkable how, by applying the term, ' Thy Word,' to the co-eternal Word of GOD, we heighten the meaning of the Psalms ; a remark which applies, beyond all others, to the 119th. Consider the following expressions in it :—' Wherewithal shall a young man cleanse his way ? even by ruling himself after Thy Word,' compared with ' Leaving us an example, that we should follow His steps.'   ' I will not forget Thy Word,' taken with reference to the ' Friend that sticketh closer than a brother.'   ' O quicken Thou me, according to Thy Word,' compared with, ' Because I live, ye shall live also.'   ' Comfort Thou me according to Thy Word,' said of Him Who is the ' Father of mercies and the GOD of all consolation.'   ' My trust is in Thy Word.'   ' O think upon Thy servant as concerning Thy Word ;' for if not thought of as concerning Him, how could we hope to stand before the Righteous Judge ?   ' I have a good hope because of Thy Word.'   ' Mine eyes long sore for Thy Word ;' which last expression can hardly be taken in any other sense than of the Son of God. 'O Lord, Thy Word endureth for ever in heaven;' to which the same remark is applicable. 'Thy Word is a lantern unto my feet, and a light unto my paths:' compare, 'A light to lighten the Gentiles and the glory of Thy people Israel:' and, 'I am the light of the world.' 'Quicken me, O Lord, according to Thy Word;' in the same sense as, 'For as the Father raiseth up the dead and quickeneth them, even so the Son quickeneth whom He will.' 'My trust is in Thy Word.' 'Mine eyes are wasted away with looking for Thy health, and for the Word of Thy righteousness.' 'When Thy Word goeth forth, it giveth light and understanding unto the simple;' with which that noble passage in the Book of Wisdom may be compared, 'For while all things were in quiet silence, and that night was in the midst of her swift course, Thine Almighty Word leaped down from heaven out of Thy royal throne.' 'Quicken me according to Thy Word:'—the constant connection of quickening with the Word is surely remarkable. So we may take those passages where there is a reference to the Blessed Trinity. 'By the Word of the Lord were the heavens made, and all the hosts of them by the Breath of His mouth:' and again, 'He sendeth out His Word and melteth them; He bloweth with His Wind, and the waters flow.'' * * *

"It may not be amiss now to offer a few remarks

on the peculiar titles which some of the Psalms
have received, either singly or in groups ; and those
which first of all present themselves are the Penitential.

"The *Penitential*, formerly also called the
Special,* Psalms, are, as every one knows, held to
be these :—6, 32, 38, 51, 102, 130, 143. It is not
wonderful that seven should have been the number
fixed upon for the Psalms of penitence. It applies,
in the first place, as those now so called are applied, to the seven deadly sins ; the 6th against
anger, the 32nd against pride, the 38th against
gluttony, the 51st against impurity, the 102nd
against avarice, the 130th against envy, and the
143rd against sloth. But why those especial seven
should have been chosen, it is a harder question to
determine. There are others which seem at least
as penitential. For example, the 88th Psalm—the
only one which has no clause of comfort or of hope
—is not among the list ; it is difficult also to see
why the 142nd has not as good a right to the title
as the 143rd ; while, again, the 56th or 57th might
seem to have as just a claim to the same character.
And so we find that, in the Churches of France and
Germany, during the first ten centuries, a very
usual reckoning of the Penitential Psalms was

---

* But *the* Special Psalm, when mentioned by itself, is the 130th,
as the only one which occurs both among the Penitential and the
Gradual Psalms.

this :—6, 51, 57, 67, 70, 86, 130. According to other rituals, the 88th took the place of the 86th ; or both these were retained, and the 67th, which can scarcely be called penitential, was omitted. It is curious to observe how, all through the Middle Ages, the English Church possessed, in one re-spect, that penitential character which now is notoriously stamped on its ritual. Not only did it add the 51st Psalm to all the Hours, (in which it simply followed the Gregorian use, afterwards dropped by Rome itself,) but in Lent—at least in many localities—it added to this Psalm one of the Penitential Psalms in order ; only at Sexts, when it would have been subjoined to itself, the 67th Psalm was substituted. This very substitution is one among many proofs of the extreme antiquity of the sources whence the Sarum ritual was derived : and it is singular that the retention of that Psalm in our own Evening Prayers should point backward to an antiquity which is attained by a very few parts of the Roman Breviary.

"Next in importance to these we have the Gradual Psalms, which, as being no arbitrary division, could never vary. Then the Baptismal Psalms, three in number ; those, namely, that form the Nocturn on the two ancient baptismal days, Easter and Pentecost ; they are the 1st, 2nd, and the 4th. Then the Psalms of the Passion : 2, 7, 22, 31, 38, 59, 69, 81, 94, 102, 123, 130, 132, 142.

The *Prostrate* Psalms, the Penitential and Gradual conjointly. * * *

"We must now speak of the rise and progress of that which especially characterises the Western use of the Psalter; namely, the system of Antiphons. Ancient as is the alternate chanting of Psalms in the Church, it may be doubted whether that of Antiphons is not of even more venerable antiquity; and the relation of Socrates about the vision of S. Ignatius, and his introduction into the service of the Church on earth of that which he had seen in the Church in heaven, more probably refers to this system than to that of responsory chanting. An Antiphon, then, in the original sense of the word, was the intercalation of some clause or fragment between the verses of the Psalm which was being sung; one choir taking the Psalm, the other the intercalated portion. An example will make this plain :—

First Choir. 'The LORD said unto Me: Thou art My Son; this day have I begotten Thee.'

Second Choir. 'The LORD said unto Me: Thou art My Son; this day have I begotten Thee.'

First Choir. 'Why do the heathen so furiously rage together: and why do the people imagine a vain thing?'

Second Choir. 'The LORD said unto Me: Thou art My Son; this day have I begotten Thee.'

First Choir. 'The kings of the earth stand up: and the rulers take counsel together against the LORD and against His anointed.'

Second Choir. 'The LORD said unto Me: Thou art My Son; his d   have I begotten Thee.' * * *

U

" It would appear that the repetition of the Antiphon after every verse lasted far down into the eighth century. * * *

" It gradually came to pass that the present Roman use prevailed ; and the Antiphon was restricted, as a general rule, to the beginning and end of the Psalm, or to the beginning and end of two or four Psalms taken together, as the case might be. The 95th Psalm, however, has its Antiphon or Invitatory additionally repeated at the end of the second, fourth, seventh, and ninth verses ; and a similar repetition takes place when that Psalm is, on the feast of the Epiphany, said at the beginning of the third Nocturn.

" The next step in abbreviation was the repetition of only the first three or four words of the Antiphon at the commencement of the Psalm, except on high festivals,—an abbreviation which, however, is sometimes not without the advantage of peculiarly riveting, as it does, the attention on the emphatic word. What force, for example, is given by a single word, as the previous Antiphon to the 56th and 57th Psalms, at Matins on Wednesday—FOR; by which word the whole tenor of the two Psalms is made to imply that trust and confidence which man may now have in GOD, because, as on the Wednesday, GOD trusted in man, and was betrayed. So again, in the Office for the Dead, the Antiphon (as cut off at its mediation) of the 7th Psalm is the word ' Lest.'

" But now, to take some examples of Psalms, the sense of which is directed throughout by means of the Antiphon.   The perfection of an Antiphon is, no doubt, when it can be taken from its own Psalm ; but even mediæval piety could not always accomplish that ; and a considerable proportion of those said are not even taken from the Psalms at all.

Let us select a few of those which occur most frequently.

" The first Psalm is said in the ordinary Sunday service, in the Common of one Martyr, in the Common of many Martyrs, in the Common of a Confessor and Bishop, on Easter Day, and Whitsun Day.   In the first, we have this ordinary every-day duty of a Christian : ' Serve the Lord* with fear, and rejoice unto Him with reverence,' eliciting no peculiar sense from the Psalm, but leaving it appropriate to the duties of common life. In the second, ' His delight * was in the law of the LORD day and night,'—not only, according to the mediæval interpretation, in the day of prosperity, but in the night of affliction, even such affliction as the pains of martyrdom; and then, immediately ' the way of the ungodly,' ' the seat of the scornful, ' the ungodly who shall not be able to stand in the judgment,' speak of the unrighteous tribunal at which the martyr stood. The ' tree planted by the rivers of waters ' is CHRIST Himself on the Cross, Whom every sufferer for the truth was in some sort ' like ;' and the ' fruit in due season ' sets forth how the blood of the martyrs became the seed of the Church. The third gives us the Antiphon, 'By the rivers * of water he planted the vineyard of the just, and in the law of the LORD was their delight.' Here, with the same general bearing, their sowing in tears that they may reap in joy is more prominently brought forth. A Bishop and Confessor's Festival directs us to another verse : ' Blessed is the man * who doth exercise himself in the law of the LORD : his will remaineth day and night ; and all things whatsoever he doeth shall prosper ;' thus referring the Psalm to the study and doctrine of the Saint which the Church commemorates. At Easter :—' I am * that I am and my counsel is not with the wicked : but in the law of the Lord is my delight ; Alleluia.' Here the whole is boldly taken, no longer of the martyrs and confessors of the LORD, but of the LORD of martyrs and confessors. He is the Man that is blessed— that stood not in the way of sinners, that exercised Himself in the law of the LORD, as in the threefold answer to the threefold temptation—Whose leaf shall not wither, because the leaves of that tree are for the healing of the nations. On Whitsun Day, in ordinary Breviaries, the Antiphon is, 'Sud-

denly * there came a sound from heaven as of a
rushing mighty wind : Alleluia, Alleluia ;' but in
some provincial German uses, ' Look, * whatsoever he doeth, it shall prosper ;' thus applying the
Psalm no longer to CHRIST or to Christians, but
directly to the HOLY GHOST. S. Thomas's Antiphon for Corpus Christi is, ' The LORD gave His
salutary fruit to be tasted in the time of His
death ;' thus riveting the sequence of thought to
the institution of the new Sacrament.

" The 51st Psalm, again, is one that occurs as
often as most. In the ordinary ferial service at
Lauds, the antiphons run on in sequence, according to that favourite rule of the Church, where no
very particular point was to be brought out. * * *

" But in the Office for the Dead the one leading
feature is, ' That the bones which Thou hast broken
may rejoice ;' or, as it is in the Vulgate, ' The bones
which Thou hast *humbled ;*' thus magnificently
bringing out the ' sown in corruption ' raised in
incorruption ; sown in dishonour, raised in glory;
sown in weakness, raised in power,' of the Apostle.
On the Wednesday in Holy Week, ' Deliver me
from blood-guiltiness ' (*de sanguinolento*), ' O GOD,
and my tongue shall sing of Thy righteousness,'
refers the Psalm to Him against Whom bloodthirsty
men did indeed rise up, and Who did indeed sing
of the righteousness of the FATHER, when He said,
' As the FATHER hath sent Me, even so send I you.'

On Maundy Thursday we have, 'That Thou mightest be justified in Thy saying'—He Who had so often prophesied that He should be delivered to the Gentiles, and spitefully entreated, and put to death, and that He should rise again the third day —'and clear when Thou art judged:' according to Pilate's own confession, 'I find no fault in this man.' On Good Friday, the ordinary Antiphon is simply borrowed from the New Testament, 'GOD spared not His own Son, but delivered Him up for us all.' But we have seen a Dutch Breviary, which, with the wonderful devotion to the Passion which distinguished the good men of that Church in the fourteenth and fifteenth centuries, gives a far finer one in the Psalm itself, 'Tunc acceptis sacrificium justitiæ.' That same Breviary gives for this Psalm on Easter-eve, instead of the usual, 'O Death, I will be thy death! O Grave, I will be thy destruction,' the same as that employed in the Office for the Dead, and, to our taste, with very fine effect.

"The last three Psalms, the *Laudes* of S. Gregory, have, of course, a great variety of Antiphons. * * * That on Wednesday, in Holy Week, is singularly happy: 'To bind their kings in chains, and their nobles with links of iron:' the reference being to 'Let us break their bonds asunder, and cast away their cords from us,' of the second Psalm. Again, in the Office for the Dead, the very exact verse to

harmonize the solemnity of the Office with the joy-
ousness of the Psalms, ' Let everything that hath
breath praise the LORD;' literally, ' Let every
spirit praise the LORD.'

"As we have had occasion to refer so often to
the Office of the Dead, it may be worth while to
point out the magnificent manner in which, its key-
note having been once pitched, the Psalms fall into
their proper place.   Take, for example, the 65th.
The Antiphon is, ' Thou that hearest the prayer,
unto Thee shall all flesh come;' *come*, that is, when
all that are in the graves shall hear the voice of the
SON of GOD, and they that hear shall live.   Of the
first verse we have already spoken; the praise of
GOD commenced in Sion, and the vow completed
in the heavenly Jerusalem.   Next, of the blessedness of those that die in the LORD: ' Blessed is the
man whom Thou choosest and receivest unto
Thee: he shall dwell in Thy court, and shall be
satisfied with the pleasures of Thy house, even of
Thy holy temple.'   Then, looking forward to the
greatest of all wonders, the general Resurrection,
' Thou shalt show us *wonderful* things in Thy
righteousness, O GOD of our salvation; Thou
that art the hope of all the ends of the earth '—of
the countless corpses scattered as it were over the
whole surface of the globe—' and of them that remain in the broad sea,' looking for the resurrection
of the body, when the ' sea shall give up her dead.'

And still, with reference to the same hope, 'Thou visitest the earth'—at that great visitation at the last day—'and blessest it.' ('Come, ye blessed children of My FATHER.') 'Thou makest it very plenteous,' when every churchyard shall bring forth its abundant crop of life—

'Saat, von Gott gesäet, am Tage der Garben zu reifen.'

'Thy clouds'—when the Son of man shall come in the clouds of heaven—'drop fatness: they shall drop upon the dwellings of the wilderness'—the unknown and lonely resting-places of so many of GOD's saints—'and the little hills'—the graves of the earth—'shall rejoice on every side.'

"Or again, take the 63rd Psalm. The Antiphon is, 'Thy right hand hath upholden me:' the protecting and providential care which, through the lapse of centuries and amidst all the organic changes of matter, nevertheless upholds and will bring together again the bodies which, 'having been sown in corruption, shall be raised in incorruption.' And, in this sense, how beautiful is the 'Early will I seek Thee,' taken in connection with 'Blessed and holy is he that hath part in the first resurrection.' 'My flesh also longeth after Thee,' while waiting its reunion with the soul. Once more, 'Have I not remembered Thee in my *bed*, and thought upon Thee when I was waking?' (Compare, 'When I awake up after Thy likeness, I shall be satisfied with it.') 'Those also that seek the hurt of my soul, they shall go under the earth.' So, in Zechariah, 'The Lord rebuke thee, O Satan . . . . is not this a brand plucked out of the fire?' 'But the king shall rejoice in GOD'—

> 'Et cum multis illic scandet
> Unde solus venerat.'

The 67th, as we have said, follows without a *Gloria*. And still the same idea is carried on : 'That Thy way may be known upon earth,'—the way by which our LORD, having conquered death, ascended to the FATHER, and by which He will come to bring His people with Him,—'Thy saving health' ('for He is the Saviour of the body') 'among all nations.' Again, 'Thou shalt *judge* the folk righteously :' and, in its full sense, 'then shall the earth bring forth her increase :'—

> 'Tu depositum tege corpus :
> Non immemor ille requiret
> Sua munera fictor et auctor,
> Propriique enigmata vultus.
>
> Veniant modo tempora justa
> Cum spem Deus impleat omnem ;
> Reddas patefacta necesse est
> Qualem tibi trado figuram.' * * *

Taken in this sense, it would seem as if these two Psalms were written for, and could apply to nothing except, a funeral office ; let us now take them with another Antiphon, and examine what meaning they may then bear.

"On the Epiphany the Antiphon is, 'When they had opened their gifts, they presented unto Him gold, frankincense, and myrrh. Alleluia.' Then the 'Early will I seek Thee,' will apply to the general expectation of the King that was to be born, and Whom the star in the East heralded. The 'barren and dry land where no water is,' to the heathendom of those distant countries from whence the wise men came. 'Have I not remembered Thee in my bed, and thought upon Thee when I was waking?' will well set forth those watches of the night in which the astronomer kings must have beheld the new star. 'Those that seek the hurt of my soul,'—to whom should they refer, but to Herod and his court? 'The king shall rejoice in GOD,' will set forth the new kingdom set up on earth, of which the following Psalm speaks more fully. 'GOD be merciful unto us, and bless us, and show us the light of His countenance,' well expresses His manifestation to the wise men. 'That Thy way may be known upon earth; Thy saving health among all nations;' the end and aim of His Epiphany, 'that the earth may be full of the knowledge of the LORD, as the waters cover the sea.' So, even more remarkably, the doubly repeated prayer, 'Let the people praise Thee, O GOD,' —the people, hitherto the LORD's only people :—

but now, from this day forward, that shall not be enough,—'yea, let ALL the people praise Thee :' in other words, 'A light to lighten the Gentiles, and the glory of Thy people Israel.' '*Then* shall the earth bring forth her increase ;' true increase, the harvest to which the fields were white, even in the time of our LORD ; ' and '—the Psalm well ends with a prophecy of the day when the kingdoms of this world shall become the kingdom of the LORD and of His CHRIST—' all the ends of the earth shall fear Him.'

"In the Eastern Church, though there are Antiphons, yet from always recurring at the end of the Psalms, they have but little of the beauty which those of the Western Churches present. So, for example, at Lauds, the 3rd Psalm is begun without any kind of Antiphon ; but at the end we have, ' I laid me down and slept and rose up again, for the LORD sustained me :' at the end of the 38th Psalm, ' Forsake me not, O LORD my GOD ; be not Thou far from me ; haste Thee to help me, O LORD GOD of my salvation.' At the end of the 88th, ' O LORD GOD, Thou strength of my health ; Thou hast covered my head in the day of battle :' after the 103rd Psalm, ' In all places of His dominion, praise the LORD, O my soul.' "

*   *   *   *   *

Appendix.

I.

The Benedictine Office.

IT might be asked why we have passed over the great Benedictine Office with a cursory mention, although it was formerly used through the length and breadth of England, in the multitudes of religious houses which followed the rule of S. Benedict. And the answer would be, that, perhaps unfortunately, that Office has not yet been republished in an English form for present use : and therefore hardly came within our province. But some account of it must find a place here, and perhaps the best plan will be to draw it directly from the Rule of S. Benedict.

"In winter, having first said the verse, 'O GOD, make speed to save me, O LORD, make haste to help me,' the words, 'O LORD, open Thou my lips, and my mouth shall shew forth Thy praise,' are next to be repeated three times. After this the 3rd Psalm is said, with a *Gloria* at the end. Then the 95th Psalm is to be recited or sung with an antiphon.

"Let an Ambrosian [a hymn] follow next, and then six Psalms with Antiphons. These being said, and a Versicle added, let the Abbot give a blessing, and then, all being seated, let three lessons be read by the brethren in turns, from the book lying on the lectern. After every lesson, let a Responsory be sung. Let two of them be without a *Gloria,* but after the third let it be added by the Cantor, and as soon as he has begun it, let all rise from their seats out of honour and reverence to the Holy Trinity.

"Let the divinely inspired books, both of the Old and New Testament, be read at Matins, together with the expositions made upon them by the most famous, orthodox, and Catholic Fathers. After these three lessons and their responsories, let six other Psalms follow, to be sung with an Alleluia. Then let a lesson from the Apostle be said by heart, and after that a verse and the supplication of the Litanies, that is, *Kyrie Eleison*. And thus let Matins or Night-watches be brought to an end.

"From Easter till the first of November, let the same number of Psalms be recited, as we have before appointed; but let not the lessons be read, because of the shortness of the night. Instead of these three lessons, let one out of the Old Testament be said by heart, followed by a short Responsory, and let all the rest be performed as we have before arranged.

"On Sunday let them rise more seasonably for Matins, and therein observe the following order: When six Psalms and the Versicle have been sung, as we before arranged, let all sit down in a becoming and orderly manner, and let four lessons with their Responsories be read from the book; to the fourth Responsory only, let the Cantor add a *Gloria*, at the beginning of which all shall rise out of reverence. After these lessons let six more Psalms follow in order, with their Antiphons and Versicles as before. Then let four other lessons with their Responsories be said in the same way as the former. Next let three Canticles be said out of the three Prophets, such as the Abbot shall appoint; these must be sung with *Alleluia*.

"When the versicle has been said, and the Abbot has given his blessing, let four other lessons out of the New Testament be read, in the same order as before.

"After the fourth Responsory, let the Abbot begin the hymn *Te Deum*, and this being said, let him read a lesson from the Gospel, while all stand with reverential fear. At the end of this let all answer *Amen*, and then let the Abbot go on with the hymn, 'Te decet laus.' Then after the giving of the blessing, let Lauds begin. This order is always to be observed in singing Matins on Sundays, both in the summer and in winter, except perchance (which GOD forbid) they rise late, for then the lessons or responsories must be somewhat shortened. But let good care be taken that this do not happen: and if it do, let him by whose negligence it comes to pass, make satisfaction for it in the Oratory.

"For Sunday's Lauds, first, let the 61st Psalm be said plainly, without an Antiphon; after which, say the 51st with an *Alleluia;* then the 118th and the 63rd; then the *Blessings* and *Praises,* one lesson out of the Apocalypse said by heart, a responsory, a hymn, a versicle with a canticle out of the Gospel, and the Litanies, and so conclude.

"On ferial days, let Lauds be celebrated thus: Let the 67th Psalm be said as on Sunday, plainly and without an Antiphon, and also somewhat more slowly, in order that all may be in their places for the 51st, which must be said with an Antiphon. After which, let two other Psalms be said according to custom; that is, on Monday, the 5th and 36th; on Tuesday, the 43rd and 57th; on Wednesday, the 64th and 65th; on Thursday, the 88th and 90th; on Friday, the 76th and 92nd; on Saturday, the 143rd and the Canticle of Deuteronomy, which must be divided under two *Glorias*. But on other days, let the Canticle out of the Prophets be said, each on its own day, according to the practice of the Church. After these, let the Praises [the *Laudate*] follow; then a lesson from the Apostles, to be said by heart, a responsory, hymn, and versicle, a Canticle out of the Gospels, and so conclude.

"Let not the celebration of Lauds, or Evensong, ever terminate, unless at the end the LORD'S Prayer be said by the Prior, in the hearing of all, because of the thorns of scandal which are wont to arise; that the brethren, being reminded by the covenant of this prayer, in which they say: *Forgive us our trespasses as we forgive them that trespass against us,* may purge themselves from these faults. But in celebrating the other Hours, let the last part only be said aloud, that all may answer: *But deliver us from evil.*

"On Saints' days, and upon all solemnities, let the same order be observed as upon Sundays, only that Psalms, antiphons, and lessons be said, proper to the day itself. Their number, however, shall remain the same as before determined.

"From the holy feast of Easter until Whitsun-tide, let *Alleluia* be said without intermission, as well with the Psalms, as with the Responsories. From Whitsun-tide till the beginning of Lent, let it be said at all the Night Offices, with the six last Psalms only. But on every Sunday out of Lent, let the Canticles, Lauds, Prime, Tierce, Sexts, and Nones, be said with *Alleluia*. Let Evensong, however, be said with Antiphons. Let the Responsories never be said with *Alleluia*, except from Easter till Whitsun-tide.

"*Seven times a day*, saith the Prophet, *have I sung praises unto Thee*. This sacred number of seven shall be accomplished by us if at the times of Lauds, Prime, Tierce, Sexts, Nones, Evensong, and Compline, we perform the Office and duty of our service. It was of these hours the Prophet said: *Seven times in the day I have sung praise to Thee*. For of the Night watches, or Matins, the same Prophet says: *At midnight I did arise to confess to Thee*. At these times, therefore, let us give praise to our Creator for the judgments of His justice : that is, at Lauds, Prime, Tierce, Sexts, Nones, Evensong, and Compline ; and in the night let us rise to confess unto Him.

"We have already arranged the order of the Office for the Nocturns, and Lauds; let us now dispose of the Hours that follow. At Prime, let three Psalms be said separately, and not under one *Gloria*. Presently, after the verse, 'O GOD, make speed to save me,' let the Hymn of the same Hour follow, before the Psalms be begun. At the end of the Psalms, let there be recited one Lesson, a Versicle, and *Kyrie Eleison*, and therewith let that Hour conclude. Tierce, Sexts, and Nones, are to be recited in the same way, that is, the Prayer, Versicle, and Hymns of these same Hours, three Psalms, then a Versicle, and *Kyrie Eleison*, and so let the Hour conclude. If the Community be great, let the Hours be sung with Antiphons;

if, however, it be small, let them be only recited. Let Evensong be said with four Psalms and Antiphons; after these, let a Lesson be recited, then a Responsory, the Hymn, Versicle, and Canticle, out of the Gospel; the Litany, the LORD's Prayer, and so conclude. For Compline, let three Psalms be recited straight on without Antiphons. After these, the Hymn for that Hour, the Lesson, Versicle, *Kyrie Eleison*, and Blessing, and so let the Hour terminate. In the Day Hours, let the verse, *O* GOD, *make speed to save me, O* LORD, *make haste to help me,* always be said first, and after it a *Gloria.* Then the Hymn proper to each Hour. On Sunday, at Prime, there must be said four divisions of the 119th Psalm. At the rest of the Hours, to wit, at Tierce, Sexts, and Nones, let there be said three divisions of the same 119th Psalm. But on Monday at Prime, let three Psalms be said, that is, the 1st, 2nd, and 6th; in the same way at Prime, let three be said, in order every day, till Sunday, as far as the 20th Psalm; yet in such a way that the 9th and 18th Psalms be divided into two *Glorias.* Thus it will fall out that on Sunday at Matins we shall always begin at the 21st Psalm.

"At Tierce, Sexts, and Nones, on Mondays, let the remaining nine divisions of the 119th Psalm be said, three at a time, during these same Hours. On two days, therefore, to wit, Sunday and Monday, the 119th Psalm being gone through, let the Psalms at Tierce, Sexts, and Nones, on Tuesdays be sung in order, three at a time from the 119th to the 128th; that is, nine Psalms. These Psalms are always to be repeated at the same Hours for the rest of the week till Sunday; a uniform order also of the Hymns, Lessons, and Versicles, being every day observed, so that every Sunday they may begin with the 119th Psalm. Evensong is to be sung every day with four Psalms, which are to begin from the 110th; and go on to the 148th; such only being excepted as are set apart for other Hours, that is, from the 118th to the 128th, and from the 134th to the 143rd; all the rest are to be said in Evensong. And because there fall three Psalms short, those of the aforesaid number that are longer, must be divided, that is, the 139th, 144th, and 145th. But let the 117th, because it is short, be joined with the 116th.

"The order, therefore, of the Psalms for Evensong being set down, let other matters, such as Lessons, Responsories, Hymns, Versicles, and Canticles, be arranged as before. At Compline, let the same Psalms be repeated every day; that is, the 4th, 91st, and 134th. The order of the Day Office being thus disposed of, let all the Psalms which remain be equally portioned out into seven Night-Watches, or Matins, and such of them as are too long, divided into two. Let twelve Psalms be appointed for every night.

"If this arrangement and distribution of the Psalms displease any one, let him, if he thinks good, order them otherwise, provided however he take care, that every week the whole Psalter of one hundred and fifty Psalms be sung; and that on Sunday at Matins, they begin it again; for Monks shew themselves to be over negligent and indevout, who do not in the course of a week sing over the Psalter with the usual Canticles, since we read that our holy Fathers courageously performed in one day, what God grant that we, who are negligent and tepid, may perform in a whole week."

II.

The Kalendar.

Communicated by the kindness of Mr. A. R. Cooke.

Although the Ecclesiastical Kalendar is generally regarded as something too complicated and abstruse for ordinary comprehension, it is really a very simple matter, and capable of easy explanation.

It should be premised, however, that the Christian year is made up of two distinct portions, which are governed by perfectly different principles. One represents the Gentile or Solar year, and extends from the week before Advent to the Eve of Septuagesima. The other is a modification of the Hebrew or Lunar year, and lasts from Septuagesima till " Stir up " Sunday, or the next before Advent.

There is some reason to think that the Nativity may have taken place at the Feast of Tabernacles, (which answers very nearly to our Seventeenth Sunday after Trinity,) and that its observance was removed to the 25th of December, in order that a series of Christian Festivals might replace the heathen rites with which the turning-points of the solar year were celebrated. It is remarkable that the beginnings of the seasons, as well as the equinoxes and solstices, have left in popular customs connected with the corresponding holidays (namely, Candlemas, May-day, Lammas, and All-Hallows,) traces of a clearly pagan origin. For the Christmas Kalendar nothing is needed but to know the day of the month upon which Sunday falls; for which purpose there has been invented

The Sunday Letter.—If you look in your Prayer Book, you will find that the Almanack there given is divided into weeks, the days of which are distinguished by the first seven letters of the alphabet. In one year it is the A-days which are the Sundays; in another it is the G-days, and so on. But how are we to tell which is the

Sunday Letter of any particular year? Nothing can be easier. As the year consists of fifty-two weeks and a day over, the Sundays fall a day earlier each year, and the Sunday Letter therefore recedes one place every common year, and two places every leap-year. If, then, we know the Sunday Letter for any leap-year (that is, every year that is divisible by 4, without a remainder) we have only to add one-fourth to the number of years that have elapsed from it, and divide by 7. The remainder will show the number of places which the Sunday Letter has gone back; or, what comes to the same thing, if the number of years, plus one-fourth, be deducted from the next multiple of 7, the remainder will give the number of places which the Sunday Letter is in advance of the year we start from. Now it so happens that the Sunday Letters of the even centuries advance one step Old Style, and two steps New Style; and that both Styles coincide in the year 1200: thus—

	Old Style :—			New Style :—
A.D. 1200—A.				A.
„ 1300—B.				C.
„ 1400—C.				E.
„ 1500—D.				G.
„ 1600—E.				A.
„ 1700—F.				C.
„ 1800—G.				E.
„ 1900—A.				G.
„ 2000—B.				A.

This gives us a very convenient and easily remembered series of starting-places, and hence the rule—To the odd years (which for convenience of calculation may be reduced by 28, 56, or 84) add one-fourth, deduct the sum from the next multiple of 7, and reckon many places forward from the centurial year, as the remainder. Thus for 1877 add to 21 (77—56) one-fourth, deduct the sum (26) from 28, and the remainder (2) shows that the Sunday Letter for the year is two places in advance of G, that is B, Old Style, and two places in advance of E, that is G, New Style.

But remember, where there is no remainder after dividing by 4, it is leap-year, and the Sunday Letter for January and February is one more place in advance than that found as above for the rest of the year. Thus the Sunday Letters for 1876 were DC Old Style, and BA New. In applying this rule to time before the Christian era, subtract one less than the year B.C. (for there was no B.C. o) from 1400 or some larger multiple of 700, Old Style, and from 1600 or some larger multiple of 400, New Style, and proceed with the remainder as if it were A.D.

The Easter Kalendar.—By far the larger part of the year depends upon Easter Day, which in its turn depends upon the Passover. In the first days of the Christian Church, it was a question whether the Resurrection should not be celebrated on the very day on which it occurred, namely, on the 16th of Nisan; but at the Council of Nicæa it was finally determined that the day of the week should also be taken into account, and that on whatever day of the week Nisan 14th, the day of the Crucifixion, might actually fall, it should be regarded as taking place on the Friday; in other words, that Easter Day should always be the Sunday after the Paschal full moon. The day on which the Passover was kept, was not originally fixed with any great nicety. The custom seems to have been that it should be held on the fourteenth night of the first month of the year in which it was possible to procure ripe barley. This fourteenth night being counted from the reappearance of the moon after her conjunction with the sun, was really what we should call in modern astronomical language, her fifteenth, or even in some cases, her sixteenth day. In the time of our LORD, it might be kept as early as the 18th of March, (see Canon Norris's *Key to the Gospel Narrative*,) and if the year of the Passion was really A.D. 29, it must have taken place on that day. Ultimately the rule has prevailed to reckon as the Paschal moon that which becomes full next after the vernal equinox, and to determine the day by means of cycles, instead of by actual observation. But the cycles which were adopted have proved so inaccurate, that the Orientals, who still go by them, keep Easter in the wrong month eight times out of every nineteen, and in the wrong week four times out of every seven. In another nine hundred years, if they retain their absurd conservatism, they will never be right at all as to the week, and in two thousand years more they will never be right as to the month.

Old Style means simply the custom of observing every fourth year without exception as a leap-year. At the time the tables were drawn up, the equinox was supposed to fall (as it really did A.D. 200) at midnight on the 20th of March, whereas in the old Kalendar it has now receded to the 8th. New Style has restored the equinox to its ancient place, and will keep it there. This has been done by suppressing in Roman Catholic countries the ten days between the 4th and 15th of October, 1582, and in our own by making September 14th, 1752, immediately follow September 2nd; and by establishing the rule that whenever the year of our LORD can be divided by 400 without a remainder, there shall be no leap-year.

For the actual lunations, of which no two consecutive ones are alike, there has been substituted an imaginary moon of twenty-nine and thirty days alternately. As twelve of these occupy 354 days, the new moons fall eleven days earlier each year. In every three years these eleven days make an extra moon, and leave three days over. In six trienniums there is a balance of eighteen days, which added to the eleven days of the nineteenth year make a moon of twenty-nine days. Thus the lunar cycle is one of nineteen years, and it was long thought that it exactly occupied that space of time; but just as the old Kalendar year was, roughly speaking, eighteen hours too long in every century, the lunar cycle is wrong by a day in every 308 years. The Golden Number is the year of this cycle of nineteen years.

To find the Golden Number.—Add one to the year A.D., and divide by 19. If there be no remainder the Golden Number is 19; if there be one, that remainder is the Golden Number. The Golden

Number may be found in an instant by omitting the hundreds of years, and adding 5, for 1600; 10, for 1700; 15 (or deducting 4), for 1800; 1, for 1900; 6, for 2000, and so on. Then deduct the twenties and add one for each. Thus for this year, 1877, omit 1800 and 4; and then from the remaining 73, cast out the three twenties, and add 3 to the 13 which remain. The Golden Number is thus 16.

To find Easter.—Having ascertained by these easy rules what is the Golden Number of the year, look for it in the annexed Kalendar (Table II). The Paschal full moon falls on the day which is opposite to it in the third column; and the Sundays printed at the top of the Table, are the days which are opposite the Sunday Letter of the year.

Thus for 1877, the days which stand opposite to the G which comes after the Golden Number, 16, are Jan. 21st for the last Sunday in Epiphany (the day when the hymn, " *Alleluia, dulce carmen,*" used to be sung); Feb. 25th for the 2nd Sunday in Lent; April 1st for Easter Day; May 6th for Rogation Sunday; June 10th for the 2nd Sunday after Trinity, and so on. From these, the other Sundays in the Easter Kalendar may be ascertained at a glance. The Paschal full moon fell on the 29th of March. As regards the Solar, or Christmas Kalendar, it is only necessary to note in Table I., the Sunday Letter of the particular year.

But the Easter Kalendar will only keep right till 1899. In the first place the Paschal moon falls a day earlier in about every 300 years. On the other hand, when the centennial correction for leap-year is made, all the Golden Numbers must be set forward one day. The rule, therefore, is this : at the commencement of every century which cannot be divided by 400, the Golden Numbers are set forward one place ; and when the century can be divided by 300, they are set back one place. These corrections, however, often neutralise each other. But note, when a Golden Number below 12 reaches April 19, it remains at April 18, and at the next remove it is transferred to March 21. In like mannner, the Golden Numbers above 11 remain two removes at April 17. The corrected places of the Golden Numbers from 1500 to 1699, and from 1900 to 2199, as well as their places Old Style, are given in the right hand margin of Table II. Old Style, sofar as the Paschal moons were concerned, was correct A.D. 600.

It is quite easy to dispense with all tables whatever. Thus to tell which is the letter assigned to the first day of each month, it is only necessary to remember an old jingle which contains twelve words, the initial letters of which answer to the twelve months of the year, namely :

> At Dover Dwell George Brown Esquire
> Good Christopher Finch And David Fryer.

If we want to know on what day of the week the 17th of July falls when A is the Sunday Letter, that is, when the days to which A is attached are Sundays, we note that the seventh word (" Good ") which answers to the seventh month, begins with G. The 1st of July being thus G, the 2nd is an A day, and the Sundays in that month are the 2nd, the 9th, the 16th, the 23rd, and the 30th. The 17th is a Monday.

To remember the place of the Golden Number in the Kalendar, observe that 19 is affixed to March 26th, and 8 to 27th. Deduct the Golden Number from one or other of these figures, multiply the remainder by 11, divide by 30, and add the remainder to the 26th or 27th of March as the case may be. Thus the Golden Number of the year 1877 (16) subtracted from 19 leaves 3, which multiplied by 11 gives 33. Deduct 30, and then add the remainder (3) to March 26. The result is the date of the Paschal full moon, namely, March 29. The Sunday Letter, we have seen, is G, which is the month-letter of April (" George ") ; and so Easter day was April 1st.

The full moons of January and February are the same as those of March and April ; and they fall in each of the succeeding months a day earlier, except the September moon, which is two days earlier

than that of August. The range of the Paschal full moon is from
March 21 to April 18, inclusive; and when the full moon falls
outside those limits, it may be brought within them by subtracting
one day from the March moon, which gives the moon for April and
vice versâ. For the two centuries 1600-1799, reckon from the
25th and 26th of March; and for the three hundred years (1900-
2099) from the 27th and 28th. For Old Style, take the 17th and
18th of April; or, if more convenient, the 18th and 19th of March.
But whenever the calculation gives the 19th of April, make it the
18th; and where the Golden Number exceeds 11, and the calculation gives the 18th of April, make it the 17th.

Sometimes in reading history, it is desirable to know the age of
the moon at a remote date. For this purpose find the Paschal full
moon, O.S., and add or subtract one day for each 300, or part of
300 years before or after A.D. 600. (To find the Golden Number
B.C., subtract one less than the given year from 1900, and proceed
with the remainder as if it were A.D.) Example: on what day did
the new moon fall in May, B.C. 585? The Golden Number being
6, the Paschal full moon would be on April 10th; add 4 days, the
correction for 1200 years, and the real date is April 14th. The
new moon would thus be on March 31st. There would be another
new moon on April 30th, and the May moon would be on the
29th—a day later than the date assigned by astronomers to the
famous eclipse of Thales. The Kalendar moon is very often one
day, and sometimes two days, different from the moon of astronomers.

To find the date on which any particular Sunday falls in any
year, it is only necessary to remember that Septuagesima is four
days earlier in January and February; the first Sunday after Trinity,
two days later in May or June; and the fourteenth Sunday after
Trinity, one day later in August and September, than Easter Day
is in March or April. The simple rule, therefore, is to multiply
the number of weeks that the required Sunday falls after those
landmarks by 7, add the product to the date of Septuagesima,
Easter, the first or fourteenth Sunday after Trinity, and divide the

sum by 30. The quotient will show the number of months in advance; and by deducting one from the remainder for each of the 31-day months that have intervened, you will have the day required. For example, on what day did the seventeenth Sunday after Trinity fall on 1877? Easter Day being the 1st of April, the fourteenth Sunday after Trinity was on the 2nd of September; and the third Sunday after that was the 23rd.

The Epact mentioned in one of the tables in the Prayer Book means the age of the Kalendar moon on the 1st of January. It is of no particular use,

TABLE I.—THE CHRISTMAS KALENDAR.

"Stir-up" Sun. Advent Sunday 2nd ,, 3rd ,, 4th ,,	1st) Sunday aft. 2nd) Christmas	1st) 2nd) 3rd) Sunday 4th) after 5th) Epiphany	6th Sunday after Epiphany
Sun. Let.:—	Sun. Letter :—	Sun. Letter :—	
B Nov. 20	C Dec. 26	G Jan. 7	Feb. 11
C 21	D 27	A 8	12
D 22	E 28	B 9	13
E 23	F 29	C 10	14
F 24	G 30	D 11	15
G 25	A 31	E 12	16
A 26		F 13	17
B 27	A Jan. 1	G 14	
C 28	B 2	A 15	
D 29	C 3	B 16	
E 30	D 4	C 17	
F Dec 1	E 5	D 18	
G 2	Epiphany	E 19	
A 3		F 20	
B 4		G 21	
C 5		A 22	
D 6		B 23	
E 7		C 24	
F 8		D 25	
G 9		E 26	
A 10		F 27	
B { Ember Week } 11		G 28	
C 12		A 29	
D 13		B 30	
E 14		C 31	
F 15		D Feb. 1	
G 16		E 2	
A 17		F 3	
B 18		G 4	
C 19		A 5	
D 20		B 6	
E 21		C 7	
F 22		D 8	
G 23		E 9	
A 24		F 10	
B Christmas			

TABLE II.—THE EASTER KALENDAR.

	Sun. bef. Sept. / Septuagesima. / Sexagesima. / Quinquagesi. / Quadragesim. (Ember Week)	2nd S. in Lent / 3rd „ / Mid Lent S. / Passion Sun. / Palm Sun.	Easters / 1st after „ / 2nd „ / 3rd „ / 4th „	Rogation S. / S. aft. Ascen. / Whits.(Emb) / Trinity Sun. / 1st Sun. aft.	2nd / 3rd / 4th / 5th / 6th	7th / 8th / 9th / 10th / 11th	12th / 13th / 14th / 15th / 16th	17th / 18th / 19th / 20th / 21st	22nd / 23rd / 24th / 25th / 26th	N.S. 1500—1699	N.S. 1900—2199	O.S.
14 3 D	Jan. 11	Feb. 15	Mar. 22	April 26	May 31	July 5	Aug. 9	Sep. 13	Oct. 18	3	14	16
. E	12	16	23	27	June 1	6	10	14	19	11	3	5
11 F	13	17	24	28	2	7	11	15	20	.	.	.
. G	14	18	25	29	3	8	12	16	21	9	11	13
19 A	15	19	26	30	4	9	13	17	22	19	.	2
8 B	16	20	27	May 1	5	10	14	18	23	8	19	.
. C	17	21	28	2	6	11	15	19	24	.	8	10
16 D	18	22	29	3	7	12	16	20	25	16	.	.
5 E	19	23	30	4	8	13	17	21	26	.	16	18
. F	20	24	31	5	9	14	18	22	27	5	5	7
13 G	21	25	April 1	6	10	15	19	23	28	13	.	.
2 A	22	26	2	7	11	16	20	24	29	2	13	15
. B	23	27	3	8	12	17	21	25	30	.	2	4
10 C	24	28	4	9	13	18	22	26	31	10	.	12

Table II.—The Easter Kalendar—*Continued.*

	Jan.	Mar.	April	May	June 14	July 19	Aug. 23	Sep. 27	Nov.			
· D	25	1	5	10	14	19	23	27	1	18	10	1
18 E	26	2	6	11	15	20	24	28	2	7	·	·
7 F	27	3	7	12	16	21	25	29	3	·	18	9
· G	28	4	8	13	17	22	26	30	4	15	7	·
15 A	29	5	9	14	18	23	27	Oct. 1	5	4	·	17
4 B	30	6	10	15	19	24	28	2	6	·	15	6
· C	31	7	11	16	20	25	29	3	7	12	4	·
12 D	Feb. 1	8	12	17	21	26	30	4	8	1	·	14
1 E	2	9	13	18	22	27	31	5	9	·	12	3
· F	3	10	14	19	23	28	Sep. 1	6	10	9	1	·
9 G	4	11	15	20	24	29	2	7	11	·	·	11
· A	5	12	16	21	25	30	3	8	12	17	9	·
17 B	6	13	17	22	26	31	4	9	13	6	17	19
6 C	7	14	18	23	27	Aug. 1	5	10	14	14	6	8
D	8	15	19	24	28	2	6	11	15			
E	9	16	20	25	29	3	7	12	16			
F	10	17	21	26	30	4	8	13	17			
G	11	18	22	27	July 1	5	9	14	18			
A	12	19	23	28	2	6	10	15	19			
B	13	20	24	29	3	7	11	16				
C	14	21	25	30	4	8	Emb. 12	17				

LIST OF AUTHORS QUOTED.

S. Augustine (*On S. John* and *on the Psalms*) † 430.

Honorius of Autun (*Gemma Animæ*) 12th century.

Hugh of S. Victor: but the three books *Of the Divine Office* under his name, are really by Robert Paululus, a priest of Metz. † 1140.

Sicardus, Bp. of Cremona (*Mitrale*) † 1215.

The anonymous author of *Micrologus*: 12th century.

Rupert, Abbot of Deutz. † 1155.

Durandus, Bishop of Mende (Rationale of Divine Office) † 1296.

The anonymous author of *The Myrroure of our Ladye,* a rationale of the Office of the Blessed Virgin, written for the Nuns of Sion House, Isleworth: 15th century.

Walter Hilton (*Scale of Perfection*) latter part of 15th century.

Louis Blosius, Benedictine Abbot (*Mirror of Monks*) † circ. 1566.

Cisneros, Benedictine Abbot of Montserrat (*Spiritual Directory*), 1500.

Jerome Drexelius, s.j. circ. 1629.

Christopher Mayer, s.j. (*Encheiridion Industriarum*) 1578.

Gavanti, † 1638, and Merati, † 1744 (*On Roman Breviary*).

Grancolas (*Commentary on Roman Breviary*) † 1732.

Martene (*De Ritibus Antiquorum Monachorum*) † 1739.

W. Palmer (*Origines Liturgicæ*).

Daniel Rock, D.D. (*Church of our Fathers*) †

J. M. Neale, D.D. (*Liturgical Essays, Mediæval Hymns, Commentary, and Essay, on Psalms*) † 1866.

Philip Freeman, Archd. (*Principles of Divine Service*) + 1875.

W. Bright, D.D. (*Ancient Collects*).

R. F. Littledale, LL.D. (*Commentary on Psalms*).

C. Walker (*Services according to use of Sarum : Plain Song Reason Why*).

J. D. Chambers (*Divine Worship in the* 13th, 14th, *and* 19th *Centuries*.

AUTHORS REFERRED TO IN QUOTATIONS FROM THE ABOVE.

Aldhelm, Abbot, + 709.

Alcuin, deacon of the Church of York, wrote Offices in France in the reign of Charlemagne, + 804.

Pseudo-Alcuin wrote on the Divine Office under the name of Alcuin : 12th century.

Amalarius Symphosius, deacon, first commentator on the Roman Office, + circ. 837.

S. Ambrose, Bishop of Milan, + 397.

S. Anselm, Abbot of Bec, 1078, Abp. of Canterbury, 1093 ; + 1109.

S. Athanasius, Bishop of Alexandria, + 373.

Baronius, Cardinal, + 1607.

S. Basil, + 379.

Venerable Bede, + 735.

S. Benedict, founder of Western Monachism, + 542.

S. Bernard, Cistercian Abbot of Clairvaux, + 1153.

S. Bonaventura, Franciscan, + 1274.

S. Cæsarius, Bishop of Arles, + 379.

Thomasius (Tommasi) an Italian collector of ancient Offices, + 1713.

Cassian, Abbot, † 433.

S. Chrysostom, † 407.

S. Cyprian, Bishop of Carthage, † 258.

S. Ephrem Syrus, † 378.

Gregory of Tours † 595.

S. Gregory, Pope, † 604.

S. Hilary, Bishop of Poitiers, † 367

S. Jerome, † 420.

S. Isidore of Seville, † 636.

S. John Damascene, circ. 756.

Lanfranc, Abp. of Canterbury, † 1089.

S. Leo, Pope, † 461.

S. Peter Damiani, Cardinal and Bishop of Ostia, † 1072.

Ralph, Dean of Tongres, circ. 1402.

Walafrid Strabo, circ. 849.

Y

INDEX.

LONDON :
SWIFT AND CO., NEWTON STREET, HIGH HOLBORN, W.C.

"Why the devil did you marry me?"

◇

Clay demanded.

"Every morning I've watched you race out of this cabin as if *you* were the one just released from prison, and every night you climb into that cursed pallet as if we were strangers instead of man and wife. Why did you marry me if you can't stand my company?"

"For the same reason you married me, Clay Penley!"

"In that case, you'll come to bed. My God, woman, I was beginning to believe that you really don't have normal feelings like the rest of us."

He rebolted the door and guided her toward the bed with a purposeful pressure. He pulled her down beside him, his lips seeking hers with an expert's aim. What areas of her exposed flesh his hands did not excite, his exploring lips did.

Lynn made no attempt to curb the tumult of her own response...

*　　　　*　　　　*

T4-BAG-432

Also by
ELIZABETH EVELYN ALLEN

Freedom Fire
The Lady Anne
Rebel

Published by
WARNER BOOKS

Witch Woman

Elizabeth Evelyn Allen

WARNER BOOKS

A Warner Communications Company

WARNER BOOKS EDITION

Cover illustration by Pino Daeni

Warner Books, Inc.
666 Fifth Avenue
New York, N.Y. 10103

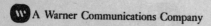 A Warner Communications Company

Printed in the United States of America

First Printing: August, 1987

10 9 8 7 6 5 4 3 2 1

Antiquity and birth are needless here;
'Tis impudence and money makes a peer.

—Daniel Defoe
The True-born Englishman

PROLOGUE

London 1665

The frail woman lying immobile in the velvet-canopied bed faced death as she had life: without a hint of the softening grace of apology for sixty wasted years. Clutched in one motionless, blue-veined hand was an amulet, attached around her neck by a slender gold chain, a good-luck charm that had been given her by an infatuated Dutch sea captain more than four decades earlier.

The only surviving offspring of the long dead but once powerful Lord Henry Trelynn and the occasional wife of the parliamentary lawyer Ephraim Penley, the Honorable Hortensia Trelynn Penley had been a lifelong gambler whose passion for wagering and the gaming tables had dominated her life. Long before the fact, she'd wagered that Charles I would be the first English king to lose his head on the chopping block if he continued his cavalier treatment of Parliament. She'd even wagered Oliver Cromwell himself that his hard-won Commonwealth would survive his death by only a year or two. When Cromwell asked her why, Hortensia had smiled and said candidly, ''We English are a quarrelsome lot, Oliver, who prefer to blame a king for all our troubles rather than to accept the responsibility ourselves.''

She was already winning her wager with her doctor that she'd die not of the rampant bubonic plague, but from what he called a worn-out heart and circulatory impediments. She'd won her wager about who would come to her rescue when her funds had been exhausted. Trelynn, Hortensia's only grandchild, had responded, as predicted, and remained to take charge in the elegant home that, like thousands of other London houses, now bore the black cross on the front door. That cross had been painted there two days before the graddaughter's arrival when the cook's husband had died, and in those two days the household had become chaotic. Nadine, Hortensia's distant cousin and paid companion, had locked herself in her room, and Hortensia's vain, foolish daughter, Lavinia, had fled to an apothecary, pleading for a magic elixer that would spare her face from the hideous black sores.

Hortensia smiled now, four months later, as she watched her granddaughter kneeling beside a small, frugal fire coaxing a pot of tea to boil. From the first day, the twenty-year-old had taken competent charge and had nursed, in turn, all five of the remaining residents. The cook had died two weeks later and then the maid, leaving the girl with all the work to do alone; Lavinia and Nadine had made no effort to help. Indeed, after a month had passed without an additional death, they'd added to the burden by resuming their afternoon visits to the only gaming house within walking distance. How dreadful they had looked without expert maids to arrange their elaborate coiffures and elegantly complicated dresses, Hortensia thought, but she'd held her peace. Let them indulge their passion for gambling even though it cost the remainder of the family jewelry; it was the only pleasure they had left in their useless lives. Those two lives had ended six weeks later; the plague was also a frequent visitor at public gaming halls.

With her work reduced to the care of one undemanding

old woman, the girl had ceased being an efficient automaton and had become a delightful companion. Released from the constraint of tending the mother who'd ignored her since infancy, she relaxed enough to reveal herself as a woman as individual and remarkable as her grandmother. After she'd rifled her grandfather's law office on the ground floor for history books and the more exciting legal papers, she read them aloud with an intelligence that was a revelation to the dying woman who had deliberately avoided the girl's company in past years.

It was for this granddaughter's future that the Honorable Hortensia planned her final gamble, a gamble that would also settle a long-standing score with a man who lived three thousand miles away. The day before her lawyer was to visit her one last time, Hortensia used her waning strength to write a series of letters and to rearrange a box of documents she'd maintained over the years. One of the letters, the first one she wrote and the simplest, was a friendly, unsentimental farewell to her husband of thirty-eight years announcing that while both his and her fortunes had been exhausted, their granddaughter's future would be secure. Far more complicated was the missive to another man whom Hortensia had known far longer than she had Ephraim Penley, a man she would have married had their respective fathers not interfered.

Sharply critical of the contents of this second letter, her lawyer had immediately protested. "You can't gamble with other people's lives, Hortensia."

"Of course I can, John, 'tis my money!"

"Much of it was Ephraim's," the lawyer murmured dryly. "Why is it you choose another man to carry out this commission rather than your husband?"

"Ephraim believes in the letter of the law; Bevil will be amused by the poetic justice."

"Will this Bevil also be amused by your plans for his own son?"

"He'll be relieved, I hope."

"How did you learn the truth about this young man?"

"I'm not as gullible as most people. I recognized the handsome rogue at a party three years ago, and I've kept abreast of his interesting career ever since."

"Did you tell your daughter about this arrangement before her death?"

"Lavinia would have resented my taking any interest in my granddaughter's welfare; she was a very immature woman."

Remembering the self-centered Lavinia with sour disapproval, the lawyer asked, "Didn't she even appreciate the risk the girl took by coming to London during the plague?"

" 'Twas Lavinia who sent for her without my permission, but from fear rather than affection."

"I'm surprised your granddaughter came under those circumstances. She strikes me as being a very independent young woman."

"You don't know the half of it, John. She's as much a hellion as I was at her age, and she has a will of iron. That's what makes all this such an interesting challenge."

"I very much doubt that either your granddaughter or the young man will find it so."

"How much would you care to wager on the outcome, John?"

As he settled to the task of legalizing the various documents, John Coleman was smiling; on the whole, he had always preferred unrepentant sinners as clients. Moreover, as Hortensia had claimed, poetic justice was frequently more effective.

CHAPTER
1

Plymouth, 1667

The young woman seated on a sea chest amid the clutter of other luggage in the cottage parlor regarded the old man with tolerant amusement. He had just completed reading the journal of accounting she'd given him and was preparing to deliver another of his legalistic judgments when she interrupted with a slashing candor.

"They spent all your brass, Grandfa, and left you burdened with a cloddish farmer for a granddaughter whom you can neither marry off nor protect beyond the grave. I'll not worry you into that grave, but neither will I be trusting that errant father of mine with my future."

"Perhaps you should, Trelynn. God knows Royce Trevor is well-landed and should be wealthier than Croesus with the money he's bled from your grandmother and me over the past twenty years. Now that my daughter is dead, you're his only heir. Did you notify him that your mother and Hortensia had died?"

"The same time I did you, Grandfa, and I've already received his response. He demanded a return of all the monies he called his 'rightful estate.' Won't he be sur-

5

prised when he learns that my grandmother wrote a new will eight years ago?''

''Since there was very little left, he shouldn't mind too much.''

''Then you don't know him as well as Grandmother did. She didn't want him informed until I was settled, and I'll not settle in Virginia. I couldn't legally inherit an acre of land in that benighted colony anyway, Grandfa; you know that estates are as 'man-tailed' there as they are here. I'd be naught but a servant in my father's home, and an unpaid one at that.''

Ephraim Penley sighed as he admitted the truth of her charges. That she understood the intricacies of property entailment in the remote American colonies did not surprise him. Over the years her avid research in his library had made her almost as competent a lawyer as he was. And God's wounds, she had just cause for her anger. She'd turned his own entailed estate from a rundown farm into a prosperous one, yet a worthless second cousin would inherit it just because he was a male. In more private matters, she'd done the job of taking care of his own family better than he had. He'd been far away following his career as legal advisor to colonial governments when the plague had struck London. Like a pair of idiot dottrels, his wife and flighty daughter had refused to leave the stricken city; but they hadn't hesitated to send for Trelynn when they ran out of money and food.

Escorted only by Jem Rigg, the indentured criminal Ephraim had hired to be her watchdog during his own absence, Trelynn had traveled to London with a wagonload of supplies and had remained there alone. Even after her mother and grandmother had been buried unceremoniously in one of the common burial pits that now held the bodies of more than seventy thousand plague victims, Trelynn had stayed on long enough to sell the house and furnishings. With a stubborn tenacity of purpose, she'd outwitted the caballers who were gulling most survivors of the victims who'd died during the plague to sell out at a tuppence to the pound. Aided by Hortensia's lawyer, she'd managed to negotiate a fair price from a Yorkshire parliamentarian. He had even paid additional money for the furniture.

When Jem Rigg had returned with the wagon, once more loaded with food and kindling wood, Trelynn had sold the food, packed up all of Ephraim's treasured books, and returned to Cornwall. A dozen times along the lawless highway cluttered with the homeless rabble from London streets, she and Jem had successfully fought off would-be thieves, flesh-flies, and blackguards who had mistakenly thought Trelynn a helpless female. Ephraim smiled faintly as he studied his unusual granddaughter. Since she'd been fourteen, she'd been more than a match for any man foolish enough to attempt an assault.

Tall for a woman, she'd inherited the unique Penley strength of muscle that had made his own ancestors some of the greatest of Cornish wrestlers. Few of these Penleys had ever been beaten in exhibitions at village fairs, and they'd made an excellent living at the trade because the wagering odds were usually in their favor. Slender men, they'd always looked like stripling youths in comparison to their muscle-bound adversaries; but they'd been swift and deadly in their attack. When she'd been a child, Ephraim had watched his granddaughter develop the same agility and speed. Because his own career kept him away from Penley Farms much of the time, he had sponsored her training in self-defense and purchased her a pair of the popular presbyterian flails—short, sturdy clubs with lead tips. By the time she was a tall, slender thirteen, she'd become expert in their use; more than an expert, he reflected proudly. By lengthening the leather wrist straps, she'd learned to whirl them with lightning speed and to strike her straw-men targets with controlled accuracy.

When Lavinia had seen Trelynn's skill, any pretense of motherhood on her part had vanished. She'd never visited the farm again; and until the plague, she'd never paid her daughter the slightest attention. When the London gaming houses reopened, Lavinia had become as addicted to gambling as her mother, but she had not a jot of Hortensia's shrewdness. During those first years of the Restoration, she had cost her mother a fortune; and it had been Ephraim's own patrimony that had supported the pair of them for the last two years of their lives. If Trelynn had not sold the house when she did, he'd now be without funds. He jerked uneasily at her sharp reminder.

"Stop woolgathering, Grandfa. You're two years too late to bid them peace; and truth, you're better off without them."

As always, he was shaken by his granddaughter's ability to read his innermost thoughts. Recalled to the current crisis, he asked hesitantly, "How did you know to sell, Trelynn? Without the brass you've saved, we'd both be penniless."

"I couldn't leave the house unguarded; there'd have been a hundred thieving squatters in it by daybreak. And Jem couldn't run the farm alone. I didn't want that house, Grandfa; and I didn't want to live in a city so rotten with human filth and misery. I felt smothered every day I was there."

"Are you certain those were the only reasons, lass?"

Peering closely at her grandfather's odd expression, Trelynn smiled in sudden understanding, a puckish grin that made her seem a young girl again. "You can stop frowning, Grandfa. I'm not the witch the local grannies accuse me of being, and I haven't a glimmer of Scot second sight. I had no more inkling than anyone else that London would be incinerated five months later in a fire that destroyed the half of it. I wanted the money, Grandfa, and the chance to leave England. I'd have left long before if I hadn't needed your help. That's why I came to Plymouth to await your ship."

"Why the rush, Trelynn? You have months ahead to decide on your future."

"That I don't, Grandfa. I'm sailing on the convoy leaving port two days from now."

"God's wounds, girl! You don't know enough about that wilderness to survive for a week!"

"I know everything you've recorded during the five inspection tours you made for Parliament. And I've found a place where there's enough freedom for a woman to live alone. You marked the colony yourself. According to your notes, I don't have to be either Puritan or Anglican to live in Connecticut; and the only property qualification is thirty pounds."

Ephraim sighed in renewed irritation. Since she'd refused her first marriage proposal at fifteen, she'd never accepted the limitations of womanhood under English law.

"For a man only, Trelynn."

"Aye, Grandfa. That's why the farm will be in your name, and I'll be using the name of Penley too—Lynn Penley—so there'll be no Trevor claim on our property there. In Connecticut, there's no law of male entailment or primogeniture; so I can inherit the farm from you."

"If you read all my notes, lass, you'd know that colonial communities don't tolerate spinsters living alone— especially in New England. 'Tis couples and families the settlers want for neighbors, not unwed, educated women."

"I won't be alone. Jem and Polly Rigg will be going with me, and there'll be others who—"

"Jem could well be a problem to you; there are many who are superstitious and cautious enough to regard him as a simpleton or worse because he can't speak."

"He's mute only because some pig of a man slashed his tongue when he was a pitboy in the cursed Pollock tin mines."

"Fifteen years later he murdered a man, and I was able to win indenture for him only because he couldn't defend himself."

"Well, he can now. Polly and I taught him to read and write. That murder he was charged with was self-defense;

the foreman was trying to strike him with a pick. The Pollocks have always hired the worst scum in Cornwall to run their pits.''

'' 'Tis ancient history now and best forgotten; he's served his indenture, and he's a free man now. But you still haven't told me why you're in such a hurry to leave Cornwall; 'twas my intention that we leave together once I've made my report in London. I'm thinking you're up to your old tricks of editing your words and telling me only the part you want me to know. More to the point, you've been keeping a close watch on the window and the road beyond. Is my reception committee about to be enlarged?''

''Aye, 'tis, Grandfa. Will Sprague reported that your charming nephew Owen has been watching the docks since the *Wayfarer* was sighted six days ago off the Isles of Scilly. He's pounding up the road right now. I should have realized he'd know which cottage was yours.''

''What business would that profligate want with me? He must realize I've no money left to waste on him.''

''He's here on other business, Grandfa; so I'll let him tell you the family news. No doubt he'll be more eloquent. But he's not to know I'm here, not under any circumstance. Meg's in the kitchen. I'll tell her to answer the door.''

With that swiftness of hers that had always unnerved him, she vanished through the rear parlor door, while Ephraim stared with annoyance at the luggage the drayman had dumped hodgepodge on the floor. He'd looked forward to an uninterrupted rest after forty-three uncomfortable days at sea; and in his exasperation at the turn of events, he'd been far sharper than usual with the granddaughter he considered his only worthwhile human achievement. His daughter had been a dismal failure, and his wife had treated their marriage with a cavalier indifference; but Trelynn had always been a remarkable scholar and, on the whole, a thoroughly sensible woman. Yet she'd just delivered an emotional ultimatum that she was embarking willy-nilly on a quixotic immigration to a wilderness she knew little about.

Concerning the second uninvited guest now being ushered into the small parlor by his aged housekeeper, Ephraim had no illusions or expectations. Heir to the once impressive Penley Farm, rundown now and productive only to the extent of Trelynn's success, Owen Penley was typical of the generation of men who had survived the civil war during childhood and the repressive Commonwealth during their early manhood without developing any loyalty to either faction. Assiduously, Owen had also avoided developing any ambition beyond his expectation of an easy life as a country squire. Until he'd married one of the innumerable Pollock women who peopled the Tamar Valley and the surrounding hills of Cornwall, he'd squandered his money on frivolous pursuits without regard for the future. His wife, though, had instituted instant reforms in his attitudes. With the avarice typical of her family, which now numbered ten branches and controlled a fifth of the stannaries of Cornwall, Edith Pollock devoted her soul to the acquisition of a fortune far beyond Owen's inheritance from his father.

Cynically, Ephraim suspected that his nephew was coming to ask for money again, a request that would be an exercise in futility in light of the disastrous depletion of his own purse over the past four years. Had the older man not perfected the art of inscrutability, his face would have mirrored his shock at both his nephew's appearance and the startling determination of his demands.

Gone was the drab attire Owen had affected during the years under Oliver Cromwell, the sober gray worsted of Puritan unpretension. Instead he looked the caricature of an arrogant cavalier in jewel-red pantaloons and coat topped by a lacy collar. Even his abundant brown hair was now long and fancifully curled. However, it was the expression of angry authority that captured the wary attention of the alert lawyer. Owen Penley had never before displayed an iota of initiative.

"I'm looking for your granddaughter, Uncle. Is she here?"

"I wouldn't know, Nephew. I just arrived home."

"I'm aware of that, Uncle Ephraim. I've been waiting for you in Plymouth for eight days. I wanted you to know that I'm charging her with theft before I report her crime officially."

While his voice remained calm, Ephraim's eyes narrowed. "Suppose you tell me the precise details of this alleged theft, Owen."

"Twenty months ago when she deserted her post as caretaker of Penley Farm, I took over the management. If I hadn't, there would have been no estate left by the time I inherited."

Leaning back in his chair, Ephraim stared at his nephew in disbelief. "On what grounds did you presume such insolence? Until my death, Penley Farm is my property, and my granddaughter had my full permission to run it as she saw fit. As for the desertion you accuse her of, 'twas a five-month absence to take care of her mother and grandmother."

"She went there to sell the house and to pocket the money!"

" 'Twas hers to sell, the inheritance from my wife. Since she was of age, she did not need my consent."

"She sold more than the house, she sold the furniture and jewelry too; and those were Penley, part of the inheritance I was counting on. Right after she sold out, I contacted your goldsmith in London, and he informed me that you were bankrupt. I'd say your scheming granddaughter did a thorough job of—"

"You audacious ass! My personal accounts had naught to do with the entailment of Penley Farm. 'Twas not Trelynn who squandered my money. Indeed, what little I have left is the result of her shrewd husbandry. Is that the extent of your charges against her?''

"Nay, Uncle, you're not the only one with access to legal protection. My petition is limited to what I can prove. When I moved my family into the manor, I took a careful inventory of everything on the property. Among the most valuable assets were the cattle; forty-four trained bullocks, twenty productive cows, and a bull. Since the farm did not need all of those bullocks, I advertised forty of them for sale. That was when some of the tenants became surly and uncooperative, and at least one of those traitors informed Sir Bevil Trevor of my intentions. The next day that meddlesome fool and that murderous half-wit you hired as your granddaughter's companion moved every head of cattle to Trevor land, and I was informed they would remain there until the bitch returned from London. When she did, she moved into one of the Trevor cottages with the half-wit."

"And with his wife, Polly," Ephraim inserted dryly. "Tell me, Nephew, did your wife's brother help you prepare these charges against my granddaughter?"

Discomfited by his uncle's caustic smile, Owen hesitated before he responded. "Aye, he did, but without malice. He even offered to wed the overgrown jade."

"Rad Pollock made the same offer seven years ago when she was fifteen, just after his first wife died from overwork. You've been gulled, Nephew. Rad Pollock knows the history of those cattle; and like you, he covets that bull, which is easily the most valuable in the county. Had Trelynn been witless enough to marry Pollock, you'd have discovered that she owns the cattle, every head of it; and you'd have discovered that your brother-in-law wouldn't have let you keep so much as a calf. My granddaughter raised that bull after her heifer died birthing it."

"But you bought that heifer out of estate funds."

"Not so, nephew. Ten years ago, on her twelfth birthday, Sir Bevil Trevor gave her three heifers already bred to his prize bull. Since then she's sold off thirty bullocks and fifty cows. Had you asked her, I'm certain she'd have shown you her record books.''

Owen Penley was silent for a moment, his eyes narrowed in calculating thought before he demanded, ''What did she do with the money?''

''That was the same question Rad Pollock asked me three years ago after his second wife died in childbirth.'' Ephraim smiled broadly and added in a voice as dry as autumn leaves, ''The Pollocks are a greedy lot and not above deception if they can gain from it. Have you told me all of your calamitous news yet, Nephew?''

Owen's hesitation was longer this time and characterized by an odd tension that had been lacking earlier. ''I had naught to do with the other petition that's already been laid before the Stannary Court in Truro.''

''Concerning Trelynn?''

''Aye. It charges her with five counts of witchcraft. I tried to deny those charges, Uncle, but I was voted down.''

Ephraim's expression no longer reflected bland contempt, and his voice was sharp with concern. So it was that cursed witchcraft petition that had driven his granddaughter into flight. For a thousand years that cruel charge had been used to destroy social misfits by superstitious Christians who practiced little Christianity!

''Your Pollock in-laws were the ones who voted you down?'' he asked.

''There were a dozen others there, mostly hill folk who reported that she'd been acting queerly for years.''

Ephraim took a deep breath, his earlier weariness forgotten. ''What are the specific charges, Owen?''

''First there's that bull. They said it acts as gentle as a lamb when she's near and follows her around like a pet dog. And 'tis said that many a witch used a bull as her familiar, especially in Cornwall.''

''And the other charges?''

"They said she speaks the ancient tongue."

"Many Cornishmen still use that language."

"Aye, but she was heard using it at the old dolmen in our hills."

"That ugly little monolith on Trevor land? God's wounds, Owen! Every Trevor and Penley child for the past hundred years has played around that spot, yourself included."

" 'Twas three years ago and she wasn't a child, Uncle."

"You said there were five charges. What are the other three?"

"That she was stronger than an ordinary mortal woman. Two of the Tamar ferrymen attested to that. They said that during a crossing four years ago when one of them attempted a harmless kiss, she knocked them both into the water with those clubs of hers."

"Those two men were convicted of that assault and sentenced to a year at Bridewell. 'Twas no harmless kiss they intended, 'twas robbery and rape. They had already bound and gagged the stockman who'd accompanied Trelynn to Devon where the bull had been hired to service a pair of cows."

"One of them testified the bull obeyed her command to keep them from climbing back on their own ferry. They had to swim for it."

"And the fourth charge?"

"That she was twice seen dancing around a bonfire with a band of roaming tinkers on Holy Rood Day last spring and at All Hallow's last November eve."

"Who were the witnesses to those remarkable celebrations, Owen?"

Unwillingly the younger man responded, "Sid Pollock, Rad's younger son, both times and his brother Jabe, too, in November."

"Which of the Pollocks leveled the fifth charge?"

"That one's not so important."

"What is it?"

"That after she moved to Trevor land, she put a curse on my wife's kitchen garden and killed every plant."

"When was that?"

"Two months ago."

"That would be in March when Cornish frost burns every seedling planted by fools who don't know farming. Tell me, Owen, does your wife think she'll be the one to profit if Trelynn is convicted on these trumped-up charges? And do you believe you'll get the cattle back as well as Trelynn's money?"

"I told you I voted against the proceedings," the accused man shouted.

"Aye, you told me. How did our tenants accept the news of Trelynn's witchcraft?"

"All but two of them packed up and moved out and went to live on Trevor land. The thieves stole all of the tools and equipment too, leaving the smithy empty and the mill all but a useless hull. There's not a beehive or a rabbit hutch or a chicken coop left on our property."

Ephraim laughed sardonically. "You fool, didn't you read the tenancy papers? Those people agreed to pay a set amount for rent and a set percentage of their earnings, but the tools and equipment belonged to them. They were among the best tenants in the valley, and Bevil Trevor has been after some of them for years. When the main farm wasn't being worked, the Spragues' mill almost supported the entire estate."

" 'Tis no laughing matter, Uncle; the farm is still your responsibility."

"Not any more. I've decided that you can have your inheritance early, and I wish you well. But when you and your wife give evidence against your cousin at the Stannary Court, remember that Cornishmen rarely forgive family disloyalty. Remember also that your cousin is a Trevor and that your Trevor neighbors will never forget an injury done to one of their own.

"You're a bloody damn fool, Owen. Do you really

think the other mine owners trust the Pollocks any more than I do? Or that they'll ever convict a Trevor? Those tin miners are political survivors like the rest of us. Since our return to a monarchy, the cavaliers now rule the nation; and the Trevors are among this county's most important links to royal favor. Did you sign the petition?''

"No."

"Did your wife?"

"She's a woman of strong religious convictions."

"So was Judas! Your new suit is very becoming, Owen; but I doubt you'll ever be able to afford another like it. Before I leave the area, I'll drop by to pick up the rest of my personal belongings and Trelynn's too. That list will include all of the Trench-marked pewter plates, the sets of silver bowls and goblets, the French china, and most of the finer furnishings. Those belonged to my wife and are now a part of Trelynn's inheritance. Our ancestors were a much humbler folk. Good day, Nephew."

Oddly, Ephraim experienced a momentary bleakness as he watched Owen leave the house far less confidently than he'd entered. The last of the Penleys, the lawyer mused as he contemplated the vagaries of nature. Why did some family lines flourish and others shrivel? Once one of the dominant clans of Cornwall with scores of proud men leading in battle and winning in sports, the Penleys were now reduced to one tired old lawyer and a morally depleted nephew. Wearily Ephraim settled back in the uncomfortably stiff chair and rested his elbows on the wooden arms, his hands templed together and his brows knit in thought. He was, by no means, as confident as he'd sounded in the dressing-down he'd administered to Owen.

Witchcraft had never been an easy charge to disprove; not even impartial juries were completely free from the primitive fear of the supernatural. Politically, too, it was an explosive issue. Cornwall still had entrenched strongholds of Covenant-like religious zealots who'd welcome a chance to shout their exhortations from the pulpit. And God knows, Trelynn was different enough from other women to have aroused masculine jealousy and suspicion. At twenty-two she was far beyond the preferred age for marriage, she was as tall as most men, and she possessed an intimidating boldness. She was also annoyingly successful in the farm business, an oversetting sin few men could forgive. He glanced up in time to intercept Trelynn's cynical smile; he hadn't heard her enter the room. As always, she moved with the surefooted swiftness of a sleek athlete.

"Owen didn't tell you all the charges, Grandfa," she murmured. "I'm accused of surviving the plague when thousands of people didn't; and Owen's goodie wife stopped just short of insisting I had caused it."

"God's wounds, lass, did you attend that cursed meeting?"

"Nay, but one of our tenants did. It was also recorded that I order Red Penny to sire more bull calves than heifers, and that I'd hexed Owen's wife so that she'd bear naught but two daughters. Do you really believe you can refute such *legal* evidence in a court of Cornishmen who still believe in the magic tales of the old people?"

"I doubt any but the Pollocks would vote to condemn you."

"I already am condemned, Grandfa. You can't stop rumor any more than you can dam the Tamar River. So 'tis the colonies for me where I hope to have neighbors other than Pollocks and Trevors."

"Bevil Trevor has been good to you, lass."

"I know he has, but he disapproves of me as much as Rad Pollock does."

Silently Ephraim studied his granddaughter's face, seeking some sign of the flirtatious hypocrisy most women assume when they seek compliments. But her composed features reflected nothing but cynical resignation. Because she'd inherited none of her mother's arch prettiness or her grandmother's classic beauty, she considered herself unattractive. Ephraim sighed. How could an old man who'd never mastered the social grace of flattery ever convince a skeptical realist that hers was an ancient beauty that needed no artifice? That her heavy dark hair did not need to be tortured into a cascade of artificial curls to be alluring? That her deep brown eyes, heavily fringed beneath black upswept brows, hinted of a long forgotten mysticism? 'Twas no wonder it had been easy for Edith Pollock Penley and her brother to raise the dread specter of witchcraft. Trelynn's face bore no sign of sanctimonious Puritanism and not a trace of feminine reticence. Ephraim knew from experience that her mobile lips could curl with instant scorn and defiance when she was asked to obey some illogical dictum of the commonwealth enforcers. Those same lips could express an inner amusement that had irritated her elders on innumerable occasions, just as it did now when she recalled him sharply to the business at hand.

"You're woolgathering again, Grandfa, and you're letting your fondness for me interfere with good thinking. You've been in the new world too long where people have better things to do with their time. But in England for the past twenty years, women accused of witchcraft were the favorite targets of busybody preachers and enforcers escaping their own little bugbears of boredom and bamboozling. 'Tis true the English churches were more civilized—they merely ordered the poor wretches hanged or thrown into Newgate—but the Scot Covenanters tortured them to death. And the charges against most of those women were seldom as damning as the ones against me."

"Aye, but we can prove yours false, lass."

"In court perhaps, but nowhere else. After I first returned to Cornwall, Owen's wife wouldn't let me have my clothing, so I had to wear the black dresses I'd used in London even when I worked on Sir Bevil's farm. People were already muttering then. 'Tis the way I look, Grandfa, like a half-wild Welshwoman or a female hunter from the early days before the Normans. I've seen the faces on the old tapestries at the Trevor keep, and even Sir Bevil noted the resemblance.''

''I wouldn't have thought you'd have worn black, especially for your mother. She failed you as a mother when she put you out to nurse even as a newborn babe.''

''Most everyone was wearing black in London during those days, Grandfa; but I guess it was partly for my mother. I felt sorry for her even though she could be annoying; she had absolutely nothing in her life that was important, and she was so pathetically vain.''

''What about your grandmother?''

''I wish I'd known her when I was a little girl. Nothing I said or did shocked her. I guess she was the wittiest person I ever knew.''

''Lass, did she tell you why she and Lavinia didn't leave the city before the plague spread?''

''When Jem and I first got there, I tried to get them all to leave with me, but my mother refused. I think she believed that the plague was limited to the slum people. As for grandmother, I think she'd been too ill to travel for months. She joked about it, of course, and said that her good-luck charm warned her to stay right there in bed. Just before she died, she gave it to me and told me that if I never lost my courage, it would bring me the same good luck it had brought her.''

''Do you wear it, lass?''

''Nay, Grandfa, I don't believe in such things. I plan to make my own luck; but I'll keep it safe anyway. 'Tis the only remembrance I have of her.''

''Did you have to spend much of your own money to support them while you were there?''

''Some, but I wouldn't finance my mother's gambling or buy her a dress she wanted; she had too many of them already stuffed into clothespresses, and enough pairs of slippers to shoe half of London.''

''I'd left them well supplied with funds, Trelynn.''

''I know you did, but my mother and her cousin Nadine

went to the gaming places as often as they could. As far as I could tell, neither of them ever won anything. A funny thing, Grandfa . . . when I sold all of Mother's, Nadine's, and Grandmother's clothing, the woman in the shop told me that my mother had been her most extravagant customer and that she was known as one of the most reckless gamers in London. But she said that my grandmother almost always won, so mayhap the amulet did work for her."

"How much money do you have all told, Trelynn?"

"I have a little over four thousand pounds, Grandfa. The other four thousand is for you, and 'tis locked in that strongbox just behind you. If Owen hadn't cheated me, I'd have more; but he sold four of my bullocks before Sir Bevil could stop him. Most of it, though, I got back. I took half of the seed grain from Penley Farm and enough fodder to feed my cattle until we reach Connecticut."

"If you'll take my advice, lass, you'll not be going to Connecticut. Instead you'll be settling in Rhode Island where I've two small farms and good friends. 'Twill be a much better place for you because the people there are guaranteed more freedom, and you'll not be so criticized because you're a lone woman."

"I told you, Grandfa, that I wouldn't be alone. Besides Jem and Polly, two of the Spragues and their wives will also be working for me. There's something else, Grandfa. Sir Bevil expects me to settle on or near his property in Connecticut."

"What property?"

"When King Charles II gave his brother James the whole of New York and New Jersey to pay off the royal family's debts, the border between New York and Connecticut was still in dispute. The parcel awarded to Sir Bevil turned out to be in Connecticut between the Housatonic River and the border."

"That's wilderness, Trelynn, thirty miles from the nearest settlement and already peopled by Iroquois Indians. You can't settle there without thirty or forty people to defend you."

"So far there's only fourteen of us."

"I count only seven. Who are the others?"

"Sir Bevil asked that I let him explain to you."

Ephraim regarded his evasive granddaughter sternly. "You'll be telling me now, girl, if you expect my help."

"They're seven indentureds Sir Bevil wants out of England."

"Volunteers or criminals?"

"The four men are from Newgate, the three women from Bridewell. When they were charged six months ago, Sir Bevil's lawyers saved them from the steps and strings by pleading for indenture."

With his eyes narrowed to thoughtful slits, Ephraim nodded slowly. "Then they'll be Cornishmen, and the charge most likely was smuggling. At least, I hope to God they weren't accused of wrecking. Devious though he is, I don't believe that Bevil would subject you to that breed of foul criminal. Did he swear that these prisoners had naught to do with luring ships to their doom off Cornish and Scilly cliffs, girl?"

"Of course, he did; and you know full well that wreckers are never given the choice of indenture. If they aren't killed on the spot where they're taken, they're hanged and often quartered right after they're convicted. These men had worked for Sir Bevil—he admitted as much. Because he was a Royalist, the Commonwealth taxed him almost out of existence until he organized a band of smugglers who earned enough to save his estate and a bit beyond, I imagine."

"Who are the women?"

"The wives of three of them captured at the same time in a house near Falmouth."

"And the fourth man?"

"Sir Bevil said he'd surrendered himself after the others were taken and claimed he'd been the one responsible."

"I don't like it, lass. The Trevor estates were cleared seven years ago by the time Charles took the throne. Why would Bevil have remained in the precarious business of smuggling?"

"Why wouldn't he? Half the gentry of Cornwall have engaged in smuggling throughout the centuries."

"Have you met these men yet?"

"Not yet. Sir Bevil paid for their indenture and took care of transporting them to the ship at the same time he paid to have my cattle boarded."

"Did he say why he didn't ship those convicts to your father in Virginia? Royce Trevor is a relative, after all."

" 'Twas the first thing I asked him, Grandfa, but he said he didn't trust my father."

"I suppose he named me as the responsible holder of their indenture papers?"

"Aye, and I agreed. I didn't think you'd mind, and we will be getting ten years of free labor."

"We will if they don't escape and return to smuggling in the colonies or to buccaneering. I'll not let you go into the wilderness with people like these, Trelynn. You'll be staying on my farm on Aquidneck Island in Rhode Island where I've friends enough to protect you until I get there. And I'll be sending those friends a complete report on every person in your party, yourself included. As I told you before, there's religious freedom in that colony so there'll be no witch-hunting or any such nonsense to worry about. The man you'll report to your first day there lives on the farm next to mine, and I expect you to listen to his advice. I'll write those letters right after supper."

"I can't stay that long, Grandfa. Jem's waiting for me with Red Penny on a farm outside of town. Meg knows where, and she can get those letters to me."

"I'll take you there myself."

"Nay, Grandfa. You'd best stay right here and play the innocent bystander when Owen's in-laws come looking for me. I wouldn't want to shock the constable by telling him that I'd rather be tried as a witch than marry Rad Pollock.''

"Pollock made the offer even after the petition?"

"He visited Sir Bevil twice with the proposition. He claimed that he'd be taking me to a Pollock plant station south of the James River in Virginia. Is there such a farm, do you know?"

" 'Twas a good-size block of land granted to the family fifteen years ago by the Commonwealth in payment for services rendered during the civil war. Four Pollock men died fighting for Oliver Cromwell at the battle of Edgehill in '42. But so far that land has not been developed, and 'tis said not to be good farmland. Did Bevil urge you to accept Pollock's offer?"

"Anything but. 'Twas just after Rad's second visit that Sir Bevil decided I'd need protection here as well as in the colonies. That same night he barged me and all my cattle down the Tamar River and arranged passage for the lot of us."

"Trelynn, there's much I don't like about all this secret planning. In my opinion, you'd be wiser to remain here and stand trial. I'm certain the charges would be dropped if I explained the circumstances, and then you'd not be labeled a fugitive."

"Can't you clear my name without my testimony?"

"Not as easily. Are any of the charges true?"

"I speak the Brythonic tongue whenever I visit the old places, because I believe the ancients and their religion were as civilized as we are."

"Don't ever admit that in public, not even in Rhode Island. Many liberal Christian folk prefer to believe all other religions are heathen. Were you near either of those tinkers' bonfires?"

"On All Hallow's Eve I was. So were Sir Bevil and his son Averill and half the servants from Trevor manor. But I haven't seen a Holy Rood celebration since I was a child."

"Were any of the Pollocks present?"

"They might have been, there were crowds of people there. Grandfa, the whole thing is nonsense, but I'll not be risking my life by staying here. I don't trust Owen, and I didn't like the look on his face when he left. 'Tis dark enough now, so 'tis safe for me to leave. I'd like it mightily if you'd decide to quit this worn-out old land and join me in Rhode Island. But if you can't, I don't want you worrying about me. I plan to survive however I can. At least, I'll never be the abused old maid I would be if I were forced to live with Owen's family."

For the next two hours Ephraim noted little of the bustle about the house as Meg and the adenoidal young factotum she had hired as an all-purpose helper unpacked his luggage. Absently, he sipped the wine he was served at supper and toyed with the untempting food, his thoughts in an unaccustomed whirl of indecision. Abruptly he left the table to rummage through the contents of his strongbox until he located the deeds to his Rhode Island farms. Trelynn was right, she'd be safer in the colonies; the more he thought about Owen's evasiveness, the more he distrusted his nephew. With renewed determination, Ephraim began to write, filling one page after another with his meticulous analysis and explanation. He'd completed three letters when his housekeeper's querulous voice interrupted his concentration.

"Ye'll no' be gettin' those letters to the lass tonight, Squire Penley. There's been a pair of constables watchin' the house—front and back—for the past hour."

"Did my granddaughter get away safely?"

"She's too slippery for the likes of those lumpish clod-pates to catch, but puir Willy wouldn't ha' the wit to gi' them the slip. And ye're too overset to go traipsin' about that open country at night."

Alarmed about the degree of official caution, Ephraim drummed his fingers restlessly on the table, then paused to ask abruptly, "Meg, do you know if Sir Bevil Trevor is still in town?"

"If he's the one who's been by here every day askin' for ye, he is. And as nervous as a prinked-up bride he was today. Said to tell ye to meet him at Drakes Inn soon as ye caught yer breath."

"Why the devil didn't you tell me earlier, woman?"

"Didn't think 'twas important compared to the young mistress's troubles."

" 'Tis all one and the same problem, Meg," Ephraim sighed, his earlier optimism forgotten.

Bundled up in his heavy cape, he left the house minutes later, announced pleasantly to the constable that he was taking his regular evening constitutional and strode rapidly to Drakes Inn on the outskirts of the dock area of town. A secure haven for monied travelers, the imposing square structure was built around a cobbled carriage court with its gated entrance well guarded by armed doormen. Before Ephraim could pull the bell cord, a servant stepped from the shadows and stayed his hand.

"His lairdship is expecting you, Squire Penley; but 'tis best we not arouse the others. There's been a constable posted here for days, and the head constable himself arrived an hour ago. You're to follow me, sir, through the postern gate and up the back way."

As upsetting as the servant's greeting was to the weary lawyer, Sir Bevil Trevor's was grim to the point of desperation.

"Thank God, you've come, Ephraim. If we hurry, we just might save your granddaughter and that rapscallion young son of mine from being hanged on the same gallows."

CHAPTER
2

Had there been any witnesses near and about the darkened Drakes Inn that night, they might have been amused to see two old men huffing and puffing as they ran after a pair of servants bearing torches. Their amusement, however, would have quickly turned into curiosity had they seen those old men board a hooded coach waiting for them five hundred feet away. If, perchance, such witnesses had been a patrol of soldiers from the massive fort atop the highest hill in Plymouth, there would have been no speculation of any kind, only a sure conviction that if they followed the swift coach pulled by four whip-driven horses, it would lead them to a pair of wanted criminals hiding somewhere in the sparsely populated countryside.

Twenty-four hours earlier in England's westernmost defense post, Henry VIII's proud Citadel erected to fend off any Continental invaders, the commander had been recruited by the combined constabulary of Devon and Cornwall counties to aid in the search for a fugitive murderess reputed to be a dangerous witch. This morning that search had been enlarged to include an escaped convict. Normally, such military intervention was called upon only for the pursuit of gangs of wreckers who operated along the rugged coast of Cornwall and the granite cliffs of the offshore Scilly Islands. In pursuit of the murderous scum who lured ships to their doom with false lights and then killed the hapless sailors, the soldiers were in their proper element as they primed their muskets and waited for the wreckers to return in long boats laden with stolen booty from the sinking ships. Since no one wanted the wreckers taken alive, the soldiers could fire at will until the enemy was exterminated.

But the current search for a single pair of fugitives was a more demanding task for simple soldiers, because they'd been ordered to take these quarries alive. The substantial indenture fee for the man had already been paid, but it would have to be returned if the man were dead. Since the needy royal government disliked the loss of any income, the man was to be taken without an injury that might reduce his ability to work. In the case of the woman, there were additional restraints. Superstitious countrymen believed in the dark powers of witchcraft, but the authorities had learned to be more cautious. This rumored witch was a member of the powerful Trevor family and under the protection of Sir Bevil Trevor himself. Even more inhibiting to the searchers was the official suspicion that the evidence against the woman was not plausible enough for a conviction.

Ten days earlier the owner of a Pollock mine in the northwestern stretch of the Tamar River valley had been found beaten to death a short distance from the entrance to his mine. In the first report issued by a local constable, suspicion was concentrated on one or more miners who'd been laid off without receiving their wages. The ancient tin mine, which had been in operation for hundreds of years, was almost played out and for fifty years had required the use of deep and unsafe tunneling. Thus, it seemed reasonable to the original investigator that men who'd not been paid for the dangerous work would be angry enough to kill the owner.

The following day, however, a small contingent of miners led by Rad Pollock, the brother of the dead man, made claim that a local woman, recently accused of witchcraft by the neighborhood, was the real perpetrator. Somewhat skeptically, the constable agreed to interrogate the woman, said to be living on the Trevor estate. Not until he found both her and Sir Bevil Trevor unaccountably missing did he attach any significance to the accusation of her guilt.

Since the Tamar River emptied into Plymouth Harbor, the search spread from Cornwall to Devon County and to the port of Plymouth itself. The official fear then became dual in nature; there were a dozen ships preparing to depart for the American and Caribbean colonies. At the insistence of the powerful Massachusetts Bay Company, a search was ordered of all ships. The stern Puritan theocrats who ruled the most populous colony in the new world wanted no woman suspected of trafficking with the devil to arrive as a colonist. Because a witchcraft trial had already been calendared for the next session of the Stannary Court of Cornwall, the search for Trelynn Trevor was intensified, and the military conscripted as the hunters.

Oddly enough, when the pursuit shifted from rural Cornwall to the more sophisticated Plymouth, no mention was made of a Devon breed bull reputed to be the witch's familiar. Nor did the Cornish constabulary report that she was the granddaughter of Ephraim Penley, an important government official well-known in Plymouth. Only after Rad Pollock and Owen Penley informed the authorities of these and other specifics, did the search include the cottage Ephraim Penley used as headquarters upon his return from abroad.

In the securely enclosed cab of the speeding Trevor coach, Ephraim listened quietly to Bevil's account of the murder of John Pollock and the subsequent accusation leveled against Trelynn.

"I'd hoped your nephew would have the courage to tell you, Ephraim, but it seems he's lost what little decency he had," Bevil concluded.

"I'm angriest that my granddaughter didn't trust me enough," his companion responded tersely.

"She knows nothing about the murder or the increased jeopardy she faces. On neither of his insolent visits to my estate would I allow that blackguard Pollock to see her. The first time he tried to blackmail me into permitting her to accompany him to Virginia by using the witchcraft petition; but the second time he was more subtle. He told me about his brother's murder and hinted that there'd been reliable witnesses. I knew it was only a matter of time before that cursed Roundhead or one of his weasely sons accused Trelynn. In a way, though, Pollock's sly warning may have saved your granddaughter's life; certainly it spared her from being taken into custody by the Plymouth constabulary.

"Except for Trelynn and the mute and the bull, everything and everyone else were already aboard two of the three ships waiting in Plymouth Harbor. Since one of the barges had returned to my estate, we'd planned to follow the others to those same ships that night. If we had, we'd have been stopped and searched as soon as we reached the harbor. Fortunately, I own a farm, tenanted by a man I've trusted often in the past, that's located just northwest of Saltash. We pulled the barge ashore there the next morning and went to the farm; my men and I returned to the barge with two wagonloads of ship's provender. Two hours later at Plymouth we were boarded and searched. That was eight days ago."

"Where was Trelynn?"

"Well hidden at the farm and busily employed turning Red Penny from a devon red into one of those queer Holland breeds. My friend's wife is an expert in the disguise of animals. I recall a time some years back when the Roundhead soldiery was close enough on our heels to have marked the colors of our horses. Within two hours Ellen Wadley had lampblacked or chalked those four bays so expertly that the soldiers rode past them without a backward glance.''

Irritated by his friend's garrulous digression, Ephraim snapped curtly, ''Disguised or not, that cursed bull would trap Trelynn. Both Owen and Rad Pollock know it too well not to recognize it and the way it follows my granddaughter around like a pet dog.''

Bevil Trevor chuckled. ''To tell you the truth, Ephraim, 'tis almost as friendly to me. I sometimes wonder at masculine conceit that male animals are always said to be the fiercer. Red Penny is the finest breeder in Cornwall; and its get—bullock or cow—is a gentle, tractable creature. When Captain Vinson—his ship's the one taking the cattle to America, and incidentally, I'm half-owner of all three of the ships—when Vinson refused to have a bull as a passenger, I brought him to the farm. He was hand-feeding Red Penny within the hour.''

Wearily Ephraim returned the conversation once again to his central worry. ''I still say Trelynn will be safer if the bull remains here.''

''The bull and Jem both are already aboard,'' Bevil retorted smugly. ''As soon as we heard that your ship was only a day out, I secreted Trelynn aboard my coach and brought her to your home. The constables weren't picketed there until late this afternoon after your nephew reported to the head constable that Trelynn had not yet contacted you.''

''How would you know that?''

''One of my men is quite familiar with the Plymouth gaolhouse; he's spent a goodly amount of time there. With your granddaughter safely hidden in your home last night, Jem transported the bull by wagon to the barge and eventually to the *Tamarlind*.''

"Then why in the devil didn't you send word to Trelynn? Why did you let her return to the farm when there was no need? It seems to me that she's in greater danger now than—" Ephraim stopped abruptly in the mdddle of his angry castigation and stared at his companion. "I just remembered the second half of the remarkable greeting you gave me tonight. Just how did one of your sons become a wanted convict? When I was last in England, both Averill and Bourke had left off sowing wild oats and settled down to responsible prosperity."

Sir Bevil Trevor's response was harshly spoken. "I have a third son, Ephraim."

"The story I heard was that your youngest son was drowned seven or eight years ago when the ship he was on went down mid-channel. If I recall the details correctly, only three crew members reached English soil to tell the tale."

"Neither the ship nor Charles Clay was lost. The captain—Peter Vinson's name was David Farnell in those days—had received word before he left Calais that the Commonwealth authorities had labeled him a pirate and condemned him and his crew in absentia. Three of his most trusted men were put aboard a longboat three miles out from Dover, and the story they told was accepted as true. They claimed that they'd been kidnapped after their merchant ship had been sunk by the pirates, and that, in revenge, they had scuttled the pirate ship and escaped.

"David Farnell changed his name to Peter Vinson and had his ship refitted in Bordeaux where he received permission to register it as a French merchantman. Three years ago I purchased half interest in the ship and registered it as English under the name of *Tamarlind*."

"Had this Vinson been a pirate?"

"Before the Commonwealth, he'd been a respected privateer with royal letters of marque from the king; after the war he became a smuggler."

"What about your son?"

"Ephraim, you were overseas throughout most of the civil war, so you don't really know how it was for those of us who fought against the Roundheads. After those bloated fools executed the king, they all but taxed the rest of us out of existence. We survived as best we could. I'm certain you know how. It was the same business half the disfranchised Cavaliers of England plied. We smuggled in the wine and brandy even the moderate Puritans craved. I was more successful than most, because I had the Tamar River outside my door and enough hiding places on the estate to conceal a ship's full cargo. 'Twas a family business, Ephraim, even for Charles Clay, who was only twelve when we began; but he quickly proved to be my most talented son."

"Spare me your family history, Bevil. What happened to him after the channel thing?"

"He changed his name to James Thayne and remained with Vinson for two years in honest merchanting, but that life quickly palled for him. With two friends equally adventuresome, he returned to smuggling; and until his friends became careless, they were highly successful. During his absence, they were caught in his Falmouth home with the smuggled goods that had been their share of the final raid. Quixotically, my son swaggered into court during their trial and announced that they were innocent dupes and that he was the only smuggler. They were all condemned equally, and I was damned lucky to get their sentences commuted from death to indenture. But Charles—James Thayne he is now—was as difficult as always in his choice of master.

"When your granddaughter decided to immigrate to the colonies, I informed him that his options were now limited to one—he would serve his ten years as Trelynn's servant and learn farming. He agreed only if the other members of his . . . his group were identically indentured. So I paid for the lot of them in your name. Five days ago they were brought to Plymouth in chains and placed aboard the

Tamarlind with thirty other convicts. Two hundred more were imprisoned aboard my third ship to be transported to Jamaica—that commitment was one of the penalties I had to pay for my son's life.''

Irritably Ephraim interrupted his friend's rambling monologue once again. ''Why was your son allowed to leave the *Tamarlind*?''

''He was the only one I could trust to smuggle the bull aboard; Jem could never have managed alone. Last night Charles Clay accomplished that mission before he returned to the farm to wait for Trelynn. But this morning his luck ran out. The military had been recruited to aid in the search for your granddaughter, and soldiers were placed aboard every ship in the harbor to prevent her escape by sea. When the sergeant aboard the *Tamarlind* inspected the indentured convicts, he discovered that my son—that James Thayne was missing.

''Captain Vinson left his ship immediately and reported to me at Drakes Inn. There we devised a plan that might solve Trelynn's and my son's problems permanently. Since the sergeant announced that unless you, as the responsible owner, came aboard to take charge, the other six would be returned to Newgate and called down—resentenced to hanging—we had to act immediately. Right after we warn Trelynn and my son, we'll pick up your gear and report to the *Tamarlind*, which will sail on tomorrow's tide.''

''Good God, man, I have to report three years of colonial statistics to Parliament within the month. I'll be as much a fugitive as your son if I fail in that duty.''

''Hear me out, Ephraim. We'll be sailing only as far as the north Cornwall coast where the *Tamarlind* will be anchored offshore from a cove that Charles Clay knows well from his smuggling days. In a week or more, Vinson will send a longboat ashore to wait for my son and Trelynn, who'll have walked across the better half of Cornwall. 'Tis the only way they'll escape the trap set for them, the mounted patrols that will be scouring the countryside once the hunt begins in earnest. By walking at night on rocky trails where horses can't travel, they'll be safe enough; and the parents of one of the indentured men live along the way, so they'll have food. If Trelynn were a delicate lass, it might not be possible; but she's a strong, resourceful woman.''

"What happens if they do reach the ship?"

"Vinson will take you and me to Bristol where the coach will be waiting to convey us to London."

"I wasn't thinking about my own safety, Bevil. My granddaughter and your son will still be listed as fugitives in the colonies the same as here."

"Not if Trelynn agrees to the rest of my plan. 'Tis possible that both she and Charles Clay will be free from any suspicion when they land in Connecticut."

"Trelynn will not be going to your property in Connecticut; 'tis still a primitive wilderness along the Housatonic River. She'll be going to Rhode Island and staying on my farm on Aquidneck Island. I suppose the others will have to remain there too. Now, tell me the rest of your remarkable pl—. Why has the coach stopped, Bevil?"

"We're waiting for the ferry to take us cross river. You can relax, Ephraim, the ferryman is another friend of mine."

"I'm beginning to think Cornwall is run by and for smugglers."

"I've not been one since the Restoration," Bevil demurred quietly before he continued his earlier explanation. "If Trelynn agrees, within the month the Tamar Valley witch will have become nothing but a ghostly fugitive on Bodmin Moor."

"Not if I'm successful in clearing the charges against her."

"You'll be legally successful given enough time, I've not a doubt. The witchcraft thing is a cock-a-hoop piece of trumpery, and our local constables will eventually locate the miners who killed John Pollock. But think, man, you'll never be able to clear her reputation of suspicion; and I'll wager you that the Puritans in Massachusetts and the other northern colonies are as quick to hunt down witches as their sanctimonious relatives here."

Tacitly agreeing to the gloomy prediction, Ephraim slumped tiredly against the cushions and listened quietly as Bevil talked.

"I blame myself for my son's unenviable position, but I have an idea that will return his dignity at least. Ephraim, I recall that thirty-odd years ago, your youngest brother left Cornwall bound for the Caribbean."

"Joseph died in Jamaica three years later."

"Aye, but 'tis logical that he may have left a son behind. You need another nephew, Ephraim, one who'll be a bit more of a man than the craven Owen. The one I've chosen for you will be named Clay Penley. Clayton was my father's name, so at least part of my son will remain a Trevor. If you're willing to commit a considerable amount of forgery, my son will be a free man in the colonies."

"Unfortunately, the system's more complicated, Bevil. The colonials count all incoming criminal indentureds very carefully; they'll expect to find a James Thayne among them."

"Already taken into consideration. One of Vinson's crew will act the part until the *Tamarlind* leaves. Then Clay Penley will announce the escape of one of his paid-for servants; 'tis said that many of them do escape from each shipment."

"Just how is all this flummery going to help my granddaughter?"

"While we're still aboard to act as witnesses, Captain Vinson will perform a private wedding ceremony in his quarters uniting Clay Penley to Lynn Penley—'tis the name she intends to use anyway. On paper, they'll be second cousins so the marriage will be completely legal."

"Good God, man, think of what you're suggesting! Trelynn is a Trevor as much as your son; 'tis too close a relationship. Our mutual grandchildren could well turn out to be two-headed idiots.''

"Not so! By my reckoning, they're only fifth or sixth cousins. Royce Trevor and I had only a great-grandfather in common.''

"But an odd suggestion, nevertheless, Bevil, and not typical of you. You wed both of your older sons to the daughters of titled men more powerful than yourself. Just why would you want the daughter of a commoner for your youngest?''

"Don't waste your clever lawyer's tongue on me, Ephraim. Ask the question that's burning your brain, why should an innocent like Trelynn be linked to a Newgate bird for life?''

"The thought does plague me, Bevil, especially since my granddaughter claims you disapprove of her.''

"She irritates me, 'tis all, because she acts and thinks more like a man than is seemly. Why the devil didn't your daughter ever buy her pretty dresses or slippers that weren't the oxhide boots of farm workers? And all the dresses she's ever owned look like the drabs only rustic grannies wear.''

"My daughter was not a good mother; but Trelynn herself prefers plain clothing. 'Tis another reason I think it best that she seek a husband who isn't quite so used to pretty women in silks and velvets.''

"God's truth, you're blind! If your granddaughter ever discovers how to use that dramatic face of hers and her proud carriage, she'll play hob with any husband's sanity. Even now, when she considers herself naught but a mawkish farmer, she's a damned disturbing woman.''

"And you'd prefer your son to have a more amenable wife?''

"Nay, she may be the only one strong enough to curb his wildness. But neither of them are going to welcome this arrangement unless we insist on it.''

"I know Trelynn won't if she learns he's a Trevor, and I

imagine your son will bristle at her plain speech. A life such as he's led with pretty women a-plenty won't let him settle seriously to a blunt-tongued realist like Trelynn.''

"We're quarreling without purpose, Ephraim. They'll both have to bend to necessity. 'Tis true Char—Clay has nine years more of stubbornness than she has, but perhaps he still has enough gentleness left to protect a woman who's been falsely accused by a pack of greedy hypocrites.''

In view of Bevil Trevor's sincere chivalry and his conviction that men were the destined protectors of women, he would have been appalled by the violent reversal that had occurred an hour earlier near the thatch-roofed byre on the Wadley farm.

As Trelynn had walked over the uneven fields from her grandfather's cottage to the farm, avoiding both beaten paths and roadways and waiting for Sir Bevil's special ferryman before she crossed the Tamar River into Cornwall, she had pondered Owen Penley's performance with Ephraim and wondered what further mischief he had concealed. Usually he was all blustery as he'd been when he accused her of theft. But he'd been reluctant to tell Ephraim about the witchcraft petition, and he'd been holding something else back . . . of that Trelynn was certain!

She knew that her money was his target, just as it had been since the day he and his wife had taken over the farm. In the opinion of Edith Pollock Penley, a spinster cousin had no right to expect anything more than frugal room and board. Stronger willed than her husband, Edith had plotted very skillfully to defeat the stubborn younger woman who stood in her way.

Trelynn shook her head irritably as she glanced around the empty fields dimly visible in the waning moonlight. Beneath the dark gray cloak that fended off the chill wind of early May, her hands gripped the flexible leather loops that allowed her to swing her flails with a well-mastered skill. Grateful for the protection they gave her, she remembered the rabid dog she'd killed when it threatened a calf and the London ruffian she'd struck down when he attempted to rob her. Not so pleasantly, she recalled what her stockman had shouted to her after she'd pushed the two ferrymen into the Tamar River.

"Don' be a bliddy fule, youn' mistress. Push the bliddy murtheres under. Dead men don' tell tales," the frightened farmhand had warned her.

If she'd taken his advice, she thought darkly, she'd have one less charge to face on the witchcraft petition. Shivering suddenly, Trelynn stopped abruptly just outside the stone wall that encircled the feeding yard and the stone byre. Thirty feet from where she stood, a group of horses whinnied nervously, and the young woman stared at them in a dawning awareness. Red Penny was no longer in the byre, else he'd have been bellowing out an angry warning. Horses were the one animal the usually amiable bull distrusted.

More alertly, Lynn looked over toward the shadow-shrouded byre and inhaled sharply. There was a dim glow of light beaming out from the cracked-open doors. Warily she followed the curved fence until she was facing the rear of the byre, and she silently climbed over the four-foot wall. Crouching in the protective dark as close as she dared beside the rear half-door, she listened intently, shuddering with fear and hatred when she recognized the voice of the speaker. It was Owen Penley, and he sounded as peevishly outraged as he had earlier in his uncle's cottage.

"Why the devil didn't your father remember this farm four days ago when we could have captured both the cattle and my damned cousin?"

" 'Twas not Da who learned of it at all, Uncle Owen. 'Twas old Fen and me located it when we followed old Trevor out of Plymouth late yesterday. We lost sight of Trevor on t'other side of the river on account of we dasn't crowd on the same ferry. Old Trevor's got some temper when he's riled. We knew this was the right farm, though, when we seen his high and mighty coach of four leaving here at a tearing speed. I sent old Fen to follow it and see what direction it took and then go tell Da and Jabe we'd located the farm.

"I hid my horse and myself by some trees and settled down to watch. 'Bout an hour later just afore dark I watched two men cart some old bull away in a wagon. Don't jerk so, Uncle Owen. 'Twern't the devon red you're so fond of; 'twas only an ugly old black and white that looked like that Dutch Holstein old man Crothers was always bragging about.''

"Who were the two men, Sid?''

"Figured one was the mute, leastwise he looked like him from where I was hiding. But t'other was the stranger who was with Trevor on the way in. Wasn't no farmhand, though; he was booted in smooth leather and dressed in a coat near as fancy as old Trevor's. Didn't look like an outdoor man at all, pale as dough he was, with a beard that hid his lower face.''

"Why didn't you follow them, Sid?''

" 'Cause I was waiting for Da and Jabe, so's we could search the byre. That's where I figured the devon red would be, and mayhap the witch woman herself. How did you find out about this farm, Uncle Owen?''

"From the constables at the gaolhouse. When I asked if there were any Trevor property nearby, one of them told me about this place.''

"Good thing you didn't bring them back with you; might be hard to explain our being here and all.''

"They won't be coming at all, only soldier patrols that begin tomorrow morning; and they'll be too late to do us any good.''

The coarse, snorting laughter of callow youth greeted the older man's complaint. Crouching deeper into the shadow outside the byre, Trelynn shivered with the thrill of fear. She now knew all of the characters in this sordid drama. The man with Owen was not yet a man, just the younger and more vicious of Rad Pollock's sons, and the Da and Jabe he'd referred to were his father and brother. Even old Fen was no stranger; he was the brutish Pollock stockman whose cruelty to animals had always sickened her. Recalling what Sir Bevil had told her, Trelynn identified the bearded man Pollock's son described as the leader of the indentured convicts, the brazen smuggler who'd surrendered after the others had been captured.

"He's a gentleman, lass," Bevil had said, "so don't you be minding the beard. When he's clean shorn, you'll find him handsome enough."

Why was it, Lynn asked herself, that human worth was so often measured by beauty? She much preferred Polly's blunt evaluation: "Handsome is as handsome does." In the primitive American colonies a man who couldn't work would be as useless as a spavined horse. Straining her ears, Trelynn listened to Sid Pollock's boast delivered between bursts of adenoidal laughter.

"The game's not over yet, Uncle, not by half. We've got the bearded man, and he's trussed up like a market pig with its snout tied shut to stop the squealing. Da and Jabe ran him down when he was returning the wagon here, and old Fen bashed his lights out with a rock. But the bearded devil didn't go down easy—slashed Jabe's leg and both horses with a sword that Da said he used like a soldier."

"Good God, Sid, how did you know he wasn't?"

"Because underneath that fancy coat of his, he was wearing a convict's shirt, the kind they give to indentured bastards about to be shipped overseas. We caught ourselves a prize on account there's always reward money for the return of a convict."

"Is the man still alive?"

"Alive and already come to, though his head's bloodied some. Old Fen's guarding him at t'other end of the byre. 'Twas a good thing I recognized that red suit of yourn when you come sneaking in here a while ago, else your head would be bashed worse than the stranger's.''

"Where are your father and Jabe?"

"In the farmhouse keeping the rustics from giving warning in case Trevor or the Trevor witch comes back tonight.''

"My cousin's no witch, Sid, and you know it; and she didn't kill your Uncle John. You'll be lucky if the tables aren't turned on you during her trial; 'twas you who lied about seeing her all those times.''

Trelynn was barely breathing as she heard Owen's words, the ones he hadn't dared utter in front of her grandfather. Her hands tightened on the thongs of the clubs as the awareness of her peril increased. Uneasily she contemplated reclimbing the wall, but she dared not return to Plymouth, not with both the constabulary and government soldiers searching for her. With the accusation of murder added to witchcraft, she stood little chance of surviving another day. Willing herself to continue listening, she heard Sid Pollock's insolent taunt leveled against his uncle.

"You'd swing on the same gibbet, Uncle, you and Aunt Edith both. You lied same as the rest of us and for the same reason; you want the gold the hard-mouthed bitch has got hid and the cattle. If you weren't afraid of old Ephraim Penley, you'd still be yelling 'witch' same as me; and I ain't so sure she's not one.''

"My uncle is a shrewd lawyer, Sid; like as not, he'll trap you as soon as you take the witness box.''

"Da and me don't plan to do any such thing. That's why we're waiting here for her to show; we're not simpleton enough to go before the Stannary Court—not now!''

The desperation in Owen Penley's voice was clearly discernible to the woman concentrating on his words.

"I thought you Pollocks dominated that court with six of your family members on it.''

"Was six with Uncle John, and he was the one who told

the others how to vote. But they don't trust Da, and they won't have the stomach for family loyalty, not against old Trevor or a slick-tongued lawyer like old Ephraim.''

"Your father will have to attend; he made both accusations to the authorities.''

"Not if he's out of the country, he won't; and that's where we'll be if we catch the slut and locate her money in time. We don't think she'll be so reluctant to wed Da once she learns about the murder charge, and Da reckons she's got at least a thousand guineas salted away.''

"She has much more than that," Owen amended grimly, "but the question is where. Did you get a chance to search this byre? If this is where she's been for the past week, chances are she hid it here.''

"If 'tis here, Uncle Owen, we won't be sharing it with you. Da says we'll need every gold coin of it to get the farm started in Virginia.''

"The devil you say! I have more legal claim to it than you do.''

Having heard all she wanted of an acrimonious falling out of thieves, Trelynn made her way stealthily around the stone byre and into the yard where the horses moved uneasily about. If two of the five had actually been sword slashed, it should prove easy to panic them into terrified action. With a fierceness born of desperation, she brought her flails down harshly on the first two rumps, striking the nose of a third and the withers of a fourth before one animal screamed in pain. Grimly, she listened to Sid Pollock's startled shout, "Get out and see to those damned horses, Fen, afore they arouse the countryside.''

Standing motionless beside the calmest of the beasts, Trelynn waited. Old Fen had been the only man inside the byre she'd feared; he had to be rendered unconscious before she could settle with the other two. The only possible confederate she had on this lonely stretch of Cornish moor was the bearded convict held prisoner in one of the byre stalls. With her eyes adjusted to the dim moonlight, she watched the shambling half-run of the Pollock stockman as he approached. Both of her clubs landed simultaneously on his head, and she stood without remorse as he crumpled to the dark earth. At that moment she felt herself precisely what she'd been called—a murderous witch. Kneeling swiftly down beside the still body, she was almost regretful that it still breathed. With the kerchief yanked from around his neck, she gagged his lax mouth, then bound his hands and feet with leather bridle straps removed from the horses. More thoughtfully now, she led one of the animals through the gate into open pasture and watched with satisfaction as the others followed. They'd not be caught again until morning.

The other two men proved easy targets. She tapped the head of the brash eighteen-year-old Sid as he stepped outside the byre to check on the servant. Only the one bellowed shout of "Fen" preceded his abrupt lapse into senselessness. Soundlessly she stood beside the open door and waited for the man she'd learned to hate. The Pollocks had always been a scrabbly lot with morality that often bordered on the criminal; but her cousin Owen had been raised a gentleman, and his cowardly treachery sickened her.

She glimpsed the torch before she saw the man and heard his sharp gasp of shock as he leaned forward for a clearer view of his companion's sprawled body. He never noticed the raised clubs that ended his own awareness. Swiftly Trelynn retrieved the torch before it was extinguished and returned it to its crude bracket inside the byre. After dragging the bodies of both men into one of the empty stalls, she bound and gagged them with the ropes used to restrain cattle. With her sense of urgency heightened, she raced through the task of untying the bearded man whose degree of consciousness was still unstable and fluctuating. As she removed the dirty cloth that swaddled his face, he groaned; hastily she retied it and looked around the dim interior for the fodder barrow.

It didn't occur to her that her chances for escape would be reduced to improbable with the added burden of a cumbersome farm barrow and a wounded man. Her thinking remained at too primitive a level for cold logic. Regardless of his convict status, she couldn't leave him to the untender mercy of Rad Pollock or to the inflexible justice of the soldiers due the following morning. By exerting all of her strength, she managed to drag and lift him into the clumsy contrivance. Pausing only to douse the torch in the water trough, she began the back-straining work of pushing the heavily laden barrow across the yard and through the gate, never stopping until she'd reached her immediate goal—a thick coppice of trees and shrubs she'd explored earlier in the week. Located near the small stream that supplied the farm with water, the wooded shelter would offer protection enough for a few hours of rest.

Less cautiously than before, she again removed the cloth from the convict's face, moistened it in water, and tried awkwardly to sponge his face. She jerked violently at the sound of his hoarse voice.

"I'd be better off if you helped me out of this damned box so I could drink some water instead of being sloshed with it. I've been half smothered in straw and manure for hours."

Despite his understandable belligerence, Trelynn noted that he leaned heavily on her shoulder as she inched him toward the stream's edge and knelt down beside him. Vigilantly, she watched as he drank thirstily, dipping his scooped-together hands into the water time and again.

"Did you understand anything of what was said in the byre?" she asked once she'd settled him against the upturned barrow.

"The polite thing to do would be to ask a man his name before you started scolding him, Trelynn Trevor. If I thought my legs would support me, I'd perform our introductions properly with a bow. But until I'm certain I still have fingers and toes, we'll dispense with formality.

I'm James Thayne, mistress, late of Newgate and points beyond.''

"And 'tis a name that'll be on the lips of every soldier from the Citadel by morning; escaped convicts are considered every bit as dangerous as witches. You'd best find your toes as quickly as you can so that we can be a long way from here when Rad Pollock finds his slimy son on a heap of manure.''

"Where do you think we should be going, mistress?''

"I was hoping you'd be able to get us aboard the *Tamarlind* as you and Jem did Red Penny, at least I hope that's where my bull is.''

"The bull's aboard and will be bound for America by late tomorrow, but not you and me, Trelynn. If I'm a wanted man, 'tis because the port authorities found me missing from this morning's prisoner muster. Once we set foot aboard the *Tamarlind*, we'd be taken; and you'd receive little reward for your heroic rescue other than a short, uncomfortable stay in some miserable prison before they hang us. By bashing those good, honest citizens and aiding a dastardly convict, you've allied yourself with the devil, mistress, and no mistake.''

"What does your devil suggest we do, Mister Thayne?''

"We'll be hiding on the moor until I can locate a ship whose captain is greedier than he is righteous. I trust you have that fortune Uncle Owen was so worried about safely stored about your person, Trelynn. Captains who accept fugitives as passengers are freebooters with an eye for gold.''

Annoyed by the impudent effrontery of the man she sensed was smiling at his own wit, Trelynn responded sharply, "I don't have a guinea with me. Like Red Penny, my funds will be on their way to America when the *Tamarlind* pulls anchor.''

"That's a dangerous gamble, mistress. Captain Vinson has a crew I'd not trust with temptation, and there're thirty resourceful criminals like myself aboard. Where did you hide it?''

''Where not many will have the courage to look,'' she retorted with a tart asperity.

'' 'Tis on the bull then,'' he murmured soothingly. ''I thought as much when I saw that great collar swaddling its neck. 'Twould explain your loving concern for that unnatural beast and Jem's watchful eye. 'Tis too bad, though, that your Red Penny loves to be petted behind its ears. Even a dull swab will soon guess your secret if he's assigned duty in the cattle hold.''

''For your information, Mister Thayne, my bull is very selective in its choice of human friends and just as defensive as the rest of the breed about trickery. It won't allow Owen Penley near its stall, and it'd charge Rad Pollock at full run. Are your toes nimble enough for walking yet? We'll need to be better hidden than this if we're to avoid those soldier patrols tomorrow.''

''You're a bold woman, Trelynn Trevor, and you're no complainer. Most females as gently bred as you would be trembling in terror at the thought of even one night on the open moor. But the good Sir Trevor warned me you were unusual when he told me about your rare abilities—all except your skill with presbyterian flails. That's something he didn't mention, that you're as expert as a London constable in their use. 'Tis too bad we'll not be using them for the next week since they're no match for a soldier's musket.''

''Just what do you suggest we use, Mr. James Thayne? You've not so much as a dinner knife about you.''

''A dinner knife would be more useless than your flails; but if you'd allow me a few more moments of rest, I'll be visiting the farmhouse to retrieve my sword and pistols.''

''Don't be daft, that's where Rad Pollock and his other son are.''

''I'm quite familiar with Rad Pollock's reputation for courage when the other man's back is turned; 'tis what he'll do when he has to face his enemy that interests me. The son will be no problem, though; that rude lad won't be walking around until some doctor stitches up his leg. Now, if you'll help me stand, we'll go forth to do battle once again before this night is over.''

"I'll do nothing so stupid, James Thayne!"

''Then you cower here and watch me, mistress. I'll not go traipsing across the moor without protection. There are smugglers all about, lass, and they're a scurvy, dangerous lot.''

Thirty feet from the rambling house, still lamplit despite the lateness of the hour, Trelynn felt her arm grabbed firmly by her reckless, arrogant companion as he motioned her to a halt. The protest that trembled on her lips, however, was quickly stifled as she listened to him shout in a reasonably good imitation of Sid Pollock's adenoidal bleat.

"Da, I need your help, Da. The bearded villain got loose and set upon old Fen and me. I need you, Da, I'm bad hurt.''

Only one repetition was needed before the door opened and the light poured forth simultaneously with the stocky, powerful frame of Rad Pollock. Trelynn jerked uncontrollably when James Thayne whispered laconically, ''Now you can use those presbyterians again, lass, and this time with as much force as you like.''

She gasped only once in shock before she fumbled desperately to free her weapons from the folds of her cloak. But she wasn't in time to save her companion from the fall he suffered when Rad Pollock slammed into him. Pollock had been ten feet away when he discovered the ruse, but his cursing shout of ''You damned trickster!'' didn't slow him down. When he jumped upon Thayne with murderous intent, Trelynn was able to strike, but it took three solid blows to still him completely.

''You're not as gifted as I thought, mistress,'' James

Thayne complained breathlessly, "and I'll be thanking you to get this overgrown boar off me. He weighs a ton."

With her self-control destroyed by a black fury, she screamed her reply, "Crawl out from under yourself, you witless simpleton. You risked both of our lives with your buffoonery, but you'll never do so again. We'll go our separate ways from this moment on."

At her scream of outrage two excited children erupted from the farmhouse door.

"They got the fat old caterpillar, Ma," one lad shrieked. "They got him good. Mister Thayne and Mistress Trevor . . . they bashed him into pudding."

From that dramatic moment on, chaos was piled upon comedy. The Trevor coach arrived with a grinding flourish before the Wadley parents could be released from the ropes that Rad Pollock had used to restrain them or before the unconscious invader himself could be trussed up. While the four coachmen rushed to drag the other villains from the byre and yard, two old men descended stiffly and rushed toward their respective young relatives.

"Are you all right, lass?" Ephraim asked shakily.

"Good God, Charles, what happened to your head?" Sir Bevil Trevor demanded imperiously.

Just why the two victors of the small battle chose to answer the wrong questions was never noted or explained. But the man whose face and neck were streaked with dried blood responded glibly, "She's right as rain, sir, with a cool head and a hot tongue."

Simultaneously Trelynn responded at cross purposes. "The Pollock stockman downed him with a rock, then used him as a kick board for an hour or two. But you're wrong about the reckless idiot's identity, Sir Bevil. He calls himself James, not Charles."

Eventually the confusion quieted into a frantic hour of activity and planning. Farm-trained and familiar with the terrain of their own grazing fields, the young lads, who'd celebrated the victory first, returned the horses to the byre yard and readied two of the uninjured ones for a predawn flight across the moors. Trelynn and James would have at least a few hours lead over their military pursuers. While the coachmen lashed the bodies of the four men onto the flat baggage platform at the rear of the coach and covered them with a tarpaulin, the older Pollock son, limp and weak from loss of blood, was hastily bandaged and secured inside the cab.

Against her will and at the insistence of the man who was to be her traveling companion, Trelynn was bundled into Owen Penley's elegant red suit, soft leather boots, and plumed hat by the sympathetic farm wife.

"Sojurs will be looking fer a woman and a convict, not a pair of prinked-up sparks in city finery," Ellen Wadley explained. "Besides, in these pantaloons ye can git up and down Cornish hills and gullies without tumbling every step, and ye'll be needing the freedom of men's garb if ye're to keep up with Master Thayne on horseback. When he was using this farm as one of his regular stops, he'd ride up like the channel wind and leave the same way. Weren't no patrols could ever catch him."

"Mrs. Wadley, does my cousin Owen know that I was the one who struck him?"

"None of them do, lass, not even the Pollock toad who tied Hugh and me up. He was muttering about a gang of convicts when he come to, and that son of his with the gashed leg was too far gone to know what was going on. Don't ye worry none about them anyway; I 'spect Sir Trevor will settle their hash soon enough. There's not many who can stand up to his temper."

Reassured that a sixth charge would not be added to the witchcraft petition, Trelynn voiced an even more urgent problem. "How do you ride a horse, Mrs. Wadley?"

"Same way ye rode our old dobbin 'round the farm last week. Reckon all ye do when the creature speeds up is hang on. I made sure my young 'uns gave ye a saddle with a sturdy pommel on it. 'Spect we'd best get to the kitchen now and garner up some food fer ye to take along. Won't be a feast, but 'twill keep ye alive until ye reach the Kenns' farm.''

Already accustomed to masculine attire and to the freedom it afforded her, Trelynn experienced little embarrassment when she rejoined her grandfather and the others in the farm kitchen. Their nods of approval seconded what she'd already guessed, that Owen's red suit was a flattering change from her usual drab dresses.

Rather, it was the appearance of the bearded convict she'd rescued that startled her. He was far younger than she'd expected, and his hair was not the grimy black it had seemed. Clean-shaven now and clad in a resplendent green suit his father had fetched from Plymouth, James Thayne was what Sir Bevil had promised—a handsome man with crisp brown curls flecked by gold and with leaf-green eyes the color Cornishmen referred to slightingly as Devon gray. However, it was the unexpected rapport between her grandfather and the smuggler that soured some of Trelynn's earlier approbation. She listened to the convict speak in respectful tones rather than the mocking ones he'd used with her by the stream, and his sentiments both startled and annoyed her.

''I'd be honored by the gift of your name, sir, and by the relationship it implies.''

Ephraim Penley's explanation to his granddaughter irritated her equally. '' 'Tis the wedge I'll be needing to force Owen to clear your reputation, lass. James here, or rather Clay, which is his real name, has consented to be presented as the son of my younger Penley brother who died thirty years ago. Owen will soon be singing a different tune when he learns he's no longer my only male heir. And you'll be using the same Penley name, lass, with that fanciful first name your grandmother gave you, shortened to Lynn just as you always preferred. 'Tis a stratagem Bevil and I devised to keep you safe in the colonies.''

''If I ever reach there,'' she retorted tartly.

"You will, lass, with a little luck and with a little obedience on your part. You're not to plague James—Clay Penley—with your usual impudent argument. He knows the land lay between here and the coast, and he'll get you to safety if anyone can. Good luck to the pair of you."

Trelynn Trevor—now Lynn Penley—stared in disbelief as Ephraim and Bevil Trevor boarded the coach without a backward glance. She'd been cast adrift in the company of a stranger without so much as a courtesy explanation from the grandfather who'd been her most reliable human mentor throughout a lonely and problem-prone youth.

CHAPTER 3

"You didn't tell her the whole of it," Bevil accused balefully as he braced himself to accommodate the breakneck speed of the coach.

Silently Ephraim shook his head and nodded significantly toward Jabe Pollock, who lay uncomfortably on the opposite padded seat. "Young ears are always alert," he said mildly.

"But the plan is unchanged?" Bevil insisted.

"Unchanged as far as I'm concerned," Ephraim agreed.

"Then you'll be interested to know I've decided on an addition," the aristocrat announced casually. "I've decided 'tis a shame for a potential colonist and his get to remain in Cornwall when the James River is so available."

For a brief moment Ephraim regarded his friend with a speculative gleam before he smiled broadly. "Does one of your ships have a doctor aboard?"

"Aye, the one now bound for Virginia. I'm not a vindictive man, Ephraim, only cautious."

Leaning forward, the lawyer tapped Jabe Pollock's arm. When the youthful eyes flew open with amazing speed for

53

someone who'd appeared sound asleep earlier, Ephraim smiled.

"Which Plymouth inn is your father using, lad?" he asked gently.

"Drakes," was the mumbled reply, and this time it was Bevil who smiled.

At intervals during the remaining predawn hours, Ephraim pondered on the shortsightedness of English officialdom in decreeing the death penalty for smugglers. The public would be better served if all captured suspects were put to work for the government. Never had the lawyer witnessed greater human efficiency than the performances of the four Trevor coachmen and the two servants who'd remained at Drakes Inn. In only a brief stop at the hostelry, the Pollocks' luggage was spirited from their room and stowed aboard; then the coach was driven to a remote waterfront area beyond the city limits. Visible in the light of breaking dawn, two longboats were waiting at the water's edge, manned by sailors who evinced no surprise when four of the prisoners were transferred silently from the coach.

"How are you going to explain those men to the soldiers already on the ship?" Ephraim asked.

"By the most plausible of explanations," Bevil responded with a smile. "Four drunken crew members overcelebrated their last night of shore leave and had to be restrained. They'll be well sloshed with rum before they board, and I'll be the one who'll do the explaining. See you aboard the *Tamarlind* within two hours, Ephraim."

When the lawyer returned to the coach, he found his nephew waiting for him inside the cab. During the twenty-minute drive to his cottage, Ephraim did all the talking, a circumstance necessitated by the gag still stuffed into the younger man's mouth.

"You will have little more than two weeks to decide your own fate, Owen," he warned sternly; "and those weeks will be spent under the protection of the men driving this coach.

"Before I define what options you do have, I want you to know that there is a second male Penley who would qualify as my heir if you should fail to carry out the orders I am going to give you. The man in question is the son of my youngest brother, Joseph, whom I'm certain your father told you about. I met the son several years ago. At that time he was not interested in leaving his native Jamaica and returning to England. Now that Jamaica has become an English colony, however, his attitude has changed; and I'm certain he'd welcome the inheritance of Penley Farm. But since he is younger than you, he cannot supersede you unless you are convicted of a crime—such as persecuting an innocent woman. Remember that your foolish conversation with Sidney Pollock at the cattle byre was overheard by several witnesses, men who will gladly testify against you if I so request. And I will make that request if you mention tonight's activities to anyone, including your wife.

"Now, as to what you're to do to redeem yourself. First, you're going to curb your wife's spite by telling her that she committed open perjury by signing the petitions she knew to be false. Second, you personally will do everything in your power to clear Trelynn's name. If you fail me in these requests, I will see you stripped more completely than you were tonight. By comparison, the loss of your suit will seem only a minor inconvenience. Since your luggage will be returned to you, I trust you will look more presentable when next we meet. Mr. Wadley's wardrobe proved quite limited, and I'm certain you've noted, unpleasantly odorous."

With little sympathy for the stricken man, Ephraim dismounted in front of his cottage and spent a busy hour repacking his legal papers and the articles of clothing he'd need for another ocean voyage. Despite his physical exhaustion, he felt a measure of satisfaction about the night's events; if Bevil succeeded in removing the two main witnesses against Trelynn, there would be little substance remaining to the murder charge.

Since none of the prisoners Sir Bevil took aboard the *Sea Falcon* that morning resembled the two wanted fugitives, the soldiers on watch revealed no curiosity about the condition of the men. Maritime laws concerning a captain's right to secure a crew had been very flexible since Queen Elizabeth's reign sixty-four years earlier. Nor did the soldiers accompany Bevil and the ship's doctor to the hold where the Pollocks and Fen were imprisoned and where Sir Trevor delivered a blunt warning to Rad Pollock.

"This kidnapping is very similar to the one you planned for Trelynn Trevor, but far more merciful. You will be free men once you reach Virginia, except for your servant. Because he attempted to murder one of my men, he will be classified as a dangerous criminal indentured to ensure that the colonial authorities keep a watchful eye on him. In time I will notify your family members of the location so that they can send you the remainder of your possessions should they feel so inclined. One word of caution, though, if you ever again attempt persecution of Trelynn in any form, I will not be so merciful."

His eyes hooded with exhaustion, Bevil Trevor studied the thickset man straining at his bonds and remembered the Commonwealth years when he'd been at the mercy of men just like this conniving bully. Barrel-chested and short of stature, Rad Pollock represented the type of Englishman the aristocrat detested—humorless, ambitious men without scruples or honor. Still, Bevil had often wondered at the courage of the fifteen-year-old Trelynn who'd refused this man's offer of marriage. At that time, Pollock had been one of the wealthiest and most politically powerful men in Tamar Valley; and at that time he'd been as acceptably good looking as his oldest son was today. Her adamant and repeated refusals had precipitated the current crisis in her life. A flicker of conscience momentarily troubled the old man as he wondered if she'd be any better off with his youngest son.

Four hours into her own escape, the newly christened Lynn Penley was convinced that she could not possibly be worse off, even if she were standing in the docket before the Stannary Court. Laden with the bulky sheepskins Mrs. Wadley had insisted she take for additional warmth, her own heavy wool cloak, and an awkward bundle of food and utensils, Lynn clung to the horse in miserable discomfort, trying vainly to keep up with her more skilled riding companion. During the final hour of the ordeal, a mizzling rain had added to her sense of futility. When she'd traveled to London with Jem, she'd known where she was every minute of the time, and she'd known the security of a sturdy, well-stocked wagon. But here on the blustery, windswept moor, she had no sense of direction, since every hill and crag and cliff looked exactly like the ones just passed.

She sighed with relief when the man of many names, who would now be known as Clay Penley, finally pulled to a halt before an uninviting cave in one of the shale-lined gullies. With her bruised posterior protesting every step she took, Lynn lugged her supplies inside and arranged the sheepskins on the floor before she turned around to look at her trailmate. To her fearful consternation, he was leaning weakly against his own mount. Worriedly she carried his gear inside; she'd seen enough of illness to realize that he was barely conscious. When she returned to his side, his face was paler than a prison pallor in the gray light of early morning. She supported his weight for the thirty long feet to the makeshift pallet where she lowered him.

Nagged by multiple fears for both him and their safety, she rushed outside once more to slap the two horses on their rumps and to watch them take off at full gallop in the direction they'd just traveled. Still in the same uneasy mood, she climbed the one small hill nearest the cave and looked around. The barren landscape was devoid of humans or human habitation; not even a sheep cote or a stretch of stone fencing broke the monotony of grassy splotches and stunted shrubbery. A hundred feet away, a straggly stand of wind-bent oak trees offered the only visible source of firewood. Wearily she limped across the rocky expanse and gathered an armful of twigs and dead branches.

She reached the safety of the cave again just as the misty rain turned into a downpour, and she shivered from the damp, penetrating cold. Not daring to pause long enough to rest, she searched through the disordered bundles until she located the borrowed tinderbox and the small pewter pot Mrs. Wadley had tied to the goat-skin water bag. In London during the plague Lynn had learned to build fires with inadequate kindling and to cook simple meals over small flames. That her survival in this cave and on Bodmin Moor beyond would be a greater challenge than London, she hadn't a doubt. The food supply was scant and unplanned, oatmeal mostly and leftovers from the Wadley kitchen. Her knees were as bruised as the rest of her body by the time she finished that first meal; and even to her uncritical palate, the oatmeal mush with shredded bits of day-old roast mutton seemed tasteless and gummy.

Ignoring her semiconscious companion's peevish protests, she spoon-fed him half the mixture before she ate the rest herself and cleaned the pot and bowl with sandy grit and rainwater. Getting him to drink the tea she boiled proved to be no problem; he thirstily consumed all of it, leaving her no choice but to slake her own thirst with tepid water, since the small fire had burned itself out. Unable to deny her exhaustion long enough to investigate the dark areas of the cave, Lynn lay down on the small area of sheepskin not already occupied, pulled her heavy cloak over both bodies, and fell instantly asleep.

Hours later in midafternoon she was awakened by a muttered request for water. Sluggishly, with her sore muscles straining at every move, she complied, awakening only gradually to the realization that her patient was more feverish than he'd been earlier—not as burningly so as her mother had been, but enough to cause intermittent delirium. Driven by the added anxiety, Lynn settled to the demanding task of saving the life of a man she'd not known twenty-four hours earlier. During a break in the rain, she searched the long gully for firewood and exulted when she found piles of dry twigs and faggots that had been snagged together during the winter runoff and deposited in one of the shallow caves. In the uncertain light of dusk she cooked another meal, mutton broth this time, and made three successive pots of it.

Patiently, for the three more days the rain endured, she devoted herself to a routine of primitive nursing, and she amassed a considerable fund of knowledge about herself as well as the man her grandfather had so inexplicably welcomed into his family. Perhaps because he was not as ill as her mother and the other plague victims had been, she found the onerous tasks less repugnant, and his firm skin and strong muscles more agreeable to touch. With a sense of victory she noted his daily improvement: the fewer relapses into mumbling disorientation, the gradual abatement of the fever, and his increasingly peaceful hours of sleep. Because the chore of preparing the simple meals, now reduced to oatmeal gruel, and the slow hand-feeding at frequent intervals consumed most of the daylight hours, she had few minutes leftover for much introspective worry about the dangers they faced. Not once had she seen any sign of their pursuers, and the remote wildness of their surroundings now seemed a familiar landscape.

No longer did she consider Clay Penley a stranger; she'd accepted the fact that their futures were bound together. Although she did not consider this man in the same class as Jem Rigg, she felt an equal degree of responsibility for his well-being. He would be a part of her life in America during the ten years of his indenture. However, she doubted he'd ever be as useful as the great hulking Jem who'd become the finest stockman ever to work on Penley Farm. Briefly, she wondered about Clay Penley's background; his speech and appearance were those of a gentleman, but his reckless daring was that of an adventurer. She hadn't forgotten his dangerous and foolhardy challenge of Rad Pollock or his boast that he knew all about the Tamar Valley residents. Certainly Sir Bevil must have had considerable respect for the smuggler to have saved him from the gallows. It was only her grandfather's sponsorship of the handsome convict that puzzled her. Why should Ephraim adopt this man as nephew? Undoubtedly, Owen Penley would be terrified by a possible usurper to the estate he'd considered his own since childhood, but this Clay Penley was much younger; and it was always the oldest male who inherited. Moreover, deported criminals were rarely allowed to return to England.

A second odd aspect of her grandfather's approval puzzled her even more. She'd been but twelve years old when he'd brought Jem Rigg to the farm; but he'd made certain Jem was safely married to Polly Henshaw, the widowed sister of one of the tenants, before he'd assigned the convict laborer as his granddaughter's watchguard. Yet that same cautious lawyer had almost casually turned her over to another convict, cautioning her only to obey the man. Contemplating this final admonition, Lynn smiled with amusement. So far she'd been the protector, caretaker, and provider. Since he'd led her to the cave, the only words the ex-smuggler had uttered were the unintelligible ramblings of delirium interspersed with mumbled requests for water.

Interrupting her own reflections with an impatient glance at the sleeping man, Lynn contemplated rousing him. He was no longer feverish, and his gaze had been sharply focused on her earlier in the morning. Still, they couldn't leave the cave until he'd recovered enough strength for strenuous walking. If he collapsed on the open trail, she'd be unable to care for him; and she had no idea where they were going or what was supposed to happen once they arrived. Restlessly, she left the cave and made her way to the vantage point from which she could survey the countryside. Seconds later she was racing back to the cave, her heart thudding with alarm. Silhouetted against the distant eastern horizon had been the figures of four men sitting astride their motionless horses.

Relief poured through her when she found her patient already on his feet, his expression alert and intelligent. "I heard you running," he whispered tersely. "How far away are they?"

"They're still a long way off, and they weren't riding yet."

"Good. Help me move that pile of rocks at the rear of the cave; they're blocking a passage to a more private entry. Don't look so shocked, witch woman; a good smuggler never allows himself to be trapped. My people and I have used this cave before."

In only a few minutes they managed to clear the concealed tunnel and to gather up their few belongings. With amazing speed and coordination for a man who'd been so recently ill, Clay helped her scatter the ashes of the small fire and spread pieces of shale around the floor to cover the signs of habitation. Crowded together in the narrow passage, they repiled the heavy rocks at the tunnel entrance before they moved farther back into the forbidding darkness.

"Spread the sheepskins out," he suggested amiably in a soft tone of voice. "We might as well be comfortable since we'll not be leaving until dusk. You needn't worry that his majesty's soldiers will be so brave as to spend a night on the open moor, not when they can find more comfortable billet in some farmer's warm kitchen."

"What happens if they find the cave?" Lynn demanded tersely.

"Some of them might know the cave right enough, but none of the patrols have ever found this passage. How much food do we have left?"

"Only the grain biscuits and cheese; I used the last of the oatmeal this morning."

"For which I'm heartedly grateful. Another pot of skilly spooned into me, and I'd have turned into the idiot I must have seemed for the past days. How many were there?"

"This is the fourth."

"Then 'tis a good thing I finally woke up. We'll have to travel ten miles a night to reach the coast in time."

"What happens then, Clay Penley?"

"Why then, Mistress Lynn Penley, we'll not be at the mercy of some greedy captain after all. We'll board the *Tamarlind* and join your grandfather and my—and Sir Trevor. But they'll not be going to America with us; we'll be on our own in that terrifying land."

"Have you ever been there?"

"Many times to the Caribbean, but never to the fiercer places where I've been told the Indians massacre white men on a regular schedule."

"That's an old wife's tale; American colonies are well established now, and prosperous."

"Keep your voice down, mistress. There's no gain in raising the hackles on some poor soldier's neck, especially if he believes in the spirit people said to inhabit Bodmin Moor. Odd superstitions abound about this section of Cornwall."

Shivering uncontrollably, Lynn moved closer to her sardonic companion. Although she'd enjoyed traipsing over the Penley and Trevor hills during her youth, she'd always avoided the dark places, even the heavily treed glades where the sun rarely penetrated. She'd never analyzed the vague aversion she felt for caves and crevasses and underground pits since she experienced only a relatively minor fear of the dark in the familiar surroundings of her bedroom. Not until she'd learned the ancient language and read the frequent references to the Brythonic gods of darkness, did she understand the universality of man's fear of the unknown. Despite a Protestant upbringing, she'd felt a strong empathy for the primitive people who'd once inhabited Cornwall. It was easy to give credence to the existence of evil forces whenever you were afraid. In this narrow, midnight-dark passage, she moved still closer to the man seated beside her on the spread-out sheepskins.

Had Lynn but known that her companion was emotionally swamped by his own spiritual bleakness, she'd have moved instantly away. Had she known that she was the cause of his current unpleasant mood, she'd have withdrawn the tentative offer of friendship she extended him while he was ill. Indeed, if she'd been informed of the totality of her grandfather's and Sir Bevil's plans, she'd have risked traveling Bodmin Moor by herself.

Clay Penley—it was the most acceptable name he'd used so far in a disoriented, adventurous life—was badly rattled by his emotional reaction to the woman he'd previously considered to be only a means of escape from the untenable choice of indenture and slave labor. Before he'd lost his freedom and almost his life, when his father had first suggested he marry this woman, Charles Clay had refused with amused outrage. But after months of the pitiless privations of Newgate, he would have agreed to any stratagem, even marriage to a farm woman whom his brother Averill had called a "Medea in homespun sackcloth." Three years ago during one of his clandestine visits to his father's estate, Clay himself had glimpsed his distant cousin while she'd been plow training a young bullock. At that time his sister-in-law Barbara had dubbed the younger woman "a plow horse hitched to a bull." Mounted on one of his father's sleek horses, Clay had ridden away from his brother's hunt party for a closer look at the girl Bevil Trevor believed to be the finest farmer in Cornwall. Never near enough to see her face clearly, he had watched her supple movements as she guided the plow along the straightest furrow he'd ever seen. Something about her determined patience with the animal, her stubborn tenacity of purpose had made him feel momentarily ashamed of his own aimless life.

Years before, Charles Clay had been as hardworking and ambitious as the rustic Medea on the neighboring farm. Only six years old when his father had joined the king's forces and his older brothers had been enrolled at distant Eton, Clay had remained at home with his mother, gaining an unbalanced education from a family tutor who preferred sword fighting to mathematics. Three years into his father's absence, his mother was summoned to her ancestral home near Bournemouth in Dorset to tend her brothers who'd fallen ill from a winter epidemic that had decimated their Royalist encampment. She'd never returned, and it was months before her youngest son learned that both she and her brothers had died. As the oldest available grandson, it had been lucky, lazy Bourke Trevor who'd inherited that estate and title.

When an embittered Bevil had returned after an eight-year debacle to find his estate almost bankrupt, he and his three sons had boarded the last clear-of-debt Trevor asset, a venerable merchant ship, and had begun to earn an often dishonest living on the channel and coastal Atlantic. Within months Bourke had been sent to Bournemouth; he'd proved useless both as a sailor and a smuggler. With a small measure of battle experience to his credit, Averill had learned the distribution end of the trade; but it'd been the fiery young Charles Clay who'd soon surpassed both his father and oldest brother in his zeal for success. He'd been seventeen when he'd attracted the notice of another disfranchised aristocrat, David Farnall, whose successful buccaneering and smuggling along the Spanish Main had already earned him two of the finest French-built ships afloat. Within the year Bevil and David were partners, with Bevil and his two older sons in charge of distribution and sales while his youngest son remained with Farnall, becoming increasingly expert in the various skills of the trade as sailor, smuggler, merchant, and occasional free-booter. Throughout those five wildly adventurous years, Clay had given all his personal profits to his father until the Trevor estates were once again completely restored and solvent.

Ordered home by his father, Clay had arrived in time to celebrate Averill's triumphant wedding to Barbara Gordon, one of Devon's most acclaimed heiresses. But it was Barbara's younger sister who fascinated Clay, and a de-lighted Lord Gordon promptly proposed a second interfamily match. Two weeks before the engagement was announced, the young woman eloped with a French count, and a disillusioned Clay returned to sea. Fourteen months later when David Farnall was declared a pirate, Charles Clay Trevor lost his home, his name, and the promise of an aristocrat's inheritance. Cut adrift from family ties, Clay had taken the ironic name of James Thayne and become a criminal without any ennobling purpose other than money and the thrill of danger. When his partners had been captured, his own surrender had been little more than a quixotic gesture; he'd had no real hope for a reprieve. Prison, however, had been a brutalizing experience that had taught him more about survival than had fifteen years of successful smuggling.

The price tag of marriage had seemed a small price to pay for freedom, a practical expediency that would solve both his own and Trelynn Trevor's legal problems. But a flesh and blood woman with the strength and resourcefulness of this one was no casual expediency; she'd been a threat to his sense of masculinity since the first minute he'd met her in the Wadleys' byre. Despite his desperate need, he'd resented being rescued by a confident young woman capa-ble of downing four vicious men with nothing more than primitive flails. The knowledge that he'd deserved the tongue-lashing she'd given him for his reckless bravado with Rad Pollock had further demoralized him. How could he explain to her that he'd been too lightheaded for rationality, and that he'd underestimated Pollock? Hell, the charging scoundrel would have killed him if she hadn't acted as swiftly as she did.

On horseback, though, during that wild ride to the cave, he'd acted even the worse fool. Maliciously triumphant when he'd discovered that riding was not one of her skills, he'd driven his horse at full gallop, expecting any minute to hear her cry for help. But she'd followed his lead with grim determination; and when he'd slipped half-conscious from his horse, she'd saved his life for the third time in the one night. During his lucid moments—far more numerous toward the end than he'd pretended—he'd watched her move about the cave with graceful efficiency as she'd tended his needs. She'd eased the pain of his pounding head with rain-soaked cloths and sponged his fever-racked body. She'd spoon-fed him with firm insistence even when he didn't want to eat, and she'd brought him water whenever he'd mumbled his need. As long as he'd been too weak to leave the cave for essential relief, she'd half carried him outside and waited until he was finished.

But damn her cold heart, she'd done it all without a quiver of emotion! At night she'd slept beside him as impersonally as a fellow sailor on a crowded deck, and not once had she smiled at him. All I mean to her, he fumed, is ten years of labor; she'd take the same care of a bull or bullock or cow! Late yesterday after his fever had broken, she'd performed the final indignity. She'd stood just inside the cave, removed her clothing, and bathed herself as casually as she would have if he'd been a blind lad of ten.

At first the sight had merely intrigued his curiosity. In build she was nothing like the buxom barmaids he'd tumbled as a brash young sailor, or the more sophisticated women who'd obliged him later, or the knowingly seductive temptress who'd been his sometimes mistress during the three turbulent years between her marriages to other men. Trelynn Trevor—Lynn Penley—was tall and leanly muscled with broad shoulders and capable hands. That there was a wild beauty to her, he couldn't deny; but he was certain that her cleanly sculptured breasts would prove to be as resiliently firm as the rest of her athlete's body. No wonder she was fleet footed and strong enough to support his weight, and no wonder she could whirl those clubs like a juggler at a village fair.

How the devil, he asked himself sardonically, could this dynamic huntress be the daughter of the pretty, feminine girl he'd seen on Penley Farm when he'd been a small child? Years later he'd watched Lavinia Trevor at a London gambling salon just after the Restoration. From across the wide room she'd seemed the same pretty woman she'd been on the farm, and she'd been as exquisitely gowned as the most regal woman there. But in spite of her finery and arch smile of invitation, she'd displayed not a hint of her daughter's strength of face or character. It was that dominating character Clay resented. He wished now that he'd insisted Ephraim Penley explain the necessity of marriage. Damn, with the sharp tongue she'd used to flay him after Pollock's assault, she could very well announce that she'd never wed a bumbling idiot. What cut even deeper into his self-confidence was Ephraim's warning that she'd be adamantly opposed to the marriage if she ever learned he was Bevil Trevor's son.

Clay smiled in the dark with an abrupt cynical amusement. Perhaps he should tell her now while she was still afraid of the soldiers; he hadn't missed the tremor in her hands as she'd helped him sit down. As his wayward humor deepened, he shook his head; he hadn't the strength yet to stop her if she decided to bolt.

Instead he leaned toward her and asked, "Is the waterskin handy, Lynn?" After he finished drinking from the awkward container, he whispered more softly, "The walk tonight will be a harsh one, mistress, so we'd both do well to get some sleep." The smile still played about his lips as she settled beside him and covered them both with her cloak. She'll survive, he thought with a twinge of envy; even when she's afraid, she doesn't lose control. Perversely, he didn't tell her that they'd know instantly if the soldiers approached the cave. The shallow ground above the narrow tunnel vibrated like thunder when even a single horseman rode overhead. To his own relief, no outside sounds intruded into their dark haven throughout the afternoon hours of rest.

Even the long walk that started at sunset and ended just before dawn at another farmhouse passed without any frightening incident. Only frequent stops for rest and for small portions of dried cheese and stale biscuits interrupted their otherwise steady progress along a ridge of granite too steep for horses to scale. Under a cloudless sky there was sufficient moonlight to light the narrow path they traversed. Dawn was just breaking as they descended onto a meadowed plain marked by sprawling farm structures in the distance. Cautiously Clay moved along the stone fences that enclosed a pasture yard, pausing abruptly when he heard the soft, aroused whinnies of horses.

"The Kenns have company," he whispered tensely to the woman standing motionless by his side. "We'll have to wait in the byre until Matthew comes out for the morning milking."

"Milking is usually finished by dawn," Lynn whispered thoughtfully. "Do you know this farmer?"

"Aye, I know him well; his son Tom is indentured to your grandfather."

"Then at least one of you knows something about farming," Lynn murmured with satisfaction.

"Don't you believe it. Tom's no farmer; the only four-legged things he claims to understand are tables and chairs."

"Well, someone here is a farmer," Lynn whispered sharply. "That rhythmic sound we hear is milk hitting a wood bucket."

"That'll be Matthew, Tom's father. You stay here while I go inside to check."

Waiting uneasily outside the byre entrance, Lynn experienced the same trepidation she had five nights earlier at the Wadley farm when another group of horses had whinnied just as nervously. Instantly the torch inside the byre was extinguished, and seconds later Clay stepped outside accompanied by a bulkily dressed man. Silently she followed them across wide expanses of unfenced pasture land to the most distant structure on the Kenn farm, a three-sided stone sheep cote.

"Ye'll be safe enough here, Jame, ye and Mistress Trevor both," Matthew Kenn said softly. "As long as the sheep are here, the soldiers won't come looking. Those sluggard jack-a-dandies don't trust their skittish horses among woollies. Just lay low until I finish the milking and return to the house before that sour-nosed captain takes another of his sly notions. I'll be back as soon as they've left for the day."

"Are those the same soldiers I saw yesterday?" Lynn asked tensely once she and Clay were alone.

"I imagine so, since they're the ones who searched the Wadleys' place before they came here two days ago. The captain in charge is the same one who arrested Tom and the others in Falmouth, so he knows me and the territory. I hope you never have to meet him, Lynn; he's a religious zealot who prays out loud at a public hanging, but who wouldn't hesitate to shoot a suspect in the back if he thought there was any danger to his own precious hide."

Shivering at the prospect, Lynn whispered, "Let's leave now, Clay."

"We can't leave until dark because Wilcox will be patrolling all around this area. He's already told the Kenns that he'll be staying here as long as necessary. Mrs. Kenn is the best cook on Bodmin Moor, and our thrifty captain doesn't believe in wasting his own brass for food."

"How did Mr. Kenn know we'd be coming here?"

"One of the Wadley lads rode over three days ago and gave warning; else the Kenns would not have been able to hide enough food for us to take with us tonight. First thing Wilcox does when he gets to a suspect farm is to check the supplies in the pantry and then recheck them twice every day he stays quartered there. Because of Tom, the Kenns' farm is invaded every time there's a fugitive hunt in this area. 'Tis a policy of our great empire system to force the public to support its army."

"Can you trust the Kenns not to peach on us?"

"Aye, they're good people, Lynn, and they're grateful to me and my fa—my friend, Sir Trevor, and to your grandfather for a merciful indenture. Tom was a wild one long before I foolishly allowed him to join me and the others. 'Twas his braggart stupidity that led Wilcox to my Falmouth home—him and the barmaid slut who was with him."

"I thought all your men were married."

"Bert Spence and Harry Cobb are, and Tom claimed he was; but this woman's not the kind a man with good sense marries, not even Tom. During her earlier stays at Bridewell, she saved herself from hanging by pleading her belly."

Outraged by the disclosure that she'd be responsible for some cheap strumpet who used motherhood as insurance, Lynn demanded hotly, "How do you expect me to take someone like that to my grandfather's farm on Rhode Island?"

"Unless we can sell her papers to some publican in New Port, we'll have to take her there. I doubt Tom would go without her, and I promised the Kenns I'd give their son another chance. She's not all that bad a worker, and I'm sure that between the two of us, we can keep her busy."

Lynn was warily silent as she digested the impact of Clay's revealing words. This arrogant man did not consider himself an indentured servant at all; he sounded as much like an estate owner as Sir Bevil Trevor himself.

"I think you'd better tell me everything you and my grandfather and Sir Bevil discussed at the Wadleys'," she whispered with a cold emphasis.

"I will, Lynn, after we've had some sleep. 'Twill be hours at least before our intrepid hunters leave on their appointed round, and we can be free from their busy ears. But for caution's sake, we'd best sleep separate this time. Mrs. Kenn belongs to chapel and might draw the wrong conclusion if she found us under one blanket."

Angered anew by his smiling impudence, Lynn moved her sheepskin as far from his as she could manage in the crude shelter and rearranged the straw to form one barrier in the middle of the cote and a higher one on the open side.

"Good idea," Clay approved smugly as he followed suit.

As tired as she was after twelve hours of walking, Lynn did not fall asleep easily. That casual comment, "if we can sell her papers," aroused her deepest suspicions. She was leaving England, not only because of the criminal charges against her, but because she could not abide the prospect of thankless servitude under the domination of any man, even her grandfather. Yet this convicted smuggler, indentured by law to ten years of proscribed labor, had just announced his intentions of being her full partner if not a good deal more.

Resentfully she remembered the years of hard, dirty work it'd taken to build her small herd of cattle, and the difficulty she'd had learning the rudiments of farm management. Recalling the early years when she'd lacked the authority to discipline the often insolent farmhands and dairymaids during her grandfather's absences, Lynn gritted her teeth. She had no intention of ever relinquishing that authority again, certainly not to a man who most probably had never shoveled a scoop of manure from a byre or tested a spade full of soil for planting warmth. Cynically, she looked over the straw barrier and noted that the "one blanket,'' her limp and soiled cloak, was now exclusively draped over his own body.

Awakening hours later, however, was one of the most pleasant moments she'd had since her grandfather's cottage in Plymouth. Matthew Kenn had arrived back at the cote laden with buckets full of heavenly, hot food: a pot of dark tea strong enough to sharpen her already acute hunger, boiled eggs, thick slabs of crisp pork, fresh-baked bread golden with melted butter, and tangy sweet-berry jelly. An hour later Matthew returned with two large buckets of hot water and a clean length of linen towel tossed incongruously over his shoulder. From a voluminous pocket in his heavy homespun jacket, he pulled forth a yellowed bar of soap; and, for the first time, he addressed Lynn directly.

"Martha thought ye might like some wash water, Mistress Trevor. Didn't think 'twould be safe enough for ye to use the house; might be the captain 'ud take a notion to return out of spite. But she'll be fixing ye dinner later on and enough tucker to last 'til Padstow.''

Pausing to shuffle his feet in some embarrassment, the man continued haltingly, "One more thing I'd like to tell ye, mistress. I know about the brangle ye're in with the law, but I don't go along with church folk who use their own bugbears t' twist the truth some. I'm sure ye'll do the best ye can for my dottrel son, but I won't be blaming ye if he fails to stop his wasteful, hell-bent ways. Martha spoilt him when he was sprouting, then tried t' correct his faults with preaching; but the lad didn't take t' preaching any more than t' farming. Didn't settle with any sense t' smuggling either. Jame was too soft with him, and it cost the lot of them.''

As Lynn listened with a growing sympathy, she wondered if people ever realized how much of themselves and the people around them they revealed as they talked. Martha Kenn believed witches were evil beings and was worried about her precious son being forced into the company of one, whereas Matthew Kenn had little hope for his son's reform. Like most Cornishmen, he also regarded smuggling as an honorable profession. Thanking him for the hot water, she watched in relief as he and Clay both left the cote and headed toward the farmhouse.

In the process of stripping off her trail-stained clothing, Lynn remembered that her companion of five days had failed again to answer any of her specific questions about the plans already formulated for their futures. Instead Clay had gulled her with an account of the immediate problems ahead of them on the open trail. Since there were no additional friendly farmers along the way, they would have to take shelter wherever they could find it. He'd also warned her that the Padstow area itself might prove to be more dangerous than Bodmin Moor. The smugglers' haven he'd known as safe in the past was now reported to be the operating arena for gangs of wreckers who'd left the Scilly Islands and the southern half of the county.

Worried equally about both the immediate and distant futures, Lynn scrubbed her hair and body absently, her thoughts busy with puzzling contradictions. Why had her grandfather confided his intentions to a stranger rather than to her? And why had Sir Bevil been the one to warn that stranger to protect her at all costs? More than anything else in life, she detested being treated as an incompetent child. Decently clad a half hour later, she was still toweling her hair when she looked up to see an amused Clay Penley regarding her.

"Two hundred years ago the papist priests would have been the ones accusing you of witchcraft because of your obsession for bathing," he murmured lazily.

"While their own bodies were covered with lice and festering sores and doused with French perfume," she retorted tartly. " 'Tis not a condition I enjoy."

"I'm not so fond of the stench of farms myself, mistress. That will be something we'll have to keep in mind once we reach our own property."

Inhaling sharply, Lynn asked the question that had been burning her brain. "Did my grandfather deed his Rhode Island farm to you?" she demanded bluntly.

"I was referring to the Trevor property in Connecticut. Sir Bevil will be deeding that land to me in payment for past services."

"That land is still wilderness and too remote for settlers. Only a large, organized colony would be safe from Indian attack."

Angered by her negative reception of his offer, Clay snapped irritably, "Then perhaps you should have accepted Rad Pollock's offer of marriage. 'Tis said his Virginia property is surrounded by civilization; and no doubt he'd make you as good a husband as any."

" 'Tis also said, Clay Penley, that there are five men to every woman in the colonies, so perhaps I'll have my choice of husbands yet."

"Your grandfather said you'd already turned down a goodly number of applicants."

"My grandfather can be a foolish old man! When I was seventeen and he still had his fortune, he offered a dowry for me that attracted every rakehell, flesh-fly, and impoverished Cavalier in the country. Not a one of them approved of me any more than you do, but the promise of money made them willing liars. Since there's no longer any dowry available, perhaps some colonial will accept me as I am."

"And what are you, Lynn?"

"I'm a farmer, Clay, with an unseemly education not appreciated in a woman. I'm too tall and muscular for a man's physical liking, and I've too sharp a tongue for his peace of mind. I've no illusions about myself, but neither do I have any faith in medieval folklore about knights in shin—" Abruptly, Lynn stopped talking; she'd just noted his altered appearance. He was clean shaven again and his gold-flecked hair had been smartly shortened.

"I see Mrs. Kenn did not consider her house too

dangerous for you. I don't suppose she thought to send along a hair brush for me?''

"A hair brush and scissors both. She suggested I crop your hair so you'll look more like the man you're pretending to be.''

"And less like the witch she imagines I am,'' Lynn retorted rashly. "As you said before, she's a true chapel-goer who believes that single women are all evil temptresses and handsome men merely the innocent victims. But she's right about my hair; 'twill be less bothersome if you cut it as short as yours. Cut it evenly, though, so that it curls under like a proper Puritan's.''

Lynn was smiling when the job was finished, and her shoulder-length tresses brushed neatly into the medieval style for pages and young squires. With an experimental playfulness, she shook her head, enjoying the freedom from the weight of a heavy waist-long mass of hair.

"Now 'twill be only my voice that'll give me away,'' she disclaimed cheerfully.

Settling back against the stone wall on his side of the cote, Clay surveyed his handiwork with a critical eye, rendered doubly so by an irritation with himself. As he'd handled the heavy silk of her dark hair, he'd become far too aware of her as a woman. Until he could gain some measure of mastery over her, he didn't want her to mean anything more to him than a ticket to freedom. Let her retain her misguided conceit that she looked like a man; Clay was already finding her far too disturbing. He'd not slept well this morning without her by his side, and he'd hotly resented Martha Kenn's self-righteous criticism. The damnable woman had tried to force him to accept her offer of an inscribed wooden cross "to ward off the temptation of a devil's handmaiden.'' Perhaps I should have taken it, he reflected derisively, until he remembered the one certain hold he'd have over her if his father and Ephraim Penley had their way.

"Would you like to hear some of the minor details about the home I'm planning in Connecticut?" he asked casually.

"What minor details would those be, Mister Penley? 'Tis common knowledge that when mad Prince James gives land to a faithful old Cavalier, 'tis more likely to be the size of Tamar Valley than a simple farm. No doubt the home you're planning to build will be as grand, with thirty servants to do your bidding and a clever woman like Mrs. Kenn to keep you beautiful."

" 'Twill be your home too, Lynn Penley, so mayhap we'll need only fifteen servants; and you can be the one who keeps me beautiful."

"If I ever cropped your hair, you'd look more the Roundhead than the Cavalier you are. I'll not be a servant to any man; and anyway, 'tis nonsense we're talking. If I remember rightly, the shoe is on the other foot; 'twas you who were sentenced to servitude, not me. At any rate, I'll not be going to Connecticut; I'll be developing a small farm on Aquidneck Island and making my own living as I've been doing for years."

"While you're looking for a husband, mistress?"

"Only if Grandfa was right when he said a woman was not welcome without one."

"What kind of a man would you be looking for?"

"One who doesn't consider himself an anointed tin-pot god with all the rights and privileges on his side."

"Someone like me, perhaps?"

Soft laughter bubbled up in Lynn's throat as she shook her head. "I'm not denying you'd be a pleasant companion to argue with, but I've no illusions about the merry dance you'd lead me on. You've had your own way with women too long for a simple rustic like me to compete for your attention. I'd be better off with a farmer who'd appreciate my ways, not with someone as unsuitable as you."

"According to your grandfather, I'm both fit and suitable, so you'll not be looking for a husband in America.

You and I are to be wed the minute we board the *Tamarlind*. Does the idea shock you?"

Oddly enough it doesn't, Lynn thought as she concentrated on keeping her breathing at an ordinary level; the only part that flustered her was her own stupidity. She should have guessed her grandfather's plan, or rather Sir Bevil's scheme; Ephraim could never have devised such a subterfuge without help. Forcing her stiffened shoulders to relax, she shrugged.

"No more than it did you, I expect," she murmured lightly. "It explains my grandfather naming you his nephew, and 'tis a good plan to hide my identity. No one expects a proper wife to have the freedom for witchcraft. What puzzles me, though, is Sir Bevil's eagerness for the match."

"He has nothing to do with the matter. What about your willingness?"

More defensively, Lynn shrugged her shoulders again. "'Twas never my plan to have an arranged marriage."

"Nor mine, but 'tis an arrangement I like."

"Are you telling me that I'd have been the woman you'd have chosen had you not been declared an indentured convict?" The mocking smile that framed her lips froze the easy words of flattery he'd been preparing to speak.

"Perhaps not," he admitted more honestly.

"But you are still willing?"

"Aye, are you?"

"I suppose marriage would be as good a way as any to gain your freedom. That is what you intend, isn't it?"

"That's part of it, but not all; you'd be equally protected."

"Perhaps, but not equally free. Am I to be given any choice in the matter?"

"What other choice is there? We need each other, and that's a better reason than most couples have. Will you accept me as your husband?"

"Since the affair seems already settled, I suppose 'twill be as good a solution as any."

Annoyed by the indifference expressed in her response and driven by a compulsion to make her aware of him as a man, Clay rose precipitously and stepped over to her side of the straw barrier. Seating himself beside her, he reached out to pull her closer to him.

" 'Tis customary to seal a troth with a kiss," he murmured lightly.

A startled gasp interrupted his practiced approach to love-making, a sharp intake of air followed by an urgently whispered warning as she pulled him strongly down into the concealing straw.

" 'Tis a custom that could cost us the wedding," she mumbled. "I'm certain that cloud of dust pulling up in front of the Kenns' house contains your Captain Wilcox and his small army of hunters."

CHAPTER 4

Had the danger not been so pressing during those remaining hours of daylight, the troth of Clay and Lynn Penley might have been sealed by far more than a mere kiss. Bedded deep in the straw and trapped in an embrace too improperly intimate for a formal betrothal, they hadn't dared move during those first few minutes for fear of attracting unwelcome attention. But while their mental faculties were focused on the distant sounds of hoofbeats, their physical senses were otherwise engaged. The incipient, unwilling desire that had plagued Clay since he'd first recovered from delirium blossomed unrestrainedly; her pliant body was not the hard pillow he'd feared, nor was it as coldly passionless as he'd half expected from her glib chatter. Her breathing was as uneven as his own, and her arms did not relax their hold on him.

Too far away to hear the voices of the soldiers or any sounds other than the muted bleating of one or two of the flock of sheep pastured around the cote, they remained motionless for the time Clay estimated it would take their pursuers to turn their horses loose in the fenced yard and return to the house. Cautiously then, Clay crawled to his side of the cote and retrieved his sword and pistols. When he returned to Lynn's side, he noted with satisfaction that she'd had the presence of mind to arm herself with an equal determination. The fact that his bride-to-be was no stranger to self-defense did not bother him as before; he might well need her assistance if one or more of those soldiers decided on a predinner stroll. Since her weapons were not as lethal as his, they wouldn't be charged with a murder from which there could be no lenient parole.

Their leave-taking just after sunset was a silent one, after Matthew Kenn deposited a bundle of carefully wrapped food inside the cote and walked away without uttering a word of greeting other than the whispered information, "They can't follow ye for a time at least, I've unsaddled their horses."

Hastily Lynn and Clay repacked their knapsacks, rolled up their sheepskins, and made another successful escape from the same four soldiers. A mile into the bleak granite hills on a trail only dimly visible in the pallid moonlight, they stopped and ate their own delayed dinner. Before Lynn could repack their loads, Clay pulled her to her feet and spoke softly for the first time in hours.

"As I was telling you, mistress, before the slight interruption, a troth is commonly sealed with a kiss."

That kiss was a revelation to Lynn, who'd frequently witnessed the practice among milkmaids and farmhands but had never tried herself. It had seemed little more to her than a foolish and meaningless indulgence that produced nothing except an annoying inattention to work. Since those stolen kisses on the farm had been awkwardly executed by loutish workers and giggling young girls, she was unprepared for the thoroughness of Clay's salute or for her own response. As is usual with a novice, she'd done little more than accept the pressure of his lips when he'd begun; but her own pulsing emotion had almost smothered her until he withdrew and allowed her to breathe.

"You've never been kissed before, have you?" he asked softly as he watched her gulp in air.

Shaking her head, she admitted ruefully, "It didn't seem like a skill that would need much practice." She was grateful then for his laughter and for the exuberant way he hugged her, but she wondered perversely why he didn't kiss her again. She received an answer of sorts at their next rest stop a mile farther along the way.

" 'Tis a skill that takes time to teach properly, Lynn Penley, although proper isn't quite the word I had in mind. But I'm thinking you're going to prove to be an apt pupil."

The next mornning Lynn discovered a second reason for his restraint. Making camp in a narrow rift between two granite slabs at the foot of a gaunt monolithic outcropping known locally as Brown Willy, Clay all but collapsed as she built a small fire and cooked their simple meal. As patiently as she had in the cave, she insisted he eat the pork stew she prepared and drink two bowls of tea. He was sound asleep when she crawled onto the pallet beside him and wrapped her arms around his shivering body. "Please, God, don't let him be delirious when he wakes up," she prayed silently before she, too, fell asleep. When he awakened at sunset, he was both lucid and subdued, and he drank the broth she'd cooked and ate his share of the heavy brown bread and soft farm cheese.

During their second day, ten miles closer to the coast, their shelter was far more precarious: a wide shelf of surviving roof atop an abandoned stone mill in a flat stretch of Bodmin Moor that offered no other shelter. Protected from view by a two-foot wall encircling the heavy timbers that had once been the drying crib for grain, they settled quickly into a sleep that promised to be undisturbed. But such complete relaxation of their vigilance was not to be that day. A small band of wanderers, the gypsylike nomads known as tinkers and distrusted by all provident Cornishmen, chose the gushing stream that flowed past the mill as their noontime camp. Tensely Lynn listened to the snatches of the ancient Cornish language she understood well enough to know the import of their desultory conversation. Decent people, she thought shudderingly, had good reason to fear these homeless misfits. They were laughing about some farmer whose market pigs they'd stolen and sold in the next village. After the interlopers had abandoned their camp, Clay muttered in relief, "I'd rather be taken by soldiers than by those damn savages."

The following day, however, in a shallow cave high on the side of another granite mountain, Clay amended his opinion. On a distant dirt road that meandered over Bodmin Moor, he and Lynn watched as two mounted patrols of soldiers met and rested their horses briefly before they spread out to search that stretch of hilly countryside more thoroughly. One diligent soldier dismounted near the base of the stone shelf that led to their cave and prowled around on foot, shoving his musket determinedly into the declivities and small caves that dimpled the lower part of the rocky hill. Lynn remembered her petulant irritation when Clay had insisted on climbing higher up the steep slope before he'd allow her to cook their breakfast.

When the soldier finally rejoined his patrol and all of the men rode out of view, Clay muttered, "We could have killed ten tinkers and no one would have given a damn; but if we'd so much as tapped that peeping-Tom soldier on his thick skull, we'd have been hunted down and murdered on the spot. I've no liking for caves that lack rear exits."

Frightened by the grimness of his words and by the narrowness of their escape, Lynn asked wonderingly, "Did you have to hide like this often when you were smuggling?"

For some reason his soft responsive laughter annoyed her, and his boastful words renewed her hatred for the capricious idiocy of English law and order.

"For more than five years until Tom's stupidity attracted the attention of the sanctimonious hypocrite Cyril Wilcox and a prudish Falmouth constable, we'd had little trouble with the law, and for a damned good reason. We supplied every head constable in Cornwall with wine and brandy, and some of our best customers were the military leaders who disliked the king's tariff as much as we did. On the few occasions we had to run from soldiers, our horses were always faster.

" 'Twas a merry life while it lasted. In between runs, we were wined and dined on some of the greatest estates in England; our richest customers didn't want to lose their source of supply to the finest of French wines."

"Under those conditions, why did you need so many haven farms and caves?" Lynn demanded.

"We couldn't afford to bribe every policeman and soldier in Cornwall, only their leaders."

Part of her growing attraction to Clay shriveled at the reminder that he had lived a social life far removed from her own isolated loneliness. To him, the only important people in the world were those with rank. They'd never suit, not in the long run of it, she reflected; he'd be bored on a farm and hanker incessantly for the footloose life he'd enjoyed among the social elite of England.

"How much longer before we reach the coast?" she asked wearily.

"In a day or so we should be secure in a comfortable billet on the Cornish cliffs, and from then on 'twill be a simple matter of waiting. But now I think we'd best get some sleep. The walking we've done so far has been holiday strolling compared to what's ahead. Mayhap you'll have to carry me on your strong back yet if the elements decide to play their usual temperamental tricks along this stretch of coast."

As if Nature disliked a flippant appraisal of her powers, she withdrew the benign support she'd given the fugitives in the forms of moonlight and bearably warm weather during the past few days. When Clay and Lynn awakened before the hour of what should have been a gold-spangled sunset, they faced instead a sky overcast with scudding clouds and a freshening wind that penetrated their inadequate clothing. Clay's earlier good humor was replaced by a knowledgeable concern.

"We're in for it, Lynn. This will be no drizzling rain like the one at our first cave; it feels like an Atlantic gale full of cold northern water. And we can't stay here; this cursed cave slopes the wrong way. We'd be awash an hour after the storm began. Get moving, woman; there's no time for hot food now. Wrap our food in the sheepskins, skin side out, your cloak too. We'll need it to keep from freezing if we ever reach the keep."

Lynn would never forget the next twenty hours; no hardship she'd ever endured could compare with the violent misery of the Cornish coast. The rains began when they had traveled three hours along the treacherous rocky trail barely visible in the fading light of day—not the steady downward rain of spring, but intermittent sheets of water hurled against the granite walls of gullies and hillsides to form freshets and cascades that undermined every footstep on the slippery surface. Drenched within minutes of the first onslaught, they dared not rest for longer than brief intervals beneath an occasional overhang. Hard boiled eggs supplied their nourishment at the first few stops, eggs that tasted insipid with old age; limp strips of what had once been dried pork fed them next; and finally only soggy oaten biscuits were left of their once plentiful food supply.

Daylight brought only a lessening of rain; the winds still blew at gale force, and the skies remained overcast. Because they found not even one suitable cave, they continued their painful climbing, sliding, stumbling travel westward. By afternoon neither Lynn nor Clay dared sit down even in a protected spot. Lynn's tortured muscles cramped painfully if she stood too long in one spot, and Clay's knee, bruised when he'd stumbled against a jagged rock, was already too swollen to risk a prolonged rest.

Almost a full day after they'd left the cave that had

sheltered them from discovery, they reached the coast; and
Lynn had her first view ever of the Atlantic Ocean.
Nothing in her grandfather's descriptions of storms at sea
had prepared her for the thundering, destructive power of
the great breakers hurling themselves against the granite
cliffs that formed the western extremity of Cornwall. For a
woman whose only water travel had been on river craft,
the prospect of a voyage upon the open sea no longer
seemed a pleasant prelude to adventure.

Clay was equally disturbed by the vista that met their
eyes, but for an entirely different reason. His eyes were
focused more distantly on the ruins of an ancient stronghold built a century after the Norman years of conquest.
Those ruins were a familiar sight to Clay, and something
about the configuration of the venerable structure bothered
him.

"We'll use the road the rest of the way," he announced
hoarsely to his partner fugitive. "I doubt there's a soldier
in Cornwall who's left his comfortable billet today."

Although the stone paved road, begun in Roman days
and repaired during the reign of Henry VIII, was a hundred fold easier for the footsore refugees, each step was
still a painful effort. As they trudged wearily toward the
ruined castle, Clay's earlier concern strengthened steadily
into certainty. There was definitely a ladder dangling from
the oceanside tower where no ladder should have been. If
what he suspected turned out to be reality, there would be
no available shelter again this night.

Had Lynn been as preoccupied as Clay about a future
problem, she might have missed the sounds of a more
immediate one. Within clear sight of the ancient keep, she
felt the sudden vibration of the roadbed before she heard
the sound of hard-driven horses. Always swift in her
reactions, she grabbed her companion's arm and with a
lunging shove tumbled them both into the deep watery
ditch by the side of the crowned road. Nor was she a
moment too soon; already rounding a curve to the south, in

clear view of the spot she and Clay had been on the road, was a pair of powerful dray horses pulling a swaying wagon. Kneeling low behind the wall of the ditch, half inundated by muddy water, neither of the fugitives dared look up as the lead wagon and the ones that followed thundered past them. Only after they were a considerable distance ahead on the road, did Clay raise his head to stare at the receding procession. His heart pounded in alarm until the wagons spun past the turnoff leading to the seaside ruins of the medieval keep. Not until the last wagon disappeared from view around a distant northern curve, did he relax his vigil. Then pushing Lynn up the steep embankment, he waited impatiently until she turned to pull him after her.

Even with the torment of an icy wind stinging their faces, he urged them forward at an increased speed until they were abreast of the ruined structure. Wordlessly he turned onto an unkempt roadbed marked by tumbled mounds of hewn stone that lined the sides. A hundred feet further on, they crossed the stone bridge that had replaced the more ancient drawbridge after the advent of cannon and gunpowder. Far beneath them only small pools of rainwater in the rock-lined channel marked what had once been a protective moat.

Vigorously now, despite his swollen knee, Clay grabbed Lynn's hand and led her through the ruins with a sure knowledge of his specific destination. Dodging broken parts of walls where no passage seemed possible, he finally reached the footing of the one tower still intact, a twenty-foot diameter structure, the seaward defense center of the venerable fortress. Halfway up the curving wall to the opening thirty feet above the ground, the stone stairs ended, the missing steps crushed into rubble on the floor below. Motioning Lynn to silence, he relinquished her hand, removed his sodden pack, and climbed the stairs alone. After listening intently for any sounds from above, he knelt cautiously and retrieved a hooked gaff hanging from below the stairs. With his back against the wall for support, he raised the gaff upward to the wood platform above and moved it a few feet along the protruding timbers. He uttered a grunt of satisfaction as a heavy rope ladder swung downward, then carefully returned the gaff to its hiding place.

"This is the snug billet I promised you, Lynn," he announced softly as he rejoined his bedraggled companion. "You wait here while I check for intruders." That one thirty-foot climb up a swaying ladder was the only ascent Clay made. Three-quarters up, his knee buckled, and he reached the top in a contorted crawl. A minute later he leaned over the edge and told Lynn to bring both packs with her. Neither as impulsive nor as overconfident, she made two trips before she pulled the ladder up to the platform. Only then did she turn around to view the comfortable room that contained the blessings of a fireplace and a bed.

"Light the fire," Clay called out from a deep recess that jutted away from the rounded contours of the room. His optimism, as usual, implied far more than the existing actualities. There were logs piled in a corner and a crate of kindling twigs, but Lynn had to hunt for the more essential tinder. She found the precious supply of shavings in a small alcove burrowed into the stone wall. Shivering violently in the icy chill of a long unheated room, she gripped the tinderbox with stiff fingers and struck again and again before she achieved the miracle of a flame. Kneeling before the open hearth she coaxed the shavings to ignite, then the dry kindling, and finally the heavy logs.

As she warmed her hands, she looked around the room and discovered it to be a blending of the ancient and modern. The fireplace itself had been rebuilt to include a chimney, and the iron pot hanging over the open flame and suspended from a hinged metal arm was also a recent addition as were the glass-walled lanterns and the glass-paned windows on opposite sides of the room. Modern too was the large bed with a neatly ticked mattress and goosedown pillows.

Lynn's questions were myriad by the time Clay emerged again into the larger room, but she quickly forgot them in her resentful envy of his changed appearance. In place of the soiled and water-soaked blue suit was a long fur-lined bedrobe, and he was both clean and clean shaven. Lynn slumped lower on the stone hearth before the now blazing fire; she felt like a dirty chimney sweep by comparison. She also felt put upon and abused. While he'd ordered her to build the fire—no easy job in the oversized fireplace— he'd groomed himself to a delicate degree of finery. She noted, though, with malicious satisfaction that his limp was more pronounced.

"Come over to the window, Lynn," he called out. "I want to show you something."

Pushing herself up from the floor, she obeyed his peremptory summons unwillingly, walking slowly across the room to stand beside him looking down from a dizzying height to the rocks and surf far below.

Impatiently he clutched her arm and pointed. "Do you see that small rock tower near the water? That's a false signal fire wreckers use to lure ships into dangerous waters. The damn wreckers use driftwood soaked in oil to give a steady flame so that navigators will mistake it for an official lighthouse after the lighthouse fire has been deliberately extinguished."

"Those were wreckers who passed us today, weren't they?"

"Most likely, perhaps the same ones who've used this tower since I was last here. But they won't be bothering us for the next few days unless they sprout wings; I've cut the ropes of their ladder enough to fell the first man who tries to climb it. The cursed villains dirtied the garderobe some, but they didn't locate the supply closet. You'll find bedding there and another robe when you finish washing, and the larder's been freshly stocked for us. Do you suppose you can fill the cooking pot with water before you start? I need some hot tea to get rid of the chill I still feel."

Lynn stared mutinously at the dry fur-lined slippers now encasing his feet and wiggled her icy toes in the water still sloshing uncomfortably in her own worn boots. In a voice that was sharp with exhaustion and exasperation, she retorted tartly, "You can put your own water on, Clay Penley, and dress your own bed. Moreover, Mr. Penley, unless there's another pair of those house boots you have on, your feet are going to remain chilled."

Grinning at her with an impudent superiority, he chided her lightly, "We'll have to do something about that temper of yours. Since you're so unwilling, we'll forget the tea until after you've cleaned up. You'll find plenty of wash water just past that door."

The wash room was little more than a wide corridor boarded up at one end, and the plentiful wash water consisted of a row of wood buckets on an outdoor shelf accessible to the rain. Exposed to the elements by a large window-high opening in the wall at the rear of the sloped waste fall, the small room was as primitive as it had been five hundred years earlier when English castles often reeked of human excrement. Lynn shivered with cold as she used the ancient contrivance and thought longingly of the civilized advances of chamber pots and warmed necessary rooms.

Shivering more violently now in the unheated alcove, she stripped off her sodden clothing and washed herself as quickly as she could soap one linen towel and dry herself with another. Before she threw the bucket of soapy water down the waste fall, she doused all her discarded garments in the water, scrubbed out the worst of the dirt, and wrung them out. In the concealed closet Clay had mentioned, she located the second fur-lined robe and pair of matching boots, pretentiously purple in color and oversized, but heavenly warm. As she turned to leave, she stumbled over a pile of sodden clothing, carelessly discarded on the floor.

Silently cursing her inconsiderate companion who'd thrown them there, she washed them as she had her own and hung both sets on a makeshift line she rigged between two chairs in the tower room. Resentfully she turned around to berate the man who treated her more like a chambermaid than a potential wife, only to find him sprawled across the bed and sound asleep. The only work he'd done before he collapsed was to drape leather coverings across the land-side windows and to bolt the heavy doors that sealed off the dangerous entry.

Returning wearily to the alcove, Lynn checked the food supply and thought longingly of a hot meal, but she knew she was too exhausted to cook it. With the last of her energy, she placed two more logs on the dwindling fire, spread blankets over the sleeping man, climbed in beside him, and fell asleep instantly, still wearing the robe. When she awoke unnumbered hours later in the gray dawn of another overcast day, the fire was out and the room once again, icy cold. While Clay slept on in total oblivion to her bustling activity, she rebuilt the fire, filled the pot with water and added the ingredients for another pork stew before she prepared a pot of tea. Only then did she take the time to wash herself and brush her hair into a semblance of order and to set the small table with the cups, bowls and cutlery she located in the supply closet.

She'd just finished laying out the bread and cheese and tempting black currant cake when her companion of ten days mumbled a sleepy greeting. "As soon as we've finished breakfast, mistress, I wish you'd look at my knee. It feels stiffer this morning."

Remembering how sore and stiff her own muscles had been until she'd moved briskly around the room, Lynn responded crisply, "I hope one of your indentured women friends is a nurse; you seem always to be needing one."

Clay laughed good naturedly as he limped to the garde-robe, returning a while later with a small cask of wine and two magnificent pewter wine cups. Silently he filled them

and raised his in a mocking salute. "I'm quite content with
the woman and nurse I already have, Lynn Penley. Now
let's drink to a speedy rescue and a long and happy life
together."

Slowly Lynn lifted her cup, not to sip the wine, but to
study the crest on the side of the richly embossed vessel.
She recognized the heraldic symbol instantly; it was one of
the most famous in Cornwall—the undulating sea serpent
of the powerful Pendrath family.

"Are you a Pendrath, Clay?" she asked quietly.

His mocking smile annoyed her. "No more than I am a
Penley, mistress. In truth, I'm no longer related to any
family other than the one we'll beget together."

Reminded of a future she hadn't yet accepted fully,
Lynn was silent as she served the food and poured the tea.
Although she ate as hungrily as he did, her thoughts were
concentrated on another probable future reality. She was
quite certain that the two men Clay had referred to casually
over the past days as Spence and Harry were his equals in
social rank. Moodily resentful as she tidied the dishes, she
felt trapped. Unless she could escape from the responsibility she'd been tricked into assuming by a devious Bevil
Trevor, she'd be the one doing the servant's work for
spoiled and demanding aristocrats like the one waiting for
her to tend his knee. She jerked uneasily when his voice
sounded behind her.

"What's the matter, Lynn? Are you disappointed that
I'm not a Pendrath?"

"I wish you weren't anything like a Pendrath. I wish
you were nothing but a farmer with modest expectations.
But you're not a farmer; you're used to people obeying
your every whim. Since the night we met, you've treated
me as your servant, not your equal. I didn't mind when
you were ill, but I mind very much your playing the
condescending lord with me now."

"Is all this bad humor the result of my falling asleep last
night? I was done in."

"So was I, but someone had to tend the fire and wash our clothes. We'd look more the fools than we are, trying to escape in these pretty bedrobes. 'Twas as hard for me as it was for you to walk those hills, but every night and morning you let me prepare the food and unpack our bundles.''

Having exorcised her twin devils of resentment and suspicion, Lynn quickly regained her customary self-confidence. "If 'tis a servant you're expecting, I give you fair warning you'll be disappointed. I've no intention of spending my life on my knees in front of any man. Now, let's look at that sore one of yours.''

A few minutes later after her capable hands had probed the slight swelling, she smiled reassuringly. " 'Tis only a bruise and not serious. You won't be scrambling over cliffs very gracefully for the next few days; but according to you, we're done with that misery. Are you ready yet to tell me just how we're to get out of here and aboard the *Tamarlind*?''

"After dark tonight, I'm to signal with a lantern from the sea window. My friends will be watching from across the cove—''

"From the other Pendrath keep?''

"I had no idea you were so well informed about Cornish estates.''

"Cornwall's a small county without many undamaged relics from the Middle Ages. What happens after you signal?''

"They'll come for us in a small boat, and we'll rendez-vous with the *Tamarlind*.''

"What if those wreckers who passed us yesterday decide differently?''

"We'll have to reach Trebuchet on our own.''

"Did you recognize those wreckers, Clay?''

"Not personally, but there's only one I know of with that big an organization—a Welsh pirate who left the sea to work his villainy on land.''

"Is he the one who mounted the ladder against this tower?"

"Probably. He wouldn't be tolerant of competition. But we've more important things to discuss, mistress, and not too much time left. What are you going to tell m—tell Sir Bevil Trevor about our marriage?"

The idea that had been forming slowly in Lynn's mind hardened into determination; there was no need for her to be responsible for anyone other than her own people.

"We can tell him that we'll be married since 'tis the safest way to protect our new identities; but that once we reach America, you'll go to Connecticut with your friends, and I'll stay in Rhode Island with mine. In that way, you'll have your freedom and I'll have mine."

Clay's narrowed eyes glinted in anger. The fact that he'd decided on the same solution when he'd agreed to the marriage only added to his frustration. Both his father and Ephraim Penley had made him promise that the marriage would be a very real one; and both men intended to make certain it was. What the devil had happened to change her mind? She'd seemed willing enough on the trail.

"Sir Bevil and your grandfather won't agree to those terms, and neither will I," he exploded.

Surprised by his vehemence, Lynn moved restlessly over to the window, disturbed anew by this man who'd dominated her thoughts since the violent night she'd met him. When she felt his arms encircle her from the rear, she stiffened defensively, but she didn't pull away. She was remembering the turbulent emotions she'd felt when they'd clutched each other in the sheep cote and later when he'd kissed her. Loosening the tight hold of his arms, she turned around to face him in protest; she had no intention of succumbing to a deliberate and calculated seduction. She realized her mistake instantly as those same arms locked her into a sinewy vise, and he bent his head the few inches needed to capture her lips. Lynn's only impression before the remembered surge of warmth entrapped her was that he was still angry, but no more in control of his emotions than she was of hers.

Minutes later, after she'd learned to avoid being smothered by the increasingly amorous pressure of his lips and the added stimulation of his hands gripping her unclad body beneath her robe, Lynn decided that she'd been right about the skill of kissing—it didn't require much practice to master. It also proved to be far more enjoyable in bed where they'd somehow arrived without her conscious knowledge. That she was now irrevocably committed at least to a temporary union with this complicated man, she didn't deny, not even when his lips left hers and traveled wantonly to her breasts. Lynn had no way of knowing that her partner had already surrendered to the sensually primitive pleasure of exploring the body of a woman whose subtle femininity was building to a passionate awakening. She knew only that there was a fiery emptiness inside her, a burning compulsion to unite her body with his.

Despite the one searing pain she experienced when he entered her slowly but inexorably, that moment of union held no real mystery for her, only a physical satisfaction, a realization of the fulfillment that had eluded her in all other pursuits. Even the tumult of their bodies moving in concerted rhythm, straining toward an unknown goal for her, seemed as natural to her as the rhythm of the changing seasons. Sensitized now to the instructions of his lips and hands, Lynn matched his final thrusts with an instinctive strength that required no willful volition. She was as much animal as human during the climactic explosion that vaulted her into a world free from mental control and moral edict, a world of physical sensation so intense she felt consumed.

Her first reaction to the abrupt cessation of the ecstatic thrill was greedy disappointment; she didn't want to leave the exalted plane of altered consciousness. That Clay's response had been quite different was readily discernible; he'd kissed her limply and rolled to his side, his arms holding her without intent or purpose, his eyes closing in pacified content. Lynn remained quietly by his side until his breathing rumbled into sleep, then she eased herself from the disordered bed and walked into the cold washroom. She needed the chill wind of a dying storm to clear her head and readjust her to a reality that held little of the enchantment she'd just experienced.

With arousing humor she washed herself and sponged off the dull smears from the fur lining of her robe; she hadn't expected the blood and certainly not the ample amount she'd shed. Ruefully she wondered if Clay had realized that she'd been ignorant as well as innocent. Despite her reputation as a stock breeder, Jem had always made certain that she was safely in the house with Polly when he ran a cow into Red Penny's small fenced pasture. Meticulously each night during the breeding season, Jem had reported which cows had been serviced, and she'd recorded the date. There'd been no such prohibition about the birthings, however; so Lynn's knowledge of procreation had remained somewhat limited to the fruition part when the calves were pushed or pulled onto the hay in a byre stall.

Her humor wobbled a little when she considered the possibility of a similar result from her impulsive mating with the trouble-prone man who would become her husband once they reached the *Tamarlind*. She still had no confidence in the permanency of their relationship, but at least the marriage would be real enough to satisfy Sir Trevor and her grandfather. Whatever happened after they reached America, they'd both be protected by the legal bond at least. Sharply reminded that reaching America was by no means certain, Lynn dressed herself hurriedly in the clothing she'd laundered the night before and began the preparation for still another flight.

She was filling the waterskins when she heard a shuffling noise coming from the timbered platform outside the heavy oak entry doors. Too terrified to move until she remembered the metal bars locked into place over both doors, Lynn snatched up her clubs and moved toward the bed to awaken Clay. When an exasperated command sounded from the entry, she jerked nervously in renewed fear.

"For God's sake, Clay, wake up and open the door. We're about to have visitors."

As instantly alert as he'd been in the cave when Lynn first reported the soldiers, Clay relayed the command, "Open the door, Lynn, he's a friend."

Still vigilant despite the reassurance, she wrested the heavy bars from their slots, opened one door part of the way and stepped backward to retrieve her clubs. The man who strode briskly into the room looked no more like a fugitive criminal than Clay did. Although his maroon velvet coat and jack boots were muddied, his plumed hat was rakishly Cavalier; and his self-assured smile was condescending as he surveyed the flails in Lynn's hands.

"Can you use those clubs, laddie, or are they just for show?" Without waiting for an answer, he called over to Clay, "Where the hell's the woman who's supposed to be with you? Without her aboard, old Penley won't let the *Tamarlind* sail anywhere."

Controlling his laughter as he walked toward the washroom, Clay returned the greeting in kind. "You nearsighted jackanapes, you just met my wife; and believe me when I tell you she can use those clubs like a professional. Lynn, hand me my clothes while Harry bars the doors, and then pour the swaggering pretender some wine."

Stunned by the premature appellation of "wife," Lynn followed the instructions dazedly, defensively wary as she filled one of the crested cups that she suspected belonged to the stranger. Her suspicion was confirmed when he accepted the proffered cup and muttered "What the hell are these doing here?" before he swept his hat off, made a cursory bow, and introduced himself. "Harry Cobb at your service, mistress."

Lynn's responsive smile belied her cynical evaluation of

the man; this was another of the indentured smugglers she'd thought to turn into a farmhand! She'd have been even more nonplussed had she known that the money belt around his waist contained a fortune in gold guineas, and that his wife of three years, also an indentured criminal, was the sister of Averill Trevor's wife. Fortunately for Lynn's dwindling equanimity, Harry Cobb's interest in her was of short duration. While she busied herself stirring the pork stew simmering over the low fire, Harry leaned against the wall leading to the garderobe and engaged in an animated conversation with Clay.

"Where's Spence now?" Clay asked.

"Six miles north of here nursing a bullet wound in his sword arm. Two of the six seamen who were with us weren't as lucky."

"What happened?"

"We ran into a pack of cursed wreckers, that's what happened! They attacked without warning just after we beached the boat, and we were damned lucky to get away at all."

"The Welshman?"

"That's what the army thinks, but they haven't caught him yet. Whoever the villains are, they've already lured three ships into their trap and perhaps a fourth during this storm. 'Tis suspected they use the towers here and at Trebuchet for their false signal lights. Did you notice any sign of them here, Jame?"

"Best call me Clay, 'tis my official name again, Clay Penley. As for the villainous wreckers, I think some of them were in this tower during this last storm. Two of the rain buckets were only half-full, and the floor of the wash room was muddied. I don't think they found our entrance, though, because they mounted their own ladder near the waste fall. Relax, Harry, I've already cut the ropes. They didn't use this tower for signaling, only as a lookout; they built their own signal tower on the rocks below here. What about Trebuchet?"

"That's where we were attacked late yesterday, right in the water in front of the tunnel, when a dozen of the devils rushed out pirate-style with cutlasses and pistols. We barely managed to reach open water in time to save the four of us; the two men already out of the boat were killed. The boat's well hidden now a mile north—you remember the cave—but we couldn't signal you, so I walked the long way around past Drathmont."

Lynn could hear the amusement in Clay's response. " 'Tis obvious you visited your brother's estate; you've not looked this grand for a long time, Harry."

"Don't sound so smug! 'Twas an eight-mile walk, the same one we'll be taking tonight, and we'll not be lonely. There's twenty soldiers stationed at Drathmont waiting for reinforcements from the south, and they're as jumpy as hound dogs before the hunt."

"My God, you didn't talk to them, did you?"

"Don't be daft. Andrew met me at the north gate house. He's the one who sent his bailey to stock the food for you after someone had sent a message from Plymouth. He'll be waiting for us on the return trip to tell him anything we've seen of the villainous scum. Have you had a chance to check the cellars yet?"

"No, we were done in, but I imagine they're using all of them as we did before I bought that cursed house in Falmouth. Trebuchet wouldn't hold the loot from two ships, much less four. God knows they've enough wagons for easy transportation between the two. I counted four that passed us on the road yesterday with fast horses and well-greased wheels."

"Full of cargo?"

"Full of men. That's why I was sure 'twas the Welshman."

"You've seen more than anyone else then; none of the guards Andrew set out to watch ever saw a sign of them. But the military insists they'll need those cargoes as proof before they attack."

"Our noble military wants those cargoes as reward, so

they can do their own searching. I've no desire to fight my way out of here at night."

Listening to the conversation from across the room, Lynn felt a dismal foreboding. The prospect of another long walk was discouraging enough, but the possibility of meeting either soldiers or wreckers made her shudder with dread anticipation. Harry Cobb, however, had not yet completed his recital of bad news. Edging more completely into the washroom, he spoke confidentially in a lowered voice.

"There's another matter you should hear of, Clay. I'm hoping you spoke the truth when you said you'd already wed the woman; because if you haven't, her grandfather plans to make sure you don't."

Clay's sharp response was clearly audible to the avid listener in the adjoining room. "The devil you say! He was in complete argreement eleven days ago. What happened to change his mind?"

"Tom Kenn announced he didn't intend to do a lick of farmwork, and his damned slut of a woman riled the old man with her insolence."

"The damn fools! They'll work all right, if I have to beat the pair of them!"

Harry sighed heavily. "They weren't the ones who really convinced Penley. My charming wife did her best to antagonize the old man."

"What the hell did she do?"

"She tried to insist he purchase the papers of one of the other women convicts so that she could have a maid."

"My God, doesn't she have any sense at all?"

"You know Amelia, she says and does what she wants."

"Why the devil didn't m—didn't Sir Trevor shut her up?"

"How could he? Her sister's his daughter-in-law."

Lynn closed her eyes in hopeless resignation. She'd met Barbara Gordon Trevor often enough to despise the arrogant conceit of such women. No wonder Bevil Trevor had worked so hard to free these particular convicts; he was protecting a member of his own family, another useless aristocrat like the two men whispering in the next room. With her lips curling in bitter contempt, Lynn set the table and placed the pot of stew in the center, making no effort to hear any more of the furtive conversation. She'd heard all she needed or wanted to know; Amelia Gordon Cobb would be an impossibility on a small New England farm. When the men sat down to eat the meal she'd prepared, their bland faces revealed no hint of the confidences they'd exchanged; and Lynn's own features were impersonally expressionless. After the hurried meal, Harry Cobb announced his intention of taking a short nap and promptly proceded to do so without an apology to his hostess, a freedom he'd never dare take with a daughter of the arrogant Devon Gordons, Lynn reflected cynically.

As she began to gather up the dirty dishes from the table, Clay rose from his chair and put his arm around her waist. "You're angry about what you overheard, aren't you, Lynn? You've no reason to be; Amelia's as indentured as the rest of us; and besides, I can handle her tantrums."

"How very cozy. But why should you be any more successful than her husband? Let Sir Bevil Trevor be responsible for his own relative."

"What do you mean by that remark?" Clay demanded with a wary bluntness.

"She's his relative by marriage, and the only reason he involved me in this scheme was to keep her safe. Did she earn her conviction or was she charged unfairly?"

Clay's eyes were no longer hooded with concern, but his admission was still vaguely cautious. "She took the same risks as the rest of us."

"Then she'll be the responsibility of you and Harry, but not a one of my people will become her personal servant. As long as your friends pay their own way and follow the legal restriction of indenture, I won't bother them. But I don't think they'll be very happy on a small farm, so you'll have to make arrangements for them somewhere else. Excuse me, Clay, while I see to the packing.''

''We won't be needing any of those things again. Sit down, Lynn, I want to talk to you.''

''There's nothing more needs be said.''

''Not even 'thank you'?''

''I doubt you'll have much to be grateful for; my grandfather usually proves to be right.''

''The future can take care of itself. I was referring to our immediate past. Did you think I'd forgotten?''

Smiling with cynical self-deprecation, Lynn shrugged her shoulders, seeking to dislodge his arm from around her waist. Clay's response was a more complete embrace, with his unoccupied hand holding her head still while he whispered into her ear, ''You've still much to learn about men, my lovely witch. 'Twas your fault I needed sleep afterwards. Had you stayed in bed with me, I'd have awakened long before Harry interrupted us. Our marriage won't be a dull one, Lynn. You've passion enough to match a man's, and even better endurance.''

Lynn's laughter was a soft burst of amusement that reflected little romantic appreciation for the compliment; she felt like a heifer on the selling block. ''I've also a sharp ear for false flattery, Clay Penley,'' she scoffed.

''Don't be so quick to misjudge a man, Trelynn Trevor; or you'll find out how hard a floor can be,'' he countered sharply before he pulled her into a tighter embrace and pressed her hips against his with strong hands. Smiling down at her startled look of recognition as she felt his readiness, he kissed her slowly and thoroughly until her body was as passionately taut as his own. But whether he would have carried out his threat was not to be tested. Both of them heard the dull thud that sounded on the outer wall of the tower and the muted curses that followed.

''The ladder,'' Clay whispered tersely. ''Someone tried

to climb it. We'll have to risk a daylight escape after all. Open those doors, Lynn, while I rouse Harry.''

The few minutes that lapsed between his muted warning and the hurried departure revealed much about the three occupants of the tower room. With efficient speed, Clay and Harry loaded their pistols and fastened their swords about their waists while Lynn slipped her hands through the leather thongs of her clubs and fastened her dirty cloak around her neck. None of them panicked when they heard the sounds of grappling hooks landing on the roof above and grinding into the low crenels of the ancient stone defenses.

''At least the bastards never found our entrance,'' Harry grunted as he lowered the rope ladder toward the pit of rubble far below. He descended swiftly and held the ladder taut as Lynn descended, her heart beating in fear for the man remaining on the platform above, holding a drawn sword in his hand. As Lynn, in turn, steadied the ladder for Clay's descent, Harry ran up the stone stairway and, with a swift sword stroke, severed the ropes just as Clay dismounted at the bottom.

Silently the three fugitives moved cautiously along the cluttered, narrow path leading to the more distant ruins of the old castle and toward the one certain escape route: the stone bridge that spanned the empty moat. Because for the most part, the two-hundred feet they traveled was protected from view by tumbled walls and overhanging timbers of the ancient structure, they felt relatively safe. But their first clear view of the bridge ended any hope for an easy escape. On the road at the far end of the bridge stood a large dray wagon with the horses facing the distant highway. Standing on the bed of the wagon, two burly men were handing down barrels, crates, and trunks to other men waiting to carry them into the remote cellars that had escaped damage throughout the centuries. In the center of the bridge, four guards armed with cutlasses watched as their companions worked.

From the deep concealment beneath a tumbled wall, Lynn stared with fascination at the faces of the wreckers, men considered to be the most vicious criminals in the whole of England. While three of them looked no different from the peasant farmhands she'd worked with, the others seemed exotically foreign to her, darker skinned and more heavily bearded. But all of them, she noted, were well-booted and more warmly dressed than common seamen; and the ones unloading the wagon were strong enough to carry heavy loads with a practiced ease as they started off on a well-pounded path that led to the distant cellars.

"They won't be back for thirty minutes," Clay whispered to his companions. "That gives us time to disarm the others."

"We'll stand a better chance after dark," Harry countered.

"By that time the ones in the tower would have found their way here, and we'd be trapped in the middle. Worse still, the other three wagons could be on the way, and then we'd stand no chance at all. Put your pistols away, Harry. We don't need any extra noise. Since when couldn't you and I handle four half-trained lumberers armed only with clumsy cutlasses? Lynn, you're to stay put inside the old portcullis wall until we engage those guards. Then you cross the bridge and keep going until you reach the other side of the highway."

A minute later Lynn was huddled behind the crumbling wall just inside the ruins, her view of the bridge obscured. As he had on the night he'd tricked Rad Pollock out of the Wadley farmhouse, Clay was talking as he approached the men on the bridge. "Ahoy, mates," he called out, "you're trespassing on private property. This is Pendrath land, and we represent the—" His speech was interrupted by the sound of clashing metal on metal, and Lynn heard her first sounds of violently sustained sword fighting, interrupted briefly by the scream of one man falling to the rocks below. Seconds later she heard an even more paralyzing sound: that of hard-running footsteps coming from the shadowy direction of the tower. As frightened as she was, she darted behind a pile of rocks just before three men appeared within feet of her new hiding place. Clay had underestimated the time it would take the tower invaders to reach the inner passage.

As she gripped the handles of her clubs, Lynn's only thought was that they were child's weapons compared to swords and pistols. But they downed the last man to pass her before he reached the bridge, and the second man five feet farther on. Only the man in the lead turned to face this new enemy, his weapon a heavy cudgel that would have crushed her with the first blow had his aim been more accurate. Fighting for her life now, Lynn was forced to rely on agility to keep out of reach of that deadly bludgeon wielded by a strong man inured to the violence of criminal battle. As surely as the sword fighters thirty feet away from her, Lynn retreated backward and darted forward in a desperate pattern of evasion, her only advantage being the doubtful one of swifter movement. Eventually it was luck rather than skill that saved her when her stocky opponent stumbled and momentarily lost control of his weapon. Both of her clubs struck him simultaneously, then struck again and again until he lay deadly still at her feet.

Lynn was still breathing hard as she turned toward the other fight being waged, but she was experiencing an emotion she'd never felt before—something a veteran soldier would have called the heat of battle. As her eyes focused on the individual figures of the other fighters, she knew with a dread certainty that Clay had also underestimated the number of guards. Two dead wreckers lay sprawled on the bridge and one on the stones below, but three others were still fighting, their heavy cutlasses slashing against the swifter defense of swords.

None of the five combatants broke their concentration long enough to notice the figure in the dark cape covering a water-wrinkled red suit running toward them. Only at the last moment did the bearded man Lynn had targeted sense her presence and turn to confront her. His lunge was an automatic reaction, as was Lynn's leap to one side, but during that brief moment the man's back was exposed to the sword held with grim intent in Clay Penley's left hand, his right arm hanging uselessly by his side. The battle ended when the remaining two wreckers turned to run across the bridge and into the castle ruins. Of the three victors, only Lynn was uninjured, and only she was in any condition to attempt an eight-mile walk.

Perhaps it was the pain of his new injury added to the older one of a bruised knee that made Clay speak so harshly to her. "You cock-a-hoop fool, you could have been killed. Now, help me get Harry aboard that wagon. Someone will have to drive the bloody thing to Drathmont."

Barely able to stand from a slashed leg, Harry proved to be far heavier than Lynn had thought possible; but the barrels and bundles she was forced to push off the wagon to make room for the wounded man were heavier still. Her arms felt leaden in their sockets as she climbed into the driver's seat and took the reins from Clay. Weakened by a loss of blood, he protested peevishly.

"I can drive a wagon," she asserted rashly, forgetting that the farm carts had been pulled by slow-paced bullocks, not by powerfully swift horses. Neither of her passengers would ever forget that wild three-mile ride to the Pendrath stronghold of Drathmont or the jarring stop beneath a stand of oak trees a hundred yards from the imposing gate house. And Lynn would never forget the terror and tension of the following twelve hours.

CHAPTER
5

In the timbered attic of the stone gate house, Lynn lay sleepless on a small pallet far removed from the larger ones provided for the wounded men. Bandaged efficiently by the servants whom Lord Andrew Pendrath had summoned and given ample doses of laudanum in glasses of wine, Clay and Harry slept peacefully through the departure of the troop of soldiers accompanied by Lord Pendrath himself. During the tense hour preceding, Harry had explained the situation to his brother, omitting only one minor detail in his recital. Lynn had been introduced only as a young cousin to James Thayne and thus been given the indifferent treatment accorded to an unimportant male relative. She was asked no questions, but rather told what would be expected of her during the final hours of escape.

Quite accustomed to command, Lord Pendrath announced that his finest coachmen would drive the wagon to the rendezvous beach just before dawn and carry the wounded men to the waiting boat. Lynn's assignment would be to locate that boat and take charge of its departure. Unfortunately, like the directions given by so many other men, those outlined by Harry about the location of the boat were

106

both lofty and vague, while Clay's clarification was muddled by sleep. That confusion, however, lost all importance to Lynn an hour later when a second troop of soldiers arrived at Drathmont. From the tiny dormer window, she watched the bobbing lanterns in the court and recognized the distinctive high-crowned hats and the red coats of the English military even before a servant crept into the loft and told her who these new arrivals were.

To her dismay, she learned that the captain had declined to join the other troop already in pursuit of the wreckers. Instead he quartered his men in the manor house, requested dinner, and announced a morning departure. It was when Lynn heard the captain's name that she felt the cold grip of renewed fear. Clay had described Cyril Wilcox as a Puritan hypocrite with the instincts of a bloodhound and the unbending morality of a prude. Lady Pendrath's plan to offer plentiful amounts of wine to her unwelcome guests would not work with a man who considered spirits of any kind another of the devil's handiwork. Like witchcraft, Lynn reflected bitterly!

Because Penley Farm had been a simple home where the old family retainers spoke their minds freely, Lynn had no idea of the army of servants who operated the Pendrath estate, or of their regimented loyalty or versatility. Somehow during the night, the two dray horses had been watered and fed, the remainder of the wreckers' loot removed and hidden from sight, and the wagon bed fitted with comfortable pads and blankets. As an added insurance against detection, the heavy wooden sides had been lined with hay, and a lightweight frame stretched across the top and piled with additional hay lashed down with ropes. The Pendrath people were no strangers to the subterfuges of smuggling. During and after the civil war, the older hands among them had participated in the transportation of illegal cargoes, both inanimate contraband and fugitive Cavaliers.

Before she fell asleep, Lynn had one additional fright.

Accompanied by the Pendrath bailiff, Captain Wilcox insisted on what he called a precautionary search of the premises; and the gate house was not spared his suspicious vigilance. Even as the authoritative footsteps of marching soldiers sounded in the larger rooms below, nine servants squeezed their bedding into the attic space and arranged their pallets tightly around the crawl-hole entry. They were feigning sleep with practiced artistry when the heads of two soldiers, silhouetted by the lanterns they were holding, poked through the opening.

"How many servants up there?" Lynn heard a voice below demand.

"An even dozen," one of the soldiers responded, "just like the bailey said there'd be, and packed together like pigs on the way to market."

Those packed-together bodies remained where they were until the appointed hour of departure. By that time, Lynn felt smothered by the odor of unwashed bodies and deafened by the discordant drone of snorts and snorings. But those sensations were minor compared to the sick horror she experienced when she was told to crawl into the prisonlike cage on the wagon beside the limp bodies of Clay and Harry. Had Clay not been next to her and had she not been able to dig an airspace in the wall of hay, Lynn might have given vent to an insane compulsion to scream.

The ride itself was as smooth as an expert driver could contrive, but every rut and rock jarred the passengers until Lynn's groans were as loud as Clay's and Harry's. Only one stop was made along the way, but that one was terrifying to the one conscious passenger. As Lynn heard the terse military order to halt, she squirmed into a cramped position that allowed her to cover the mouths of her sleeping companions with her hands. Only slightly relieved when she heard the gruff, authoritative voice of Lord Pendrath, Lynn tried to ignore her cramping muscles as she kept her two companions quiet.

"The wagon's mine, colonel, making its regular delivery of fodder to Padstow," the aristocrat assured the officer blandly before he addressed the wagon's driver more aggressively, "Dickson, have the other troops arrived yet?"

Lynn heard the sly insolence in the voice of the resourceful man who'd directed most of the night's activities at Drathmont. "Aye, yer worship, they did that; but yon Captain Wilcox refused to heed the message that Bailey give him about joining you on the chase. Claimed morning 'ud be soon enough; but won't be early morning. The captain kept his men on the hop for hours after he come; checkin' the premises, so to speak, as if we 'uz hidin' the murderin' pirates there."

"Was he finally satisfied we were not?" Pendrath asked sharply.

"Aye, but only after her ladyship served him and his men enough mutton stew and skilly broth."

Certain that Lady Pendrath's skilly broth had been liberally laced with laudanum, Lynn started to relax, only to tense again when the officer Pendrath had addressed as colonel spoke angrily. To her relief, the man was a Cavalier with little discernible interest in the search for a suspected witch or an escaped convict.

"Curse King Charles and his tolerance for cowardly Roundheads! The only damn thing they're good for is chasing down harmless fugitives, and Wilcox is the damndest of the lot."

Lynn heard no more of the roadside dialogue; the wagon was in motion again, a smoother ride this time on the stone-paved coastal highway. It was two hours before the driver stopped again, and Lynn emerged stiffly into gray daylight along a protected stretch of beach whose cliffs were gentle slopes rather than perpendicular walls. Fearful of what lay ahead on the path leading down to the water, she once more gripped her flails defensively. She saw the man crouching behind a rock just before he stepped out to confront her, but it took the whole of her failing reservoir of courage to call out softly, "Are you from the *Tamarlind*?"

"Aye, lad, but where's Harry Cobb and the others?"

"They've been injured," Lynn rasped tiredly as she turned around to signal the driver.

"Damn to hell, lad," the sailor exploded angrily, "them'll make three dead weights fer us t' row a bloody mile against the tide, and you don't look sturdy enough t' spell us off."

Lynn was, however, considered sturdy enough to sit in the bow of the longboat with two pistols in her hands to watch both fore and aft for pursuers during the short voyage. Crowded together on beds of straw laid athwart the craft were the "dead weights" of the three injured men, the one called Spence muttering in intermittent delirium while Clay and Harry slept peacefully. The morning was well advanced by the time the straining oarsmen pulled the boat alongside the heavy timbered hull of its parent ship. Never had any sight been more welcome to the exhausted woman who'd survived eleven days of traumatic flight, but even more welcome were the davit ropes and pulleys that hoisted the longboat up to the deck of the *Tamarlind* without disturbing the ailing human cargo. Lynn had been certain that her stiffened hands would have prevented her from negotiating another rope ladder.

When Captain Vinson tried to question the odd young passenger he did not at first recognize as the Mistress Trelynn Trevor he'd met at the Wadley farm, a vigilant Ephraim Penley whisked her to a cabin away from the bustling activity on deck. Inside the cabin Polly Rigg was waiting with two buckets of hot water and a breakfast that still contained the rich provender of land. Sound asleep within the hour, Lynn awakened late in the afternoon to find her grandfather seated patiently on the one chair in the small cabin.

"I've heard all the sorry details of your escape, lass," he began what was to be a lengthy and discouraging warning, "so 'tis not that I want to talk to you about.

Clay . . . Clay Penley said that you'd agreed to wed him. Have you?''

"Yes. Wasn't that what you and Sir Trevor wanted me to do?"

"Bevil still does, but I've changed my mind."

"Why?"

"Not because of the man himself; I've a notion he's a charming rogue. But the collection of parasites he means to foist on you will make your life miserable."

"Two of those 'parasites' risked their lives to get me safely aboard this ship, Grandfa," Lynn reminded her grandfather slyly.

"Point well taken, lass," Ephraim admitted. "If you'd be dealing with just the three men, I'd give my approval, although they're an irresponsible lot. After the doctor stitched up your sword fighters and removed the bullet from the other man, the three of them acted as if the danger had been merely good sport. That's their problem, Trelynn. They've been taking foolish chances for so many years, I doubt any of them will ever settle down to sober, hard work. To begin with, none of them have learned an honest trade; and they'll be useless on a farm, especially on a farm in Rhode Island. I'm well-known there, and my friends would be very curious about my sponsoring indentureds as undisciplined as this lot. You should have heard your intended husband boasting about his plans for a future that will be as footloose as his past."

"You're the one who freed him from indenture, Grandfa, when you named him your mythical nephew."

"I don't regret that decision. As a free man, he'll be able to take care of his friends without endangering you; and he'll have a choice of colonies. He can take them to Bevil's property in Connecticut or to the Pendrath lands in Virginia."

"What about me, Grandfa?"

"You'll live with my friend Edward Fulton on Aquidneck Island until I'm free to join you."

"Did you tell Clay about your decision?"

"No. I doubt he'd have taken me seriously; he seemed very sure of you."

"He has reason to be, Grandfa," Lynn responded with a blunt honesty. "Perhaps Clay isn't a sensible choice of a husband, but I've given him my word. Now tell me about his friends."

"He said you'd know that Harry Cobb is Lord Pendrath's brother and that he's the only one who is still a wealthy man. His ill-gotten gains were safely stored in his brother's stronghold when he was captured. The Pendraths are an arrogant lot, lass, who'd ride roughshod over the likes of us if given a chance."

Remembering Harry's condescension to her in the tower room, Lynn promised grimly, "He'd do it only once to me, Grandfa. I've already decided that he'll be Clay's responsibility. What about Bert Spence?"

"He's better educated than the other two and as well born, but not as lucky as Harry Cobb. The Roundheads confiscated his family estate, and King Charles did not reinstate it because it was bankrupt. In spite of his years in smuggling, he's the most sober of the three; under different circumstances, he might prove to be an excellent colonist. As I said before, I've no hard and fast objection to these three. 'Tis the others who are worthless."

"What is Mrs. Spence like?"

"On the surface, Leona Spence appears to be a gentlewoman. Her father was an Anglican minister who died before his church and holdings could be returned to him, so she's as penniless as her husband."

"Is she willing to work?"

"No, she's naught but a childish dreamer who'll never accept the harsh reality of colonial life. One minute she prattles prettily about the home she expects her husband to establish for her, and the next she whines about the unfairness of her prison sentence. She'll be nothing but a burden to her husband and to you."

"I already know about Tom Kenn. Even his father admitted that he was a ne'er-do-well."

"He's a good deal worse than a mere wastrel; he's a swaggering bully without the ability to be anything more than a six-shilling pickpocket. Jem won't let him near your cattle because I suspect the young blackguard is as vicious as he is insolent. Even the woman he calls his wife is not the fool he is. I'll let Polly tell you about Nell Wallis; I found her too rebellious to be civil."

"But she's not the villainess Amelia Cobb is, am I right, Grandfa?"

Ephraim sighed heavily. "What do you know about her, lass?"

"I've met her sister, and I've heard all I care to about the glorious history of the Gordon family."

"They're scoundrels, the whole lot of them, but this one is worse. Harry Cobb blames the Wallis woman for their capture, but his own wife was the real culprit, the real criminal what's more likely. Before she wed into the Pendrath family three years ago, she'd been a part of the hangers-on around Barbara Villiers, the Duchess of Cleveland, when the royal court was still exiled in Holland. After the Restoration and, incidentally, after Villiers had presented our monarch with a third bastard, there was a celebration ball in London on which occasion a necklace the king had just given his mistress disappeared. No charges were made at the time, but the description of the costly jewel was circulated throughout England. A year ago in Falmouth an alert constable became suspicious of a necklace being worn by Tom Kenn's woman. In the company of Captain Wilcox, the constable listened to Tom's drunken boasts about new-found wealth and followed the couple to the Falmouth house where a cache of smuggled goods was uncovered."

"Did Amelia Cobb tell you this story, Grandfa?"

"No. The Wallis woman did, claiming that Tom had stolen the jewelry from Mrs. Cobb. The necklace was quietly returned to the Duchess of Cleveland, and again no charges were made. I imagine Lord Gordon paid an impressive sum to King Charles to save his daughter from hanging. When I questioned Amelia Cobb about the theft, she denied any wrong-doing entirely. But she's an arrogant liar and, in my opinion, an immoral whore as well. You'll be no match for her, lass; she has a conceit about men that bespeaks a ten-year career of playing the courtesan.''

"Well, she's nothing but an indentured servant now!" Lynn declared defensively.

"She has no intention of serving a day of that indenture; as far as I could tell none of them do. And indenture laws are strict, girl, especially in New England! As registered owner, I'd be the one responsible for their actions.''

"Not if you deeded them over to Clay."

"I've already lied too much over this sorry affair."

"Why did you lie at all, Grandfa?"

"To keep you safe, lass."

"Won't I be safer still if I'm wed?"

"Aye, but—"

"Then Clay and I will take responsibility for the others."

"You're that determined to wed this man?"

"I suppose I am, Grandfa."

"Then I pray you'll not regret your decision. Best now you get dressed; the captain wants to perform the ceremony before Bevil and I transfer to another ship bound for Bristol. Polly's waiting outside to help you."

Cloistered in Captain Vinson's quarters an hour later were seven people, the only ones aboard who knew the intention of the gathering. Of those seven, only Jem seemed to be in full approval; he was the only one who had worked with both principals. His wife Polly still retained her ingrained prejudice against the social privileges of landed gentry, and Captain Vinson was worried about an extended anchorage in open water. Ephraim Penley and Bevil Trevor were poles apart in their regard for the bride and groom; the groom was irritably incapacitated by a swollen leg, a stitched together arm, and a pounding head; and the bride was miserably aware that her shabby black dress was as unattractive as sackcloth and her cropped hair as mannish as a knight errant's.

Clay's petulant complaint at the conclusion of the unemotional ceremony did little to relieve the general gloom. "I hope you're satisfied," he muttered to Bevil Trevor. "Why the devil couldn't we have waited until I felt better?"

Before he climbed down the ladder to the small boat waiting to take him to a Bristol-bound ship, Ephraim Penley bid his granddaughter a brief, recriminatory farewell, "I warned you he'd be a difficult husband, Trelynn."

Bevil Trevor's departing advice was only slightly less gloomy. "Don't let him bamboozle you, girl; he can be a bit of a limp cully when he's sick. But 'tis his own fault this time; he was well enough to celebrate with his friends this afternoon."

Clay's illness, however, was not merely the result of overindulgence in wine. The ship's surgeon, a twenty-year veteran in dealing with sailors' hypochondria, was bluntly clinical about this patient's multiple problems. Concussion to the head originating from a vicious blow and exacerbated by a violent assault shortly afterward, combined with overexertion, undernourishment, painful bruises, and loss of blood from a slashed arm would necessitate weeks of slow recuperation without excitement. Denied the privileges usually accorded a newly married man, Clay was perversely quarrelsome with his wife when she arrived in his cabin after seeing the two old men off. Having been stopped by the doctor outside the door and warned about the extent of her husband's injuries, Lynn entered the large well-appointed cabin expecting Clay to be asleep. Instead he greeted her with a peevish protest.

"I don't give a damn what the doctor said, I want you to sleep with me, and that's that!" he mumbled.

Looking down at the three-foot-wide bed so obviously

designed for double occupancy, but now crowded by her husband's splinted arms and heavily bandaged knee, Lynn murmured placatingly, "Until your arm is healed, I'll remain in my own cabin, Clay."

"The devil you will! You're a married woman now, and your place is with me. I don't want some hammer-handed deck swab taking care of me; I want you right here with me."

Flattered despite the undiplomatic phrasing of his demand, she agreed to the addition of a sleeping pallet in the corner of the stateroom, but her promise to remain with him throughout each day was broken at dawn the following morning by the arrival of a flustered Polly Rigg.

"Jem and me need help with the cattle, Lynn," she declared flatly, "else you're going to be losing some of the animals."

"What about the Spragues?"

"Roy and Will and their wives ain't aboard, not enough room for the cattle and their mill equipment. 'Spect they was put on the ship that's headed first to Virginia. Any of those indentureds his royal nibs promised us ever worked with cattle? The one good-for-nothing his lordship sent to help Jem was meaner than old Fen around the bullocks."

Recalling her grandfather's evaluation of the other five indentureds, Lynn shook her head. "The others are just as useless. Polly, have you had a chance to meet any of the thirty prisoners aboard?"

"Happens I have, Lynn. A woman 'bout my age named Kate Horton. She's the one the Cobb bitch wanted for a maid."

"What was her crime?"

"Stealing three guineas from a tight-fisted mistress who hadn't paid her salary for two years. Reckon she'd know if any of the men 'ud be worth the salt you'd have to pay for their papers."

"Then let's talk to this Kate of yours, Polly; if she's as good as you say, I'll buy her papers too."

Lynn's meeting with the outspoken Kate Horton was a revelation. Before the potential employer could ask a question, Kate boldly listed her own qualifications and her own restrictions.

"I'm an experienced lady's maid and an expert seamstress. I'll work for you, Mistress Penley, because Polly tells me you've had enough dirt beneath your own fingernails to know the value of the people under you. But if you're planning to turn me over to the Cobb woman, I give you fair warning; I'd strangle the shrew and go happily to the gallows."

Smiling in whole-hearted agreement, Lynn confided bluntly, "You'll be working for me, Kate, and no one else. I don't suppose there's much you can do to change my appearance, but I'd appreciate your trying. I'm a farmer, Kate, and I never expected to be anything else, certainly not the wife of a spoiled aristocrat. Now I want to look more like the women he's used to seeing; I'd not like him to be ashamed of me in public."

Kate Horton looked appraisingly at the young woman standing before her with arms akimbo and booted feet planted firmly apart on the rolling deck. Responding to Lynn's plain-spoken request with an equal candor, she asserted, " 'Twould take a miracle to make you into the likes of that prinked-up breed, mistress; you've too much of the wild in you. But if you'll trust me, there's no man alive who won't find you attractive."

More than pleased with the assurance, Lynn persisted in her second request. "Polly said you could also help me select three prisoners who'd make good farmhands."

"Not many in that lot who'd be any good in the rough and tumble of cattle. I grew up on a Sussex farm, so I know the likes of them who can't stand the stench of manure. There are two of the men, though, who are farm-bred and decent enough to be grateful for the chance to work for someone like you instead of a bully. Aye, and there's an Irish rogue who'll work well enough if he's watched.''

Four days later Jem handed Lynn a laboriously written note containing a brief evaluation of the three applicants. John Bram ''weren't afeared to work the bullocks,'' Kerry Egan ''could milk a cow most as good as a dairymaid,'' and Jonas Hale ''knowed fodder and grain as well as a fat field mouse.'' Jem's final approbation was a general comment about the ages of the men, ''old enough to know there's no easy way of it.''

That same day Lynn purchased the indenture papers of Kate Horton and the three men from a relieved Captain Vinson, but not until she read the specifics of their convictions did she learn that for ten years she'd be working alongside a horse thief, an Irish highwayman, and a farmer who'd shorted a government requisition for naval supplies.

With her animals provided for and with Kate busily stitching on a pale gray wool dress and cloak from a bolt of fabric purchased from Captain Vinson's stock of sale goods, Lynn returned her attention to a complaining husband who demanded a daily accounting of her morning stint of work in the cattle hold. The day after she'd purchased the four servants, Clay was particularly irritable.

''Why the devil didn't you put Tom Kenn to work?'' he asked sourly.

''Tom's your responsibility,'' she replied evenly. ''Jem won't let him near the cattle.''

''Good God, woman, he'll have to earn his keep somehow. We can't be feeding half the exodus from English prisons without getting labor out of them.''

''Just what would you say Bert Spence and Harry Cobb can do on a farm, Clay?''

Lynn regretted the rash question instantly; she hadn't meant to open that Pandora's box until after she'd secured her marriage. But her husband was equal to the challenge. ''Harry will be providing for himself as long as he's with us; and that reminds me, he sent a note asking that you turn the woman you've hired over to his wife. He's willing to pay you double for—''

"His precious wife would not be safe with Kate Horton, and I'm fond enough of Kate to prevent trouble," Lynn retorted, her temper rising to a pitch that destroyed her earlier good humor.

"Why the devil would you take the part of a low-born criminal?" Clay's disbelief sounded genuine, so did the subtle warning that followed. "In case you've forgotten, mistress, you and I will both be living a lie in America; and Amelia Cobb knows all of our secrets."

"Do you really think she's going to add blackmail to her already impressive list of crimes?"

Clay's jaw was clamped shut in anger; his own thinking on the delicate subject had not come close to a blunt accusation of blackmail. He glared at his wife, now smiling at him with a baiting look of triumph, and silently cursed all women and their interference in his life.

"It seemed a small price to pay for peace," he muttered.

"Not for Kate Horton," Lynn snapped. "She's not a negotiable piece of merchandise, and she hates your Amelia Cobb. If you like, I can ask her to locate another maid among the prisoners."

"Amelia wouldn't be happy with a substitute."

"Amelia's not in a position to pick and choose. Just why have you been elected to be her protector, Clay?"

"She and Harry are old friends," he mumbled evasively. "I merely thought—"

"That I'd be more gullible than my grandfather?" Lynn interrupted sharply.

"No, that you'd have the sense to realize the vulnerable position you're in!" he snapped.

For a moment Lynn stared at her husband in disbelief; it was the first time he'd reminded her that while he'd escaped from ten years of indentured labor, she was still a wanted fugitive. Turning swiftly away from her angry husband, she fled from the cabin. When she returned hours later with his supper, she fed him with the same silent efficiency she'd employed in the cave during his earlier collapse, forcing him to drink a cup of milk and shaking her head when he requested wine instead.

"You're still feverish," she murmured without expression. "Until you're well, the doctor doesn't want your head muddled with wine or with any more argument. So I've decided to return to my own cabin and see you only when necessary."

"Why? So that you can have more time to arrange our future without consulting me?" he complained bitterly.

Resisting the impulse to tell him that he hadn't planned any future beyond a carefree life for himself and his friends, Lynn denied the charge. "I don't know anything more about the future than you do. As you reminded me, our marriage doesn't make me any less the suspect."

"I'm sorry I said that, Lynn. 'Tis just that as yet we haven't had a marriage; you've refused to sleep with me, and now you're threatening to leave my room entirely."

Reminded of Polly Rigg's warning that "sick men are naught but puling babes," Lynn rescinded her determination to return to her old cabin now occupied by an industrious Kate Horton.

"I'll remain here as long as you need me, Clay," she promised flatly. "But I won't argue with you, and I won't criticize your friends again."

Curiously enough, during the following week, two of her husband's old band of smugglers joined Lynn's small work force. With Kate's and Polly's help, she developed a friendly relationship with the woman Ephraim Penley had described as too rebellious for civil talk. After she'd heard the story of Nell Wallis from Polly, Lynn decided that the rebellion and foul language were probably justified. Indentured by a dying mother to a London innkeeper when she was nine years old, Nell had become an experienced whore within four years with the innkeeper himself as her most frequent bedfellow. It had been the innkeeper's wife whose unfounded accusations of theft had led to Nell's first two imprisonments at Bridewell. Since she'd never been allowed to keep any of the money she'd earned, the young girl was unable to fight either conviction. Released the second time, she had eluded the innkeeper who had reported dutifully at the prison to reclaim his property. In the company of an older, more experienced strumpet, Nell had worked at her profession in the Cornish town of Falmouth until she had become Tom Kenn's mistress two years before her third confinement in Bridewell.

Expecting a painted bawd like the ones she'd seen in London, Lynn was startled by Nell's appearance. Despite the bedraggled, overruffled dress, the girl's face was clean and her hair neatly brushed, but her words of introduction were an uncompromising declaration.

"Pol says I can work for you if I prove myself useful. She says she told you all about me, so you can stop biting your tongue and say what you want."

Flustered by the brash approach, Lynn asked the most obvious question, "How old are you, Nell?"

"Nineteen—near as I can figure, but don't think I'm too young to know hard work."

"That's just it, Nell, you've only worked in . . . in public houses. My grandfather thought you might be happier in a New England inn."

"Was he the old man who looked like a sour-faced judge?"

Lynn smiled at the description; in his legal capacity Ephraim did tend to appear overly severe. "He wasn't condemning you, Nell," she protested mildly. "He just didn't think you'd know what to do on a farm."

"I can do the job you're doing and do it better," the nineteen-year-old stated with a confident assurance. "For six years I shoveled sawdust out of a drinking room, and it smelled worse than that stuff. There were some of the drunken fleshflies who pissed a pint for every ale they guzzled.''

More amused than shocked, Lynn looked down at the shovel she'd been using to clear Red Penny's stall. Thus far, the new men had been afraid to tend the bull.

"What about Tom Kenn?" she asked. "I've been told he hates farming."

"Tom's his own man and I'm me. I've been in prison three times because of men, and I don't plan on going back. I have six years of indenture time to learn something better than being a slut for every stinking gorebelly who thinks he owns me. And Tom's not all that different. He's the one who gave me that bloody necklace. How was I to know her highness had pinched it from a duchess, and the king's whore at that? I know what I am, mistress, but there are some who are worse."

Since she'd controlled little of this remarkable interview, Lynn could only agree and offer the limp warning that she wouldn't be an easy taskmistress.

Her admonition was greeted by a gamin smile and another blunt admission. "I'm no dim-witted old grannie, mistress. Polly and I watched you work before she sent me down, and I heard old Harry tell how you knocked the lights out of three men with your presbies. There were times when I'd have used one myself if I'd had it handy."

Lynn was slightly more than dazed by the acquisition of this particular worker, but her skepticism decreased daily. Under Jem's benign tutelage, the outspoken Nell Wallis buckled to the job of learning a variety of new skills; nor did she brangle about performing the dirtiest tasks aboard; scrubbing the floor of the cattle hold and lugging the buckets of manure up the steep companionway to toss overboard. It was during one of Lynn's own brief excursions on deck that she watched an interesting confrontation between Nell and a young man Lynn thought must be Tom Kenn.

Too far away to hear the tersely exchanged words, Lynn

could only guess their content. But Nell's fierce shove when the man tried to embrace her indicated a distinct difference of opinion. From the partial concealment of the raised quarterdeck, Lynn studied the face of the angry man whose age seemed nearer to her own than to Clay's. She recognized his expression as that of a ne'er-do-well loitering around English docks. Vaguely she wondered just how such a lazy, bored wastrel had proved useful to an expert band of smugglers. Abruptly startled by the sound of another masculine voice to her rear, Lynn turned around swiftly to confront the newcomer. She recognized him instantly as the man who'd been injured on the beach.

"Bert Spence at your service, Mistress Penley," he introduced himself with a polite bow. "I was hoping to see you today. I'm afraid your grandfather may have given a sorry description of the three of us: your husband, Harry, and myself," he elucidated when he noted her confusion. "On the afternoon he talked to us, we were acting the fools, a rather commonplace behavior for us; and I was certain you'd show the good sense not to marry our intrepid leader."

Ephraim had described Bert Spence as an educated man, but an embittered one. He was also, Lynn noted, a few years older than Clay and quite handsome, a Cornishman as dark-eyed and dark-haired as she was.

"What do you want to talk about, Mr. Spence?" she asked.

"The future, mistress. I imagine that Jame—rather Clay— has told you that Harry and I were not to be treated as common prisoners. But as you can see, I'm common enough and as penniless as the rest of the Newgate birds aboard. I also know that according to indenture laws, it'll be hard labor if my wife and I are to survive. So I'm asking to be put to work the same as Nell."

Unable to refute his argument, Lynn hesitated to respond. Jem would not appreciate having such a man as this one assigned to him. Moreover, Bert Spence still looked too weak to survive the heavy work needed for cattle maintenance in the small confines of a ship's hold.

"You need more time to recuperate, Mr. Spence," she equivocated. "You were delirious when we brought you aboard three weeks ago."

"Only a touch of lead poisoning, mistress, and the lingering curse of prison fever; but I still won't accept Clay's charity. Like you, I plan to survive in that savage land ahead of us."

"Have you ever visited the colonies, Mr. Spence?"

"For five years at the request of the Roundhead Parliament. I helped a distant cousin build his first cabin along the James River in Virginia."

"Then that's what you'll do for Clay and me," Lynn exclaimed with a relief born of inspiration. "I doubt Clay's given a thought to the problem of housing us before winter."

"How many of us are there, mistress?"

Calculating the number rapidly, Lynn shuddered. "There are eighteen humans so far and sixty head of cattle. The byre will have to be built first, because a severe winter might destroy the animals otherwise."

Bert Spence smiled for the first time during the conversation and regarded the woman Harry Cobb had called a "mannish clod" more closely. In spite of her heavy shoes and coarse wool dress, the more perceptive Spence recognized her sharp intelligence and even more acutely the incipient beauty of her strong body and face. Clay had always been the lucky one, he reflected with a twinge of jealousy; this woman would be capable of building the byre without his help. Her next words informed him that she was also a competent business woman.

"We'll have to build a mill too, Mr. Spence, as quickly as possible. The sooner the farm starts making money, the better off we'll all be."

"Have you talked these plans over with your husband yet, mistress?"

Recalling her one argument with Clay since they'd been aboard the *Tamarlind*, Lynn shook her head, recovering her poise only when she noted the skeptical smile on her companion's face.

"Clay is still concerned about maintaining the social order," she snapped bitingly, "but his disapproval won't change reality. And the reality is that none of us have any choice. Indentureds are not as welcome in New England as they are in Virginia; so we'll have to be as inconspicuous as possible. Mr. Spence, is that man leaning on the taffrail Tom Kenn?"

"That's our lad."

"Has he done any work since he's been aboard?"

"Tom rarely works, Mistress Penley."

"Do you know Captain Vinson well, Mr. Spence?"

"Very well."

"Then tell him to assign Tom four hours of hard work each day for the remainder of the voyage in return for his meals. Once we're on land, he'll continue to do his share of the work or he won't eat there either. As for you, Mr. Spence, your shipboard duty will be to determine the materials we'll be needing for the shelters."

Bert Spence was still laughing minutes later when he approached Captain Vinson and relayed Lynn's message about Tom Kenn. His lightly delivered comment about the determination of Mistress Penley received an instant agreement. Peter Vinson had his own reasons for being grateful to her. Since she'd taken over the maintenance of the cattle hold, his ship had ceased to reek of animal excrement and urine; and the milk delivered daily to the galley was a welcome addition to shipboard diet. In the past, the cows he'd transported to the colonies had gone dry within a week at sea; but this herd, he reflected, seemed peculiarly adaptive and placid.

On her way to Kate Horton's cabin for her daily salt-water bath, Lynn was not nearly as sanguine or confident as she'd sounded during her conversation with Bert Spence.

She knew with dismal certainty that she was dabbling in the dangerous quagmire of masculine conceit; Clay wouldn't appreciate her bold words to his friend nor her casual assumption of the prerogative of leadership. For once, she submitted meekly to Kate's ministration and agreed readily to try the forehead bangs the skilled maid thought would be attractive. Half an hour later with the ends of her ragged hair neatly trimmed and a heavy fringe of dark bangs obscuring her forehead, Lynn waited nervously as Kate surveyed her handiwork.

" 'Tis the very style for you, Mistress Lynn; you don't need the masses of artificial curls most women do, and you don't need cascades of ruffles around your neck to look pretty. This white kerchief I've finished will be ornament enough to make your dark hair gleam in contrast," Kate declared in satisfaction. Three weeks of freedom without the carping demands of some fat goodie to be made beautiful had given Kate an increasing appreciation of her current mistress who required so little in the way of complicated grooming. Worldly wise, though, about aristocratic fetishes for lavish costumes and ornate hair styles, Kate doubted that a spoiled husband would have the sense to appreciate the clean handsomeness of Lynn Penley.

As she hurried toward her husband's stateroom an hour later than usual, Lynn herself was quite certain he would not approve of her at all if he ever learned about her meddling. Hoping he'd be asleep, she edged around the door and closed it silently behind her, only to stare in dismay at the sight of Clay standing in front of the transom window with his back turned toward her. He was wearing a green bed robe even more elegant than the one he'd used in the tower; and sometime during her five-hour absence, his arm had been unsplinted. Lynn felt suddenly drab in her plain dark dress and white shawl, as if she were a Puritan goodwife at chapel meeting, she thought bleakly, while her husband looked magnificently Cavalier.

Looking around the other changes in the familiar cabin,

Lynn noted that the small table was set for dinner with a silver tureen in the center and a bottle of wine beside it. Not until she studied the space beyond, though, did she notice the main reason for the altered appearance of the cabin. Her bed pallet was gone! With her heart beating uncomfortably fast, she walked hesitantly across the room only to have a startled husband swing violently around when she was three feet away.

"Good God, woman," he exploded, "I'm going to put a bell on you so I'll know where you are. You move like a bloody cat stalking a bird. Where have you been? I've been waiting over an hour."

Lynn was only able to gasp "I've been," before she was interrupted by a low whistle and the candid demand "Did your Kate Horton fix your hair? 'Tis very becoming, wife. I agree you were wise to keep her."

"How are you feeling, Clay?" Lynn managed to ask.

"My arm and leg are almost mended, and my head feels clear for the first time since that ugly brute knocked me cock-a-hoop with rocks."

"Did the doctor give you permission to leave your bed?"

"To leave my bed four hours a day and to feed myself for a change. Will you join me in drinking a cup of wine to celebrate my recovery?"

Already too tense for comfort, Lynn shook her head, but her refusal went unheeded as he filled her cup to brimming. "That's another of the bugbears you'll be discarding," Clay informed her companionably. "You're not the Puritan you pretend to be, and I'll not have you prudishly sober while we eat. 'Tis my first day of feeling human again."

Noting the speed with which he drained his cup, Lynn was tempted to remind him that the last time he'd overindulged with Spence and Harry, he'd been depressingly human and irritably sick. Instead, she murmured an inane warning, "Better not overdo your first day up."

"What can happen to me now that my nurse is here?" he retorted with a challenging smile.

Throughout the simple meal of lukewarm soup, biscuits, and cheese, Clay maintained a light patter of inconsequentials: the excellence of the weather, the limitations of shipboard meals, and the possibility of reaching New Port by early July. Other than two additional refusals of more wine—both of which were ignored and her cup refilled—Lynn contributed only minimally to the conversation, mumbling agreements with whatever Clay said. Why, she asked herself in disgust, should she suddenly feel ill at ease with a man she'd known intimately for five weeks? She'd washed him, fed him, dragged him out of danger, and saved his life; and God's truth, she'd had no trouble tongue-lashing him when the occasion demanded. Even after the emotional turbulence of their lovemaking in the tower room, she'd regained enough equilibrium to indulge in a lively dialogue with him.

So why was she acting like a tongue-tied rustic dolt now? Because that's what she was, she concluded dismally, a Cornish farmwoman who'd never learned the social art of flirting, and whose speech was still slurred by country vernacular. She'd realized that particular flaw during her earlier conversation with Bert Spence. As Cornish by birth as she was, he'd learned to speak without a hint of his county origin, so had Clay and even the loutish Harry. She was the outsider, the one who didn't belong with these aristocrats who'd retained their attitudes of confident superiority even in prison.

"What are you thinking about, Lynn?" Clay interrupted her unpleasant ruminations abruptly. "You look as if you wanted to be far away from here."

"I suppose I do, Clay," she retorted with a defensive candor. "You don't really need me anymore, and I'd feel—"

"Would you like to put that absurd opinion to a test? Why do you think I've been trying to get the doctor to remove those damn bandages for the past two weeks? Every morning I've watched you race out of this cabin as if *you* were the one just released from prison, and every night you climbed into that cursed pallet as if we were strangers instead of man and wife. Why the devil did you marry me if you can't stand my company?"

"For the same reason you married me, Clay Penley!"

"In that case you'll help me put the crockery outside and then come to bed. My God, woman, I was beginning to believe that you really didn't have normal feelings like the rest of us."

Surprised by the vehemence of his declaration and badly disturbed by her all too human response, Lynn cleared the table nervously and carried the remains of the half-eaten meal to the door held open for her by a watchful husband. Even as he rebolted the door, his other arm was around her, guiding her toward the bed with a purposeful pressure. Throwing back the covers, he seated himself on the edge and pulled her down beside him, his lips seeking hers with an expert's aim. Not once throughout his deft removal of her clothing did he break his concentration on anything so trivial as endearing conversation. What areas of her exposed flesh his hands did not excite, his exploring lips did; and Lynn was once again sucked into the inferno of a man's aroused passion. And once again she lost all awareness of herself as an entity apart.

Almost automatically, her hands caressed the familiar body she'd tended during illness, instinctive in their possessive touch. The only thought that penetrated the sensual haze of physical absorption was one of relief; Clay had not lied to her in the tower. Their marriage was not to be one of mere protective convenience for him; he was taut with impatient desire as he pushed her naked body onto the sheeted mattress and followed her down without a second's hesitation.

Having never been counseled by another woman about the established rules of marital intimacy or about the more passive role a bride customarily played, Lynn made no attempt to curb the tumult of her own response. She welcomed him with a throbbing urgency and countered his turbulent thrusting with an equal strength, her senses sharply focused on the instinctive urges of her own body. Unaware of the bruising strength of his fingers gripping her or of their perspiration mingling together from the heat of their exertions, she concentrated only on the primitive need to experience once again the hypnotic thrill of ecstasy. It began as a poignant quiver just as her partner moaned during his own moment of fulfillment and ended for her in a consuming explosion of pure sensation.

Rousing from the magic moment in time to return her husband's dazed smile, Lynn murmured happily, "I'd say my feelings were every bit as normal as yours." Clay's warm laughter followed them both into a peacefully drugged sleep.

CHAPTER
6

Except for the happier, more relaxed hours she spent each afternoon with Clay in their cabin, Lynn's shipboard routine remained unchanged. Leaving her sleeping husband snug in bed, she arose at dawn and went to Kate Horton's small cabin to change into her work clothes before reporting to the cattle hold. Now on good terms with both her new and old employees, she supervised the morning milking and cleanup, breakfasted with Nell Wallis and Polly Rigg in the dining quarters allotted the ship's crew, and then returned to Kate's cabin for additional fittings of the dresses still under construction. To her surprise, on the second morning after she'd spoken to him on deck, Bert Spence was waiting for her at breakfast, and the hour was extended as they consulted the ship's carpenters about the construction details of Bert's half-completed sketches. During the following week, that morning conference with Bert became routine.

Satisfied that the practical aspects of her immediate future were under control, she returned late to the cabin she shared with her husband. He wasn't there, but spread out on the table was a profusion of maps, scrolls, and

131

papers. Lynn's first reaction as she studied the top paper covered with notations in an unfamiliar handwriting was one of wary suspicion. These notes were the labor of several days, yet Clay had consistently refused to answer her questions about the Connecticut property. Her second reaction when she unrolled the heavy parchments containing the two deeds was shock. On the larger deed was the description of the property and the impressive signature of James Stuart, Duke of Albany and York; but on the smaller one above the signature of Bevil Trevor was a paragraph deeding the land to Clay Penley and a following paragraph that detailed the rules for a subsequent inheritance. The land could be inherited only by Clay's son or by one of Averill's or Bourke Trevor's sons. Sir Bevil had followed the entitlement laws of England to the letter!

In the event that Clay died without producing a son, Lynn realized bitterly, she'd be as homeless as she'd been when Owen Penley had taken control of her girlhood home. The only land she could ever be certain of owning was her grandfather's farms in Rhode Island. Ephraim Penley's will, now locked in one of her trunks in Kate Horton's cabin, named Lynn as his sole heir to both farms without any mention of Clay or Owen Penley.

Lacking her earlier enthusiasm for her husband's Connecticut property, Lynn studied the map, which delineated its boundaries and its history. In 1664 King Charles had deeded all the land between the Connecticut River to the north and Delaware Bay to the south to his brother Prince James, without regard to the settlers already there. At the strong protest of Connecticut leaders, James agreed to honor the original boundary between New York and Connecticut, provided the three grants he'd already given away were also honored. The large plot of land marked by the names of Trevor and Penley began some thirty miles southwest of New Haven and extended to the New York boundary. Cynically Lynn wondered how the other colonists with small, hard-purchased farms would feel about the munificence of James's gift to an aristocrat who hadn't participated in the courageous pioneering of the colony.

More minutely now, she reread Clay's notes, but his concerns had nothing to do with moral considerations, only with the physical drawbacks of the estate. Only a fourth of it lay within the tidewater flats of the Housatonic River, and the river itself was not navigable by ocean ships on the stretch along the property. In addition to his notation that the king had requested that the resident Indians not be disturbed, Clay had written, "As if they could be. Ninety percent of the damned place is mountainous and forested." In another scrawled comment, he'd described a more damning fault: "The only settlement close enough for trade is a colony of psalm-singing Puritans in New Haven. Within a year they'll be forcing everyone in a hundred-mile radius to support their damned church, and in another year they'll force everyone to join."

Frowning at the possibility—Lynn had less enthusiasm than most Englishmen to return to a government dominated by fanatic Puritans—she remembered the prolific notes she'd cribbed from her grandfather's reports. Racing back to Kate's cabin, she reread her notes; and within an hour she knew more about the New Haven colony than her husband did. New Haven was indeed a Puritan stronghold that had given sanctuary to two of the last unpunished regicides of King Charles I. Edward Whalley and William Goffe, who'd served as colonels in Oliver Cromwell's army, were now politically active in New Haven government and indirectly in the overall government of a united Connecticut.

More convinced than ever that her safest refuge would be Rhode Island, Lynn finally read the letter her grandfather had given her before he disembarked from the *Tamarlind*, a letter she'd forgotten in the rush of organizing her shipboard life. It began with the opening, "Trelynn, it has been my experience in the courts of English justice that lies are the most harshly punished of all crimes. To protect you, myself, and, to an extent, the others involved in this subterfuge, I have revealed the entire truth about yourself and the others and an explanation of my motives to three of my most trustworthy friends. To spare you the danger of temptation, I have asked Captain Vinson to deliver those letters. The first letter goes to Edward Fulton, an old friend, and the neighbor who will help you settle safely on Aquidneck. My second contact is Roger Williams, also a friend of more than thirty years and, more important, the spiritual and political leader of Rhode Island. Both of these men will respect my confidence, and both will treat you fairly despite your fugitive status and your husband's altered identity. My third correspondent is Captain Clive Dunton, the leader of the New Haven militia and another firm friend. In the event your husband insists on settling in Connecticut, Dunton will give you what protection he can from the less sympathetic religious leaders of that colony. Included in the information I have given these gentlemen are a complete accounting of the false accusation made by the Pollocks and your cousin Owen, and a thorough description of the part Sir Bevil and your husband played in rescuing you from jeopardy.''

After she'd read her grandfather's letter twice over, Lynn returned it to the trunk, oddly relieved that she'd not be living a total lie, but worried about the probability that Clay would feel betrayed. Lynn was still seated on the trunk staring thoughtfully into space when Kate returned from dinner.

"For goodness sake, Lynn," the maid exclaimed, "the first mate has been scouring the ship looking for you. You're supposed to join your husband in the captain's quarters for a celebration of some kind."

"Did Mr. Carey say what we were supposed to be celebrating?"

"Your husband's and Harry Cobb's recovery; so if I were you, I'd wear the light gray dress. It'll make you look the lady. I imagine you'll be meeting the Cobb woman and Bert's wife."

Frowning at the gray dress hanging from the bulkhead, Lynn wished that she hadn't insisted on such plain styling. "I'll look like a Puritan goodwife if Amelia Cobb dresses as elegantly as her husband."

"Stuff and nonsense," Kate chided her. " 'Tis a becoming style for you. Just don't let the woman annoy you. Treat her like you did Nell Wallis at first; you'll soon discover that Nell is more the lady than that prinked-up pretender."

Lynn remembered this advice when she was admitted into the only luxurious quarters aboard the *Tamarlind*, admitted not by an attentive husband, but by a polite Bert Spence. No one else even heard her circumspect knock; they were all too busy listening to the dulcet voice of a woman who reminded Lynn of her own mother in coloring and mannerisms. But Amelia Cobb was more beautiful than Lynn had expected from Kate's description. Curled russet hair cascaded gracefully over a rich blue velvet suit rendered delicately feminine by flounces of lace around the neck. One of her hands held a crystal goblet of wine, while the other rested lightly on Clay Penley's arm; and her voice was merrily gleeful in its entreaty.

" 'Twas not the way Harry told it, Jame. 'A red-breasted crow flapping across the bridge, swinging her clubs like a demented witch' were Harry's words. 'Twill be a delightful story to tell in court some day."

Only Bert Spence heard Lynn's small gasp, and he was swift to respond. "You'd be a widow, Amelia, if Mistress Penley hadn't swung those clubs with an expert's aim. Your poisoned tongue would have been a sorry weapon in comparison."

As the caustic reprimand registered with the four people playing audience to Amelia Cobb's entertainment, they turned around to stare at the latecomer with differing emotions. Captain Vinson's welcoming smile was one of relief, but Clay appeared startled; and Lynn suspected the sudden flush on his face was that of guilt. Since it had been his insulting description his wife had quoted, Henry Cobb began a blustery apology about too much wine and stopped abruptly. He, too, had become aware that the tall woman with the raven wings of hair framing her face possessed a commanding look of pride and, damn, a kind of beauty he'd not dreamed possible.

Controlling her breath, which threatened to explode from her lungs, Lynn ignored the three men, focusing her eyes instead on the second woman who'd been standing next to Harry, the woman Ephraim Penley had described as a "childish dreamer." But Leona Spence did not appear childish to a more perceptive Lynn; the expression on her vapidly pretty face was antagonistic. Even as her husband introduced her, Leona's perfunctory smile did not reach her pale blue eyes, which remained warily suspicious; and her murmured response held no warmth.

With a belated realization that Bert Spence had usurped his position as champion, Clay performed the remainder of the introductions in a strained voice that sounded more belligerent than proud. The only verbal response came from the woman who had been holding sway when Lynn had entered the room; this time Amelia Cobb's comment was an amused scolding. "Don't look so grim, Jame, love; I'm certain Mistress Penley doesn't enjoy being considered so much of a burden."

In spite of her own conviction that she possessed no second sight, Lynn was acutely aware of the subtle innuendos of Amelia Cobb's lightly delivered chiding. Remembering her grandfather's blunt warning, Lynn wondered how much of Amelia's confident charm had been used on "Jame, love" in the past and how successful it had been. Certainly throughout the dinner that followed the awkward scene, Amelia was a lively participant while Lynn was a mute observer whose only conversation was exchanged with Bert Spence. After Clay's one attempt at gallantry—when he'd seated her beside him at the table and inquired limply about her tardiness—had elicited only a sardonic smile and an indifferent shrug, he had returned his attention to the others and ignored her pointedly. She would have to learn the casual give and take of social intercourse, he reasoned irritably; but he jerked nervously when she did.

During a lull in the crosscurrents of light bantering among old friends, Amelia leaned forward and addressed Lynn directly, gesturing dramatically with the wine glass she used as a theatrical prop to sip from occasionally.

"Tell me about yourself, Mistress Penley," she cajoled prettily. "Harry has informed me all about the trouble you're in with the Cornish authorities, but I would have thought that witches were much more extraordinary in appearance."

"You sound like an expert on the subject, Mistress Cobb. Have you known many witches?" Lynn asked with a smiling venom, vindictively pleased when Bert Spence raised his glass in a salute. Clay, however, placed a warning hand on Lynn's thigh, and she subsided into satisfied silence as she pushed his hand away.

Before Amelia could respond to the subtle insult, an alert Captain Vinson plunged into the conversation he'd ignored earlier with a rambling commentary about the location of Clay's property in Connecticut. Lynn could have blessed him with loud huzzahs when he announced authoritatively that it would be two years at least before the ladies present could safely travel into that wilderness. In two years, Lynn vowed silently, her grandfather's farms in Rhode Island would be in full production and making money.

The dinner ended a few minutes later when Captain Vinson was summoned on deck, but the party continued for another hour after Amelia suggested a round of brandies in Clay's stateroom. " 'Tis the only one big enough to hold us," she murmured. That the size was not the only information she possessed about the cabin was apparent in the sharp exclamation of surprise she uttered upon entry. "What happened to the other bed, Jame?"

"We needed the space," Clay retorted shortly and added in a more conciliatory tone, "Clear the table, Lynn, while I locate some cups and brandy."

The table, however, was not to be cleared easily. Amelia's eyes were as rapacious as her tongue, alighting on the spread-out map as swiftly as iron filings to a lodestone. That her intelligence was as sharp as her eyes was obvious in her outraged gasp. "Why is Jame's land bigger than yours, Harry?" she demanded of her wine-befuddled husband.

With a speed that astonished Lynn, Clay intercepted the question. "You've nothing to worry about, Amelia; Harry's property is in the heart of tobacco country and ten times more valuable. From the look of this map, mine is nothing but forests and mountains."

"Then why are we planning to waste any time there?" Amelia asked avidly. "The people in Virginia would be more our sort anyway, and we could make money in tobacco."

All of which would belong to you, Lynn mused cynically as she waited for her husband's response. When he seemed lost in a contemplative assessment, she intervened quietly, "My grandfather will expect his Rhode Island property to be developed, and I imagine Sir Bevil Trevor expects the same about the Connecticut land."

"Then let them do the work themselves," Amelia retorted angrily. "We're not farmers, and I have no desire to become—"

"You're forgetting something, aren't you, Amelia?" Bert Spence interrupted tartly. "The four of us are nothing but indentured laborers, consigned to do exactly what Ephraim Penley orders for the next ten years."

"That's absolute nonsense, Spence," Amelia denounced swiftly. "That old man told me that Jame—that his *nephew*

Clay Penley—would be responsible for me and Harry. Isn't that right, Jame?''

"To an extent," Clay replied warily, his eyes resting uneasily on his wife's expressionless face as she filled the pewter cups with brandy. "But we *will* be going first to Rhode Island," he added more aggressively, "until I decide what will work best for all of us. We're in this thing together just as always."

Except for me, Lynn thought with a gloomy certainty; he doesn't have the foggiest idea what he's going to do with me. I'm the odd one out, and Amelia's dense husband is a close second. She was grateful when Bert Spence ended the awkward silence.

"Don't strain yourself on my account, Clay," he demurred blandly. "Leona and I will be staying with your wife in Rhode Island. There are more than a few minor items that you and Amelia seem intent on ignoring, such as sixty head of valuable cattle that will require winter shelter and cabins for us greenhorn humans so that we don't freeze to death during our first winter in a country that can be as savage as hell. That reminds me, Mistress Penley. There are some questions I need to ask Jem Rigg about fodder storage. If you've had enough of this foolish celebration, I thought we might—"

Lynn didn't wait for Bert to finish his welcome invitation. Without looking in her husband's direction and still carrying her untasted cup of brandy, she moved swiftly to the door and into the companionway beyond. She was out of sight before a furious husband could follow her or before an equally angry Bert Spence could silence his wife's shocked reprimand.

"I forbid you to leave, Spence," Leona hissed. "You have been as rude as can be to Amelia, and I insist you apologize. She is my oldest and dearest friend, and I won't have you insult her by taking the part of an outsider."

"That *outsider* is the only hope we have for survival. Are you coming with me?"

"No. I can't hurt Amelia's feelings. She's been looking forward to this party for weeks all the time we were taking care of Harry."

"Then you go right on playing the lady's maid to her lady, Leona; but don't you ever again join her in insulting Lynn Penley as you did today."

"What the hell are you talking about, Spence?" Clay demanded harshly after he returned from a futile search for his fugitive wife. "No one insulted my wife today; she has to learn not to be so damned thin-skinned."

"Have it your own way, Jame love," Bert murmured as he strode away, leaving an open-mouthed wife and a badly rattled old friend behind.

Clay located Lynn early the following afternoon, seated beside Bert Spence at one of the crude trestle tables in the crew's quarters, their heads bent over the intricate sketch of a byre loft.

"Would you mind leaving my wife and me alone, Spence?" Clay asked coldly.

"That'll be up to her," Bert retorted.

"The devil you say!"

"What devil would that be, Clay? The one still driving you to act the fool?"

"I'll talk to him, Mr. Spence," Lynn interposed quickly. "We can't do much more planning about the byre anyway until we know what materials are available. In the meantime—"

"Get the hell out of here, Spence!" Clay interrupted furiously, glaring at Lynn with narrowed eyes when she smiled in farewell to her fellow worker and then turned toward her husband with a polite expression of bored disinterest.

"Where did you go last night?" he demanded stridently.

"After walking by your cabin and finding it still occupied by your friends, I went to bed."

"Whose bed?"

"Not Mr. Spence's, if you're thinking to ease your own conscience."

At the sound of masculine laughter coming from the companionway, Clay rasped, "Damn it, you've made me the laughing-stock with my friends! Why the devil do you take everything so damned seriously. Nothing was said yesterday that—"

"Oh, but it was, Clay. I'm just sorry I didn't hear *your* description of my crossing the bridge. Was it as amusing as Harry's!"

"God's truth, Lynn, Harry and I are both aware that we wouldn't have survived without you."

"I don't believe Harry is aware of anything. How long have you known his charming wife, Clay? You needn't answer if you don't want to. I'm certain Amelia plans to tell me all about your killing her first husband in a duel."

"I tried to avoid that fight, Lynn; it cost me my . . . it cost me."

"I dare say, but still she married your best friend instead of you."

"Who told you about the duel?"

"Nell Wallis."

"Do you listen to everything that slut tells you?"

"Nell learned about it from listening to Amelia boast of her numerous conquests, so I'm not entirely certain which one is the slut."

" 'Tis past history, Lynn."

"Not so past as all that. My grandfather warned me that I'd be no match for her; I just wish he'd told me why. How often did she visit you while you were ill?"

"She merely dropped by to amuse me while you were busy with your damned bulls. And while we're on the subject of company, when did you and Spence become such good friends?"

"Since he's been working. Unlike Amelia and Harry, he knows he has no other choice. His wife's been working too, but not at anything worthwhile. She's the one who's keeping the beautiful Amelia so beautiful, or did you think those lovely curls arranged themselves?"

"For God's sake, shut up about her! I want to talk about you and me."

"Until we know what the future holds, we'd be wasting our time. You have your choice of homes, I don't. Now, if you'll excuse me, I need some fresh air."

Clay joined her on deck five minutes later; and for the next interminable twenty-one days, he rarely left her side even to the extent of accompanying her to the cattle hold and of sharing with the work. In return, he demanded she accompany him to the two daily meals they shared with the Cobbs, the Spences, and whichever of the ship's officers were not on duty. Each afternoon he insisted she watch his deckside sword-fighting exercise with Bert and Harry; and occasionally after supper he asked her to participate in the dice and card games, seeming to be genuinely proud of her rapid mastery of both skills.

But Lynn had been entirely accurate in her assessment of Harry's wife. Amelia Cobb did not abdicate her throne gracefully. By the time the *Tamarlind* docked in New Port harbor, Lynn knew the ten-year romantic history of the relationship between Amelia and Clay, and she knew her husband's complete identity. At twenty-two Charles Clay Trevor had expected to marry the youngest daughter of Lord Geoffrey Gordon; but according to Amelia, she'd been forced to wed a French comte by her ambitious father. After a desperately unhappy year, Clay had "helped" her escape from that marriage; but because of an unlucky twist of fate, they'd been unable to wed each other once again. The comte's vindictive son had notified the English authorities that the *Tamarlind* was a pirate ship, and Clay had been forced to change his name.

"Naturally my father would not allow me to wed a

nameless man without any expectations," Amelia had confided to Lynn during one of the sword practices. "So Clay and I did the next best thing until my father forced me to marry Harrold Pendrath four years later. Of course, I didn't know that Harry was a member of Clay's smuggling band until after the wedding."

The story was not related to Lynn in any chronological order, but in tantalizing snatches whispered whenever Clay's attention was diverted elsewhere. In every episode, Amelia was the heroine and Clay the pursuer; but with a pretty pout on the final day at sea, she admitted that she'd erred in not marrying Clay at whatever cost. "We're bound together by emotional ties that neither of us can break," she concluded wistfully. It was at that dramatic point that Amelia called him by his real name.

Stunned by the realizations that she'd married a Trevor and that her grandfather had known the truth, Lynn completed the alienation that had existed between herself and Amelia Cobb since the night of the celebration dinner. Shaking her head, she stated flatly, "I don't believe Clay intends to kill this husband as he did your first one. You'll have to settle for that other-than-legal relationship, provided, of course, that my husband is the fool you so optimistically claim."

Perversely, Lynn did not mention any of Amelia's revelations to Clay; she was too busy analyzing her own reactions. In a curious way, she felt a greater freedom in planning a complicated duplicity; and she was completely agreeable when he admitted that she might have to remain in Rhode Island until he could learn more about his own Connecticut property.

"I don't suppose we can leave those damned indentureds of yours without someone there to keep them out of trouble," he complained. "Have you any idea where to find the friend your grandfather said would look after you?"

"I know exactly where Mr. Fulton lives," Lynn replied cautiously.

"Good. As soon as we land, you'll go see him and find out if he's willing to board your animals until I can find a—"

"I'll ask him," Lynn interrupted hastily. She had no intention of allowing her husband any control over her ability to earn a living in the only way she knew. She wanted both her cattle and her money safely lodged with Edward Fulton, the friend her grandfather had described as both shrewd and trustworthy. Even before the reentry of his former mistress into his life, Lynn had learned to distrust Clay's reckless impulses; Amelia's presence had more than doubled that distrust. Until she could secure some measure of financial safety, Lynn wanted all temptation removed from her husband's reach.

On the morning the *Tamarlind* docked, Lynn was aided in her unaccompanied departure by the New Port officials who boarded the ship. While they insisted Clay be responsible for the eleven indentureds registered to Ephraim Penley, they gave Ephraim Penley's granddaughter ready permission to go ashore. To her relief, neither her husband nor the officials commented on the oddity of her carrying a heavy cloak during the heat of summer. One of the more gallant of the Rhode Island men even accompanied her to the edge of town and pointed to the path that would take her directly to the Fulton home. Lynn's arms were numbed by strain when the well-meaning Samaritan finally left her side and returned to the ship. In a leather knapsack beneath the cloak were four thousand and two hundred odd gold guineas whose combined weight had been bearable as a backpack, but leadenly heavy for her arms.

Switching the knapsack to its proper position and then donning the cloak so that it covered both her and the bundle, Lynn smiled in ironic appreciation. She really didn't need the flails she'd brought along for protection; she knew she looked like some hunchbacked old hag in a soiled and well-worn cape. Not until she climbed to the roofed porch of the Fulton house did she remove her burden and smooth her tousled hair. To her surprise, she was expected, and the door was opened by the very man she'd come to see.

"I received your grandfather's letter a half hour ago," Edward Fulton told her with a smile and then added an explanation. "I always send a man to meet every ship coming from England; 'tis a precaution that keeps the busybodies from knowing my business. In this case it proved a very wise precaution. I dare say, even in this liberal town, there are folk who'd not approve of my following Ephraim's unusual instructions."

"Are you willing, Mr. Fulton?" Lynn asked bluntly. "I *am* a fugitive from English justice."

"I suspect that half the people in New Port are, one way or another; but most of the citizens don't believe in witchcraft, so 'tis not you I'm worried about. 'Tis the former profession of the seven indentureds you brought with you, your husband included. I'm surprised Ephraim approved your marrying such a criminal."

"My husband and his father saved my life, and our two families are old friends and neighbors. But Grandfa wasn't too happy about the marriage despite my husband's gallantry."

"So he said in his letter. Like me, Ephraim believes in criminals accepting their punishment; and he's afraid this group of aristocratic rogues intends no such thing. Does your husband plan to settle here permanently?"

"I don't think so; at present he intends to sail to Connecticut when the *Tamarlind* leaves New Port."

"What about you, Mistress Penley?"

"I'll be living on my grandfather's farm until Clay decides what he wants to do. That's why I need your help, Mr. Fulton. I want you to protect my cattle and my money."

"From your husband?"

For a bleak moment, Lynn stared at the shrewd eyes

watching her, and nodded in defeat. In a rush of words as unemotional as she could manage, she revealed all of her fears and suspicions.

"First, the money," Fulton interrupted her. "Does your husband know about it?"

"Not the exact amount."

"How much is it, and where is it hidden?"

"Four thousand, two hundred and forty pounds in gold guineas, and 'tis all in this knapsack."

"You carried that much weight in a packet on your back?"

"I've always been strong," she admitted defensively, expecting the usual masculine buffoonery.

But Edward Fulton had lived for thirty-five years in a harsh new world that killed off fragile women in a seventh that length of time. What a shame, he reflected, that this obviously strong and healthy woman had been rushed into marriage to a man who sounded as light-a-foot as the buccaneers who inhabited New Port part of each year. There were a hundred good men on Aquidneck Island who'd welcome her as a wife. Regretfully he thought of two of his own sons and his one grandson who were already widowed. Returning his attention to the business at hand, he became brusquely businesslike.

"Your amount of gold is no paltry sum, mistress; by colonial standards, 'tis a small fortune."

"By my standards too, Mr. Fulton, but unfortunately, not according to my husband's."

" 'Tis often the case with men who had none of their own. How much will you tell him you have?"

"Just half the actual amount."

"How much do you intend to give him when he asks?"

"A thousand pounds."

"A goodly sum that should satisfy any man. And now you want me to prevent your husband from selling your cattle?"

"They're blooded animals, which would be easy to sell in any colony, Mr. Fulton."

"If they're as good as Ephraim claims, they'd sell in an hour's auction right here in New Port, a circumstance your grandfather wisely anticipated. In his letter, he claimed them as his own possessions with you as his only agent empowered to sell. Well, now that we have our stories straight, young woman, we'd best get to work. Those cattle will have to be drayed into my pasture yards. I doubt many of them will be able to stand, much less walk, after that long a time at sea. First, we'll stow your money in my strong box, which is safer than any on the island. Several years ago when the first of the freebooters arrived in harbor, I had the iron box embedded in stone. If you'll help me push this desk aside, you'll find it beneath the carpet."

A few minutes later Lynn breathed a sigh of relief; her money, at least, was safe. And if the cattle could be brought to pasture before nightfall, they, too, would survive. Now all that remained of her immediate responsibilities was to locate temporary shelter for her workers. She hated to ask still another favor from Edward Fulton, but she had no other choice. "Would it be possible for my people to board here for a few days until I know more about my grandfather's farm?"

"I've already made arrangements, though I doubt your fancies will appreciate the humble accommodations. The women will sleep in the house, and the men in the barn."

"Are there no existing facilities on Penley land?"

"It has a cottage, which will need little more than cleaning. 'Twas the first home I built when I moved my family here thirty years ago. There's a piggery that is still usable, but the barn—'tis what you call a byre—was damaged in a storm six years ago. The two stone walls are intact, but you'll be needing to rebuild the rest."

"That's more than I expected. I don't suppose there's any fencing?"

"Wasn't needed in those days, but now 'twill have to be your first consideration, that and fodder. The land's not all that productive, so you'll be needing a supply to last until harvest next year."

"Then we'd best leave, Mr. Fulton. How do you arrange for drayage?"

"Two of my sons will meet us at the dock with their wagons, and one of them will be supplying your fence rails and posts."

Recalling that her grandfather had described Edward Fulton as shrewd as well as trustworthy, Lynn nodded in appreciation. "You're a good businessman," she murmured.

The smile that softened his craggy, weatherbeaten face was a merry one. "Aye, but I suspect I've met my match. And if that bull of yours is as good as Ephraim said it was, you'll be making money. The only one on the island now has to be controlled with chains, and its get are nothing but cantankerous calves. I'll be wanting to breed my own cows come spring."

"Several of the cows I saw in your field, Mr. Fulton, are too narrow in the flank to bear Red Penny's calves, so I'll be paying part of my debt to you with three cows that can."

Lynn's first impression of the two bullocks pulling the wagon that carried her and Edward Fulton was one of disbelief that animals so old and mismatched could function at all. The wagon itself, however, was well sprung and strongly built with wheels that didn't wobble in the ruts. Addressing the driver who'd been introduced as Edward's oldest son, Lynn asked where he'd obtained the excellent vehicle.

"Twenty years ago in Boston," the man responded promptly, "but we've even better wheelwrights here in New Port now."

"Is there much call for draying in the colony?" she persisted.

"More than we can handle, mistress, especially with the new road to Portsmouth."

"Have you thought of using work horses? They'd be faster than your bullocks."

"Horses are still too skittish for this country. The road I mentioned is the only one except for those in the towns, and horses can stumble over rocks and into ditches before a driver has a chance to pull the reins. But this sorry old pair of oxen need only a little guidance."

Lynn was thoughtful as the wagon stopped on the dirt waterfront road near her sixty head of cattle swaying on unsteady legs as they tried to readjust to land after fifty-two days aboard ship. Standing nearby with their faces smeared with sweaty dirt were her own seven workers; not a one of Clay's group was in sight.

"You'd best go aboard, Lynn," an exasperated Polly whispered. "His royal nibs has been swearing up a storm since he found your money missing an hour ago."

"Where's Spence?" Lynn demanded.

"Reckon he has his hands full tryin' to calm his wife. The pulin' female chose this morning to announce she's expectin', and she's caterwaulin' to be taken to the inn same as t'other bitch."

"Poor Spence," Lynn murmured. "Where did my husband say he'd be?"

"With the captain, I reckon. Leastwise that's who he was yellin' at a while back."

The greeting Lynn received when she stepped into the captain's quarters was a harshly rasped question delivered by her furious husband. "Why the hell didn't you have the sense to put your money in the ship's strongbox? I warned you what would happen, but you wouldn't listen, would you?"

"The money is safe," she gasped.

"Where? We've searched the damn ship over."

"I've already put it into Mr. Fulton's strongbox."

For a moment Clay glared at her in fiery disbelief before

he shouted another reprimand. "You senseless idiot. You dared to carry that much money through this town without protection?"

Taking a deep breath to quell her own rising temper, Lynn replied to the insult in a flat voice, " 'Twas not all that much money."

"How much?"

"A little over two thousand guineas."

"The devil you say! My fa—my expectations were for triple that amount. According to Sir Trevor, you sold a London house and—"

"Sir Bevil was always an optimistic accountant," Lynn murmured caustically. "I sold that house during the plague and was lucky to get three thousand pounds for it, half of which I gave to my grandfather. Was there anything else you wished to ask me?"

"Why the hell did you register those four criminals in your grandfather's name? I could have sold them this morning when Vinson sold the others."

"They aren't for sale; I'll be needing all of them to work the farm."

"The devil with the farm! Come along, mistress, we're returning to this Fulton's home right now to reclaim that money before something happens to it. I'll be needing the lot of it."

"You'll be getting exactly half!"

"You're forgetting, wife, that English law applies here the same as it does in Cornwall."

"And you're forgetting, husband, that we'd be worse than idiots to appeal to the law right now. Did one of the crew take your place during indenture inspection?"

Clay's eyes were still sparking anger as he nodded curtly. "The second mate was the only one who looked enough alike. Nate's agreed to work for you during the three weeks we'll be in port."

Lynn heard Clay's final words with a heavy heart; she'd hoped that he might change his mind and remain in New

Port until she was free to join him in Connecticut. But the other news he'd given her was cheerful enough. Nate Stokes was one of the most competent officers aboard, and a good carpenter as well.

"Will you be going to Connecticut alone?" she asked her husband.

"What good could I do alone? I'll be taking Tom, Harry, and Spence with me."

Covertly studying his face, which appeared more ruthless than she'd ever seen it look before, Lynn's own resolve hardened.

"You won't be taking Bert Spence," she contradicted curtly. "I need him here. Besides, Leona announced this morning that she's carrying a child, so she'd be about as useful to you as a worn-out cow."

"Damnation! Spence is the only one who knows his way around this cursed country. Why do you need him?"

"He'll be building shelter for us to survive the winter."

"I'll be back long before that."

"Then you'll need shelter too."

"Why can't you stay with this friend of your grandfather's?"

"Mr. Fulton is a businessman, not a Father Christmas. He's waiting on the dock to dray the cattle and the rest of the fodder to his farm. Will you be coming with us?"

"I'm no farmer and you know it. I've appointments in town with some merchants and a sea captain. Do you have any money on you?"

Mechanically Lynn nodded and dragged ten gold coins from her pocket, remaining stoically expressionless when he frowned at the amount. "Where will you be staying, Clay?" she asked woodenly.

"I had planned to be at the inn, but now I guess you and I'll remain aboard ship. I'll drop by the farm to pick you up about sunset."

"Then will you tell Bert Spence that his wife can ride in one of the wagons if they leave the ship now."

Not pausing to hear his response, Lynn fled from the cabin and from the ship. An unexpected sheen of tears glazed her eyes when Red Penny bawled a greeting to her and stretched its massive head out to be petted. "You silly clown," she murmured, "at least you're still my friend. Come on, big fellow, let's show the others the way to our new home."

Had Lynn not been so tired six hours later when Tom Kenn arrived at the Fultons' with a hastily scrawled apology from Clay that he'd see her later aboard ship, she might have voiced a very unflattering opinion about the uselessness of aristocrats. Even Bert Spence had disappeared long before the necessary work was done, returning only in time for the supper the Fulton servants served on trestle tables outside the house.

"The cottage isn't bad," Bert announced, "but it won't sleep all of us; we'll need two more cabins before winter."

"How did you know where the farm was?"

"One of Fulton's sons took me there. He begins draying the fence posts tomorrow and the rails the—"

"Bert," Lynn interrupted, "Clay wanted you to go with him to Connecticut. If you'd rather—"

"I'm staying here, and Leona can't—" He broke off with an abrupt stiffness. "My wife won't be able to do her share of the work; but if you'll trust me, I'll get the necessary building done for you. Can you afford to pay for the materials and minimum of outside labor?"

"Provided you keep the cabins simple."

"*Basic* would be a more appropriate word. Remember, I'm an unskilled, untalented fool who's wasted twenty years without learning much of anything."

"My grandfather called you an educated man."

"If I hadn't tried to reclaim a worthless estate, I might have become a scholar. Who knows?"

"What kind of a man is my husband?"

"Damned if I know anymore. He's luckier than he has any right to be—we all are—but Clay's devils are still riding him, I suppose because he can never reclaim his own name."

"I'm glad he can't. I spent twenty-two years as a Trevor, and that's punishment enough."

"He told you?"

"Amelia did."

"The cat-clawed harpy!"

"She also told me that you're Sir Spencer Burtram."

"Not since my bankrupt estate was confiscated twelve years ago and I was exiled to Virginia. Tell me, Mistress Penley, are you related to the Trevor I met in Jamestown—a Royce Trevor?"

"Since we're both in exile, Bert Spence, I'd prefer you call me Lynn. Mr. Trevor is my father, but I wouldn't recognize him if he were seated three feet away from me. I wouldn't want to anyway."

Repressing the abrupt surge of kinship he felt for this articulate woman, Bert glanced uneasily toward the house where Leona was already in bed in one of the Fulton guest rooms. After seven barren years, nature had chosen the worst of times to grant him his wish for an heir—and the weakest of women to mother his child, he reflected cynically. Not physically weak, he amended, but morally and mentally as devoid of character as an undisciplined ten-year-old.

Irresistibly Bert's attention returned to the vibrant, dark-haired woman who was moving around the table, pausing long enough to speak to each of her workers in turn before she finally seated herself between Nell Wallis and Kate Horton. Remembering that blunt Nell had called her the only lady she'd ever known, Bert's thoughts were speculative. Lynn Penley was the daughter of one of the most flamboyant settlers in Virginia, a man who'd maintained the Cavalier traditions in grand style throughout the prosaic Commonwealth years. Yet the daughter he left behind on a bypassed farm had kept pace in sophistication. Even as she'd walked beside her bull today, encouraging the great brute to keep the pace, she'd emanated more dignified power than her father ever could. For the first time in many years, Spencer Burtram's smile was not tinged with bitterness.

Not until evening the following day did Clay Penley locate his wife. Had he begun his search early in the morning, he might have avoided hours of inconvenience and irritation. Unfortunately, he'd been unable to arise at dawn as his wife had, because his first intoxicating day of freedom had ended only a few hours earlier. He hadn't kept his appointment with either of the merchants, only with the sea captain who supplied the New Port inns with imported wine, rum, and brandy to augment the local hard cider brew. What had begun as a serious investigation into money-making opportunities had gradually accelerated into a drinking party after Amelia and Harry Cobb had joined the group, which then included several other ship captains.

Only when the bustling landlord had begun serving dinner did Clay remember his promise to Lynn, and he sent Tom Kenn to the Fultons' with a message. Clay remembered her again when he and Peter Vinson reached the *Tamarlind* and were told that Mistress Penley was not aboard. Drunker than he'd been in years, he was momentarily worried, but his concern was quickly replaced by defensive anger and sodden sleep. Late the following morning when he learned that the stores of household goods shipped by his father had been unloaded, Clay realized his mistake.

At the Fulton home, Leona Spence greeted him with a querulous complaint about the woman he'd come to see.

"You'll have to do something about your wife, Jame

Clay. She forced Spencer to start work at dawn this morning, and she took everyone with her... everyone, even the woman who lives in this rustic—"

"Did my wife seem angry about last night?" Clay interrupted impatiently.

"Who can tell what she's thinking? 'Tis Spencer's idiocy that worries me; he's acting as if he doesn't have any sense at all. Talk to him, Clay. Tell him that we have to go with you and Amelia. I'll die if I'm left here in this awful place."

After another long walk under a July sun too hot for his English coat of green worsted, Clay finally located his long-time friend supervising the construction of a log and split-rail fence.

"I don't know where Lynn is," Bert responded to Clay's brusque question. "She's been rushing around with the Fultons all morning, and last night she worked until after dark. She's not a helpless female who waits around for someone to tell her what to do."

"Why the devil is she doing all this, Spence? I want to sell those damned animals so we won't be tied down."

"Those *damned* animals are already making money, Clay. Fulton drove Lynn and your replacement over to—"

"My who?"

"Nate Stokes, or have you forgotten he's standing in for you?"

"He wasn't supposed to do any work."

"Nate enjoys work. Anyway, he and Lynn sold two barrels of our leftover milk to some farmer who makes cheese. I'll say this of the colonials, they don't believe in wasting time or anything else. Fulton's son put Tom to work this morning splitting rails."

"How did he convince Tom to do any hard work?"

"The Fultons employ indentureds so they know the law."

"What else has been going on while I was—"

"Doing what, Clay?"

"Trying to find something other than this kind of slavery. There's more money to be made in shipping."

"I remember the kind of money we made in our brand of shipping and the risks we took making it. I'm willing to wager you that Fulton has amassed a greater fortune without breaking a single law."

"What the devil's happened to you, Spence?"

"Age! I'm thirty-six and haven't a farthing to show for all those wasted years. While I was talking to your wife last night, I realized that she knows more about—"

"Just why were you talking to my wife instead of your own?"

"Not for the same reasons you talk to Harry's wife, Clay. Were she and Harry with you yesterday during your quixotic search for the pot of gold?"

"There were seven other men in the room!"

"But the fair Amelia had eyes and ears only for her knight in tarnished armor! Poor old Harry! Don't waste your temper on me, Clay. I have work to do. But if I were you, I'd locate Lynn damn fast."

Furious at the friend he'd believed incorruptibly loyal, Clay rasped contemptuously, "You're a hypocrite, Spence. I don't remember your complaining when Amelia flirted us safely past English and French tariff agents or when she risked her life to save ours two years ago in Paris."

"I'll grant she proved her worth in smuggling, Clay; but it was her own hide she was saving in Paris when she shot that man. He wasn't a policeman who'd come to arrest us as she claimed. He was a discarded lover she'd robbed six years earlier when she was still using the name of Comtesse d'Auberge."

"How do you know?"

"The man was grateful enough to talk after the doctor I'd summoned saved his life. Since neither you nor Harry would have believed me, I didn't bother to tell you."

"Why are you telling me now?"

"So you'll keep her away from your wife before she

does any more damage. Amelia is not a woman who enjoys sharing someone she's considered her personal possession for ten years.''

''Lynn knows damn well I haven't been unfaithful to her.''

''Lynn knows only what Amelia told her—and that, my poor friend, was everything—your name and the years you've danced attendance on that bitch's whims. My wife was a delighted member of that little audience because she's fool enough to believe Lynn a stupid woman.''

Leaving his dumbfounded friend abruptly, Bert returned to his interrupted work. Morosely thoughtful, Clay wandered aimlessly in the direction of the distant cottage, surveying the utilitarian stone structure and its roughly shingled roof with distaste. From the threshold he stared at the barrels and containers stacked on the hand-hewn table and freshly scrubbed stone floor.

''Who brought all this stuff here?'' he demanded of the kerchiefed woman vigorously scrubbing the fireplace.

Nell Wallis swung around and glared at the intruder. ''Your wife, that's who, when she came back from town early this afternoon.''

As Clay absorbed the shock of learning that his wife had been aboard the *Tamarlind* while he'd slept, he felt a burning resentment. She'd disobeyed his instructions that he'd expected her last night, and she hadn't even bothered to awaken him today. Angrily he turned to leave only to be stopped by the insolent command of a woman he'd detested since Tom had first introduced her into the Falmouth household.

''Not so fast, James Thayne,'' Nell admonished him sharply. ''Tom says he's going with you when you take French leave of your wife. Is that right?''

''That's right!'' Clay snapped as he turned to leave, stopping short when he heard Nell's second insolent command. ''Then take the slimy bastard with you now, and good riddance to the pair of you. I'll trust my future to the mistress.''

Concern for the futures of twelve human dependents and sixty-one animal ones had driven Lynn on a ceaseless round of activities since dawn. Plagued throughout the previous night by a sense of failure and an aching loneliness, she'd awakened tired and discouraged. But farmwork doesn't wait on human happiness; twenty cows had to be milked and the workers fed. Suppressing her resentment at the speed with which she had to make decisions, she assigned the work in order of priority and spent the morning aboard a wagon traveling from one supply source to another. At a Dutchman's farm two miles distant, she traded two barrels of milk for three balls of cheese and a crock of honey. Thus was Lynn introduced to the barter system that replaced money transactions in much of the bustling colony. Since her own trading stock was limited to surplus milk, forty bullocks, and a productive bull, she quickly learned to follow Edward Fulton's example and haggle for value.

It cost her one bullock to secure sufficient animal fodder to last until the first harvest from her own farm could be reaped, and it cost another four for the lumber needed to rebuild the barn and to construct two small cabins. At a wheelwright's busy establishment on the edge of New Port, she became a partner in an interisland draying enterprise. A canny trader, Caleb Winslow offered to supply the wagons while she supplied the oxen and drivers. Lynn's stubborn insistence that the drivers be paid before any profits were divided among the partners resulted in a faint flicker of respect on the part of the wheelwright. However, it was Edward Fulton who realized the extent of her astuteness when he asked about her reasons.

"Last night your son George offered to make me a

partner in his ferry services in exchange for four of my bullocks, and I accepted. As soon as Mr. Winslow mentioned the word interisland, I knew that some of the deliveries would take a full day or longer. Unless the drivers were paid separately, I could lose money.''

Fulton was still chuckling when he pulled the wagon to a stop on the dock where his son and Nate Stokes were waiting with a second wagon. While Lynn went aboard to direct the removal of the household equipment supplied by Bevil Trevor, the old man ruminated on the vagaries of fate that had sent this determined woman to his doorstep. Ephraim Penley had called his granddaughter headstrong and sharp-tongued, and that she was, but considerably more as well. She'd taken an accurate measure of colonials, a stubborn breed of Englishmen separated from the mother country by twenty or more years of independence; and she'd met the challenge of survival with an enterprising fortitude few men could match. And she had done it without a sixpence of help from the husband whom Fulton had heard the youngest of the indentured women describe as a handsome scoundrel.

Aboard the *Tamarlind* Lynn had only a brief glimpse of that handsome husband, although his good looks were considerably obscured as he slept in ugly disarray in his stateroom. Sniffing the brandy fumes still lingering in the stale air, she sighed in resignation and left quietly to gather some of her own clothing from the smaller cabin. She still had hours of work to do before she'd have the time to coax an errant husband into a semblance of good humor. Recalling with a twinge of conscience that she hadn't as yet given him the thousand guineas she'd promised, Lynn contemplated the tempting alternative of withholding the money indefinitely. As long as he was without funds, he couldn't leave New Port.

The afternoon hours whirled by as she accompanied Edward Fulton on another pair of procurement missions. A month's supply of food was paid for by the promise of Red

Penny's stud service for four cows, and a year's supply of firewood cost her two more bullocks. Upon returning to the Fulton house, she gratefully accepted her host's offer of a civilized bath in an outsized cooper's barrel located in the washroom. She was freshly dressed in one of the summer gowns Kate had made for her when she learned the discouraging news that Clay had already come calling for her and left. Quietly at sunset, she told Bert Spence to take charge of the work on the following day.

"You can't go alone to that part of town," he warned her when he realized her intention. "Some of those sailors are as bad as London street scum. Wait for Clay here; eventually he'll come to his senses."

Lynn shook her head, relieved that she didn't have to voice her fears to this man. He knew Clay Penley far better than she did. "Or perhaps I'll come to mine," she retorted lightly. "In the meantime, the less public notice of our oddity, the better. As long as the daylight holds, I'll be all right on the dock." She didn't mention the fact that her knapsack held her flails as well as a thousand gold guineas. For a woman who'd faced the savage viciousness of Cornish wreckers, a chance encounter with a drunken sailor held little fear.

It was as well, however, that she didn't tarry along the way; the *Tamarlind* was already untied, about to move out to harbor anchorage while another ship waited for its turn at dockside. Lynn remained on deck to watch the exchange and to study the incoming ship that carried no flag to mark its national origin.

" 'Tis a Jamaican pirate that Captain Vinson has no great liking for," the first mate informed her. "There'll be no peace in town tonight."

"Is my husband aboard, Mr. Carey?"

"Aye, him and as much of the crew as we could locate. Yon pirate has a way of convincing unwary lads to change allegiance, but I'd not envy any fool who did. 'Tis a short life, regardless, and none too merry at the best of times."

"Do you know which cabin my husband's in, Mr. Carey?"

"He's at dinner in the captain's quarters with a pair of locals, merchants would be my guess, although one of them is as heavy booted as a farmer. Do you want me to announce your arrival, Mistress Penley?"

"No, I won't disturb them, but thank you anyway."

"Then would you be doing me the honor of a simple sup, mistress, as soon as I put this wooden beauty to rest again. There's a small matter of a wager with the cargo mate concerning your bull. Did the animal walk all the way to the farm or did it collapse halfway there?"

"Eight of the cows had to be carried, but Red Penny and the others completed the journey."

"Then, except for the cargo mate's gloom, 'twill be a merry meal. I was certain the great beast would have the pluck to endure."

An hour later in the officers' dining area, Lynn was pleasantly relaxed for the first time in two stressful days, watching a hotly contested game of chuck-a-luck. As absorbed as the players in the outcome of each toss of dice, she was unaware of a second audience until she heard the sweetly derisive voice of Amelia Cobb.

"I told you your wandering witch would return, Jame."

CHAPTER
7

"What the devil took you so long getting here, Lynn?"
Clay demanded brusquely. "I sent word to Leona that you
were to return to the *Tamarlind* as fast as you could. And
why in hell did you eat dinner in the officers' mess when
you were supposed to report directly to Vinson's quarters?
I'd arranged a damn good sale for every head of cattle with
the men who just left the ship, but they wouldn't sign
without talking to you first. It seems your friend Fulton
warned them off with some balderdash about your grandfather's claims."

Clay's lengthy castigation was delivered during an often
interrupted walk along the lower gangway without a long
enough pause for Lynn to respond to any of the separate
allegations. Not that she was inclined to do so at any rate;
she was too busy digesting the bits and pieces of information revealed. Leona Spence had mentioned only Clay's
earlier visit, not his subsequent summons; and Mr. Carey
had neglected to inform her that she'd been expected at the
captain's dinner. Far more irritating was the purpose of
that dinner: a peremptory sale of her property without even
her tacit permission. The timing, too, intrigued her. Last

night during the outdoor supper, Edward Fulton's widowed daughter-in-law had announced that he'd had two visitors, obviously the same men Clay had entertained tonight. After those men had learned that she was the only one commissioned to sell, they'd convinced her husband to summon her to a meeting that would exclude Edward Fulton. Lynn's estimation of her grandfather's friend increased measurably; under his careful guidance today, she'd committed the services of her bull and nineteen of her bullocks. Quite obviously, Fulton had not considered her strong enough to resist her husband's blandishments. Unsure of how she would have reacted, Lynn concluded that the old man had acted wisely in removing the temptation.

Other aspects of the meeting tonight also puzzled her. Why had the meeting been held aboard ship, rather than at a New Port inn? And why had Amelia Cobb been invited? Despite her arrogant airs, she was still a registered convict; moreover, she and Harry had announced their intention of remaining at the inn until the *Tamarlind* sailed in three weeks. Following the woman whose stiffly wide skirts filled the narrow companionway, Lynn wondered if Harry was also aboard or whether—. Her angry thoughts were abruptly terminated by Amelia's petulant demand.

"Help me up these stairs, Jame, love," she ordered imperiously. Of necessity, Lynn crowded against the bulkhead while Clay pushed his way past her to obey the command. A minute later Lynn climbed those same narrow steps without assistance, still carrying her heavy knapsack. Nor was she reassured by the firm hand her husband clamped on her arm when she emerged into the upper companionway. It was a guiding hand, lacking in affection or concern; and it remained firmly in control until he ushered her into his own stateroom in the wake of Amelia Cobb.

The presence of Harry Cobb and the remains of a dinner for two still spread over the table answered two of Lynn's questions. Someone had shown the wisdom to exclude the

Cobbs from the captain's dinner. Within minutes, Harry's rumbling explanation addressed to Lynn had answered the rest.

"B'God, we barely had time to get aboard, and I'm still not sure we're safe from that cursed pirate. Bad luck all around his coming here. Wouldn't have thought New England colonists would allow his breed in harbor, much less welcome him. If I hadn't recognized his blackguard second mate when he first swaggered into the inn, we'd have been in for it . . . swords and all."

"You're exaggerating, Harry," Clay intervened hastily. "Rambert could have exposed our identities, that's all. He's known Vinson and me for ten years and Harry for five. We were just unlucky enough to be in port at the time."

"Won't he recognize the *Tamarlind* anyway?" Lynn asked.

"No, it was rebuilt eight years ago."

"How well did you know this pirate, Clay?"

"Ten years ago during England's first attempt to invade Jamaica, his ship and ours fought against the Spanish; and Vinson and I met Rambert in Port Royal. A month later he tried to take our cargo at sea, and we retaliated by capturing his ship."

"That's only half the story." Harry plunged into the narrative. "Five years ago in Bordeaux, we *borrowed* a consignment of stolen brandy from him. When he recognized Clay, he vowed revenge."

"Does he know Bert Spence?" Lynn asked worriedly.

Clay paused for a moment to glare at her before he responded curtly. "Spence will have the sense to remain hidden. He was blunt enough today about staying on that barren farm; he sounded as if he planned to remain there the rest of his life. While we're on the subject, Lynn, what did you tell Fulton about us?"

"Whatever he knows about any of us he learned from my grandfather's letter."

"I meant about our plans."

"How would I know anything about your plans," Lynn rasped with growing asperity. "You seem to change them on a daily basis, and I don't believe the Cobbs are interested in our private business," she added tartly.

"Hoity-toity," Amelia drawled. "Be careful, Jame, your wife has a temper; and she brought her little toys along with her to keep you in line." With a mocking laugh, the auburn-haired woman pulled the flails from the knapsack Lynn had laid on the bed and waved them around experimentally. Not unpredictably, those experimental waves were aimed closer to Lynn than to the men.

"Put those damn things down before you hurt some-one," Harry shouted from across the room. His warning proved unnecessary, though; with a swift lunge, Lynn had retrieved her clubs from the other woman's hands. Efficiently she relatched the knapsack and picked it up before she turned around to confront her silent husband who was staring speculatively at Amelia.

"I brought them along for protection from waterfront loiterers," Lynn murmured with ironic inflection. "But I think I'd have been safer with drunken sailors than I am here. If your unfriendly pirates leave port before you do, I think I'd feel more comfortable if you visited me on the farm." She'd almost reached the door when Clay stopped her.

"Harry," he snapped, "take your wife to your own cabin. I want to talk to mine without—"

"I won't stay in that dark closet, Jame," Amelia interrupted in a shrill protest. "And I won't be put away like a naughty child. I'm not to blame if your wife is a jealous savage. I was only funning with her, and she hurt my hand."

Lynn watched the performance with cold dispassion. Remembering the practiced technique her own spoiled mother had employed to escape responsibility, she waited for Amelia's cerulean eyes to fill with limpid tears and for her lips to purse into an appealing pout. On cue, the actress displayed her artistry, treating each man equally to her displeasure.

"I'll go, but I won't forget that both of you took her part." Amelia had, however, reserved enough venom for one final barrage hurled at the taller woman who stood silently watching her. "Remember what I told you the other day. You may be married to Jame, but you don't own him."

As she always had with her mother, Lynn made no attempt to defend the indefensible. She was no match for a woman who could flaunt her power over one man so openly and still retain her husband's blind adoration. Prying her arm loose from Clay's fingers, Lynn walked over to the transom windows to peer morosely out over the water now darkened to an inky gray. Tensing angrily, she heard the bluff good-night exchanged by the men and the snap of the closing door; but she didn't turn around even when Clay asked his first defensive question.

"What did Amelia tell you, Lynn?"

"The truth about you, and a charming fabrication of the romantic life of Lady Gordon—something or other—Pendrath."

"That's all past history."

"I know, about twenty minutes past when you rushed to help her up the stairs and let me climb alone."

"I haven't been unfaithful to you, Lynn."

"I know that too, Clay, but I think only because you're loyal to Harry, not to me."

"I avoided both of them when we weren't working."

"You're not avoiding them now."

"Are you still angry about my not coming for you last night?"

"I didn't really expect you."

The cross-purpose dialogue had eased neither of their differing tensions; but of the two, Clay's defensive frustration was more volatile than his wife's emotional resignation. Abruptly he abandoned his attempt at apology and launched into a more characteristic offensive.

"I looked all over for you today. Where were you?"

"On some errands with Mr. Fulton."

"Was it your decision or his not to sell the cattle?"

"Neither. Technically they belong to my grandfather."

"But you can sell them if you want to."

"I suppose I could; but since they're the only means I have of earning a living, I won't."

"But they're not the only way; that's what I'm trying to tell you. For three thousand pounds and Harry's three thousand, we could buy half interest in a ship that would earn ten times the amount."

"Neither you nor Harry are shipmasters, and neither of you can return to England."

"The ship's already captained and crewed, so we'd be only sea-going merchants. And we wouldn't be going to England; we plan to operate between the American colonies and the Caribbean."

"Then you'd be breaking the law, and you'd be guilty of smuggling again since English ships are required to trade with England."

"Hundreds of other captains break that law without being caught. We'd only be doing it for a few years, just long enough to earn the money for a decent life."

"Is that what you and Harry decided yesterday?"

"Yes, and 'tis a damn good opportunity for only three thousand pounds."

"Did Harry, by any chance, mention the fact that you and he were experienced smugglers?"

Damn her, Clay cursed silently, she's as relentless as a prosecutor! It hadn't been Harry who'd mentioned smuggling yesterday; it'd been Amelia who'd become boastful. As a result, Harry and he had been forced to offer another five hundred pounds each to convince the skeptical captain that they intended honest merchanting. Clay's scowl deepened; the hypocrite had been breaking the trade laws for a score of years, but he wouldn't admit to smuggling. Still, he was the best in the business and highly respected by his customers; the only alternative would be criminal freebooters and buccaneers. Grimly Clay reopened the subject of finances.

"The business would be honest enough, and you'd make your money back within the year. It seems to me that a few cattle are a small enough price for you to pay for a chance at—"

"I'm not selling them, Clay, but I brought you the amount I promised. That's why I came tonight, to give it to you. I don't imagine you'll be leaving the ship any more in New Port, and you'll need funds wherever you go. You have expensive friends."

"So we're back to that again."

"We never left."

"How much did Spence tell you about . . . about Harry's wife?"

"Nothing, other than calling her a harpy. He didn't tell me anything about you either, even when I asked. Clay, I don't know how to play your kind of games, so I'm not going to try."

"I haven't played any games with you, except about my name, and that was your fault. Why do you hate my father?"

"I don't hate him, I just feel that . . . that he used me."

"Why? We're both safe; and if you'd only forget your prejudices, we could have a good marriage. There was nothing wrong between us until you—"

"Until your former mistress reclaimed her property! What happens when her current husband removes his blinders? Will you be able to avoid still another duel of honor?"

"Don't be a fool! I was forced to defend my own life in that duel, as for Harry—" Clay stopped talking abruptly; he'd just remembered the story Spence had told him, a story he'd labeled as only jealousy on Spence's part because Harry's fortune was still intact. God, what had happened to the friendship and trust that had once bound Harry and Spence and him together? The answer tore at his own conscience. He'd been fool enough to believe everything Amelia had told him, that she'd been forced into both marriages by her father, but that she'd loved only him. Bleakly he wondered how many others had been honored equally by the same confession. She'd been his mistress only at intervals during those years before Harry, and he'd gradually lost the fierce protectiveness he'd developed for her when he'd been in his early twenties. How the devil had he been so blind as not to have noticed the essential bitchiness of the woman: she'd been as vicious as a street slut to Lynn, even to the extent of threatening her with physical assault when she'd swung those clubs around. But tonight he'd jumped to help her up those damned stairs and ignored his wife.

What in hell was wrong with him? He no longer desired Amelia, not in the way he did the woman watching him now with knowing eyes from across the untidy table. Even when Amelia had come tripping into this cabin, flirting with him, promising him the love he'd never collect, he hadn't been tempted. His senses were still dominated by the woman he'd married, but whom he'd not yet mastered in bed or out. The enigmatic witch woman had matched him in passion without reservations; but other than during those moments, she'd eluded him completely. Perhaps it had been nothing more than childish petulance that had driven him backward into the familiar quagmire of Amelia's flattering attention. Spence had been right about old devils being the hardest to placate, Clay admitted ruefully; he'd resumed his irresponsible habits because he'd never learned to accept discipline or domination.

As if attuned to her husband's plaguing dilemma, Lynn broke the uncomfortable silence. "I imagine Captain Vinson will sail as soon as possible to avoid trouble. Have you any idea when?"

"Are you that eager to get rid of me, Lynn?"

Rising from her chair with an effortless ease that marked all of her actions, she smiled sadly. "No, but neither am I eager to hold an unwilling man. I hope you find what you're looking for, Clay."

Alarmed by the finality of her words, he shoved his chair back and stood up uneasily. All bluster had left his voice when he held out his hand in entreaty. "I'd like you to stay with me until we do sail, Lynn."

"I wasn't planning to leave tonight, only to take a walk on deck and then go to bed. 'Tis been a long day, and I didn't sleep much last night."

"I'm hoping that's because I wasn't there," Clay murmured impulsively. "I don't sleep well without you either."

Lynn's responsive laughter was spontaneous; he'd been all but unconscious when she'd seen him this morning. He has a glib tongue, she reminded herself with a perverse humor; like a greedy child, he wanted the best of both worlds—a wife to tend him and a mistress to amuse. The last thought was a sobering one, and she arrived on deck in somber contemplation of the realities of Clay Penley's complicated personality.

There was not the peace on deck she'd hoped for, though; Amelia had not retired for the night nor forgotten her earlier complaints about the accommodations she'd been assigned. In a voice no longer dulcet, she was arguing vigorously with her husband and Captain Vinson. Just how the angry woman recognized Clay in the dark, Lynn had no idea; but he was immediately recruited as an ally.

"Jame, 'tis half your ship! Please tell your stubborn captain to give us the quarters he's saving for some doltish colonials who're not even aboard yet. I can't breathe without a window, and I'm not going to be squeezed into some dark cavity to smother to death."

Peter Vinson's strident whisper cut across her complaint

with a repressed fury. "Madam, I've warned you three times to keep your voice under control. Sound travels across water, and the crew is in no shape to repel a boarding raid by pirates tonight."

Increasing the volume of her taunting threat, Amelia began, "In that case, Peter Vinson—" only to be silenced by her husband's hand across her mouth.

"For God's sake, shut up, Amelia! Clay, help me get her below before she causes us any more trouble. What in hell am I going to do with her?"

"All you have to do, Harry, is to keep her quiet for this one night." Vinson intervened in a harsh whisper. "She goes ashore tomorrow morning when we pull anchor. I've put up with her demanding nonsense because she's your wife, but tonight she endangered my ship. I won't have a drunken woman aboard. Kindly remind her that as an indentured, she can be remanded into custody and returned to England; and her accommodations then would be a lock-in. After tonight she'll be the responsibility of Mistress Penley."

Lynn listened to the grim announcement with violently mixed emotions, bitter disappointment that she had only the one night to regain any kind of a hold over a wavering husband, and a black fury that her own immediate future was to be handicapped by a vindictive shrew. Determinedly she followed the others into the ship's interior, leaving a relieved Peter Vinson behind. When they reached the door to Clay's stateroom, Lynn issued several sharp orders of her own.

"Put her in here, Harry, and bind her mouth if she starts to scream, or Captain Vinson will do it for you if he doesn't throw her overboard first."

Before Harry could protest her rough language, Lynn shoved the door open wide enough to admit the struggling husband and wife. Remembering that the money she had given Clay was still in the cabin, she retrieved the knapsack and her flails just as Harry released his hold on

Amelia. Before Lynn could reach the safety of her own husband's side, the irate woman tried to grab hold of the leather pouch.

"Whose money is that?" she demanded.

"Mine," Lynn snapped with a grim satisfaction. Her instincts had been accurate; earlier when Amelia had opened the pack she'd surveyed its contents thoroughly. But as swift as Lynn's reactions had been, her rival's were swifter.

"Then it belongs to your husband!" she lashed out. "Jame, is it enough for your half of our ship?"

Controlling her outrage with difficulty, Lynn fled from the stateroom, blotting out the sounds of Clay's and Harry's sputtered comments, but hearing Amelia's final shrill outcry. "Don't be such a fool, Jame; we're three against one. We can force her to sell those hideous animals."

With a relief rooted in despair, Lynn located Captain Vinson on deck, still anxiously watching the distant ship.

"A piece of bad luck," he said quietly when he recognized his visitor.

"Are those pirates really dangerous?" she asked in a whisper.

"Aye, they are. Rambert and his crew are all fierce fighters, and they're convinced they have good reason to hate us. We bested them in fair enough fights, but I doubt we could again. I've lost my taste for such violence. 'Tis ironic, mistress; ten years ago Rambert was a good friend, but in the profession he chose to follow, friendship doesn't count for much."

"Why would New Port allow such a man to use this harbor?"

"'Tis good business. He can sell the cargoes he's stolen from Spanish and French ships cheaper than honest merchants can. Did you get the woman quieted down?"

"She'll be staying in my husband's cabin."

"Only until the morning, Mistress Penley. 'Tis my

opinion the shrew was deliberate in her attempt to attract Rambert's attention."

"Captain, please keep her aboard," Lynn implored desperately. "I wouldn't know what to do with her."

"Are you certain you know what you're asking, lass? She's never been a reasonable woman when she wants something."

"I know, and I also know what she wants. But I'll be safer if she's here rather than on my farm. Will you allow her to remain?"

Vinson was slow to respond; he'd been looking forward to a voyage without any women aboard. Still, he was fair enough to admit that he was better equipped to handle the arrogant termagant than another woman.

"Aye, I'll keep her for this one trip," he consented heavily. "The future, though, is another matter; I'll never welcome her aboard the *Tamarlind* again."

"I hope you don't, and I hope she never returns here. Captain, I have one more favor to ask. I want you to lock my husband's money in your strongbox. I'd rather Mrs. Cobb not have access to it."

"I don't blame you, but 'twould be safer from her grasp if you remained aboard with Clay."

"I can't; there are too many people depending on me."

"Lass, do you mind my giving you a piece of advice? Bert Spence has a bit more sense than the other two; he'd be a good friend to you if you'd let him."

"He already is, Captain."

"Then there's naught more to be said. Come along, mistress. We'll lock that money up now."

Fifteen minutes later, Lynn knocked on the door of her husband's stateroom and motioned him outside when he opened the door.

Without waiting for his predictable question, "Where the devil did you go?" she plunged into the speech she'd wanted to make since the day she'd met Amelia Cobb.

"Your money's safe in the captain's strongbox, and he's

agreed to let your . . . to let Harry's wife remain aboard.
She's your problem . . . and Harry's, Clay, not mine. Don't
be idiot enough to underestimate her; she was no more
drunk tonight than I was. Regardless of the danger to other
people, she meant to have her way about the stateroom just
as she means to have you.''

"You're forgetting that I'm married to you."

"You wouldn't be if my grandfather had told me what
he knew about her. I'd never have agreed to compete with
a jealous mistress."

"For God's sake, Lynn, I've already told you—"

"Then you'd better tell her the same thing. Afterward,
if you want to see me, you'll find me in Kate's old cabin."

"Damn it, woman," he exploded, but his exasperated
protest was hurled only at her departing back; and his
belated attempt to follow was circumvented by a tight-
lipped Harry Cobb.

"Amelia wants to talk to you, Clay," he said tersely.

"What the hell about? She's your wife, Harry."

"We both know that she should have been yours twice
over. Don't look so shocked, Clay. She told me about you
right after we were married and once a day ever since."

Chilled by the matter-of-fact candor of his friend, Clay
blustered, "Harry, I never—"

"I'm not the complete fool I may seem. I knew why
you always stayed at another inn and why you turned your
house over to the rest of us. Christ, we've been friends too
long for me to doubt you. Do you know something? I'll be
glad to leave her behind tomorrow and get on with my own
life. Did your wife agree to give you enough money?"

"No."

"Amelia said she wouldn't. What a pair of bitch-ridden
dolts we are, Clay—me with an immoral slut and you with
a—"

"Lynn has nothing to do with our problem, Harry, and
she won't have. Your wife isn't going ashore tomorrow.

You and she can have my cabin for the duration, and I'll
avoid her as much as possible until—''

''Well, you can't avoid her now, old friend; I promised
to bring you back alone so that she can make one of her
pretty apologies. And don't be ass enough to tell her the
truth tonight; I'm not in any shape for a sword fight
against the likes of Morse Rambert. God's truth, Clay, I'm
damned tired of trouble.''

As Clay made his way down the steep steps to the
'tween-deck row of airless cabins, he was more depressed
than at any time since he'd walked out of Newgate prison.
Although he'd shared only two of the five brandies it'd
taken to dry Amelia's copious tears, he'd been forced to
listen to her repeat the same drunken plans they'd all
agreed upon yesterday in the crude comfort of a colonial
inn. How dismally asinine they sounded to him now, and
how dangerously similar to their old life. Despite his
earlier assurance to Lynn, he realized bleakly that within
months, they would have become as recklessly foolhardy
as they'd been before their capture. When Harry had left
the cabin in search of another bottle of brandy, Clay had
learned that Amelia's plans for the future extended far
beyond mere criminal smuggling.

''We belong together, Clay; we always have,'' she'd
told him then. ''Harry will understand when we become
lovers again; I've already told him that I love you. God
knows, I didn't realize how much until you brought that
black-eyed devil woman into our lives. Why did you have
to marry her? Why couldn't you and Harry have left her in
England when you had the chance? She'll never be one of
us.''

Desperately Clay had waited for Harry's return so that
he could escape from the horror of watching the face of the
woman he'd always considered classically beautiful crum-

ble into a caricature of a wheedling strumpet with the same
sly pouts and fluttering eyelashes. For the first time in his
memory, Amelia was drunk enough to forget her sophisticated acting talents, drunk enough not to be instantly
aware of his complete rejection of her blatant overtures.
God, what a fool he'd been and how blessedly lucky he
was to have avoided her domination. Mercifully, just after
Harry reentered the cabin, brandishing a dusty bottle in his
hand, she'd fallen asleep, sprawled limply across the bed
like an overdressed, overcurled rag doll.

On deck, where he'd remained long enough to clear his
head and to breathe deeply the salty air of a muggy July
night, he'd looked across the water at the lanterns swaying
on the masts of the unflagged ship. With an ironic gratitude, he gestured a salute to his unseen enemy. If Morse
Rambert hadn't arrived at New Port when he did, Clay
might still be tempted by the will-o'-the-wisp lure of
picaresque adventure with equally unprincipled companions. It had been the maudlin confession of a self-centered
woman that had revealed the hypocrisy and deceit of his
own character. He'd been all too willing to use his wife's
small fortune for his own ambitions without a thought for
her security. He wasn't sure he'd even planned to return to
her; it would have been easy to drift from one smuggled
cargo to the next. Spence had the right of it when he'd
called him a damn fool, but Spence would have to swallow
those words when Clay Penley and wife arrived at the
Fulton farm together.

His optimism lasted until he reached the lower deck and
he remembered Lynn's warning to him. She'd sounded as
impartial as a judge passing sentence and as remotely
disinterested. How could he expect any intelligent woman
to feel otherwise? Odds were she'd be relieved to see the
end of him; and more than likely, she'd refuse his offer to
remain with her.

He recognized her cabin easily, her two small sea chests
were stacked in the narrow space outside. Inside the

crowded room, a low-burning lantern cast a dim amber light over a scene that eased his conscience and eliminated the remainder of his doubts. Neatly arranged on the bare ropes of the narrow bunk were Lynn's clothing and empty knapsack, while on the floor side-by-side were two pallets made into one bed. He gazed down at the figure of his wife sleeping motionless on her side and experienced a surge of relief. Hastily he removed his own clothes, extinguished the lantern, and joined her with warm gratitude. The desire came minutes later when he felt her move against him in a sleepy welcome.

He might never understand her entirely, he thought before the fire she'd aroused in him since their first tempestuous lovemaking obliterated his ability to think at all. She never played the game most women did of punishing a man by denial; her passion had always been free of feminine whims of pretended reluctance. Nor did she seem to consider her participation as a reward for some gift or other generosity. If ever a woman had a right to anger, this dark-haired, enigmatic woman did on this disagreeable night when he'd treated her so ungallantly. Yet her arousing passion kept pace, and her strong body moved in easy consort with his.

Unaware that Clay's regard for her had increased beyond mere physical desire, Lynn responded with as much relief as sensuous abandon. He hadn't forgotten her, at least not yet; and in the months ahead, he might remember her with an emotion other than regret. It was this hope that drove her to make what might be their final night together memorable. Uninhibited as she'd always been with him, since it seemed incomprehensible to her that mating should be considered any more sinful with humans than with animals, she encouraged him with caresses that prolonged their ultimate ecstasy. Lynn would have been surprised to learn that many women never experienced the throbbing magic of fulfillment or that some wives dreaded the intimacy of marriage.

Because neither she nor Clay ever indulged in intimate confessions before or after, she had no idea that their mutual satisfaction was unique. His instructions had always been physical rather than verbal, and Lynn had been an apt pupil. She'd learned which caresses had increased his enjoyment—and, incidentally, her own—and which speed best suited his variable moods. But always she had loved the silent communication of their bodies from the first exploratory kiss to the wild turbulence of their climax.

Tonight in the pitlike darkness of the cabin, she felt an added urgency. With her legs binding him to her, she met his slow, mesmerizing thrusts with an intense desire to keep him buried inside her long after their racing pulse beats slowed and their breathing quieted. When he started to roll over, her arms tightened and she murmured in protest. For a moment he lay still, and then his perspiration-drenched body shook in quiet laughter. "If you only knew how often I've been tempted," he murmured indistinctly.

"I didn't know if it were possible," she whispered. "You never..."

"I thought about it our first time together when you acted as if I'd raped you."

"It wasn't rape."

"I know it wasn't. You were as ready as I was, even though you were as green as grass about men. But after we were married, you climbed back into your shell and wouldn't come near me until I ordered that damned bed removed."

"You were in no condition to—"

"I would have managed if you'd given me the invitation you did tonight."

Lynn's laughter was softly exultant as she moved experimentally against his rebuilding desire. "You're managing very nicely now," she giggled.

"I'd have to be in my dotage if I didn't. You're full of surprises tonight."

"So are you. Why was it we never talked like this before?" she whispered.

"I had other things on my mind—like now." But there was a difference in his lovemaking this time. Her humor and unexpected aggression had surprised him into an emotional warmth that had little to do with sensual enslavement. Until she'd clung to him earlier, he'd had little faith that she felt anything other than physical lust for him. Intrigued by the possibility that this self-possessed woman might be in love with him, Clay caressed her with a growing possessiveness and was rewarded by a more confident response on her part. There was an awareness of something infinitely desirable building between them that transcended even the throbbing excitement of culmination. Neither of them dared define the difference as love, but both were aware that their relationship had undergone a subtle change. Clay held her close to him after he'd moved to his side, and Lynn made no attempt to pull away. Even as they fell asleep, there was a peaceful unity of spirit they'd never experienced with each other before.

Clay's sleep was deeper, however; Lynn had drunk none of the soporific brandy he'd consumed. He was awakened late the following morning by the pitching rolls of a ship under full sail being driven by brisk winds. He awakened alone on an untidy pallet occupying the floor of a small cabin. Not until his mind began to function, did he realize the extent of his loneliness. Lynn's clothing and the trunks that had been piled in the gangway outside were gone. After dressing himself as rapidly as he could in the confining quarters, he raced upward to the deck and stared westward toward the distant shore with a sense of irreversible loss.

"You disappoint me, lad," Captain Vinson reprimanded him quietly. "I didn't think you'd let her go alone. I was hoping you'd gained a bit more sense about women after you married her. She might not have been what you wanted, but she's more the lady than the perfumed courtesan she left behind. The least you should have done was to see her safely ashore. In case you're interested, David Carey was all too eager to act as your substitute."

"How long have we been underway?"

"Three hours."

"Is it too late to turn back?"

"Aye, and you know it, with Rambert still in New Port."

"I meant to go with her, Peter."

"Did you tell her so?"

"No, damn it! I thought she would know that was my intention."

"Why would she have had any such reason? Last night you announced just the opposite with small regard for her feelings. And this morning Madame Cobb arose in time to bid your wife a vicious farewell with the message that you'd be making your new home on Pendrath land in Virginia. It should be quite a household, what the decadent French would call a *ménage à trois*."

Clay's eyes were narrowed as he continued to stare westward. "How soon do we reach New Haven?"

"If the winds hold, within a day or so, no longer than three I'm hoping. I still have the necessary ship repairs to make if New Haven has progressed enough to have a shipwright in town. If not, we'll have to backtrack and sail thirty-eight miles up the Connecticut River to Hartford. May have to anyway to locate a replacement for the cargo we were forced to pass over in New Port."

"Then you'll be leaving Harry and me in New Haven. I want to find out if there's any hope for my land there."

"Are you taking the woman with you?"

"Not a chance! I don't want to arouse the prejudice of people who might someday become my neighbors."

"What are your permanent plans for her?"

"As soon as we reach Virginia, Mrs. Harrold Pendrath will be deposited on her cousin's plantation; and as soon as you've taken on enough tobacco cargo, we'll sail away on the fastest winds we can find."

A broad smile appeared on the sun-wizened face of the veteran mariner. "If I were you, I'd take the time to send that message to your wife on the first ship headed north. But in the meantime, my reformed young friend, you'll have to serve as second mate. In the rush we forgot all about Nate Stokes."

"Is Tom Kenn still aboard?"

"No, he left about an hour after you delivered him yesterday. Can't say I'm sorry, though; he openly defied my order to help clean the bilge. I hope your wife will be more successful at disciplining the young scamp than I was, but I imagine she'll have the sense to turn him over to Nate."

Recalling the confrontation he'd had with Nell Wallis, Clay frowned. "Tom can be damned difficult."

"Nate's used to getting work out of the worst slug-a-beds in my crew, as you'll be finding out unless you plan to waste the day with the pair who've just emerged on deck looking for you."

Out of the corner of his eye, Clay recognized Amelia's bright blue dress and grimaced. "Not a chance, Peter, I'll take the crew; you can have the Cobbs!"

Vinson frowned with distaste as he watched Clay disappear into the fo'c'sle's gangway, but the smile he managed at the last minute for the overdressed couple approaching him held a grim satisfaction.

CHAPTER 8

Having read most of the literature published about the American colonies, largely as a result of her grandfather's work, Lynn Penley was better prepared than most newcomers to meet the hardships and challenges of life in sparsely settled Rhode Island. Since her own unique life in remote Cornwall had denied her the elegant ease generally accorded daughters of highborn gentry, she had developed the necessary skills and physical endurance. Upon returning to the farm on the third day of her new life, she tackled the goals she'd set for herself with determined perseverance. Indeed, on that particular day, she welcomed the hard work as an antidote for the lonely desolation she'd felt when she left the *Tamarlind* for the last time. Despite her best efforts at winning the loyalty of a skittish husband, Clay had made no avowal specific enough to be considered a binding pledge.

The vague promise he'd made about returning after he'd explored his Connecticut property was now meaningless. He'd already committed himself to an exploration, if not considerably more, of the Pendrath lands in Virginia as well. Although Lynn did not believe the entirety of Amelia

Cobb's farewell boast, she knew that Clay had not renounced his former life completely, if at all. His reckless gambling with the fragile security so dearly purchased by his father was incomprehensible to Lynn. For a man who had barely escaped the hangman's noose to risk the freedom he'd gained through the chicanery of two old men seemed the height of folly to her. But Lynn herself was not entirely devoid of prejudice against both of those same old men. Sir Bevil's timely help in her escape from the vindictive Pollocks had been a carefully planned extension of his imperative to save his own son. As she faced the responsibility of establishing a colonial home alone, she resented the fact that her grandfather had also conspired to keep her in ignorance of her husband's identity and his already complicated life. Lynn was honest enough to admit that she would have married Clay even if she'd known he was a Trevor. She'd accepted him long before he made love to her in the tower; but his relationship with Amelia Cobb was a more formidable obstacle. Now she had no choice but to wait out the weeks, months, years to learn whether she had won or lost.

With the stoic resolve that had sustained her throughout the physical desertion of her father and the spiritual denial by her mother, Lynn turned her energies toward survival in a frontier world. Within three months her people were securely housed in sturdy unadorned cabins, and her remaining animals in a half-wood, half-stone barn that would withstand the heaviest of winter storms. When the four Spragues— soon to become five—arrived aboard the *Merline* after a detour to Virginia, Lynn had taken the two brothers to her grandfather's second farm on the banks of the Seekonk River near Providence. Following Ephraim's instructions, she explained the terms of the Spragues' potential ownership; for the next ten years only, the profits would be evenly divided between them and the Penleys.

"They're generous terms, Mistress Lynn," Will Sprague said quietly.

"Aye, they are, Will," she agreed readily, "but we'll both profit in the long run."

The first major commercial trip made by the combined draying and ferry companies—the delivery of four wagon-loads of mill equipment and lumber—was not profitable, except for its superb advertisement value. The citizens of the mainland town of Providence would no longer be dependent on unreliable barge transportation of heavy equipment across Narragansett Bay; they could now depend upon the safer overland delivery. Caleb Winslow's wagons and Lynn's bullocks had drayed the huge stone grinding wheels and deposited them without damage on the site the industrious Spragues had already chosen for their mill. Within days, despite the approach of winter in two months, Will and Roy began construction of a stone mill, and their farm-bred wives moved uncomplainingly into a dirt-floored log cabin deserted by the former owner of the farm.

Not until mid-November, four months into the new life of never-ending work, did Lynn pause long enough to measure her expenditures against her profits and to take careful inventory of her ten co-workers on the Aquidneck farm. Faithful to his promise, Edward Fulton had located buyers for the bullocks not otherwise consigned, but Lynn had received money for only half of them. The others had been paid for in bartered goods: enough pigs and chickens from one farmer to keep her people supplied with eggs and winter meat; a wagonload of tanned deer hides, which Polly and Kate used to make trousers, coats, and capes; plain but sturdy beds, chairs and tables from a farmer as capable with carpentry tools as he was with a plow; and a shipment of dried grain, root vegetables, and kegs of hard apple cider from the most productive farm in the Providence area.

A small but steady income had resulted from the first business transaction Lynn had made at the remarkable farm that supplied honey and cheese to townspeople and ship captains. The Reikerks were a large family of Walloon Dutch who'd lost their New York farm during the English conquest of that colony. Because Lynn supplied more milk than was necessary for a weekly allotment of cheese and honey, she received a monthly stipend. In addition to the money they paid for milk, the Reikerks had become the first regular draying customers.

That draying service had taken more of Lynn's time than she liked, not because it was extensive enough to warrant tight scheduling, but because in his business practice Caleb Winslow was more sharp than ethical. Believing the drivers Lynn supplied to be illiterate indentureds, he juggled the accounts in his own favor. After a week of being cheated, Lynn ordered Jem and the others to keep a record of the miles and the goods delivered, crude records that she and Winslow haggled over at each accounting session. Only when she threatened to withdraw from the business did the wheelwright relent enough to suggest she keep the books.

She learned from the experience, though, and avoided being bamboozled by the farmers who requested Red Penny's services as stud bull. Remembering the Cornish farmer who'd tried to breed six cows for the price of one, she insisted that the servicing take place on her own farm and under Jem's watchful eye. It was always the same, she reflected sadly; not many farmers could afford the cost of a bull for their few cows. Except for breeding purposes, a bull was a useless animal on a farm; even good-natured Red Penny would rampage if a pulling yoke were to be placed around its neck. But her bull had paid for its care many times over in eight years, and it still had fifteen or more years of productivity left.

As Lynn completed her tabulation, she studied the results thoughtfully. She had not had to use any of her funds stored in the Fulton strongbox, and she'd made a little money even after the expense of work boots and shoes had been deducted. There had been other unavoida-

ble expenditures as well. The shrewd Spragues had estimated the potential market for meal and flour as too small
for much profit, and they had suggested adding a saw mill
to their enterprise. Lynn requested another year of partnership and sent to England for the intricate saws that could
be operated by water power. The Spragues, she reflected
enviously, had adjusted to the driving acquisitiveness of
American colonials as if they'd been born in the log cabin
they now occupied.

She wished she could be as certain about the other
people in her employ. Although she'd had to pay higher
wages to Nate Stokes, she'd be sorry to lose the genial
second mate who'd filled in for the missing James Thane.
Used to long hours and hard work, he'd been an inventive
jack-of-all-trades, even to the extent of building a rock-
lined bathing pool and rerouting the small stream that
supplied the farm's water. That pool had been Lynn's
special project. In the crowded cottage there'd not been
enough room or privacy for bathing; and she'd felt unbearably
grimy. Now she bathed each day at dusk despite the
increasingly cold weather.

Nate Stokes had proved his worth in other ways too.
Experienced at disciplining sailors, who'd often been forcibly recruited from the streets or from the dirtiest ale
houses, he undertook the training of Kerry Egan, the
one-time Irish highwayman. Egan's fault was not unruly
defiance of authority; it was evasive laziness. On hot
summer days he could always find a cool spot for an
unscheduled nap; during a critical period of building, he
would waste time talking nonsense in his amiable Irish
brogue; and invariably during those early weeks, he had
glibly wheedled extra rations of food from Polly. Nate had
solved all three problems with a warning delivered out of
Lynn's hearing; either Egan would do his share of the
work, or he'd spend the remainder of his indenture as a
deck swab aboard the *Tamarlind*. Not surprisingly, the

Irishman chose the less cloistered life on the farm and became an adequate, if not overly diligent, worker.

But now on the eve of winter, Nate Stokes was eager to return to his ship and to England. More and more frequently he volunteered for draying jobs that took him to the waterfront in New Port where he could ask the officers and crews from the ships in port about news of the *Tamarlind*. Until late fall, Lynn's eagerness for news had equalled Nate's, but gradually, resentment replaced her hope for her husband's return; and she began to make more permanent commitments in the small colony. Because her friendship with Bert Spence had progressed to the level of trust, she made him her business manager. With Edward Fulton's help, she acquired a wardrobe of clothing that fit Bert's lean frame reasonably well, and informed him of his new responsibilities.

"We're going to increase the draying services," she announced. "At present, Caleb Winslow won't have anything to do with the captains he calls 'unhung pirates'; but those men pay in gold coin, not barter, so we're going after their business."

"The townspeople may resent me," Bert cautioned her.

"These townspeople will respect anyone who makes money, and we're going to do just that. We're going to open a shipping order service for the specific English goods people want and charge a commission when we deliver. I think colonials are tired of the cargo auction system because they can't always get what they need, but you knew exactly where to locate those saws the Spragues wanted. And there are hundreds of other products the people with money will be willing to pay for: good riding horses instead of spavined nags, crockery sets that match instead of odd and end pieces, pumps that work, stronger plows, and furniture that doesn't look homemade. 'Twill make a permanent career for you, Spence."

"What about your husband?"

"He isn't here obviously."

"He may have made other plans for you."

"I doubt it. In the meantime, we'll make more money in transportation and merchandising than we will from the farm. You'll be good at the job because you know more about ships and people."

On the day Lynn accompanied Bert to meet Caleb Winslow, she was confident she'd made a wise decision. Even knowing that he'd be working with a convict bondsman, the cantankerous wheelwright treated Bert with greater civility than he'd ever shown her. As she walked home alone, Lynn felt a sharp relief; she hadn't enjoyed forcing herself into public notice.

That afternoon she remained in the cottage she shared with the Riggs and Kate Horton. It was the first time since their shipboard days together that she was able to visit informally with the two women who had made this farm life so bearable for everyone else. Polly Rigg had cheerfully met the challenge of preparing two meals a day for eleven people, frequently twelve because Edward Fulton was a more than occasional visitor. Although the Cornish woman had never seen an ear of corn or baked with cornmeal, she'd adjusted as quickly to this American grain as she did to venison, turkey, and butternut squash. Like the Sprague women, she found the new world similar enough to the old to be bearable. And as always, Jem was the least complaining of husbands. As long as he could work with his beloved animals and return to a cheerful wife, he was a happy man.

Kate Horton, too, had accepted the hardships with equanimity, confiding frequently to Polly that it was the first freedom she'd ever known. "My father worked me like a slavey on his Sussex farm," she admitted, "and the women I hired out to were demanding despots."

"I'll wager you never slaved for any of them as hard as you work here," Polly chided amiably. "You wash and sew and hoe in that durned vegetable garden more hours a day than there be sunlight.''

"But each night I sit down to eat with a woman who hasn't once carped at me and who pays me a salary when she doesn't have to."

Both women spoke as freely in Lynn's presence as they did to each other—Polly from long years of association and Kate with a genuine admiration. When Lynn told them her decision about Bert Spence, Polly snorted her approval.

" 'Bout time. Farm work's not for the likes of him; he couldn't milk a cow any better 'n he could plow a straight furrow. Jason Hale swears he made the chickens too nervous to lay eggs, and John Bram says he's the worst driver of the lot. But he'll be right good with those purse-proud townfolk, because he's got the nerve and learnin' to outface them. Besides, missy, you kin get off that durn treadmill you've been on since we set foot ashore. S'truth, Lynn, you've been harder at it than you were in Cornwall.''

"I had to make sure we'd survive the winter."

"Pish tosh, lass, we'd have survived anywhere, what with most of the durn parasites long gone—your scatty husband included.''

"I imagine he'll be back, Polly," Lynn protested heavily.

"Don't doubt it for a minute; but he's a light-o'foot who'll be gone again, chasing those rainbows his kind never manages to harness. Too bad your grandpa saw fit to saddle you with a scat-around.''

More knowledgeable about Lynn's regard for Clay Penley than Polly was, Kate hastily intervened, "He'll stay anchored once he's taken stock of what he's got here, and once Lynn takes a mind to act the woman again. You've been wearing those ugly old rags since you got here, young mistress.''

Lynn looked down at the drab black wool of her skirt, already showing the green fade of hard usage, and smiled ruefully. "A farm's no place for pretty dresses, Kate.''

" 'Tis for some! The one next door is always prinked-up like a painted doll. Mind telling me why Bert Spence's wife is treated like visiting royalty? Near as I can figure, she's got the same number of years to serve as Nell and me."

Regretting her impulse to spend the afternoon with her two friends, Lynn sighed in irritation. How could she defend such an obvious unfairness in treatment?

"Leona is ill," she began tiredly.

"Was ill," Kate amended sharply. "Last two months she's been feeling spry enough to entertain old Fulton's daughter-in-law like she was owner instead of servant and to upset Polly's cooking by asking for tea and biscuits. Did you know Nell's moved out of that cabin and into the barn?"

"Why?" Lynn demanded.

"Fortnight ago, the madam asked her to clean the cabin as if Nell didn't have enough to do with the barn and the cows."

"I wish Nell had told me."

"Nell's not one to peach, Lynn," Polly volunteered. "I 'spect you best know the rest of what's been goin' on. Mr. Fulton's grandson Ned has been sniffin' around Nell whenever he gets a chance, and she don't deserve another man treatin' her the way that worthless Tom did."

"What way was that, Polly?"

"Refused to wed her, as well he should have; and last day he 'uz here, he beat her around some when she'd have naught t' do with him. Nell ain't trash like the durn prissy next door seems t' think."

"No, she's not," Lynn agreed thoughtfully, "and I'm not going to let anyone treat her as such. Kate, is there anything useful Leona can do?"

"She wasn't raised to the royal purple like the other bitch was; she can sew right enough—remade four dresses to hide the fact she's child bearing—and I expect she knows the working end of a spinning wheel. Most parsons' daughters do, that and waiting table whenever there was company. If she weren't such a lazy whiner, she could help Polly with the cooking.''

"Not me, Kate," Polly demurred. "I can't abide the woman. I just don't want Nell t' get the short end of the stick."

"She won't anymore," Lynn promised grimly. "I'm giving her my room here and moving next door, and this afternoon I'll take care of the Ned Fulton matter. I won't have—"

"Best you change into your pretty gray dress if you're going visiting," Kate interrupted hastily. "Polly and I'll bring you some hot water so you'll not have to use that ice pond tonight."

Left alone with Polly, Kate lowered her voice to a confidential whisper. "She'll raise more hob than any of us can handle if she moves in with Bert Spence. For a sharp woman, she's as blind as a bat when it comes to men."

Nodding in a worried agreement, Polly whispered in return, "Always has been. Her worthless mother saw to that, grandmother too, for that matter, Told her often enough that she wasn't pretty. When the time came for her to wed, she couldn't believe any of those sparks were interested in anything except money. I just wish her footloose husband had been as bright as Bert about seein' that rare beauty of hers. But you're right about her movin' in over there. Best Jem and I—"

"The lazy slattern would make your life miserable, but she won't dare order me around. Besides, I'd be more use come birthing time. Soon as Lynn leaves, I'll fetch Nell to help me move."

Intent on her resentment about Leona's selfishness and angry about Ned Fulton, Lynn agreed absently to Kate's reasons for moving in with the Spences and failed to note the relieved glances exchanged between the older women as Kate arranged her hair in its becoming page boy.

" 'Spect you'll be asked to stay for dinner," Polly advised sensibly. "Lord knows, the old man has mentioned it often enough. So you'd best take your clubs, and wear the new cloak Kate made you; 'twill keep you warm."

In no mood for a social evening with Edward Fulton, who could be as shrewd as her grandfather in asking questions, Lynn shook her head about dinner; but agreed to take her clubs for protection. She hadn't forgotten that New Port was host town to several hundred half-savage sailors who wintered there. Oddly enough she had no fear of the native savages who occasionally left their mainland villages to visit Aquidneck Island, despite the fact that they had scant respect for fences. During her limited dealings with the Indians, Lynn had found them more civilized than the brawling seamen.

Perhaps it had been the reminder that people like Leona Spence automatically considered themselves superior to the Nell Wallises of the world even in a pioneer society that had aroused Lynn's anger. And the idea that a member of the Fulton family regarded Nell as he would have a waterfront whore infuriated her. Nell's fierce resolve to gain respectability had increased daily as had her mastery of farm chores. With her own jaw clamped tight with determination, Lynn was ushered into the Fulton parlor where the man she'd come to see was warming himself before the fireplace.

"Well now, Mistress Lynn," Edward Fulton greeted her cordially, "you've finally condescended to visit me, or is it merely business again? Either way, you'll be staying for dinner as repayment for the hospitality I've enjoyed in your home."

"You won't be repeating that invitation, Mr. Fulton, once you've heard what I've come to say about your grandson. He's been bothering one of my employees with unwanted attentions, and I mean to keep him off my property."

"I wondered where he's been going these past weeks. Is it your pretty milkmaid he's bothering?"

"Nell Wallis, and you know her background; so we'll not pretend he is seeking a replacement for his dead wife."

"Are you certain the young woman objects, lass?"

"Most strenuously, according to my housekeeper, Mr. Fulton. Nell's been victimized by enough men, and I'll not let her be hurt again."

"What about that scamp who left with your husband? She'd been living free-style with him."

Lynn's dark eyes burned with a hot fire; she'd been right. Edward Fulton was no different from the gentry in Cornwall who considered unattached females as fair game and who easily forgave themselves for licentious living, but never the women.

"When Tom Kenn refused to wed her, she broke off the relationship and suffered a beating for her courage," Lynn said harshly. "She'll make some farmer an excellent wife, Mr. Fulton; and in time I'll locate that farmer for her. Meanwhile your Ned is to keep away. I'm sorry to lose your friendship, but I won't permit—"

The old man's chuckle broke into laughter as he shook his head. "You'll not be losing my friendship over a trifle like this, mistress. Relax that fierceness your grandfather warned me about, and tell me about this Nell you're defending like a Cornish jay hen. Seems to me, you'd be ahead of the game if you married her off to one of your own workers."

"She's only nineteen years old, and they're all over forty."

"Aye, but she has six years to serve, and she'll be too old to begin child bearing by the time she's free."

"She's already borne two children when she was little more than a child herself, shoved into prison by the jealous wife of the rake-hell landlord who brutalized Nell."

"Healthy babes were they?"

"Healthy and pretty enough to be adopted by a warden's wife. Why do you ask?"

"My grandson's wife died bearing a puny offspring who didn't live but a few days. 'Tis a tragedy that occurs all too often in these harsh colonies. A woman who births a child without problems is always a desirable rarity."

"Not out of wedlock, Mr. Fulton," Lynn reminded him bluntly.

Again Fulton's laughter shook his sturdy frame. "Agreed, lass. We've enough bastards here already. But now we'll talk of more pleasant subjects. You'll be meeting a man at dinner tonight I expect you'll admire without restraint. He's one of Ephraim's oldest friends and in a fair way of being considered a saint by local folk. Roger Williams knows all about your own problems lass, and he feels as I do that the noses of some church leaders are too busy sniffing out evil that only they can smell. Twice Roger has kept Massachusetts busybodies from taking over our colony. Now, of course, those long-nose clerics will have naught to do with us since we've become polluted by Quakers, Baptists, a Jesuit or two, and the Lutheran Reikerks. Have you thought to enroll your people in one of our churches yet?"

"I doubt any of them would welcome us."

"Your miller folk have already joined Roger's own congregation, but the one for you would be the church in the Portsmouth village. Did Ephraim tell you its history?"

"He told me the story of Anne Hutchinson, if that's the church she founded."

" 'Tis the same, and its people have retained her tolerance and beliefs. You'd be welcome there the same as the others of us. 'Tis the church I prefer to attend whenever my old joints will permit."

It was Lynn's turn to laugh. Whenever Ephraim had been at home in Cornwall, his "joints" had kept him from attending church more often than not. "If you'll gain permission from your minister, Mr. Fulton," she told her host slyly, "some of us will accompany you the next time you feel well enough to attend."

Smiling in response to her subtle jibe, Fulton was well pleased by the prospect of a lively dinnertime conversation. Despite his sixty-four years and intense religious convictions, Roger Williams was a fighter both mental and physical. Twice during the Commonwealth years he'd gone to England and shouted down the Roundhead Parliament to gain an independent charter to keep church and state separate in the colony. Even more stubbornly, he had persisted in establishing laws that prohibited slavery and that required white colonists to pay the Narragansett Indians for the land.

"I'm thinking you will get along with him very well, Mistress Lynn," Fulton informed his young guest. "Like you, he speaks his mind regardless of the cost; and because of him, we've had none of the Indian massacres that Massachusetts has suffered. A few years ago the settlers there were forced to exterminate the entire Pequot nation in the name of peace."

"Now they exterminate only Quakers, Baptists, Jesuits, and witches," Lynn demurred.

"Ephraim's kept you well informed."

"He warned me not to travel to Boston or Salem until he's cleared my name," Lynn admitted.

"That will be something else you have in common with our leader. 'Twas just such cruel nonsense that drove him out of Salem thirty-odd years ago."

Roger Williams proved to be precisely what her grandfather and Edward Fulton had claimed: an articulate and educated man who lacked any trace of the pomposity Lynn had expected from a religious leader. That he remembered her personal history was evident in the first question he asked her concerning her reasons for learning the ancient Cornish tongue.

"Some of the hill folk still speak it," Lynn responded hesitantly. "And it seemed a part of my own heritage."

"Did you learn anything from it?" Williams persisted.

"Yes," she replied more boldly to this challenge. "They were a very enduring and open-minded people. They welcomed both the Romans and the Normans without bloodshed, and they adopted Christianity in the sixth century without giving up all of their own beliefs—the ones that taught them to respect nature. Have you ever visited Cornwall, Mr. Williams?"

"No, but I can understand the people you describe, because they are much the same as my Indian friends who also accept Christianity with reservations. 'Tis their belief that white men cut too many trees and take too many fish from the waters. Only time will tell which of our differing cultures is right."

Throughout the dinner, Lynn listened as the two old men discussed communal problems she'd never considered: the growing need for schools, the difficulty in luring doctors away from England, and the critical shortage of weaponry for the colony's defense. She learned that five, not two, of the doubtful captains had announced their intentions of building homes in New Port. Abruptly Roger Williams asked her how many weapons and men she could supply in case of attack.

"I don't know if there are any guns," she admitted.

"A very foolish oversight, Mistress Penley," Williams warned her bluntly. "With that many undisciplined crews roaming about a town ill-equipped to house or entertain them, there's bound to be trouble unless we're prepared. I'll be over to check your farm before I leave the area and to find out if any of your male servants are dependable enough to bear arms. Moreover," he added in a lighter tone, "I want to see for myself if your bull and bullocks are as gentle as Edward claims. If ever I can afford the price, I may be wanting to buy one of your animals to help me on my own farm."

The idea that a man who wielded as much power as this one did throughout an entire colony could be impoverished embarrassed Lynn. In London the only two minor magistrates she'd met lived in opulent homes and traveled around the city in impressive carriages, but this important and dynamic leader was only a poor farmer. To her added embarrassment, both Roger Williams and Edward Fulton insisted that she be escorted to her home; and the escort they chose for her was Ned Fulton. The young man, not quite her own age, had sat mutely through the dinner without contributing a word to the conversation; and Lynn had suspected that both he and his equally silent mother resented her and her interference. But Ned Fulton proved neither resentful nor shy nor sullen! His first words to her were an urgent plea that she help him convince Nell that he'd be a good husband.

"If you'd let me buy her indenture papers, I could pay you some each year until the cost was made up. But Nell won't even listen to me unless you say so, Mrs. Penley; and I don't want to wait six years."

"Do your mother and grandfather know your intentions?" Lynn asked dazedly.

"Reckon my mother will give her approval since she already talked to Nell. She says Nell's got a sharp tongue and is honest to a fault, but she don't hold that a sin. Ma's got a temper of her own. As for Grandpa, he thinks Nell's strong enough to make me toe the line better than I usually do."

"Your grandfather didn't even know you were interested in Nell," Lynn protested.

"Grandpa can twist the truth some when he's a mind to. After I told him I wanted to wed her, he made it his business to talk to her whenever he visited your farm. Point is now, do you have any objections to my courting Nell? I heard you tell Grandpa tonight that I was to stay away."

"Under the circumstances, I withdraw my objections," Lynn murmured faintly, "and I'm sorry you overheard that conversation."

"Ma's already chewed my ear off for eavesdropping, but I made Grandpa promise to let me walk you home."

Later, during her first sleepless night in America, Lynn's thoughts spun around on a ceaseless treadmill going nowhere. It seems, she reflected miserably, that she could solve other people's problems, but not her own. Eight months into her married life, she'd had a husband for only a few weeks, and then only on loan from another woman. There were moments that night when she wished she'd remained with her grandfather in his Plymouth cottage and never walked those long miles to the Wadley farm. Her life had held little of her girlhood serenity since she'd met Clay Penley!

That it was a more challenging life, she couldn't deny on the following afternoon when Bert Spence returned from New Port with a report of trouble. An English ship had arrived in harbor with a crew the captain had recruited in Mediterranean towns; and the exotic garb and coloring of the Turks, Arabs, and Spaniards had triggered a confrontation on the waterfront. Only the timely intervention of the ship's officers had prevented any serious injury to the poorly armed colonial youths.

A week later a more dangerous episode occurred in the street market where the farmers who still had produce to sell congregated each week with their chickens, pigs, and winter vegetables of butternut squash, pumpkin, cabbages, onions, and dried corn. When one of the farmers left his young daughter in charge of selling to the sparse crowd of shoppers, a sailor—English this time—assaulted the girl, dragging her into a littered alley between two buildings. Her piercing screams prevented the sailor from raping the twelve-year-old, but the guilty man escaped in the ensuing confusion.

As a result of those unfortunate incidents, the Winslow-Penley draying business more than doubled on market day after Bert Spence announced that a dray wagon with armed drivers would carry the food down residential streets so that housewives could shop in safety. It was the sight of Nate Stokes, Kerry Egan, and John Bram armed with pistols and knives that reminded Lynn of Roger Williams's warning.

"Polly, were there any other weapons in the crates Sir Bevil sent with us?" she asked the housekeeper.

"Don't rightly know, Lynn; we were in too big a hurry to open them all that first day. Jem stored what was left in the attic loft, and I forgot about them."

Lynn frowned in annoyance when she opened the first chest; Sir Bevil had wanted his son to be gentleman-dressed even in the wilderness. There were two pairs of handsome jack boots, a gray-blue superfine wool suit, elegantly soft linen shirts, and a plumed hat that would have been suitable for a royal garden party. Cavalier Trevor arrogance, she fumed silently, meant to intimidate poorly dressed colonials.

The contents of the second two chests were far more welcome: badly needed wool blankets, bed warmers, and a long handled copper skillet that made Polly gasp with pleasure. The heavy wood crates, however, were an eloquent testimony to the thoroughness of Sir Bevil's preparation; they contained twelve muskets and enough powder and shot to withstand a prolonged siege. Lynn regarded the cache nervously, frightened by the prospect of ever needing such an arsenal. Cautiously that night, she asked Bert Spence and Nate Stokes what she should do with them.

"Teach everyone including the women how to use them, then lock them up until they're needed," Stokes advised with a blunt practicality. "No use putting temptation into anyone's way. There's little chance of an Indian raid here, and I doubt the town scum would ever roam this far afield."

"In that case, I don't think it's necessary for all of us to learn how to use them," Lynn persisted.

"Yes, it is," Bert contradicted flatly. "I disagree with Nate about the sailor scum floating around town. Some them have been bottled up in port for over a month without enough shipboard work to keep them occupied and without any money for rum or women. If twenty or thirty of them decide to band together, they could wipe every man out from here to Portsmouth, leaving the women completely unprotected.

"Besides," he added with a twisted smile, "except for you innocents, most of us here already know the working end of firearms. Those were the tools of our inglorious trades. Even Leona knows how to handle a pistol, and Nell was the fastest loader and third best shot of our jolly little band. Tomorrow Nate and I'll start training the rest of you."

Doubtfully Lynn gave her consent, and within a week Polly and Kate were expert at loading and priming while Lynn and Jem no longer closed their eyes when they fired the heavy muskets. The farm seemed a secure fortress on the afternoon Roger Williams paid his promised visit. With a professional eye more reminiscent of a military man than a minister, he surveyed the seven men confronting him and decided they'd serve as a nucleus for an island militia. Overlooking Ned Fulton, who'd become a regular visitor at the farm, Williams selected Bert Spence and Nate Stokes as the leaders.

Twice during the remainder of his stay at the Fulton home, he ordered this "militia" to accompany him. Aboard a wagon, they traveled to Portsmouth and to other farms on the first occasion, recruiting additional men for the island's defense. Three days later with this martial display of strength, Williams marched through New Port, meeting with the town and church leaders. They were told to summon the militia at the first sign of trouble by ringing all the church bells simultaneously. After sending the newly formed militia to escort every ship's captain in town, whether merchant or freebooter, to a meeting with the colony's founder, Williams announced quietly that henceforth any one of them who did not keep his crew in check would be expelled and denied access to the port. Because New Port offered the best winter harborage on the Atlantic coast, the captains were forced to agree to Williams's terms.

Before he left the island, the leader paid a final visit to the Penley farm and spent an hour closeted with Bert Spence in one of the smaller cabins before he located Lynn in the barn. Expecting the same friendliness he'd extended her at the Fultons, she was surprised by the gravity of his greeting.

"I wish to talk to you about your husband, Mistress Penley. As you know, I am quite familiar with his background from the information supplied by your grandfather; and Mr. Spence has told me that he is a resourceful fighter in an emergency. What I want from you is an evaluation of his character."

Hating the necessity of lying to this perceptive man, but unwilling to voice her own unhappy thoughts about Clay Penley, Lynn was evasive. "I didn't know him long before we married, and he left me shortly afterwards—on business."

"In view of the profession your husband followed for a number of years, I'm surprised Ephraim approved of the match."

"My grandfather didn't, Mr. Williams, not because of Clay's character, but because of other difficulties. Clay had saved me from capture by the English soldiers, and I was . . . grateful to him. Why are you asking about my husband?"

Instead of answering her question, the minister responded with another of his own. "What do you know about slave trafficking?"

"Only that 'tis a thriving business among all of the nations represented in the Caribbean and that thousands of Negro slaves are being transported into the American colonies."

"Do you approve of the practice, mistress? Remember that these pathetic Africans are enslaved for life without any hope for the freedom indentured criminals are allowed to earn.''

"I don't really approve of either practice,'' Lynn asserted thoughtfully, "except that in the case of criminals, 'tis usually a better life.''

"So Mr. Spence informed me. He was entirely honest about his background and enthusiastic about the opportunities you've offered him here. His disapproval of slavery stems from his experience in the Virginia colony. 'Tis his belief that it will create a worse social order than exists in England. Yes, he told me about his own lost title and estate and about your husband's connection to the aristocracy. When do you expect him to return?''

Suppressing her impulse to blurt "I don't,'' Lynn shook her head and added a word to her initial intention, "I don't know.''

"Is the name Pendrath familiar to you, mistress?''

Mutely Lynn nodded, fatalistically convinced that whatever the rumor was, Clay and Harry and Amelia had found an easy way to earn the money and adventure they craved.

"One of the reliable captain-merchants and a long-time resident of New Port, Elwin Carter first informed me of the rumor a week ago, and one of the less desirable mariners reaffirmed it yesterday. Your husband and this man Pendrath are reported to have hit upon a scheme to supply specified types of slaves demanded by wealthy customers in England and the colonies,'' Williams confided with dry disapproval.

"The practice of slavery for raw agricultural labor is wicked enough, but this refinement of the trade reduces those pathetic people to a less than human status, to the level of your bulls, cows, and bullocks—animals bound for life to perform only one task. If your husband has chosen this deplorable career, I doubt he'll be welcomed by the decent settlers in this colony.''

"I don't believe he intends to live here,'' Lynn demurred with a dull sense of defeat.

"If that's the case, I trust he'll be generous enough to allow Mr. Spence to remain with us. We need men with his education and leadership both for defense and for business. And now, mistress, I'd like to meet your bull so that I'll be better able to defend you in case your grandfather fails in his efforts. Although we're a part of England, we do not subscribe to the entirety of its common law. We believe in offering sanctuary to those who need it."

The meeting of the colonial leader and the placid devon bull spared Lynn any need for explanation, because an alert Jem, whose ears were as sharp as his tongue was mute, led Red Penny out of his stall. Thus it was upon the broad shoulders of the veteran stockman that Red Penny rested its great head as it gazed with peaceful eyes at the strange man in the dusty black suit. A minute later, Williams laughed with appreciation when the bull placidly accepted the visitor's offer of a handful of dried corn.

" 'Tis no devil's creature, but one more touched by the hand of God than most of its breed," the minister declared firmly as he took his leave. "Have no fear that folks locally will condemn either that beast or you. More likely, they'll be clamoring for its offspring. Fare thee well, mistress. If you have need of my services, just send a message to Providence. Mr. Spence has promised to deliver it."

Smiling in relief that the disturbing conference was concluded, Lynn murmured her gratitude, vowing silently to avoid this perceptive and candid individual, this "seeker of truth" as he called himself. She had no premonition that one day his second-hand testimony would possibly save her life.

Most pleasant among the surprises this new land held for the Cornish farm woman was the mild climate of Aquidneck Island and the Providence plantation in general.

Protected by a great hook of land projecting eastward from Massachusetts Colony and warmed by the ocean's Gulf Stream, Rhode Island was not the frozen, blizzard-plagued, brutal winterland of northern New England. What snows there'd been by late January had been light, and even the frost was merely an inconvenience annoyance. Only a few of the chickens had perished in the one prolonged cold snap, and the native forage grasses had endured long enough to allow the cattle out of the barn. Thus the pace of life had varied but little from the fall routine.

Under the leadership of Bert Spence and Nate Stokes, the militia had grown to thirty armed men who'd maintained order in New Port with only an occasional show of force. Because of the five new homes being built by buccaneers, the town's merchants and tradespeople had ceased to complain about the invasion of pirates since their own pockets were being filled with Spanish gold. The Winslow-Penley draying company was equally enriched, and Bert had no compunctions about accepting shipping orders for hundreds of luxuries the pirates wanted from England. Put to work as construction laborers by their captains, the erstwhile idle crews had less time for vandalism and lawlessness.

At the Penley farm, life had assumed a pleasant tenor with enough variation in activity to prevent corrosion from boredom. On the draying trips to the mainland, the drivers frequently took time off to hunt for deer and turkeys, and the native foods offered a pleasant change from the familiar staples. Subdued by the growing burden of impending motherhood, Leona had ceased being such an audible irritant to the less pretentious household members, although she had yet to contribute to the communal work. More dramatic in its impact on the residents was Nell's consent to marry Ned Fulton in the spring. That promissory alliance had resulted in a spate of informal parties, celebrated with enough hard cider to ease the objection a few of the farmers held for indentured criminals. Ironically, the four men under Lynn's control had gained a measure of respect for their militia activities and from their now regular church attendance.

Some of Lynn's own concerns about the future were alleviated when the Sprague brothers sent word that the saw mill was now in operation. That first consignment of lumber was sold within days to the pirates whose large homes were still under construction. Busier than at any other time in her life, Lynn helped keep the various account books, juggled manpower assignments, and kept a close watch on her breeding cows, one of which had almost reached the ten-month term for delivery. Despite the potential income from the other projects, she knew that cattle would remain the mainstay of her farm's economy.

The first disruption in the even tenor of farm life was Jason Hale's announcement that a dozen chickens and two market-ready young shoats had been stolen on the night following the arrival of a Caribbean-based ship of doubtful integrity. The second upsetting incident was Nate Stokes's discovery that one of his pistols was missing. Having been spared any intrusion by the resident pirates in New Port, everyone immediately suspected the crew of the latest ship in port. A guard system was organized, and a large brass bell was installed over the barn door, its heavy clapper attached to a rope within easy reach of the shortest person on the farm.

But Nate remained a worried man. " 'Tis not like sailors, even pirates, to raid so far away from their ship the first night in port. These thefts were too efficiently committed for men stumbling around strange territory at night."

Lynn, too, was puzzled by the sequence of the two crimes, but for a less logical reason. Having become firm friends with Nell over the months, she was suddenly confronted by a tense young woman who was increasingly hollow-eyed with fatigue during the morning milking. On the fourth day after the raid, Lynn asked her companion bluntly, "Have you and Ned had a disagreement, Nell? I haven't seen him around for a few days."

"I told him to stay away for awhile," the girl responded with a vaguely sullen brevity.

"Make up the quarrel, whatever it is," Lynn counseled. "Ned's a nice young man."

" 'Tis my business what I say to Ned, Mistress Penley," Nell retorted with a formality she hadn't used with Lynn since summer. Oddly, however, despite her apparent hostility, Nell dogged her mistress's footsteps with a vigilance that only added to the general tension. One week after the thefts had been reported, Lynn learned the identity of the thieves at the same time her husband returned after seven and a half months of absence.

Nate Stokes and the other three bachelors had left the cottage after an early supper to conduct a nightly patrol of the premises, when the unaccustomed sound of neighing horses startled those remaining inside. In an automatic response, Bert and Jem barred the door and reached for the muskets hanging on pegs on either side. Reacting just as swiftly, Lynn raced to her room where the other weapons were stored. She didn't hear Nell speak in a grating whisper of bitter resignation.

"You can open the door, Bert Spence. Our visitors will be their royal highnesses. I've known they were on their way for the last ten days."

Nell's quiet announcement was confirmed a second later by a loud hail from outside and a louder complaint delivered in Harry Cobb's boisterous voice.

"Let us in, Spence, 'tis started to snow and 'tis iceberg cold out here." Before the heavy bars could be removed, Harry shouted again, "Best send the stockman out to take care of these horses; they're Pendrath bloods and as valuable as all hell!"

When the door was finally flung open, the two men who stepped inside spent the first few moments brushing the clinging flakes of snow from their elegant attire before they swept their plumed hats in a courtly greeting to the silent spectators. It was Harry who made the joyous introduction.

"The Honorable Harrold Pendrath and the Honorable Charles Clayton Trevor at your service. We did it, Spence, b'God we did it! We won a full pardon from King Charles! You too, Sir Spencer Burtram and Lady Burtram. We're as free as birds, and within the month we'll all be in Virginia!"

In her private, lean-to bedroom at the rear of the house, Lynn heard the jubilant words and reached for the heavy leather cloak Kate had made for her. She had no desire to join in the celebration of the four aristocrats who'd been forgiven their crimes by an indulgent monarch. She also had no hope that she'd be equally forgiven for crimes she had not committed. King Charles was a devout survivor who'd taken an oath not to interfere in church business. Shaken by a barrage of emotions she didn't want identified, Lynn removed the deer skin that covered her window and was preparing to climb over the sill when a strident whisper sounded from the doorway.

"I'm going with you," Nell Wallis hissed tensely, "and we'd better take a pair of those muskets and your presbies."

CHAPTER 9

The awkward silence that greeted Harrold Pendrath's ebullient boast was broken by the soft bubbling voice of Leona Spence, now miraculously elevated to Lady Burtram.

"How glorious, Spence. Now we can return to your estate in England and forget all this misery!" she gushed excitedly.

Her husband's smile was harshly sardonic. "There's no Burtram estate in England or anywhere else. Is there, Harry?" he asked quietly.

"No, but b'God, you have a pardon. It cost Andrew a bloody fortune to obtain that much for the five of us, six including Tom Kenn."

"Did your brother think to request an equal clemency for the others?" Bert asked quietly.

"What others? If you're talking about the woman Clay married, Lord no! He wouldn't have dared. Her cousin's wife has publicly accused her of murdering Rad Pollock and his two sons. As for Nell—where the hell did she disappear to? She was here a minute ago. Nell already had a long prison record. Andrew asked for Tom's clearance because Tom's mother is a distant relation of ours—where the devil is Tom? He said he'd meet us here. Sounded damn queer when he met our ship at the dock today."

"Hasn't he been with you the whole time?" Bert demanded.

"Tom? Lord no! He'd have slowed Clay and me to a crawl just when we needed to race. Wait until you hear—"

"We've already heard," Bert rasped. "New Port's a busy town for rumor. Odd thing about that rumor though, you were using your real name, but Clay was still hiding behind his nice, safe alias." In cold anger, he turned toward the tall man who'd become a cautious observer after his one ironic gesture of greeting when he doffed his flamboyantly plumed hat.

"You've been damned quiet, Clay. Did you forget something, or has Harry become your conscience?"

"That's because I know you better than Harry does," Charles Clay Trevor retorted with anger as hot as Bert's was icy. "Where is my wife, Spence?"

"What wife, Clay? If you mean Lynn Penley, she could be any place on Aquidneck Island. Her interests are no longer limited to the farm."

"Spencer, what is the matter with you?" Leona shrilled petulantly. "You've been acting like . . . I don't know what. Clay, your wife is in her bedroom at the back of the house. Kate, will you or Polly kindly—"

"Not our mix," Polly Rigg retorted bluntly. "Lynn knows what she's about, and her ears are as sharp as Jem's. If she wanted to be here, she'd be here. Something more important t'do now anyways if Harry Cobb expects them fancy horses t' last the night. Red Penny don't tolerate horses in the same barn he's in. Jem, we'd best go ask Mr. Fulton if we can stow them in his barn, but Harry can do his own herdin'! Kate, take Bert's wife home; we don't need the added mess of a child comin' tonight."

Prior to Leona's attempt to order the two older women on an errand, no one had taken any notice of Polly or Kate. But Polly's brisk orders and her insulting use of the name Harry Cobb focused attention on her plain, middle-aged features now set with mulish determination.

"To hell with the damned bull," Harry exploded. "These horses will need special care for the month we're going to—"

"Harry, you'd better do what Polly says," Bert interrupted curtly. "You too, Leona."

"Don't you give me orders, Spencer," his wife shrieked, "not until you've apologized to Clay. He's come a long way to see his wife, and you've no right to stop him. Harry, where's Amelia?"

"She's staying with a cousin in the most beautiful country I've ever seen. Amelia loves the life there and the people."

"Those people she loves are the spoiled refuse tossed out of every titled family in England," Bert countered. "I'll take Rhode Island where accomplishments count more than titled relatives."

"Where you're working fourteen hours a day to make someone else wealthy!" Leona challenged bitterly. "Why can't you at least listen to what Harry and Clay have to say?"

"You can listen all you want, Leona. Jem and I'll take care of your horses, Harry. I've a sudden need for fresh air. We'd better take the muskets, Jem. I've a feeling we might need them."

"Just a minute, Spence," Clay called out as Bert and Jem left the cabin. "I'm going with you."

"That's up to you, but you might ruin that stylish new hat. This is no country for pretty greenhorns; and I warn you, I won't be pleasant company. Good God! There are six damn horses here, and they look half dead."

"We hit one storm after another on the crossing, and they were battered around. I was hoping someone here would be able to patch them up; we'll be needing them in Virginia."

"Is that where you've decided to settle, Clay?"

"Temporarily, yes."

"What happened to Connecticut?"

"Indians happened and waterfalls and mountains! There's no money to be made there."

"Why did you come back, Clay! This isn't for you either. You and Harry come prancing in like spoiled royalty, announce that you've been forgiven for ten years of crime, and insult a pair of decent women who are earning their freedom."

"You were pardoned too, Spence."

"I don't want the pardon, and I sure as hell don't deserve it. You stood there tonight like a bloody fop and let Harry condemn your wife without saying a word in her defense. Like father, like son! Why did the noble Sir Trevor allow Lynn to be accused of murdering the Pollocks when he was the guilty one? We learned about the abduction three weeks after you left."

"Ephraim Penley knows all about the Pollocks. I brought a bundle of letters that'll explain the situation. We've played this game long enough, Spence. Now, tell me where my wife is."

"Not a game, Clay. Lynn's building a life here, and I won't let you destroy it. If you're after more money, I suggest you ask your old mistress for it. How is the beautiful Amelia these days?"

Clay was silent for a few minutes as he trudged along the snowy path, leading two of the stumbling horses. Cursing his stupidity for having brought Harry with him tonight, he frowned in angry concentration. Admittedly, he'd broken his promise to return to Rhode Island months ago, but he'd explained his reasons in the letters he'd sent to Lynn from Connecticut and Virginia. A sudden ugly suspicion jarred his shaken confidence.

"Did my wife receive any of my letters?" he demanded harshly and sensed rather than saw the caustic smile that formed on his companion's face. Clay knew what the answer would be! How she'd done it, he could only guess, but Amelia had intercepted both letters and then played the conquering bitch all the way to Jamestown. Eventually he'd had to move in with the crew to avoid her aboard ship, but on land she'd been even more tenacious.

Clay winced when he remembered the last time he'd seen Amelia. He'd taken a room at one of the waterfront inns while Harry had escorted Amelia to her cousin's plantation before he'd gone farther upriver to explore his own land. Relieved to be left alone, Clay had busied himself by studying the slave trade now thriving in the royal colony. On two occasions he'd watched a shipload of motley Negroes deposited on the docks, and he'd been highly critical of the lack of selectivity on the part of the slaver captains. Some of the blacks had been too old for productive work, others were immature boys too young to be good economic risks, and some were women whose distended bellies indicated imminent childbirth.

During his successful smuggling career, Clay had learned that auctions of any kind were hit-or-miss propositions; far more reliable was the order-and-delivery business. For years he'd supplied the French wine and brandy his elite clients had ordered, and never had any of them refused to pay upon delivery. The same principle would apply in the slave trade, he reasoned, and it would be completely legal. Mingling with the potential buyers at the second auction held on the Jamestown commons, he garnered his first three customers: practical men who wanted twenty strong, young black males to be delivered before winter. Clay had been jubilant. He'd be able to select the best from among the thousands of raw slaves being dumped into Jamaica, and he'd never have to suffer the ugliness of the longer transportation from Africa.

Returning to his room in an exultant mood, he'd discovered that the visitor his landlord had mentioned was not Harry as he'd hoped, but Amelia. She'd paid one of her cousin's grooms to escort her into town on horseback, and she'd come prepared to stay without regard for scandal. Clad in only a blue velvet bedrobe, she'd handed him a cup of wine and announced that she was finished with propriety and the silly pretense they'd maintained during her three years of marriage to Harrold Pendrath.

"When he learns we've become lovers again, Harry won't mind, not really," she insisted. "I don't plan to ignore him completely, so he won't feel left out; and you and he can still be good friends. We'll all be together anyway, so why shouldn't we be happy?"

Shivering now in the light intermittent snow falling on Aquidneck Island, Clay recalled with repugnance her screaming fury after he'd told her that he wasn't interested. He hadn't bothered with any explanations, and he'd shoved her away when she'd attempted a frantic embrace. Picking up his small sea chest, he'd left her in the room and returned to the *Tamarlind* riding at anchor in the harbor. Clay wished now that the reason for his refusal had been his memory of Lynn Penley, but the truth was that he hadn't been tempted. Amelia had lost all the allure she'd once held for him, and he'd felt only a bored disinterest in her naked body.

During the following five months, he hadn't even remembered her in the rush of buying slaves in Jamaica and delivering them to the customers in Virginia. Flushed with triumph over the substantial profits after their second delivery, he and Harry had risked a return to England. Summoned from London by Harry, Lord Andrew Pendrath had arrived with news of the pardon and with an enthusiastic promise to handle the English end of the new business.

The demand for Negro maids had resulted from the combined circumstances of a greatly expanded social life inspired by the loose morality of King Charles's court and by the increasing expense of the available English maids. Such women now demanded annual salaries of eight pounds a year in addition to the money they made in *douceurs*, the bribes they were paid by mercers, drapers, and tradesmen. Since slaves were not allowed to possess money, they were

far cheaper than their white counterparts. Lord Pendrath
had also discovered a second market for women slaves,
particularly those of mixed Arab blood. Entertainment
parlors were thriving, and the bored men who frequented
them requested more and more exotic bed partners.

Part of Clay's ballooning dreams of immediate wealth
were shattered by the cold reception from his father, who'd
adamantly refused to advance any money for the working
capital Clay needed in order to share equally with the
solvent Pendraths. Sir Bevil had also demanded that his
son return to his wife. It was during that bitter fight with
Bevil that he'd learned Lynn's fortune was considerably
greater than the two thousand pounds she'd admitted
owning.

Abruptly Clay's attention was returned to the unpleasant
present when he was shoved onto the porch of the Fulton
house and introduced to an unsmiling Edward Fulton. The
request to shelter the horses in the barn was readily
granted, but the old man made no effort to be gracious to
the overdressed husband he'd already decided was worthless. In the barn, a nervous Ned Fulton ignored the
stranger and spoke urgently to Bert Spence.

"How's Nell, Bert? She ordered me to stay away from
her as long as that bastard's in port, because he threatened
to kill me if he caught me visiting her. But I've kept watch
anyway from a distance. Did you know she carries a pistol
with her all the time now?"

Bert nodded with an abrupt understanding and hastened
to reassure the worried man. "Nell's fine and I'll see she
stays that way, Ned. If you'll help Jem with these horses,
I'll get back and make sure she's safe tonight."

During the next few minutes of brisk walking, Clay
regained a shred of humor. "I see Nell's up to her old
tricks; it didn't take her long to forget Tom."

"Ned Fulton is marrying her in April," Bert rasped
harshly.

"My God! The damned young fool!"

"You're the fool, Clay. Nell's paid the price of admission into decent society. And the last member of our old band of smugglers is about to pay *his* debt. The mystery of Tom Kenn's activities for the past months has been solved. More than likely, he joined a pirate crew the day you sailed, and 'twas him and some of his fellow scum who robbed the farm sev—'' His speech broke off mid-word; the bell attached to the Penley barn was being rung with a clamorous urgency. As Bert Spence began to run, he gripped his musket with tense fingers.

Constrained by the need for silence and burdened by heavy muskets, Lynn and Nell climbed out of the cottage window and walked the distance to the barn without exchanging a word. Once inside, Nell bolted the wide doors while Lynn manipulated the tinderbox and lighted two of the lanterns hung on pegs against the wall, a familiar routine they'd followed each day for the morning milking. Nell's next movements, however, were not a part of that routine. With sure steps, she walked to Red Penny's stall and unfettered the great beast who remained quiescently tranquil as the young woman petted his head with practiced ease.

"I figure Red's the best protection we can have," she announced, adding casually, "I've been guarding the barn ever since we were robbed."

"You've also been guarding me, haven't you, Nell?"

"'Twas my fault you were in danger, mistr—Lynn. Come on, we might as well be comfortable while we wait."

"Wait for what?"

"I'll tell you once we're settled in the loft over the door. I've fixed it up so we won't freeze to death, but I crack the gate window open to keep me from falling asleep."

As Nell had promised, the forward loft had been carefully prepared for a sustained vigil with straw banked against the wall and spread thickly over the vented floorboards. A bucket of drinking water was sitting a few feet away on the bare floor, and still farther away was a painted china chamber pot. Nell giggled as she pointed to the innocuous object.

"Ned lent it to me when I told him my intentions. Have you ever seen a fancier one? He said we'd use it in the bedroom once we're married."

"Then you didn't quarrel with him?"

"Only when he threatened to stay here with me. I didn't want him hurt."

"When did Tom Kenn return, Nell?"

Letting her breath out slowly in relief, Nell spoke in a swiftly delivered whisper. "Ten days ago. We'd best blow out the lantern before I tell you the rest."

"Why didn't you inform Bert and Nate the minute he came?"

"Neither of them would have considered him dangerous. Bert thinks he can still handle him, but Tom's three stone heavier than Bert now; and Nate doesn't know how mean he can be with a knife. Tom wasn't an innocent when he turned to smuggling. He'd done far worse things when he was younger, things he didn't want to talk about."

"Like robbing people on highways?"

"Not Tom. He doesn't like facing people in an open fight. His style is more to hit from behind, like poor drowning sailors after their ships had been deliberately sunk. Fasten your cape around you, Lynn. I'm going to crack the gate and pull in the bell rope."

Lynn's admiration for Nell's precaution increased; she'd been conjuring up visions of fighting men like the Cornwall wreckers she'd seen on the bridge with only one slender girl as her ally. But the bell would summon six armed men who'd been trained militia style.

"When Tom came here ten days ago, what did he want?" she asked.

"He wanted to hide here until his ship left port. Pirating had proved to be hard work, and he's lazier than a milk-fed cat. And then he wanted to use me as he had before I got good sense. That first day, he waited until you and Jem left to deliver the milk; then he came out of cover when I was cleaning the barn. He tried to grab me, but I was working with a pitchfork, so I squirmed away. I told him that you wouldn't let him on the property and that I wouldn't have anything to do with him even if he offered to wed me, and that I was going to marry Ned Fulton come April.

"He hit me when he learned about Ned; Tom always does his thinking with his fists. I decided right then it was time for me to become friends with Red Penny. I ran toward the stall, but Tom grabbed my arm just as I reached your bull. He'd have broken my arm if Red Penny hadn't become nervous and lowered his head some. After that, Tom backed off and started cursing. First, he threatened to rob the farm—he sure did that all right—then he said he'd burn the barns one night and 'cook that damned bull to a crisp.' Next he shouted that he'd cut off Ned's b—that he'd make Ned into a half man.

"I stayed next to Red Penny and let Tom yell until he turned his spite on you. I knew then that he wasn't just blowing off temper. He'd thought a long time about what he planned to do to you."

"Why should he hate *me*? I've hardly ever spoken to the man."

"Tom was used to having his own way; and according to him, you made me stop sleeping with him the first time you talked to me aboard ship. And he said that you'd ruined Jame—Clay Penley—as if that conceited dottrel needed any help in making another mess of his life. Tom was afraid of you, Lynn, from the first time he saw you;

so was I for that matter. You have a way of making a body turn to jelly when you look at him straight on.

"When Tom started making good his threats, I stole one of Nate's pistols, because it was easier to hide than a musket; and I've been waiting for him to show. I think he will tonight."

Unconsciously Lynn reached for the comforting feel of her clubs, trying to repress the tremor of fear expressed in the brief question, "Why tonight?"

"Tom knew when the *Tamarlind* was due to arrive in New Port—not much pirates don't know about the comings and goings of ships. Anyway, he boasted that Harry and Clay would protect him no matter what he did, so I reckoned he'd wait until they got here. He also said that Clay would force me to go back to him."

"Clay wouldn't be that stupid, Nell!"

"Then you don't know him as well as I do; he's always acted as if I was dirt under his feet. Highborn rakehells like him despise sluts except when they're using them."

"You're no slut!"

"I was and I'll never be fool enough to deny it. I didn't want to be, but I was. Still I was luckier than most. Old Higley used me himself; and he was so dead afraid of catching the pox or clap he made sure the customers he chose for me were clean. I never had to serve the floor like Peg or Jenny. They were covered with sores by the time old Higley threw them out on the street."

Feeling like an ignorant child being counseled by a knowing adult, Lynn changed the indelicate subject to one she was better equipped to discuss. "With your background, Nell, where did you learn to speak as well as you do?"

"Some from the warden's wife who took my babies to raise. I was lucky there too; she brought me food and helped me stay clean. Both times I was brought to bed, she moved me into her house and read to me while I was nursing because she wanted each child in turn to hear only her voice. But mostly I learned from my mother. She never talked about herself, so I don't know where she came from; but she could read and write and she wasn't like the others forced out into the street. I expect she was a tradesman's daughter who was fool enough to let some damned, lying man have her because he promised a wedding.''

Recalling her own foolish surrender in the tower room nine months ago, Lynn winced. What if she'd been as unlucky as Nell's mother, and what if Clay had been as callous as Nell's unknown father? Again Lynn guided the conversation into less provocative channels. Her softly murmured question, ''When did Ned propose to you?'' was greeted by amused laughter.

''When he couldn't get me any other way,'' Nell retorted candidly. ''He wasn't like Tom though. Tom just packed me off, not that I screamed much in protest. Tom was the best-looking man I'd ever known, and I thought I'd have a better life until I wound up in Bridewell again. But Ned just smiled and joked with me until he decided I was serious. Then his mother came to look me over and to ask Leona about me. Well, Leona can be as much the simpering bitch as any other female goodie who thinks she's better than anyone else. So I beat her to it. I told old Janet Fulton everything about me, and I didn't waste my breath in apologies, because I really didn't care. Ned's as plain looking as a country rustic, and he can be as lazy as any other man. He's no fool, though, and he's honest; and after awhile, I didn't mind his big nose and floppy hair. Someday I expect he'll be as much a man as his grandpa is.''

Lynn listened to her companion's matter-of-fact acceptance of a less than perfect reality and felt a twinge of jealousy. At the moment, she reflected, she would gladly trade the handsome and *honorable* Charles Clay Penley Trevor for an unromantic colonist like Ned Fulton.

''You'll have a good life, Nell,'' she murmured.

"I will if Clay and Harry don't spoil everything by forcing us to move to Virginia."

"They won't do that, I promise you."

"Harry was bursting with excitement when he talked about Virginia."

"That'll be his home, not ours."

"Not if Clay's going into business with old Andrew Pendrath. Old Andrew doesn't pay out good money unless he's sure of getting it back, and Clay didn't deny anything Harry said. That's why I left the room to warn you."

"It wasn't necessary, Nell. I know what business my husband and Harry are engaged in."

"Smuggling again?"

"I almost wish it were. They're buying and selling slaves this time."

"Then what are they doing here? Ned says Rhode Islanders are dead set against having those blackamoors in the colony."

"I suspect my husband has come for a more practical reason; he'll need money to get started."

"You going to give it to him?"

"I don't know."

"Well, at least Bert Spence won't have anything to do with them or with slavery."

"How do you know?"

"He said so just after old Mr. Williams was here."

"That was before he learned about his pardon, Nell. Now that he and Leona are free, I expect they'll join the others in Virginia."

"Spence won't, not as long as you're . . . not if you were to make him another one of your partners like old Caleb and the Spragues."

"If he stays, I will. He's already doubled the business."

"Then he won't be leaving you no matter how much Leona caterwauls. Does Clay have anything to say about Kate and the others?"

Lynn hesitated before she answered, "No, I indentured them to my grandfather."

"If you're smart, you'll stay right here with the rest of us. You wouldn't like living with Harry's wife; she takes over everyone and everything."

"What was it like before you were captured? When you were all living together?"

"We weren't together that much. Jame—your husband— was usually off making contacts, of one kind or another. He usually stayed at a different inn from the rest of us."

"Was it an exciting life?"

"No, it was ugly and dangerous, and I didn't have any more money than I did back at old Higley's. Jame always gave my share to Tom, and Tom spent it drinking or gambling. He gave Amelia her separate share, though; she'd have screamed the house down if he hadn't. She screamed whenever she was upset anyway. You should have heard her when Jame was with any of the other women who chased after him, but she usually managed to win him back again. Poor old Harry was as relieved as the rest of us when she did; nobody was sure what she'd do otherwise. I thought Jame would stop dancing attendance on her when he married you, but I guess he's still a fool."

Both women were silent after Nell finished talking, each one contemplating her own separate memories. Restlessly Lynn pushed the window gate wider open and gazed out over the white landscape now silvered with bright moonlight.

"The snow has stopped," she announced softly; but her companion made no responsive sound other than the even breathing of exhausted sleep. Left alone with her own miserable thoughts, Lynn remained on her knees looking outward toward the lamplit cottage. Bitterly, she wondered if her husband had laughed when he'd learned that she'd bolted like a skittish girl. Had he been as amused as Harry Pendrath was when he'd boomed out the words, "If you're talking about the woman Clay married, Lord, no!"? Harry hadn't even remembered her name! Bleakly she wondered if Clay had any interest in her other than money; in the logical core of her mind, she decided not. He'd have returned months ago if he'd remembered her as a woman. As her resolve hardened, she recalled what Nell had said about Bert Spence and hoped the optimistic prediction was true. If Spence stayed on to manage everyone including the Spragues, the Penley interests would continue to thrive even if Clay insisted she accompany him. Lynn smiled derisively at her own foolish fancy. She'd be about as welcome in Virginia as the plague; only her money would be needed there, the money her husband could claim by law anytime he wanted.

Concentrating so intently on the unpleasant future, Lynn almost missed hearing the sounds that heralded a more dangerous present. Not until Red Penny bawled in warning, did she become aware of other noises, not those made by awakening cows and bullocks, but the stealthy scratching of a tinderbox held by human hands. Staring intently into the darkness, she watched as a lantern flickered into life before she grabbed the rope from Nell's hand and pulled it frantically with a pent-up fear. She'd seen the dark silhouettes of four men standing in front of the open rear door, which was now hanging loosely from its severed leather hinges. The terrified shouts of two of those men were simultaneous.

"The gor-damn bull's loose and h'its chargin!"

"Damn ye to hell, Tom, there's some bloody bastard up there on top of us."

For the two women watching frozen from the loft, the action at the far end of the barn was too swift to follow as three of the shadowy figures pushed past the taller man holding the lantern in a frantic effort to reach the doorway. Twenty feet away from them, the massive shape of Red Penny was also in motion, lumbering toward that same opening, its head lowered and its breath expelled in violent bovine snorts. The tall man hesitated only a second before he threw the burning lamp into the mound of hay in the empty stall and then shoved through the door only feet ahead of the enraged bull.

Before Nell could aim and fire the musket, Lynn grabbed the water bucket and ran toward the ladder now clearly visible in the light of the ignited hay. Her only thought was the fire and the doomed animals if she couldn't extinguish it. In the urgency of the moment she forgot weapons, Nell, and her own safety. The one bucket of water, already half empty by the time she reached the packed dirt of the floor, did little more than produce a hiss of steam when she threw it on the spreading conflagration. In desperation, she whipped off her heavy leather cloak and plunged it into the water trough, and beat at the flames until her arms felt leaden. Repeatedly she sloshed the garment into the water and continued the frantic flailing until the fire was reduced to glowing embers of red. Even when that feeble light was gone, she continued to stumble back and forth in the dark from the water trough to the smoke-filled stall.

Throughout the ordeal Lynn heard only the terrified bawling of the cows and bullocks tethered helplessly to the barn walls. She didn't hear the discharges first of Nell's pistol and then of both the muskets the younger woman had carried down from the loft. Lynn's belated realization that the emergency had ended came when other lamps were lighted, and she felt the strong, comforting arm of Jem Rigg holding her sagging body. Unable to focus her smarting, tear-filled eyes, she gasped the words, "Get Red Penny, Jem; he crashed out of here after those men. Don't let them kill him."

It was Nell's shrill voice, still high pitched with tension and remembered horror that responded. "Red Penny's safe, Lynn. He gored one of those murdering bullies and stomped another."

"Was Tom one of them, Nell?"

"Aye, 'twas Tom all right; he was the one who threw the lamp. But as always, he had the devil's own luck. I only grazed his cheek with one of my bullets and hit another piece of scum instead. Spence and the others are out looking for Tom and the fifth bastard now.''

''I counted only four of them,'' Lynn insisted.

''Four inside, but Tom was coward enough to post a fifth man outside to guard his back. If they catch Tom, I hope they bowstring him and throw him in the pond. Stay here a minute with Jem while I fetch my fancy china, then you and I are going back to the house. I feel like a Bridewell slut, and you look like a beaten blackamoor with that soot all over your face.''

With her hands already blistering, Lynn made no protest about leaving the barn or about having Polly and Kate fuss over her once she reached the cottage. By the time the two frightened women had finished their expert ministrations, Lynn had been sponge-bathed, her singed hair cropped, her reddened hands wrapped in clean linen bandages, and the burning pain deadened by a liberal dose of laudanum administered in a cup of hot tea. Gratefully the benumbed young woman allowed herself to be tucked into bed like a child; and like a tired child she fell asleep, unaware and uncaring that the grim activities begun in the barn continued without let-up until well past dawn. When she awakened at noon the following day, she surveyed the remnants of her burned dress and heat-twisted oxhide shoes and wondered if she'd ever again find the courage to fight a fire with nothing but a water-soaked cloak.

After receiving the first accounting of the near tragedy from Kate, she realized she'd need a different kind of courage to face the aftermath. She was in no condition to hide again from the problems that had sent her fleeing to the barn the night before. Despite Kate's protest that she should remain in bed, Lynn insisted on dressing, reluctantly allowing Kate to choose her newest and most attractive gown of cramoisie red wool with a ruff of white ruching around the neck.

'' 'Twill look prettier with your short hair and help hide the gloves you'll have to wear over your burned hands.

I've stitched a pair of bed slippers to put on your swollen feet, but don't you be trying to do any fancy walking. Fact is, you'll be better off seeing them that's waiting for you right in here. The kitchen has been more crowded than a London street during a hanging.''

"Who wants to see me, Kate?"

"Bert Spence for one. He and that husband of yours have been glaring at each other for half an hour. If I was you, I'd talk to Bert first. He was the one who took charge last night and got those good-for-nothings put away before the whole town turned into a lynch mob.''

"I thought Red Penny killed two of them.''

"Not those thieving caterpillers! Three of them were messed up some, but I reckon poor Ned Fulton was hurt worse than they were. That scoundrel Tom attacked Ned from ambush with a knife. If Nate Stokes hadn't used the butt of his musket to knock that rakehell villain to kingdom-come and back, Ned would have been killed for sure. I'll let Bert tell you the rest; I get riled just thinking about what happened.''

After she finished hearing a haggard Bert Spence chronicle the night's events in a more orderly fashion, Lynn was more helplessly angry than Kate. Jem and Ned had heard the bell, and Ned had outrun all the others to reach the Penley barn just before Nate and Kerry arrived on the scene. Unarmed except for the wooden broom he'd grabbed when he'd raced from the Fulton barn, Ned had the misfortune to meet the fugitive Tom Kenn. Before Nate could immobilize Tom, Ned had been injured. An hour later in a more remote part of the snowy battlefield, Clay and Bert had located two others of the armed culprits and subdued them after a brief violence. By the time the five injured pirates had been loaded on a wagon and driven to New Port, dawn was breaking. In their official capacity as militia leaders, Nate and Bert had imprisoned Tom in the hold of the *Tamarlind* and the other four on their own ship with orders that all of them be kept aboard and not released into New Port ever again.

"Why weren't they charged with attempted murder?" Lynn asked furiously.

"We didn't dare," Bert rasped tiredly. "When Tom came to, he claimed that Harry had arranged to meet him in the barn, and that he'd dropped the lamp accidentally when someone in the loft had shot at him."

"That's a lie, Spence! He threw that lantern deliberately, long before Nell and I could even pick the muskets up."

"I know, his confederates admitted as much; and they confessed to the earlier theft. But we still can't charge them, because Tom threatened to expose you publicly. It took me an hour to convince Edward Fulton not to arouse the local authorities and bind all of them over for trial. Only after Captain Vinson and Nate Stokes promised to keep Tom permanently out of Rhode Island, did Fulton agree to remain silent."

"Why doesn't Captain Vinson just return Tom to England to finish his sentence?"

"Because Tom was forgiven his sins along with the rest of us."

"All except Nell! Why would anyone pardon a murderer like him and not an innocent like Nell?"

"Did you meet Tom's mother while you were hiding at the Kenn farm?"

"No. According to her husband, she was chapel folk; and chapel folk believe in witches."

"She's worse than that. She could never admit that her wastrel son was—"

"Tom was a wrecker, not a wastrel!"

"I'm not surprised, but his mother insisted that Tom had been in no trouble until he'd taken up with Nell Wallis."

"Did Lord Pendrath really believe her?"

"No, Andrew's too sharp to be so easily misled. But Martha Kenn threatened to expose the details of your escape from Cornwall, and he was afraid she'd endanger the pardons he'd already arranged. Now Harry will have to take the useless young fool to Virginia if Vinson declares him unfit to remain aboard the *Tamarlind*. None of our pardons permit a permanent return to England.''

"Are you planning to settle in Virginia too, Spence?''

"Good Lord, no! If you've no objection, I'm staying in Rhode Island to continue building what we started. After the child arrives, Leona and I will be moving into town; otherwise nothing's changed.''

"Everything is changed, Spence! I imagine Edward Fulton is having second thoughts about allowing his grandson to marry Nell.''

"Anything but. He took Nell home with him to nurse Ned.''

"Was Ned badly hurt?''

"He was cut up, but he was too fast on his feet for Tom to do any real damage. Harry was the one who made the old man furious by insisting that Tom had some kind of a claim on Nell. Like most of our useless class, poor Harry still believes in the nobility of blood lines. He'll be paying for his prejudice this time, though. Fulton is going to charge him enough for taking care of those horses to pay for Nell's papers.''

"What did Harry do when he heard the bell?'' Lynn asked curiously.

"You can't accuse him of cowardice, Lynn. He didn't even know where the barn was, but he raced out to do battle anyway; and he helped Jem make certain the fire was out. My only complaint was that he didn't tell us that you'd been injured.''

"Spence, did you get a chance to warn Tom never to come back here?''

"I told him that he'd be a dead man if he did, and I confiscated everything of value he owned to pay for the damage he did. I also collected a fine from the pirate captain that'll replace the stolen animals and supply the lumber we'll need for the barn.''

"How badly was it damaged?"

"One wall and the one stall were charred, but Nate will be bringing enough ship's carpenters later today to do the repairs. The only thing we lost was this morning's milk. I wouldn't have thought it, but even your placid cows can act like temperamental females."

"Only when they're breeding or frighten—"

"Lynn," Spence interrupted her brusquely, "we've talked about everyone and everything except your main problem. What are you going to do about your husband? Since he found out you'd been hurt, he's been acting as if he finally remembered he has a wife."

Lynn's smile was a twisted grimace. "He's two letters and several months too late."

"Then there were letters? He claimed he'd written to you, but I didn't believe him."

"He didn't, Amelia did. Her explicit messages arrived together just before Christmas. When you read them, you'll know the answer to your question about my marriage. Read the letters, Spence; you'll find them just inside the sea chest you're sitting on. And don't feel you're intruding; you already know all about that sordid history."

"I don't have to read them, Lynn. Leona received one of the same kind that hinted broadly that Amelia had finally overcome Clay's objections to a ménage à trois. But she could be lying; Amelia has the morality of a bitch in heat when she doesn't get her own way."

"I know she's vicious, but the fact remains that Clay has no interest in me other than . . . did he mention anything to you about needing money?"

When he made no response other than a grim frown, Lynn shrugged with a cynical acrimony. "You're a loyal friend to him, Bert Spence. But I imagine that by this time, he's discovered that I was not entirely honest about the extent of my grandmother's estate, and I imagine he'll feel most slighted when he learns you're my business manager. At any rate, I've decided to give him another two thousand pounds and be done with it.''

''My God, Lynn,'' Bert protested hotly, ''that will leave you with only a thousand reserve. We've made some money, but mostly from the sale of your bullocks, and we have a year to go before the other enterprises are really profitable.''

''And two years before we have any more trained bullocks to sell,'' Lynn added. ''But I'm in no position to fight the law which gives a husband control. If you don't mind the chore, I'd prefer you tell him and make the arrangements. At the moment, I don't feel courageous enough to face the conquering hero.''

''Well, you'd better damn well find the courage,'' an explosive voice sounded from the doorway, ending in a curse of furious pain as the tall man banged his head on the door's lintel, an inch too low for his height.

''Get out of here, Spence; I want to talk to my wife alone now that the pair of you have finished assassinating my character,'' Clay rasped.

Instead of obeying the angry command, Bert stood up and removed the two letters from the chest, scowling with distaste as he noted the broken wax signet stamp of the Pendrath family. Handing them to Clay, he announced flatly, ''Before you criticize Lynn and me, I suggest you read these letters from an expert in the art of assassination. Since you sailed merrily away from here almost eight months ago, these secondhand accounts are the sum total of the news your wife has received about you. So I'm not leaving you alone with her until I know she's safe.''

''What the devil is my wife's safety to you?''

''Exactly what you care to make of it.''

During the acrimonious exchange of challenges, Lynn studied the differences between the two men with as much objectivity as she could muster. After months of working alongside Bert Spence, she was as familiar with his dark,

finely chiseled features as she was with her own. But his
intense antagonism today baffled her. Not until she noticed
the shabbiness of his boots and plain gray suit, did she
interpret the reason for his anger. Unlike his richly clad
friend, Bert had not taken the time to change his clothing
or to shave; Lynn suspected that he hadn't even gone to
bed. How he must hate looking the colonial rustic in front
of his social equals who'd returned to Cavalier grandeur.

Her emotional comparison included no such sympathetic
understanding as she watched her husband read Amelia's
letters. As always, his facial control frustrated her; he
appeared neither guilt-ridden nor embarrassed. Only an
occasional upward flick of his mobile eyebrows indicated a
reaction that was more humorous than concerned. After
refolding the expensive parchments, he handed them to the
other man and shrugged indifferently.

"Have you read them, Spence?" he asked.

"No, but I read the one she sent to Leona."

"Amelia at her bitchiest! She told Harry essentially the
same thing. Fortunately, Peter Vinson was able to supply
me with a safe alibi on both occasions, and Harry finally
found the courage to leave her with her relatives in
Virginia." Abruptly Clay turned to face his wife whose
face reflected none of his own easy assurance. "Do you
still consider me the world's most idiotic rakehell, Trelynn
Trevor?" he demanded.

Aware that she'd been placed on the defensive and
resentful of his arrogant confidence, Lynn responded brashly,
her irritation concealed behind a skeptical half-smile. "No,
Clay Penley, or whatever name you're using now, I think
you have a convenient memory. The lady in question
described the cabin you were occupying aboard the *Tamarlind*
quite accurately and the room at your Jamestown inn with
explicit details."

"I'm not denying that she visited me in both places, but
not at my invitation; and I didn't accept the one she offered

me on either occasion. If Spence had been honest with you, he'd have told you that I never played Harry false."

"Spence has been very loyal to you," Lynn affirmed tartly. "If 'twill relieve your conscience, I'll accept your exclamation that you're equally loyal to Harry and that you cater to his wife's whims only when 'tis safe. I do believe, though, that you'll be leading an interesting life in Virginia."

"A life you'll be sharing with me, Mrs. Trevor."

"I prefer the name of Penley," Lynn murmured vaguely. "Did you see my grandfather while you were in England?"

Clay frowned slightly in annoyance and answered curtly, "I saw him."

"And?" she prompted.

"He sent you a packet of letters."

"May I have them, please?"

"Not until we settle our differences. Whether you like it or not, you and I are—"

"I know what we are," she interrupted, "and we'll settle those differences according to law. I've instructed Spence to give you two thousand pounds to finance your—"

"What the hell does Spence have to do with your money?"

"He's my business manager. Now, if you'll give me my grandfather's letters, I won't detain either of you any longer. Spence looks ready to drop from fatigue, and you're in an unpleasant enough humor to need Harry's cheerful company."

Bert moved restlessly from the corner of the room where he'd been standing in uncomfortable silence and nodded curtly at the stiff-necked man glaring at Lynn. "Come on, Clay, if you want your money today, we'll have to walk over to the Fulton house."

"To hell with the money!"

Bert's eyebrow was raised in spurious surprise, and his voice was acidly caustic. "You don't want the money? Harry said—"

"The devil with Harry. Here are your precious letters, madam; but I'll be back, so don't try to run away on those burned feet of yours. In case you're interested, I did write to you, but my letters were intercepted. And if you hadn't been so damned eager to leave me that morning aboard the *Tamarlind*, you'd have learned that I'd planned to remain in Rhode Island."

The stiff pride that had sustained Lynn throughout the unpleasant reunion crumbled as she tried to pick up the small packet her husband had tossed on the bed before he strode from the room, remembering just in time to duck his head. It was Bert who remained behind for the moment it took him to untie the cord and break the seals of the letters before he left her alone with her seething thoughts.

Her depression deepened as she read Ephraim's letters. The murder of John Pollock was still unsolved; and despite Owen's efforts to silence his wife's tongue, Edith Penley was too much a Pollock to obey docilely. Slyly, out of Owen's hearing, she'd kept the neighborhood stirred up about the dangerous, murderous witch reputed to be still hiding on Bodmin Moor. In reference to Edith's charge that the fugitive "witch" had also murdered Rad Pollock and his sons, Ephraim Penley had been cheerfully contemptuous. "Bevil will inform the authorities about their enforced immigration to Virginia as soon as the other charges against you are dropped."

To Lynn's surprise, the second letter was a copy of one that Roger Williams had written to Ephraim concerning her. It was a declaration that the colonial leader had found her to be an industrious and honest woman, incapable of committing the criminal offenses lodged against her. Williams also praised her fair dealings with other colonials and with the Narragansett Indians, whose language she had promised to learn. As payment for the services Ephraim Penley had rendered to the Narragansetts several years earlier, the Indian leaders had promised to grant sanctuary to Lynn Penley in the event of a threatened arrest. She would be safely hidden in a remote Indian village until Ephraim could prove her innocence in the courts. Although Lynn was grateful for Williams's support, she winced at his suggested solution that she live among a primitive people in the wilderness. Even on the rare occasions she assisted in a delivery to one of their villages, the Indian men had spoken only to Jem Rigg or to John Bram. She'd been ignored. But at least, she grimaced with a twisting pain, she wouldn't have to worry about a disguise. With her dark coloring, she would appear enough like the natives to be overlooked by outside strangers.

The third letter in the packet was a stern warning from her grandfather that she not leave Rhode Island under any circumstances, regardless of her husband's announced intention of moving her to Virginia. "Your husband," Ephraim had written, "will be away much of the time in pursuit of a business I heartedly deplore, and you will have no one to protect you. Your father has already notified me that he intends to sue for your grandmother's estate. Because Hortensia had excellent legal advice, Royce Trevor stands no chance of winning his suit; but the resultant notoriety might prove very dangerous for you."

Scanning the remainder of the letter, which contained praise for her accomplishments and a promise to join her as soon as he was able, Lynn reflected glumly that her grandfather had as little faith in the future of her marriage as she did. She no longer believed in the specifics of Amelia Pendrath's claims of possession; but neither did she have any illusions that it was love of his wife that had brought Charles Clay Trevor back to Rhode Island. Only his unexplained anger against Bert Spence had driven him to claim her at all. The fleeting hope that he might really have intended to remain with her months ago was instantly replaced by the cynical memory of his demand for money the night before he'd sailed.

Unable to resort to hard physical work as an antidote for her momentary depression, Lynn reread her grandfather's correspondence, trying to glean some measure of reassurance from his cautious lawyer's optimism. But the only doubtful hope she could find for her defense was the opinion Ephraim had wrung from a parliamentary lawyer who was an authority in church affairs. According to him, she did not qualify as a witch under the official definition set by Lord Edward Coke in 1600, "A person who had consulted with the devil or done his bidding," because none of the witnesses against her had sufficient education in demonology. Ironically the only fact Lynn could recall about Lord Coke, other than his reputation as the greatest authority on English law, was his treatment of his own daughter. Coke had kidnapped the fourteen-year-old girl from her mother, dragged her screaming to the altar, and forced her to marry an old man she hated.

Lynn smiled sourly at the reminiscence. No wonder a hundred times more women were condemned as witches, since men like Lord Coke were the devils who did the condemning. As her anger roused, so did her curiosity about the laws pertaining to witchcraft. Sore hands and all, she located the one law book she owned, Lord Coke's *Reports on English Law*, and awkwardly located the brief chapter she wanted. After an hour of discouraging study, her only hope in the event she was forced to face "twelve good men and true" was that they'd be considerably less than Puritan good.

While Lynn wrestled with the weighty problem of a future legal defense before she fell into an uneasy sleep, her husband was interested in a more immediate consideration—the extent and profits of his wife's commercial enterprises. At Clay's insistence, Bert led him to the cabin next door and showed him the account books for the draying and customer ordering business. To Bert's relief, Clay was contemptuously unimpressed by the earnings.

"You're wasting your time here, Spence," Clay disclaimed bluntly. "I made more money than this on one slave run between Jamaica and Virginia. Why bury yourself in a pence-and-shilling business when you could make a fortune if you joined Harry and me?"

"Because this pence-and-shilling business allows me to sleep at night; your kind of trade wouldn't."

"Why not? Slaves are as much products for sale as the pots and pans you're ordering for these colonists."

"Pots and pans don't die during transportation, and they don't need special training to be salable. Who's going to educate those raw primitives to become ladies' maids for ladies who wear three-foot-high French wigs and dresses that require expert seamstresses to stitch on? And are you and Harry planning to train the more exotic *products* who are going to be used as whores in fancy brothels?"

"Don't be a bloody ass! Harry told you about only part of the trade. Our main customers will be Virginia planters who need strong field hands, slaves we'd choose ourselves in Jamaica. That's the part of the business we'd like you to handle, Spence."

"Not me, Clay. I'm staying right here."

"Have you considered the fact that Leona would be much happier in Virginia?"

"Somehow I'm not interested in your considerate regard for other men's wives. I'd rather hear what you intend to do about your own."

"That's none of your concern, Spence. You're already too involved in my wife's business to suit me, and you're beginning to sound damned possessive."

"If I thought you were jealous, I'd tell you to go to hell. But since you're only concerned with her money, I'll tell you the truth. She's the most challenging woman I've ever known and one of the most beautiful. If she hadn't made the mistake of marrying you, she could have her pick of all the single men in this colony; and if I can, I'll stop you from ruining her life any more than you already have. Take the two thousand she offered you, Clay, and leave her alone in the future. After your last scot-free departure, she worked like a demon in an effort to forget you; but she's not a gullible fool. She knows you'll never be anything more than an occasional visitor who drops by to mark his territory like a herd animal in rut. So find yourself another territory.''

"And leave this one to you? It sounds to me as if you've already staked a claim of your own.''

Bert Spence's harsh laughter resounded throughout the small cabin he shared with Leona and Kate, both of whom had left when he and Clay had begun their antagonistic meeting.

"I'm tired as hell, Clay; so why don't you take your wife's advice and locate Harry. If you're simpleton enough to make that same accusation to Lynn, she'll save me the trouble of knocking your bloody head off. This is the real world of hard work, not that fool's paradise you're still seeking.''

Without a backward glance at the angry man seated at the table, Bert left the room and carefully latched the bedroom door after he'd slammed it shut. We're two of a kind, he thought sardonically, both of us more interested in other men's wives than we are our own. God, he wished Leona weren't becoming such a complaining, dull slattern; she'd made no effort to wash the linen sheets in months. What the hell was she going to do with a child?

CHAPTER
10

Even before Lynn roused completely from her troubled nap, she was aware of her husband's presence in the bedroom. From beneath the dark lashes that shrouded her half-opened eyes, she studied his face in the dim light of a flickering lantern, trying vainly to determine his mood. Feeling disadvantaged and vulnerable, she swung her legs over the side of the bed and sat up defensively to return his speculative stare.

"Guilty conscience, Mrs. Trevor?" Clay inquired blandly.

"No, Mr. Trevor, merely the oddity of having a man in my bedroom."

"You showed no such alarm when Spencer Burtram was here."

"Bert Spence is not an alarming person. You are. Was there something else you wanted?"

"Not particularly, since I'll be sharing this room with you."

"The bed isn't—"

" 'Tis as wide as our bunk aboard ship was. We'll manage for the next month before we leave."

"Before *you* leave, Mr. Trevor; I'll be remaining here. If you'd care to read my grandfather's letters—"

"I read them while you were asleep. I'm sorry the news wasn't better, but somehow I don't have much confidence in your Roger Williams's idea of protection. He's an old man."

"He's the same age as my grandfather; they attended Cambridge together."

"All right, I'll admit they're *educated* old men; but neither of them could have gotten you out of Cornwall as I did. When it comes to dodging authorities, I qualify as an expert. I don't suppose I'll be a very good nurse; but right now, I'm going to feed you your supper before it gets cold. Is there anything you need before I fetch it?"

"Where's Kate?"

"Next door with Leona, and I sent your housekeeper and Jem to bed. Nate and a pair of his carpenters are spending the night in the barn, so you can stop worrying. I'll be taking care of you until your hands are healed. What's the matter, Lynn? Are you afraid of my helping you use the chamber pot? I didn't complain when I was the one who needed assistance."

Provoked by the baiting challenge and embarrassed by the prospect, Lynn muttered aggressively, "I'm not that helpless."

"No? Let's see you unbutton your dress and untie your underskirts."

Taking refuge in silence, because she knew she could do neither—she'd had to use her elbows to turn the pages of the law book—Lynn submitted to her husband's ministrations, which proved less oppressive than she'd anticipated. Because his occasional comments were cheerfully impersonal and he attempted no intimacy with his hands, Lynn survived the indignities with only an occasional flush of exasperation when a small glob of stew dribbled down her chin or a piece of bread broke off and caught in her hair.

"I'm not as deft as you were when you fed me," Clay

apologized lightly. "Tonight you'll have to make do with a face scrub, but tomorrow I'll give you the bath Kate said was a daily obsession with you." Clay smiled impudently at her flushed face and added a more personal reminder: "I'll never forget your soaping yourself inside our first cave before you stepped outside to let the rain wash you off."

"You were delirious when I did that."

"After the first day, I made a point of being lucid whenever you reached for the soap. What do you use here on the farm?"

"I generally use the small pool we dug along the stream, but the others use large cooper barrels."

"No imported copper tub for cold winter nights?"

"Spence ordered one from France, but it hasn't arrived yet."

At the mention of the other man's name, Clay became brusquely businesslike as he shoved the bed against the wall, blew out the lamp, and undressed in silence. Only after he'd climbed into the narrow bed did he renew the interrupted conversation.

"Now that I've made sure you can't climb out of bed and disappear as you did night before last, we'll talk. Just how essential has my faithful old friend Spence become to you?"

Resentful of the presumptuous tone of voice, Lynn retorted curtly, "He represents me in public and is indispensible to the town business, but I didn't ask him to stay. He made that decision himself and for good reason. He's respected in the colony, enough so that Roger Williams appointed him head of the island militia; and he's trusted by all the other businessmen and the ships' captains. Is that the reason you were glaring at me when I woke up, because Spence refused to go with you?"

Cautiously Clay paused in his attack. She'd answered his blunt question without a hint of fear or guilt, neither speeded-up breathing nor tell-tale jerks. Either she was a better actress than any woman he'd ever known, or she hadn't an inkling that she'd aroused more than platonic respect from a man who previously had little regard for any woman. More subtly now, he continued his probing.

"You can't blame me for being curious. I come back to find out that he knows more about you than I do, and that you've made him your business manager. Why did you think it necessary to pay him a salary all these months?"

"Since I had to pay Jem and Polly and Nate for their work, I decided to pay the others as well, all except Leona."

"Why in God's name? They were nothing but indentured criminals."

"They're friends and loyal employees now."

"Well, you'll not be paying Spence anything after today. He can earn his own money. I plan to dismiss him from his present position and prevent him from having any more influence in your life."

The emotional reaction that had been lacking earlier now flamed into a physical violence that almost tumbled Clay from the bed as Lynn sat up and turned to glare in his direction.

"The devil you will! Before Spence took over dealing with some of the dim-witted males in this colony, Caleb Winslow tried to cheat me, George Fulton acted as if I didn't know a byre from a piggery, and the Indian men treated me like a squaw. If I'd been an unmarried woman or a widow, they'd have at least credited me with a little sense. But a deserted wife is considered the most useless of females."

Muttering irritably as he reclaimed his share of the bed and anchored the covers more securely around his shoulders, Clay countered with exasperation, "You weren't deserted, damn it! And you were treated no differently than any other woman. If you'd had the sense to limit your activities to simple farming instead of trying to rearrange the colony's economy, there wouldn't be any complications in selling out here and moving to—''

"No one here is moving to Virginia," Lynn interrupted hotly. "Technically, except for Spence and Nate, my people work for my grandfather; so you can't order them to go anywhere. And I'm not fool enough to risk placing myself at the mercy of the Pollocks or your damned mistress or my greedy father in a colony run by people like Andrew Pendrath. In case you've forgotten, you're a free man while I'm still a fugitive whose location is no longer secret. Did you make a point of visiting my father while you were becoming a lordly Virginian?''

"No, but I learned his home is one of the finest in the county. I thought perhaps we might ask him for a few months of hospitality. As his daughter—"

"I'd be dragged into court and sued for my grandmother's estate! I thought you said you'd read my grandfather's letters.''

"I read the first one and the Williams thing. What the devil do you mean that your father would sue you?''

"Royce Trevor is an expensive parasite whom my grandparents supported. Now that he's probably remarried, he needs a new source of income; and I'm afraid our mutual relative is as unscrupulous as a pirate when it comes to money.''

"Then 'tis a good thing you're married to me," Clay murmured sententiously, unaware of the irony his words implied.

Still sitting bolt upright, Lynn grimaced in contempt as she tabulated the monetary problems stemming from her male relatives: a grandfather who'd been too indulgent to guard his own fortune, a cousin who'd accused her of witchcraft to line his own pockets, a father who was suing her, and a husband who considered her small inheritance his own. She'd had better luck with strangers, she reflected cynically: Jem Rigg, Bert Spence, and Roger Williams—

men who owed her nothing, but who'd offered her their protection anyway.

Suffocating from an abrupt sense of entrapment so overwhelming she forgot her sore feet and hands, Lynn moved swiftly to escape from the imprisoning bed. She'd reached the heavy wood barrier at the foot when her startled husband grabbed her and dragged her backward.

"What the hell's the matter with you?" he exploded.

"You are, Mr. Trevor," she rasped in a voice that shook with anger.

"Why?" he demanded. "Because I showed a normal husband's interest in knowing what my wife had been doing with another man all the time I was away?"

Clay regretted the words instantly when Lynn's pliantly muscled body stilled to immobility and her breathing stopped for the moment it took to understand the import of his accusation. When she finally spoke, it was with an impersonal calm.

"In a civil law case, 'tis a wise defendant who can make the plaintiff seem equally guilty. Unfortunately, in your case, the counter accusation is invalid, because neither Bert Spence nor I have indulged in your kind of social recreation by playing the fool for someone else's spouse."

Tiredly Clay repeated his earlier denial. "I told you I've had nothing to do with Harry's wife since I left you."

"You told me that you ran for cover when Amelia Pendrath demanded what you'd promised with your gallant and constant flattery. Do you really believe that Spence and I have been playing such a ridiculous game?"

"According to Leona, he spends most of his time with you."

"Leona is a stupid woman who has refused to do her share of the work. I've no doubt she blames me for her own unhappiness and for her husband's boredom whenever he's around her. Believe her if you want to, but I'd be careful about accusing Spence; he's not a man I'd care to have as an enemy."

Clay shook his head in annoyance. Despite his frustration at her cold counterattack, he knew that she'd usurped his initiative and done it convincingly. He'd not make the mistake of underestimating her again.

"I've known Spence for ten years," he asserted more mildly. "He hasn't always been such a blameless hero." Clay could feel her shrug as she settled back beneath the covers, and he sought vainly for a conversational opening that would establish some kind of rapport between them.

" 'Tis a shame you sold all your bullocks, Lynn. Virginia has fifty times the land of this small colony. You would have earned double the money you did here."

"Why Virginia, Clay?"

"That's the first time you've used my given name since I returned. Did you finally remember that we're not exactly strangers?"

Refusing to be drawn into intimacy with a man she could no longer trust, Lynn returned to the safer path of practicality. "You've so many names. Is Virginia the place where you've decided to plant the Trevor one?"

" 'Tis the most beautiful of the colonies."

"Then did you think to buy a parcel of land there?"

"Royal grants are the rule in Virginia, but Andrew Pendrath promised to sell me a part of his."

"In return for what?"

"That depends upon the success of our business."

"In the meantime," Lynn murmured reasonably, "Lord Pendrath suggested that my people and my bullocks could clear his land and develop his fields in tobacco. I imagine at Harry's insistence, he also included Kate Horton's services as personal maid to Amelia Pendrath in order to keep peace in his own family. Did you agree to any of those terms as a price for a small, not too choice part of Pendrath land?"

"We'll make more money under those conditions than you're making here."

"We've just begun, Clay. As soon as the Spragues' flour and saw mill goes into full operation—"

In a deceptively calm voice, Clay interrupted her boast. "There was no mention of any mill in the accounts Spence showed me."

"I keep those books, but Spence has sold every piece of lumber the Spragues have produced."

"Produced where? There's no mill on this farm."

"My grandfather owns another piece of property on the mainland that's still covered by forest. For eleven years he and I will share the profits equally with the Spragues. Rhode Island is a fast-growing colony, Clay, and its port is one of the best. Even though slave ships aren't very welcome here, you could still use it for the few weeks each year you might want to visit us."

Clay was silent for a moment, his thoughts busily cursing Spence for not having told him about the mill. Wondering how many other potentially productive enterprises had been concealed from him, he hedged his answer to her half-hearted invitation. "I don't suppose we'll have any choice but to spend a part of each year here to check on your investments . . . and on Spence. Still, with him so completely in charge, there's no reason now why we can't go to Boston next week with Harry and Vinson."

"Clay, I can't go to Boston or anywhere else with you."

"Why not? You'd be safe enough aboard ship."

"I'd be apprehended in the first English port by cargo inspectors who are as interested in human cargo as any other kind."

Again her relentless logic defeated him; he may have won a royal pardon, but the customs officials in every port of England had long memories and unforgiving dispositions. Clay's eyes narrowed in concentration as he weighed the comparative dangers of taking her with him or leaving her behind. Except for the threat of Spencer Burtram, she'd be physically safer right here in this odd little colony where everyone seemed in league to protect her. What the devil had she done to make a sophisticate like Spence call her the most challenging and beautiful woman he'd ever known? It hadn't been mere gratitude that had inspired Spence's anger this afternoon.

Abruptly a twinge of guilt spurred Clay's memory. He'd been too angry himself to really look at her when he'd crashed into the bedroom earlier today, but now he remembered vividly the picture she'd made seated on a crude bed in a primitive cabin. There'd been an arrogance about her at that moment that had fueled his already heated temper, and he'd responded by acting the condescending fool. No wonder Spence had lashed out at him; and no wonder she'd used the derisive words "conquering hero" just before he'd entered the room.

Ironically, her mocking description had been an accurate assessment of how he'd felt since the day he'd regained his own identity. For weeks after he and Harry had arrived in London, they'd cavorted like a pair of school lads on holiday, ordering the most expensive clothing and attending lavish parties. At one of these pretentious receptions, he'd remembered his farm-born wife and decided she'd appear an awkward outsider among these glittering social queens. He'd been wrong! Even in the subdued red dress she'd worn today, she'd have looked unique, dramatically different enough to have startled the most jaded eyes.

His memory had played him equally false on the occasion when one of the reigning beauties, the thirty-year-old wife of a country recluse, had invited him to remain as a guest in her town house after a gala dinner party. Having been relatively celibate throughout the months of challenging work, Clay had been flattered by his acceptance into a social circle he'd thought forever denied him. But his stay at the opulent town house had lasted only a few hours, only until he could flee from his hostess's perfumed bedroom after an insipid union with the demanding and jaded woman.

Returning on foot over rain-dampened London streets to

his own rooms at an expensive inn, he'd remembered the last night he'd spent with his wife aboard the *Tamarlind*. Bleakly he'd wondered if he could be as content throughout a lifetime with the unusual woman he'd married as he'd been that night. When he'd married her, he'd had few expectations of permanency despite her physical attraction for him. Two years earlier he'd been adamantly opposed to his father's insistence that she'd make him a good wife. Oddly enough, she had; he'd been the one who'd failed. But now that their social levels had been widely separated by his return to his own class, he'd become even more doubtful that he'd be able to accept such a limited life.

Perhaps if Connecticut had not proved so disappointing, he might have been willing to settle down. In New Haven where the people had been inhospitable and suspicious, he'd paid for the services of a guide and a surveyor and had traveled with them a short distance up the Housatonic River to his own land. For a week they'd hiked through primeval forests and past cascading waterfalls in the most forbidding wilderness in Connecticut. The New Haven men had been awed by the size of the property and its potential, but Clay had been appalled by its isolation. Nor could he force himself to return to Rhode Island until he'd found some means of escaping the dreariness of a small farm. Jamestown and a profitable form of slave trade had solved that problem; and the ensuing months of exciting challenge had all but erased his memory of the small New England colony that harbored a wife he remembered guiltily only at intervals.

Arriving back at his London inn in the predawn hours of early January, he'd found his disapproving father awaiting him with the news that he'd overstayed his welcome in England. Lord Pendrath had neglected to inform either Harry or Clay that the royal pardon had specified complete freedom in the colonies only. In the following half hour of stern parental lecture, Clay learned that Sir Bevil would neither invest in the slave business nor pay any of his son's bills.

"Andrew Pendrath informed me that he expects you to pay four thousand pounds as investment capital. Do you have that amount?"

"I've already paid him a thousand," Clay had responded defensively.

"Then you'll find him a harsh partner who'll take most of the profits. I'm glad Trelynn had the sense to limit your access to her small inheritance. How much of her money have you squandered so far?"

"She gave me only a thousand pounds; I earned double that amount in a few months."

"And squandered it in half the time. Trelynn was wise to save three-quarters of her small inheritance for her own support."

Clay's eyebrow had been lifted in surprise when he'd learned of his wife's duplicity, but he hadn't interrupted his father's continuing castigation.

"I've asked Peter Vinson to nursemaid you for another few months as far south as Virginia since that is where Harry tells me you intend to settle. If, by chance, you should see Trelynn while the *Tamarlind* is in New Port, tell her that I deeply regret my part in burdening her with a worthless husband."

More amused than angry, Clay had defended himself: "Of course I intend to see her. Why else would I even go there?"

"I dare say, you'll think of a reason," Bevil had murmured dryly as he strode from the room.

Two mornings later when Clay arrived at the London docks, he'd found both his father and Ephraim Penley awaiting him. Having just spent an hour imprisoned in the Pendrath carriage assuring Lord Andrew that he would be able to contribute his full share of the investment capital once he reached America, Clay was in no mood for additional recriminations from either his father or the man whose fictitious nephew he'd been for six months. He'd been spared the necessity by the timely arrival of Harry Pendrath in a second carriage piled high with luggage. Unfortunately, Harry had also seen fit to bring the two sisters who had been his and Clay's most frequent companions. Although Clay had never been seriously attracted to the widowed sister, he had been momentarily intrigued enough by her impressive fortune and by her eagerness for his company to remain mute about his own hasty marriage. Under the disapproving glare of his father, Clay had bid the woman a constrained farewell, gratefully relieved when she returned to the carriage.

The damage, though, had already been done. His father made only one request, that he deliver a packet of letters to Trelynn Trevor, a request that was instantly canceled by Ephraim Penley's cold rejoinder, "I have already assigned that commission to Captain Vinson. I'm certain my granddaughter would prefer a less forgetful messenger."

Lying beside that granddaughter now in the humble wilderness cottage, Clay reflected that she'd proved as forgetful of their marriage as he'd been. She'd also become lawyer-shrewd in countering his arguments and in defending her employees. With a canny accuracy, she'd guessed Andrew Pendrath's plans for his family's Virginia estate; she'd been right about the danger she would face with cargo inspectors; and she'd convinced him that she would be safer in Rhode Island. More cautiously Clay contemplated the options still open to him: he could take her advice and money, and leave without any more unpleasantness; or he could try rebuilding a marriage that had never really had the time to begin. Reluctantly, he admitted to himself that he wanted her as a woman, just as he had every time they'd been together. She possessed a subtle magnetism that had nothing in common with the feminine ploys used by more socially adept women, and she possessed a capacity for passion that still intrigued him.

The jarring memory that Spence had recognized these

qualities in her goaded Clay's determination, that and his own suspicion that his wife might be resourceful enough to escape the marriage bond if he failed her again. He had four weeks between now and the time the *Tamarlind* sailed to Virginia to convince the cynical, independent woman that he was a serious husband, not merely what Spence had accused him of being: a male animal marking territory before it wanders off. Perhaps it was time to follow Spence's example and start a family. Even a woman as adventuresome and energetic as his wife could be restrained by motherhood.

Intrigued by the thought of a child and aroused by the desire that had been building despite the coldness of her reception, Clay put his arms around her and whispered her name softly, remembering as he did so that the last time he'd awakened her from sleep, she'd welcomed him with an eager warmth. But tonight, his tentative caress elicited not even a stir of response. Disappointed, but not particularly discouraged when he recalled her burned hands and feet, Clay followed her into sleep with a gambler's optimism that she'd still be by his side in the morning. Regrettably, he failed to take into account that a farmer's morning begins at dawn in contrast to the nine o'clock arousal of a vacationing gentleman.

When Clay awoke, he found his wife already gone and the house empty of human occupants. Grumbling from the icy chill, he dressed in his oldest and warmest clothes, ate the cold breakfast laid out for him on the kitchen table, and walked to the barn. He found Lynn seated alone on the driving bench of a wagon loaded with crated goods and barrels.

"What the hell do you think you're doing?" he shouted from twenty feet away.

"I'm driving a wagon," she retorted sharply as she pulled at the reins looped over her arms.

"Are you crazy? You can't even use your hands."

"I don't have to drive far, only to the Reikerks'. One of the men there will go with me on the other deliveries."

"Where are all your own workers?"

"Doing things I can't with these hands of mine. Jem's waiting for a calf to be born, and Bram's in town helping Spence load two other wagons. The ship that docked yesterday carried three months' worth of the goods we'd ordered."

"What about the others?"

"This is market day for Jonas, and Kerry's at the Fultons helping tend your friends' horses. Nate's repairing the barn, and Nell's cleaning it. She came over this morning to do the milking . . . that's what's in those barrels and that's why I have to leave now. Milk can sour even on a cold day."

"Move over," Clay ordered as he climbed aboard, "I'm not letting you go alone."

"You'll be happier in town with Harry," Lynn protested, "especially today. Polly and Kate may be busy with Leona; it could be our resident lady will finally give birth."

"Why the hell isn't Spence staying home?"

"This will be the fourth time this month Leona has announced impending motherhood. I suppose he thought it just another false alarm, and Kate was glad to see him go. According to her, husbands are more trouble than mothers during birthing."

"Do you want children, Lynn?" Clay asked abruptly as he headed the wagon down the trail.

Her ready response was honest and unembarrassed. "Not as much as I want my cows to produce more bull calves than heifers. I'm not nearly as enthusiastic about human offspring, not even my own."

Forgetting that his own decision about a child was very recent, Clay demanded harshly, "Why not?"

"I'd want any child of mine to have a resident father, not some shadowy man who visits once every five years."

"You don't mince words, do you?"

"I don't believe in hypocrisy either. In England, fathers were often absentee, but in America they're considered as essential as mothers. That's why both widows and widowers remarry as quickly as possible; but since I wouldn't be a widow, I'd have a hard time raising a child and earning a living. That's the Reikerk farm ahead, Clay. You turn left at the gate and head for the barn."

Silenced by her candid analysis of their marriage, Clay observed her closely during their brief stay at the Dutch farm. As Spence had told him, she'd become an expert in dealing with customers, combining business and friendship with a light touch. She'd chatted amiably with the women while he and three burly Reikerk men wrestled the heavy barrels of milk into the whitewashed barn that housed the vats of forming cheese. Casually she introduced her husband as Clay Penley and, just as casually, held up her freshly bandaged hands and admitted there'd been a small fire in her own barn.

"When are you going to announce you've had a change in name?" Clay asked as he steered the bullocks back to the Portsmouth road.

"Since my grandfather agreed to the lie, I think it best that he explains his reasons. In the meantime, I'd appreciate your continuing the pretense."

"I hope someone remembers to tell Harry and Vinson."

"Spence said he would when he left this morning."

"You've talked to him already this morning?"

"I talk to him every morning and every night and usually in between, so don't bother to repeat the silliness you spouted last night. Regardless of your contempt, this is a complicated business. Slow down, Clay, we're delivering the two crates of crockery at the farmhouse over there."

Clay's jaw was set as he climbed stiffly down from the driver's bench to be surrounded by the eight family members who came rushing out of the house, barn, and piggery to greet the arrival with eager anticipation. Like the Reikerks, these people were not the reserved and disapproving Puritans he'd met in New Haven; they were cheerful and friendly. But Clay noted with skepticism that they did not pay any money for the merchandise they received.

"Most of the farmers pay eventually," Lynn assured him, "when they sell a pig or enough butter and eggs. But not the man you just met; he'll pay in furniture. He made the bed you slept in last night and the tables and chairs."

"He's also created quite a litter of offspring and another addition on the way," Clay muttered.

"Joab Markley loves children; he teaches all of the local ones twice a week at the Portsmouth church. I've promised him a heifer calf so that he'll have a supply of milk for his pupils in a year or two. In return, he'll make Polly and Jem a pair of rockers." Lynn laughed at her husband's sardonic expression. "Once you get used to our island barter system, you'll find money's not that important."

"But you do make some money," Clay reminded her sharply.

"From the Reikerks, the townspeople, and our pirate customers; and everyone pays in coin to use the ferry. We charge for the lumber the Spragues are sawing, and eventually we will for the flour. We also make a fair commission on the goods we order from England."

"Will we be using the ferry today?"

"One of them, unless we go all the way to Providence and take the other two as well."

"How did you get involved with ferryboats?"

"Six of my bullocks power the capstans that haul the ropes; the old oxen and horses weren't strong enough for the heavier barges. George Fulton asked me to join his company the first day I was here just as his father set up the arrangements for the draying business. 'Tis a fast-growing colony, Clay; people who aren't welcome in Massachusetts and Connecticut come here."

"Where they're met by my ex-partner in crime and my energetic wife. Who's next on your delivery list?"

"On Aquidneck there are three more farmers, the tannery, and the Portsmouth church. Once we cross the Sakonnet River, there are only two farmers, one of them Fulton's oldest son George.''

It was at the church that Clay discovered still another facet of his wife's complex new life; she and most of her people were members of the congregation. The shambling man who'd been shoveling snow from the stone steps leading to the double doors of the rustic church smiled in greeting as he walked over to the wagon.

"Did the windows come then, Mistress Penley?''

"They did, and only one small pane is crizzled. Bert Spence said to tell you that you'll be getting a small refund for that damage. Reverend Tyler, this is my husband, Clay Penley. He'll help you carry the crates inside.''

Still beaming, the untidy minister wiped his hand on his worn leather breeches and extended it to the startled man climbing down from the wagon.

"I was hoping you'd arrive in time for the April festivities,'' Reverend Tyler announced jovially. "Now you'll be able to do the honors.''

Rescuing her floundering husband with a broad smile, Lynn shook her head. "I'm afraid not, Reverend. Mr. Penley will be leaving again on business in a few weeks. Nell would have liked Jem Rigg to give her away, but Jem's too shy; so Bert Spence has promised to stand by her. If all goes well today, you'll be combining the wedding with a christening.''

"I trust Bert's wife will be in better spirits than when I talked to her last. 'Tis a difficult time for a delicate woman like Mrs. Spence.''

Lynn shrugged indifferently. "I expect Leona will be happier once she's established in her own home in New Port.''

Instantly the minister's fluttery conviviality disappeared behind a frown of concern. "As much as I appreciate what Mr. Spence has done to control our doubtful visitors, what you suggest, Mrs. Penley, is impossible. He is still an indentured criminal, and as such, must be maintained by the person who has undertaken responsibility for—"

"Not any longer, Reverend," Lynn interrupted smoothly. "My husband can tell you that Bert Spence and his wife have been granted royal pardons and are now free British subjects. In time he will repay the money expended for his transportation to the colonies."

Again Reverend Tyler's expression changed with mercurial speed, this time to a thoughtful contemplation. "A royal prerogative I do not condone and, in this case, do not understand." His pause was followed by a smile of sudden comprehension. "Ah, I see! Mr. Spence is an educated aristocrat just as our founder claimed he was. Are you certain he intends to remain in our humble colony? It seems to me, he would be more tempted by New York or Virginia."

Lynn shook her head impatiently; she had correctly interpreted her husband's expression as one of chagrin at the subject and at the delay. "Mr. Spence has no money other than his present salary, and he has already turned down another offer."

"Is this news confidential, Mistress Penley, or may I relay it to Roger Williams? I'm quite certain that for a man of Mr. Spence's varied abilities, our governing officers will be delighted to offer him a permanent position in the community."

Agreeing hastily, Lynn politely reminded the well-intentioned cleric that she had other deliveries to make. Within a minute she and her irritated husband were underway, and she was forced to listen to his explosive scolding.

"For God's sake, Lynn, do you tell everyone on the island your business? I thought that neighborhood gossip was a damned laborer when I first saw him."

"He is when he isn't teaching in the church school or administering from the pulpit. He's one of the finest carpenters on the island. When we were buildi the barn, he walked over from Portsmouth to help us. That's when he and Spence became friends.''

"Whose idea was it to tell him all of our business?''

"I asked Edward Fulton to show him part of the letters my grandfather had written. I didn't want any public embarrassment.''

"What the hell did your grandfather write?''

"The truth about everyone including you and me, but Mr. Fulton and Roger Williams are still the only two who know about your past.''

"My God, Lynn, that magpie minister could expose you to immediate arrest.''

"Not Jeremiah Tyler! Thirty years ago when he was a child, his family was among those who followed Anne Hutchinson into exile after she'd been charged with another kind of witchcraft in Salem. He's very protective of all of us, even Leona who refuses to associate with people she calls rabble heretics. In some respects, she's a worse snob than your . . . than Harry Pendrath. For a penniless parson's daughter, she's—''

"Before the civil war, her father was well-connected and wealthy. I suppose, like the rest of us, she's had a hard time adjusting. Not everyone has your capacity for . . . for survival.''

Briefly Lynn wondered what it was her husband had intended to say before he hesitated, but she decided she didn't really want to know. In the two days since he'd returned, he'd made no real gesture of reconciliation other than to salve his own guilty conscience by accusing her of infidelity. The only person he'd listened to with sympathy had been Leona Spence, another of the women he considered his social equal. Regretting her impulse to accept his offer of accompanying her on this delivery run, Lynn became brusquely businesslike as she directed him about the mechanics of ringing the bell at the ferry landing and driving the wagon onto the flat barge connected to the heavy hawsers that spanned the river.

"We have a half-hour wait," she announced flatly. "I saw Mr. Ludlow using the bullocks to pull a stump when we passed his farm a few minutes ago; so we might as well be comfortable. There's a fur rug in one of the containers in back and a knapsack of food Polly prepared. I thought we might—"

"Do you mean to tell me that I've been freezing to death unnecessarily?" Clay demanded as he located the designated items. "I was about to ask you to share your cape as we did in Cornwall. I'll be damned. 'Tis the same old cloak; and as I remember, it kept both of us warm on many an occasion."

He's at his best when he's being deliberately companionable, Lynn reflected ruefully, emotionally flustered despite her resolve to maintain an impersonal relationship. As he wrapped her heavy cloak around both their shoulders and tucked the beaver skin rug over their legs, she felt the same fluttery warmth she'd experienced the first time he'd kissed her on that remote Bodmin Moor trail.

"We'll eat later," he murmured into her ear now within inches of his lips. "There's something else we've postponed long enough. Did you really think I was going to let you bargain your way out of marriage to me? And don't waste your time leapfrogging me into legal traps, Trelynn Trevor, or I'll disconnect this barge mid-river and we'll move to the back of the wagon. I dare say, the wooden boards won't be any harder than some of the beds we've slept on together."

As he talked, one of his hands clamped around her waist while the other immobilized her head. He kissed her then, but disconcertingly on the pulse throbbing on her neck in wild agitation, rather than properly on her lips. By the time he corrected his oversight, both of his arms were around her as his kiss deepened to a smothering intensity. His eyes were half-closed with a sensuous anticipation when he finally relaxed his hold and allowed her to catch her breath. During those drugging moments in a close embrace, Clay had made his determination. Once across the river on the island that appeared densely forested, he would reclaim his property well away from the prying eyes and ears of her partisan defenders on the farm. He'd been a fool last night to waste time in argument; the response she'd just given him was proof enough that she remembered as well as he did the uninhibited passion they'd once shared.

Predictably, the capricious laws of Rhode Island winter had altered Clay's plans by the time the ferry deposited the wagon safely on the far shore of the Sakonnet River. In mid-stream a light snow began to fall, and the ferry operator shouted a warning.

"Best turn around and come right back, Mistress Penley. 'Tis not safe to operate this capstan once the snow gets heavy."

"We'll stay the night on Bristol, Mr. Ludlow," Lynn returned the shout.

"Encourage your bullocks to run then, mistress. 'Tis six miles to shelter, and this looks to be more than a flurry."

Having been ignored by the taciturn individual who'd silently hitched a pair of Devon bullocks to the capstan ropes, Clay was decidedly irritated about his wife's high-handed decision. The trees that had seemed a welcoming shelter were now forbiddenly frosted with snow; and to a man who preferred the warmer climates of Virginia and Jamaica, the prospect of a six-mile drive beneath those laden branches was intimidating.

"What kind of an inn can this godforsaken island support?" he demanded gloomily.

"Very primitive," Lynn retorted cheerfully, "we'll be sharing a barn with four bullocks."

"Good God! Why didn't we turn around when we had the chance?"

"Because it was twice as far back to the farm. Jem and Bram stayed overnight in the barn during a storm and said it was snug and comfortable. But since my share of it cost

me a bullock, I wanted to see if it really is. Besides,''
Lynn added with a humor that had been building since
Clay had kissed her, "we'll be able to argue privately
without Polly threatening to add wormwood to your cider.''

"I've no intention of risking another cross word,'' Clay
responded in kind.

"In that case,'' Lynn suggested prosaically, "stop sawing on the reins. Quince and Robin know their way to the
barn better than I do, and they hate snowstorms enough to
make a run for it.''

"Are you telling me that these two great lumbering
rumps have names?''

"Certainly they have names, and they'll resent being
rubbed down by anyone who doesn't use those names with
respect. Robin is the one with the white patch on the
forehead, but Quince is the animal you'll take care of
first.''

"Why, in God's name?''

"He's the pacesetter.''

Despite his interest in things other than a pair of pampered
bullocks, Clay was well aware that the team had doubled
its speed without any signal from him and that the two
animals were still moving in synchronized unity. Having
helped train his childhood pony, he could understand his
wife's defensive pride in her cattle. In ten years since his
father had given her the three heifers, she'd learned more
about breeding and training than most farmers did in a
lifetime. She'd also acquired an impressive number of
other skills in her twenty-two years. His thoughts paused
at the number; she could be twenty-three now if she'd had
a birthday during his absence. Guiltily he remembered that
while he'd replenished his own wardrobe in England, he'd
neglected to purchase so much as a lace kerchief for her;
and he had yet to present her with a single piece of
jewelry. No wonder Polly and Spence held him in contempt; no wonder they resented the legal power he held
over her . . . and her income. Clay added the final three

words unwillingly. They conjured up the images of too many impoverished Cavaliers who'd callously married the daughters and widows of wealthy tradesmen, and then treated those women with scandalous neglect.

Moodily preoccupied with rare self-castigation, Clay roused only when the wagon stopped in front of the wide doors of a compact barn. Startled by the realization that Lynn was holding the reins in her swaddled hands, Clay jumped awkwardly from the snow-covered vehicle and opened the doors, noting as he did so the sturdiness of their construction. Once the wagon was inside and the entry resealed, he noticed other innovations as well. Unlike most English byres whose foul air could smother anyone except nose-hardened farmers, this structure was well ventilated without being drafty. Separated from the animal stalls at the far end by twenty feet of equipment storage area was a partitioned room designed for human occupancy. It was this room that Clay inspected first.

"At least we don't have to sleep in manure," he admitted grudgingly as he tested the thickness of the straw pallet reserved for stranded travelers and checked the chimney structure of the small fireplace. "We won't have to eat cold food either," he added with satisfaction.

For a moment Lynn watched in silence as he set about laying a small fire and spreading the leather blankets over the bed. Sighing in resignation, she loosened the bandages on her hands, released the tired oxen from their confining traces, and led them toward the other pair of bullocks already comfortably ensconced in their stalls. Despite the stiffness of her hands and the soreness of her feet, she rubbed Quince's and Robin's snow-dusted pelts with a practiced efficiency, soothing them with familiar, softly spoken reassurances. Not until they'd been watered and fed did she return to the partitioned room where her husband was coaxing a smoky fire.

Picking up an armful of dry straw and several small logs from the neatly stacked pile, she squatted down beside the frustrated man. "I'll take care of the fire while you fill both of the kettles with clean snow," she ordered him tonelessly.

Irritated by his own ineptitude, Clay rose to do her bidding, returning a few minutes later with his jaw clenched in defensive anger. "Why the devil didn't you wait for me to tend those damned bulls?" he demanded.

"They needed food and rest more than we did," she retorted crisply. "They've been working since early morning; and in this country, we take care of our animals first."

"There's such a thing as pampering them," he rasped.

"None of these animals are pampered; they all work for their keep and care. That other pair of bullocks not only operate the ferry on demand, they are hired out to all of the farmers at this end of Bristol Island, all of those who can hear the bell. Those farmers are the ones who built this barn, and they're still glad to pay for the services of the bullocks. Don't just stand there glaring at me, Clay. Hang the kettles over the fire and fetch the box of provisions from the wagon. I think we both need a mug of cider before we eat."

Again Clay's irritation flared, this time with suspicion. "When did you learn to drink hard spirits?"

"At our barn-raising celebration and at every social event since. The settlers here are especially companionable to newcomers."

"Which one of them beside Spencer Burtram was your special companion?"

"None of them and all of them, but the only couples who ever pair off are newlyweds and those promised to each other. But since you introduced the subject, I'd be interested to know what kind of companion you partnered at all the London parties you and Harry attended."

"What parties?"

"The ones to celebrate your freedom. You certainly didn't buy that beautiful new wardrobe to impress colonials, not even Virginians. I know it wasn't Harry's wife who was with you, but I imagine 'twas some London lady very like her. Was she the one you were thinking about during the last twenty minutes of the drive today?''

''What the devil are you talking about?''

''You didn't even blink when I took over the reins,'' Lynn challenged him crisply, ''so who were you thinking about? I know it wasn't me, because your expression was neither amused nor angry. Was your lady friend really that memorable?''

''There was no lady friend in London or anywhere else,'' he declared with a reckless fury.

Recalling her grandfather's veiled warning in his last letter and Nell's uninhibited revelations about Clay's popularity with women, Lynn greeted his declaration with an ironic smile. ''How lovely to know that you were a good and faithful husband all these months,'' she murmured softly before she reverted to the sharp tones of authority. ''You'd better light one of the lanterns before it gets too dark in here.''

Grateful that her deep brown eyes revealed little of the seething agitation she was experiencing, Lynn returned his glare of baffled anger briefly before she walked to the barn entry and eased herself outside into the chill air of a powdery snow flurry. Hugging the walls of the barn beneath the overhang, she made her way to the crude lean-to shed that housed the water bucket and the oak chamber pot. Not until she'd finished with the more intimate function, did she remove the soiled bandages from her hands, sighing in relief when her fingers flexed with much of their accustomed strength. At least tonight, she would be free from the oppressive ministration of a disinterested husband.

When he'd kissed her aboard the ferry barge, Lynn had been hopeful that at least his passion was sincere. But immediately afterwards he'd retreated into memories she didn't share, memories that turned him into the stranger he'd been since his return. With helpless frustration, she scooped up handfuls of snow and scrubbed her flushed face and reddened hands. Once she reached the safety of her own farm, she vowed silently, she would follow Nell's example and hide in the loft until this self-centered, disturbing man left Rhode Island. Roused from her gloomy introspection by the sound of her name being furiously bellowed from the front of the barn, Lynn saw her husband twenty feet into the open snow, looking worriedly toward the roadway.

"The washroom's around the side," she called out to him as she slipped into the barn. Hissing in irritation, she shoved the skillet of cornbread and cold chicken over the hot coals and filled the two pewter mugs with the hard cider she hoped would be as numbing as the brandy she'd once consumed to ward off the London plague. Without a pause, she pulled a pair of gloves over her hands, picked up her own mug and the small keg of cider, and plumped herself down on the straw pallet. When Clay returned a few minutes later in a predictably explosive mood, she raised her mug in a defiant salute and drained its contents.

"Now you can add drunkenness to the charges against me," she announced and poured herself a second full portion. Her hands were no longer throbbing with pain, and her feet felt warm for the first time in hours.

"Along with stubbornness and stupidity," Clay muttered.

"Oh, I don't know," she retorted with a wayward amusement. "At least I had the sense not to walk out in the snow."

"I thought you might have known the trick of using the wagon ruts to disguise your footprints."

"Where in the world did you think I'd be going?"

"God knows, but you seem determined to avoid me. Tell me, Lynn, would you have shared these accommodations with one of those fat Dutchmen?"

Returning his scowl of disapproval with a taunting smile, Lynn nodded her head. "And with his fat Dutch wife," she admitted flippantly. "The people here may be liberated, but they're not foolish gamblers."

"Some of them are," he snapped. "Why did you take the bandages off your hands? You'll be lucky if they aren't permanently scarred."

Having been worried about that possibility despite Polly's assurance, Lynn's response was unduly caustic. "In that case, you'll remain the undisputed beauty of the Trevor clan. And after tomorrow, you can accompany Harry to Boston and be spared any more concern about me. If you'll take Spence's word that the second Penley farm in Providence is doing well, you can forget about me for another year . . . permanently if your own business is successful. Since you've regained your name, you no longer need the protection of the Penley one; and since you're in possession of most of my money, you no longer need me. So I'd appreciate your leaving without any more pretense or hypocrisy."

"What do you plan to do without me?"

"What I've always done—manage my own life. Of course," she added with sardonic humor, "if you could persuade King Charles to terminate our marriage as he did your sentence, I might be tempted to seek a more suitable husband. But perhaps the king's royal intervention won't prove necessary. When the honorable Charles Clayton Trevor settles down to squiredom on his Virginia estate, I'll announce the untimely demise of Clay Penley and become an available widow. Don't look so shocked. I've heard rumors that there are hundreds of bigamously married men in the colonies, so why not one unattached Cornish woman?"

Clay's lips were pursed in a silent whistle as he studied the vividly bold face of the woman he'd recklessly undervalued. Because she'd tolerated his puerile behavior aboard ship after their marriage, he'd assumed she had accepted its limitations. On their last night together before he'd sailed irresponsibly away, he'd hoped that her attachment to him had developed into a permanent bond. As he watched her now in the dim light of a snowbound barn, he realized that she'd felt no more bound than he had—far less so, if her dramatic declarations were sincere. In spite of his own cavalier neglect, he'd expected her to be waiting for him regardless of the delay. Instead, he'd been greeted by a possessive and antagonistic Spencer Burtram and by a wife who hadn't wanted him to return at all, a wife who'd just casually announced her intention of acquiring a more suitable husband.

"What kind of a husband do you intend to seek?" he inquired with bland deception.

"One quite different from you. When he kisses me, he won't be remembering another woman; he won't accuse me of infidelity to justify his own; and he won't treat me with an aristocrat's contempt for a peasant dairymaid."

"What if I should become that ideal husband?"

Lynn's smile mirrored regret as well as resignation. "Clay, you couldn't stand a year of boredom, much less a lifetime; and the occasional attraction we feel for each other will never be strong enough to overcome your temptation to roam."

There was a glinting determination in the man's eyes as he phrased his next provocative question, "Are you planning to resist that occasional attraction tonight and the rest of the time I *am* here?"

More than any of the other analytical commentaries about their marriage, this one revealed the depth of her conviction that it was a failure. "No. As a matter of fact, I allowed you to accompany me today because I thought you'd forgotten that I'm neither a reluctant nor passive woman. As long as we're still married, I thought that it might even be prudent to conceive a child." A rueful chuckle accompanied her explanatory afterthought. "I've been told by an expert that the ability to bear a healthy child is the only recommendation a widow needs among the wife-hungry men in this or any other colony."

CHAPTER
11

The meal that followed Lynn's candid admission was a stiffly silent one, due mainly to the angry reaction her husband was experiencing. Throughout his fifteen years of association with women, not one of those he'd pursued successfully—not even Amelia Pendrath—had ever treated him with such overbearing arrogance. Yet this farm woman, whom he'd married more for her protection than for his own and who was his social inferior despite her Trevor blood and her obvious talents, had dared to imply that his child could be a useful asset in her quest for another husband. He ignored the facts that he'd planned to use the same unconceived child to keep his wife quiescent during his next prolonged absence, and that his own brief flirtation with bigamy had not been as theoretical as hers. He'd actually gone to the trouble of finding out that the eager widow's fortune had been a hundred times larger than Trelynn Trevor's.

Then what was he doing here where he wasn't wanted, he asked himself furiously; she was making it very easy for him to escape her domination. He could leave this smug colony of farmers and pirates and in a few months

265

time, contrive a believable death for Clay Penley. The only two people who might challenge the rumor were safely in England, and Clay doubted that either his father or Ephraim would fight to reinstate the marriage they'd initially engineered.

He roused briefly from his angry mood when the woman who'd caused it removed the lantern from its hook on the partition wall. "I'm going to check on the animals," she announced softly before she left him in the darkness of the crude room. Although he noted that she was limping, he made no move to relieve her of the chore, remaining stubbornly seated on the pallet. When she returned, her instructions were impersonal reminders. "If you're finished eating, put that metal plate over the fire and extinguish the lantern. I don't want to risk a second disaster." Then, without another word, the infuriating woman spread her cloak over the fur rug and climbed underneath.

"For God's sake," Clay exploded into speech, "aren't you even going to remove those damned wet boots?"

"I can't untie the laces," she admitted stiffly.

"And you were too obstinate to ask for my help," he accused her, "even after last night when I took complete care of you."

"Especially after last night."

"Why not?"

"I don't care to be treated like a half-witted child again."

"So tonight I'll treat you like the half-witted woman you are," he countered with the first faint smile he'd worn since the ferry barge. "You were the one who fell asleep last night," he reminded her as he removed first one and then the other of her heavy boots. He added laconically, "Your skirt is also damp; do you want it on or off?"

Since he'd already unlaced her bodice, skirts, and petticoats, the question was academic; and by the time her damp clothes were festooned over the partition wall,

Lynn's attire consisted of a soft linen underblouse and pantaloons. When Clay joined her beneath the fur robe, he was similarly clad, but dissimilarly shivering from the cold.

"I can understand why a wife is a necessity in New England," he grumbled as he caressed her warm legs with his icy feet.

"Hot bricks wrapped in flannel are more efficient," Lynn murmured.

"That depends on the wife. Would you care to prove your boast that you'd make a good one for some backwoods Rhode Island bumpkin?"

"If you're referring to yourself, the answer is 'go to sleep.' I've heard enough argument for one day."

"Then stop arguing and start acting like a wife instead of a virginal spinster."

Despite her resentment over the petulance of his complaint, Lynn giggled involuntarily; he was an illogical man, as incapable of accepting blame for his own faults and oversights as a meandering tomcat.

"I will," she challenged him, "provided you stop pretending to be an abused husband or a husband at all. At least in bed, let's be honest with each other."

Seconds later Lynn discovered that whatever kind of husband he was, he was capable of violence. The hands that gripped her now and shoved her pantaloons roughly down her legs made no attempt at the gentler seduction he'd always employed before, and the heavy strength with which he pinned her into the resilient straw threatened to smother her. As swift in her reactions as Clay had been in his attack, Lynn used both hands to push his head away from her face.

"I can't breathe," she gasped and gasped again as he drove into her with a force that momentarily immobilized her. Had he not paused long enough to mutter an apology and to roll over on his back pulling her atop him, their reunion might have ended abruptly. Even so, Lynn was barely able to catch her breath before her own sensibilities were overwhelmed by his fierce passion. Adjusting to the novelty of the position and to the altered rhythm that gave her a measure of control, she experienced a wild exhilaration, a sensation of floating in spite of the strong hands that held her hips firmly bound to the man moving powerfully beneath her. Without any signalled warning, his arms pulled her downward, and his seeking lips found hers just as he climaxed. She was still shuddering with her own ecstasy when she collapsed on top of him.

"Was that honest enough for you, witch woman?" he demanded softly a minute later. As she tried to pull away, his arms tightened. "Just stay where you are, Trelynn Trevor," he murmured. " 'Tis the first time I've been warm in three days, and the first time I've raised such a sweat since our last night aboard ship."

Lynn held back the question that raced through her head, Just what kind of a sweat did you raise all of the times in between then and now? Instead she mumbled evasively, "We'd better get some sleep, Clay."

"I'm not sleepy."

"You will be in the morning when George Fulton comes to roust us out at dawn. This is his working barn."

"Why on God's green earth do farmers feel compelled to start work at dawn?"

"You'd know the answer if those four bullocks were cows in need of milking. Besides, if you still want to go to Providence, we'll need to be underway while the trails are still frozen and the Narragansett River is still calm."

Restlessly Clay rolled away from the woman he'd been holding, and his voice lost its amused cajolery. "Don't you ever think about anything but work?"

"It has to be done."

"Then hire more workers. I don't want a laborer for a wife."

"What kind do you want?"

"Someone who doesn't hide from me whenever I return from a voyage, and someone who doesn't make me jump through hoops when I want a little simple entertainment."

"Then you should have accepted Amelia's invitation; she's—"

"I'm damned tired of telling you that I had nothing to do with Amelia."

"And I'm just as tired of being reminded that I'm a cloddish frump who doesn't meet any of your specifications. But let me tell you something, greenhorn; I'm going to become the most successful clod in this colony with or without your cooperation or permission." Simultaneously, with the final word of her defiant vow, Lynn threw off the covers and swung her bare legs over the side of the pallet.

"God's truth, woman," Clay cursed violently as he dragged her backward, "you have the devil's own temper. Where did you think you were going?"

"To sleep with my bullocks. They're not as particular as you."

"That's because they're gelded; but I'm not, Trelynn Trevor, and the sooner you get used to the idea, the better."

As abruptly as Lynn's temper had flared, it subsided. Shivering with cold, she curled back into the warm cocoon she left. "Was that the kind of entertainment you meant?" she asked bluntly.

"What the devil kind did you think I wanted?"

Shrugging defensively, she snapped out the words with a long-stored bitterness, "Pretty clothes and pretty manners, vicious chatter about other people, and a simpering pretense of helplessness even when you're as well-armed with poison as a rattlesnake. Someone with a witty enough tongue to slash their opponents to ribbons. Someone like your . . . your brother Averill's wife."

"I don't expect any of those things, especially nothing

like my sister-in-law's nasty conceit. How well did you know Barbara?''

"Well enough to despise her."

"Did you attend any of her parties while you were living on my father's estate?''

"I wasn't invited; but I'm certain that had she been asked, she would have signed the petition against me."

"What really happened while you were there, Lynn?''

"I overheard her screeching at your father, but I didn't know why she hated me until I learned you were Sir Bevil's son. When did your father first ask you to marry me, Clay?''

" 'Tis ancient history now and unimportant. How was I to know that the rustic neighborhood witch was a fiery woman?''

Indistinctly mumbled against the pulse throbbing in her neck, Clay's foolish question did little to dispel Lynn's doubts; but his demanding passion aroused a primitive response from deep within her own intense, half-tamed nature. There was no logic in her love for this man, no assurance of permanency, no certainty of security. There was only a need to possess and be possessed. Her body that had cooled to an icy rejection after their first violent reunion now throbbed with a hunger more compelling than any emotion she'd ever experienced. With a fierce compulsion she burrowed deeper into his encircling arms and sought his lips with a pulsing ardor that transcended mere physical sensuality.

Whatever the difference in her response this time, Clay was too experienced not to realize that he'd broken through her guard, and that she was offering him far more than she ever had before. He didn't try to analyze his own pounding excitement as he welcomed her. Only afterward did he recall the long-ago advice he'd received from a ship's captain. "Aye, lad," the man had told him as they'd emerged together from a discreet brothel in Bordeaux, "I'm driven to use them the same as you whenever I reach

safe harbor. But 'tis a sorry sham compared to being with
a woman who loves you."

At eighteen, Charles Clay hadn't believed in love; at
thirty-one, he hoped that he wasn't merely spinning cobwebs about the enigmatic woman sleeping peacefully by
his side, her legs still entwined with his. From their first
time together, she'd been the most satisfying partner he'd
ever known; but he'd played the fool because he hadn't
wanted to be bound permanently to any woman, certainly
not to an Amazon warrior with her physical strength and
mental control. Now he wasn't certain that he'd have the
willpower to leave her long enough to fill the contracts
he'd already made with Andrew Pendrath. His father had
been right; it was time for him to settle into a permanent
marriage. And God knows, even in this primitive barn
amid a snowy wilderness, he could find no fault with the
prospect of spending his life in the company of this
passionate and challenging witch woman.

To Lynn's embarrassment, Clay awakened long before
she did the following morning. Prompted by a rare mood
of contentment, he'd felt inspired enough to disprove his
wife's accusation that he was a greenhorn. Having survived as a younger man through several enforced sojourns
in more savage Caribbean settlements, Clay had no real
doubts about his ability to prosper in this not too primitive
wilderness. He surprised both his wife and the prickly
George Fulton by doing a creditable job of hitching the
bullocks and helping in the cleanup of the barn. He
displayed an even more impressive knowledge when he
advised Fulton that the capstans that operated the ferries
should be raised two feet for easier turning.

"Why?" the Rhode Island man demanded brusquely.
"It works all right the way 'tis. Any higher and the ropes
mid-river could be snagged by boat traffic."

"Not if you slacken the ropes twenty more feet. Right
now you're working your animals too hard; and yesterday,

even with an almost empty wagon, your ferry barge bucked some in the current.''

George Fulton glared at the man whom his father had called an aristocratic parasite, and he nodded curtly without openly admitting that Clay was right. Twice already there'd been near accidents when the barges had almost foundered in the surging currents of the Sakonnet and Narragansett rivers. Fulton's farewell actually held a hint of reappraisal after Clay had described a more secure method for anchoring the capstans.

At the Spragues' mill site, Clay startled his wife even more profoundly. Because Bert Spence knew nothing about mechanics, Lynn had assumed Clay was equally ignorant. Instead, he understood the intricate functions of the gears and waterwheels; and his eyes lost their customary contempt for the working world as he studied the separate arrangements for lumber and grain.

Lynn knew that part of his interest was due to Will Sprague's recognition of the "young laird" and his subsequent respectful attitude. While all the Spragues called Lynn by name or by the appellation "the lass here," their mode of addressing Clay was strictly formal. When he mentioned casually that his Connecticut land had swifter water power and a thousandfold more trees, he received such avid attention that Lynn was instantly on guard when Clay asked Will if he knew anyone in England who might be interested in establishing a mill similar to this one.

"My oldest brother and Da aren't happy where they are," Will responded promptly.

"Why not?" Clay demanded. "My father never mistreats his tenants."

"The old laird is seldom there, and the young one—" Will stopped talking in sudden embarrassment.

"What about my brother?" Clay prodded sharply.

"Naught against the young laird," the miller replied heavily. " 'Tis his wife. The lass here always treated us fairly, but that one—"

"What did she do?" Clay prompted.

"Treated all of us like bondsmen and our women like servants. Once she tried to order the lass here t' wait table during one of her parties for her roughshod Devon kinsfolk, and Da says she's more demanding than ever without Lynn's sharp tongue t' keep her in check."

Glancing briefly at his wife, Clay nodded in understanding. "I'll speak to my father when I return to England," he promised Will.

" 'Twill do no good. Da's already set his mind on the colonies."

"Then I'll be talking to you again before I leave. In the meantime, are my wife and I supposed to deliver that lumber stacked over there?"

"Aye, 'tis marked for delivery, half to Providence and half to New Port. But the lass here is not fit for heavy work with those burned hands of hers, and 'tis not proper for you t' do such rough labor."

"I didn't think there was any other kind in this colony," Clay murmured, responding to Lynn's sardonic expression with warm humor. "I can manage that load," he assured Will Sprague more soberly. "I've done enough hard labor in my time."

"Aye, just before we left Plymouth, the old laird told us about your troubles at the same time he told us you'd be wedding the lass here. Sir, will you be staying in the colony now that you've come back?"

"Long enough," Clay answered briefly and then asked, "Will, do you do any trading with the local Indians?"

"Aye, ever since Bert . . . Mr. Spence talked them into letting us cut one of their trees for every wagonload of their corn we milled, leastwise three villages of them agreed. My brother's there now in the nearest village marking the tree they promised us: hard pine and two hundred feet as straight as an arrow. I'll be joining Roy tomorrow to help with the cutting and to deliver the cornmeal."

"What kind of people are these Indians, Will?"

"Reverend Williams calls them his brothers, and I reckon they're as civilized as we are once you get used to their ways."

"What would happen if my wife and I took their food to them instead of you?"

"They know the lass here well enough; and Indians like company same as the rest of us during winter. Good thing for us they do; 'tis the only time we can sled the logs out. But you'd best be prepared to stay the night. The sachem arrived there to watch us fell the tree tomorrow, and he's a rare one for asking questions."

"This sachem is the village chieftain?"

"More like the head of the whole tribe, and smart enough to make a body feel like a scat-brained cully if you pretend to knowing more than you do."

"Does he speak English?"

"Aye, and well. But the lass here is learning their tongue, so 'tis likely you'll get along with the others same as with his nibs."

"Good. Let's get the wagon loaded."

Throughout this remarkable conversation, which had so neatly excluded her, Lynn had stood slightly apart, preoccupied with the same thoughts that had plagued her since Clay had awakened her this morning. Already fully clothed, he had managed to light the fire and arrange the leftover food in the warming skillet. Silently, but with hands that were boldly caressing, he'd helped her dress. Still wary that his relaxed humor was only condescending pretense despite his passionate possession of her much of the night, Lynn steeled herself against the hope that he intended any permanency. Realistically, she was convinced that once he left this small, isolated world, he would revert easily to his old adventurism; and she would once again be the safely forgotten wife. As genuine as his interest in the ferry mechanism and mill operation seemed, she suspected that he was merely playacting the interested husband. But the proposed trip to an Indian village baffled her enough to break her imposed silence.

"Why in the world would you want to go there, Clay?" she asked.

"'Tis where your Reverend Williams has threatened to hide you, and I wanted to find out if I'd approve of the idea."

"Clay, compared to an Indian village, the barn we used last night was a luxurious accommodation; and there's no available shelter for the bullocks. They can't stay out in—"

"'Twill be no problem, Lynn," Will interrupted eagerly. "Roy is still a bairnie when it comes to staying away from home at night, and he'll be glad of the ride back. Your bullocks will be housed with ours in a snug byre tonight."

"Where's your sense of adventure, Lynn?" Clay challenged her. "I've a wish to meet these primitives of yours, and 'twill be an experience to tell our grandchildren."

What adventure there was at the Indian village was a two-day vacation from work for Clay and just the reverse for Lynn. Accompanied by the sachem himself and a half-dozen braves, Clay had gone on a hunting trip for the small herd of half-starved deer he and Lynn had seen along the crude trail. Hours later the triumphant hunters returned with the carcasses of two deer, which they dumped in front of the bark shed where the women were preparing the communal dinner. While the men proceeded happily to the long, fire-warmed, bark-covered structure reserved for the sachem's use whenever he was in residence, the women began the task of skinning, cleaning, and butchering.

Lynn's own afternoon had been vastly different. Except for a brief glance of recognition from the sachem, she'd been ignored at the initial greeting of the tall Englishman with the magnificently plumed hat. Instead she'd been roughly pulled aside by one of the older women she vaguely remembered.

"Chénock wonch Jem Rigg cuppeeyeâumen?" the agitated squaw demanded.

"Nétop tatta," Lynn replied vaguely, wondering why Jem's presence was so urgently sought.

She discovered the reason when she was led to an animal pen where an aging cow was in dire straits with a rump-first calf trapped in its womb. Pausing only long enough to remove her cloak and to order the older woman to grease her right arm and hand, Lynn set to work, hopelessly aware of the weakened condition of the cow. Inch by inch, she pushed and pulled the still-alive calf until her arm felt torn from its socket. Two hours later she yanked the tired bull calf onto the hay, tore the smothering membrane from the struggling creature's body, and sank down beside it on the damp straw. To her horror, one of the younger women grabbed the calf's head, and Lynn was just in time to prevent its killing.

In a muddled conversation of Narragansett and English, Lynn learned that Indians never emasculated the male of any species; and the prospect of an adult, unrestrained bull roaming among the flimsy buildings was untenable. Lynn hesitated for only the moment it took her to determine the health of the calf and then offered a heifer in exchange. Her business was dependent upon bullocks; the Indians needed a future source of milk. Aroused from exhaustion by the need to provide survival for the cow and calf, she told the older woman that some kind of protective shelter would have to be constructed around the pair. Within an hour she knew what Roger Williams had never written in his accounts of these Indians; the women were the builders!

Lashing slender logs together into a mobile framework that they placed over the animals, three of the younger women quickly covered the structure with long pieces of bark secured into place with lengths of leather thonging. Only after the calf was nursing lustily did Lynn think to look down at her bloodied and filthy dress. She made no protest when the women led her into a bark wigwam where a central fire pit was glowing red with hot coals placed around a blackened iron pot full of steaming water. Hesitating only momentarily in the presence of the several women crowded into the small interior, Lynn stripped off her clothing—even her pantaloons were reeking with the fetid gore of afterbirth—and washed her body vigorously. Forgetting both modesty and embarrassment, she ripped a piece of linen from her underskirt, and dipped it repeatedly into the hot water until she finally felt both clean and warm.

The fact that the only garments she had left to wear were her cloak and boots didn't particularly bother her; she'd already decided to return to the Spragues' mill with Roy. Wrapping her cloak securely around her, she sat down to tug the boots over her reddened feet. It was then her silent audience stirred into life. At the guttural command of the older woman, one of the squaws produced a container of aromatic grease and began to rub it over Lynn's hands and feet. Recognizing enough of their words to know that these Indian women were no strangers to burns, she submitted to having her feet and hands bound in soft leather wrappings, demurring only when they pulled her to her feet, untied her cloak, and slipped a shapeless leather dress over her head. By the time knee-high boots were added to the costume, Lynn felt more Indian than white and uncomfortably aware that she was being honored.

All ceremony stopped, however, when she was trooped along with the Indian women and handed a heavy wood salver loaded high with what she recognized as *nokehick,* the flat rounds of cornbread drizzled with maple syrup that Polly misnamed hoecake. Another woman carried a tray of roasted butternut squash, which the older squaw called *asquutasquash,* while others bent with the weight of iron pots filled with hominy and deer stew. Silently the women filed into the sachem's quarters where all the village men were now gathered, and just as silently deposited the food in front of the individual groups and then left the building.

Only the one white man paid them any attention, and Lynn noted with irritation that his eyebrow was raised in amusement. She also noted that his elegant plumed hat was now firmly set on the graying head of the sachem.

That was the last Lynn saw of her husband until she awakened in the bark wigwam to find him sleeping heavily beside her as fully clothed as she was. Without rousing him, she walked outside to find a young girl waiting to escort her down the well-worn trail to the latrinelike trenches that served as the women's half of the village privy. Since anything resembling privacy was impossible, Lynn used the facilities and then walked far enough afield to locate a bank of clean snow. Removing the leather bindings from her hands, she sighed in relief; whatever native medicine had been in the grease, it had worked a miracle of healing. Lynn felt newly liberated when she returned to the wigwam and stirred Clay awake.

"'Tis time for your next adventure, husband. The Spragues are here and asking for your help in keeping your Indian friends safely out of reach while they fell the tree."

Groaning as he sat up, Clay rubbed his back. "My God, this ground is hard. Why didn't you put pine needles underneath?"

"By the time the women were allowed to eat, 'twas too dark. What did you and the honorable sachem talk about until all hours?"

"He told me what you did to save the cow."

"How would he know? I didn't think the men and women here ever spoke to each other."

"If you'd returned to the lodge with the other squaws, you'd have discovered they do considerably more than talk." Grinning at her as he stood up, he put his arms around her. "If you hadn't looked like a forest priestess when you served our dinner, I'd have been tempted to fetch you and join the celebration."

"You might have considered coming here earlier," Lynn

retorted with a glint of humor. "Even Indian newlyweds are allowed some privacy."

Clay's expression became abruptly serious. "No, I couldn't have, Lynn. I've learned enough about Indians to know that when you're their guest, you follow their rules. We'll be leaving here as soon as I've talked to the Spragues."

They left mid-afternoon after hours of hard labor shared with everyone in the village except the male elders and the youngest children. Soon after the forest giant crashed to the ground, the Indian men used their steel-headed war axes, imported from England, to hew the branches away while the women used smaller tomahawks to strip the bark. Nothing was wasted, not the needles nor the smallest twig. Every branch the Spragues ruled too small for milling was chopped into building lengths and piled on the wagon along with the bundles of faggots and the sacks of needles the children gathered. Six times Lynn drove the wagon to and from the village with the precious stockpiles of supplies that would increase the margin of survival for the villagers. By midday the skeletal remains of the symmetrical tree lay glisteningly bare in the snow, already sawed into eight twelve-foot lengths and one sleek hundred-foot long bole that would someday become the mainmast for an oceangoing ship.

With the manpower of twenty Indians and three white men, the first massive log was rolled onto the heavy wood sledge; and the four patient bullocks began the ordeal of dragging it the three miles to the mill. Left alone with the women who were no longer strangers, Lynn continued to work with them until the older squaw whom she had now identified as the sachem's village wife, ordered Lynn's hands to be regreased and rewrapped. Afterward her contributions were only verbal warnings about the cow and calf; the cow was to be kept sheltered, fed heavily, and milked only once a day for two months until its bull calf could be safely weaned and replaced by a young heifer.

In mid-afternoon after the second huge tree-trunk log

had been secured to the sledge, Clay climbed briskly aboard the wagon to drive the load of smaller logs through the narrow forest trail. Not until they reached the Spragues' cabin did Lynn discover that her Indian friends had given her another gift: a small white fur so luxurious she gasped with pleasure.

Clay's response was a low whistle. "'Tis winter ermine," he told her. "A shipload of them to the royal court would bring us a lifetime fortune."

Lynn smiled and shook her head. This one she would keep as a souvenir of her two days as an Indian squaw.

Arriving back at the Penley farm after three nights and four days away, Lynn glowed with an illogical happiness. Although Clay had made no commitment of any reliable worth, his enthusiasm now seemed centered on Connecticut and lumbering rather than on slavery profits. And in the snug, dry grain loft of the Spragues' mill the night just passed, he'd been unrestrained in lovemaking, despite his aching muscles. Both with the Spragues and with the Providence cooper awaiting his supply of flexible oak staves, Clay had been openly friendly. Without the sweeping hat that more than any other accoutrement of dress marked the Cavalier, he'd seemed more New Englander than Virginian in his cheerful talk of trade and commerce. As satisfying as these small signs of change had been to Lynn, his actions in the more sophisticated town of New Port had delighted her. As he'd driven down the windy embarcadero toward the shipwright's work yard, Clay had again shared her cloak and kept one arm tightly around her waist even while they talked to the crusty Mr. Bigelow.

While workmen unloaded the lumber from the wagon, Bigelow wasted no time in polite conversation. "Mr. Spence tells me your mill will be cutting hard pine this next week, mistress. I want the lot of it."

"Then you can talk to my husband about the sale tomorrow. He knows more than Mr. Spence does about the wood and the cutting of it. But I warn you, 'twill be expensive."

"Aye, but if 'tis good wood, I'll have to pay. There's been no hard pine hereabouts for a year. How big a tree, Mr. Penley, and how much board feet will it supply?"

Still sharing her cloak on the drive home, Clay was thoughtful. "Spence won't appreciate my interfering, Lynn."

"He didn't help cut that tree down, you did; and you know more about milling than he does."

Clay had only grunted his response; but impulsively, he'd bent his head down to kiss her cheek. Outside the barn, he'd lifted her to the ground and grinned broadly at her. "I'll make an adventurer out of you yet, Trelynn Trevor; you've got enough daring for the pair of us," he murmured.

Before Lynn could ask his meaning, a dour-faced Jem Rigg stepped out from the barn, beckoned them inside, and pointed to the three new calves: all placid, unmistakable heifers. Amused by the irony of this small fate, Lynn told him about the Indian bull calf and suggested that he choose the best of these three for the trade. Smiling at the glum-faced stockman, she assured him lightly, "The female of the species does have its uses, Jem."

When she learned about the fourth birth that had taken place while she and Clay were absent, Lynn had no such flippant answer, however. Within an hour much of her glowing optimism had been replaced by a less pleasant reality. Looking unkempt and worried, Bert Spence and Kate Horton met them outside the cabin they occupied. While Bert and Clay stepped aside for a more private conference, Kate exploded into angry speech.

"She's as full of milk as a dairy cow, but she's too mule-stubborn to nurse her own daughter."

"Was it a difficult birth, Kate?"

"No harder than most, she just squalled more. She caterwauled a whole day before she even started labor pains, and then Polly and me had a devil of a time getting her to do a thing to help herself. 'Tis a wonder we got the babe out at all, much less in good shape; but now that little tyke's in real trouble, Lynn, and weakening fast. Poor Bert's at his wit's end, and I'm wore out trying to get that mite to take a drop of cow's milk. I don't expect you'll have any better luck with that fool woman, but I wish you'd try.''

''Use Nell's bedroom and get some sleep, Kate. I'll take over here,'' Lynn promised grimly.

Her jaw was clamped shut as she entered the small cabin and surveyed the evidence of Kate's unceasing work. A small wooden infant bed sat in the middle of the table surrounded by piles of infant garments, which Lynn suspected Kate had made. Festooned on ropes suspended across a corner of the room were freshly washed bedding, diapers, and feminine clothing. Briefly Lynn glanced at the tiny body mewling fitfully in her bed before she strode purposefully into the rear room.

''Where's Kate?'' Leona greeted her peevishly.

''I sent her to bed, and she won't be returning,'' Lynn retorted crisply. ''That infant in the other room is your job, not Kate's. Do you want me to bring your daughter to you, or are you planning to let her starve to death?''

Leona's reaction was a furious protest. ''You talk to my husband about neglect, not to me! I told him months ago to have a wet nurse available. Not that I expect someone like you to understand, but I am not going to be disfigured for life when there are hundreds of colonial peasants who can be hired to nurse that baby. Now that my title has been restored, I refuse to act like a common mill hand. Spencer knew how I felt, and he did nothing to supply me with that one simple amenity. Would you kindly leave me now, and ask him to come in here. Perhaps by this time, he will have come to his senses.''

Lynn stared at the petulant face glaring at her amid a welter of pillows and burst into harsh laughter. ''I'll send for him after I've had my say,'' she asserted firmly. ''I've tolerated your laziness and lack of cooperation all these months because I didn't want you to lose your child. But your position, Lady Burtram, is still only that of an incompetent beggar, and your illusions of grandeur are ridiculous. You can't return to England because you were a convicted criminal, and here in New England your husband's title is a liability. Spence will make money in time, but only provided you don't drag him down to your level. Right now he's a tired and discouraged man who doesn't know what to do with a child or with a wife who refuses to tend that child."

"If he had any gumption," Leona snapped, "he'd take me to Virginia where Harry has promised us enough money to live decently among people of our own kind. I refuse to raise my daughter among the heathenish people in this God-forsaken wilderness."

"God isn't forsaking that little girl in the other room, Leona; you are! But I'm not going to let her die just because she has a selfish fool for a mother. If you still refuse to do your duty, I will take her to my friends in an Indian village where the women are more generous and more civilized."

Leona began to scream even before Lynn left the room, and her piercing shrieks, interspersed with curses that the daughter of a high placed minister should not have known, reverberated through the small frame house. Smiling with contempt, Lynn closed the door firmly and turned her attention to the infant child whose weaker screams were far more disturbing. With competent speed that belied her complete inexperience with human young, Lynn checked the freshness of the milk in the small crock, scrubbed her hands in the basin of water, and cradled the infant in her arms. With the same technique she'd used to feed newborn calves, she dipped the rolled edge of a clean diaper into the milk and forced the soaking material into the small mouth. Seconds later the tiny human child was sucking as ravenously as Red Penny once had, and Lynn's smile became one of satisfaction. Humans were no different from animals when it came to survival, she reflected with warm humor as she watched the small face contorting with the vigorous exercise of nursing.

She didn't glance up as two worried men burst into the room, pounded across the wooden floor, and jostled against each other as they shoved their way into the bedroom. The screams stopped instantly, and a sobbing, high-pitched speech began. Bert was the first one to return to the main room and to sit down wearily on the bench opposite Lynn.

Making no attempt to explain his wife's behavior, he nodded toward the spectacle of his daughter eating her first meal. "Kate and I have taken turns trying to feed her for two days and a night, but we couldn't spoon a drop into her. Where did you learn that trick?"

"Jem and I have lost a few cows along the way, but we saved every live-born calf. I think both kinds of young have to suck on something before they can swallow. Did Leona tell you my suggestion?"

A cynical smile lighted Bert's face momentarily. "That was the first, second, and third scream you heard. But the Indian village won't be necessary, Lynn; I located a woman in town today."

"Had Leona told you before that she wouldn't nurse a child?"

"She began telling me six months ago to locate a wet nurse, and she wanted someone just like the pathetic nanny who relieved her own mother of the chore. I tried to tell her that this wasn't England, and that we were nothing but poor servants now ourselves. But Leona hasn't matured a jot since her fifteenth birthday; she still believes that wishing will make all of her childish dreams come true."

"Why did Clay remain in the room with her?"

"As you've undoubtedly learned by this time, Clay can charm any woman he's ever met into a state of abject agreement; and he's always had a protective attitude about Leona. But this is one time I hope he fails."

Unpleasantly reminded that she'd become one of those easily manipulated women, Lynn asked dully, "Why should you, Spence? Your daughter needs a mother."

Shaking his head in defeat, Bert responded bluntly, "Leona will never stop thinking about her own disappointments long enough to become a good mother to any child . . . or a good wife." Changing the subject abruptly, he asked more calmly, "What do you think of the name of Jane for her?"

Lynn looked down at the child still sucking lustily and nodded her approval. "It has a solid Rhode Island ring to it. Did Leona agree?"

"I didn't ask her because I don't think she'll be around long enough to care. Harry wants to take her to Virginia to keep another useless woman company."

"Amelia will make her into a servant," Lynn warned.

"No, only an obedient and servile companion. Amelia suffers from the delusion that standing next to Leona in public makes her appear more dramatically beautiful."

"Amelia *is* a beautiful woman, Spence."

"She used to be, but she isn't anymore. That's one of the reasons she hates you so intensely, because you make her look like the overage, prinked-up whore she is; and she's damned afraid that Clay will eventually recognize the difference between you."

Lynn sucked her breath in sharply and glanced up in time to see her husband regarding her with narrowed eyes from the bedroom doorway.

"Take the child to your wife, Spence. She's agreed to perform the chore until you can make other arrangements."

"You take young Jane in, Clay," Bert replied with a laconic irony. "I'm certain Leona will appreciate the gesture more from you than from me."

For a moment Clay was too startled to protest, but finally he approached Lynn and held out his arms. Equally surprised by his response, she gently handed him the small blanket-wrapped bundle and giggled with amusement as he stiffened his arms to receive the child.

"She's not a roasted turkey, Clay, and she won't bite you. Cuddle her next to your body." Lynn's breath caught painfully as she watched her husband follow her instructions and direct his smile involuntarily downward.

"God's truth, she's too little to cause so much trouble," he mumbled, adding impulsively, "I'd like our first child to be a son, Lynn."

Recalling her rash boast of a few nights ago, Lynn shivered with cold apprehension. The ability to bear children might be a good recommendation for a widow; but for a wife without a husband in attendance, the burden would be too inhibiting. As she studied the accumulated paraphernalia needed for one infant, she shuddered anew. If she were tied down to a houseful of children, she'd be unable to earn the money for their support. Not for the first time, Lynn wished she'd been born a man with the broader option of being able to sail away from responsibilities as Clay and Harry had done or to ship an unsatisfactory wife to another colony as Bert proposed.

"What happens now, Spence?" she asked curiously.

"I'll wager you that Leona leaves on schedule. She'll soon tire of the demands of motherhood, and 'tis always her nature to take the easier way. But this isn't your problem, Lynn. In a few days I'll move her and the babe into town."

"There aren't any houses available in New Port."

"We'll be renting two rooms from the woman I told you about."

"Who is she, Spence?"

"Elwin Carter's daughter. Her husband was the captain of the Carter ship that went down last December. They need the money, and the house is large enough for two families."

"What about his daughter?"

"Like you, she doesn't ask for pity even though she was left to raise her infant son alone."

"I don't know whether I'd have that kind of courage," Lynn murmured thoughtfully.

"You?" Bert demanded with a smile. "I'd hate to be the one who threatened any child of yours. I've watched you with your animals and with my own daughter a few minutes ago. I only wish Leona had a hundredth of your spirit."

"Perhaps she would if you flattered her as much as you do my wife," Clay suggested quietly from across the room. "Leona wants to see you, Spence. I imagine she wants your agreement on a promise I made her."

"You're losing your charm, Clay. You didn't need to bribe women in the old days. What did you promise her?"

"An indentured woman or a slave, depending on where you intend to settle. You know damn well Leona can't take care of a child without help. She's never done any hard work, and she's—"

"She's too damned lazy to try," Bert interrupted harshly as he shook his head in resignation. "You're a gullible fool, Clay. You let your own wife do harder physical labor than most men, but you cater to the self-centered women you consider your social equals. Don't bother about the servant. Leona won't be needing one, and I'll take care of my daughter. I think you'll find that my *helpless* wife has already made plans to *help* herself."

On their way to their own cottage, Clay's pleasant humor of the past four days vanished. "What plans was Spence talking about?" he demanded of his own wife.

" 'Tis his business, not ours, Clay. Leona hasn't adjusted well to this new life."

"She wouldn't have to if Spence would use his head and accept the job the Pendraths are offering him. I know Leona's weak, but she's just undergone a late-in-life child-birth. And you frightened the devil out of her. Why did you find it necessary to threaten her with that Indian nonsense?''

Lynn shrugged restlessly and remained silent. She was far more preoccupied with the ironic truth of Bert's revealing accusation. Despite all of his glib gallantry of the past few days, her husband still considered her a social inferior.

''While we're on the subject of Indians,'' Clay persisted, ''you're to change from that damned squaw dress. I'm tired of seeing you look like a primitive.''

The last of Lynn's optimistic hopes shriveled and died. ''I'll remember to wear silk the next time you insist on my accompanying you into the wilderness,'' she murmured expressionlessly. She was five feet ahead of him before he could grab her arm and pull her to a halt.

''I didn't mean to criticize you, Lynn; I was just upset about Spence's treatment of Leona and about his—''

''He had more important things on his mind. If you'll excuse me, Clay, I'm going to help Polly with supper. She hasn't had much sleep lately.''

''Damn it, Lynn, I was just trying to help.''

An understanding fairness forced Lynn to agree. ''I know you were, Clay,'' she admitted softly.

Whether or not her husband was aware of her tacit withdrawal during the fortnight following the unpleasant scene with Leona, Lynn couldn't be sure since his schedule had become as busy as hers. Preoccupied with supervising the milling of the hard pine to the shipwright's specification, he made four separate trips to the Spragues' mill, accompanied by Lynn on only the first one. After Bert moved his family into New Port, Clay visited his old friend each morning and volunteered to fill in for Jem on the delivery runs. This particular consideration puzzled Lynn until she learned that her husband had ordered the stockman not to sell any of the bull calves.

On that occasion Polly had asked suspiciously, "Is his nibs planning to settle down here?"

"I don't think so, Polly."

"Then why in tarnation did he tell Jem he wanted all future bullocks trained for lumber work?"

"I suppose he plans to put the rest of the Spragues to work on his Connecticut land."

"You going with him this time?"

"No, I'll be staying here."

"If you're not careful, he's going to strip you clean, girl, and then dance out of here like old light-o'foot hisself. He sure hasn't paid you much never-mind since you lit into her ladyship with a well-earned tongue lashin'. And you've been acting as close-faced as your grandpa whenever you talk to him. Did you finally get over your foolishness for him or are you jest playactin'?"

"We're good friends," Lynn had assured the older woman before she'd fled from the cottage to avoid any more prying questions. Ironically, her answer had been close to the truth except for the nights she spent with Clay in bed. During the daytime hours they were together, their conversation was pleasantly devoid of friction since Lynn avoided any hint of argument. At night Clay's passion easily overrode her token resistance; that much of a marriage, at least, Lynn would have to remember. There were moments during those two weeks when she almost succumbed to the temptation of hope, but even that faint euphoria was vanquished on the Sunday morning when Harry Pendrath returned from Boston a week ahead of schedule.

Alone in the cottage with Clay since everyone else was attending church in Portsmouth, Lynn fled to the bedroom when she recognized Harry's booming voice outside. For the next hour while she dressed and tidied the room, that booming voice bounced against the walls; and she was a captive eavesdropper to a conversation she would never forget entirely. Harry described the Boston market in detail, cursing repeatedly the pair of "Roundhead scoundrels'' who'd already cornered the Massachusetts slave trade.

"We'll have to hop lively if we're to get the New York and Virginia trade. Those damnable hypocrites are well enough funded to outbid us in all of the colonies. Did your wife give you enough brass to make up your share of our capital?"

"She's been very generous," Clay responded vaguely. "I hate to—"

"Damn it, man, you have no choice. Three thousand is the smallest amount Andrew will accept, and you know it. Even so, we'll be stretched thin. Take the money, Clay; 'tis yours by right anyway. Can you get your hands on it without her knowing?"

From the bedroom Lynn strained to hear her husband's answer; his hesitant yes ended her unwilling eavesdropping. Picking up her ancient cloak and, as an afterthought, her clubs, she climbed out of her window as silently as she had on the night of the fire. Pausing in the barn only long enough to inspect the six cows that hadn't as yet calved, she left by the rear door to walk across the fields to the Fulton home. Two hours later she was in the kitchen with Nell and Janet Fulton when Clay and Harry were ushered into the study; and for the second time that day she eavesdropped. It was a brief, unfriendly meeting that Edward Fulton conducted and controlled.

"Is my wife here, Mr. Fulton?" Clay demanded.

"The lass? She's generally at church of a Sunday, Mr. Penley."

"Not today she isn't. Have you any idea where she might have gone?"

"Well now, she and Bert sometimes work on company records even on the Lord's day, Mr. Penley. You might try the Carter house in New Port; 'tis the large one near the Carter sheds. Would there be anything you want?"

"I'll be taking my wife's money with me."

"Aye, Bert said you'd need two thousand."

"I need the three thousand, Mr. Fulton."

"You'll be leaving the lass short of funds, Mr. Penley."

"Her income is ample enough to support her until I return. May I have the money, please?"

"Aye, I don't deny you have a legal right to it, and I'll not voice my opinion of you; but 'tis in an inconvenient storage. So I'll be asking you to step outside my home while I fetch it. Mr. Pendrath, before you leave, I'd like to know if you brought your cousin back with you on the ship that docked this morning."

"My *who*?"

"The murderous thief who tried to kill my grandson."

"Tom Kenn is only a distant relative, not a cousin; and he's aboard ship under restraint."

"Make sure he stays there, but I've notified the militia just in case you take a mind to claim, as you did the night he set fire to Trelynn's barn, that he's naught but a simple prankster. Now about your horses, when do you want them delivered to the ship?"

"We won't be sailing for nine or ten days, but I'll want to use them while I'm here," Harry blustered.

"They're in no condition yet to be raced around the countryside, Mr. Pendrath."

"Damn!"

"You can check on them tomorrow if you like. 'Tis not possible today, since my stockmen aren't here. Good day to the both of you. If you'll kindly leave now, I'll bring the money to you in a few minutes. But I advise you to put it in a strongbox as quickly as possible; New Port has its full share of blackguards and cheats."

With a numb sense of betrayal, Lynn helped pack her hoard of gold coins in an ancient knapsack supplied by a somber and disapproving host.

"Did you know he'd be taking the whole lot, lass?" Edward Fulton asked.

"Yes, I knew."

"And you agreed?"

"He's my husband, Mr. Fulton."

"Aye, but 'tis one time I disagree with the law that gives him the right."

Lynn bid her friends good-bye after Nell reported that Clay and Harry had left the farm and headed for town. The only cheerful comment she'd received had been from the recuperating Ned. "T'other's the rum one, Mistress Lynn, not your husband. Nate Stokes says he's a fair man who'll make a go of whatever he tries just like you; you'll not be losing your money."

It wasn't the money that had driven her into retreat, Lynn admitted to herself hours later. It had been the ease with which Clay surrendered to Pendrath domination, cutting her out of his life as surely as he'd taken her money from the Fulton strongbox. Unable to face any more sympathetic pity, she moved her personal belongings from the cottage into the cabin vacated by Bert and Leona, leaving only a brief note for her husband stating her intention. Clay found her there when he returned from New Port long after supper. His greeting was an aggressive demand.

"I hope you have a good explanation for your idiocy today."

With residual anger far more deeply rooted than his, Lynn retorted insolently, "I have several; which one do you want?"

More cautiously now, Clay retreated into polite cajolery. "I'm sorry you overheard Harry this morning."

"I was much sorrier to overhear you."

"Did Fulton tell you that I'd come there looking for you today?"

"He didn't have to. I was the one who packed your money."

"I'd have told you my plans a long time ago if you hadn't given Spence control."

"The only thing Spence will control in the future, is the

income we've made from business, unless you intend to take my share of that as well.''

"Don't be a fool; I made sure you had sufficient income to last until I return.''

"Very thoughtful of you.''

"Lynn, I had no choice. I owe Andrew Pendrath for my freedom.''

"You had more freedom of choice as Clay Penley. Was there anything else you wanted to discuss?''

"Just one more thing, Trelynn Trevor. I've decided you'll be less of a problem if I take you with me.''

"You've a convenient memory, Mr. Trevor. I won't leave the safety of this colony, and I won't gamble what little financial security you've left me.'' Rising from the table where she'd been working on the mill account, she left the room with an icy invitation of sorts. "You're welcome to stay here if you like. I don't imagine either of us would be too popular next door right now.''

The estrangement was harder on Clay than on Lynn; she'd endured far more years of concealing her emotions than he had, and she had the advantage of harder work. Two hours after dawn each day, she was aboard the milk delivery wagon with Kerry Egan, whose lively Irish patter kept her gloom under control. Nursing a guilty conscience and a borderline headache from the consumption of the brandy he shared with Harry Pendrath at the inn, Clay returned to the cabin only at night, and he no longer displayed any interest in his wife's business affairs.

On the fourth day, he arrived in mid-afternoon, located Lynn in the barn, and escorted her forcibly back to the cabin.

"Get dressed in something decent,'' he ordered. "We'll be spending the night in town.''

"You may be, Clay, but I'm not. You and Harry will have to make do without me.''

"You'll go if I have to drag you there, and 'tis not mine or Harry's idea. Captain Vinson is the one who insists you come. My father appointed him as watchdog to make certain you remain a Trevor daughter-in-law.''

''What your father wants is no concern of mine, and I shouldn't think it'd be of much interest to you either . . . not now.''

''Are you still angry about that thousand pounds?''

''I was never angry about the money, only about the means you employed to earn it. I would have preferred you ask for it outright and avoid the pretense.''

''What pretense?''

''Your convincing performance that our marriage had become something other than what it is and always has been—an arrangement your father made for *your* safety and *your* convenience. I'll go tonight only because I don't want to start any more gossip about us. Who else has Captain Vinson invited to this inspection party?''

''I don't know, and I don't give a damn! Just get dressed.''

In the bedroom Lynn found Kate Horton waiting with buckets of hot water on the bench and the cramoisie-red dress laid out on the bed. On top of the dress was the pendant Lynn's grandmother had given her three years before.

''I'd forgotten all about it. Where did you find it, Kate?''

''Bottom of your trunk when I was looking for another pair of gloves. Thought it might perk up your dress some.''

'' 'Tis not very pretty.''

''No, but it has style; and I won't have the others looking prettier than you tonight.''

''What others?''

''Nell for one, and in a new dress the Fulton woman made her. Then, of course, Bert's wife will be strutting around in her worn-out finery.''

''How do you know?''

"Bert told us last Sunday when you and your husband began your feuding."

Lynn sighed. "I'd hoped that my moving out of the cottage would keep the rest of you from knowing."

"Couldn't tell from you, but your husband has been growling like a hungry bulldog."

"Kate, why didn't you tell me about tonight?"

"Bert thought you might take off again, and he said 'twas important you be there. Now let's get you washed and dressed."

"Kate, where did those shoes over there come from?"

"Bert brought them when he came; said the woman who ordered them couldn't pay. Don't turn up your nose, young lady; they aren't silk slippers, but they're not the clods you usually wear, and they'll fit you since you and me wear the same size."

"I'm not objecting, Kate, 'tis only that—"

"Don't worry about your husband taking your money, Lynn. Bert said he'd made enough on those last loads of lumber to keep us going for months."

"The money's not important, Kate, not really."

"I know, 'tis his leaving you again. Seems it always takes a man longer to settle down than it does a woman, and he's a hard one to figure. As for you, girl, you've got the stiff pride of old Queen Bess herself, and a slashing tongue that would dry up a man's juice."

Smiling at Kate's unabashed language, Lynn asked, "Why didn't you ever marry, Kate?"

"Not many takers for a serving woman except for the fly-by-nights who'd let you support them until they found a better nest. Polly thinks your man's a light-o'foot, but she's not met the ones I have."

"I wish I had your cheerfulness, Kate."

"Yours for the taking, girl. Stand up and let's take a look at you. I was right; your grandmother's gewgaw adds a spark, and the cloak I made you will finish you off nicely. Color's not very cheerful, but that Indian fur is downright elegant.''

"Clay said it was ermine."

"Thought it might be; it looks expensive enough."

When the two women reentered the main room, they stood still in deflating shock; their efforts at beautification now seemed countryfied and homemade. The full-caped, full-length, superfine greatcoat Clay was wearing was nothing short of magnificent. His greeting, though, was sardonically lacking in both elegance and good taste.

"I think I should be the one to run off and hide this time, since I seem to be the center of tonight's witch hunt. It sounds as if your friends have planned quite a reception for me."

Cringing in embarrassed understanding, Lynn realized that the walls of the cabin were even thinner than the ones in the cottage.

CHAPTER
12

Although Kate's warning should have prepared her, Lynn was still startled by the number and identity of the guests gathered in the private entertainment room in the largest of New Port inns. Grouped around a table were the Fultons—Edward, Janet, and Ned—and an attractive young woman whom Lynn recognized only after Nell Wallis smiled at her. Looking more prettily innocent than any Puritan ever had, Nell was easily the most femininely attractive woman of the half-dozen in attendance. With her brown curls controlled by a ribbon and in a simple blue dress adorned only by a white kerchief around the neck, she looked younger than her nineteen years and happier than Lynn had ever seen her.

By contrast, Leona Spence appeared overdressed in an ornate lavender velvet gown, and her face seemed tired and jaded despite its lavish make-up. In the flickering lamplight, with her light hair that was almost colorless, Leona appeared years older than the husband standing by her side. Bert looked as he always did, poised and subtly commanding despite the shabby plainness of his suit and his worn boots. That he was also popular, Lynn noted with pride, was evident in the number of other men who walked over to talk to him.

It was the curious composition of those other men that puzzled Lynn; they seemed like such an odd mixture. What was a cantankerous wheelwright like Caleb Winslow doing in the company of Captain Elwin Carter and three other respectable New Port mariners? And why was Elwin Carter talking so intently to David Carey, the first mate of the *Tamarlind*? A very odd combination of businessmen and party people, Lynn concluded as she returned her attention to the host who had greeted them at the entrance. Still engaged in talking to Clay and Harry, Peter Vinson looked anything but a man who would ever interfere in someone else's private life. But when he turned his attention abruptly to Lynn and announced that he wished to speak to her in private, she wondered if she might not have misjudged him. He sounded very determined. From the corner of her eye, Lynn noted the expression of angry warning Clay bent on her before he granted tacit permission for the interview.

With an amused chuckle, Peter Vinson chided her good-naturedly. "Relax your guard, mistress, 'tis not an inquisition I intend, but a simple business proposition that involves many of our friends here tonight. These past weeks Spence has been busy organizing an order-and-delivery business that will keep five ships plying the Atlantic in a convoy, and two singles that will work the coastline. Since 'twas your idea initially, we want you to be one of the twelve partners."

"Will Spence be one of those partners?" Lynn asked sharply.

"Not without you, Mistress Penley. And without him to manage, 'tis doubtful the rest of us can succeed. I'll be lending him the money to buy his way in."

"Is the *Tamarlind* going to be a part of the fleet?"

"She'll be the flagship."

"But I thought you'd be supplying transportation for Clay's . . . for my husband's cargo."

"Two short trips as a slaver were enough for me. My ship still reeks from the stench of those poor devils' misery. Clay and Harry will work aboard the three armed ships that Andrew Pendrath is sending to Virginia."

Lynn glanced across the room at her husband and asked quietly, "Why would slave ships need to be armed?"

"Slaves have become a favorite booty for pirates. 'Tis said a third of the Negroes in Jamaica arrived through the back door, yet few of the western pirates ever sail to Africa."

"But Clay's ships won't be carrying raw slaves."

"No, their cargoes will be carefully selected slaves and even more valuable. I'm thinking our buccaneer brethren will be far more interested in those cargoes than in our pots and pans."

"Captain, did anyone ask my husband to join your group?"

Vinson sighed heavily. "Aye, lass, but he refused. Our profits will be only a fifth of what he expects to make. His father was hoping you'd be able to change his mind, but Clay's not one to take the slower way."

"Is Sir Bevil a part of your group?" Lynn asked suspiciously.

"He will be as soon as I reach England. None of us want to risk our ships on lone voyages any more, and Bevil feels as I do about importing alien slaves to the mother country—too many labor problems there already."

"Can my husband really make the hundred percent profit he claims?"

"He did on the first two trips to Virginia, but he spent the money fast enough. And now he'll be in partnership with a man who knows more than a few ways to cheat. I've known some of Andrew Pendrath's former partners, and they're poor men by comparison. But now about our own partnership, mistress; are you willing to join us?"

Lynn shook her head with regret. "At the moment, I don't have any funds to invest, Captain Vinson."

"Aye, Clay admitted he'd taken all of your money, and I suspect he'd rather not have you involved. But you see, lass, we'll be needing your bullocks, so they'll be your investment capital, just as Caleb Winslow's wagons will be his. 'Tis land transportation that bottlenecks most sea-going operations. We plan to deliver direct to our customers just as you and Spence are doing now."

Again Lynn shook her head. "Rhode Island is too small a colony for that much expansion."

"We plan to cover all the American colonies; and with more forming each year, 'twill be a lively trade. Are you willing to take part in our gamble?"

"Of course I am," she agreed readily, "provided I'm allowed to work."

" 'Tis expected you will since Spence claims you'll be indispensable, and Nate Stokes does little except boast of your skills. Did you really help in the roofing of your barn, lass?"

"Pounding pegs and nails is no harder than any other farm job," she retorted crisply. "Besides, it was my barn. When does this company you're forming go into operation?"

"My ship's already half-full of Massachusetts pine, and I'll be completing the load with Virginia tobacco. But now, mistress, 'tis time you join the party. Your husband looked like a thundercloud when he brought you in, and I'll wager he hasn't appreciated my monopolizing you."

"He doesn't mind, Captain Vinson. He's only impatient to get underway with his own life. As you can see, he's well occupied at the moment with his special friends."

Vinson's eyes were shrewdly calculating as he glanced across the room at the three people standing apart from the others, all of them dressed in clothing too Londonish for a gathering of colonials. The Spence woman looked ridiculously overdone, and Harry Pendrath's ruffled and lacy shirt was almost laughable. Even Clay, Vinson reflected sadly, was out of place in his leaf-green suit that bespoke the expert skill of a London tailor. The captain was smiling, though, as he returned his attention to his companion. In her dark brown cloak with the pretty white fur banding the hood and trimming the front, she was both more attractive and more suitably clad. Belatedly remembering his duties as host, he said hurriedly, "I'd best be taking your cloak, mistress, before you smother from the heat in here."

As she handed him the heavy garment, his smile broadened. No wonder Clay's mood was as black as ship's tar, Vinson reflected with an amused understanding; in her crimson dress, Lynn Penley looked as regal as a queen. Suddenly his eyes fastened on the dull stone pendant hanging around her neck, and he frowned in concentration.

"Forgive my curiosity, mistress, but where did you get that necklace you're wearing?" he asked brusquely.

Surprised by the question, Lynn glanced downward and shrugged. "'Tis but a trinket my grandmother gave me before she died. She called it her demon talisman and claimed she'd worn it every time she gambled."

"That's no trinket, mistress. Forgive my asking, but what was your grandmother's name?"

"The same as the odd one she wished on me . . . Trelynn . . . Hortensia Trelynn Penley."

"I'll be damned! So the legend was true after all!"

Responding cautiously to his excited outburst, Lynn asked, "Did you know my grandmother?"

"She was a bit before my time, but I heard about her from my school days on. What Cornish lad didn't! The daring Hortensia Trelynn whose luck with dice was famous and who was said to have won a fortune in a London card game when she was only a girl."

Lynn shook her head skeptically. "If 'twas the same woman, her luck failed her later in life. During the plague when I arrived in London, my grandmother was penniless."

"Not with that necklace, she wasn't, mistress."

Looking down at the drab pendant, Lynn murmured, "It

looks like an ordinary milk stone to me, and the gold chain is scant enough. What makes you think it valuable?''

"Unless the legend is wrong, that 'milk stone' is an unpolished, uncut diamond that once belonged to a Hottentot tribal chief in southern Africa.''

"My grandmother never left England, not even to accompany my grandfather to America. She had no access to Africa.''

"Aye, but a roguish Dutch sea captain did, and 'twas common practice for all sailors to trade with the natives there. But the stone you're wearing was said to be the largest one ever traded in those early years.''

"How did my grandmother get it?''

"According to the legend, the captain had deliberately lost a two-guinea wager he'd made with her and paid off with the diamond instead of money. 'Twas said that Hortensia had planned to elope with the adventurer. But Lord Trelynn was so furious when the smitten man pursued her to Cornwall, he ordered the Dutchman expelled from England; and he married his flamboyant daughter off to a commoner Cornishman, your grandfather, as it turns out.''

For a stunned moment Lynn was silent, recalling the only argument she'd ever heard between her mother and grandmother. She could still hear her grandmother's sharp ending to that dispute. "If it suits your fancy to claim relationship to the Trelynns, do so, Lavinia; but my granddaughter is a Penley and a Trevor, nothing else.''

Taking a deep breath, Lynn turned to face her present informant. "You know more about my grandmother than I do, Captain Vinson. No one ever told me who her father was, if she even *was* whom you say. I'm not certain about this trinket either. I've never seen a diamond, but I've heard they're supposed to sparkle. This thing doesn't.''

"When 'tis properly cut and polished, you'll be the envy of every queen, crowned or uncrowned, in King Charles's court.''

"Then 'tis only a useless trinket after all; I'll never meet people like that or want to. Would it fetch any money in this ugly, raw state?"

"Every jeweler in Holland would jump at the chance to purchase it, and I've heard there's a Dutch collector in the New York colony."

"Then perhaps I can—"

"Nay, mistress, that would be a mistake. Has your husband ever seen it?"

"I've never worn it before."

"Then hide it right now as your grandmother was said to have done, and don't show it to him. I might not be the only one who has heard of its existence, and there's more than one pirate in town who'd know the look of a raw diamond. Can you keep it hidden until—" Vinson abruptly stopped mid-sentence and pursed his lips.

"Until what, captain? I don't have any use for the thing."

"I'd estimate its value at many thousands of pounds sterling, lass; and that's not a useless sum of money, particularly to an ambitious man like Clay."

Lynn sucked in her breath and swiftly slipped the pendant inside her dress. She didn't need Vinson to remind her that her husband would appropriate it as casually as he had her other funds. But if she could locate the Dutchman in New York, she would have enough capital to ... to do nothing, she concluded dully. Until her grandfather cleared her name, she couldn't leave this one small colonial haven. The necklace whose weight she hadn't noticed before now seemed like a millstone around her neck. Paying only scant attention, she heard Vinson's next question.

"Clay doesn't know about your Trelynn blood, does he?"

Shrugging stiffly, she shook her head and responded more candidly than proper wifely devotion dictated. "Why should he? Neither of us knew the other one existed when I was growing up. He considers me a peasant farmwoman without the refinement to understand or appreciate such delicate ladies as the one now pouring out her shallow little heart to him or the sluttier one you took to Virginia eight months ago.''

Vinson's laughter was a low rumble that shook his trim frame. ''Lord Harry would be devastated to hear your low opinion of his haughty wife even though he can no longer abide the woman himself. You can also absolve your husband of having any more tolerance for her treachery. He hid from her aboard ship during that last voyage and fled to safety when she invaded his room at a Jamestown inn. Give him time, mistress; Clay's never been one to welcome a leash of any kind; but he's not a complete fool. He's been watching you like a tomcat pretending to be asleep, and he hasn't missed a toss of your sleek head.''

As he watched Nate Stokes and David Carey converging on them with determined strides, Vinson's chuckle deepened. Clay Trevor hadn't been the only one watching the unusual woman who could roof a barn and run a farm and still challenge a man with her uncommon beauty. Without realizing it, Vinson reflected with wry humor, Trelynn Trevor had inherited more than money and a priceless diamond from the Honorable Hortensia; she'd also inherited a commanding presence of spirit.

Clay was moodily aware of the ostracism being leveled against him by the roomful of people Harry Pendrath had contemptuously labeled ''the chamber potters.'' When Bert Spence had first mentioned the expanded company to him, Clay had been unimpressed by the proposed profit margin. He'd made five times that percentage in his first two deliveries to Virginia, and Andrew Pendrath had projected an even larger profit in England. Within five years, Clay reasoned, he'd be able to retire while Spence would still be a mere tradesman.

"What will you do when you retire?" Spence had asked reasonably.

"Anything I want. In the meantime I plan to put share-tenants to work on the land in Connecticut."

"That worn-out system will never be popular in the northern colonies, not when cheap land is so available."

"The Spragues seem content enough in that mill you neglected to tell me about."

"They'll own the land and the mill in eleven years. Lynn and her grandfather will have made their investment many times over by that time."

"I'm counting on that support for her, but I don't want her involved in this crack-brain company of yours," Clay had warned.

"She already is; most of it was her idea."

"She doesn't have the capital to invest in it now; I needed the whole of her money."

"So Fulton informed me. Have you told her yet?"

"She overheard Harry asking about it, but I'd appreciate your not reminding her."

"Lynn's memory is accurate enough not to require a prompter. How long do you plan to keep her dangling, Clay?"

Now as he watched his wife engaged in animated conversations with other men across the room, Clay was experiencing emotions he'd never expected to feel about any woman. He was jealous and resentful! He'd been a fool not to have told her about the money the first night they'd been together. Wincing from the playful elbow being jammed into his side, Clay responded to Harry's amused *sotto voce* comment with sour irritation.

"Your wife seems to prefer the company of other men as much as mine does, old lad. I've never seen Pete Vinson even smile at a woman before, but he's near to doing nip-ups over yours. I will admit that she's a damn sight more attractive in that red dress than I ever thought she could be. 'Tis a color that doesn't become Amelia, but she'd be snapping with envy if she were here.''

"Amelia would never stoop to such a vulgar color, Harry," Leona scolded him. " 'Tis the color of the streets as well you and Clay both know, and 'tis the color Nell Wallis should be wearing instead of the blue trickery she has on.''

"I'll be damned," Harry exclaimed as his eyes located the girl he'd always thought of as Tom's barroom whore. "I didn't recognize her. I hope Vinson had the sense to post a double guard on Tom while the *Tamarlind*'s in port. Christ, old Tom would be ripe for murder if he saw her looking like a virgin bride.''

"Bride-to-be," Leona amended swiftly. "That poor young man is in for a nasty shock when he weds her.''

None of the three had heard Bert Spence approach, and Leona jerked in annoyance when his low voice responded to her sweetly spoken slur. "That *poor young man* and his grandfather have known all about every one of us since our first day here, and they're still delighted Nell agreed to marry Ned. Moreover, my gossipy wife, I very much doubt my own mother would have approved of you as heartily as Janet Fulton does Nell.''

Turning to the glum-faced man who'd been paying little attention to the conversation, Bert spoke more briskly. "Are you planning to ignore Lynn the entire evening, or do you want me to fetch her?''

"She looks content enough with what she's doing," Clay snapped.

"Stokes and Carey look even more so. Nate's just a friend; but if you remember, David's no raw beginner when it comes to appreciating a beautiful woman. There's something else you might find of interest. Dave will captain the ship we'll be using as a coastal freighter to collect American and Caribbean cargoes for us; so New Port will be his home harbor.''

"I wouldn't worry if I were you, Clay," Leona advised

with biting petulance. "Mr. Carter's ships aren't very lucky. He's that prattling man nearest the fireplace, and he's poor enough to take boarders into his home. For all of these dreadful days, I've been forced to listen to his dull chatter."

"He's our landlady's father," Bert explained with a sardonic smile, "and Mistress Hayes is the reason my wife now feels free to resume what she chooses to call her interrupted life."

"What Spencer is implying so rudely, Clay, is that I've decided to accompany you and Harry to Virginia," Leona simpered.

Clay's eyes narrowed in speculation. "A sea voyage can be dangerous for a small infant, Leona," he warned.

Smiling appealingly, Leona linked her arm through Clay's. "I know I promised to try, but Spencer can tell you that I found that . . . that part of motherhood too exhausting to endure. The Hayes woman is used to it, but I just couldn't . . . it was too degrading."

" 'Tis Leona's belief that motherhood shouldn't be allowed to interfere with the important things in life," Bert intoned caustically, "and Harry has convinced her that Amelia needs her more than a three-week old infant does."

"I'll be gone for only a few months, Spencer, a year at most, and Jane doesn't need a mother yet. I'm hoping, of course, that Spencer will join me in Virginia once he's had his fill of this primitive existence."

Leaning forward eagerly, Harry added his smiling persuasion. "How about it, Spence? Why not join Clay and me, and earn pounds instead of pence? Once Leona's gone, what the devil are you going to do here alone?"

Clay stiffened as he noted the dangerous glint in Spence's dark eyes and heard the softly voiced counter question. "Are you offering me a full partnership, Harry, or am I going to serve another period of indenture?"

With a cynical smile of futility, Clay heard Harry's

blustering explanation, and watched with apprehension as the heavier man placed his arm around Bert's trim athletic shoulders and pleaded for a more private conversation. As the two men walked toward an unoccupied corner of the room, Clay scowled in frustration; now he'd be forced to entertain Leona until one of them returned. Feeling an unpleasant trepidation, he listened restlessly to her gush of words.

"Oh, Clay, if you only knew how much I've wanted to talk to you alone these past weeks, but, of course, she wouldn't allow you out of her sight long enough for you to do what you wanted. Why can't Spencer be like you and just walk away from her? But, no, he feels responsible—as if she weren't manlike enough to do her own work. I hate her, Clay. She's tried to treat me just as she does all of those terrible people who're just like her; and Spencer has refused to understand how I feel. He always takes her part, and he accuses me of being a heartless mother. Goodness knows, I love my daughter; but I just can't seem to convince him that I'll go out of my mind if I don't have a little harmless fun in my life."

Clay heard the complaining drone of her voice, but his thoughts were churning around the conviction that Spence had deliberately engineered his wife's departure. Damn him and damn my stubborn wife in that flaunting red dress who had no intention of letting Spence go! Concealing his anger behind half-hooded eyes and a vacuous half-smile, Clay voiced the hopeless suggestion, "Perhaps you should remain in Rhode Island, Leona."

"No!" she snapped her answer. "Spence will have to come to me and apologize for his neglect. Right now, he is more polite to that human cow of a nursemaid than he is to me, and after all the misery I went through to bear his child."

With his attention concentrated on watching his wife laugh unrestrainedly at something David Carey had said to her, Clay barely heard Leona's continuing complaints about her present life or her feminine titillation about the forthcoming journey. Repressing a fervent sigh of relief, he welcomed the brusque approach of Peter Vinson.

"Spence tells me you're to be my passenger, Mistress Burtram," the captain announced with crisp disapproval. "I wasn't expecting a woman aboard this trip."

"I won't be a bit of trouble," Leona promised. "You won't even know I'm aboard. I plan to remain in my cabin the whole time and sew; I surely don't want Amelia to be ashamed of me when I arrive in Virginia. Goodness knows, after this terrible place, I'll need everything new from the skin out."

"Very well, but don't expect a pleasure cruise. Clay, if the lady will excuse us now, I'd like a word alone with you; and then I think you should rescue your wife from my overzealous officers."

The years of friendship and frequently hazardous adventures he'd shared with the younger man did not inhibit Vinson's blunt language as the two men moved hastily away from Leona. "Clay, you're either a cock-a-hoop simpleton or a knavish rakehell; I can't decide which. You treated your wife cavalierly enough aboard ship when you were still dancing attendance on the Pendrath shrew, but to subject an intelligent woman to the sight of her husband paying solicitous court to a childish, spineless jade is beyond understanding. There was a time when I thought you'd acquired enough sense to appreciate Trelynn Trevor; but after tonight, I realize you're nothing but a freebooting nomad."

"Is that what my wife told you during your extended conversation with her?"

"No, we were talking about more important things. Tell me, Clay, did you ever meet any of Trelynn's family other than Ephraim Penley?"

Clay shrugged impatiently. "I saw her mother a few times, but I never met her formally. Why?"

"Curiosity. Do you know anything about her grand-mother?"

"Nothing beyond the fact that the old harridan gambled away a fortune."

"For a class-proud peacock, you're not very knowledge-able about Cornish aristocracy. Hortensia Trelynn Penley may have been a gambler, but an old 'harridan' she wasn't. She was the only daughter of Lord Henry Trelynn and one of the most sought-after women of her day."

"Did my wife tell you that?"

"Trelynn didn't know, but I would have thought your father would have mentioned the relationship to you. Bevil generally knows everything about the county's entitlement families, especially since there are so few of them. I can't imagine that he didn't know Hortensia Trelynn; they would have been about the same age."

"Are you sure about this, Peter? It doesn't seem logical to me that a lord would marry his only daughter off to a commoner."

"Well obviously, Henry Trelynn did. Tell me, Clay, do you really think titles and the claptrap about bloodlines are all that important in a wife?"

With a deflating rush, Clay's gloom returned, and he shook his head. "Not a damn bit and especially not my wife; she'll be as hard as hell to control now."

"She will be if you don't start acting like a husband instead of an unwilling visitor. I'll be returning to my ship tonight, so you're welcome to use the room I reserved here at the inn. Perhaps if you could separate her from that partisan crowd of friends, you might be able to rewin her trust. God knows how, though; this past week you've treated her like a leper."

The first greeting Clay received from the people seated around the Fultons' dining table was a sardonic smile from David Carey who reluctantly moved from his position next to Lynn. The second was a murmured suggestion from his wife.

"Perhaps you should ask Leona to join us, Clay. She looks unhappy about your desertion."

"Let Spence take care of his own wife for a change," he growled softly in response. "If he hadn't ignored her all these months while dancing attendance on you, Leona wouldn't feel so unwanted."

Although Clay's accusation was scarcely more than a raspy whisper, it was intercepted by a vengeful Nell Wallis, who moved swiftly from her place across the table to stand defensively in back of Lynn. "If you believe what that puling bitch told you, *Lord* Trevor," she whispered harshly, "you're the same great booby you've always been. 'Twas Bert who waited on her hand and foot while she complained, and 'twas Lynn who let her loll around in comfort while the rest of us did her work. And now 'tis Elvira Hayes who'll be raising her child while that simpering twit skips off to play the lady again. Well, good riddance to her and to Harry and to you. We've better things to do with our time than be unpaid servants to the likes of her."

With a satisfied flounce of her head, Nell returned to her seat, leaving a pair of silenced people behind, Clay from angry embarrassment and Lynn from wayward humor that threatened to erupt into laughter. Nell's brash words were the ones that Lynn herself had longed to say since the night Clay had emerged from Leona's bedroom, words that crystalized a problem far deeper than the flight of a cowardly wife. The other causes of Lynn's bubbling mirth were equally gratifying. After Captain Vinson's revelation about her grandmother and a wealth she hadn't known she possessed, and after a pleasant hour in the company of a man well versed in flattery, Lynn felt like a butterfly emerging from its ugly chrysalis. More confident than she'd ever been in her life, she turned to the discomfited man by her side.

" 'Twould seem that your gallantry was misdirected tonight, husband, and more than likely you owe Spence an apology."

''Do you share the other sentiments that unmannered female blasted me with as well?''

''About your leaving? No, but then you're the one who made the choice, and life does go on even among the peasants left behind to till the fields. You can stop scowling now, Clay; we've already caused enough stir for one evening. 'Tis time I was going home anyway.''

Without waiting for his compliance, Lynn rose with an easy grace and bid goodnight to her dining companions, adding a special warmth to the words she spoke to Nell and to David Carey. Both of them had added considerably to the unusual occasion. Halfway toward the entrance, she paused long enough to wish Leona and Harry a pleasant voyage and to tell Bert that she'd be working full schedule after Clay's departure in a week. At the rear entry, she allowed Clay to help her with her cloak before she pulled the door open and stepped outside into the chill March night. Clay grabbed her arm before she'd taken two steps.

''Where do you think you're going, Lynn? I told you we'd be staying in town tonight. Peter Vinson has offered us his room.''

''That was generous of him, but I've no liking for the bedbugs and dirty sheets this inn is rumored to supply its guests. I've no objection of you choose to stay; but if you're going to walk home with me, you'd best put on your pretty coat before you freeze.''

Damn her, Clay fumed, her tongue had been sharper than a rapier tonight. Shoving his arms viciously into the fashionable greatcoat he'd had made in London, he glared at the back of her averted head. She'd taunted him about his clothing at every opportunity, he reflected savagely, flinching only slightly as he remembered the exorbitant cost of this richly caped garment. But he wasn't at fault this time, she was! She'd played the grand dame all evening, ignoring him deliberately and exchanging flippant comments with the men who'd clustered around her without a hint of the caustic sarcasm she used on him. How the devil had she learned so much party prattle in eight months, and damned witty repartee at that? Aboard ship, she sat like a sphinx and let Amelia do the talking; but now she could bandy words with the best of them and with only a trace of her former Cornish accent. Her light farewells to Harry and Leona had been so skillfully executed, both of them had burbled awkwardly in response.

Not Spence though, Clay recalled abruptly. Spence's dark eyes had glinted with approval, and his conversation with her had been the cryptic one of complete understanding. And why shouldn't it have been, Clay realized with biting resentment; Spence had been the one who'd taught her all those social tricks she now used with devastating skill. The jealousy that had nagged Clay earlier now returned full strength, all but obliterating his own sense of guilt.

"I thought Spence was my only rival," he blurted incautiously, "until I watched you lure David Carey into hot pursuit tonight. Which of them are you going to favor once I'm gone?"

"Spence already *is* a good friend, and I've no doubt Mr. Carey will soon become one. I have better luck with friends than I do with—"

"With lovers?" Clay interrupted harshly.

"I was about to say 'with husbands.' Mine is either missing for months on end or merely misplaced whenever there's a nearby damsel in distress."

"Good God, you can't really believe I'm interested in Leona! I was only trying to convince the damned woman to remain with her husband."

"How thoughtful you are of other people's marriages."

"I wasn't doing it for hers; I was hoping to save my own."

He cringed when he heard her soft chuckle and ironic inflection. "I've read that on the eve before many chivalrous knights of old departed on their own little adventures, they locked chastity belts on their wives. But you don't have to worry about Bert Spence; Mistress Hayes is not the milk cow Leona thinks she is.''

"What *do* I have to worry about then?''

"Why should there be anything to fret you? I'm the one who's captive here in Rhode Island until my grandfather clears my name.''

"What happens when he does?''

Lynn's facile lips curved into an impish smile. "I might take a trip to Holland.''

"Holland's the dullest country in Europe. Why would you want to go there?''

"'Tis said its merchants have unusual skills; and I want to learn the trade from experts.''

"For God's sake, Lynn, you're a woman!''

"A drawback I'll admit, but not necessarily a fatal one for me, especially since I'll have enough men to blame for any miscalculations I might make during the coming year.''

"You once claimed you were only a farmer.''

"No more than you were only a smuggler, Clay. This is a new world that's ripe for the taking; you'll be reaching for its gold in your way while I'm trying for it in mine.''

"What happened to your plan of using motherhood to attract a more suitable husband?''

Again his taut nerves were jangled by her soft laughter. "That was but an old wives' tale to keep you entertained,'' she murmured lightly. "You'll be more pleased to know there'll be no child.''

"Why should I be pleased? I told you I wanted a son.''

"Whatever for? So you could pat him on his head during your once-a-year inspection tour? And perhaps if our spawn were female, you'd not bother with any more devotion than Leona intends to give her daughter.''

"I don't approve of Leona leaving Spence, but the practice of wet-nursing is an old and established custom.''

"Only among aristocrats who didn't care about the peasant babes who starved to death as a result.''

"You belong to the same class as I do, Lynn.''

"You mean because of my unsaintly grandmother?"

"Until Vinson told me, I had no idea you were related to that family."

"How could you? You were never home; but your father and my grandmother were good friends. For your information, no one ever thought to tell me about her family either, but I'm just as happy I never developed any silly pretenses. That's why I like this part of America so much better than you do and why I'll never want to live in Virginia where worn-out entitlement still determines who's rich and who's poor."

As abruptly as she'd begun her militant harangue, Lynn ended it when she glimpsed her husband's face in the faint light of the late winter moon. He appeared less assured and more vulnerable than she'd ever known him to be, and his expression was one of bleak frustration.

"Clay, let's not spend the rest of our time together bickering. Until Leona's problems and Harry's demand for money interfered, we were happy with each other; and neither of them is important any more. I don't care what happens to her, and Spence and the others have offered me a chance to earn my own money."

And the chance to make you forget me all the faster, Clay finished the sentence in glum silence. Aloud he expressed his disapproval more diplomatically; he didn't want her to withdraw the tentative truce she'd just extended. "Don't become so involved, you won't want to accompany me as soon as you're free."

Repressing a sigh of irritation—he was still a heedless child about facing reality—Lynn responded dryly, "According to Harry, you'll be working steadily for years before you even consider returning here."

"You asked him?"

"He was eager to volunteer both that information and the fact that the plans you and he have made didn't really include me."

"He wasn't speaking for me, Lynn. I'll be doing the

scheduling, so I'll be here as often as I can. I really don't want to leave you at all, but—''

''But you're already committed,'' Lynn concluded for him flatly.

''I'm sorry I am now.''

''At least, that will be something to remember,'' she murmured.

For the few minutes it took to cross the field leading to their cabin, they were silent; but Clay's arm was around her waist and their long strides were synchronized. Inside the lamplit cabin, Lynn smiled as she looked around; someone had recently lighted a fire and laid a small supper spread on the table.

''Was this your idea?'' Clay asked suspiciously.

''No, but Kate and Polly know that I'm usually too busy to eat much when I'm with a crowd of people. For that matter, you didn't have any supper either. Put the kettle on, Clay, while I change my clothes.''

When she returned wearing a robe that was drab in contrast to the one he had donned, she accepted the glass of wine he handed her. ''You didn't drink anything tonight,'' he reminded her.

''I had other things on my mind,'' she answered lightly.

Throughout that shared meal, Clay was thoughtful. It would be pleasantly easy to make love to her, he knew, but there was a difference about her tonight that aroused a reckless desperation in him. He'd never made an honest declaration of love to any woman before, and he had no idea how he would feel a sobering few months from now. Cautiously he began a roundabout approach.

''Have you ever regretted that night we spent together in the tower?''

'' 'Twas morning when you made love to me, and I never regretted it; but I wish I'd known your plans then.''

''My only plan then was to convince you to marry me, and I certainly didn't *plan* on being separated from you because of a damned pirate.''

"I doubt Captain Rambert had any such intention. He seems peaceful enough now that he's making New Port his home."

"What the devil do you mean, 'his home'?"

"Inbetween voyages, this is where he lives. He's building a big house here, and he is one of our best customers."

"My God, he's a damn criminal!"

"Not here he isn't. He respects the militia the same as all of them do, and he keeps his men in line better than most."

"I don't want you to have anything to do with men like that."

"I'm in business, Clay, and Captain Rambert and some of the others are customers."

"You're not going to face that kind of danger unless I'm here to protect you. I'll speak to Spence about it tomorrow."

"Do what you like, Clay; but right now, I'm going to bed. If you've had enough supper, I'll bank the fire and turn out the lamp; the idea of fire still frightens me."

As he followed her into the bedroom and into the brick-warmed bed, Clay was uncomfortably aware of her defensive evasions; but he still felt compelled to win this one argument.

"Lynn, I know Morse Rambert. One day he can seem like a friend, and a month later he's a dangerous enemy. I just don't want you hurt; I care very much what happens to you."

Waiting for her response, Clay could feel her move restlessly on her half of the bed. "Did you hear what I said, Lynn?" he demanded impatiently, but her answer was another evasion.

"So far, the only person who's proved dangerous to me was Tom Kenn."

"I mean about my caring for you."

"Don't, Clay."

"Don't what?"

"Don't spin me any fairy tales; reality is the only thing

that matters. I'll admit that I wish our lives were combined, but they're not and perhaps never will be. So we're better off without illusions; our lives are muddled enough already.''

"We're still man and wife regardless of your distrust."

"So were our parents until both of our mothers died, but they were separated from their husbands most of the time. There's no profit in my mourning your absence any more than there is in your worrying about my safety while you're away. The same is true of telling each other what to do or not to do. We've separate lives to lead and separate decisions to make. Let's just enjoy the present, Clay, and let the future take care of itself.''

Frustrated by her unemotional logic, Clay remained stiffly silent for the length of time it took him to probe the subtleties of her declaration. Without any concern for her wedding vows, she intended to do what she pleased; and he was powerless to stop her.

"What kind of decisions do you intend making?" he asked finally, only to wince at her responsive answer.

"The same kind as you," she murmured.

"Will infidelity be one of them?"

"That's an odd question for you to ask, Clay; I didn't have the freedom you did on your last trip. Harry claimed that you were in demand wherever you went."

"Damn Harry! Lynn, I told you that—"

"I'm not asking for any promises!"

Biting back the words *Well, I am!* Clay demanded instead, "When did you learn there'd be no child, Lynn?"

"Four nights ago."

"Are you free yet?"

"I'd not have invited you into my bed tonight if I hadn't been."

His heart pounding with confused emotions, Clay moved swiftly to pull her into his arms and to kiss the mobile lips that had been tantalizing him all evening. A witch woman with a will of iron she might be, but she was still a woman whose independence could be tamed by nature. There was still time for a child, though she'd been slow to conceive so far. For a moment the warmth of her reception soothed his anger, but only for a moment until he recalled the rankling words she'd flung at him. As one of his hands pushed the swaddling nightdress from her shoulders and over her hips, his other held her head firmly so she couldn't avoid his ravaging kiss or start again any of her disconcerting dialogue.

As always though, when he embraced this woman whose inward fire was always so well concealed from public view, his own senses were quickly swamped; and he soon forgot any motives other than fulfillment of the passion that swelled through his groin and drove him relentlessly to reclaim her vibrantly firm body. Kissing her now with a more primitive purpose and caressing her breasts already tightened with responsive desire, Clay felt only the excitement of the possession she had aroused in him since their first time together. Driven by a compelling urge to weld their bodies into one, a compulsion that had been sharpened by days of anger and jealousy, Clay claimed her body in a swift attack, relaxing long enough to savor the throbbing excitement of consummation. As her sinuous legs wrapped tightly around him, he began the slow rhythmic thrusting that required no volition, only blind obedience to human instincts. Although his own need was the imperative that impelled him, he experienced a savage satisfaction when he felt her body shudder with the approach of ecstasy. They climaxed within seconds of each other, their exquisite pleasure joining and overlapping.

Clay was still breathing heavily as he rolled over and pulled her on top of him before they separated. Hesitating to tell her that their physical unity was a rarity and that she might be disappointed with another man, he whispered instead, "I feel the same as I did the night we spent in the barn: as if there's nothing else I want in life. I hope you aren't sleepy."

Already half-asleep, Lynn giggled happily.

* * *

The final week of Clay's month-long stay in Rhode Island was unlike the earlier three, as both of them reached a plateau of acceptance of each other and their limited time together. By mutual consent they remained isolated, separating themselves from other people as much as possible. At the Spragues' mill, Clay kept her by his side as he talked to the hard-working brothers. With Kate's understanding contrivance, they ate their meals alone in their cabin; and only once did they visit the *Tamarlind* where Clay conferred briefly with Captain Vinson and Harry while Lynn visited with Nate Stokes. They were together in the barn when the last of Lynn's twenty cows delivered its oversized bull calf, and Clay had the grace to laugh when Lynn named it Red Clay.

"It looks exactly like its papa did eleven years ago," Lynn announced excitedly. "I didn't think I'd ever be lucky enough to duplicate a breeder like Red Penny."

Since the dark red animal looked exactly like the other bull calves already delivered, Clay asked with amusement, "How the devil can you tell?"

"Its strength and its size, but mostly its aggression. It stood up sooner than the others and has already started eating. Look at his eyes, Clay; even on a farm, that animal will eventually challenge Red Penny to become the herd ruler."

"That's because Red Penny isn't aggressive," Clay argued.

"Don't you believe it. Red Penny's gentle by nature and by pampered nurturing and care; but there's nothing wrong with its herd instincts. My big baby could tear this barn apart if it were angry or frightened or if it sensed danger."

More impressed than he cared to admit, Clay was silent as he watched his wife complete the arduous task with skillful efficiency. No wonder she was so self-confident, he thought with pride; she was a better midwife than any stockman on Trevor Manor. Frowning with a sudden vivid memory of the one glimpse he'd had of her when she crossed the tower bridge with her clubs whirling and three downed men behind her, Clay felt a chill of fear. Previously he'd considered the charges of witchcraft leveled against her to be merely the persecution of a lazy cousin and his jealous wife, but now he knew with a certainty that most bigoted Cornishers of both genders would resent her usurpation of masculine prerogatives. She had defied convention in farming and business, in education and intelligence, and most damning of all, in her mastery of self-defense. Apprehensively, he wondered how long it would be before colonials became equally intolerant. In his limited survey of colonial women, he'd met not one who could compete with her, except—Clay paused in an honest evaluation—Nell Wallis, who had her full share of an equal courage, and perhaps the unknown Elvira Hayes who'd taken over the burden of raising another woman's child in addition to her own.

Half an hour later, Clay was even more thoughtfully impressed by his wife's unique character. As he stood shivering by the small bathing pool, he watched as she stripped off her sweaty and stained garments and plunged into the icy water. She's a throwback to a hardier, more dynamic race whose women had not yet been enslaved by vain artifice and social restrictions, he concluded irrelevantly. In this sylvan setting, she looked as primitive as an Indian, but more beautiful than in her red dress. Experiencing a sharp desolation at the thought of leaving her behind, Clay vowed that this would be their last separation. Only a fool would risk losing this rarity among women!

As she dried herself off with one of her petticoats, Clay noticed the dull pendant hanging about her neck and asked with a casual interest, "What's that thing about your throat, Lynn?"

"A foolish piece of milk stone my grandmother gave me for good luck," she responded promptly with a rippling smile.

"I didn't think you liked your grandmother very much."

Lynn's smile broadened with amusement. "I'm learning to appreciate her sense of humor, but some day I shall expect you to present me with a necklace of real value."

Late the following morning when the *Tamarlind* was two hours out of port, Clay recalled the pendant and his wife's smile; and a vague memory stirred his consciousness. Why would an arrogant old woman who gambled away fortunes keep such a crude necklace, especially a woman like the flamboyant aristocrat Vinson had described? As his memory focused, Clay recalled Amelia Pendrath's exclamation when she'd learned that he'd married a woman named Penley. " 'Tis too bad your witch wife isn't related to the grand old dame of London gamblers. That old woman was supposed to own a diamond necklace that would support us for life."

Clay's eyes were glinting with humor as he realized that the milk stone Lynn had joked about was a raw diamond that would indeed support them for life. His heart was as thistle-down light as it had been sixteen years earlier at the start of his adventurous years before cynicism and boredom had taken their toll. That necklace, he reflected with a warm gratitude, had already given him a week of happiness he hadn't expected; and it had restored Lynn's tolerance and humor.

"What the devil are you celebrating?" Harry grumbled as he joined his partner at the railing.

"The luck of a gambler, m'lad!"

"I hope your good mood lasts until we reach Virginia. I'll need your moral support when I see Amelia."

"Not any more, Harry. 'Tis long overdue that you bring her to heel without my interference."

"Christ!"

"Do you have enough wherewithal to satisfy her?"

"Money's no problem this time. Lord Gordon finally delivered the dowry he promised me four years ago."

Clay studied his friend's insensitive face thoughtfully. "If you had that much money at your disposal, Harry, why did you feel it necessary to strip *my* wife of all of her meager funds? In the past, you and I never had any problems about sharing."

"My God, Clay, they're two different women. Amelia would have my head if I touched her money."

"Why? As you told me when the situation was reversed, 'tis yours by right."

"In Amelia's case, that's not so certain. I'm hoping to convince her to build our Virginia home with it. Your wife doesn't have the needs mine does, and she's able to support herself. But I'll admit I was wrong about her in other ways; she's not the untamed rustic I thought she was. Except that she's a commoner, she might even fit in with Virginia people."

Clay shook his head in hopeless resignation; Harry would always be an obtuse dunderhead about people. Smiling as he recalled Lynn's sly humor about her grandmother, he murmured, "My wife's remarkable enough to overcome that slight disadvantage."

Standing with Bert Spence and David Carey on the New Port embarcadero, Lynn watched the *Tamarlind* until only the billowing sails were visible on the distant horizon. Despite her brave words of farewell to her husband, she felt desolate and empty, already dreading the lonely months ahead. Her two companions were equally silent, each man lost in his own thoughts. David was the first to voice his gloomy preoccupation.

" 'Tis the first time she's sailed without me in twelve years. I've a foolish feeling that I deserted the old ship."

"You've your own to worry about now, Dave, and a strange crew to whip into shape before the week is out. The sooner we're underway, the sooner we'll locate enough trade goods to fill five ships. Lynn, are you ready to go to work yet?"

Lynn nodded indifferently in response to Bert's question. She was prepared to work only as an antidote to assuage her sense of loss, but her enthusiasm of a week ago had deserted her. Dreading the six hours she'd spend each day in town doing Bert's work while he was searching colonial ports for enough of the raw products needed by English manufacturers, Lynn felt doubly deserted.

"How long before Captain Vinson returns with the fleet?" she asked dully.

"Three months more or less. In the meantime, we'll have to make at least that number of coastal runs. Dave, you'd best get the *Narragansett* in order while I check Lynn out in the operations at this end, but don't forget we're due to meet our American partners this afternoon."

Recalling Clay's foolish concerns about David Carey, Lynn watched the newly appointed captain stride jauntily toward the small boat waiting to take him out to the ship that would now be his to command. Even if he had been interested in her, she concluded cynically, she'd be no competition against the lure of the sea and ships. Bert Spence, too, she realized, was experiencing the same sense of being left behind that she was. As the *Tamarlind* had pulled away from the dock, she'd caught a glimpse of his face. He'd been saying goodbye to a wife of seven years; and despite his disillusionment about Leona, Lynn suspected that he was still hurt by her callous desertion. As if his thoughts were attuned to hers, he recalled her attention to the gloomy present with a pungent comment.

"The difference between us, Lynn, is that your wandering spouse will return; mine won't."

" 'Tis more likely the other way around; a man has more freedom in his roamings than a woman."

"I would have agreed with you a week ago, but not now. Clay's not going to risk losing you."

"That's what he said, but I'm still wagering Leona will return first. I don't think she'll find any more acceptance in Virginia than she did here; colonial men need working women, not ornamental parasites. What is she going to do without something to occupy her time?"

"She'll drift into old age without ever realizing that she's become one of those useless parasites. Before she met Amelia, I entertained false hopes that Leona might eventually grow up; but 'tis too late now. Still my marriage wasn't a complete failure; I do have a pretty daughter."

"I'd have thought that you'd have wanted to remain here to take care of little Jane."

"She'll need a secure future more than she needs me for the while."

"What about the island's security, Spence? Without you and Nate Stokes leading the militia, this waterfront could become as dangerous as the Cornish coast."

"There are forty trained militiamen and homegrown officers who know the territory better than I do. And last week, Fulton and Carter convinced Morse Rambert to police the brethren of the sea. Not many colonial ports will give him and his kind safe harborage, and Rambert is too sensible to risk expulsion."

A week later, the day after the *Narragansett* sailed, Lynn learned first-hand that Morse Rambert was as shrewd as he was sensible. Minutes after she'd arrived at the small, street level office in the Carter home, she was startled by a discreet knock on the door. Carrying her lead-tipped flails, which she kept close by her during her working stint in town, she unlocked the door cautiously and peered at the elegantly dressed Captain Rambert standing respectfully some five feet away.

"You won't be needing your weapons, Mistress Trevor," he advised her lightly. "I mean you no harm. I've come to offer you a business proposition that should prove mutually profitable."

"I think you should wait until Mr. Spence returns, Captain Rambert," she countered, guardedly aware that he'd called her Mistress Trevor instead of the Mistress Penley he'd used during their less formal encounters at the site of his new home.

"I trust neither Sir Burtram nor your husband, mistress; nor do I want to deal directly with your other partners."

"In that case, Captain, this interview is concluded."

"You're not that foolish, mistress. I know you'll have to inform the lot of them, but 'tis your agreement I want. Unless Peter Vinson can return to England with full loads each trip, your company will lose money. I propose to supply half of your cargo with five of the most reliable money-makers in the trade: indigo, rum, sugar, molasses, and cacao beans. Now, do we talk business, or do I contact the individual merchants in port?"

Having studied Bert's prolific notes during the past eight days, Lynn knew the profit margin of every new-world product needed in England. She'd also learned that the supply of American products was limited; there was too much competition for the tobacco trade, the supply of lumber was unpredictable, and the availability of leather and furs was happenstance at best. By far the most consistently lucrative trade had been the sugar and rum produced by the Caribbean colonies, which had attracted almost three times the number of colonists as had the sparse settlements stretched out along coastal America.

With a gambler's instinct for survival, Lynn admitted Morse Rambert into the cluttered office, gesturing brusquely toward the visitor's bench as she resumed her own chair behind the desk. Smiling an apologetic warning to her unlikely guest, she laid her clubs on the littered desk top and waited silently for him to speak. His introductory remarks turned her smile into one of wry humor.

"I was watching the day you leveled two of my men with those pretty weapons, mistress."

"Since they were both drunk, Captain, their injuries were slight."

"Aye, they were until the fools suffered the ten lashes I ordered for each of them. You've a rare skill with those clubs, and 'tis one of the reasons I'm here; you'll not be easily cowed."

"What is your offer, Captain Rambert?"

"The products I mentioned earlier are not the favorite cargo of my breed of mariners. Aye, mistress, I've been many things during my thirty years at sea; and more than likely, my reputation has been well earned. But I'm as much merchant as I am buccaneer, and most of my cargoes and those of the men I represent are Spanish or French in origin. We've yet to prey on honest English shipping. Still and all, we'll never be given the royal pardons your husband and his partners received, and thus we'll be forever denied entry into the home ports of England. Therein lies our problem. In the past two years, since Spain no longer ships as much gold and the French now garden every acre of their colonies, over half of our bounty has been Caribbean produce; and we've no way of selling it. Until the English took over New Amsterdam, we'd have sold to the Dutch privateers; but we're denied even that port now."

"I've no money to buy even a dozen barrels of rum, Captain Rambert," Lynn warned.

"Aye, I know you'll have to consult Edward Fulton about payment."

"You're well informed," Lynn murmured neutrally.

"Harry Cobb has always had a careless tongue when

he's drinking, and I've a harmless looking bosun's mate with sharp ears. Not only was Harry informative about your company, he boasted loudly of his own enterprise." Pausing to note the suddenly wary expression on Lynn's face, Rambert smiled with reassuring cynicism. "You needn't worry about your husband's safety at sea, mistress. He has an uncanny way of attending a ship's defense that discourages attack from those of us who know his reputation.

"And I'll ease your mind about the money payment as well," he added. "The proposition is that we'll be paid half the profit you'll make in England for the goods we supply you, provided you're the one who determines that sum."

Lynn suppressed a gasp of surprise; she'd expected far more demanding terms. " 'Tis a generous offer, Captain Rambert."

"You'd not be considering it otherwise, mistress. I'll expect your answer tomorrow morning."

"One thing before you go, Captain. Why would you trust a man like Harry Cobb and not my husband or Bert Spence?"

Rambert's expression was no longer bland, and his harsh bearded face lost all semblance of amiability. "One does not need to trust a fool to make use of him. Harry Cobb Pendrath is not a man to inspire either trust or fear, unlike the other two. My only objection to the man you call Bert Spence is simple self-preservation. He now represents the law, and I've reason enough to be wary."

"And my husband?"

"Did he tell you that we fought together in winning Jamaica for England?"

"I've heard something of that matter and a little of your subsequent clashes on land and at sea; but from what I understand, Captain Vinson and the others were equally responsible."

" 'Tis a more personal matter between Charles Trevor and myself, an affair of honor."

"Suppose you tell me, Captain Rambert; I cannot do business with someone who hates my husband."

" 'Tis not a pretty story for a young wife to hear."

"Tell me anyway."

"Six years ago in France I'd been made a French privateer with letters of marque to give me a measure of respectability. About that same time I met a young English widow who agreed to become my wife until your husband interfered and claimed her for his own."

Lynn's lips curled in bitter realization that one way or another Amelia Pendrath was still a threat. Eight months ago it hadn't been Harry who'd recognized Rambert's first mate in the New Port inn; more likely it'd been the observant Amelia. And later aboard the *Tamarlind*, the damnable woman had been deliberately noisy in an attempt to attract Rambert's attention so that Clay might once again be forced to defend her honor.

"Was the woman's name Amelia Gordon something or other French?" Lynn demanded harshly.

" 'Twas Amelia d'Auberge; I didn't know about the Gordon part. According to her, Charles Trevor had destroyed her earlier marriage and killed her husband, and he now threatened her life and mine. At first, I didn't believe that the man I'd known would be so dishonorable; but the woman seemed terrified, and so I let her go."

"Clay killed her first husband in a duel she'd arranged; he fought only to save his own life; and that duel cost him his name. He was James Thayne at the time you met Amelia, and I doubt he was even in France."

"He was in France, mistress. I received word that my letters of marque had been rescinded because of a complaint by Charles Trevor."

"More likely 'twas the Comte d'Auberge, the son of Amelia's husband. He was the one who had my husband declared a pirate. Tell me, Captain, had you given Amelia many trinkets of value prior to her remarkable story and 'terrified' departure?''

"Aye, a chest full of them."

"Then your hatred is misdirected, sir. The lady in question has quite a history of jewel acquisition and of promising what she had no intention of delivering. 'Tis true my husband played the fool for a number of years until she married Harrold Pendrath, the younger brother of Lord Andrew Pendrath. She would never have married you under any circumstances; Gordon women marry only into wealthy, aristocratic families. Imagine her chagrin when she discovered that the Honorable Harrold Pendrath was also Harry Cobb, a member of my husband's band of smugglers. But she soon became a talented smuggler too."

"Are you certain of these facts, mistress?" Rambert demanded.

"Absolutely. 'Twas a necklace she'd stolen from one of the king's mistresses that led to the capture of the entire group; and until the royal pardon, she was an indentured criminal the same as they were. If you're really interested in resuming your interrupted pursuit for her favor, you'll find her in Virginia. But if you do, question her more thoroughly than you did the last time; she is the most gifted liar I have ever known. I'd also keep a close watch on your strongbox; her last store of jewelry was confiscated at the time of her arrest."

"The thieving bitch!"

"My informant was a woman who should know; she was the only one of the seven smugglers *not* pardoned."

"Then she'd be the one Harry Cobb referred to as Tom's . . . I beg your pardon, mistress, 'twas an ugly word he used."

"I'm familiar with Harry's vocabulary; as you said, he has a loose tongue. But Nell Wallis is honest to a fault."

"Then the matter's settled, Mistress Trevor . . . Mistress Penley. When you see your husband next, you can tell him so."

"I doubt he knows anything about the incident. Until quite recently, he believed Amelia's lies as readily as you did. Are you still tendering your business proposition in good faith?"

"Far better now. I think we understand each other. You're not a woman to quibble, and you're gambler enough to trust me."

Lynn nodded thoughtfully. "Aye, I'm gambler enough," she admitted.

It needed only a few minutes in the Fulton study that afternoon for Edward Fulton to convince the other partners to accept the offer. " 'Twill mean the difference between a long slow haul and a guaranteed success. We've allowed the scurvy lot to settle in our colony; now 'tis time we profited. If we don't, the others will and we'll be the losers. I'll admit I prefer knowing all the people I'm dealing with; but Rambert's proved trustworthy so far, and I can't fault his terms."

The following morning, Lynn learned that those terms made her the permanent go-between. Rambert and his cohorts insisted that she, Jem Rigg, and John Bram be the only outsiders present during the transfer of goods from the stronghold cellars of the buccaneers' homes to the Carter storage sheds along the embarcadero. Each predawn morning, the work was accomplished under cover of darkness, and the only noise engendered was the creak of wagon wheels. After Rambert and his fellow freebooters had left New Port bound on their annual hunting voyages, Lynn informed Edward Fulton who readily agreed that the secrecy had been necessary.

"Not all the pirates hereabouts fly the Jolly Roger," he intoned sententiously.

When Elwin Carter returned with the *Aquidneck* at the same time as the *Narragansett* with David Carey and Bert Spence aboard, all three men enthusiastically approved both Rambert's offer and the secrecy. "Until we can hire enough capable guards, the less attention we attract, the better," Carter declared.

"Did you bring full loads back with you?" Fulton demanded.

Carter shook his head gloomily. "Only half. The Massachusetts market has already been cornered by its own shippers."

"Then we'll concentrate on the south," Bert volunteered. "We'll need both ships to collect the lumber we bought from every sawmill between here and the Carolinas, and we've located a source for tar and turpentine."

Exhausted after weeks of fourteen-hour working days, Lynn left the four men huddled over the spread-out tally sheets in the office to begin the second half of her grinding schedule. She found the cottage in a pleasant uproar of busy preparations. For a moment she stared blankly at Polly and flinched guiltily when Kate called out, " 'Tis Nell's wedding day tomorrow, and Ned's already gone into town to remind Bert of the fact. Lands sake, girl, you look like you've forgotten all about it."

Lynn nodded morosely; she'd been too busy to remember her own marriage except during the lonely hours of night.

CHAPTER
13

Few experiences in her own life had ever given Lynn the satisfaction that Nell's wedding did. In the long weeks between the pre-Christmas promise and the April fact, Nell had won approval beyond the Fulton family circle; her blunt honesty and humor had eventually outweighed her doubtful past among all but a few purists in Reverend Tyler's congregation. In her simple blue dress, she had spoken her vows in a clear voice; and no one present had any doubt but that she'd keep them.

Almost as touching a ceremony was the brief christening that followed the wedding, when Bert Spence stood beside the woman who'd undertaken the care of his motherless daughter and who now assumed the official position of godmother. With Elvira Hayes's bluff father, Captain Carter, completing the small procession as godfather, young Jane Spence was welcomed into the humble congregation with a simplicity that ignored her father's title and her absent mother's social pretentions. During the weeks preceding the dual celebration, Lynn had gradually won a guarded offer of friendship from the retiring young widow largely because of Lynn's tolerant fondness for Elvira's toddling son. Having monitored the gamboling playfulness of a hundred-odd calves, Lynn had found the antics of the curious and adventuresome fourteen-month-old Melvin Hayes a welcome diversion from dull office work.

Now as she watched Bert and the Carter family from across the room at the wedding reception, Lynn remembered Leona's fading prettiness and postured mannerisms with humor. Ten years younger and as many pounds heavier, Elvira Hayes was comely enough to make any man forget the petulant, childish woman who had deserted her husband and child.

Lynn's own interest in Elvira other than a needed friendship was a sincere admiration for her quality of motherhood. Content in her limited role of homemaker, Elvira lavished her love on both infants equally; and Lynn found herself wishing that her own disposition were as placid. Five weeks after Clay's departure, she'd known for certain that she was to bear his child; she'd worked with breeding animals too long not to recognize the symptoms. Within days she'd accepted the fact with inner satisfaction, vowing only to contain the secret as long as possible.

Her energies, however, remained concentrated on the task she'd undertaken: to make all of her separate and combined businesses successful. She worked unstintingly throughout the weeks prior to Captain Vinson's return with the fleet of five ships, surviving the strenuous unloading and reloading of cargoes and the speeded-up delivery of those items bound for Rhode Island customers. More difficult for her was the suppression of her emotional reactions to the letters Vinson had brought her. The one from her grandfather expressed Ephraim's bitter disappointment that John Pollock's killer had still not been apprehended, and a firm reminder that she was not to consider leaving her present sanctuary. When Peter Vinson had handed her Clay's letter, he was openly jovial.

"Your husband took no chances that this message might

be lost. I was instructed to deliver it personally even if it meant a delay."

"Can you perform the same delivery service for me?"

"Aye, to your grandfather, but not to your husband I'm afraid. He'll be using London port while we alternate between Plymouth and Liverpool. So that one letter from Clay will have to do you until he returns. Your grandfather was insistent that you not trust anyone other than me with your personal mail."

Had Clay's letter been a more recent one, Lynn might have rejoiced in its contents. The reminders were humorously fond, and the promises firm; but Lynn's current mood was rooted in an existing reality, not in a romantic, sometime-in-the-distant-future possibility. She had to plan her life around a child now, not on a husband plying the distant seas between the Caribbean and England. Nor could she reveal the child's future existence to her grandfather; she had already burdened him enough. The one letter she wrote to Ephraim was an edited description of her life and the people around her, the very people she was already learning to avoid. She wanted neither their sympathy nor their advice nor a well-meant supervision of her activities. She still faced the necessity of providing financial security for her child.

Throughout the second three-month period of rebuilding cargo stocks, she wore a lightweight cloak in town and on deliveries and a concealing apron when she worked on the farm. Her only concession to impending motherhood was the fewer number of times she drove the delivery wagons. But even in the beginning of the sixth month, she still manned one of the wagons that transferred the cargoes from the buccaneers' ships to the company storage sheds. Ironically, it was the sharp-eyed Morse Rambert who informed Bert Spence of her condition when the *Narragansett* arrived in port.

Furious at the missing father and at himself for avoiding

seeing her, Bert visited the farm that same afternoon and spoke privately to Kate and Polly.

"Why the devil didn't one of you stop her from trying to kill herself?" he demanded.

Polly was first to answer the rude question. "Lynn ain't one to back away easy when she gets the bit in her teeth, and she never did take to being fussed over. No credit to her feckless mother or overweening grandmother, Lynn has enough good Cornish hill blood in her not to be the weakling your wife was, Bert. She'll not be working beyond her strength, and she'll want the babe as healthy as her bulls."

Kate's response was less practical, but more perceptive. "'Tis not a happy time for her, so I made her dresses looser without nagging her. I think she's been working like a drudge to help her forget that it might be years before her husband returns."

"Has she tried to reach him by letter?"

"Not likely," Polly snorted in contempt. "Lynn's as proud as Lucifer when it comes to asking help from any man, much less that light-o'foot excuse for one."

Lacking Polly's greater experience, Kate was cautious. "Don't be in too great a hurry to bad-mouth him, Bert. Could be we're all wrong about his intentions. Lynn expected him to be gone at least a year, so likely she's not too upset yet. Matter of fact, before you start bellowing at her at all, best you talk to Nell. She generally comes over to work with Lynn every afternoon."

"Why should Nell be working here at all? She has her own home to run now."

"Nell insists on paying her own debts. Besides, she's known about the babe longer'n any of us."

Although he was considerably calmer by the time he located the two young women in the barn, Bert was no less determined. "I'll be taking over the work in town, Lynn, until after you deliver your child," he announced without his usual diplomatic preamble.

"There's one job I still have to supervise regardless of my untimely condition," she responded with an equal lack of pretense.

"Not any more; I talked to Morse Rambert today. Why the devil didn't you tell me months ago, Lynn?"

" 'Tis no one's concern but my own, Spence."

"I dare say, Clay might be concerned if he knew. How many letters has he written you?"

"Only one, but New Port's not one of his ports of call. He promised to return, and I've no doubt he will... eventually, but probably not until long after my child is born. And there's something else he might be more interested in than fatherhood at any rate." Lynn's voice was tinged with irony as she removed the gold chain from around her neck.

"Nell," she called out to the woman seated on a low stool twenty feet away, "leave the milking for the moment; I want you to see this."

In an explanation to Bert, Lynn added casually, "Nell has promised to raise my child if something happens to me, but I'll want you both to look after his inheritance in case his father is reluctant. I didn't know I'd have an inheritance to leave until Captain Vinson told me its worth six months ago. Since Clay has seen it, too, he might also have learned its worth. If so you'll have no say in the matter; but if you do, I want my child protected from poverty at least. Was Captain Vinson right about its value, Spence?"

Holding the stone up to the light, Bert whistled in awe. " 'Tis a raw diamond, Lynn. I've never seen its like before. My God, woman, why have you been working like a beaten slave when you had this fortune hanging around your neck?"

"I prefer to earn my own; besides I had no access to a market. Nell, I want you to lock it up in Mr. Fulton's strongbox until 'tis needed."

"What happens when Clay gets here, Lynn?" Bert asked harshly.

"If I survive, I'll deal with him. He said he wanted a child, so perhaps he wasn't spinning cobwebs. If I don't survive, you and Nell will have to face him. I don't really suppose he'll have much interest in raising a child alone, but you'll have to tell him anyway."

"Have you written a will yet?" Bert persisted.

"No. Until my name is cleared of the suspicion of witchcraft, any will I made would be invalid. That's why everything I possess is in my grandfather's name—everything except this necklace; so I've kept it secret."

"Gor!" Nell exploded into speech. "I'd like to get my hands on the bastards that hung that charge on you. But as of right now, both of you can stop spouting gloom all over the place. Lynn has the edge over most women caught in the trap; she knows to a week when the sprout is due, so she'll not be caterwauling in terror whenever she gets kicked or feels a pain. Childbirth is no blinking romp, Lynn, but you're as strong as any woman can be; and you'll be coming through it with a son that'll weigh half a stone or more. With Kate and me there to tell you what to do and with Polly keeping Jem and the others from plaguing you with worry, you'll be more than all right."

Nell's optimistic prophesy proved accurate in every detail except for the infant's size. Charles Ephraim weighed in at ten pounds, almost three over the half-a-stone prediction. While not an experience Lynn looked forward to repeating on a yearly schedule, the eight hours of labor had been bearable. And Jem's look of satisfaction when he inspected the red-faced child brought the laughter of relief bubbling to her tired lips. Jem had looked just as he did whenever a newborn calf was bull rather than heifer. But Lynn's most deeply rooted gratitude went out to Nell, a gutter waif who'd become a staunch friend, and to Bert Spence who promised solemnly to protect another man's son.

Because Lynn had worked steadily until the day she gave birth, the farm was prospering and the trading company was well afloat with three round-trips successfully completed. With a renewed sense of hope, she was out of bed in two days, alternating the chore of nursing an uncomplicated infant with regaining control of her own life. Her first tour of the farm was a triumphant one, rendered emotionally touching by the paternal interest of the three indentureds who'd been her working companions for eighteen months. It was Kerry Egan, the irrepressible Irishman who'd once been the bane of Irish travelers in County Sligo, and now the fiercest member of the Aquidneck militia, who expressed the sentiments of the less effusive John Bram and Jason Hale.

"Niver did we doubt 'twould be a lad ye birthed, mistress; and he'll not be wantin' for a man's carin' as long as we're here."

Lynn smiled her gratitude for his degree of Irish tolerance; more than once she'd blistered his ears in a well-deserved reprimand. But she'd never docked the wages of any of them! That incentive had more than paid off during the speeded-up work schedule of the past months, and it had gained her friends instead of resentful prisoners.

Jem, of course, had a deeper sense of possession for her child. He and Polly had been more parents to her than anyone else in her life, and both of them made frequent excuses to hover over the sleeping infant. Lynn's own emotions about her son were as uncomplicated as he was; it didn't matter that he resembled neither of his parents, he was hers. She now had someone of her own blood to share her life with; and as the weeks passed, the bond strengthened. Far less frequently was her peace of mind shattered by resentment against a missing husband, and no longer did she fret inwardly about letters that never arrived. Clay

Trevor was what he was, and nothing she could do would change his wanderlust into domesticity. She vowed, however, that her son would not follow in his footsteps. Charles Ephraim would become a solid merchant farmer, an American rather than a misplaced Englishman. With that goal in mind, Lynn began to plan a permanent home.

The pressing need for one had become apparent within a week after Charles Ephraim's birth. The small cabin that he shared at night with his mother was large enough, but woefully lacking in comfort, while the cottage next door where he spent his days was overcrowded and inadequate. As the rainy winter replaced a blustery fall, infant laundry dangled from every corner; and the communal meals now lacked any pretense of graciousness. Ignoring her nostalgia about the rambling stone manor house on Penley Farm in Cornwall, Lynn planned instead the practical two-story, central chimney structure that conserved both firewood and warmth. Hers would be a frame and sawed-lumber house with four rooms upstairs and four below and with washrooms elegant enough for guests. It was time, she reasoned with a practical fortitude, for her to abandon her phantom dreams of a home supplied by a fond and constant husband, and to develop a social life of her own as full as the one the Fultons led.

On the day she finalized her thinking on the matter, Clay had been missing from her life for well over a year, and his son had become her chief confidant and confessor. "You're not to worry about your life being lopsided, little son," she told him. "I grew up without any sides at all, and I survived."

Impatient as she always was once she decided on a project, Lynn turned her just-fed son over to Polly and walked into town to join Bert Spence in the office. For a moment he stared at her silently before he spoke.

"You look like you've just found a pot of gold," he challenged her.

"Just the opposite. I'm going to spend one. I've decided to build a house."

"Why now, Lynn?"

"I want my son settled down."

"You know that's impossible until Clay returns."

"My son may be full grown by that time. Clay's been gone over a year, and it could be another five before he finds the time to visit me again."

Bert's voice held a bitterness that startled her when he responded to her lightly spoken cynicism. "But when he does, you'll fall into his arms and do whatever he asks. Last time you said you wanted no part of him, yet you gave him all your money and then bore his son."

"I don't regret the money or the child, Spence. Like all the partners, I've almost earned back the money; and I'm a little tired of pioneering. What is your real objection to my building a home here?"

Feeling as bleak as the overcast March weather, Bert was tempted to gamble, to salvage something from the lives that were being wasted by two selfish partners. His own private life had become one of avoidance. Had he been free a year ago, he would have married Elvira Hayes out of gratitude; but a clandestine relationship had proved impossible for both of them. She was too fine a woman to be subjected to public scorn; and Leona had not forgotten the stranglehold she had on him. Shoved under the less irksome papers on his desk was another letter from her, this one dictated by a far brighter mind, a subtle threat to reclaim her daughter and a subtler account of a neighboring Virginian who'd displayed an uncommon interest in the whereabouts of the witch woman.

"Imagine finding anyone in this colony who'd ever heard of that mawkish farmwoman," Leona had written. "The last time Clay and Harry were here, they didn't mention her. Is she still tending her bull on that hideous farm, or has she been returned to England? I know better than to criticize her to you, Spencer; but I do hope that by this time, you'll have realized that she's not our kind of people and never can be."

In these pages of script, there was no interest revealed in her daughter's health or in Bert's work, except for an urgent request that he increase her allotment of money. Everything else in the letter had been devoted to description of the home Amelia was having built, the beautiful clothing Amelia wore, and the devastating popularity with the Virginia gentry that Amelia enjoyed.

"Lynn," Bert checked his bitter recriminations abruptly, "what would you say to moving the company headquarters to New York? We'd have a bigger market there, and we'd both be free."

"Free from what?"

"Our damnable idiot spouses. Clay has forgotten you exist, and all Leona wants from me is money."

"No, Spence, I made the mistake of running away in Cornwall and of leaving a tired old man to fight my battles for me. I'd rather wait for the future here among friends than in a strange colony among strangers."

"I wouldn't be a stranger, Lynn."

Again she shook her head in denial. "Neither of us is the kind who can ignore reality, Spence. I don't need any more complications in my life, and neither do you. Now will you help me build my house?"

Bert sighed in resignation. What was there about her that made her seem a second half of himself? She'd even used the same words that he'd been thinking, and he'd known what her answer would be before she spoke. As always, she'd been swift in her comprehension and unhesitatingly honest in her response.

"Wait until I return from this final trip to New York. Dave and I will be making the last of our deliveries there and picking up the cargo we've already contracted."

"Then will you do me one favor before you leave? I want you to tell Captain Rambert that I'd like to see him.

One of his men is a superb builder, and I plan to hire him."

"Good God, Lynn, Rambert's a pirate, and so are his men."

"He prefers the term buccaneer merchant; and since we're making money from his endeavors, I don't feel all that sanctimonious in contrast."

"I was referring to the fact that you're a beautiful woman again, Lynn."

"As far as he's concerned, I'm a business partner; and he always treats me with respect. Since I'll be working in the office again for three hours in the morning and afternoon, I won't be able to go to his home."

"Why don't we just close the office down for a month?"

"If one of us isn't here, Caleb Winslow would revert to his old tricks of overcharging. Besides, I need to get back to work; I've had a long enough holiday. And I want you to spend your last days in port with your daughter; and while you're about it, I want you to give Elvira's son a big hug too. He's another of our half-way children."

"Lynn, about what I said a while ago—"

"You didn't say it, Spence, and I'm grateful. But don't forget your promise about Rambert. I'd like to thank him for the vacation months he gave me before my son was born."

A week later, just after Lynn finished a brisk morning of supervising the loading of three wagons hired to cart a valuable cargo of wine from a docked ship to the shop of the most prosperous merchant in town and completing the tally sheets at her desk, she glanced up and nodded absently to the man who'd just entered the office. Because the visitor was flamboyantly garbed in a colorful, full-pantalooned velvet suit and was wearing a lavishly curled wig and a plumed hat, her first impression was one of mistaken identity. The only New Port resident who dressed in such extravagant style was Captain Rambert, and she almost spoke his name until she looked more closely at the saturnine face of a complete stranger.

The cultured voice held a note of caustic condescension when he addressed her. " 'Tis like turning the clock backward, Mistress Penley; you grew up to look just like my mother, devil eyes and all. I'm your father, Royce Trevor, and I've come a damnably long way to find you."

Ten years ago in London when the hot passions of youth still ruled her mind, Lynn would have fled from this meeting, so intense had her hatred been. During one of her mother's and grandmother's rare visits to Penley Farm, she'd overheard an emotional conversation between the two women and learned that her father had ordered his wife to remain permanently in England. Later Lynn had read the letter she'd found crumpled in the waste bin, a report from the agent Hortensia had hired to investigate her son-in-law. Royce Trevor hadn't wanted his wife to come to Virginia because his household there consisted of a housekeeper-mistress who'd already borne him a son and a daughter. In the ensuing years, Lynn's hurt fury had cooled to icy contempt. Now as her gaze swept disdainfully over the father she hadn't seen in twenty years, she felt nothing but a cynical malice.

"Please have a seat, Mr. Trevor," she murmured. "I'll be with you in a minute."

Dipping her quill carefully into the ink pot, she proceeded to complete the tally sheet and to reread what she'd written before she laid the quill down. She knew her numbered total was wrong by several pounds, but her face was expressionless when she finally glanced up and spoke with pleasant impersonality.

"Now tell me about this grandmother you say I resemble."

"Like you, mistress, she was a Cornish hill woman who brought disaster to my family."

"She *was* a member of your family then?"

"She was an embarrassment and worse. Throughout the civil war, she accompanied my father into military camp; and like the fool he'd become, he didn't send her packing. That was where she lost my family the title and the estate King Charles had promised us. When the king visited my father's regiment, she dared to use the ancient Cornish tongue and to threaten the king with a traitorous prophecy of defeat and his eventual death. King Charles never spoke to my father again."

No longer disinterested, Lynn stared at her father. "Were her prophecies always that accurate?"

"No one had paid much attention to them before, and she and my father were both killed in that battle of Edgehill in '42. What paltry estate my father left me was gone within a year. Had she not been the troublemaker she was, I'd have been spared the subsequent indignities of my life. As I said earlier, you have her look of insolent deviltry."

"I may resemble her physically, Mr. Trevor, but unfortunately I do not possess her gift of second sight. When you first entered my office, I mistook you for one of the local freebooters who would have been most welcome by comparison. Was your poverty the reason you wed my foolish mother when she was but fifteen years old?"

"That cursed marriage was the *Honorable* Hortensia's idea, and therein lies the reason for my seeking you out today. I have come for the inheritance Hortensia promised me, the money you embezzled after the old harridan died."

"Then you've come a long way for nothing," Lynn snapped with cold authority. "Ten years ago, my grandmother wrote a new will naming me her heir. Perhaps you should journey to England and consult with her lawyer, John Coleman, who survived both the plague and the fire."

Royce Trevor's smile was smugly triumphant. "I have just returned from England where I learned from your Mr.

Coleman that while he survived the fire, his records did not. But all of my records are still intact, especially my copy of your treacherous grandmother's original will naming me her sole beneficiary. You'd be very foolish to contest my claim. So before you blurt any more of your unfilial insolence, you should know that I took the time to investigate the charges against you thoroughly. For your own protection, I advise you not to anger me further. Where is the money you stole from me?"

Suppressing the impulse to tell her father that Ephraim Penley had her grandmother's final will in safe custody, Lynn countered the implied threat with a deceptively mild question. "Look around you, Mr. Trevor. Do you think I'd be working in this office for a few shillings a week if I had access to a fortune? While in England, you should have talked to my grandfather. He would have told you that during their lifetime, my grandmother and my mother gambled away both the Trelynn and the Penley fortunes. All that was left after they died was the London house and furnishings, which realized very little money in a city stricken by plague."

"How much was the total?"

"Eight thousand pounds."

"What about the Trelynn jewelry? That hoard was worth triple that amount."

"A week or so before she died of the plague, my mother lost the last necklace over the gaming tables."

"You tell a convenient lie, mistress, but not a convincing one. Hortensia owned a pendant, a diamond she'd worn around her neck for years, always concealed from the public, but 'twas public knowledge none the less. Before I wed your mother, I made it my business to learn all about that diamond and about Hortensia's attachment to it. She would never have gambled it away herself or allowed her scatterbrained daughter to touch it."

Lynn's heart was pounding with alarm, but she forced her voice to reflect only disbelief. "The only thing my grandmother wore around her neck was an ugly trinket: a dull, shapeless stone of some kind, certainly not a diamond. She called it her good-luck charm and was clutching it in her hand when she died. As far as I was concerned, it had no value. The officials who buried her in the plague pit didn't think so either. They stole only her gold hairpins before they bundled her into a shroud and put her body into the collection cart."

Royce Trevor stared at her in stupefaction before he exploded into furious speech. "You bloody damn fool! You imbecilic dunderhead! That was an uncut, unpolished diamond worth a fortune, and you threw it away!"

Watching his agitation with relief, Lynn continued the fabrication. "How was I to know its worth? I've never owned a piece of jewelry in my life, and I didn't think it was worth a tuppence. At any rate 'tis gone now; no one is allowed to dig in those pits."

Mastering his anger with difficulty, Trevor snapped out his next order, "Then get me the eight thousand pounds from wherever you've hidden it, and I'll be done with you."

Again Lynn's eyes widened in spurious shock, although this time her protest required very little deception. "I don't have a farthing of it. My grandfather was without funds when he returned from the colonies, so I gave him half; and my husband took the rest to start his business. As you had with my mother, he considered my money to be lawfully his."

Trevor was silent for a moment as he studied her face and then shrugged in angry acceptance. "In that case, you leave me no alternative but to reclaim my money in whatever way I can. As you know, I remarried three years ago, and I now have a son."

"You had another son and daughter before that," she accused him.

When she noted his furious flush and compressed lips, Lynn silently blessed the merciful fate that had spared her the indignity of resembling him. Despite his florid good looks and well-trimmed beard, his face was flawed by self-centered conceit and petulance, and much of the cultured assurance of his voice had been replaced by an unpleasant rasp.

"My private life is none of your business!" he snapped.

"But you did have two children while you were still legally married to my mother," Lynn persisted. "Is the woman who bore you those children the one you married after you were free?"

"Don't be a fool! My wife is a woman of quality."

"What happened to the other woman and your children?"

"Not that the matter concerns you, but she married a cooper who emigrated to the Carolinas after he'd served his indenture."

"And the children?"

"She took them with her."

Smiling faintly in subtle contempt, Lynn murmured, "You have a way of ridding yourself of any responsibility for your unwanted offspring, Mr. Trevor. As a point of curiosity, how did you locate me so quickly after ignoring my existence for two decades?"

"I had excellent help as well as your scandalous reputation to guide me, and last spring I met your husband in Virginia."

Lynn's heart thudded with an abrupt heaviness. "He told you where I was?" she asked dully.

"He was as insolent as you, and as unobliging as your grandfather when I challenged his claim to being a Penley. I'd been told that there was only one Penley nephew until your arrogant husband persuaded me otherwise."

As she realized the import of his words, an illogical happiness flooded her being; Clay had not betrayed her, and he was still using the name of Penley. "Was he the one who told you he'd married me?" she asked curiously.

"No, 'twas the wife of his partner who informed me some months earlier about your situation."

"Did Amelia Pendrath tell you anything about my husband other than the fact of our marriage?"

"She mentioned his conceit and his knavish reputation with women, and she said he'd used many aliases in his various attempts to earn a living. Her report to me is the only reason I accept your claim that he absconded with the money."

"You found her all that trustworthy?"

"Why not? Like my wife, she's a woman of quality, connected to one British lord by birth and to another by marriage. Moreover, she is well sponsored by her Virginia cousin who is a long-time friend of mine."

"I hope you're a better judge of your present wife's *quality* than you are of Amelia Pendrath's," Lynn murmured. "What did she tell you about me?"

"The truth—that you were a fugitive charged with murder and witchcraft."

"And you accepted her word about my guilt without any proof?"

"You forget that I already had good cause to believe the witchcraft charge. I'd known for years that you'd inherited my own mother's taint. Had my need for funds not been so acute, I'd have denied the relationship; but unfortunately Mistress Pendrath was not the only one in Virginia who knew you were my daughter. A newly appointed deputy sheriff in the county showed me a copy of the specific charges against you: damning facts that left no room for doubt."

For the first time since her father had intruded into the office, Lynn experienced a thrill of fear. "What is that deputy's name?" she demanded shakily.

"His name is not important. He's a cloddish Cornishman who knows you well."

With her remaining doubts eliminated, Lynn retorted hotly, "Aye, Rad Pollock knows me well; he asked me to marry him often enough."

"So he said; and until he learned of your ill-considered

marriage, he was still willing to accept the risk. Had you wed him while you were still young enough to be disciplined, you'd not be in the damnable situation you are now. And you'd have had enough children to have kept you too occupied for the devil's mischief. In the case of my mother, 'twas I and the three who died who gained her any tolerance at all among my father's friends. Regrettably, you'll not have the benefit of motherhood to help in your defense if you're returned to England and placed in the dock. According to Harrold Pendrath, who was as agreeably informative as his wife, you've seen your husband only once since you arrived in the colonies, and you'll not be seeing him again for a long time.''

Rendered abruptly cautious by the odd satisfaction reflected in her father's voice, Lynn did not contradict his claim. Instead she added to the lie. '' 'Tis just as well I don't have children. My grandfather's farm here on Aquidneck Island produces only one sparse crop a year, so I've scarce enough money for my own support.''

''Don't take me for a fool,'' Trevor warned her coldly. ''When I talked to your cousin Owen, he told me you'd stolen a goodly herd of breeding cows and forty salable bullocks worth a small fortune.''

''Owen and his wife have always been gifted liars. 'Twas your cousin Bevil Trevor and I who owned that cattle jointly. I brought the beasts to America right enough; but as you should know, Bevil never gives away aught for naught. He made me responsible for eleven indentured criminals he wanted out of England. The money those forty bullocks earned was spent to build cabins for the indentureds and a barn for the cows. I now earn a pittance for boarding sixteen of the bullocks, but I don't own them anymore. The man who operates the local draying company does, and he is not a person I'd want to cheat.''

Since the mention of the word *indentured*, Trevor's eyes had held a gleam of interest. ''Never mind the bullocks for the moment; what are the lengths of service for those eleven people?''

"There are only four of them left after King Charles was paid to grant a royal pardon to the other seven. Colonial life has not been as merciful to me as 'tis obviously been to you," she added boldly.

Her irony was lost on the man now frowning heavily as he continued his tabulation of her wealth. "There was a bull mentioned in the official charges against you, and the deputy was positive that you'd never part with that particular animal.''

Lynn sighed in defeat; her father had been well informed. "I still own Red Penny," she admitted, her eyes narrowed in speculation. He means to strip the farm, she concluded with a heavy anger, and he considers me as guilty of witchcraft as he did his mother. Lynn shuddered involuntarily as she recalled his words about two other of his unwanted children. Without a hint of conscience, he'd packed them off to another colony; and he would send his oldest daughter back to Cornwall to stand trial just as callously. He might even prefer me dead, Lynn brooded; in that way, there'd be no one but a tired old man in England to challenge the theft of her animals and servants.

Sharply recalled to the present danger by his demand that she escort him to the farm, Lynn rose swiftly, gathered up her cloak and clubs, and walked toward the rear door that led to the Carters' entry hall. As she stepped from the office into that darkened haven, she turned toward the man who'd started to follow her.

"You're a fool, Royce Trevor, if you think I'm going to contribute to your support," she snapped as she slammed the door shut in his face. Shoving the lock bar into place, she raced to the back door of the house and into the alley behind, and then began to run with the racing speed she'd once practiced in the isolation of the Tamar Valley farm. She had no doubt that he'd locate this new farm and carry out every one of his threatened intentions. She had to warn the others in time to support the lies she'd told a father she had no reason to trust. And, dear God, she had to hide the son she'd denied having!

When her uncaring father had first mentioned his satisfied conviction that she had no children, Lynn had been perplexed; but now that memory filled her with increasing dread, and she ran as if pursued by the devils he'd accused her of serving. Seconds after she'd flung herself through the cottage door, she picked up her sound-asleep son and wrapped him and a pile of his infant clothing into the wool shawl that covered his small bed. As she turned to face the two women staring at her in consternation, she exploded into tense speech.

"Polly, you and Kate are to do exactly what I tell you. As soon as I've left to take Charles Ephraim to the Fultons, you're to hide everything that belongs to him in the root cellar."

"Lands sake, Lynn," Polly blustered, "why in tarnation would you want us to do that?"

"My father—my cursed damnable father—thinks that I robbed him of my grandmother's estate, and he's coming here to collect whatever he can. He was also very curious as to whether or not I had any children, so I don't want him to know a thing about my son."

"Lynn," Polly protested again, "there's enough of us here to protect that little mite from one man, even if Royce Trevor is the world's most unnatural father."

"That's just it, Polly, he might not be alone; and the man who may be with him is Rad Pollock."

Polly's florid face blanched in sudden fear. "God in heaven! Don't you dare return, girl, no matter what. If that lying son of Satan gets his hands on you, you'll pay a dear price. Run as fast as your legs will carry you, and tell Ned to fetch Mr. Williams."

"I don't think Mr. Williams can help. Rad Pollock is now a sheriff in Virginia, so he's a government official with the power to arrest me. Dear God, Polly, he can also arrest Kate and the others! I want all of you to get as far away from here as you can. Take one of the wagons and go to the Spragues.''

"Pshaw, girl, Rad Pollock don't frighten me none; he knows Jem's served his time, and he knows I'm a free woman," Polly insisted. "Just you take care of yourself and the babe, we'll look after things here."

In motion before Polly finished speaking, Lynn reached the boundary of her farm within minutes, pausing only to grab the halter rope of Red Clay, the half-grown bull grazing near the gate. In another fifteen minutes, she was inside the Fulton home, pouring her fears out to an alarmed Ned and Nell and to their concerned grandfather.

"Roger Williams is with part of the militia in the backwoods searching for renegade foreign Indians who raided a Narragansett village," Ned volunteered excitedly.

"We don't need them," Nell declared hotly. "Ned, you get over there and tell Jem and the others to arm themselves, and then you bring three of those muskets back here. Reckon we're allowed to defend ourselves same as everyone else."

"Not against a Virginia sheriff," Edward Fulton snapped. "We'd be accused of murder. We need someone official who can refuse to accept the warrant for Lynn's arrest and who can stop her thieving father. Ned, you go into town and see if you can locate any of the councilmen; but before you leave, get one of the field hands to put that bull in our barn before it gives the show away."

"I'm not leaving Nell and the rest of you unprotected," Ned insisted stubbornly.

"Do as I say, grandson. Nell and Lynn and the babe will be safely hid in the attic; and your mother and I will lock the house. If you can't locate anyone with authority enough in town, fetch your uncles and any of their hired men who might be willing to help us."

Normally an imperturbable man, Edward Fulton was frowning as he reread Ephraim Penley's letters with their

specific details about Rad Pollock's persecution of Lynn
and their equally blunt accusations about Royce Trevor.
Both of these men were ruthless, Fulton concluded; but
unfortunately, they were well armed with evidence supporting
their claims. Trevor had taken the precaution of bringing
his copy of an ancient will naming him heir, while the
newer, contradictory will was two thousand miles away in
Ephraim Penley's strongbox. In an even more secure
position as a Virginia deputy sheriff with official warrants
for Lynn's arrest on criminal charges, Pollock would be
difficult, if not impossible, to dissuade.

Fulton was familiar with Roger Williams's promise to
secrete Lynn in an Indian village, but Fulton himself did
not have the power to carry out that promise. Furthermore,
he was worried about the colony's reaction to the witchcraft charges. During his brief tenure in Massachusetts, he
had seen evidence of the hysteria such a charge produced.
While most Rhode Islanders were more tolerant, there
would be a few who might insist on her expulsion from the
colony; and an uncontrolled search for her might place her
and the child in greater danger than they now faced. But
under no circumstances, Fulton vowed, could he allow her
to be taken by these two villains whose motives were
despicable.

Four hours into his increasingly concerned vigil, long
before Ned could return with reinforcements, Fulton admitted an agitated stockman into his study.

"Gor," the frightened man exclaimed breathlessly,
"they've took everything, even the chickens and pigs.
Slicker than an Injun huntin' party they was, and even Red
Penny went along peacefullike when they roped him to one
of them wagons. 'Course ole Jem was in that wagon,
hog-tied along with t'others. And now there's two of them
furrin' bastards comin' here, not the fancy-dressed one,
but the one what did the ordering around the barn and the
young 'un what bashed the lights out of Kerry and Bram.
He and t'others was hidin' in the barn when Bram and

Kerry came back with a wagon, and he hit them from behind with a club.''

"My God, man, why didn't you warn me when the villains first arrived?" Fulton rasped.

" 'Cause Ned says you weren't t'be tole unless those thieves come here. And the big 'un who took Jason and Jem prisoner was bigger than a bear and twict as mean. 'Twas him what took the animals away, him and the young 'un while the others stood guard.''

"How many of our own workers are here, Rafe?"

"Jest me. Ned tole me t'watch, and he sent the others to fetch help, but I reckon there ain't many militia men left on the island what with them Injuns on the loose.''

"All right, Rafe, I want you to slip out the back door and run as fast as you can into town. You're to tell the preachers to start ringing the church bells and then—''

"No, he's not!" Lynn interrupted harshly as she entered the room. "Nell's already been to town and back to tell the one man who can help me. Captain Rambert has promised to follow the other ship and report back here when he learns where they're taking my people and animals. I imagine my grandfather will want to know when all of this is over.''

"Get back upstairs, mistress," Fulton ordered sharply. "Unless those men plan to break into my home, they'll not take you.''

"Those men wouldn't hesitate to burn your home, Mr. Fulton; and I want my son safe. Rafe, get up to the attic as fast as you can and hide. If they took Jem and Polly, they'll take anyone they can sell as an indentured.''

Stoically Lynn waited until the frightened stockman had fled toward the stairs before she continued her fatalistic instructions. "Mr. Fulton, all I want you to do for me is to protect my son until my grandfather arrives. Nell has promised to care for him.''

"God in heaven, woman, I can't turn you over to lawless men like these. Are you sure about their identities?"

"I could see a long way from your attic window. The big man Rafe described is named Fen, and he's a loyal servant to Rad Pollock. He's a vicious brute who was hated and feared by the neighbors in Cornwall. The younger man is Sid Pollock who did all the necessary witnessing against me for his father, and he's as vicious as Fen. Neither of them would hesitate to silence you if need be. I should have realized this morning that my father would not dare leave me here."

"Damn the lot of them to hell!" Fulton exploded in helpless anger.

"I'd prefer them indentured to me for twenty years' hard labor," Lynn murmured as she walked toward the entry door and pulled it open before the first knock sounded. Wincing involuntarily at the sight of the man lighted by the last rays of sunset, she awaited his pronouncement with the hopelessness of the already doomed.

Aggressively Rad Pollock pulled a rolled parchment from his pocket and announced, "You're under arrest, Trelynn Trevor Penley, to answer charges duly leveled against you by sovereign British edict. Do you want the specific charges read?"

"No, Mr. Pollock, I'm quite familiar with the lies you and your family told about me."

"Very well, mistress, if it suits your humor to be insolent. Who else is in the house?"

"An old man, half senile with fear, and his housekeeper hiding in the kitchen. You'd be wasting your time questioning them, since they know nothing about my past. I'm ready to leave with you now."

"Search her, Da," a nasal voice shouted from the bottom of the steps. "And use the manacles, Da. I don't relish another bashed head from those devil clubs of hers. Old Fen weren't as senseless as he pretended the night you did us in, witch."

Holding her empty hands stiffly out, Lynn submitted to the indignity of the heavy irons snapped around her wrists before she walked determinedly down the stairs. She wanted to be as far away from the Fulton home as possible before Rad Pollock remembered that he'd searched neither her nor the house. Despite her fear of what lay ahead, she experienced an increasing sense of victory with each step. Her son was safe, and her abductors would not go unpunished; there'd been too many reliable witnesses left behind.

Halfway to town on the darkening path, she spoke to the heavy-jawed man striding by her side. "Will you be taking me to England yourself, Mr. Pollock?"

While Rad Pollock made no response, his son sniggered, and Lynn felt the beginning of another kind of fear. They weren't planning to turn her over to responsible authorities at all! None of them, neither the Pollocks nor her father, could stand the glare of an official investigation any more than she could. She shuddered from the cold that was now more inward than out; they were waiting until dark to smuggle her aboard ship. Her father could easily have appeased any curiosity about the other kidnappings with his glib tongue and elegant mannerisms, but he could never have silenced her in town where she was well-known.

Sensing the tense vigilance of the two men pacing on either side of her, Lynn knew she had no chance of overpowering them, not even if her hands had been free to reach the clubs concealed beneath her petticoats. Cautiously she exercised her fingers within the restraint of the iron bonds and then relaxed; given privacy and time, she could free her left hand. The manacles had been designed for larger, less flexible hands than hers. Once she had one hand free, she reckoned with a chilling, sardonic resignation, she'd be able to swim a few strokes before she drowned if their intention was to throw her overboard. Lynn's mirthless half-smile did not go unnoticed.

"What's the witch smiling about, Da?" Sidney Pollock demanded suspiciously.

"At your gullibility," Lynn answered swiftly. "How did

my father ever convince the pair of you to do his dirty work for him? I'd have thought by this time you'd be wealthy Virginians, too high and mighty to act the servants for an aristocratic peacock like my father.''

"Our land there is naught but swamp," the younger man declared with pent-up bitterness. "The snotty bloods got all the river land. What ain't swamp on ours is good only for raising the cattle we got us today."

"Do you really think Royce Trevor is going to let you keep even one of the cows you stole?" Lynn demanded with incredulous contempt. "My nefarious parent has been cheating people successfully for more years than you are old, Sidney Pollock. He'll have sold every head of cattle before you're off the ship in Jamestown."

Lynn jerked convulsively when Rad Pollock gripped her arm with brutal strength. "You can stop playing your clever games with my son, and start using your head. Your father's not a complete fool; he can't let you roam free in Jamestown any more than he can let you stay here. And my price for keeping him safe from your wagging tongue is the cattle, but the five indentureds and the rest will be his to sell."

"Jem's indenture was finished long ago, and Polly's been a free woman all of her life," Lynn exclaimed in angry distress, only to cringe in fear at her tormentor's coarse laughter.

"Aye, and 'twill be my official duty to remind your father of the fact after I've taken you to wife and you've borne my children. He'll be paying a price to keep me quiet then: a bit of his rich land for each child you bear. The strutting cock cannot afford a damaged reputation, so he'll pay and keep on paying."

Lynn's heart leapt in revulsion; she'd believed that her existing marriage, however unsatisfactory it was, would protect her from the horror that Rad Pollock had just described so casually. When she thought of his thick-set body, grown more bullishly heavy over the past two years, she shuddered. Without much hope that her protest would be heeded, she murmured mechanically, "I already have a husband."

"That popinjay Penley relative your grandfather found rotting in Jamaica? Not much of a husband for a woman like you, mistress. I'll never be fool enough to leave you alone as he has; you need the discipline of a man, not a coward who flees from the marriage bed."

Stung to rashness by the conceit of the middle-aged braggart whose touch made her skin crawl, Lynn responded with an impulsive taunt, "He's more of a husband than you can ever be, Rad Pollock; and he's anything but a coward. He's the youngest son of Sir Bevil Trevor, and not a Penley at all; and as your brutal servant Fen discovered, he's a difficult man to kill. He was the one who lamed your son Jabe, and helped me capture all of you at the Watkins's farm in Cornwall."

"That man was an indentured criminal!"

"Not with a royal pardon he isn't! Do you really think you can outwit a man who has been a successful adventurer for fifteen years! He'll smash you and your puling sons like the slimy vermin you are once he locates you!"

Instantly Lynn regretted her rash boast; she'd risked what little safety she had, and far worse, she'd endangered her son. While her scheming father and the Pollocks had scant respect for the revenge capabilities of Ephraim Penley, all of them knew that Bevil Trevor and his sons were men of action rather than words. As casually as she could manage, she added the warning, "I'd not be telling Royce Trevor that 'twas his cousin he robbed if I were you. I don't imagine that your sheriff's badge would protect you in a Virginia court of law if an established aristocrat, even one as despicable as my father, testified that you were the one responsible for today's crimes. Remember that your son's violence was witnessed by several people."

Lynn heard the whispery rush of air as Sidney swung his club toward her head. Dodging instinctively, she succeeded only in avoiding the full brunt of the vicious blow that sent her reeling to the ground. Barely conscious, she heard the shrill command of the younger Pollock.

"Kill her, Da, before she ruins us for certain with her devil's tongue. God damn the goddamned witch!"

"Don't be any more of a fool than you already are," Rad snapped furiously. "She's no more witch than any other woman; she's just a smart enough liar to make a dull wit like you jump in fear. That Trevor son drowned ten years ago in the English channel, so her husband is naught but a cowardly Penley."

While Lynn fought to retain what little awareness she had left, she felt herself pulled roughly upward and hefted over a man's massive shoulder. As her head flopped downward against the hard muscled back, she felt the sickening rush of blood for an instant in time. And then she felt nothing!

CHAPTER
14

Lynn's return to consciousness was not a simple awakening; it was a sluggish struggle to overcome the painful throbbing of her head and the oppressive lethargy that threatened to envelop her again. For indeterminate minutes she wasn't aware enough even of the Stygian darkness that surrounded her to feel any emotion other than a vague conviction that she was more dead than alive. Eventually it was her long-established fear of darkness that focused her mind with tormenting clarity. Pushing herself into a sitting position, she huddled against the dank, musty wall and forced herself to remember the advice Polly had given her years before. "Just breathe easy, girl, and use your head. Ain't nothing in the dark that ain't there in the light."

Methodically as she had in her youth, Lynn followed Polly's instructions with a dogged determination, concentrating her altered awareness on perceptions other than sight. She identified the sounds of the creaking timbers of a ship underway and of the whipping of wind-driven sails overhead. She listened to the muted footsteps on the decks above her and to the occasional shout of a human voice too remote for her to understand the words. She sniffed the fetid air around her and shuddered at the unpleasant odors of mildew, rotting hay, and an unwashed waste bucket. With stubborn persistence she investigated the other conditions of her imprisonment and discovered that someone had removed the clubs from beneath her dress and the heavy manacle from her right hand. Gritting her teeth to ease the abrasive pain, Lynn worked her left hand free, satisfied that she now had a replacement weapon: two heavy metal bracelets connected by a length of flexible chain.

Grimly she thought about Sidney Pollock; he'd meant to kill her, not just to silence her momentarily. Vaguely she remembered that his father had called him a dull wit after she'd fallen; but Sidney was more dangerous than a mere fool. He was afraid of her and of the mental powers he imagined she possessed. Her own father, too, had accused her of inheriting her grandmother's taint.

"I wish to God I had," she whispered aloud and paused abruptly in her reflections; both her own words and those Royce Trevor had callously flung at her reminded her of the descriptions she'd read in her grandfather's books about the ancient people of Cornwall. One medieval priest, whose records had been included in a more modern study, had claimed that the ancients had exhibited strange powers of communication and concentration, which he'd interpreted as godless devil worship. They'd been able to withstand the pain of purifying Christian flagellations and to perform Herculean feats of strength whenever they were in a devil's trance. According to that scholarly priest, the women among those ancients had been particularly susceptible to the devil's influence, learning such abominations as prophecy, sorcery, and most damning of all, enslavement of animals and fellow beings by thought control.

What if those abilities had survived the ages and been inherited by modern women, by her unknown grandmother as her father had claimed? Or by Polly Rigg who often knew what Jem was thinking without the use of words?

God, Lynn implored desperately, if only I could talk to Polly now to learn whether or not Jem had survived old Fen's brutality, or if Kerry and Bram were even alive after being struck down by Sid Pollock.

Lynn heard the sound of her own derisive laughter and shook her head; Polly would never "tempt the devil" by listening to voices even if she heard them. For Polly, there was no unseen spirit world, no mysteries that she couldn't explain with common sense. On the one occasion she'd accompanied Lynn to the old Druid dolmens, her only comment had been, "'Spect they had the same worries we do about keeping body and soul together, and I don't reckon they had any time left over for the nonsense you keep talking about, girl."

Never again had Lynn talked to Polly about those ancient ruins or the people who had built them. Only to quiet, gentle Jem had she tried to explain her sense of belonging more to the past than to the present. Odd that Jem had understood her better than anyone else; but then Jem had understood every animal on the farm, and they, in turn, had obeyed his silent orders. Especially Red Penny, Lynn remembered as her disoriented thoughts darted inexorably ahead. Even as a rambunctious calf, the young bull had seemed able to read Jem's thoughts, to come running when Jem called out a silent summons. More than any bullock or cow, Red Penny had displayed an intelligence that had made him seem more than just a coddled animal. If only the affection it had always displayed for Jem and her were strong enough to protect them now that they were helpless.

Listening intently, Lynn tried to determine where her prison cell was located in relation to the ship's hold where the animals were housed. As far away as possible, she concluded hopelessly; all she could hear was the faint lowing of one cow and the hungry bawling of its calf.

"Wake up, Red Penny," she cried out desperately.

"Don't let old Fen hurt Jem again. Fight the same way you did the night Tom Kenn tried to burn the barn."

For an elusive moment, Lynn felt as fierce as she had on the night two years earlier when the vicious Fen had pushed Clay's face into the manure of the Watkins's barn. If she'd known then that the Pollocks and their sadistic stockman would return to destroy her, she might have had the courage to use her clubs as Sid Pollock used his. With a helpless moan of regret, she slipped weakly back down onto the moldy straw pallet, too miserably defeated to care any longer about the darkness or the filth. Her last waking thought was the confused illusion that she was once again in the cave on Bodmin Moor with a delirious Clay by her side. She slept heavily through the violence that almost destroyed the ship.

Two thousand miles east of the troubled coastal vessel hugging the American waters, two men bore the vicissitudes of an ocean crossing with equanimity. Although Bevil Trevor was less tolerant of shipboard tedium than Ephraim Penley, he'd still been determined to make this voyage.

"How did you stand the boredom of traveling back and forth across this dismal expanse of water all those years?" he asked his companion as he reset the chessboard.

"Work mostly and reading whenever the weather was calm enough. I'd never have survived the food if my mind hadn't been occupied. Unfortunately, on this trip, my preoccupation has not been as pleasant as in the past; I keep wondering why you insisted on accompanying me. Do I continue to formulate my own conclusions, or are you going to tell me what new deviltry you've devised for my granddaughter?"

"You can stop playing your lawyer games with me, Ephriam. There's no mystery, and I've no devious schemes concerning Trelynn. I needed to escape from my daughter-in-law's tongue before I heaved the meddlesome woman into the Tamar River. I don't have Averill's tolerance for female bitchery. Thank God, Charles Clay was spared a permanent entanglement with the younger sister."

"Aye, he was that," Ephriam agreed dryly. "But I wish his freedom had not been bought at my granddaughter's expense."

"You can't deny that he's redeemed himself during these past five months."

"I'll not deny he's proved himself more devoted than I thought possible, although I confess I'm at a loss to explain his motives. This visit he'll be making her in a few weeks will be only his second in the years they've been wed, and I suspect he visited her the last time only out of the necessity for money. Did he tell you why he quit the slaving trade after making only two deliveries to England?"

"Clay's never been one to confide in anyone, especially me. I'm guessing that the business sickened him; he's not as thick-skinned as Andrew or Harry Pendrath."

"Perhaps not," Ephraim murmured judicially, "but he's callous enough about his marriage. I doubt Trelynn is expecting him to return at all."

"I'll grant you she has good cause for resentment, but the gift he's bringing her this time should make him welcome enough. He accomplished what you and I could not, Ephraim, with all your law and all my influence. He located the miner who killed John Pollock, and he paid for the poor devil's defense; and he bribed everyone of those cursed grannies and biddies to remove their names from the witchcraft petition, even Owen's wife."

"And took a bullet in the process that almost cost him his life," Ephraim admitted grudgingly.

" 'Twas Captain Wilcox who shot him, but not because of Trelynn. That odious Roundhead hated my son for escaping the gallows. Had the villain's ambush proved a fatal one, I'd have seen him hanged for murder. God's wounds, I despise religious martyrs in public office. You heard him at his trial; the fool even declared King Charles a sinner for granting royal pardons."

"He almost won his case with that particular declaration. We commoners have small sympathy for his majesty's penchant for preferential treatment of his favorites."

"Are you still bitter that he forgave my son but not your granddaughter? Our present king doesn't have enough power to meddle in church affairs."

"He finds the power whenever he wants to pay off another of his father's debts," Ephraim contradicted brusquely. "He's free enough with royal divorces when the mood suits him, as you well know."

"Why the devil should you be angry about the divorce I secured for Spencer Burtram? I've known the man for twenty years, and he wouldn't have asked for my help without good cause. The stupid woman left him strapped with a newborn infant, and I suspect he's found someone with more sense by this time."

Ephraim nodded gloomily, unable to resolve the vague worry that had plagued him for months. It had been Burtram rather than her husband who'd been Trelynn's advisor throughout her stay in Rhode Island. God knows, her letters had been cryptic enough, but the name Bert Spence had dominated her brief descriptions of her business dealings. And Edward Fulton had been blunt enough after Clay had sailed away the second time. Since then, Ephraim had received only one letter from Trelynn: an evasive, rambling missive that had sounded more like Hortensia than it had their granddaughter. God help them all if Trelynn had adopted Hortensia's cavalier attitude toward the sanctity of marriage! Discreetly he attempted an oblique warning.

"You may have secured the wrong divorce, Bevil."

"Let's have it plainly, Ephraim. You've been as sour as green apples since we began this voyage. Did my son tell you he wanted a divorce?"

"What reason would *he* have for complaint? According to Edward Fulton, Trelynn is the one who should be discontent. She's no longer the raw farm girl she once was."

"She never was a raw or a stupid farm girl. I've already admitted that my son has treated her badly, especially about money. I was hoping that she would have had a child a long time ago to settle him down."

"Settle him to what, Bevil? He doesn't even know what he wants to do yet. He stripped your estate of its tenants months ago to develop the Connecticut property, but now he's talking about an entirely different career. I think we made a sorry mistake when we forced him and Trelynn to marry."

"I'm not so sure they're all that unsuited, Ephraim; and I'm certain he's not as indifferent about her as you seem to think. He sacrificed a good deal to clear her name, and he seems impatient to see her again. At any rate, as long as the ship's doctor keeps him bedridden in his cabin, he'll have little else to think about during this voyage."

In the glare of the lantern held aloft by a sternly disciplined second mate, Polly Rigg shook the sleeping woman frantically. "Wake up, Lynn, you're needed as you've never been before, lass. God in heaven, look at her head! She's been beat about by the same scum that downed my Jem and killed poor Kerry back at the farm." Accusingly she turned around to glare at the man watching her anxiously. "Do you still think she's responsible for the trouble down in the hold?" she demanded stridently.

"Don't be a fool! Of course, she wasn't. She was unconscious or asleep both times I checked on her during the night. But the fact remains we've a maddened bull running amok in the hold with enough weight and fury to crush the ship's timbers below water line. Shake her again, mistress; I promise I'll protect her from the crew."

"Who'll protect her from the villains who dragged us aboard?"

"For God's sakes, woman, just wake her up!"

Lynn's tongue felt inches thick as she struggled to speak. "What's the matter with Red Penny?" she mumbled.

"That devil Fen clubbed the poor beast onct too often and was gored to pulp as his just reward. Jem's leg is broke so he can't move. You're the only one who can control the creature. Can you stand up, girl?"

"I need some water to stop my head from spinning first," Lynn pleaded hoarsely.

"Best you sip easy," the mate warned her as he proffered a ladle of tepid water drawn from a scummed-over bucket standing in a corner of the six-foot-square prison cubicle.

On legs that shook uncontrollably, Lynn managed to walk the narrow gangway unaided, but the second mate had to half carry her down the ladder into the ship's hold and to steady her when they reached the bottom until her dizziness passed. Still dulled by the need for sleep, Lynn peered around the dimly lit cavern, comprehending only part of what she saw: the nervous cows and bullocks crowded into inadequate numbers of stalls, straining against their tether ropes. Not until she head the thundering bellow coming from a darkened corner, could she make out the restive silhouette of the animal she'd loved and petted for twelve years. But now the sound of its heavy hooves pawing the wood decking made the great beast seem a stranger.

Fully awake now, Lynn experienced the cold chill of fear. Familiar with the uneven tempers of most of its breed, she knew that any sudden movement would send it charging with a terrifying strength. Praying that she could control her voice, she began a soft crooning. "You know me as well as I know you, Red Penny. Be quiet, sweetheart, there's nothing to be afraid of any more. I'm going to walk toward you, my pretty big penny, and you're to let me see where you're hurt.''

Step by shaking step, she walked toward the shadowy corner; but until she was only a few feet away, the nervous animal continued its threatening pawing. Only when she stretched her hand out to pet the familiar head did the savage bellow mute to a soft bawl. Lynn's soothing speech faltered helplessly when she saw the bloody lacerations on its great head and the pitchfork wound on its neck.

"Merciful God," she whispered softly, "you've reason to hate; but 'tis all over now, and you'll soon be well." Gently stroking the shuddering animal behind its ears, she continued her wheedling patter. "Come on, Red Penny, let's go back to your stall so I can treat those sore places. I promise I'll not hurt you any more than I can help, and then I'll stay with you. Is his stall clean?" she called out softly to Polly.

" 'Twill be as soon as I drag that piece of filth away. Mr. Pingree," Polly spoke softly to the second mate, "she'll be needing a bucket of laudanum salve if you've got such aboard, and she'll be needing a pair of you to help her when she starts to treat the beast. Get on with it, man. Red Penny'll not rampage as long as she's here."

Farm-bred efficient in her own movements, Polly dragged the bloody corpse of the Pollock stockman into a far corner and covered it with armfuls of straw before she returned to the stall and swabbed the floor with a bucket of water.

" 'Tis ready for him now," she called out to Lynn. "Do you want me to help you, Lynn?"

"You'd better stand clear, Polly. Is Jem conscious enough to watch me while I treat Red Penny?"

"Nay, lass. He's got the same sore head as you do, but more'n that his leg's broke. Happened just before Red Penny broke out his stall when my Jem tried to keep that devil from clubbin' the poor animal. Got clubbed himself and then stomped. Kate and I dragged him to safety up the ladder."

"Red Penny's rope isn't broken, Polly; it must have been deliberately untied. Did any of you see Fen untie it?"

"As much a brute as he was, he wasn't fool enough to loose a bull. 'Twas that murderin' young Pollock that must have done that piece of mischief. Leastwise he was down here whisperin' to old Fen not long before the villain turned berserker and started hittin' Jem. Reckon that young 'un turned out worse than his no-good pa."

"Polly, why didn't any of our men come to Jem's rescue?"

"Kate and me was the only ones here. Sometime last night they took poor Bram upstairs somewheres and ordered Jason Hale to go along to help out."

"What about Kerry?"

"Dead, poor old laddie. That one blow did him in, and Bram's not much better off; but I don't reckon that devil's spawn of a Pollock will ever be punished."

"Oh, yes, he will! One of the Fulton stockmen saw the attack. Where was my father when Kerry was killed?"

"Holdin' a fancy pistol on Kate and me in the cottage, but he seen to it that the other three was hid in the barn before Jem and our men got back from town. Jem and Jason was first to arrive, but there was no way we could warn them. Jason says the big brute took Jem out of action soon as they walked into the barn while Rad hisself bashed Jason."

"Did my father ever go to the barn?"

"Not that jack-a-dandy fop. He sent one of the pesky sailors he had workin' for him with orders for the Pollocks to strip everything just like your pa was doing to all three houses and the root cellar too."

"Oh, my God!"

"Ain't nothin' to worry about, Lynn; Kate's a smart one; she said 'twould be better if we hid the babe's things in the manure heap that Jason was gettin' ready to plow in. Claimed no fancy gentleman would go near the smelly place, and she was right. But he sure ordered all our food supplies piled on the wagon along with everything else that wasn't nailed down.''

"Polly, did you tell him that you weren't an indentured?"

"Right off; but when he located all the indenture papers inside your trunks, he decided for hisself that I was Nell Wallis and Jem was Tom Kenn. But don't you worry none 'bout Jem and me, there'll be someone in Virginia with the sense t' listen to me. 'Til then we'll last out whatever's comin'! So will you, lass, once you're in the hands of a decent constable and away from that schemin' pack of thieves."

With jarring suddenness, Lynn remembered the fate one of those schemers had already decreed for her, and she was almost regretful that she'd subdued Red Penny. Minutes later when the second mate returned with a bucket of poultice hastily drenched with laudanum, she listened to the boasting of the garrulous ship's cook who'd been the only crew member who "warn't afeard of witches and haunts."

Resisting the temptation to untie Red Penny, Lynn advised the man sharply, "Then if I were you, I wouldn't stand too close to my bull. He might try to prove you an overtrusting fool." She smiled with bitter cynicism as the cook's fat, ruddy face blanched.

"What do you want us to do, mistress?" the second mate interrupted impatiently.

"Take the ropes I attach to the animal and wrap the ends around the ship's timbers that can take the strain, then hang on. My bull has never been injured before, and it may react violently."

Beginning her soft crooning again, Lynn gently applied the first handful of the pain-deadening medicine.

Above decks in the ship's chart room, two angry men were listening to Captain Denby's coldly delivered ultimatum. "Both of you will be put ashore with the woman, the bull, and the two injured men as soon as we reach New Haven."

"What the devil are we supposed to do there?" Rad Pollock blustered.

"I don't give a damn what you do. My only concerns are the safety of my ship and my own reputation. When you showed me the warrant for the woman's arrest, Pollock, it mentioned only the crime of murder, not witchcraft."

"I was afraid your crew might be superstitious."

"Then you should have bound and gagged this jackdaw son of yours. The fool babbled like a water gusher all the time my men were rowing you and the woman out to the ship. Within an hour after you'd boarded, the scuttlebutt had spread from the lookout sentries to the bilge swabbies. And three hours ago, long before the bull began to rampage, your fool son goes screaming around the ship that the woman had turned her bull loose in revenge. Yet he knew damn well the woman was locked in a cell that's impossible to break out of, and she was unconscious when she'd been put there at your partner's insistence."

"Witches don't pay no attention to locked doors," Sid Pollock protested.

"Belay that nonsense, you jack-a-napes; you're the villain as far as my ship's concerned, you and your father both. There's something else I'm damned curious about. Your reports don't agree with the stories two of your prisoners told me. You abused all of those prisoners; and by God, that man you left below deserved what he got."

"He was murdered," Sid shrilled, "by the cursed witch when she ordered her bull to loose itself and turn on Fen. You seen her, Captain Denby. You were standing alongside of me looking down the hatch when she sweet talked that devil animal into a trance."

"What I saw, you young fool, was a woman with a bloodied head perform the miracle that saved my ship."

"Captain," Rad Pollock demanded with an abrupt truculence, "why didn't you order the damned bull shot when it first broke loose? Your delay cost me a good stockman."

"I'd have needed a cannon to down that beast, and we'd have sunk all the faster. Now back to business. Which one of you struck the woman?"

" 'Twas self-defense," Sid admitted sullenly.

"Against a woman wearing manacles?"

"She ain't no ordinary mortal woman."

"That's for the courts to decide. In the meantime, you'll be leaving that weapon you have tied around your waist aboard. New Haveners are law abiding people, and I don't relish the prospect of your finding any of *their* women to defend yourself against."

"Captain, I'm a duly appointed officer of the royal Virginia colony," Rad began aggressively; but his authority was no match for the angry Captain Denby's.

"You can be whatever you damn well please, Pollock, but not aboard my ship. My report to the New Haven authorities will read that you beat two of your prisoners almost to death and you abused the woman badly. And if you're thinking that you'll finish the job once you're ashore, you have my word that I'm personally turning all of your prisoners and the bull over to the port authorities as well as my written report of the story the woman called Kate Horton and the man named Jason Hale told me."

Rad's eyes were dangerously narrowed when he made his next demand. "Then I insist you leave the other prisoners and all of the animals in New Haven too."

"Why should I? Mr. Trevor is the one who paid their passage."

"He's as responsible as we are for what happened."

"Not so, Pollock. He had nothing to do with the violence on the farm or in the hold."

"Da didn't either," Sid rasped loudly, " 'twas all my doing. So Da can stay aboard and take care of the cattle and things here. I'll take charge of the prisoners ashore."

For a moment Rad Pollock studied his son's fierce

expression and then shook his head. "You've already done enough damage, son. I'll be going ashore with you."

"You have no say in the matter, Pollock," the captain countermanded sharply. "Both of you will be put ashore and without weapons. So I'll take your pistols now and your son's club; I've a sudden fear of armed fools aboard my ship. One further warning: this colony's Puritan, but not the Salem variety. They're not ignorant Cornish hillsmen who can be easily bamboozled into a witch burning. They'll be asking questions of the woman as well as you, and I mean to see that she's in a fit enough condition to answer them."

That the final promise Captain Denby made to the Pollock father and son remained unfulfilled for two weeks was no fault of his. The young woman whom he dared not keep aboard with a crew already threatening mutiny if she remained, was again comatose when she was hoisted to the dock with her equally drugged bull. Throughout the hours it had taken her to treat Red Penny's wounds, Lynn had remained reasonably alert. She'd even managed to obey the second mate's order to walk the groggy animal to the loading platform placed beneath the cargo hatch.

"Where are they taking Red Penny?" she asked.

"Ashore, mistress. You'll be going too. Your servant will be returning in a few minutes with clean clothes for you and some food." For a brief moment the man's eyes mirrored an understanding pity, but twenty years at sea had taught him never to question his captain's orders.

Left alone in the poorly ventilated hold whose air was now laden with the pall of laudanum, Lynn drowsed, awakening long enough to eat a few mouthfuls of cold porridge Polly spooned into her mouth and to help remove her stained cloak and dress. Frowning in confusion when Polly asked about the chained-together manacles tied to her petticoats, Lynn shook her head in a weary lack of comprehension and fell asleep. She didn't stir all the time a weeping Polly sponged her face and arms and dressed her.

"Take care of my Jem," the older woman whispered as the cargo hoist was winched aloft and swung over the deck onto the dock already occupied by the litters holding an unconscious Jem Rigg and John Bram.

Lynn knew nothing of the hour-long drama that took place in the New Haven meeting hall, a tense discussion that decided her immediate fate and those of her wounded companions. They were to be detained in a small, unused barn adjacent to one of the town's churches until they were sufficiently healed to attend the public hearing that would determine their permanent disposition. The first to regain consciousness, Lynn learned the details of her detention from the doctor who'd volunteered to care for the three strangers now disrupting the peaceful life of the small, insular colony.

"Where are we?" she asked the man concentrating on the intricate task of swaddling her partially shorn head in bandages.

"In a barn, mistress, but a comfortable enough one for the while."

"What town?" she persisted.

"New Haven."

"Connecticut?"

"Didn't they tell you while you were tending the bull?"

"I don't think I was awake enough to hear," she admitted.

"'Tis a wonder you were awake at all, but you did a fine job all the same. Your bull will be recovered long before you and the others are up."

"What others, doctor?"

"The two men the captain thought would die unless they received attention."

"Is one of those men a mute?"

"The big one. He's badly hurt but I've splinted his leg and tended the abrasions."

"Will he recover?"

"Hard to predict about head wounds, but he's a strong man."

"What about the other one?"

"I don't know. His skull was cracked, but he's lived for two days; so I'm hopeful he'll survive the damage. I'll be remaining here until I know for certain."

"Were we the only ones put ashore?"

"No, the captain insisted your two guards be left behind too."

"To guard us here?"

"Not exactly. The captain warned our officials about the younger one of them, so you'll not be abused in New Haven."

"Do you know the charges the older man has leveled against me, Doctor?"

"He insisted he was only carrying out the king's orders."

"He and his sister are the ones who created those false charges two years ago in Cornwall. The man they claimed I killed was Rad Pollock's brother, but I didn't even know him. Does everyone in New Haven believe me guilty?"

The doctor hesitated before he replied. "Perhaps not the murder thing, mistress; but they believed your father."

Lynn took a deep painful breath. "Did Royce Trevor accuse me of stealing my grandmother's estate?"

"That and the admission that you'd inherited his mother's unfortunate proclivities. I was told he was most sorrowful that he was forced to leave you here."

"Until he stripped my farm in Rhode Island, my 'sorrowful' father hadn't seen me in twenty years. Did he return to the ship?"

"He sailed on it an hour later. Now, mistress, as soon as my wife has fed you supper, you're to rest and not move about. As I've told you, there's need to stay abed until your head is clear."

"Red Penny may not let strangers tend him," Lynn protested.

"My lad's had no trouble so far. 'Tis a gentle beast you've raised and a valuable one I imagine, since your father announced he'd be sending for it."

Lynn slept fitfully that first night in her strange new prison, her thoughts an angry whirl of hatred against her father. "If I were a witch," she vowed, "I'd turn him into the jackal he is." Toward morning she was awakened by a frightening dream that she knew was no dream at all, but rather a sobering memory of her first period of consciousness aboard ship when she'd ordered Red Penny to protect Jem. If only she'd awakened sooner, she reflected without a shadow of remorse for old Fen's death, Jem would have been spared a second beating. During that waking hour before she drifted into sleep again, she allowed her imagination to roam freely into the forbidden realm of supernatural revenge against the men who'd destroyed her life.

The comfort of such a half-hoped-for power ended abruptly the following morning when Rad Pollock entered her bedroom stall as robustly healthy as ever. So much for her powers of witchcraft, she concluded with a dull disappointment; the devil protects his own! The man standing at the foot of her pallet showed no sigh of the fatal, agonizing plague she'd wished upon him.

"You're awake then," Rad said gruffly. Lynn closed her eyes to blot out the sight of her presbyterian flails hanging from his belt. Her throbbing scalp tingled in anticipation of another blow.

"I'm not here to hurt you, Trelynn," he told her. "You'd not have been hurt the first time if you hadn't invented that lie about your husband being a Trevor. And I caution you not to mention the Trevor name to Sid again. He has good reason to hate Sir Bevil for shipping us to this wilderness. 'Tis been a harsh life for Sid so far."

Aroused to sarcasm by Rad's concern for his savage whelp, Lynn murmured, "I'd have thought he'd be a great help to you in your new profession as an 'expert' witness against your prisoners. Is he going to claim that all of my workers fell on their heads?''

"He struck only in self-defense."

"You're a liar, Rad Pollock; he struck to kill them just as he did me. Will you return my clubs to me or not? I'd like to be able to defend myself the next time your murderous son attacks me."

"You won't be needing any defense; the doctor's made that very plain."

"Where is the doctor? He said he'd remain on duty here."

"I waited until he'd gone home for his breakfast, because I wanted to warn you not to rile the religious folk in this town. If you'll hold your tongue with them and act the modest woman for a change, I may be able to get you safely to Virginia. 'Twas never my intention to have you bound for trial; and if your cursed father hadn't interfered, you'd not be facing a public hearing in this church-bound town. Remember, you've no friends here who'll come to your defense or who'll care what happens to you except me."

"Then I'll trust my life to strangers!" Lynn closed her eyes again, but this time, to conceal the gleam of excitement his final warning had inspired. She might have no friends in New Haven, but her grandfather did: one man in particular, a Captain Clive something or other who headed the colony's militia. There were two other men with reason to be grateful to Ephraim Penley, two men who'd been sentenced to death by King Charles because they'd helped murder his father. Four years earlier, Lynn's grandfather had encouraged the New Haven colonists to grant them sanctuary.

Explosively eager by the time the doctor returned, she asked the name of the militia captain before the harried medic had time to remove his hat.

"Why would you want to see Captain Dunton?" he demanded.

"He's a friend of my grandfather."

"You're not allowed to have visitors without Reverend Wainwright's approval."

Forbearing to mention the fact that she'd already had one unpleasant visitor, Lynn asked the doctor to send his son to notify Captain Dunton that she was kin to Ephraim Penley.

"He's not in town at present, but I'll send the message when he returns," the doctor promised tiredly.

The next ten days were agony for the restless woman imprisoned in a narrow stall, one of six lining the side of the small barn. Her only moments of relief in the unnumbered hours of anxious contemplation about her future occurred when the doctor announced that Jem was out of danger and that John Bram had regained a measure of consciousness.

"May I see them?"

"As I told you before, not without Reverend Wainwright's permission."

"Then tell Rad Pollock to stop bothering me whenever you're gone," she exclaimed in anger.

Frowning in concern, the humorless doctor promised "to mend the problem," a promise that precipitated the most traumatically dangerous hour of Lynn's life. As had become his daily habit each morning, the doctor checked his three patients before reporting to his own home some blocks away from the barn. Although Lynn still chafed in irritation about remaining helplessly in bed, she'd been an obedient patient mainly because she remembered how long it had taken Clay to recover from a similar blow on the head. The only exercise she took was a daily washing and a few practice swings with the manacle weapon she'd hidden beneath the straw. On this, her eleventh day of inactivity, she drowsed through the doctor's perfunctory examination and was still drowsing when Sidney Pollock slipped furtively into her stall and stood at the end of her pallet, staring down at her.

Physically weakened by her injury, Lynn started with fear when she awoke enough to recognize her visitor. With her instinct for danger sharply honed by the events of the past weeks, she knew that his intentions were as deadly as they'd been on the path leading to New Port. Seeing his face clearly for the first time since that long ago night in the Wadleys' barn in Cornwall, she realized that he was no longer the callow youth he'd been then. His face was narrow instead of broad like his father's, and he'd inherited none of Rad Pollock's strength of feature. He looked, she thought, more like a cornered weasel, but she knew that his cowardice made him doubly dangerous.

Willing herself to remain motionless after she'd dug her makeshift weapon out of the straw, Lynn looked at him steadily for a few seconds before she spoke. "You were warned to remain outside this barn."

"Who's to stop me?" he demanded insolently.

"Your father, for one."

"Da don't know I'm here any more than the town cullies do. Da took himself off so he wouldn't have to stand for the bugbear doctor's bullying. Jawed Da into the ground last night he did, and Da was fool enough to listen. But Da's been making a fool of hisself over you for more years than I can remember. He should have taken you when you first growed your witch's body when he saw you taking those baths down by the river. But now Jabe and me don't want you messing Da's life up again."

" 'Twas Red Penny your father wanted, not me; and except for my refusal to marry him, I've not disturbed his life."

"You got old Bevil to throw us out of England, and you got Gabe turned into a cripple. That slimy prisoner bastard hamstrung him for life. Now all Jabe can ever be is a dirt farmer, and the only woman who'll have him will be a squaw or some worn-out trull."

"My husband only defended himself when he was attacked."

"That piece of trash was the cully you wed? I should have told old Fen to kill him that night and saved Da and Jabe and me a peck of trouble."

"If you had, Sir Bevil would have ordered all of you heaved into the deepest part of the ocean. As I've already told you, my husband is his son."

"Da says that's a lie, but I ain't so sure. The devil sure didn't look like a Penley, and he used that cursed sword of his like a blood instead of one of us. But that don't make any difference now; he won't ever learn what happened to you."

"Oh, but he will! You were all followed here by a New Port pirate who knows exactly where I am and who is responsible. And if you kill me, who do you think the people here will blame?"

With his eyes gleaming with triumph, Sid boasted, "The folks hereabouts will know 'twas me right enough, but most of them'll be grateful. Some's even afraid to walk past this barn, you've got them so scared."

"They'll hang you for murder all the same, Sid Pollock!"

"Not me, they won't! I won't be here for them to catch, and they won't be blaming Da 'cause he'll have the people at the inn to speak up for him."

Breathing slowly, Lynn asked, "How will you get away?"

"I got me a friend who's waiting in a boat just outside of town. He'll be talking me north of here to join up with a crew of men who ain't afraid to take chances. Him and Jabe tried wreckin' a few years back in Cornwall, so's he knows a thing or two 'bout outfoxing the likes of the simpletons and gulls hereabouts."

Gripping one bracelet of the manacles beneath the covers, Lynn controlled her fear enough to ask, "How did you know this friend of Jabe would be in New Haven?"

" 'Twas all arranged. More'n a year ago, he came

hightailing to our farm in Virginia after he'd jumped ship in Jamestown, and he had enough gold with him to make Jabe's eyes bug. Three months ago this friend sends a message to Jabe and me asking us to join up with him somewheres north of here. Jabe says 'no' on account of his leg; but me, I figure 'twas time to cut traces. That's why I offered to come with Da to get you. But Da wasn't supposed t' get off the ship here . . . just old Fen and me with you and the bull.''

"How did you expect to be put ashore in New Haven so conveniently?"

"Wasn't hard, not with your own da helping me. He didn't want you in Virginia any more than me and Jabe did. He paid me to start a ruckus in the hold by untying the bull, so's I could go screaming to the crew that the witch's pet demon was loose. They was already scared white-eyed.''

"Are you the one who struck Jem?"

"Only once, him and old Fen were too busy fighting each other t' pay any attention to me.''

Despite her fear, Lynn was outraged. "Jem's hands were tied.''

"Didn't slow him down none. When I slipped away, he was still on his feet. The bull was snorting right enough, but he wasn't charging, not until you sent him on a berserker to kill old Fen.''

"How could I have? You were the one who untied Red Penny. I was locked in a cell and manacled.''

"Not by half you weren't! Da removed one of them before we left you there, same time as he took your presbies,'' Sidney added with a snigger.

Lynn felt the cold chill of raw terror! She knew now what he was holding so carefully behind his back. He planned to kill her with her own clubs that he'd taken from his father. Desperately now, she tried to refocus his attention. "Why do you believe I'm a witch, Sidney? You know that those petitions were a pack of lies you and your family made up.''

"They were lies all right; Da even knew the miner who killed my uncle, and he paid the devil to lay low until Da could get you to Virginia. But what Da don't know is that you're a witch all the same. Even your own da says so; he says you ordered your bull to do the dirty on old Fen. He says you don't need to be anywhere special to work your Satan mischief. Well, you won't be cursing anybody ever again; witches can die just like the rest of us."

Praying that her muscles would obey her will, Lynn tensed herself to move swiftly enough to escape the first onslaught. With a smile that was now as reckless as his, she gambled one more time in an effort to keep him off balance.

"You're right, you know, poor little doomed Sidney Pollock, I am a witch and my special bull is but twenty feet away. Do you think it won't do my bidding with you the same as it did with Fen?"

Without warning, she screamed the two words "Red Penny" and rolled off the pallet. As she'd hoped, the startled man hesitated long enough to delay his lunge until she was on her feet, whirling the heavily chained manacle with lethal rhythm. Inexpert by comparison in the use of the unfamiliar clubs, Sidney backed slowly out of the stall, the savage hatred on his face mingled with terror.

Once again Lynn shouted the name "Red Penny," this time with a commanding authority, and listened with tense relief to the animal sounds of arousal coming from the distant stall. Her third strident shout brought an answering bellow, and the fourth the ground-shaking pawing of restless hooves. Backing slowly down the wide dirt corridor, Lynn dodged the clubs now being swung at her in maddened fury. One blow glanced off her shoulder and another numbed her idle arm, but that second strike cost her enemy one of his clubs. Step by step her stockinged feet moved steadily backward toward the sanctuary stall, her eyes never leaving her opponent, her short heavy weapon in constant motion. She didn't have to turn around when she reached her goal; Red Penny was already straining at his hold rope, his great head thrust forward beyond the partition wall.

Hoping urgently that the doctor's son had tied the rope with a slip knot rather than a stay, she edged cautiously into the stall, pushing past the muscular body, careful to keep her vulnerable feet away from the crushing, moving hooves. Dropping the now useless weapon, she reached for the dangling end of the rope and pulled, shaking in relief when the knot gave way. Bracing herself to hang on to the rope, Lynn watched helplessly as the snorting beast lowered its head and charged, leaving her with an empty, lacerated hand.

With a scream of uncontrolled fear, Sid Pollock threw his remaining club at the wild-eyed animal and then ran in stumbling panic toward the half-open door. The brief chase ended when the shrieking man tumbled through the door, picked himself up from the packed dirt outside and continued his frantic escape down the empty passageway. With the last of her energies, Lynn urged the frustrated beast back into its stall and stood petting it on the sensitive spot behind one ear.

"The next time, my wonderful big friend, you have my permission to stomp that particular piece of human filth into the ground."

CHAPTER
15

"Merciful God," the flustered doctor exclaimed when he and his son returned to find all three of his patients in a disturbed state. The woman was huddled in the corner of the bull's stall, John Bram was collapsed on the floor five feet away from his bed, and the powerful mute had pulled the wallboards loose in his efforts to free his broken leg from the ropes the doctor had used to immobilize it.

"What happened here?" the doctor demanded of the woman as he helped her return to bed. Fighting the tears of nervous exhaustion, Lynn told him with angry brevity, only to have her anger renewed a few minutes later after the doctor's son had been sent to tell Captain Dunton to go after the fleeing Sid Pollock.

"How long has Captain Dunton been back?" Lynn asked.

"The better part of a week, mistress, but Reverend Wainwright would not allow me to deliver your message."

"Then the captain doesn't know anything about me?"

"The council didn't consider your particular problem of any military significance. Now of course, he will be

385

consulted since obviously we cannot permit a potential murderer to run amok in our community.''

Thus two weeks after she'd been brought to New Haven, but only after she had survived a brazen attempt on her life, Lynn was finally asked to tell her story officially. Escorted by two leather-clad militiamen, she walked the short distance to the communal meeting house, still wearing the disfiguring bandages on her head. Ignoring the two black-robed ministers seated on the platform, Lynn addressed the third man the two young soldiers had identified as their commander.

"Captain Dunton, I am Ephraim Penley's granddaughter. He told me to seek you out if I were ever in trouble.''

Instantly Clive Dunton was on his feet, striding toward the young woman who'd been left standing in the middle of the room. Placing a protective arm around her, he led her to a bench and seated himself beside her.

"Why didn't you send for me as soon as you arrived?'' he asked quietly.

Noting the disapproving frowns on the stern faces of the ministers, Lynn knew that her only hope for defense rested with the brusque military man. Knowing full well that one of the two religious leaders was the repressive Reverend Wainwright who had dictated the terms of her imprisonment thus far in New Haven, Lynn decided that it was neither the time nor the place for diplomatic humility.

"I tried,'' she admitted bluntly, "but I was told I could speak to no one but the doctor.''

"Was that your idea, Hadley Wainwright?'' Dunton demanded of the cleric seated behind the central podium. "Didn't it occur to you to ask her name or circumstance? In the name of God, man, your negligence almost cost this young woman her life.''

"Her father had identified her to our complete satisfaction,'' Wainwright replied tartly. "Furthermore, the warrants the deputy sheriff showed us were bonafide.''

"That 'deputy sheriff' left town today in the company of his murderous son and some accomplices who were waiting for them with a boat," Dunton shouted.

"Regardless of the man's dereliction of duty, Captain Dunton, we had ample reason to keep her separated from our people. What her father told us precluded any doubt about her culpability and made her kinship with Ephraim Penley immaterial."

"You accepted the word of the father without talking to the daughter?"

"She was in no condition for interrogation when she first arrived, and we certainly didn't think that *she* was the one who was in any danger in our community."

"That was a sorry miscalculation, Reverend, and one that could have ended tragically. Had you consulted me, I could have identified this young woman far more thoroughly than her father did. In the past two years, I have received several letters from Ephraim Penley detailing the complete story of those erroneous charges leveled against his granddaughter. You chose to believe the very man who manufactured those lies and forced her to flee from her home in Cornwall. I also received a copy of a testimonial written by the Reverend Roger Williams of Rhode Island. Since I have no doubt of her innocence, I propose to offer her the protection of my home. And as soon as she is well enough for a public hearing, I will undertake her defense. Do either you or Reverend Quiller have any objections?"

"Most strenuous ones, Captain Dunton," Wainwright responded promptly. "We are not nearly as concerned about those criminal petitions as we are about the information her own father gave us. This woman has been tainted from infancy because of an abominable inheritance from his own mother. We cannot allow such evil to be loose in our community."

Roused to fury by the unquestioning assumption of her guilt, Lynn cried out, "Reverend Wainwright, did Royce

Trevor also claim that I had embezzled the inheritance he'd expected to receive from my other grandmother, the Honorable Hortensia Trelynn Penley?''

"He did indeed, and he produced the will that proved his claim."

In a voice that shook only slightly, Lynn delivered the speech she had been rehearsing for two agonizing weeks, a logically organized recital that recounted every fact she knew about her grandmother, her father, and the disposition of the funds she'd realized from Hortensia's estate. She described her father's callous boast that she was in no position to prove the existence of a second will.

"He was wrong," she concluded hotly. "That document is safely hidden in my grandfather's strongbox in Plymouth, but I never spent a shilling of that inheritance. What my father stole from me in Rhode Island was mine and had nothing to do with my grandmother's estate."

The silence that greeted her outburst lasted long seconds as Reverend Wainwright studied her somberly. "What do you know about your paternal grandmother?" he asked finally.

"I knew nothing about my father's parents until he sought me out in New Port. Since he lied to me about everything else, I assumed that tale was another attempt to silence me."

"It just might be," Wainwright admitted judicially, "but it might be equally true that his mother's taint was indeed passed down to you. 'Tis rarely inherited by men, only carried through them to the next generation of women. I venture to say that the present charges against you may prove false, but you could very well possess the capacity for evil without knowing it. You can understand my dilemma, Captain Dunton. I am responsible for the spiritual well-being of our people. Until I am satisfied that this woman does not harbor the seeds of destruction, I cannot permit her the freedom to move unrestrained in our colony."

"As far as I'm concerned," Dunton countered sharply, "I intend to keep Mistress Trevor in my home for her protection, not the colony's."

"Very well, Captain, we grant your request with the proviso she be confined to your home and farm. Now, mistress, suppose you clarify the confusion about your name. Your father identified your husband as Penley rather than Trevor."

It was another hour before Lynn had satisfied her inquisitor about the details of her life, accurate in every aspect, except for the omission of any mention about her grandmother's diamond pendant. She wanted no public record of what might be her son's only inheritance. Enduring the frequent interruptions with suppressed irritation, she was bluntly factual about her income and the methods she'd employed to earn it and about the unconventional circumstances of her life in Cornwall and Rhode Island. After she was finally released into Captain Dunton's "custody"—the term Reverend Wainwright had used to describe her forthcoming detention—Lynn survived the long walk to the Dunton farm and the cold reception she received from Mrs. Dunton.

In obedience to her husband's command that she supply her unwanted guest with a bath and clean clothing, Hertha Dunton grudgingly monitored the tepid water bathing in the outdoor cooper's barrel used by the farm workers. Despite the presence of two household maids, she insisted Lynn wash her own soiled clothing before the parsimonious housewife offered her a spartan supper of oatmeal mush and a pallet in an attic alcove. Too tired to protest the ungracious accommodations and still aching from the bruises she'd received during the violent fight with Sidney Pollock, Lynn slept through the terse conference conducted in the Dunton parlor.

Only two of the men in attendance had been invited, men responsible for the town's policing and men whom Dunton considered flagrantly derelict in their duty to protect the granddaughter of Ephraim Penley. Defensive of their own reputations, and with good reason, Colonel William Goffe and Colonel Edward Whalley had invited Reverend Wainwright to accompany them.

Dunton's opening attack was the result of the report he'd received from his own men about the successful escape of the Pollock father and son. "They weren't alone in the boat that had been waiting for them. According to witnesses there were three confederates who'd been frequent waterfront loiterers throughout the past month, during which time several of our merchant shops were broken into and robbed."

"How were we to know which of the alien sailors who visit our port were the guilty ones?" Goffe demanded.

"These particular men were not crew members of either of the two ships currently in our harbor according to the captains my men consulted this afternoon. It is my opinion that these probable thieves are as dangerous as the younger Pollock."

"Both of the Pollocks had been forbidden to visit the woman," Goffe insisted defensively.

"And both of them disobeyed you," Dunton continued relentlessly. "May I ask why none of you paid any heed to the ship's captain who labeled young Pollock a violent, brutal man?"

"The woman's father insisted that the captain's suspicions were based on evidence given by indentured criminals and highly unreliable," Wainwright protested. "We still have only her word that she was attacked this morning. If her father's accusation that she inherited unnatural powers proves to be true, perhaps Pollock was merely frightened into running away."

Furiously Dunton refuted the minister's speculation. "We have the evidence of two witnesses that she was threatened with murder; and that if she hadn't been able to defend herself, *we* might be the ones charged with criminal negligence."

"Only one witness and that one with a damaged head," Goffe insisted. "The other man is a mute."

"A literate mute who can read and write," Dunton snapped. "Whether you gentlemen like it or not, we are still subject to the laws of England, which insist that we provide safety for outsiders who visit our colony."

"We provided food, housing, and medical treatment for all of them," the third man protested.

"An unheated barn stall for the granddaughter of a man who has been a loyal friend to all of us? Have you forgotten, William Goffe and Edward Whalley, that you owe your lives to Ephraim Penley? Had he not championed your cause, you'd have been returned to England and hanged for your part in the regicide of King Charles. Did neither of you think to offer her the protection of your homes?"

"We were not certain of her identity at the time, only that the prisoner was a suspected witch," Goffe murmured.

"We gave you shelter when we *knew* you were guilty of a far worse offense," Dunton countered icily.

"Not so," Wainwright disavowed with a stern authority. "New Haven is a religious colony, and nothing could threaten our salvation more than giving sanctuary to an ungodly evil. What Colonels Goffe and Whalley did was merely political by comparison. I do agree that we'll not return the woman to England until we hear officially from her grandfather. While we're waiting for his advice, I will personally interview the culprit to determine for myself the degree of her guilt."

An hour later the still-provoked Captain Dunton sought out his wife. "Where did you bed the two men, Hertha?"

"Where they belong and where they're used to being—in the barn."

The steely look she bent on him might have cowed a more timid man, but Clive Dunton had long established cause to distrust his wife. "They'll be moved into our home tomorrow. What room did you supply to Mistress Trevor?'' When she failed to respond, he answered his own question with a heavy certainty, "I'll wager you put her in the attic and gave her discarded servant garb to wear."

"I'll not be wasting our coin on the likes of her, Clive Dunton. Why should we pay her keep when her own father refused and labeled her guilty besides?''

"You've become a miserly shrew, Hertha."

"I tithe my full share to church support," she hissed angrily.

"With my money, and you make certain that your *amens* are louder than anyone else's; but you're still an un-Christian woman. I'll be responsible for Mistress Trevor, and I'll ask my sister to supply the clothing."

"Nay, Clive, ye'll not shame me again with your overbearing relatives. 'Twill be disgrace enough to harbor that unnatural woman. Ye should have seen her in the bath; tall and muscular as a man she is and devil proud of that Satan face of hers."

Smiling maliciously at his shapeless, overplump wife, Dunton ended the unpleasant interview with a taunting threat. "You'd do well to remember that she's also brighter than the prattling goodies of this town with an ability in business that would turn our greediest merchants green with envy. You're to provide her with our best, Hertha, and you're to avoid inflicting your sour tongue on her. If I thought it would do any good, I'd also forbid you to gossip with your equally unkind cronies; but I know you too well to expect miracles."

While Lynn overheard neither of these separate conversations, she learned the import of both on the following day when a purse-mouthed Hertha Dunton moved her to a proper bedroom and, later, when Reverend Wainwright reported dutifully for the first of his promised interviews. Experienced from youth in concealing the fact that she much preferred the contents of her grandfather's library to the scriptures as reading matter, Lynn quickly reverted to the same evasive tactics she'd used to pacify the Commonwealth ministers who'd visited Penley Farm on a monthly schedule. Pleading confusion over one of the passages he quoted, she asked Reverend Wainwright for his interpretation. "Experts," her grandfather had often told her, "enjoy talking more than they do listening." Within the week Wainwright was reciting long sections from what Lynn was certain were his carefully filed sermons on the need to resist the devil's temptations. Occasionally Lynn countered with legalistic definitions from Lord Edward Coke's published opinions, reminding her present inquisitor that according to the Cornishman Coke's interpretation, evidence of witchcraft had to be proved rather than merely assumed.

Two weeks later Lynn's education about the Puritan community of New Haven was expanded beyond one disapproving goodwife and one evangelistic minister. Although the "suspect witch" was scrupulously avoided, her magnificent bull was not. With a shrewd eye toward bettering their own breeding stock the neighboring farmers approached Captain Dunton with the proposition that their finest cows be serviced by the devon red. Without a stir of conscience, Lynn set the price at double the one she'd charged Rhode Island farmers. Aware that her chances of regaining her own herd in time for spring breeding were remote, she scheduled Red Penny's maximum of fifty cows.

To her relief, that schedule was the prod needed to rouse Jem Rigg from the despondency that had kept him bedridden as much as his injuries had. Hobbling to the barn on homemade crutches, he supervised the appointed breedings as he'd done in Cornwall and Rhode Island; and in the process, he won the grudging admiration of the more perceptive farmers. On those days Lynn remained housebound, tending the remaining patient who was now fretful to be allowed out of bed. When the doctor finally granted permission, bandy-legged John Bram regained his health with amazing speed, spurred on by the sight of the dozen militia horses pastured on the Dunton farm and by the captain's permission to tend those animals.

With both of her fellow prisoners returned to work, Lynn's own restlessness increased measurably. Although Clive Dunton was a friendly man who gave her cheerful moral support, he was away most days and frequently on overnight patrols. Unlike the Narragansett Indians who'd been pacified by Roger Williams's equitable treatment, the Connecticut Indians bitterly resented the encroaching white settlements and frequently threatened the more remote farms. In addition to the problem of Indians, the multiplicity of the colony's rivers that fed into Long Island Sound attracted lawless white smugglers, freebooters, and renegade trappers. Never an aggressive church member, Clive Dunton had proved an effective militia leader who dealt fairly with the Indians and harshly with the renegade whites. The respect he'd gained among his fellow colonials was evident in the fact that none of them criticized him for harboring a woman whose daily activities were well chronicled by his talkative wife.

During Dunton's absences from home, Lynn had no relief from her overwhelming desperation, except for hard physical work on her prison farm. Her memories were torturous: the half-remembered face of an infant son twisted her heart with grief, the failure of a husband to protect her aroused her sense of hopelessness, and the burden she'd placed on an aging grandfather to clear her name made her feel guilty. Even worse, the corrosive hatred she bore her father and the Pollocks took an equal toll on her dwindling courage. Even though she was not closely watched by any of the authorities in town, she knew that the only route of escape was a wilderness that could prove more dangerous than imprisonment in New Haven.

For the first time, Lynn could understand Clay's reluctance to accept the restrictions of marriage. After a year in a prison far worse than hers, he'd wanted no new bonds to inhibit his return to freedom. Lynn wondered if she wouldn't feel equally reluctant if she ever regained her own . . . if she ever could! She'd been condemned without a trial here in New Haven; how could she expect any better treatment from a Stannary court in Cornwall where there were few restrictions against the persecution of witches, where even educated aristocrats like her father believed that women rather then men were the devil's disciples? It was the knowledge that her father had hated his mother intensely enough to defame her memory that eventually destroyed Lynn's resolve to return to Rhode Island. She didn't want her own son's life to be blighted by the ugly specter of rumors and suspicions any more than she wanted to spend the rest of her life in hiding.

Midway through the sixth week on the Dunton farm, Lynn's dilemma ended, and she was allowed to choose her own fate. Requested to attend a public meeting by the colony's religious leaders, Lynn was clad almost identically to the townswomen who would attend the meeting. That she was neatly attired in a well-cut black cloak and dress softened by a snowy white kerchief, and with her uneven lengths of hair concealed beneath a traditional white winged cap was not due to Hertha Dunton. Despite her husband's express requests, Hertha had continued her niggardly ways; it was Dunton's tolerant sister who had supplied Lynn's clothing, and who had taken care to make this particular outfit both suitable and attractive.

Lynn's similarity to the other women, however, ended with her clothing. While their faces mirrored avid curiosity, hers reflected alert vigilance. Despite the protection of Captain Dunton by her side as they walked toward the meeting house, she did not intend to submit tamely if any of the onlookers lining the streets became violent. Attached to the lining of her cloak were her clubs, which she had recovered after Sid Pollock had dropped them before he'd fled. In the privacy of the Dunton barn, she'd practiced daily until she'd regained her former competency in their use.

Such self-defense did not prove necessary during that public walk; Dunton had also anticipated trouble and had assigned three of his men as guards. The half-grown boys who shouted derisive insults were promptly driven away, the two grinning sailors who tossed handfuls of mud were themselves tossed into the swirling harbor waters, and the housewife who flourished a broom threateningly in the air was unceremoniously carried to her front door and deposited inside. Such prompt reactions rendered the remainder of the walk uneventful; and not until Lynn was seated on a low platform in clear view of both the elevated ministers and the hundred or more citizenry, did another incident occur. A well-aimed rock hurled through an open window landed near her feet and splintered one of the floor boards. A moment later everyone in the stilled room heard the roar of pain coming from the culprit and the stern order "Begone!" issued by a militiaman. It was after that dramatic interruption that the hearing officially began, and Reverend Wainwright rose to his feet and addressed the young woman on display.

"I regret very deeply that your former companions saw fit to spread ugly gossip throughout our township. We are not ordinarily vindictive people, nor do our people customarily break the law. But the circumstances surrounding you are unusual, and the problem of your continued residence is a delicate religious and legal matter.

"In keeping with our traditions, we have acceded to Captain Dunton's request that he act as your spokesman; so unless I ask you directly for a response, you are to allow him to be your defender. To acquaint everyone here with the particulars of the charges leveled against you, he is empowered to present your defense before he answers any challenges. Since I, too, have interrogated you on a number of occasions, it may be that I will be the one to offer information about you. Be assured, mistress, we intend to pass no judgment upon you; we are concerned solely with your effect upon our community."

Gruffly undramatic, Clive Dunton began with a matter-of-fact report on the criminal activities of Sidney Pollock and the suspected activities of the three men who'd spirited the two Pollocks out of New Haven. He then detailed the chronological story that began when Royce Trevor met his daughter after a twenty-year desertion. A blunt veteran of militia action against criminals in Connecticut, Dunton described the violence on the farm in Rhode Island and aboard the ship, the theft of both animals and housegoods, and Royce Trevor's callous betrayal of his daughter. Without giving pause enough for audience interruption, Dunton read all of Ephraim Penley's letters that pertained to the Pollocks' duplicity in manufacturing the petitions against Trelynn Trevor and to Royce Trevor's twenty-five years of polite blackmail in gaining a fortune from Ephraim and Hortensia Penley by threatening to return to England. Not until Dunton read the copy of the letter from Roger Williams was he challenged by one of the ministers.

"Such an opinion is not permissible evidence, Captain. Roger Williams is no longer of our faith. He tolerates evil in his colony that we would find an abomination here, and he welcomes all manner of heretics into the citizenry of Rhode Island. He has another conviction that we consider particularly abhorrent—that Divine Providence has no place in government."

During this pithy castigation, Lynn relaxed slightly. For the preceding nights when she helped Clive Dunton prepare her defense, she had carefully written a rebuttal to this particular challenge. Now she watched with inward satisfaction as her defender held forth a black bound book.

"In this book of sermons, which I borrowed from Reverend Wainwright," he announced dramatically, "there are six sermons written by Roger Williams when he was a minister in Salem. Reverend Wainwright has assured me that these sermons do not differ in any way from our own beliefs. 'Tis not Roger Williams's alleged political beliefs that are important at this hearing, 'tis his word as a respected man of God—for such he was and still is despite Reverend Davis's objections. Roger Williams has declared Mistress Trevor to be 'an industrious and honest young woman incapable of the criminal complaints lodged against her.' In his letter he offers to shield her against unjust prosecution until her grandfather can clear her name. Can we of New Haven do less and still hold our heads as high?''

For a moment Lynn thought the eloquent appeal had won her freedom, but she'd reasoned from ignorance. Hertha Dunton had been as diligent as Sidney Pollock in assuring other New Haven housewives that her unwanted guest was indeed an "unnatural" woman. Instead of respectful silence, Dunton's final question was greeted by an angry buzz emanating from a group of women seated near Hertha. To his credit, Reverend Wainwright proved politician enough to know his constituents and the source of their information. Of each of the several goodwives he allowed to voice their disapproval, he asked the one stern question, "Did you see or hear this incident or are you merely quoting someone else?" The farmwife who claimed the Devon bull was as unnatural as its mistress was silenced by her husband, one of the farmers who'd paid to have his cows bred. The aggressive woman who stated that Mistress Trevor spoke the devil's language was routed by an angry Clive Dunton.

"How is it you know the devil's language, Mistress Pelkey? The tongue Mistress Trevor uses on occasion is Narragansett Indian, not the devil's."

Knowing of the discord that existed between the Duntons, Reverend Wainwright acted to repress the other women by calling upon Hertha Dunton herself, warning her to be specific rather than merely spiteful. His reasoning about

Hertha Dunton proved to be as faulty as Lynn's; Hertha had organized her testimony with an efficient thoroughness. Rising ponderously to her feet, she addressed Wainwright directly.

"As ye well know, Reverend, she's not read the scriptures since she's been here; but she's read everything else in my husband's library—books that don't concern a woman. Each night at supper, she prates the law to my husband with the devil's own sly tongue. Aye, and much more beside—tales of visiting savage Indian camps and barbarous pirates, boasts about surviving the London plague when nobody else did, about driving teams of bullocks across rivers, and about acting the midwife come calving time."

Annoyed by the venomous loquacity, Wainwright was repressively stern. "Mistress Trevor admitted all of these activities to Reverend Quiller and myself weeks ago, and none of them are against the law, unusual though they may be for a woman. Neither is her ignorance of scriptures. 'Tis not needful to be a member of the church in this or any other Connecticut town. Were those the extent of your accusations?"

"Nay, I've just begun. She's turned my servants against me by tempting them with the devil's own coin."

"Last week Mistress Trevor told me that she paid your servants for their services, and that she paid you for her board and that of her own servants and her animal," the reverend asserted forcefully.

"Aye, she did that," Hertha admitted and then pounced triumphantly, "but she kept the main sum that her bull earned for herself—a mark of greed, Reverend, as ye've told us often enough from the pulpit. She's full guilty of worse things, too. She bathes every day she leaves off working in the barn, and in water that would freeze ordinary folk. She washes her clothes every week as if soap were easy to come by.

"But 'tis not so much what she does; 'tis her powerful

way of forcing others to do her will. The crippled mute obeys her like a dog, and t'other one would do her bidding if it killed him. Aye, and Captain Dunton's no exception. When she asked him to explore a spot of land on the Housatonic River, he raced to do her favor on his next patrol. She'll enslave the whole colony if you let her, Reverend; and she'll turn the decent folk among us into outcasts!''

Throughout the shrill tirade, Lynn watched Hertha Dunton in dismal fascination. Except for the unpleasant greeting she'd extended to Lynn on the first day, Hertha had avoided her unwanted guest assiduously and had been only a silent spectator at the supper table. But she hadn't been idle, Lynn reminded herself; she'd done a remarkable job of spying, saving up all of the private details for the grand public exposure. Lynn felt stripped of all dignity, the momentary object of curiosity for some and of suspicious distrust for others.

As his wife resumed her seat, Clive Dunton rose from his and reclaimed his leadership of the hearing. While Reverend Wainwright better understood the motives of discontented women, Dunton knew the motivations that drove the colony's men—the acquisition of enough wealth to ease the grinding hardships of pioneering.

"That 'spot' of Housatonic River land," he began mildly, "is a royal grant that was given by Prince James to the father of Mistress Trevor's husband. 'Tis several times the size of New Haven with enough virgin timber to build a city. The survey completed last year shows sufficient waterpower for a dozen mills, and a section of delta-soil tidelands for crops and cattle, in addition to a small harbor that can accommodate ocean ships. Last year when the deeded owner, Mistress Trevor's husband, visited his land for the second time, he made contact with the small Iroquois tribe of Indians who claim the mountainous third of the grant as their tribal lands.

"According to a pair of white fur trappers who accompanied the owner to the Indian village, Charles Clay Trevor promised the chieftain that his future lumbering business would not encroach upon their land if the Indians granted permission for the removal of an occasional tree. He also extended an offer of future employment to selected Indians who might want to learn the lumbering trade. Because of his wise precautions, Mr. Trevor will have far less trouble with his red brothers than some of us have experienced. Within a year, he will have transported enough settlers to his land to begin operation; and I don't have to remind you that his business will prove of benefit to our own colony.''

Shocked out of the leaden poise she'd maintained for hours, Lynn stared at her defender. All he'd told her when he'd returned from that patrol was that the land was a primitive wilderness, the same description Clay had given her over a year ago. Not until her wayward husband had met the Spragues in Providence had he realized even a fraction of the potential wealth Clive Dunton had just outlined. No wonder Clay had wanted to met the Narragansett Indians on that same day, and no wonder he'd danced attendance on the Narragansett sachem. He wanted to know how to deal with his own Iroquois. Perhaps the Iroquois chieftain Dunton had mentioned was now wearing another of Clay's richly plumed hats. Lynn's momentary surge of wild hope subsided quickly. Clay had never told her about his plans for the Connecticut land because he didn't really consider her a part of his life. At any rate the development of that land would be too late to help her.

Wearily she returned her attention to the proceedings and was shocked again by the altered expressions on the faces of the judges both official and unofficial. Hertha Dunton's mouth was open, and she was glaring at her husband in undisguised fury. People were out of their seats and engaged in buzzing conversations among themselves and with their governing ministers; even the erstwhile antagonistic women were now arguing with each other.

So much for their moral indignation against witchcraft, Lynn reflected with a curdling revulsion. They'd accept her now that they knew she had a husband potentially richer than their richest. Cynically she wondered if there had ever been a wealthy witch among the thousands in England and Europe who'd been burned at the stake or hanged on the nearest gibbet or drowned in a convenient ducking pond. Still quaking inwardly from the fear this roomful of people had inspired just moments earlier, Lynn knew in the part of her mind that was primitive and instinctive that any possible reprieve would be only temporary. The first time some other carping, unattractive woman accused her of husband-tampering—for that was what Hertha had really suspected—Lynn would be returned to this same judgment seat. Her half-formed resolve hardened into grim determination.

Gaveling the meeting back to order with an authoritative pounding on the wooden surface of his protective podium, Reverend Wainwright arose in robed dignity to address the disordered assembly. Disciplined to obedience after a lifetime of church government, the people quickly settled to attention; and the minister began what was intended to be a beneficent forgiveness.

"As I announced earlier, this meeting was never a trial; and the council and I had already made our findings, which need now only the approval of our people. During my frequent interviews with Mistress Trevor, which I conducted as much for her safety as for yours, I found her to be as Reverend Roger Williams had—an honest, industrious woman too intelligent to be guilty of the crimes listed in these false petitions. If there are no further objections, we are offering her open sanctuary in our colony with the same rights and freedoms enjoyed by all of us. How say you, townsmen?"

The approval given was not an enthusiastic roar, but rather a thoughtful murmur stemming from much altered opinions and from the provocative fact that the central figure had risen to her feet and now stood facing them in dignified defiance. Lynn's voice when she began to speak sounded harshly alien to her own ears.

"Reverend Wainwright, I am grateful for the generosity you have extended me, but I cannot accept your offer. If I am free to leave, I plan to return to England to fight legally for my own exoneration. I have but one boon to ask. Sailors are a superstitious lot, and I do not wish to be locked into a ship's cell to pacify them. Nor do I want to be blamed for a storm at sea or a broken mast or a ruptured hull. Since even the sailors in town know all about me by this time, I cannot embark on any ship leaving your harbor. Therefore I request that you allow my grandfather's friend and my kindly defender to escort me by land tomorrow morning to the settlement north of here at the mouth of the Connecticut River. There I hope to locate a ship whose captain and crew know nothing about the contents of the papers Sheriff Pollock gave to Reverend Wainwright. The money I was accused of hoarding will pay for my passage, and Captain Dunton may claim that I am a nagging wife being returned to her parents in Plymouth or a wayward daughter being sent to cloister."

Unheeding of the cries of protest, Lynn strode swiftly down the aisle and through the open door accompanied only by Clive Dunton.

"Wait for your husband to return, lass, before you make such a rash decision," he pled with her earnestly.

"My husband may never return, Captain Dunton; he's engaged in a present business that keeps him on the sea and away from home. I haven't seen him in fifteen months."

"Then let me take you back to your son in Rhode Island."

Lynn shook her head sadly. "No, I don't want him to hate me as my father did his mother. Only if I become a free woman will I see him again."

Understanding the need that drove her despite his fears

for her safety, Dunton turned to more practical considerations. "Can you ride a horse, lass?"

"Only once and that time in a man's clothing. If I could borrow a pair of your old leather breeks to wear beneath my skirts, I'd not be an embarrassment to your men. Perhaps I'd even be able to sit more comfortably when we make camp."

" 'Tis a harsh journey, lass, with renegades of both races along the way."

"It can't be any worse than the two weeks my husband and I spent on Bodmin Moor where we were pursued by soldiers and attacked by wreckers. What is the name of the town at the mouth of the Connecticut?"

"Saybrook, a decent town where you'll not be mistreated."

"Unless one of your men tells the minister there that I'm a witch."

"You needn't fear my men; they've been on your side for weeks."

Lynn smiled with sudden impish humor. "Since your visit to the Housatonic River?" she asked lightly.

"You can't blame them for being impressed, lass. Many of them are young and impatient to be free of the restrictions here in New Haven, but they'd have been loyal to you anyway."

"Then if Saybrook is as decent as you say, you'll not have to wait there with me. I don't imagine your young men would be very pleased with that kind of boredom."

"I've no wish to return early," Dunton replied heavily. " 'Tis a daughter I wish you were in fact, but 'tis a daughter I'll be protecting this afternoon when the busybodies are flocking to the house to bedevil you with their nosy curiosity. We'll be sharing a keg of cider with Jem and Bram in the barn."

"Will you allow them to earn their board after I'm gone?"

"You should have known me better than to ask. I'll

keep them safe and your bull, too. There's more than one who might be tempted by that great brute.''

"My father will try," Lynn warned bitterly.

"He'll not succeed, lass. I doubt he'd dare return to New Haven with everyone knowing him for the thief and villain he is. And don't worry about Hertha abusing your men or your animal; she's finally earned the discipline she's needed for years. God's truth, until today I hadn't realized just how much a haggish shrew she's become.''

CHAPTER
16

Lynn's leavetaking from the Dunton farm at dawn the following morning was a sadder occasion than she'd dreamed possible. She'd known that Jem would be mournful, of course; the afternoon before he'd watched her with sorrowful eyes. But John Bram's fierce loyalty was something she hadn't anticipated. As he held her horse steady enough for her to mount, his voice broke over the words, "God keep you, Mistress Lynn, and bring you back safe to all of us." It had never occurred to her that she and the others had become the only family he'd ever had. Nor had she expected tears from the two women servants who'd helped her prepare for the strenuous journey by cropping her hair to an evenly short length and packing her meager wardrobe. But this morning they'd risen even earlier than was their wont in the harsh life they led under Hertha's demanding domination and walked out to the remote pasture to bid her farewell.

During the first day of travel that had been thoughtfully slowed to accommodate her inexperience in the saddle, Lynn's emotions fluctuated from doubt about the wisdom of her impulsive decision to moments of wild exhilaration.

Even knowing that happiness was a temporary illusion in her case, she still experienced a joyful release as she bounced ungracefully whenever the caravan of eight riders speeded up over an open field. As her resilient muscles toughened to the demand and she no longer had to concentrate on the mechanics of steering her cooperative horse, her thoughts traveled backward in time to the night she'd first met the reckless convict smuggler, James Thayne. He'd been feeling the same illogical hilarity, the same unrestrained sense of freedom she was experiencing; but she'd thought him as crazy as the wild birds who feasted annually on the fermenting blackberries at Penley Farm. Even with a cracked head that must have been painful, he'd still made lighthearted jokes until he'd collapsed in front of the cave. What a drab, humorless companion she must have seemed to him!

As she thought of those early months with the man who'd become her husband, Lynn's mood sobered to self-recrimination. If only she hadn't been so determined to have her own way, she might still possess a husband. If she'd taken his advice and sold both her animals and the indenture papers of the servants she purchased aboard the *Tamarlind*, she would have had two years of marriage to remember rather than a few fleeting months. Jem and Polly could have managed the farm, and Kerry Egan would still be alive. Because of her ambition to prove herself more capable than her husband, all of their lives had been shattered, her marriage destroyed, and her infant son deserted. Even more depressing was the suspicion that her willful return to England might prove to be just another defiant gesture on her part.

By the time the small trail party had made its camp for the second night, Lynn had discovered that wilderness travel was not conducive to emotional extremes; survival alertness was far more important. Without well-defined trails to follow, progress was slow and detours frequent. On the fourth day Lynn had her first experience in fording a river, not on a securely engineered ferryboat, but on the back of a horse during a squalling rain that added to her physical discomfort.

It was while everyone was hunting for enough dry wood to maintain all-night campfires that Lynn noticed something that was as out of place on the shores of a wilderness continent as a medieval castle would have been. Two hundred yards north of the Hammonasset River they'd just crossed was a symmetrical pile of rocks, some six feet high, with a scooped-out and fire-blackened pit at the top. For a moment she wondered if it might not be an Indian shrine of some kind until she remembered the similar structure Clay had pointed out from the tower on the Cornish coast. A false fire signal used by wreckers to lure ships into dangerous waters, Clay had called it. Frightened by memory, Lynn raced back to the camp.

"Are these offshore waters navigable?" she asked Captain Dunton.

"Not close in," he told her. "For a mile out 'tis mud shallow at low tide, rocky in some spots, swampy in others. Small boats can manage, but ships would be mired down except in the deep river channels."

"How do ships' captains locate those channels during a storm or at night?"

"Usually they send a pair of longboats ashore, and the men light signal fires on both sides of the river's mouth."

"Is there much traffic on this part of the ocean?"

"That's not the Atlantic Ocean out there; that's an inland stretch of sea. Forty miles straight across from where we're standing is Long Island; and ever since England took New York from the Dutch, this stretch of water has become the busiest traffic lane on the American coast. But this is no time for a geography lesson, lass; you need to get that wet clothing dried out."

"I'm not interested in the geography, Captain; there's something I think you should see."

A half hour later, a sober-faced Clive Dunton spoke

quietly to his men. "We post double sentries tonight, lads, and we make certain our weapons are at the ready. Mistress Trevor's sharp eyes have uncovered a new type of devilment that's not visited our colony before, but one that's cursed Cornwall waters for centuries. Someone has built a signal fire tower that's two hundred yards away from the Hammonasset channel. Any ship that followed that light would have been aground a mile offshore, completely vulnerable to attack by wrecker scum in small boats."

Lynn slept uncomfortably that night with the leather straps of her clubs looped around her wrists, and the next day she rode with them hanging from the pommel of her saddle. As vividly as if she'd seen them only last week, she remembered the bearded faces of the wreckers who'd attacked Clay and Harry on the tower bridge. If a gang of those cutthroats had moved its operation to the New World, which had only isolated groups of local militia to guard the coastline, ships such as David Carey's *Narragansett* and Elwin Carter's *Aquidneck* would be in constant jeopardy. So might the *Tamarlind* and Clay's fleet of slavers.

Captain Dunton's actions the next morning added to her fears. He ordered the party underway at dawn after a cold breakfast of water and leftover hoecake, and announced they'd be breaking trail through the inland forests, rather than taking the easier shore route. Just how different the day's travel was to be, Lynn learned when Dunton signaled everyone to dismount near a small clearing while two men on foot scouted the area ahead. At irregular intervals the procedure was repeated until the sixth such patrol, when the scouts returned at full run instead of a cautious walk. Instantly everyone huddled around the excited men; and the one named Seth Wilson, who'd gone on every patrol, made his report.

"Half a mile ahead by a small river, maybe eight or ten men with their faces smeared black . . . charcoal, I reckon."

"Any horses?" Dunton demanded.

"No horses, only small boats and piles of barrels around."

"What about weapons?"

"A bearded man with a pair of pistols stuck in his belt."

"Any muskets?"

"Didn't see any."

"Any concealment close enough for us to use if we attack?"

"No. We'd have to ride in and take them by surprise."

"We can't risk the horses on unfamiliar terrain, and we don't have the manpower for a frontal attack on foot. No use getting ourselves killed when Saybrook is less than a day away. If their camp is as permanent as it sounds, we can come back next week with the Saybrook militia. Mount up, we'll move farther inland and avoid them this trip."

As militarily sound as Dunton's decision was, it proved to be a sorry mistake. The suspect encampment was better defended than it appeared to be. Just as Dunton had sent scouts ahead, so had the enemy leader posted sentries some distance from their camp. One of those sentries had been on a high enough bluff to spot the band of New Haven militia. A mile upstream along the small river Seth Wilson had described, Dunton's soldiers were ambushed by a motley band of men who'd been concealed in thick underbrush before they leapt out to attack with clubs and knives.

Having been placed at the rear of the column, Lynn watched the initial attack in horror. Two of the horses were the first victims, their forelegs broken by well-aimed blows of heavy clubs. Watching the soldier in front of her dismount swiftly and fire his musket with practiced ease, Lynn, too, slid to the ground after she'd retrieved her clubs.

"Get behind a tree and stay hidden," the militiaman hissed at her tersely, laying aside his empty musket and cocking his pistols before he ran toward the protection of the next tree.

Left alone, Lynn looked cautiously around. She heard the gasp of surprise before she saw the man who uttered it. Ten feet away from her, half concealed by a shrub, was the figure of a man in dark seaman's garb that matched his charcoal-smeared face. With a knife gripped in one hand and ship's belaying pin in the other, he approached her with a threatening swagger.

"Ye'll be a likely prize once yer friends are downed," he boasted with the grating accent of a coastal Cornishman.

Standing motionless in dread anticipation, Lynn waited until he was three feet away before she swung her clubs. She never saw the expression of disbelief that suffused his face; her eyes never left his knife and truncheon. As he stumbled backward with the arm that held the knife benumbed with pain, Lynn's clubs struck again more accurately this time and more deadly. She was breathing hard as she watched him fall, but the sounds of battle were too close for any sense of triumph. She turned around in time to see another dark figure sidling cautiously toward the soldier who'd been her companion minutes before. Engrossed in reloading his pistols, the militiaman didn't see the enemy approach; and only Lynn's shout of warning saved him from having his head crushed by a heavy quarterstaff. Even so, the glancing blow had rendered him unconscious.

Knowing that her own weapons would be useless against the six-foot-long weapon the attacker was already raising for a killing blow over the fallen militiaman, Lynn threw first one and then the other of her weighted clubs at the man's head. The second one struck its target, but only hard enough to stun him momentarily. Desperately she wrenched the knife from the limp hand of the first ruffian and ran toward the more dangerous one who was already recovering his senses. Her action was an instinctive defense, not a planned killing, as she plunged the knife into his broad back. Groping swiftly on the ground until she located one of her clubs, she waited silently for any sign of returning life before she dragged the leaden body away from the stricken soldier. No longer gripped by paralyzing fear, she stood up cautiously and peered toward the now silent, heavily treed area fifty feet ahead. Her knees began to tremble in relief only when she heard Captain Dunton's gruff voice, oddly weak, but still in command.

"That's it, lads. We'll cross the stream before we assess the damage; this lot may not be the whole of them. One of you get back to Parkman and find out if he needs any further help with Mistress Trevor and the pack animal."

Lynn's lips curled with the ironic cynicism she'd felt since she was fourteen; even men like Clive Dunton who knew all about her fight with Sid Pollock still considered women incapable of defense in any battle situation, even one as disorganized as this. She greeted the militiaman coming to her 'rescue' with a quiet announcement: "Mr. Parkman will need a litter."

Squatting beside his fallen comrade, the soldier nodded in satisfaction as he surveyed the two dead bodies. "At least Parkman got the two who slipped past our guard before he was stopped. Are you all right, mistress?"

Lynn's response was laughter, not the laughter of feminine hysteria, but that of humor. "I'm fine," she murmured.

"Then the captain wants you to look at the two prisoners we took before we move out."

"What happened to the rest of the murderers?"

"Dead except for the prisoners. There were only ten of them including the ones here; and compared to Indians, this bunch was just untrained water-front scum who'd never met militia before. Just our lead men were hurt. Gifford was bashed on the head like Parkman; and the captain took a bullet in the shoulder, but he'll be all right. Better get along and talk to him now, mistress."

Gingerly Lynn walked the short distance past the carcasses of two horses whose suffering had been ended by bullets and past the bodies of six men. She located Dunton sitting on the ground with his back to a tree. To her inexperienced eyes he looked more seriously wounded than his messenger had claimed, and his voice sounded weaker than it had minutes earlier.

"I want you to look at that bearded man over yonder," he rasped. "Some of my men think he's one of the loiterers they saw in New Haven several months ago. And if your stomach can stand it, lass, I'd like you to look at the dead ones as well. 'Tis important we know who they are."

Lynn shook her head as she looked over at the heavily bearded man tied to a tree. "I never saw him before."

"Take a closer look; I think he recognizes you."

Experiencing as nervous a fear as she'd felt for the men she'd killed, Lynn stared at the prisoner whose long unkempt hair and straggly beard covered most of his face. As she started to turn away, she swung around to stare at him again; she'd heard the curse he'd muttered: "You goddamned witch! Sid said you'uz locked up in New Haven."

Still unable to recognize the man or his voice, she asked the soldier standing nearby to show her the others. At the third body, she stopped short. Even unshaven with most of his face stained black, she recognized Sid Pollock.

"He was the villain who destroyed one of the horses and took Gifford out of action before the captain shot him. Did you know the man, mistress?" the soldier asked.

Nodding mutely, Lynn fought against the gorge that rose in her throat at the thought of looking at any more dead bodies. But she had to know whether or not Rad Pollock was among them. Minutes later she shook her head again, this time in renewed fear. The thought of the vindictive father lurking somewhere nearby made her skin crawl with nervous apprehension.

"I think we should leave as quickly as possible," she mumbled.

Spurred on by the growing certainty that there were

other criminals in the area, Lynn and the four uninjured
soldiers completed the demanding task of carrying their
injured comrades and the two prisoners across the wide,
shallow stream in tense silence. Only after they'd reached
the concealment of the thick forest on the opposite bank
did Lynn and two of the soldiers attempt to treat their own
injured, binding their wounds with bandages torn from
Lynn's petticoat. Of the three, only Captain Dunton was
conscious.

"You'll have to make Indian litters, Selwin, and you'll
have to get back to the shore route where there's sandy
surface," he muttered to his second-in-command. "You'll
find leather thonging on the pack animal."

"No, we won't, sir," Selwin responded gloomily. "That
cursed horse bolted midstream at the last crossing and was
long gone before we could catch it. We'll have to cut the
leather from our shirts."

Before Lynn remembered that all her other clothing had
been in a bundle aboard the missing pack animal, she
impulsively offered her heavy wool cloak as the sacrificial
garment. Using the strips one of the men cut for her, she
helped to tie the crossbars to the twelve-foot-long poles the
other men fashioned from the slender boles of the scrub
pine trees in the area. One by one the crude litters were
completed and attached to the stirrups of four of the six
horses by still more strips of heavy wool, these contributions cut from Lynn's discarded skirt. As silent as everyone had been throughout the tense hour of work, one of
the soldiers handed Lynn a leather shirt he'd taken from
his saddle pouch. Gratefully she removed the remnants of
her mutilated dress and donned the supple garment behind
a clump of screening underbrush. Emerging minutes later,
she found the four injured men already lashed to the litters
with the last remains of her skirt and cloak. Thoughtfully
she folded her dress bodice into a pillow for the young
militiaman whose head had been struck by Sid Pollock.
Tears flooded her eyes as she remembered the cheerful

Irish highwayman who hadn't survived such a blow. "Your murderer will never again hurt another human being, Kerry Egan," she whispered, fiercely glad that one of her own tormentors had been eliminated. If she survived England, she vowed to avenge herself against the other two whose persecution had almost destroyed her.

Jamming the injured soldier's fur cap over her own head, she picked up the reins of the horse and joined in the single-file procession already formed. Only the bearded prisoner was mounted, his hands tied to the saddle pommel and his feet lashed together beneath the belly of his horse. As a final precaution, his mouth had been gagged with a kerchief.

At a plodding pace that seemed interminably slow, the small caravan paused once to water the horses and once again to rest the weary walkers before it reached the shore. Although there'd been no sign of any additional enemy, no one relaxed his vigilance. As they paused beneath the bluffs on the sandy beach, Selwin handed Lynn a pistol and slipped a musket into the saddle holder of the horse she was leading. "Do you know how to use these weapons, mistress?" he asked softly. At her nod of compliance, he added more harshly, "If they come at us again, aim the best you can. 'Tis not likely you'll have time to reload."

Before Selwin called another halt, the soldier who'd been assigned to guard Lynn before the attack had regained consciousness, but the injured prisoner had died. "That leaves just one beauty to tell the tale before he hangs," Selwin announced grimly. "And if the captain or Gifford dies, he'll hang slow."

With a mounted militiaman now to scout the rocky beach ahead, the pace accelerated to a faster walk; and by midafternoon the torturous journey was half complete. Suddenly, without warning, Selwin led the procession behind an outcropping of granite rocks at the base of the small bluff that lined the section of beach.

Untying the bearded prisoner's fetters, he dragged the

man down from the horse and shoved him to the ground. "This slimy piece of filth has been looking out over the water for the last mile; and damn me, the hair's crawling on the back of my neck," Selwin rasped tensely. "Wilson, get down off of that horse and scout over these bluffs. This renegade is waiting for something to happen, and we're in no shape for another ambush."

As he spat out the words in an angry rush, Selwin retied the prisoner's hands and feet. Taking his knife from its sheath, he removed the kerchief, and with swift strokes, he shaved off the concealing beard and hacked away the long hair. With a few rough swipes of the kerchief, he scrubbed away the sweat-dampened charcoal, and then looked up with gratification as he pointed to the puckery red scar that marred the prisoner's once handsome face.

"I had to satisfy my own curiosity, lads, and I did," he spoke softly to the others. "I thought I recognized him; I just wasn't sure. He's the one I saw in town with a pair of scum just like him, but he wasn't bearded two months ago. What's your name, scum, and what were you doing in New Haven?" he demanded harshly.

Licking his dry lips with a thickened tongue, the prisoner smiled. "Ask the witch, she knows who I am. Won't matter what she tells you because you'll all be dead meat by sundown anyway once Captain Wellyn gets his hands on you."

Looking down on the face of a man she hadn't seen in two years except as a dark silhouette in a burning barn, Lynn shuddered. "His name is Tom Kenn," she confirmed in a leaden murmur and shuddered again at the hatred expressed in his voice.

"Aye, I'm Tom Kenn, witch, and I hope the captain turns you over to me after he's made fish bait out of these cullies. You blasted my life, and I'll make you pay for every piece of demon luck I've suffered since. Sid said you were hard to kill, but I know a thing or two more than—"

"What happened to Rad Pollock, Tom?" Lynn interrupted grimly.

"Old Pollock was the fool Sid said he was. Tried to stop Sid and me from leaving New Haven until I coshed him on the head and dragged him into the boat. He'uz warned what would happen if he riled Captain Wellyn, but he'uz too pigheaded to listen. Second day in camp, he tried to steal a boat; and he died screaming with the captain's knife in his gut."

Swallowing repeatedly for the moments it took her to regain a slight measure of poise, Lynn asked more quietly, "This Captain Wellyn is a pirate?"

"The best of them until our ship was swept south of Saybrook Point and foundered in the mud.'

"And now you're wreckers?"

Kenn's gloating smile included all of his avid listeners. "With the devil's own bounty for the taking from New London to New York."

"Who built that signal tower near the Hammonasset River, Tom?"

"There's another twenty of them ready and waiting. They weren't hard to set up when a dozen of us are Cornish. 'Tis not like home where there's a cursed army always on the snoop; this coast is wide open and free."

"Bind his mouth again, Mr. Selwin," Lynn ordered tiredly. "You've learned what you wanted to know; and I'll tell you the rest about this weakling braggart and about two of the dead men."

More to relieve her own depression than to entertain the nervous men hiding behind the uncertain protection of the stone barrier, Lynn talked about Cornwall and Rhode Island, answering the questions of the men who knew little beyond the narrow confines of an isolated Puritan settlement. It was the most companionable hour she'd known in months; it might also be her last pleasant one, she mused with bittersweet regret. Once she separated from them in Saybrook, she'd be alone. Moodily she dribbled a cup of tepid water past Clive Dunton's feverish lips and wondered if anyone, bad or good, had ever lived a happy life.

Jerking in alarm when a light hand touched her shoulder, she turned around to look at the sympathetic face of Parkman, the soldier whose life she'd saved. "Don't worry about what you had to do today, Mistress Trevor. All of us felt sick about our first combat, so I know what you're feeling. Killing isn't easy for someone who's decent, but sometimes it can't be helped."

Lynn smiled with a grateful humor; the tense fear of the more recent hours had all but obliterated the memory of the morning ambush. "You're the one who was given credit for those killings, Mr. Parkman, not me."

"Not for long. After I came to, Selwin asked me how I'd done it; and I didn't even know what I was supposed to have done. Besides, Seth Wilson saw you right after he'd wrestled the bearded wrecker to the ground and tied him to a tree. Not much ever escapes Seth. Some of the younger militia think he's got eyes in the back of his head because he catches all their simpleton mistakes. That's why you don't have anything to worry about; Seth's the best scout in the whole of Connecticut. There's no one who can outwit him on the trail, and he's faster than an Indian with the bow and arrows he always carries with him on a mission like this one."

The scout whom Parkman had praised so highly returned to his companions two hours after he'd been ordered to search the bluffs, delivering his report with a laconic brevity of words.

"Backwater cove half-mile ahead. Fifty men there, same kind as the others. Three ships listing in the shallow waters, two coastals being stripped and one old Spanish-type galley still flying the pirate black. Could be the leaders have the wind up about something; twenty of them in two longboats will be rounding the curve up yonder any minute. We stay hid until they pass."

Standing at alert with their hands stroking the flared out

noses of their horses, the five soldiers silently watched the puppetlike display of the distant longboats pulling slowly south, too far out at sea for the viewers to see anything but vague silhouetted shapes. Lynn saw nothing of this enemy; her assigned task was guarding Tom Kenn, a task she carried out with grim diligence. The margin of safety was too slight to take any chances with a criminal whose eyes now held the feral cunning of a trapped animal.

When the two boats were mere dots on the southern horizon, the small caravan moved out of its sanctuary with Seth Wilson in the lead. On a trail that seemed dangerously close to the enemy cove, Wilson led his companions through the thick stands of low branching trees, carefully avoiding any open space. As senior militiaman, Selwin was in charge of the prisoner, who like everyone else was on foot. With the rope around his neck tied to the pommel of the horse Selwin was leading, his hands bound, and his mouth gagged, Tom Kenn was forced to maintain the pace.

Near the rear of the procession, Lynn led the horse that was dragging Captain Dunton's Indian travois, and behind her the recovered Parkman walked beside his horse and an empty litter. Once during the silent passage, they were close enough to the cove to hear the voices of the pirates who'd remained at the foot of the coastal bluffs in a small protected cove. Doggedly, step by step, the column reached the comparative safety of denser forests; but not until they were a mile from the cove did Wilson signal for a rest stop.

Whether or not Selwin had relaxed his vigilance along the trail, not even the soldier following could be certain; but sometime during the long walk, Tom Kenn had worked one hand free. As soon as the horses were brought to a halt, he snatched the noose from around his neck, lowered his head, and rammed it into Selwin's chest with the stored-up power of desperation. His next action, though, was sheer viciousness; seconds before he disappeared into the underbrush, he stomped over the prostrate man with his heavy boots.

No one issued any pursuit order to Seth Wilson as the scout reached for his bow, slung a leather quiver of arrows over his shoulder, and took off on the run. Just as silently two of the soldiers carried Selwin's limp body back to the empty litter and strapped him in. In a low whisper, one of the men told Lynn and Parkman what had happened. Parkman nodded in understanding, tied the lead of his horse to the saddle of the one ahead, and took a sentry position ten feet away.

When she heard that Tom Kenn had escaped, Lynn's initial reaction was relief. With him gone, there'd be no one to inform the Saybrook people about her. The militiamen had become her friends, but Tom would have shouted the word *witch* to everyone in the small coastal settlement. Within minutes her relief had turned into anxiety; if Tom succeeded in warning the pirates, no one in their beleaguered party would survive. Apprehensively she looked up at the darkening sky as she stooped down to tend Clive Dunton and to listen worriedly to his shallow breathing.

Neither she nor Parkman heard Seth Wilson return, only the whispered order of the soldier ahead of her to get underway again. For another hour they wound around trees on what had been an ancient Indian trail, but abruptly they emerged onto a straight dirt passage many feet wider.

"Only a mile further, Mistress Trevor," Parkman asserted cheerfully in a normal tone of voice. "I told you Seth wouldn't lose us, but I'll be as glad as you when we leave the trees behind. I like open sky at night."

With only a half-moon to light the way, Lynn wasn't aware that they'd reached the town until Seth Wilson called out the order to halt. In the next moment the incessant ringing of a bell broke the peaceful silence with an urgent clamor. Dimly Lynn made out the dark outline of a building she thought might be a church. Accustomed to the greater sophistication of New Port, she wondered if anyone in such a sparsely settled community would have the courage to leave his home after dark. When torches began to appear with an immediacy that startled her, she felt a nervous trepidation. In New Port, only the militia was prepared to respond that promptly, and then only if they were expecting trouble. For a crushing second, she wondered if the trouble these people were expecting was her own arrival. The harsh challenge, "Captain Clive Dunton?" completed her demoralization; someone from New Haven had given them warning.

When Dunton himself tried to articulate a response, Lynn called out in a voice that was raspy with fatigue, "He's alive, but he took a bullet during an ambush this morning and needs a doctor. So do two of his men."

"Aye," the spokesman admitted without surprise, "we were afraid there'd been trouble."

As Lynn's eyes adjusted to the fluctuating torchlight, she leaned weakly against the trembling horse and watched the swift efficiency of the Saybrook men as they unlashed the three litters and carried them away. In a few minutes while the overworked horses were being led away, the spokesman issued new commands: "You other men are being taken to shelter where you'll find food and lodging. Mistress Trelynn Trevor, you will accompany me."

For a frantic moment, Lynn contemplated flight, and then subsided into resigned apathy. Even a jail house, if they had such, would be preferable to the horror she knew was lurking six miles south. The only words her captor spoke during the ten-minute walk were illogical ones of concern. " 'Tis not much further, mistress, but I can carry you if you're feeling too weak."

Lynn shook her head dumbly and made no reply; the fierce pride that had been her only defense throughout the months in New Haven sustained her now. She blinked uncaringly when a house door just ahead was thrown open, and lamplight poured out in blinding profusion. With little remaining volition, she walked into a large room that seemed crowded with people rushing toward her. Unable to focus her eyes on anyone except the tall man who was closest, she heard his explosive words, "God's truth, witch woman, you look worse than you did the night of the fire!" Without warning, all consciousness deserted her; and she sank to the wooden floor in an ungraceful faint.

More than a clock around later, Lynn was awakened by the rolling rhythm of a ship slicing its way through ocean swells. Her first conscious reaction was wonderment that she wasn't confined in a prison cell in the hold. This cabin was airy and well-lighted by transom windows; and the bed was comfortably soft. Unwilling to probe further into the strange reversal of her expectations, she closed her eyes again, ignoring the slight discomfort of both hunger and thirst.

"'Tis time to wake, mistress," a gentle feminine voice called out softly. "Ye've been without food nigh unto thirty hours, and 'tis weak ye are from the lack. Ye'll feel human again once ye've supped and bathed."

It was the final word that roused Lynn to full consciousness. "Who instructed you about the bath?" she asked sharply.

"Yer husband, mistress. He said ye'd not be civil without it."

Silenced by the relief surging through her that she hadn't been hallucinating the night before, Lynn arose shakily and accepted the scarlet velvet robe that the woman handed her and sat down at the table.

"'Tis not ship's fare, mistress, but fresh food from the port we left this morning."

After days of spartan camp meals and weeks of Hertha Dunton's often miserly dinners, the repast spread before Lynn on the table looked sumptuous. There were roast turkey and pork both, buttered bread, garden greens spiced with sweet apple vinegar, and egg-rich custard. Lynn didn't notice when the smiling stranger left the cabin; not even Polly had ever prepared a more appreciated meal. By the time the woman returned, followed by four burdened seamen carrying a copper tub and buckets of warm water, Lynn was tingling with anticipation. Her hair felt alive with unwelcome lice, and she itched all over from the accumulated filth of wilderness travel. Even as the door closed on the backs of the departing sailors, she was stripping off the robe and the limp remains of her underclothing that had escaped being used as bandages. Without questioning the rarity of perfumed soap after two years of coarse homemade lye, she lathered herself lavishly and scrubbed with vigorous determination to be clean again. Only when that pleasurable task had been completed to her satisfaction, did she remember a problem slightly more critical then cleanliness. The only garments she possessed after yesterday's violence were borrowed leather breeks and a shirt.

As her eyes lighted on the crimson robe, her mind began to function logically. Thus far, her needs had been too well met for an embarrassing lack of clothing to have been overlooked. Rubbing her damp hair with a soft linen towel, Lynn opened the first of the four sea chests secured to the bulkhead and studied the contents thoughtfully. The neatly folded men's suits were colored the soft greens and blues that were Clay Trevor's favorites. By no means reconciled to the idea of another brief reunion with the man she'd seen for only three months out of the twenty-five of their marriage, she closed the lid of that chest and the next one since it contained more of the same elegant masculine attire.

When she first viewed the contents of the remaining chests, she thought these garments, too, belonged to Clay, except that they were simpler in style and more vivid in color. The green suit on top was as bright as new-sprouted grass, and the blue of the dress underneath was clear cerulean, the hue of an English sky on a cloudless spring day. There were four other dresses as well: one rich crimson, another the burnished orange of sunset, the third a summery gown of pale pink, and the last a black velvet evening costume as elegant as those her mother had worn in London. The remaining chest was equally overflowing with the accessories of feminine grandeur: shoes to match the dresses, frothy undergarments, clocked stockings, a trio of delicate shawls, and a costly cloak of pale marten fur. Lynn smiled wryly at the display. If she were returned to Cornwall now, she'd be the most flamboyantly clad witch in English history. She was still contemplating the choice of dress while the tub was emptied and removed, and only the serving woman remained behind.

"Yer husband suggested ye wear the green one, mistress, so ye'll be warm enough."

"Where is my husband?"

"He said ye were to report to the captain's quarters."

"How did he know where to find me?"

"I don't know, mistress."

"Are you one of the passengers?"

"Nay, mistress, I'm one of the indentureds yer husband hired in Plymouth to work on his land in Connecticut. My name is Ellen; and when this voyage is over, I'll be joining my husband and his family there."

"Are you related to the Spragues, Ellen?"

"My husband is a Sprague, cousin to the Will and Roy who're already working in America."

"Ellen, do you know where this ship is headed?"

"Nay, mistress, 'tis back and forth we've been so far."

Lynn's heart pounded with excitement; if Clay had gone first to New Port, he knew about his son and about what had happened there. Hastily she pulled on pantaloons, a shift, and petticoats without much appreciation for their exquisite quality, grateful only that the green suit lacked the frilly femininity she'd always avoided. Since there wasn't much she could do with her short-cropped hair except to brush it vigorously and smooth the bangs over her fore-head, her grooming was completed in a matter of minutes.

With a nervous smile for Ellen, who'd been a patient if unskilled helper, Lynn left the cabin, only to have her courage fail her in the companionway outside. What could she say to a husband after fifteen months of separation? Especially to a husband who'd lacked the courtesy to come to her cabin? One thing she wouldn't say was "Welcome home." She no longer had a home, merely a deserted farm with empty cabins and an empty barn. For a moment she felt desolate; after New Haven she doubted she'd ever have the peace of mind to feel at home anywhere. There'd always be someone like Hertha Dunton or Edith Pollock Penley to spread their poisonous gossip, or someone like Royce Trevor to do far worse. At the memory of her father, Lynn's anger reignited; at least Clay would be able to help her rescue Polly and Kate and Jason Hale from her father's clutches. Determinedly she opened the door to the familiar captain's quarters and gasped in shock when she recognized the solitary occupant. The old man seated at the table looked up from his spread-out papers and smiled.

"You look better than you did when we brought you aboard last night," Ephraim Penley greeted her, "and you'll be looking even better after you've heard my news. The troubles that have plagued you so cruelly these past two years have all been resolved, and you're a free woman. Sit down, Trelynn, there's much to tell, and I was the one elected to do the telling. Clay didn't want you fainting again at the sight of him, though I expect by this time he knows 'twas merely exhaustion. Your name has been officially cleared and all charges against you dropped, but not through any efforts of mine I'm sorry to say. If you'll not interrupt, I'll tell you what your husband did for you and what it cost him. He was shot and almost killed in Cornwall by the vicious Captain Wilcox."

Lynn was silent for a moment after her grandfather had finished his often grim report of Clay Trevor's months-long crusade to eliminate the jeopardy the Pollocks had caused his wife. "Why did he do it, Grandfa?" she asked finally.

" 'Tis hard to say, but he was fiercely angry after he'd located his son and learned about the new danger you faced. Relax lass; the young lad's aboard, and you've already met the woman who's tending him. He's a thriving babe who was well loved while you were gone."

"Where is he?" Lynn cried eagerly.

"Just stay seated, Trelynn, there's more to be told. Captain Vinson, your husband, and half the crew remained on guard in Saybrook last night in case those cursed wreckers learned their strongholds had been discovered. All of our men are aboard and sleeping now, and your son is in his cabin with his father. 'Tis what Clay has insisted on since we left New Port."

"Did any of those wreckers follow us to Saybrook?"

"No, and the ship's doctor was able to save the lives of the three injured men. 'Tis a wonder any of you survived your encounter with that nest of vipers, but Clive Dunton and the one named Selwin are already recovering. The other one, poor man, will be months in the sick room, and even then he might not regain his senses. The villain who struck him meant to kill."

" 'Twas Sid Pollock, Grandfa."

"We heard all about his murderous attacks from the people in New Port and New Haven. He and his father deserved the fates they met, although I suspect the son was worse than the father. Tom Kenn, of course, was already a condemned criminal. Had he lived, he would have been hanged for the murder of two of the *Tamarlind* crew. When he jumped ship in Jamestown more than a year ago, he robbed the captain's strongbox and killed the men who tried to stop him."

"They were only three of the wreckers, Grandfa, and we killed just eight others during the ambush. There are still fifty of the murderers who could destroy the shipping along this coast.''

"They'll not take another victim. The Saybrook people are notifying the Hartford militia, and we'll be delivering the same message to New London and New Haven. As soon as those militias combine their strengths, that pirate pesthole will be exterminated. If the renegades attempt to escape by sea, they'll be met by a pair of your friends. Spencer Burtram had returned to New Port just before we arrived, and he and Captain Rambert were preparing to wrest you by force from your New Haven jailers. Now they're even angrier about the idea of this coast becoming a duplicate of the Cornish one. Such a criminal stronghold here would be disastrous since shipping is the only means of travel and communication among the colonies.''

"Grandfa, you know that Captain Rambert is a buccaneer, don't you?''

"He prefers the term *merchant buccaneer*, and I found him a reasonable man. After this action, he may even qualify as a royal privateer. He was certainly a good friend to you on the night your weakling father played the villain.''

Lynn's bright new hopes crashed into gloom at the mention of her father and the memory of the evil heritage Royce Trevor had claimed for her. "Grandfa, was my other grandmother anything like he said?''

Ephraim's eyes glinted with anger. "So he told you she was a witch, did he? That will be one more score I'll settle with him. His mother was naught but an intelligent Cornishwoman, lass, who had good cause to be disappointed in her knavish son. He was ambitious far beyond his family's humble estate.''

"Did you know her?''

"Not while she was alive, but I investigated her thoroughly after her Trevor son married your mother. I was overseas at the time of the marriage and unable to prevent the disaster. Like many men left penniless by the civil war, Royce

Trevor was in the market for a rich wife; and he persuaded your foolish fifteen-year-old mother to elope with him. However, he offered marriage only after your grandmother Hortensia agreed to name him as her heir. When you were born a few months afterwards, he terrified Lavinia by convincing her that you'd inherited what he called his mother's taint. Hortensia did the best she could; she bribed him to emigrate to Virginia, leaving you and Lavinia behind.''

Frowning in confused memory, Lynn asked hesitantly, ''Didn't he visit Penley Farm when I was a little girl?''

''Only once, to demand his wife return to Virginia with him. When she refused, he threatened to remain in England unless the income Hortensia supplied him was considerably increased.''

''How was my grandmother allowed to manage her own estate without your permission, Grandfa?''

'' 'Twas an agreement made before our marriage. Lord Trelynn was an overbearing man, and I had sufficient fortune of my own at that time.''

''Why is it you never told me about her family before today?''

''Another of your grandmother's whims, lass. In truth, she wagered that you'd be better off if you didn't know. Lavinia had been a sorry disappointment to both of us. Hortensia didn't want me to tell you about the value of the amulet either; she wagered you'd be bright enough to learn on your own, as well you did. But I think she would have been very pleased that you kept it out of sentiment. I've often thought that you and she would have been great friends, had not Lavinia been such a problem. I'm returning the diamond to you now, lass. Poor Edward Fulton worried about it being in his strongbox and was relieved to be rid of it.''

Holding up the familiar pendant to the light, Lynn shrugged. ''I learned about it only through a stroke of luck, Grandfa; but Royce Trevor knew its worth to the shilling. He was furious when I told him it had been buried in a plague pit.''

"He's a greedy scoundrel, Trelynn; and he'll pay for what he did to you. But now, 'tis time for you to stop dwelling on the dead past when you've a lively future ahead of you. I'm hoping you've tamed down enough to accept an old man's advice. Your husband has done his best to make up for his earlier neglect, and he's in a business now that will support you well enough.''

"He'll be gone eleven months out of twelve, buying and selling those slaves; I'd almost rather be a widow.''

"He lasted through only two deliveries to England in that ugly business before he sold his share of the company to the younger brother of Barbara and Amelia Gordon, a man who won't flinch at the cruelty and who'll be more than a match for Andrew Pendrath. Clay will be handling only voluntary indentureds from now on, in partnership with a ship's captain who was equally disillusioned. Since there are thousands awaiting transportation in every port in England, the captain will do the selection while Clay arranges for their employment in the colonies.''

"He'll still be gone most of the time.''

"No, he's promised his father he won't be separated from you again.''

"I refuse to be his jailer, Grandfa!''

As he studied her proud young face, Ephraim sighed. America had changed her, but not as it did most women. While they weakened or grew bitter under the wearing hardships of pioneer life, she'd grown more independent and stronger, too strong for a world that had scant tolerance even for the most worthy of women.

"Do you love him, Trelynn?'' he demanded bluntly.

For a moment she glared at her grandfather resentfully before she answered with equal candor, "Yes, I love him, but I won't be a millstone around his neck simply to please Sir Bevil.''

"Forget your foolish pride, girl; you have to please the

man himself, not the scheming father. Tell Clay that you love him; I think you'll find he's more afraid than you are of being hurt. Just remember he's earned your love this time. At any rate, he's waiting for you in the cabin you used last night.''

As Ephraim had promised, Lynn found her husband lying on the bed she'd vacated two hours earlier, and seated on his bared chest was an infant who looked too big and too old to be her own. She leaned weakly against the door as she absorbed the emotional impact of the scene.

"If you're going to faint again," Clay called out in alarm, "please do it on the bed. I doubt I could manage the pair of you."

Annoyed at her own weakness, but unable to stem the tears that flooded her eyes, Lynn walked on rubbery legs to the bed and sat down. "He's grown so much, I hardly recognize him," she whispered.

Watching her through half-closed eyes, Clay smiled. "His memory is better than yours, Mama, a sure sign of his Trevor blood to prefer a beautiful woman over any man ever born."

Lynn's arms felt leaden as she wrapped them around the small muscular body that wriggled quickly into a sitting position on her lap and looked upward to stare at her through eyes the color of his father's but with the shape of her own. Clay's amiable conversation continued without pause.

"He's more like you than appears at first glance, Mrs. Trevor; he's inherited your unfortunate proclivity for early rising. The artful little devil interrupted my sleep this morning on the flimsiest of excuses, and he's bewitched his two grandfathers into pathetic dottery. Neither of them—"

"His father, too," Lynn interrupted with a tremulous smile.

"You have to admit he was a pleasant surprise for a weary traveler since you'd vowed you'd not have the time for such nonsense."

"I had more time alone than I wanted. I'm glad to see you, Clay."

"Is that all you have to say after what I went through in Cornwall?"

"Why did you risk your life there, Clay?"

"An odd conceit that I was the only one who had the right to call you 'witch woman,' but it really wasn't all that great a risk. Why did you refuse Spence's invitation?" he asked abruptly.

Repressing her momentary shock, Lynn mimicked his light tone. "It really wasn't all that great an invitation."

"Spence claimed you weren't interested because you loved me. Do you?"

Recalling her grandfather's blunt advice, Lynn looked into her husband's oddly vulnerable eyes and forgot the bitter past. "Of course, I do," she admitted boldly. "Why else would I have waited fifteen months?"

"Fourteen-and-a-half, the last two weeks were your fault. At least I remembered to bring you a dress or two this time."

"If you hadn't, you wouldn't have known whether you'd married a woman or a New Haven militiaman."

"The soldier you saved yesterday sure knew the difference."

"Mr. Parkman was recovering from a blow on the head. Clay, why didn't you join me this morning when you returned to the ship? This is your cabin after all."

"You're not going to trap me that easily, witch woman. I haven't forgotten that you become a human being only after you've had a bath. Besides I didn't want you fainting again at the sight of me until Ephraim had a chance to smooth the stony path. Did he?"

"He was very convincing. I'm grateful to you, Clay."

"In that case you can stop drizzling all over our son and put him to bed. This is the first time he's gone to sleep without an argument in a week, and you've another Trevor male who expects the same consideration."

Lynn hated the blush that reddened her face as she rose to do his bidding. Throughout the process of disrobing in a small space that offered no privacy, she was acutely aware that his eyes never left her and his accompanying words were unabashedly candid.

"That blush is very pretty, Trelynn Trevor, but I prefer the brazen nymph who entertained me while she cavorted in an icy pond on a Rhode Island farm. You've a body that doesn't need any feminine wiles to lure a man or to keep him enticed. If you need a confession, I'll tell you again what you wouldn't believe the last time I tried. There's no one else who can satisfy me; and in all this time I was apart from you, I didn't play the wanton."

With her heart beating more erratically than it had on yesterday's battlefield, Lynn walked back to the bed, dangling her grandmother's amulet in her hand. "'You're as big a spendthrift with words as you are with money, Clay Trevor. You'll be needing this trinket to support the family you didn't know you had."

Clay grinned at her in appreciation as he put the chain around her neck. "More likely we'll need it for the other sons we'll have, and for the two small black-eyed witches I've set my heart on." Pulling her toward him with a gentle insistence, he whispered into her closest ear, "Do you recall the lesson I taught you the night we slept with Robin and Quince?" At her startled look, he chuckled softly, "For a few weeks, you'll be acting the man's part; but if I remember rightly, it didn't take you more than five seconds to become an expert."

Swiftly Lynn pulled the covers back and stared in shock at the still livid scar so low on his left shoulder she knew that Wilcox's bullet had barely missed being a fatal wound. "You're in no condition—" she began in protest, only to be stopped by a groan.

"I've learned to bear that slight discomfort; 'tis the rest of me that's being bedeviled," he complained as he tugged her tense body over his.

Bracing herself with her elbows and knees, Lynn hesitated until his unimpaired arm pulled her downward, and she discovered the truth of his urgent boast. The explosion of her own long pent-up passion ended her resistance, sweeping her into the compulsive heedlessness of sensualism. It didn't matter that his caresses were awkward and his participation incomplete; her own fiery need was sufficient, and her own readiness as imperative as his. Uniting her body with his seemed as involuntary as breathing to her as she began the slow caressing movements of fulfillment. She heard his whispery encouragement and bent down swiftly to claim his lips; she didn't want the wailing cry of an awakened infant to destroy the intense pleasure of this mating. In the primitive, instinctive part of her consciousness, she sensed his nearing climax and released the restraints she'd placed on her own. The moment when it came for both of them was a pulsing ecstasy that left her physically spent, but more emotionally satisfied than she'd ever been before. This consummation was not merely the beginning of another unhappy interlude until he sailed away; it was the first real bond of a marriage that held the promise of a permanent union.

As she moved to nestle by his side, it was her husband who spoke the words first, "Welcome home, Trelynn."

CHAPTER
17

As intolerant of shipboard convalescence as he'd been two years earlier, Clay was a difficult and irrepressible patient who obeyed the doctor's orders only when it suited his convenience. Allowed out of bed officially for a few hours each day, he rarely maintained the schedule, insisting on going ashore at each of the three ports of call and on exercising too vigorously on deck for a man still recovering from a near fatal wound.

From a protective Sir Bevil Trevor, Lynn learned how close Clay had come to death on the cobbled street in front of the Stannary Parliament in the Cornish town of Truro. In the company of Sir Bevil, Ephraim Penley, and the two miners who'd witnessed the killing of John Pollock, Clay had delivered the guilty miner to court and waited until all charges against his wife had been dropped. Ephraim and Bevil had remained an hour longer, obtaining arrest warrants for Rad Pollock and his two sons on charges of perjury and bribery. They were still there when Captain Cyril Wilcox dragged Clay's bloodied body into the courtroom and announced the apprehension and execution of a wanted criminal.

"The hypocrite had shot from ambush," Bevil stormed furiously to Lynn, "claiming that my son had violated the conditions of his royal pardon by remaining overlong in England. The zealous fool was still spouting scriptures, when the court ordered him detained and released Clay into my custody. With a doctor in attendance we raced a carriage to Plymouth and boarded the *Tamarlind* with all possible speed before that Roundhead court could change its collective mind. 'Tis an uneasy time for English justice, Trelynn."

After her experience in New Haven, Lynn was doubtful that justice was any more reliable in the American colonies. Apprehensive when Clay insisted she accompany him into New London, New Haven, and New York, Lynn was grateful that her grandfather went along. Despite his semiretirement into private life, Ephraim Penley was too highly respected for his word to be disputed; and his sponsorship of Clay's new business venture virtually guaranteed its success. The need was the same in all of the expanding towns of Connecticut and New York where church membership was not required. Community leaders wanted doctors, teachers, skilled artisans to work in an increasing variety of businesses, and unmarried women young enough for childbearing. By the time the *Tamarlind* left New York and headed toward Virginia, Clay had received orders and payment for two hundred specified emigrants to be delivered within the year.

Buoyed up by the magnitude of his business success, Clay was too restless to be a cooperative patient aboard ship. Only as long as his wife was with him would he consent to remain in bed; and Lynn quickly learned that shipboard life was a complicated one with both a husband and a child to tend. Even though Ellen took care of the infant's clothing and fed him his four daily meals of cow's milk and farina, Lynn found it difficult to keep a six-month-old child entertained in the confines of a small cabin. Adding to the stress were the frequent visits of a grandfather, great-grandfather, and Captain Vinson, whom Clay had appointed godfather. Instead of the uncomplicated infant she'd left in Rhode Island, her son was rapidly developing into a petty tyrant who'd already learned the power of the winsome smile he'd inherited from his father and of the loud voice he was developing on his own.

Because Clay's own smile was in evidence much of the time, Lynn often felt the only sober member of the family. She was the one who had to cajole Clay into drinking the milk he hated instead of the wine he ordered the cabin boy to fetch, and to taking undisturbed naps instead of trying to wheedle her to join him in bed. Although she was a willing and passionate partner once every night, she was often forced to remind him of the doctor's restrictions even in that intimate activity.

"What the doctor doesn't know . . ." Clay began his invariable protest, only to be silenced by Lynn's firm rejoinder.

"What the doctor *does* know is that you were as weak as a premature calf after our first night together."

Much of her inability to accept her new-found happiness without reservations, Lynn knew, was due to her fear of the ordeal that awaited her in Virginia. During the stopover in New Haven, she learned that Jem, Bram, and Red Penny had been repossessed by Royce Trevor two days after she'd left town with Captain Dunton. A Virginia-based ship had arrived in port carrying papers of ownership signed by her father and countersigned by the James County sheriff.

"Reverend Wainwright had little choice in the matter," Ephraim explained patiently. "You and Clive were gone, and Clive's wife accepted the captain's word that your father was the rightful owner."

"She knew the truth, Grandfa. So did the reverend and all his little reverends."

"They know it now, Trelynn, but at that time, they had only your word."

"And the word of a mere woman is never considered as valid as a man's," Lynn parroted with bitter sarcasm.

"Unfortunately not, but all of your people will be located and returned to you; and if possible, your cattle, too. I've known Governor William Berkeley for many years, and he's a stern upholder of the law."

Lynn suppressed her impulse to remind her grandfather that the Virginia governor was an old man who might prove as ineffectual as Ephraim and Sir Bevil had been in Cornwall. Clay's reassurances were lightheartedly over-confident. Since his respect for the law was still only minimally prudential, he promised more direct action.

"We'll get our people and our cattle back one way or another. We'll be needing every one of those great rumped bullocks to pull our lumber wagons in Connecticut."

"I'm more worried about the people, Clay," Lynn insisted. "No Virginia planter is going to release a stock-man like Jem willingly or an expert farmer like Jason Hale." And none of them will surrender a trained bullock or a productive cow, she added silently with depressing conviction. Neither her grandfather nor Clay had ever earned his living on a farm; neither had any idea of the worth of finely blooded livestock. She had a more private reason for her concern, as well; she dreaded a future that would eliminate the last measure of her independence. Clay was too adept at business to require her help either in his own company or in the one she'd helped establish in Rhode Island.

Most of her apprehension, however, was centered on her father; he'd lived too long by his wits to be easily outwit-ted; and he'd been a major landholder for too many years not to be firmly established in government circles. Recalling that Bert Spence had called the Trevor home in James County one of the most ostentatious and Royce Trevor himself one of the most ambitious of social leaders, Lynn doubted that he could be as quickly brought to account as Ephraim so optimistically expected.

Even the *Tamarlind*'s delayed arrival in Jamestown brought Lynn no relief from the nagging fear that she'd meet the same reception there as she had in New Haven; and the four men who now controlled her life did little to dispel her anxiety. Singly and in unison, they ordered her to remain hidden aboard the ship with her son. With his health restored to a functioning level, Clay wanted a free hand in conducting his own investigation among the contacts he'd made during prior business trips. "God knows what rumors your scurvy father has spread about you," he warned. "So until I know you won't be insulted in the streets, you'll remain aboard."

Ephraim's reasons were sternly legal. "I have official standing with the law; you do not, Trelynn. You could damage our case with that temper-hot tongue of yours or with your sarcastic wit. You'll have to be content with playing the woman's role here, lass."

Knowledgeable about the rebellious discontent of the motley crowds of waterfront riffraff who greeted each ship's arrival, Captain Vinson's concern was for his cargo, ship, and crew. He hadn't forgotten that some of the criminal indentureds who worked as dock loaders had helped Tom Kenn escape after the villain had murdered two good crewmen and robbed the strongbox. "They're as bad here as they were in New Port before the militia took control; and there are enough superstitious sailors beached here to overpower my own lads," he told Lynn apologetically.

Most annoying to Lynn was the jocular insistence by her father-in-law that she remain in seclusion aboard. "The simple folk here might be shocked if they saw you whirl those clubs of yours like a juggler at a county fair. According to the New Haven lads I talked to, you've become even more adept in their use. But you'll not be lonely while Clay is gone, Trelynn; I'll be keeping you and my grandson entertained after I've completed one brief errand ashore."

Mutinously resentful of Bevil's condescending humor,

Lynn remained stiffly silent the next afternoon when he returned to the *Tamarlind* to keep his promise. Seated on a secluded spot of the offshore deck that Nate Stokes had ruled safe from prying dockside eyes, Lynn and Charles Ephraim had been able to escape from the stifling heat of the cabin. Companionably Sir Bevil seated himself on another of the chairs placed there by the considerate Stokes and played briefly with his grandson before he smiled at his silent daughter-in-law.

"You remind me of your grandmother Hortensia when you set your jaw like that, Trelynn. I've an idea you inherited her temper as well; whenever she was displeased with me, she made certain I was aware of her displeasure. You already know, of course, that she and I were old friends."

"Why didn't you ever tell Clay about her?" Lynn asked, her interest aroused in spite of her irritation.

"She didn't want him influenced by the wrong reasons. Your grandmother was a remarkable woman."

"Does my grandfather know the contents of that packet of letters I delivered to you after her death?" Lynn demanded with little pretense at diplomacy.

"No, he doesn't; Hortensia knew he was too ethical a lawyer to carry out her instructions."

"What was it she asked you to do, Sir Bevil?"

"I can't tell you that yet. Did you know that you have a half brother six years younger than yourself with the pretentious name of Alexander Trelynn Trevor?"

"I knew about him and a half sister a long time ago, but they have a different last name now. Royce Trevor boasted that he'd married the mother off to a cooper and shipped the lot of them to the Carolinas."

"So that's how he solved the problem after your grandmother had discovered his duplicity, was it?"

"My unnatural parent has a penchant for ridding himself of unwanted children."

"Aye, he's a disgrace to the Trevor name. But no

matter, we've this young lad here who'll more than compensate. I've great hopes for him."

"You have other grandsons, Sir Bevil," Lynn reminded him pointedly.

Trevor shrugged indifferently. "Since they're becoming more Gordon than Trevor, I take little pleasure in the relationship. Your son has better blood and a finer mother."

Embarrassed by the unexpected praise, Lynn hastened to ask, "What about your other son's family?"

"Bourke was luckier than Averill in his choice of wife, but so far the woman has produced naught but daughters."

"How tragic!" Lynn murmured dryly.

Repressing the smile that twitched about his lips, Trevor responded in kind, "Except that they're said to bedevil the father, I've no objection to daughters; but the law being what it is, sons are somewhat more necessary. And yours, my lass, is a welcome addition to the Trevor family."

Relieved to hear Clay's voice as he boarded the ship and spoke briefly to Nate Stokes, Lynn made no response to her father-in-law's oblique flattery. It had been an odd conversation all around, she reflected suspiciously; and as always, Bevil Trevor had said only what he wanted her to hear. Minutes later when Clay joined them, she discovered that the father was not nearly as tolerant of his son's evasiveness as he was of his own.

"Did you take care of that small errand I requested?" Bevil demanded impatiently.

Clay shrugged and nodded. "Next time you can be your own messenger," he drawled resentfully.

"Well, what did the woman say?"

"She cursed me roundly before she summoned her confederate to complete the job. The only good to come out of that long, hot ride was that I located Kate Horton."

Lynn stiffened angrily; Clay had spent his first day ashore in the company of his old friends, Amelia Pendrath and Leona Burtram; and only incidentally had he conducted any of his own or his wife's business. Of all the women in

Virginia, only those two would have rushed to secure Kate's papers from Royce Trevor. With a swift economy of motion, Lynn arose from her chair and swept up her sleeping son from his blanket on the deck.

" 'Tis time for his supper," she murmured and was striding toward the companionway before either man could react. Dimly she heard Bevil's sputtered apology, "I'm sorry, son. I'd forgotten that you were once as big a fool as your brother over a Gordon woman. I'd have gone myself if I'd remembered."

Within the hour, Lynn's humor was restored; she'd learned more from Nate Stokes than from the Trevor men combined. Although he was now the first mate and the busiest officer aboard, Nate had remained an unpretentious man who still preferred the crew's company to that of the passengers with the exception of Lynn. Through the complicated journey from New Port, he'd kept a protective eye on her son, tending to the practical consideration of obtaining fresh milk at every port of call and insisting that the child be fed in the crew's mess hall next to the ship's galley. Outraged by the thefts from the farm he'd helped establish, Nate was keenly interested in retrieving the five people who'd been his friends, and the valuable cattle. Thus while the others were contacting the officials, he had questioned men who knew the most about incoming cargoes—the dockhands who worked on the waterfront. From them, he'd learned that when Royce Trevor had returned two and a half months earlier, Lynn's cattle had been prodded down the docks and auctioned in town while the stolen trunks and household items had been sold surreptitiously aboard the ship itself.

After a busy day ashore, supervising the unloading and reloading of the *Tamarlind*'s cargoes, Nate was relieved to find Lynn in the dining hall watching her son being fed by the nurse. Eagerly he recited his news to the woman who'd been his tolerant employer for eight months.

"Did you know that your father had stolen all your clothing and all the furniture Joab Markley made for us?"

Lynn nodded impatiently. "What about our people, Nate?"

"Only one man reported seeing what had happened to them. He said that one woman—I reckon that was Polly—started shouting the minute she walked down the gangplank, and that 'the squire' had shoved her into a waiting carriage. The other two—Kate and Jason—were auctioned off in town right before your cattle were put on the block. The man who watched the sale said that three 'prinked-up' women bid Kate's price up to two hundred pounds."

"The prinked-up woman who won the contest was Amelia Cobb Pendrath," Lynn snapped. "Did anyone see the delivery of Jem and Bram a week ago?"

"Several of them saw that one. Your bull and Jem were loaded onto a waiting barge and poled upriver while Bram was met by one of the planters. Reckon they'd already been sold and paid for. But at least they were all settled around here and weren't shipped so far away we'd never find them. Did Clay say anything about the dirty assignment he pulled today?"

"He mentioned that he'd visited Amelia Cobb and Leona Spence."

Nate chuckled warmly. "Sir Bevil tried to bribe me to deliver the message to Leona, but I'd heard her in full shrill too often to risk it."

"What message, Nate?"

"Divorce papers. The king granted Bert his freedom after Sir Bevil presented the petition in London. I'd say Bert was well rid of the whining bitch, but I sure didn't want to be the one who told her. Clay looked like a thundercloud when I talked to him."

Wincing when she remembered the greeting she'd given her husband, Lynn changed the subject abruptly. "Nate, do you know if my grandfather has returned yet?"

"He won't be back for a day or so, Lynn. The captain

sent word that they'd be staying at the governor's while his nibs is deciding what to do about your father. If what I hear about Governor Berkeley is true, 'twill be a lively day in court. There are those who say he runs the colony with an iron hand and a whip to match.''

''Virginia's a royal colony, Nate,'' Lynn countered cynically. ''The king's idea of justice will prevail here, and our bonnie King Charles is known to favor all of the people who fought for his father, even people who fought as little as my father did. The Berkeleys are too much the favorites to risk the king's displeasure. Sir William was given Virginia to run according to royal edict, and his brother, Lord John Berkeley, owns half of New Jersey and the Carolinas. I don't doubt that Sir William would condemn people like you and me quickly enough; but my father is a big landowner here who might well be praised for disciplining a wayward daughter, instead of being tried for theft and murder.''

Lynn heard the laughter coming from the galley and stiffened defensively as her husband entered the crew's quarters and sat down on the bench next to her.

''If the governor heard the treason you just spouted about our gracious and generous monarch, more likely he'd charge me with failure to discipline a wayward wife,'' he chided her genially, adding abruptly, ''Kate sends you her regards.''

''You talked to her?''

''The other way around; she was waiting for me on the verandah after I escaped from Harry's new home. I doubt even the governor will be able to shut her up once she takes the stand. It seems your father added five years to her sentence.''

''Did she know where Polly was taken?''

''Not only Polly, but the men and some of the cattle. According to Kate, Amelia and Leona took great delight in telling her how completely your father had punished you.

Lynn, how did you know to hide our son the day he kidnapped you?"

"Something he said about children frightened me."

"Thank God it did! Kate said he searched the house from attic to cellar."

"I hope you didn't tell your lady friends about me or our son."

"I didn't tell them a damn thing; all I did was deliver the divorce papers to Leona and Harry's letter to Amelia. They did all of the talking; and before I got away, I was being called worse names than Spence and Harry."

"That must have been a shock! Did either of them say anything about my father?"

Clay hesitated a moment before he responded. "Leona mentioned that they'd recently attended a party in celebration of his son's first birthday."

"His legitimate son's," Lynn amended expressionlessly. "Did you know he had one?"

"He told me . . . to make certain I'd have no illusions about any future inheritance."

"What a bastard he is! But all that really means is that we'll have to work harder to earn an inheritance for our own children."

"I don't want them to have vainglorious expectations, Clay. I want them to be Americans, not dilettante Englishmen who're so worried about inheritances, they never learn how to survive on their own."

If Lynn had any regrets about the wisdom of her decision, they were eliminated the next day when she overheard a furious Amelia Pendrath berating Bevil Trevor in the next cabin. Grateful that Clay had been summoned to the governor's home an hour earlier, Lynn listened with amusement to the woman's shrill recriminations, which were centered on the fact that her younger brother rather than Clay was now her husband's partner.

"Your son," she lashed out at Sir Bevil, "didn't have the courage to tell me himself that he'd betrayed the

Pendraths. I had to learn it from the letter he delivered from my dull-witted husband.''

Lynn heard Bevil's ironic protest and smiled in amused surprise. ''Surely you can trust your own brother, Mrs. Pendrath.''

''My brother has already squandered his own inheritance, and he'll cheat Harry out of every pound earned,'' Amelia rasped.

''I doubt Lord Pendrath will permit anything like that degree of greed,'' Bevil disclaimed with a sardonic satisfaction clearly evident to the willing eavesdropper. ''Your brother certainly didn't cheat my son; he paid full price to buy into the company.''

''My father paid, and your son had nothing to do with the arrangements. You're the one who engineered everything,'' Amelia accused her host.

''I'll admit I spoke to your father after Clay requested my help in the matter.''

''And you're the one who arranged for Clay to marry that freakish woman,'' the angry Amelia continued her relentless attack.

''I am most assuredly guilty of taking that precaution, madam. You'd plagued him long enough, and I didn't want my son or your husband hurt by your shameless lack of morals.''

''You're as big a fool as your son! Neither of you will get any satisfaction from that benighted union. Her father knew her for what she was. After I told him where he could locate her, he shipped her back to England.''

''You might well regret your disloyalty to my family, madam. Quite likely, Clay's wife will some day expose you and Royce Trevor for the liars and thieves you are.''

''Clay hasn't seen her in over a year and will never see her again. If Cornish justice is as swift as it was a few years back, he's already become a widower; so all of your scheming was useless.''

''If that is so, madam, I advise you never to seek my

son's or my company again. Neither of us forget nor forgive treachery. Right now, you have a choice of leaving this ship voluntarily or of being forcibly removed. I've suffered your shrewish tongue long enough.''

Unable to resist watching her old rival's undignified departure, Lynn cracked the door open enough to see the retreating back of a woman who bore scant resemblance to the Amelia Cobb she'd once known. The overcurled russet hair bounced unbecomingly against a beruffled scarlet dress, several inches too tight for the wearer and several shades too bright for genteel fashion. Repressing a giggle of delight, Lynn closed the door quietly. Kate Horton had already extracted a small measure of revenge!

As uplifting as the brief flash of humor had been, Lynn's mood quickly resettled into the fitful anxiety of waiting. To her relief, Sir Bevil, too, was subdued and far less irritating than he'd been the day before. Seated together in the captain's quarters where an occasional breeze wafted through the open windows, they played a desultory game of piquet and sipped lime water enlivened with a spring of mint. What conversation they exchanged was deliberately devoid of substance. The only oblique reference Bevil made to the subject that occupied both their minds was a comment addressed to the half-naked infant playing fitfully with a wooden teething ring.

''Well, old lad, the justice here is as slow and fickle as it is at home.''

When he joined them at sunset, Clay was in irritable agreement with his father. ''God save me from a trio of cautious old men. Ephraim quotes the law at every turn, while the governor and the county magistrate demand proof of every claim.''

''They've proof enough for a conviction ten times over,'' Bevil rasped.

''Not quite, according to the magistrate. He asks for a 'more proper' christening of Charles Ephraim in a 'more proper church.' Lynn, he wouldn't accept the record your

Reverend Tyler gave us in Rhode Island, in part because you used the name of Penley and because Spencer Burtram didn't sign his real name as godfather. So tomorrow morning before the hearing, our son will undergo the most witnessed christening in Jamestown history.''

Shaking her head in exasperation, Lynn protested the indignity. ''Why should he? What right does anyone have to investigate either me or our son? Royce Trevor should be on trial, not us.''

''You aren't on trial,'' Clay assured her hastily.

''Then why am I a prisoner aboard this ship? All I want is to get my people and the cattle back and get out of here. Oh, I'd like to see my father hanged by the thumbs and fined out of house and land, but that will never happen...not in a benighted colony run by men who consider women slightly less necessary than horses.''

''So much protest over a brief ceremony,'' Bevil murmured soothingly, ''a small, needful ceremony to prevent your father from disputing your claims. Be patient a while longer, lass; all of this unpleasantness will be over by this time tomorrow.''

Lynn's first impression of the men assembled inside the Jamestown Anglican Episcopal Church was one of well-practiced pomp. Even the red-brick building itself had seemed unnecessarily pretentious compared to the simpler wooden churches of Rhode Island. But it was the men themselves who more clearly demonstrated the differences between the Englishmen who governed Virginia and their northern colonial counterparts. Elegantly clad in richly colored suits that bore the mark of London tailors, the five burgesses who greeted Sir Bevil Trevor as one of their own could have been the twins of the aristocratic gamblers Lynn had once seen in her grandmother's town house right after the Restoration. Their faces all held the look of confident arrogance that came from a long heritage of wealth and authority. The minister himself was wearing a flowing robe so exquisitely tailored that it bespoke wealth far beyond a mere pastoral salary. Smiling faintly, Lynn recalled the somber, threadbare garment Jeremiah Tyler wore each Sunday at his small, weathered Portsmouth church of vague denomination.

Standing apart from the others, his plainer, dark suit drab by comparison, Ephraim Penley was watching his granddaughter and her husband as they waited for the ceremony to begin. Studying the pride on the young father's face as he held his son, the old man wondered if Clay would have been so satisfied if the infant hadn't been a Trelynn as well as a Trevor. Never an apologist for his own heritage—during his long career he'd wielded more power than any of these men present—Ephraim had always felt a vague antipathy for aristocrats whose fortunes had been effortlessly inherited. He and his father before him had earned theirs through diligent excellence in the profession of law. Grimacing inwardly, he remembered how that hard-earned money had been squandered by a wife who'd never really wanted to share his life and by a feckless daughter. But at least, no other Penley would add to the family's ruination; Owen Penley had already paid a dear price for his disloyalty. He'd been fined into permanent poverty by the Stannary Court for his own and his wife's treachery against his cousin. This afternoon, if Governor Berkeley's promised justice prevailed, the last of the family's miscreants, the son-in-law who'd proved the most cowardly villain of all, would be called to account.

Grimly judicial in his attitude toward criminals of any kind, Ephraim felt no pity for Royce Trevor, only a cold hatred for the man who'd tried to destroy his own daughter. Today's legal proceedings would be hard on her, the veteran lawyer knew; but she'd survive whatever the outcome as she'd survived Cornwall, Rhode Island, and Connecticut. She'd won the full approval of Edward Fulton, who'd had nothing but praise for her bold mastery of business, and she'd gained the grateful respect of Clive Dunton and his men for being an effective soldier rather than a hysterical woman during the deadly trek from New Haven. Against all odds, she'd earned a protective loyalty, at least, from her husband. When Clay found her missing in Rhode Island, even before he'd learned of her father's actions, he'd vowed to return to England to rescue her despite the danger to himself. Yesterday he'd revealed another kind of courage in front of Governor Berkeley by freely admitting his own criminal past. Ephraim had not expected that degree of honesty from a man who had callously stripped his wife of all of her money to finance his own short-lived ambition and had twice left her to support herself financially.

Ephriam felt no guilt about his own acceptance of the money his granddaughter had offered him; he had already taken the precaution of insuring her safety with his Rhode Island friends. With a clear conscience, he could take pride in her accomplishments and in her appearance at this ridiculously redundant christening of a thoroughly indifferent infant. She was standing straight and tall beside her handsome husband, gowned in a pink muslin dress that lacked all pretense of ornate elegance. Ephraim smiled faintly as he identified the straw hat covering her cropped hair. Instead of the lavishly plumed hats of Restoration fashion, it was a commonplace Jamaican straw of the kind workers wore to ward off the sun; but somehow it had added to her unusual beauty. Hortensia would have approved of the choice, Ephraim reflected irrelevantly. Certainly she would have approved of Trelynn's amused smile when her son gurgled with delight as the christening water was splashed in his face. A veteran of solemn rituals, Ephraim could understand the minister's disapproval of Captain Vinson's accompanying laughter; in the Anglican rite, the godfather was supposed to respect the gravity of his vows.

As the lawyer's eyes lighted on another participant of the brief ceremony, he frowned in annoyance. The approbation he'd extended provisionally to the son did not include the father. Since the beginning of the voyage from Plymouth, Bevil Trevor had been irritatingly secretive, answering Ephraim's questions with skillful evasions and half-truths. Not even a friendship that spanned five decades could eliminate the lawyer's entrenched distrust, a distrust that had begun long before Lord Trelynn selected Ephraim as Hortensia's husband. The lawyer had known that he hadn't been Hortensia's choice and that her friendship with Bevil had been life-long, but it had remained just that, a friendship; and the marriage had endured reasonably well. Despite their differences, the three of them had remained on amicable terms for almost forty years.

Only since Hortensia's death had the more scholarly man's suspicions been aroused, suspicions centered around Bevil's increasing interference in Trelynn's life. He'd manipulated her into a marriage that neither she nor her husband would have sought willingly. And now that same veiled excitement was focused on the six-month-old product of that marriage. Ephraim's frown deepened, and he hoped tiredly that today's legal proceedings would answer the questions that plagued him.

After the christening ceremony had ended, he discovered that he was not alone in his suspicions about Bevil's preoccupation with his grandson. After the infant had been taken aboard, Captain Vinson was equally curious as he confided privately to the lawyer, "You'd think that after fifteen years of partnership, I'd know what Bevil was up to; but I rarely do. Since we arrived in Jamestown, he's ordered the ship doubly guarded; so you can tell Trelynn that my godson will be safer aboard ship this afternoon than he was in church. I'll be watching out for the babe myself while you and his mother are in court."

Ephraim returned to the waiting carriage with a keen sense of anticipation; truth was far more difficult to conceal in a courtroom than amateurs like Bevil Trevor suspected. Inside the stately House of Burgesses, which had been selected in preference to the more public court house, the lawyer studied the assembled officials with satisfaction. It wasn't to be a formal trial since there was no sworn jury, only the twelve burgesses whom Governor Berkeley had summoned yesterday to study all of the documents Ephraim had prepared and much of the evidence the county sheriff had collected. But the governor himself would not be in attendance, only the magistrate who informed Ephraim privately that neither he nor Trelynn would be called upon to testify. Instead they would remain secluded in a screened compartment in the visitors' gallery.

"We won't need your direct evidence, Ephraim; and women are not welcome on the floor of these chambers," the magistrate explained. "When the first assembly met in 1634, that exclusion was one of the first pieces of legislation passed. 'Tis said those early burgesses were eager to escape from their wives for a few hours each month. In the case of your granddaughter, the less confrontation she has with a father such as Royce Trevor, the better for her peace of mind."

Since he'd helped organize the procedural agenda, Ephraim knew that the real reason for Lynn's exclusion was more serious. The shrewd magistrate wanted to force damning lies from her father before her safe arrival in Jamestown as a free woman was announced. That it was justice by indirection, the lawyer knew well; but that it would be more effective, he had no doubt. Royce Trevor would be led deeper and deeper into a tangle of lies until he could no longer extricate himself.

Cheerfully now, Ephraim climbed the narrow stairs to join Lynn and the two Trevors in the small balcony screened across the front by louvered wood slats that allowed them to see the floor below without revealing their own identities. In more normal legislative proceedings,

Ephraim suspected it was where Governor Berkeley kept a watchful eye on the government of his colony.

Taking the empty seat beside his granddaughter, Ephraim whispered a severe warning. "Regardless of what you hear today, you're not to interrupt. This is not a town meeting like those in Rhode Island where public comment is welcome. As you're so fond of telling me, Virginia is a man-dominated colony where ancient prerogatives still apply. So you might as well enjoy your first day in court and find out if any of that theoretical law you've learned is valid."

Ephraim's advice ended abruptly, and all four gallery observers leaned forward to watch a crowd of men troop nervously into the chambers below and arrange themselves on chairs facing the tiered rows of burgesses and the forbidding judicial bench.

"Gentlemen," the magistrate began calmly, "I have summoned you here for several reasons, the first and foremost is to warn you to keep this matter from becoming a public scandal. When the sheriff contacted you, he informed you that your ownership of three male servants and of the Devon cattle you acquired several months ago is in doubt. But because you purchased them in good faith at a public auction, you will be refunded your purchase prices according to the auctioneer's records. Had you bought them illegally from the pirates who frequent our shores to rid themselves of stolen contraband, you would receive no such consideration. The servants have already been removed from your homes, but you will be responsible for returning the cattle to the town commons within the week. Failure to do so will result in severe penalties."

"Are you planning to get the money from Trevor?" one of the men asked.

"Most certainly since he is responsible for the possible fraud."

"You won't get it," the man declared. "He's bought

himself eight blooded hunting horses and nineteen new slaves."

"He has also paid off two years of delinquent public debts; but I assure you, he will be forced to make prompt and proper restitution to each of you. Now, gentlemen, you will leave these chambers through the rear entry, and you will remember my request that you hold your tongues. 'Tis an ugly scandal at best, and loose talk will only make it worse."

In the balcony Lynn murmured bitterly, "My father won't even be charged openly with scandal."

"Tush," Ephraim scolded her in a sharp whisper. "The proceedings have just begun. Before this day is through..." His words trained off into silence as an unscheduled disturbance interrupted the prearranged agenda. Lynn recognized the shrill voice before she saw the woman uttering the protest. Even when the trio of two women and one man swept into view, the balcony spectators could see only the backs of Amelia Pendrath, Leona Spence, and the man Clay identified as John Gordon, Amelia's cousin.

"I demand to know why one of my servants was taken from my home and why I was not summoned here the same as the men you just dismissed," Amelia demanded angrily.

Although the magistrate was equally furious, his reprimand was couched in icy tones. "You are in contempt, Mrs. Pendrath."

"Oh, no, I'm not. I paid three hundred pounds for Kate Horton's papers, and I mean to see her returned to me."

"How did you learn of these proceedings?"

"My cousin received a summons and he informed me."

"That was very foolish of you, Mr. Gordon, because now you'll learn what I don't believe you know about Mrs. Pendrath. But first I wish to hear the particulars of your purchase of the indenture papers of a Jem Rigg and of a Devon bull called Red Penny."

"I bought the bull and its keeper sight unseen from

Royce Trevor and paid to have them transported here from New Haven, Connecticut. When Trevor told me the animal was available, I paid the price he asked—and that was plenty—because I'd seen some of its calves and young bullocks on other plantations. The bull turned out to be as magnificent as I'd hoped, and the mute is the finest stockman I've ever known."

"Did Mrs. Pendrath ever see that stockman on your property?"

"Of course she did when she came to see the bull."

"And she told you nothing about him?"

"How could she?"

"Very easily. Mrs. Pendrath knew that man, and she knew that he had completed his indenture four years ago. She also knew the precise period of indenture the woman she purchased was serving. But she said nothing about the five extra years Royce Trevor had added to Kate Horton's term."

"How the devil would Amelia know a woman like that?"

"Because Mrs. Pendrath had been sentenced to an equal term; only in her case, the sentence had been overly merciful. Had she been tried for the crime she committed before she became a smuggler, she would have been given the death penalty or life in prison. Your cousin stole a valuable necklace from the Duchess of Villiers, but her father was able to suppress the charge after the necklace was returned."

Abruptly the magistrate refocused his attention on the woman herself. "Mrs. Pendrath, when did you inform Royce Trevor about the location of his daughter?"

"I didn't," Amelia snapped, "and if you dare speak another lie about me, I'll insist that Lord Pendrath sue you for libel."

John Gordon's face was a mottled red, and his voice was sharp with restrained anger. "My cousin informed

Trevor during the first hunt she attended two years ago. I thought at the time that she was unduly vindictive.''

"Did she inform Trevor that a Rad Pollock also knew his daughter?''

"About a month later at a dinner party Trevor hosted, she told him all about the Pollocks; and at the dinner table she regaled the assemblage with stories about a Cornish witch.''

"Your cousin knew full well that those stories of witchcraft were false, Mr. Gordon.''

"The devil I did!'' Amelia exploded.

"If you interrupt these proceedings again, Mrs. Pendrath, I will fine you for contempt in addition to your other monetary loss. You will *not* be refunded a pound of the money you paid for Kate Horton because you were party to the fraud. Incidentally, the sum you paid was two hundred pounds, not the three hundred you claimed.''

For the first time Leona Burtram entered into the acrimonious combat, her protest almost as shrill as Amelia's. "That's not fair! Half of that money was mine!''

Deliberately slow to respond, the magistrate leafed through the papers stacked neatly before him and pulled out a single sheet, reading its contents silently before he addressed this new plaintiff.

"You are Leona Burtram?'' he asked. At her hesitant nod, he continued with an inflexible contempt, "I find you more reprehensible than your friend. As a criminal indentured, you lived with Kate Horton for eight months while you were childbearing; but unlike her, you did little or no work to expiate the punishment you'd earned. A month after you received a royal pardon, you deserted both your husband and the child you had birthed. The servant was most precise in her testimony to the sheriff, so I'll tolerate no further protest from either of you.''

"Mr. Gordon, you will return these women to the Pendrath property where they will remain in seclusion until Mr. Pendrath returns to take control of the pair of them.

Since you yourself were merely an innocent dupe, you will be reimbursed.''

As the embarrassed and furious John Gordon herded the two women out of the chambers, Clay whispered to Lynn, ''Poor Harry!''

''Poor Harry will find someone else to console his wife as he always has,'' Lynn returned the whispered confidence with a dry lack of sympathy. ''Was her new home attractive?''

'' 'Tis only half-finished, but the proper description would be as outrageously conspicuous as your father's.''

''No wonder they found each other so quickly.'' As Lynn noticed the sheriff escorting a lone man to the dock, she asked her grandfather sharply, ''Who is he?''

''The older of Rad Pollock's sons. Don't glare so harshly, Trelynn. Remember that the law is supposed to give everyone the benefit of doubt.''

''He was one of the witnesses against me, Grandfa!''

''Just listen, lass.''

When she heard the magistrate's opening comment, Lynn turned her head to glare at her grandfather.

''Mr. Pollock,'' the magistrate announced mildly, ''had you cooperated with the sheriff yesterday, you'd have saved yourself this trip into town.''

''He wouldn't answer my questions about Da and Sid,'' Jabe Pollock declared defensively.

''The sheriff did not know the full story at that time, Mr. Pollock. The information I want from you concerns your father's appointment as deputy sheriff.''

''Best you ask Mr. Trevor about that; 'twas his idea, not Da's.''

''Why did your father accept?''

''Same reason we're stuck in a muggy swamp. He wanted the woman and those fancy devons of hers.''

''Then he had no intention of returning Trelynn Trevor to England?''

"Not likely. He was going to bring her to our farm and settle her down no matter what Sid and I said."

"Did he inform Royce Trevor of his intentions?"

"Trevor was there when Da told Sid and me."

"Why did your brother agree to accompany your father?"

"Sid had reasons of his own."

"Did those reasons have anything to do with a man named Tom Kenn?"

Startled by the question, the witness stared at the magistrate before he answered, "Sid could be a cully fool at times, and Tom made pirating sound like a May Day sport."

"Pirating or wrecking, Mr. Pollock?"

"First time when Tom came here, 'twas pirating; but four months ago when he sent word by a friend, 'twas wrecking."

"Did your brother know the location of Kenn's operation?"

"Close enough. All Sid had to do was to get to some town called New Haven."

"Were you tempted to join your brother in the enterprise?"

"Not me."

"But you were a wrecker in Cornwall at one time, were you not?"

"Tom got me into it when him and me were sprouts, but I got out as fast as I could."

"Mr. Pollock, how responsible were you for the charges your father manufactured against Trelynn Trevor?"

" 'Twas my aunt more than Da, and I only said what I'd seen. I saw her once at an All Hallow's bonfire, and once I heard her talking the old tongue in front of some ruins."

"Did you believe her to be a witch on either occasion?"

"Not her. She was just smarter than Aunt Edith and old Owen Penley and even Da. Sid didn't believe she was either until Tom got to talking that first time. Tom was always a liar when he was covering up his own doings."

"I appreciate your cooperation, Mr. Pollock, although I

do not condone your activities in Cornwall. However, since you have not broken the law in this county, you are free to leave. The sheriff will inform you about your father and brother.''

''Da and Sid are dead, aren't they?''

''Yes.''

''I guessed as much when that bastard Trevor returned without them.''

In spite of her hatred for all Pollocks, Lynn felt a momentary pity for Jabe as he limped heavily from the hall. At twenty-two, he was what his brother had called him—a crippled dirt farmer with a future already savaged by the past. Her attention quickly reverted to the magistrate who'd begun still another speech of explanation.

''This morning with my clerk and the sheriff in attendance, I interviewed the three men and two women who are critical witnesses in this investigation. I learned what happened during the initial violence on the Rhode Island farm and what transpired on the subsequent voyage. I also learned what Royce Trevor obviously did not, since he permitted the mute man to witness several damning acts: Mr. Jem Rigg is a literate man who can read and write. Mr. Rigg is the one who overheard Royce Trevor *order* the captain to lock Trelynn Trevor in an unlighted cell aboard ship. According to both Ephraim Penley and Polly Rigg, Trevor had known about his daughter's fear of the dark since her early childhood. Jem Rigg also informed me that he'd overheard Sid Pollock boast about his cooperation with Royce Trevor just before he attempted to murder Mistress Trevor. Mr. Rigg was unable to go to her rescue because his broken leg was strapped to a wall.

''Even more damning was the testimony given by Polly Rigg. She watched Royce Trevor alter the indenture papers he'd found at the farm. Despite her protest that neither she nor her husband were indentured, he merely altered the ages on the papers belonging to two younger people who were no longer on the farm. A minute later she watched as he added five years to everyone's indenture time. Like her husband, Mrs. Rigg can read and write.

"The woman named Kate Horton was helpful in apprising us of the value of the clothing and household items stolen, while a Jason Hale reported the theft of thirty-four pigs and a full coop of chickens, which Royce Trevor sold to the captain to defray the cost of transportation. In my conservative estimate, Mr. Trevor stole in excess of seven thousand pounds. Technically this should be a criminal trial; but because it involves the reputation of other people, Governor Berkeley has recommended a measure of clemency. I suggest that we now inform Mr. Trevor that he is being held accountable for his actions."

Ephraim's strong bony hand tightened its grip on his granddaughter's arm. "It took me hours of argument to win that decision, Trelynn. Think, girl, you'd be as marked as your father if he went to prison."

Remembering the weeks she'd spent recovering from a head wound and the indignity she'd endured in New Haven, Lynn glared down at the man striding belligerently across the floor below. Dark-gold suited this time, his brown boots spurred with silver, Royce Trevor swept his plumed hat off only when he stood before the magistrate.

"Would you please tell me, James Norwell, why you have summoned me into this place and why I have been treated like a common criminal for the past three hours?" he demanded.

"Mr. Trevor, while I am wearing this robe of office and conducting a court of justice, you will address me as magistrate or judge. You have been summoned here to answer charges laid against you by Ephraim Penley. If the informality of these proceedings is not to your liking, we will gladly reassign you to criminal court with a jury and witnesses. I advise you to consider your decision carefully. You'll be guaranteed some anonymity and some consideration under this procedure, whereas the alternative will expose you to candid publicity."

"I wasn't complaining, Magistrate Norwell, only curious," Trevor responded smoothly. "I was also irritated by the inconvenience. Just what charges did my former father-in-law instigate?"

"A goodly number, which we will enumerate in logical order. First you will inform us why you coerced our county sheriff into appointing a deputy whose qualifications of good character were nonexistent. I refer, of course, to your remarkable sponsorship of Rad Pollock."

"I knew nothing against his character; he seemed a worthy man to me, and courageous enough to give me assistance in reclaiming a stolen inheritance" was the prompt reply. "The other two men were Pollock's idea."

"But you paid the transportation costs for all three. Why?"

"Because the town in question is known to be infested by pirates. As to my choice of Mr. Pollock, he was in possession of English arrest warrants that accused the person who had stolen my inheritance with murder and witchcraft. Since he was eager to arrest the criminal, I believed our mission would serve a dual purpose."

"Tell the assemblage what transpired during the pursuit by you and Pollock of that 'dual' purpose."

"I discovered that the guilty woman had already squandered the inheritance, leaving me no alternative but to confiscate what few possessions she owned."

"Describe what happened during that ... 'confiscation.'"

Lynn's jaw was clamped shut with frustrated anger as she listened to her father's glib recital that sounded as if the brutal raid on the farm had been a legal and mercifully executed operation. His concluding narrative almost ended her own grim silence.

"After we had the animals aboard ship, Mr. Pollock went in search of the woman who'd fled into hiding upon our earlier arrival. Personally I had no interest in her apprehension, but the Pollocks were determined. Unfortunately before they returned to the ship with the woman, the two female indentureds had spread word among the crew that she was tainted, the word they used was *witch*. Immediately the captain ordered her confined.''

"What about the voyage to Jamestown, Mr. Trevor?''

"Unpleasant from the start. The next morning, the bull—said to have been the woman's familiar—broke loose and ran amok in the hold of the ship, killing the Pollocks' stockman and injuring two of the male indentureds. Because the crew was close to mutiny, Captain Denby decided to dock the ship at New Haven and rid himself of the woman, the two injured men, and the bull, which had finally been restrained. The Pollocks decided to remain ashore with their prisoner. There were no further unpleasant incidents aboard ship during the remainder of the voyage.''

"Did you go ashore in New Haven?''

"Both Captain Denby and I did; we informed the authorities there of the circumstances and made certain the injured men received medical help.''

"Do you know what subsequently happened to the woman prisoner?''

"I presume Mr. Pollock arranged for her to be transported back to England to stand trial. I suggest you ask him about the details when he returns to Jamestown. Now, what precisely were the complaints Ephraim Penley has charged against me?''

"Mr. Trevor, what was the name of the woman prisoner?''

"She called herself Lynn Penley.''

"Ephraim Penley's granddaughter?''

"Yes.''

"Is she not, in fact, your own daughter?''

For a moment the urbane poise that had made Royce Trevor sound bored and disinterested, deserted him, and his response was a harsh admission. "I didn't want that information revealed in this colony; the disgrace will be hard enough for my family to endure. My daughter—I own up to the relationship—inherited her strange abilities and unfortunate proclivities from my own mother. I recognized the taint while she was still a young child; I had hoped that she might outgrow her evil heritage, but obviously she did not.''

Ignoring the outburst, the magistrate continued his questioning in a calmly judicial tone. ''Mr. Trevor, prior to your quest in Rhode Island, you took an extended trip to England. What was your purpose in doing so?''

''To replenish my stables mainly, but also to make inquiries about the inheritance promised me by my former mother-in-law, Hortensia Penley. If you doubt the validity of my claim, I have a copy of her will in my strongbox at home.''

''What did you find out from those inquiries?''

''Hortensia's lawyer informed me that all of his records had been destroyed in the London fire of '66. Since the will had been made eighteen years earlier, he confessed that he did not remember the details.''

''Just why did Hortensia Penley make *you* her heir rather than her own daughter?''

''My former wife was a very immature woman who refused to accompany me to Virginia. Hortensia hoped that the reversal of the inheritance would force her daughter to accept responsibility.''

''Did Mrs. Penley continue to supply you with money after your arrival in Virginia?''

''Occasionally she did, but the sums were paltry. You still haven't informed me about Ephraim Penley's complaint, Magistrate.''

''Quite correct, Mr. Trevor; but before I do, I find it necessary to correct some flaws in the remarkable tale you have just told to the people here assembled. Constable, bring Mr. Trevor a chair. I believe he'll find what I have to say more palatable if he is seated.''

''I have told you the simple truth!''

''That you have not; you have perverted the truth from your first admission through your last. Do not bother to protest again until I have completed the charges; and do not be so rash as to challenge my authority. Everything I am about to reveal has been substantiated by reliable witnesses, sworn affidavits, or incontrovertible evidence.

"When Mrs. Pendrath first informed you about your daughter's whereabouts and told you of Rad Pollock's interest in her, you went to see Pollock, and you proposed the joint venture. At that meeting you learned that in spite of her marriage, Pollock did not intend to return her to England. As he had for seven years, he planned to claim her as his own even if it meant keeping her prisoner on his property here in James County. Afterwards you lied to our sheriff when you asked him to appoint Pollock as deputy.

"The rest of your story is a malicious mixture of omissions and untruths. For example, you forgot to mention the murder of one of the men at the Penley farm in Rhode Island."

"That was self-defense!"

"I warned you not to interrupt me. A blow struck from behind during an ambush is murder, and it was witnessed by a worker on the neighboring farm."

"You can't hold me responsible for the actions of another man."

"You were the one who brought that man there, and you were the one giving the orders. Your next omission was your failure to inform us that when the Pollocks brought your daughter aboard, she was unconscious from a blow on the head; and it was you, not Captain Denby, who ordered her to be placed in a dark cell. You lied about the rumor of witchcraft circulated among the crew; you paid Sidney Pollock to frighten those men and to untie the bull. You lied when you claimed the bull had injured Jem Rigg and John Bram. The bull struck down only the Pollocks' brutal stockman; the others had been injured during their capture and during subsequent brutality aboard ship.

"Now we come to the most reprehensible part of your duplicity, a series of facts Sidney Pollock admitted in front of witnesses. Without his father's knowledge, he had privately informed you that he wanted to be put ashore in New Haven. You saw your opportunity to get rid of all your problems by persuading Captain Denby to put your daughter, the bull, the injured men, and the older Pollock ashore at the same time. In New Haven you informed the authorities about your daughter's 'taint' and advised them to keep her confined until she could be returned to England."

"Nothing that I did was criminal! She *was* a fugitive from justice."

"Several things you did were very criminal. You altered the numbers on five papers of indenture, and you stole more than seven thousand pounds worth of property."

"That was mine by right of inheritance!"

"I have here a letter that John Coleman, the late Hortensia Penley's lawyer, sent to Ephraim Penley, stating that he'd informed you about a subsequent will that disinherited you and named her granddaughter as sole heir."

"That letter's a forgery; all of Coleman's records were burnt in—"

"The letter is unquestionably valid, Mr. Trevor, as is this copy of Hortensia Penley's last will and testament. The two documents alone prove your claims fraudulent. In view of these findings, I order you to make complete restitution of all property you stole from your daughter and to repay the money you bilked from some thirty of your fellow colonials."

"You know damned well I can't, James Norwell!"

"You can and you will. I have already authorized the sale of your horses, your hounds, and as many of your slaves and personal possessions as will be needed."

"I'll be paupered!" Royce Trevor shouted.

"If I had my way, you'd be stripped of everything you own; but since the governor decided not to make this a criminal trial, you will retain your estate."

''No, he will not!'' a strident voice shouted from the concealed balcony.

Before Lynn and her grandfather could do more than stare at Bevil Trevor in shock, he tapped Clay on the shoulder and spoke quietly to his son. '' 'Tis time you and I contribute our bit to the ruination of our scoundrel cousin, but you'll allow me to do the talking.''

Left alone with his granddaughter, Ephraim muttered, ''Damn, if I don't believe Bevil is as much a trickster as that greedy fool down there. For weeks he's been gloating like a fat moneylender.''

CHAPTER
18

Until she watched the two men walk across the floor below, Lynn had never realized how different the father and son were in appearance and stature. Although the relationship was unmistakable in the strong noses and lean jaws, Clay's face projected a handsome appeal the father's lacked. Taller by a hand span, Clay moved with an easy grace while his father strode with belligerent determination. In coloring they were even more dissimilar; like his older sons, Bevil was dark haired and eyed, while Clay's light brown hair seemed burnished with gold in the slanted light of the chamber.

"Did Clay and his brothers have the same mother?" she asked her grandfather impulsively.

"Of course they did. Why did you ask?"

"She must have been a beautiful woman because Clay doesn't look like his father."

"I'm happier that he doesn't seem to have inherited Bevil's penchant for interfering in the lives of other people. Now pay attention, Trelynn; I want to hear what that devil is up to," Ephraim scolded as he craned his head forward to watch the older Trevor lay a sheath of papers on the magistrate's bench and then step back to make a perfunctory bow before he addressed the judge.

"Magistrate Norwell, I am Sir Bevil Trevor, a distant cousin of the man at the dock. Governor Berkeley suggested I wait until you'd concluded your other business before I revealed the contents of these documents publicly. My cousin has no legal claim to the Virginia property known as Trevalon. For over twenty years, he has been nothing but a highly paid custodian, but now that sinecure is at an end."

Frowning as he concentrated on the first of the legal papers in front of him, Norwell demanded sharply, "The governor has read these?"

"I sent him copies several years ago when the originals first came into my possession. As you can see by the signature on each separate document, the author was the Honorable Hortensia Trelynn Penley, who was the only surviving child of the late Lord Henry Trelynn. You will also note that they're all countersigned by John Coleman, the same lawyer my deceitful cousin recently consulted in London. In her deathbed confession, Hortensia requested that the contents remain secret until all conditions had been met."

"Perhaps you should explain the contents to the people here, Sir Trevor. It would appear to me that some fraud has been committed."

"Several times over, Magistrate, but not against the crown or the colonial government—only against my cousin who made the mistake of underestimating Lord Trelynn and his daughter. Twenty-five years ago, Royce eloped with Lavinia Trelynn Penley, the then fifteen-year-old daughter of Ephraim and Hortensia Penley. As a price for marrying the girl after he learned she was carrying his child, Royce demanded that he be named Hortensia's heir; but that promise of future independent wealth did not satisfy him for long. Because he quickly proved to be as callous a father as he was a husband, Hortensia devised a scheme to separate him from her daughter and granddaughter. With her father's full approval, she offered him the Trelynn land in Virginia.

"Since 1612 that plantation had been owned by Lord Trelynn when he acquired it from the Virginia Company under the old head-of-household system. Until 1644, Trevalon had been the home of Lord Trelynn's younger brother, Alexander; but in that fateful year, Alexander and his entire family were killed during an Indian massacre. Because the estate had been ravaged as a result of that raid and needed to be redeveloped, Lord Trelynn readily agreed to Hortensia's suggestion and signed over the 1612 deed to her son-in-law, seemingly delighted to be rid of the problem.

"For four years Royce worked hard to develop what he considered to be his own property. But in 1649 when hundreds of disfranchised aristocrats arrived in Virginia with land grants issued by a desperate King Charles during the final years of his life, Royce learned that his deed was invalid. Since 1624 Virginia had been a royal colony, and only royal grants were valid. Lord Trelynn had retained possession of the valid deed issued by the late King Charles in the first year of his reign. When he discovered the fraud, Royce returned to England and consulted a lawyer. At that time he learned the bitter truth; he could never legally own the Virginia property. The same laws that governed royal grants in England applied in this colony; only male blood descendants could inherit. Armed with his shrewd lawyer's advice, Royce visited his mother-in-law and made specific demands. You'll find Hortensia's account of that unpleasant interview among the papers I gave you, Magistrate.

"Royce demanded that he be made custodian in perpetuity, a legal device frequently employed by absentee landlords to ensure continuing productivity of their lands. He also demanded that his wife and child accompany him to Virginia. By that time Lord Trelynn was a broken, dying man; his only son and heir had been killed during the final year of that tragic war. His estate and English lands had already been confiscated by the Commonwealth government. The Virginia property and Hortensia's personal wealth were now all that was left of the once extensive Trelynn holdings. Faced with her son-in-law's demands, Hortensia gambled that she could outwit Royce Trevor for the second time and still protect her family. That the document she dictated to her lawyer was fradulent to an extent, she readily admitted in her deathbed confession.

"That complicated document seemingly satisfied all of Royce's demands. Pending the birth of a direct Trelynn descendant, he would be in complete control of Trevalon until that potential male descendant was of age, at which time he would share custodial duties. Since the only possibility of such a child was one born to him and Lavinia, Royce was confident that he was not being cheated again. However, his lawyer had advised him to secure other guarantees as well; in the event of his wife's death, he insisted on retaining control whether he remarried or not. My cousin made one final demand, one that had *not* been recommended by his lawyer; he demanded that the custodial control of Trevalon would be extended to any legitimate son he produced during his lifetime.

"Had he not been so greedy, he could have spent the remainder of his life in Virginia. But that one final insistence gave Hortensia and John Coleman the wedge they needed. By acceding readily to the demand that any legitimate son of Royce Trevor would retain his father's position, the document could be amended to substitute the family name of *Trevor* rather than the personal name of *Royce Trevor*. My cousin signed the agreement without protesting the omission of his first name in the critical paragraphs, and that oversight is what will cost him his comfortable life here in Virginia."

"The devil it will!" Royce Trevor exploded into furious speech, only to be silenced by the magistrate's stern warning.

"Mr. Trevor, I can still call you up on criminal charges; and if you interrupt this hearing again, I will do just that. Sir Bevil, will you inform us what happened to his demand that his wife return to the colony with him?"

"All I know is what Hortensia claimed in her report, that Lavinia refused to see him. According to Hortensia, Royce had told his wife the same things about his mother as he told his daughter; and Lavinia's reaction was revulsion for both him and her child. But there *is* something I do know first hand; my cousin's mother was not what he claims. She was an expert in medicine, not in witchcraft. Prior to the battle of Edgehill, fever spread through two of our Cornish regiments, and she came to our camp to nurse her husband and some of the other officers who were ill. To my certain knowledge, she never met the king, and she never prophesied his death nor her own nor her husband's. Robert was killed during the battle, and she died a week later of fever. I have no idea why her son invented those lies about her or even if he really believes them."

"Did you know her personally, Sir Bevil?" the magistrate asked.

"Yes. She was a fine woman despite her humble birth; I believe it may have been her lack of wealth that alienated her son. At any rate, his stories to his wife destroyed his marriage. In order to protect her daughter and granddaughter for the second time, Hortensia persuaded him to return to Virginia without them by promising him a generous supply of money to build the home he wanted and to indulge his hobbies. One of those documents is an accounting of every pound she sent him, every consignment of building materials, and every piece of furniture and artifact she took from the bankrupt Trelynn estate in Cornwall. As I stated earlier, my cousin has been a well-paid custodian."

The look on the magistrate's face was oddly speculative as he leafed through the papers until he located the one he wanted. Ignoring the man now straining forward in the dock, he addressed Bevil: "Sir Trevor, if his wife did not accompany him to Virginia, can you explain the contents of this paper you borrowed from our colonial files?"

"That was my cousin's most blatant mistake. Before he left England the second time, he purchased the indenture papers of a young woman called Margaret Rylan. When she gave birth to a son, he named the child Alexander Trelynn Trevor and registered the lad—without the benefit of christening—as his legitimate heir he'd brought from England. That deception endured for six years until 1657, by which time the Commonwealth government had become oppressive. Disturbed by her daughter's increasingly reckless gambling and by her frequent insolence to the civil authorities, Hortensia decided Lavinia would be safer with her husband in Virginia. My cousin's response to her letter requesting his permission was an adamant refusal to allow his wife to join him. Hortensia dispatched an investigative agent on the first ship leaving London. Royce was then given the choice of removing his new family from his home or of facing public charges of fraud. Predictably he chose to preserve his own reputation. He located a man who'd completed his indenture and paid the man to marry Margaret Rylan and to take her, her son, and a younger daughter to one of the Carolina settlements. Then he announced publicly that his son had died."

The magistrate nodded. "That would explain the word *deceased* added to his son's name in this document. Continue your narrative, Sir Trevor."

"Hortensia changed her will after that incident, an action she admits she'd intended all along; but she continued to send her son-in-law money to keep him in Virginia. Her main concern now was the safety of her granddaughter; she knew that Royce Trevor had not forgotten the possibility of a legitimate Trelynn heir. At his request she sent him an annual report on his daughter's progress that was entirely fictitious. She described the girl as dull of wit and unattractive. Lulled into a false sense of security and well-supplied with money, he ceased considering his daughter a threat until he learned that she was married and living in Rhode Island. That was the reason he went to England to search for the inheritance; before then he had not been too concerned since Hortensia had instructed her lawyer to continue the payments for three years after her death.''

"The one thing that puzzles me, Sir Trevor,'' the magistrate stated quietly, ''is Ephraim Penley's part in this duplicity. I have know him for several years, and I would not have thought he would submit to blackmail or be a party to fraud.''

"His only contribution was to allow his wife to have access to his own funds; he distrusted my cousin as much as Hortensia did. But he knew nothing about either of the agreements Hortensia had made with their son in-law; he was overseas at the time of his daughter's marriage, and again when my cousin returned to England. In her confession, Hortensia admits to telling her husband that before his death, King Charles had agreed to the transfer of Trevalon from Lord Trelynn to Royce Trevor as payment for Robert Trevor's service. Since the late king had permitted such an irregularity in two other cases, Ephraim accepted the lie as truth. He was told that the estate was part of the bribe Hortensia had been forced to pay my cousin to marry their daughter.''

"Did you know about any of these contrivances, Sir Trevor?''

"Only about the marriage, not about the problems until I returned to my estate after the war. The only promise Hortensia extracted from me at that time was to keep a watchful eye on her granddaughter whenever Ephraim was overseas. I received the documents now before you several months after Hortensia's death.''

"In that case, there is no need to continue this hearing. I hereby order Royce Trevor and his present family deported to England as undesirable colonists.''

"The hell you say, James Norwell!" Royce Trevor shouted. "Unless you plan to charge me as a criminal, that custodial agreement is as valid today as it was when it was written. At the time of her arrest, my daughter was childless; so there is no Trelynn heir. Even if there were one, I would still control Trevalon. Read the contract if the old bitch sent you her copy."

Turning to face his furious cousin, Bevil smiled sardonically. "There *is* a Trelynn heir as half the burgesses here can testify. When you kidnapped your daughter, her son was safely hidden in a neighbor's home. She is anything but the dull-witted woman you believed her to be."

"That's a lie, and whatever child you showed these gullible cullies is a false pretender. Ask the man standing next to you. Did you think I'd forgotten you, Clay Penley? You deserted your wife two years ago when you absconded with the money that should have been mine. When I searched the woman's house, there was no sign of a child . . . not a garment or an infant's bed; and there were none in the neighbor's house where she was hiding. The Pollocks said they searched it thoroughly before they brought her to the ship."

"The Pollocks lied to you, cousin. They didn't even enter the Fulton home; Trelynn met them outside the door," Bevil announced triumphantly.

Absorbing the shock with a cornered man's bravado, Royce Trevor blustered, "Then the child is my grandson; and since his mother is not here—"

"His mother *is* here," Bevil rasped harshly, "and she is a free woman, cleared of all the false charges against her, your own included. But now 'tis full time you hear the rest of Hortensia's revenge against you and the blackmail you forced her to pay you for twenty years. This dumbfounded man by my side is not a Penley at all; he's my youngest son, Charles Clayton Trevor. Hortensia's dying wish was that he marry her granddaughter, and I made certain that wish was fulfilled."

In the concealed balcony, Ephraim Penley sagged helplessly against the back of his chair. "Dear God, what a blind old fool I've been," he muttered.

Tight-lipped with her own seething anger, Lynn snapped out a terse response. "It runs in our family, Grandfa. Even with the promise of a magnificent Virginia estate he'd always wanted, Charles Clayton Trevor refused to marry me until he had no other choice. No wonder he was pleased when he learned he had a son!"

Alarmed by the scathing bitterness expressed in her voice, Ephraim suppressed his own emotional shock to comfort the sensitive young woman who'd just heard the character of her worthless father publicly stripped of all dignity. "I'm certain your husband knew nothing about any of this."

"You can be as certain as you like, Grandfa. I was the one who was tossed aside like a moldy sack of grain until I produced a son. How damned obliging of me to have secured a fortune for my husband and father-in-law."

"If you would use the legal knowledge you've gained, girl, you would realize that your grandmother devised the only means possible to give you and your children lasting protection. Why do you suppose she tricked your father into signing that custodial agreement? Now the name Charles Clayton Trevor can be legally inserted, as the magistrate is doing right now."

"No doubt she wanted revenge, Grandfa; who wouldn't under the circumstances? And no doubt she considered it a challenging gamble to appoint me the one to deliver those papers to Sir Bevil. She said as much when she gave them to me."

"I'll admit Hortensia was a gambler, but she was a shrewd one who protected you far better than I did. If she hadn't bribed that scoundrel to marry your mother, your life might have been as harsh as the one your Nell Wallis endured. Illegitimacy is a cruel burden for any child to bear. Hortensia was not the one who squandered our combined fortunes; your vain, foolish mother and that knavish blackmailer down there did. But it would seem that my wife managed to salvage a goodly portion of the money. Trevalon is a productive plantation despite that fool's extravagance; and your grandmother made certain he would not be able to claim a piece of furniture or a hanging of drapery in the beautiful home she paid for."

"I don't care if the damned estate is a royal palace; I won't have my son made into the bargaining pawn I was."

"You cannot deny him his Trelynn inheritance, lass."

"No, but I can keep him in Rhode Island until he learns true from false. Let his victorious grandfather and father revel in the inanities of red-coated hunting and velvet-breeched partying; these are their kind of colonials, not mine."

Lynn paused abruptly and smiled at her grandfather, a cynical smile that he knew from long experience was a better indication of her deep hurt than angry speech. "Don't pay any attention to me, Grandfa. I know you're itching to go below and scold Sir Bevil for his clever chicanery before you congratulate him for the well-deserved flogging he just administered to the main villain in my life."

She understands me better than I do her, Ephraim reflected sadly as he stood up and flexed his stiff joints. "'Tis not like you to pass judgment before you've heard all the evidence, lass," he chided her.

"I've seen enough to know that I'll never again be as easily manipulated as I was the day I married Clay Trevor. Ironic, isn't it? I thought I was being so independent when I ignored your advice; instead I was merely falling into a well-laid trap."

Ephraim was still frowning as he made his way cautiously down the narrow stairs. God's wounds, perhaps he and Hortensia had been wrong to allow the overbright minx to have had such an undisciplined childhood. She was a more determined fighter than Hortensia had been at her most contrary, and she'd developed an intimidating self-confidence. Shaking his head, the old man smiled with a gentler humor. He would have her no other way, this bold granddaughter; she'd already conquered one small colonial world peopled by settlers tougher in spirit than these misplaced aristocrats. Ephraim's smile broadened as he recalled what the buccaneer Rambert had said about her kidnapping. "I wouldn't want her a prisoner aboard my ship. She has a way of looking at a man that would strike terror in the cowards amongst us."

Whatever the look Morse Rambert had described, Lynn's dark eyes were glowing with somber fire as she followed her grandfather down the stairs a minute later and walked rapidly out of the building into the blinding sunlight of late afternoon. She wanted to run, to race across the green sward of grass that covered the town commons. For weeks now she'd endured the restraints of shipboard life and before that, the months of spirit-crushing imprisonment on the Dunton farm in New Haven. Now unless she could escape from this stultifying colony, she'd be strait-jacketed for life by social decorum. Repressing her violent urge to run, she settled to a rapid stride that took her past the blocks of homes and shops that lined the streets in the higgledy-piggledy fashion of colonial port towns. Gradually her confusion of thoughts had narrowed down to the one all-pervasive determination that neither she nor her son would be forced into the mold of plantation aristocrats who relied upon hundreds of slaves to do the work.

Lynn didn't see the two waterfront loiterers who'd been watching her with lustful eyes and who now moved to block her progress. Her first awareness of the grinning pair was their bare feet planted in the dust of the roadbed, but her only reaction to their threatening presence was renewed fury. Even broken-toothed flesh-flies with brains the size of chickpeas considered themselves superior to any woman. With hot anger born of frustration, Lynn sidestepped with a swift economy of movement and flung one arm wide.

Her doubled fist caught the shorter man squarely on the side of his head, sending him reeling against his partner; and Lynn ran as she'd wanted to do since she'd left the hearing. Experiencing the wild joy of reclaiming her own identity, she didn't see the man smiling down at her from the docked *Tamarlind* until she reached the gangplank.

"That was quite a show, Lynn," Nate Stokes chuckled.

"I hope they weren't your men, Nate. One of them won't be hearing much for a week."

"My men have better sense. Where's Clay?"

"Still celebrating, I imagine. He's finally won his Virginia estate."

"How come?"

"My stupid father proved to be no match for Sir Bevil and my late grandmother. Nate, where's the *Tamarlind* going when it leaves here?"

"Straight to England as soon as we take on passengers tomorrow morning. We're already behind schedule, and you know the company rules: late deliveries reduce our profit by ten percent. Why did you ask?"

"I want to go back to Rhode Island."

"Not a chance, Lynn. His nibs said you'd all be staying here until the muddle was cleared, but Polly said that might not take too long."

"Is Polly aboard?"

"They all are."

"Thank heaven! How are they, Nate?"

"Kate's still spitting nails, but the others are cheerful enough. They're waiting for you below. Come on, I'll take you there. I don't suppose things will be like they were on the farm much longer, not in this Royalist town. I can't see Sir Trevor sitting around a kitchen table with common folk."

Tempted to insist that she had no intention of following the dictates of Sir Bevil or anyone else, Lynn resisted the foolish impulse. But Nate's shrewd prediction bothered her throughout her reunion with the people who'd shared her life in America. Once she walked through the door of the estate now owned by the gurgling infant glorying in the attention of his old friends, she would no longer have a freedom of choice. She'd be trapped in a social system she hated. Polly's description of Trevalon only added to her resentment of the prospect. " 'Tis as big as the Trevor manor in Cornwall and just as fancily furnished. There's enough room in the kitchen to whirl an ox around, and the servant quarters are strung out like a city block. Don't reckon you'll find it cozy enough for your liking, Lynn.''

Kate was even more negative of her appraisal of life in the Virginia colony. ''Won't be the house that'll get you down; 'twill be the neighbors who'll choke the life out of you. There's a dozen more like the two Madame Prinks who've kept me hopping for three months. What's the matter with your hand, Lynn? You've been rubbing it like you've been in a nettle patch.''

''I hit it on something.''

''What?''

''An idiot who mistook me for one of your simpering Madame Prinks.''

Kate's grin of approval was balm to Lynn's troubled mind, but Polly was less optimistic. ''You'll not be able to play the man here, lass. Even your villainous father treated his wife like a china dish, as if she'd break if she did a lick of work. The gentlemen farmers hereabouts expect their womenfolk to be showpieces more'n anything else.''

''At least they expect their womenfolk to have more sense than to go running through a port town like a half-wit hoyden,'' Ephraim accused his granddaughter angrily as he walked stiffly into the crew's quarters. ''You'll now show the decency to apologize to your husband. He's waiting for you in your cabin.''

Clay was waiting for her right enough, seated at the table with a wine goblet in his hand, which he raised in an insolent salute as she entered the cabin.

"What was it, madam, a guilty conscience or a victory celebration that made you flee the scene a while back?"

"The victory was all yours, Clay Trevor. You're the one who wanted to live in Virginia, not me."

"The devil you say! You're the one who knew your cursed grandmother's plans to trap me into marriage and to keep me bottled up on a farm."

"They're called plantations here, and Trevalon is said to be larger than your father's estate in Cornwall. But if I'd know his and my grandmother's scheme, I wouldn't have been so eager to save your life on the Wadleys' farm."

"You'll pardon me if I don't believe you. You're the one who brought those damnable papers to my father, and you've too busy a nose not to have read every word of them. I don't appreciate having been the fox at your private hunt."

Absorbing the shock of his anger, Lynn asked curiously, "Wasn't the promise of the estate the reason you finally promised your father you'd wed me?"

"Hell no! One of your Hortensia's restrictions was that my father not tell me anything until after you and I had produced a son. You should have stayed for the finale of today's little show."

"What happened?"

"The magistrate made me read every one of those documents because he wanted no more misunderstanding about custodial responsibilities. Then he ordered your father to vacate by tomorrow morning so that we could take immediate possession. By that time I was willing to let the lying fool keep the damn job; I sure as hell don't want it."

"What do you want, Clay?" Lynn asked quietly.

"Freedom to move about. What am I going to do with the thirty people I've already hired to start those lumber mills in Connecticut if I'm not there to do the initial planning? And how do I handle the indentured business if I'm stuck ten miles up the James River?"

"What were you planning to do with me while you were moving about?"

"Until today I was planning to take you with me and put you to work."

"Clay, were any of my grandmother's papers intended for me?"

"The great Hortensia was too thorough a planner to forget the main character in her plot. She left you your instructions the same as she did the rest of us."

"Where are they?"

"The sealed letter is in my gloating father's pocket, but you won't be allowed to read it until we've spent a month on that damned plantation."

"Do you intend to glare at me the whole time, Clay?"

"A man doesn't enjoy being trapped."

An impish smile curved Lynn's lips until she broke into soft laughter. "How do you think your father will feel when you turn the job over to him? As a Trevor, he qualifies as well as you do; and he's titled enough to become a social leader long before our month is finished."

"Are you serious?"

"Of course, I am. I left the hearing because I thought I was the one who'd been trapped. If I'd known what was in those papers, I'd have burned them in the London fire. Until Captain Vinson told me who my grandmother was, I didn't know a thing about her family. I knew she supported my villainous father, but I thought that he owned the land here at least; and I certainly never expected to have anything to do with it. Now do you pour me some of your wine, or do I tell your father that I found our son behind a cabbage patch and have no idea who he is?"

Clay's laughter was the rolling, bubbling sound of relief as he rose to pull his smiling wife into his arms. "You're a witch woman regardless of all the judges who decided otherwise. They didn't know how you can twist the truth and make a man feel like a dolt. How do you intend to persuade my father?"

"Very easily. Since no one wants an embittered Royce Trevor running around loose, I suggest your father hire him as his estate agent in Cornwall. Believe me, your brother is the world's worst farmer; and as you recall, his wife has alienated every tenant on the place. Whatever else he's done, my father does seem to have learned how to develop an estate; and he's shrewd enough to keep Barbara from meddling, particularly if his wife is the lady he claims and as well-blooded as the Devon Gordons. They could live in the old bailiff's house, which isn't exactly a tenant's cot, not with twelve rooms and a private garden. I'm sure my grandfather can write a contract that will keep my dishonorable father on the straight and narrow and well away from us and our children."

"My father would have to return there once a year."

"He can go back every winter, and we could return here for those few months. You'd hate the cold in Connecticut anyway. I'll wager Sir Bevil will approve of the plan if he hasn't already decided on it himself. I'll promise to maintain his social reputation while he's gone; I'll even promise to entertain the country gentry . . . I have to find some place to wear that black velvet gown you gave me. I'll also try not to act the country clod as I did today."

"Is that how you hurt your hand?"

Startled a little by his shrewd perception, Lynn grinned without remorse and nodded. "I didn't say I'd become a genteel lady, only act like one whenever necessary."

That night at dinner in the captain's quarters, Sir Bevil Trevor acceded to Lynn's suggestion with an alacrity that brought a smile of abrupt understanding to Ephraim Penley's face. For him, the last piece of the puzzle had fallen into place; Bevil had intended all along to make Virginia his permanent home. Why else would he have encouraged Clay to develop the Connecticut land grant? Even without the timely arrival of a Trelynn heir, Bevil had meant to oust Royce Trevor from Trevalon.

Concerning the future of Royce Trevor, Ephraim Penley

felt a measure of relief. As much as he hated the man for his brutality toward Lynn, Ephraim experienced a twinge of guilt. In spite of the means he'd employed to secure success, Royce had been led down the primrose path by an expert in the art of deception; and he'd been stripped clean of any monetary reward for a quarter century of work. Agreeing judiciously with Lynn that there should be no word sent to England about his ruined reputation in Virginia, Ephraim helped Bevil write the letter of explanation to Averill Trevor and devised a contract that would limit any unreasonable ambition and still guarantee him life-long security. As an added safeguard, the lawyer convinced Bevil to offer a large enough percentage of profits to provide initiative.

"Your Gordon daughter-in-law can be depended upon to keep him honest," Ephraim murmured dryly, "and all of us in America will be able to sleep better in our beds at night. I have little faith in the adage that punishment reforms a criminal."

Expecting only additional vilification when he arrived aboard the *Tamarlind* the next morning with his family, an indentured nurse, and the twelve trunks of possessions the sheriff had allowed him, Royce Trevor was suspiciously astounded to be greeted with civility by the two older men awaiting him. Cautiously he listened to the proposal and read the contract three times over before he demanded, "Did you write this, Ephraim, or did my cousin?"

"I did," the lawyer responded dryly, "and I've yet to be accused of dishonesty by any man. You'll note that there are proper leashes on you; you're to make a profit for the estate without cheating the tenants, and you're to keep an honest accounting."

Turning toward the other man, Royce was more speculative. "Why are *you* doing this, cousin?"

Bevil's answer was as blunt as the question. "I've reasons enough. I don't want the family name dragged through the mud of debtors' prison, not after the damage you've already done our reputation. But I'm not offering you charity; I expect you to increase the productivity of my estate. There's a personal matter as well; I was once stung by Lord Trelynn, and I've not forgotten the affront. That's the reason my oldest son has been told nothing about your actions here, so you'll not be working under a cloud. Make no mistake, though, cousin, you'll be walking a tightrope until you prove yourself."

Minutes after the contract had been signed, Ephraim and Bevil climbed aboard the handsomely appointed carriage that until yesterday had been one of Royce Trevor's most ostentatious possessions. Reflecting sourly on how much of his money and Hortensia's had been squandered to pay for such luxuries, Ephraim experienced the same frustration he had for twenty years with the Cavalier colonists in Virginia. Most of them lived beyond their means without a thought for the future when they'd be outnumbered twenty to one by freed indentureds and slaves. Compared to the solvent settlers of New England who were already planning a diversified economy, Virginians were dependent on a one-crop basis of wealth.

"Do you know anything about tobacco?" he asked his companion.

"Nary a bit."

"Then if I were you, I'd talk to one of Trelynn's indentureds. Jason Hale is an experienced farmer, and he'd like to settle here permanently."

"Won't you be needing him on your own farm, Ephraim?"

"Jem tells me he can manage with a pair of young farmhands I've already ordered from your son. Mine is only a small farm that I expect will be swallowed up as New Port expands."

"Then I'll take the man and be grateful."

"You'll also be taking Red Penny. Jem believes the bull would savage the next ship it boards."

Bevil sighed, his enthusiasm of the preceding evening muted somewhat by the realization that it'd been many years since he'd made a living from the land.

"In a way I'm sorry Clay is so averse to farming. He and Trelynn would have a good life here; 'tis the only civilized one of the colonies. They may change their minds once they meet the people Governor Berkeley has promised to invite to the hunt I'll be hosting in a fortnight. They'll be the ones with money enough to buy the string of high-bred horses our mutual relative foolishly purchased with stolen money."

Ephraim smiled grimly but held his peace; Trevalon was still ten miles away, and the day was already overwarm.

The irritation that plagued Ephraim during the long drive had also bedeviled his granddaughter since her first glimpse of Trevalon hours earlier. There was a beguiling beauty to the white colonnaded house that overlooked both the James River and a shady grove of towering oak trees. Inside the large, two-story home, however, a sense of alienation had overwhelmed her as she'd followed the well-trained English housekeeper on a tour of one handsomely furnished room after another. Settling her son and Ellen in the nursery, Lynn looked around the room at the reminders of the three other children who'd been its unlucky tenants— two young brothers and a sister she'd never know. Rejoining her husband in the drawing room, she was further dismayed by the look of rapt appreciation on his face.

" 'Tis a virtual palace," he exclaimed enthusiastically.

" 'Tis twenty-four rooms that require ten cleaning women, two cooks, and four footmen," Lynn contradicted. "No wonder my father was always short of money. Have you toured the grounds yet?"

"I was waiting for you. I don't suppose you've learned to sit a horse properly yet."

"Proper or not, I sat one for five days between New Haven and Saybrook. If you'll not cavil at militia garb, I dare say I'll maintain the pace."

"You'll learn to ride sidesaddle here in feminine attire. I've ordered a footman to hitch up the plantation chaise. According to the housekeeper, we've three hours until dinner, enough time to see the grounds set aside for hunting and the river picnic area."

He's already adjusted to this useless elegance, Lynn thought rebelliously; within the month he'll have found a dozen excuses not to leave it. Resettling the wide-brimmed straw hat firmly on her head, she was silent as he led her through the formal dining room, the smaller family one, the sitting room, the library, and out into the porte cochère where the one-horse chaise awaited them. Within ten minutes Lynn learned that Polly had not exaggerated. There was indeed a city block of servants' quarters ranging from the white painted cottages for the white servants, and beyond the low-roofed barn and stable sheds, a row of unpainted, unfloored cabins for the slaves. Sixty-two blacks, not counting the nineteen the sheriff had removed the day before, the housekeeper had informed her proudly, had already been whip-trained into obedience. Lynn shuddered at the sight of the dark, impassive faces staring at two white people they'd been told were their new owners.

She jerked nervously when Clay spoke. "My father's agreed to replace them with indentureds after I convinced him he'd need only half the number. The farm-trained English lads swarming into the port cities will work twice as efficiently as these poor wretches."

"Is that why you gave up slaving, Clay? At one time you claimed they were as necessary as pots and pans."

"I was wondering when you'd get around to reminding me of that miscalculation. We buried more than a hundred of them at sea, and most of them died of fear. Spence was right when he said I'd sleep better in another trade."

Lynn's heart seemed thistledown light as she nestled closer to her husband. "Welcome home, Clay," she murmured.

Smiling at her with his lazy, knowing smile, he deposited the reins in her hands. "Since I'm in your good graces again, I'd as soon your arms take the strain. One of mine still feels as weak as a starved bairnie's. I'm not going to risk it during the hunt either."

"What hunt?" Lynn asked warily.

"The one the governor suggested we hold before we auction the prize horses. If you promise not to reset your jaw, I'll tell you the other reason Governor Berkeley wanted us to entertain the local gentry. He said the people would all want to meet the woman who'd caused such a stir in their placid lives."

. The stir Lynn caused the day twenty neighboring owners and their wives arrived on horseback was imperceptible at first and never intentional even at its most dramatic, except for one small precautionary alteration she and Clay had dictated. During the second day of their tenancy at Trevalon, they'd toured the vast acreage with Jason Hale and discovered some alarming facts. Less than a third of the rich river-bottom land was planted in the cash crop of tobacco, the rest was nothing but a carefully tended preserve for mounted hunters. Cleared fields that had borne crops in prior years had been replanted in native grasses with occasional hedgerows of shrubs to provide a more sporting challenge. Annoyingly as Jason quickly pointed out, even the limited tobacco crop had already been ravaged during an earlier hunt when the horsemen had pursued the quarry through the fields of tender young plants.

"Your father must have expected a huge inheritance," Clay murmured dryly.

Lynn's eyes were narrowed to calculating slits as she asked the stocky man who'd managed her crops at the Rhode Island farm, "Jason, is there still time to plant more tobacco?"

"Tobacco needs five warm months to ripen, but indigo will mature in time. So will corn, beans, peas, and a crop or two of animal fodder."

"Then start plowing all the fields around the existing tobacco. No use letting the idiots destroy what's left," she ordered briskly.

Jason shook his head dismally. "Our trained bullocks haven't been returned yet, Lynn; you can bet no farmer's going to part with them until he can get his own fields plowed regardless of what the judge told them. Jem and Bram are going after some of the cows today."

"Then we'll use workhorses."

"Only two left; the sheriff sold the others right off."

"Let's try the young bullocks. Jem had some of them almost ready for rough plow work."

"They'll be too skittish if there are going to be horses and dogs around on hunt days, especially if—"

"One hunt day only, Jason," Clay interrupted brusquely, "and those damned hunters will stay away from planted areas or use the path. Christ, unless we can get enough crops in, this place will cost us the profit from everything else."

"Begging your pardon, Mr. Trevor, but if these Virginia folk are as reckless as the ones in England, they won't care whose crops they ruin."

"On Trevalon they're going to learn to be damned careful even if I have to stand guard with pistols and a sword."

"That won't be necessary, Clay," Lynn asserted thoughtfully. "We'll let Red Penny graze in that fenced pasture near the fields the young bullocks will be plowing that day.

No rider in his right mind would jump a fence that contained a bull.''

"There'll be packs of hounds, Lynn, and Red Penny is too valuable an animal to risk with a dog attack," Clay persisted.

"Dogs won't hurt that bull," Jason chuckled. "A year ago Red stomped three wild curs into the ground and sent the rest of the pack shrieking for cover. He's even less fond of horses!''

"All right, I'll tell my father to warn the hunters away from this area. In the meantime, Jason, you're to order the overseer to get those idle Negroes back to work."

The morning of the hunt dawned clear and bright with an awakened household staff already busy preparing the prehunt breakfast and the posthunt dinner to be served alfresco on the wide colonnaded terrace. For the twelve guests who'd remain overnight, there was the additional bustle of readying eight guest rooms. In their own bedroom, a large enough one but not the master suite, Lynn and Clay completed their uncomplicated dressing. At Clay's insistence they were both clad in blue—Lynn in a simple muslin dress, her tall husband in an unadorned suit and plain linen shirt.

Looking at their images in the mirror, Clay smiled with satisfaction. "We look innocent enough to attend a May dance. Are you nervous?''

"I hate being on display like a two-headed calf at a country fair; and if one more person tells me to be pleasantly vague whenever I'm asked rude questions, I'll announce that I'm as mute as Jem and retreat into permanent silence."

"I plan to tell them the truth," Clay murmured lightly, "that I was indentured to a witch and have remained happily captive ever since. Wear your amulet, Lynn, and stop frowning. Once the hounds scent the fox—''

''The six foxes that were trapped yesterday!''

''No one will care who we are or what we've done as long as the breakfast table is overflowing and the stirrup cups are refilled promptly. Time we go, wife; the governor's carriage has just pulled to a stop.''

To Lynn's relief, Bevil proved so adept a host she was required to say little to the guests whose appetites were well honed by a brisk ride. Since Bevil planned to lead the hunt, no one questioned his explanation that his son was recuperating from an injury and that his daughter-in-law had not yet had time to select a mount. Actually Lynn found the sportsmen an agreeable lot on the whole and their conversation undemanding. She was aware of an occasional eye bent on her in speculative curiosity; but her flashing smile was always returned, and her murmured comments were heeded no more than anyone else's in the general crush.

When Bevil issued the mount-up order, Lynn helped two of the women remove their excess of outer garments and accompanied them to their horses near the head of the forming line. Enjoying the first really friendly contact she'd made, she didn't hear the noise of four late arrivals grinding to a halt on the driveway until a feminine voice fluted out the words, ''Jame Clay, help me down.''

''Oh, dear,'' the woman next to Lynn sighed softly, ''I was hoping we'd be spared today. Are the Pendraths friends of yours, Mrs. Trevor?''

''My husband's,'' Lynn replied briefly, but her voice now held an ironic edge.

''Then please go help him greet them, dear. Mrs. Pendrath can be a trying guest.''

What greeted Lynn was the sight of Amelia falling into Clay's arms from the back of her horse, while Harry Pendrath helped Leona dismount more sedately. The bold-eyed stranger already standing apart was unfamiliar to

Lynn until she met his searching glance. There was no mistaking the arrogant Gordon look of appraisal or the vain self-confidence stamped on his handsome features. By the time Lynn reached the quintet of people, Clay had disentangled himself from Amelia's grasp and was reaching out determinedly toward his wife. She felt him wince when she touched his arm, but his introductions were accomplished in a voice that was pleasantly controlled.

"My wife Lynn . . . Manville Gordon, Amelia's brother."

Had not Harry stared abruptly at Lynn and whistled, the moment might have passed without attracting general notice. But Harry was too much the impulsive extrovert to keep his reactions to himself.

"My God, you look the lady, Trelynn Trevor," he exclaimed enthusiastically. "Clay, old friend, you always did have the devil's own luck when it came to women. Your wife looks positively blooming. After the rumors Gordon and I heard on the waterfront when we arrived yesterday, I expected both of you to be in seclusion. What the devil is all the flap about, and what happened to Royce Trevor?"

"My father has returned to England," Lynn murmured. "He was merely serving as caretaker until there was an heir to the estate."

"How the devil could you be his heir, Clay?" Harry demanded.

"I'm not." Clay responded with a broad smile. "My son is. After the hunt I'll introduce you to him."

"To hell with waiting that long. I want to see the gilded lad right now. Come on, Clay, just you and me."

Lynn heard the urgency in Harry's booming voice and knew that her son was just an excuse. Harry was badly rattled about something and wanted to talk privately to the old friend who'd taken care of him in earlier scrapes. One look at Amelia's studiedly indifferent expression and Lynn knew what Harry's current problem most assuredly was. Amelia had dragged her husband and brother to the hunt without mentioning the magistrate's edict. Sir Bevil, too, was aware of the oddity of Harry's request, just as he was of the mounting impatience of his other guests. Walking over to the late arrivals, he was gracious enough in his greeting; but his invitation was tinged with asperity.

"The rest of us will be starting now, but you're welcome to join us after you've breakfasted. One word of caution, though, you're to avoid the southeastern section and the area already planted in tobacco. Manville, I'd appreciate your seeing to your sister's safety and to Mrs. Burtram's. Newly plowed fields can be quite destructive of good horseflesh, and the fenced-off areas contain cattle and a bull I don't want disturbed. Trelynn, my dear, may I have a word with you in private?"

Bevil's "word" was a terse series of instructions, delivered in a strident whisper as he strode back toward his waiting horse. "Keep that damned woman away from Magistrate Norwell and Governor Berkeley. They're in the library with your grandfather. And keep her away from Clay; she almost broke his arm a few minutes ago. See them through breakfast and then pack them off on their horses so they don't bother our other guests."

That breakfast was a difficult half hour for Lynn, not because of the rude silence of the two women she knew, but because of the flattering loquacity of Manville Gordon. Ignoring Leona who tried on several occasions to capture his attention, he concentrated his remarks and questions exclusively on his hostess. Certain that he'd already been regaled with a complete history of her past, she responded with polite brevity that did nothing to discourage him. The only contribution his sister made was an abruptly avid question about Lynn's pendant.

Noting the knowledgeable gleam in Amelia's bright blue eyes, Lynn shrugged negligibly. "Just some sentimental trinket that belonged to my grandmother."

"You've become more adept at lying than you used to be," Amelia snapped.

"Don't be a bitch, sister dear," her brother scolded. "Mrs. Trevor is quite aware that she's wearing one of nature's most valuable rarities. The immortal Hortensia's good-luck charm is quite famous, Trelynn Trevor, and it looks entirely beautiful around your lovely neck."

Exasperated by the blatancy of the compliment, Lynn looked up to meet her husband's eyes glaring at her from ten feet away. Rising swiftly from her chair, she decided that she'd been the gracious hostess long enough and that her irritated husband deserved these people more than she did.

"If you'll excuse me," she murmured, "I must see to my son and my other guests."

Clay's uninjured arm encircled her waist as she attempted to pass him, and his voice was subtly commanding. "Our son is fine and our other guests are well entertained. Harry won't be going on the hunt, Amelia, so I advise you to mount up. You'll find the others still on the river run if you hurry."

It was a firm dismissal, but none of the three made any motion to rise from their chairs. "Why isn't Harry going?" Amelia demanded.

"He and I have some business to discuss."

Instantly all hint of flirtatious gallantry fled from Manville Gordon's eyes, replaced by a flinty shrewdness. "Since Harry is now my business partner, I think I'd better attend that conference, too, Trevor. Waterfront rumor has it that you'll be working in competition against us."

Lynn felt her husband's body stiffen and sensed his growing anger. Hoping to avert an argument, she interposed smoothly, "Not at all, Mr. Gordon. Very few Virginians mix indentured with slave labor, so you'll have entirely different customers in this colony. As for the northern ones, the needs are equally distinct. Slaves are illegal in Rhode Island and very unpopular in Connecticut. Besides, the more indentureds my husband exports from England, the more market you'll have for your 'products' there."

"My business with Harry has nothing to do with either trade, Gordon," Clay disclaimed stiffly. "But my wife's explanation is entirely accurate. In the meantime, you're missing the hunt."

The charming smile was firmly in place as Gordon arose with studied grace and turned toward his companions. "Come on, Amelia, you promised us a day of sport, and Leona and I mean to enjoy it. We'll leave our charming hostess to her son, and our busy host to Harry."

While Leona was entirely cooperative as she took Gordon's proffered arm with a pretty feminine simper, Amelia's face had assumed a mulish pout. "I'll remain with Harry," she stated firmly. "I insist on knowing just what business he thinks he has with Clay Trevor."

Glancing briefly at Clay's stony expression, Gordon grabbed his sister's arm and hustled her toward the horses and the Negro groom waiting patiently beside them. "Oh, no, you won't, sister mine. You're the only one who knows the trails. I don't want Leona and me to wind up in the river."

"At least, he's not a complete fool," Clay muttered a few minutes later. "Come along, wife, we're putting that damned necklace into the strongbox. We don't need a theft on top of everything else."

"Was that *everything else* your business with Harry?"

"Not mine. The magistrate was the one who summoned him here today. Lynn, do we have any laudanum? My arm feels twisted out of its socket."

"That's what you get for being the gallant cavalier."

"I was trying to warn Harry to take his damned wife home when she tumbled down on top of me."

"In that case, I'll see what I can do about your arm," Lynn giggled.

Harry was waiting for them at the foot of the stairs when they descended a half hour later with Clay's arm bound in a sling and his mouth puckered from the bitter taste of the opiate.

"What happened to your arm?" Harry demanded.

"Your wife happened. What did Norwell have to say?"

"Exactly what you did, but with official muscle. I'm to keep Amelia under restraint until she meets with 'colonial standards.' Christ, I'd have better luck with a wild cat. I need a drink, Clay, and I think you could use one too."

"Clay can't have anything stronger than tea until supper." Lynn countered sternly. "What both of you need is breakfast and a dose of common sense. The law is always on the husband's side, Harry, so a wife has no legal choice but to obey her lord and master. You could leave Leona to tend your house here, and you could take Amelia with you and put her to work. She would probably be excellent at teaching ladies' maids how to obey promptly. But I don't think you need worry about her today. What trouble can she cause in a hunt with forty disapproving neighbors watching her?"

Two hours later Lynn learned the answer to her own question in the most disagreeable of ways. Amelia did not believe that either civil or natural laws applied to her. After Clay had retreated to the bedroom when he could no longer keep his drugged eyes open, Lynn and Harry had joined the other nonhunters in the library. Seated next to her grandfather, she listened with only desultory interest to Governor Berkeley and Magistrate Norwell debate the limitations of government. The governor had just declared that in his colony, rebellion would be a hanging offense, when he was rudely interrupted by the usually discreet Jason Hale.

Bursting into the room, his broad face reddened by anger and by a bleeding cut across one cheek, Jason ignored the four men and urgently addressed Lynn.

"Three of the damn fools are pinned down in the bull's pasture, and no one can get close enough to help them. I tried to stop the idiots after they raced through the tobacco and across the field I was plowing, but all I got for my efforts was the woman's whipstock against my face. All three of the riders cleared the fence; but when they passed the bull, the damned woman struck it on its head and the beast charged. Now they're down in the drainage ditch and can't get out. At least one of the horses is injured—broken leg would be my guess—and its rider is pinned underneath.''

Lynn heard the last of Jason's excited explanation as she fled from the library. Racing through the office, she prayed that he'd had the sense to use a farm vehicle. If she had to ride horseback, Red Penny would smell on her the scent he hated and take after her. The contraption that awaited her in the porte cochère was a crude platform loader pulled by a workhorse. By the time she'd succeeded in turning it around, Harry and Jason were both aboard. Long minutes later they reached the remote pasture where forty curious workers were watching the drama from a safe distance.

For years Lynn had been smugly amused whenever she'd heard the term *maddened bull*, but today it was an accurate description of the powerful animal thundering back and forth along the top of the ditch that traversed the pasture.

"We'll have to shoot it," Harry exclaimed urgently. "We can't risk those people's lives."

"The devil we will, Harry Pendrath," Lynn hissed at him. "One of those people is your damned wife, and she was told to stay away from here. Now keep your mouth shut while I rescue my bull!"

"I'll go with you, Lynn," Jason offered quietly.

"Thanks for the offer, Jason, but you've been working with horses all day; and Red Penny would charge you just as he would the others."

It took Lynn a tense half hour to get close enough to the snorting, charging brute to talk to it in the low, soothing sounds she'd used aboard ship. Earlier when she'd tried to place herself between Red Penny and the ditch, the bull she'd known and loved since the day it was born threatened to charge her. After she'd walked to the distant center of the pasture and stood still, the confused, tiring animal gradually lost its belligerence and approached her in recognition. Taking the lead rope, she tugged gently; and the danger was over. As she walked slowly toward the gate, Red Penny followed her amicably as it had hundreds of times in other pastures. Just outside, she spoke softly to Jason.

"Post the workers across the path on each side of the barn to keep the other horses and riders away until I get Red Penny inside; and then keep everyone out of the barn except Jem. Harry, you can rescue your wife now."

Lynn was perspiring profusely by the time she'd tied the bull in its stall. God, how she wished Jem was there to help her if her bull broke loose and charged again. For the first time in the years she'd raised and trained the beloved animals, she was afraid of one of them; but Jem, she knew, wouldn't be. She'd often wondered how he communicated his orders to them without a voice; but even the nervous cows that other farmers had brought to Red Penny for breeding had obeyed Jem's silent commands and settled placidly to the ordeal. In the meantime she was the only one available to soothe the disturbed bull whose eyes were still restlessly vigilant. In three months of unsettling change, Red Penny had lost much of its gentle trust in human beings; and Lynn was no longer sure of its temper. Tired and disheveled herself, she slumped wearily down on the straw outside the stall and continued the soft talk of endearment. By the time Jem arrived, the emergency was over; the devon red was peacefully asleep.

Emerging from the barn, Lynn blinked at the sight of her husband waiting patiently on a bench. "What are you doing out of bed?" she gasped.

"No one could sleep through all that ruckus. We had to destroy the three horses," he added quietly.

"Who were the two men?"

"A pair of young fools as stupid as Amelia."

"How badly hurt was the one who'd been pinned under his horse?"

"He'll be limping for a month on a swollen ankle the size of a melon, and he'll be lucky if his father doesn't warm his backside for losing a good horse."

"Isn't the hunt over yet?"

"I don't know and I don't care. I was worried about you. Why in hell did you take such a chance?"

"Harry was threatening to shoot Red Penny."

"Well, he's threatening to shoot his wife now. She was screaming like a banshee when we shot her horse."

"Did she tell you why she disobeyed your father's orders?"

"She claimed she didn't hear him and that she'd always had the free run of Trevalon."

"Did she admit that she'd struck Jason and Red Penny?"

"She denied the accusation, naturally; but one of her former admirers had lost enough of his infatuation to contradict her. He said she'd boasted about her ability to handle the animal. Come on, Lynn, I'm taking you back to the house."

"I don't want to see Amelia; I'm not sure I wouldn't be tempted to return the favor."

"You won't mind seeing her at all this time. She has a black eye and a swollen jaw, and don't you believe her when she tells you she was injured in the fall. Harry hit her when she attacked him with her damned whipstock, and he refused to take her home until after she'd faced the crowd at dinner."

"Then there's some hope for Harry after all."

"I'd say so; he was grinning like a Roundhead sergeant when he dragged her out of that pasture. Did you know that your dress is filthy and your face is smeared with dirt?"

"You should see yourself, Mr. Trevor. You look as if you've been wallowing in mud."

"Who do you think dragged the injured lad out of two feet of dirty water and shot the horses? Harry was too busy keeping his wife from attacking me."

The first guest to greet Lynn and Clay after they'd changed their clothing from blue to green was a bluff, middle-aged man who thanked them for saving his son's life. " 'Twas a valuable lesson for him in more ways than one. In the future, I dare say, he'll be more selective in his choice of women," the man admitted candidly.

Sir Bevil, too, was forthcoming with gratitude. "I rather wish you two were staying on. You enhanced the family reputation today considerably: Clay by the way he handled the emergency, and you, my dear, by a display of courage that dazzled the two young fools who'd been dancing attendance on our disgraceful relative by marriage."

It was the younger of those infatuated fools, though, who rendered Lynn the greatest service. Only a brash seventeen and, ironically, a nephew of Magistrate Norwell, the youth seemed as unabashed by his propped-up foot as he was of his disloyalty to his former idol. As ingenuous as he was unrepentant, he blurted out the story from beginning to end. At Amelia's invitation, he and his friend had left the hunt and disregarded their host's warning because she'd told them that the bull had been raised by a witch and was no ordinary animal.

"It turned out to be as ordinary as our cranky old humpback in its dislike of horses, only it was bigger and a whole lot faster. It sure wasn't anyone's pet; it charged Mrs. Trevor the same as it had us. But she was cattle-smart enough to let that bull run itself out before she grabbed its rope."

Standing next to her grandfather, Lynn listened in grim silence until Ephraim shook her arm. "You should be smiling, Trelynn. As foolish as that young man was to risk his horse, he's done you a tremendous favor. Nothing Amelia Pendrath can ever say about you in the future will reverse the impression his testimony made. You've just been cleared of the suspicion of witchcraft by the most difficult jury in the world—the ordinary citizenry."

The truth of Ephraim's shrewd observation was quickly

borne out as Magistrate Norwell raised his wine cup in a toast to his courageous young hostess, and the smiling guests responded with prompt flattery. As the afternoon waned, Lynn found herself more and more an accepted member of the James County gentry, both by the larger crowd that departed just before sunset and by the fewer people who remained as overnight guests. Oddly enough some of the goodwill overflowed to include Harry Pendrath, mainly, Ephraim noted to Lynn in whispered confidence, because he'd had the good sense to chastise his wayward wife. Lynn giggled in happy response; she'd just seen her husband pointedly rebuff Amelia's attempt to gain his support. Like everyone else, his sympathies were with Harry, not with an undisciplined thirty-one-year-old whose waning beauty no longer compensated for her heedless malice.

He wasn't, however, as gallant to his own wife as Lynn had hoped. Although he hovered close to her side most of the evening and announced an early retirement for the pair of them soon after an informal ten o'clock supper in the dining room, his manner was more reflective of guard duty than adoration.

"I'll be glad to leave this place behind us," he announced bluntly as she helped him ease his coat from his injured shoulder. "Any more heroics on your part, and you'll be the target of every randy Virginia male for miles around."

"Manville Gordon was the only jack-a-dandy here today, and he's as obnoxious as his sister," Lynn retorted tartly.

"He wasn't the only one ogling you as if it were open season," Clay muttered. "You were too busy chattering with the women to notice their husbands. My God, if we stayed here, we'd never get a damn bit of work done; and we'd be spending a fortune on senseless entertainment. I don't want our son to grow up as useless as those idiot pups I dragged out of the ditch."

"I remember when our son's unarmed, idiot father once

challenged Rad Pollock to a fight," Lynn murmured. "I hope Charles Ephraim inherits at least some of that idiocy."

"More likely, he'll inherit it from you. You still go charging into a damned bullpen as if you were guaranteed a charmed life."

Smiling with a gamin confidence she'd never felt before, Lynn climbed into bed beside her grumpy husband. "I think I must have been. How else would I have convinced a freebooting adventurer into becoming a staid husband?"

"Not so damned staid as you think, witchwife," he growled into her ear before his lips found a more purposeful employment. She was right, he admitted guardedly to himself before the onslaught of passion obliterated his ability to think coherently. He'd never intended to be trapped by any woman; he'd enjoyed the freedom of not having to account to anyone for his actions. But now he couldn't imagine being content without her sharp wit to prod him, and her muscular body to respond to his with her unrestrained passion. Clay relaxed into blissful expectancy as he caressed her sleek body and felt her strong, gentle hands caress him in return.

EPILOGUE

The Honorable Hortensia Trelynn Penley's letter to her surviving granddaughter was opened the day following the hunt after the overnight guests had departed, their satisfaction with their new neighbors evident. Not only had Sir Bevil Trevor proved a more charming host than his displaced cousin, he hadn't tried to cheat them on the prices of the horses they'd come to buy. As an added mark of goodwill, he'd promised them first choice of Trevalon's trained slaves once their indentured replacements arrived from England. Raw Negroes were the very devil to train; and deceitful cheat though he'd turned out to be, Royce Trevor had known how to turn the Africans into effective colonial servants.

Young Mrs. Trevor, too, had turned out to be a pleasant contrast to their expectations; she certainly wasn't the gauche rustic the unmannered Pendrath woman had described. She and her handsome husband would be lively additions to the winter party season. This tentative acceptance as a social equal was what delayed Lynn's arrival in the library. Unlike their husbands who were impatient to be underway, the hunt ladies dawdled over their departure, chatting busily with their hostess even as they mounted their horses. Lynn remained standing on the verandah, smiling inanely as she watched the colorful procession move down the driveway and into the concealment of the oak grove. Vowing never to acquire a passion for following a terrified fox across a carefully tended countryside, she wondered if she'd ever be able to endure even one more winter in the company of people whose lives seemed dedicated to little more than a pursuit of pleasure.

Arriving in the library at the same time as her husband who looked equally irritated with the tedium of hosting, Lynn accepted the thick letter Sir Bevil handed her. Her only thought as she broke the ornate seal was the fervent hope that her dead grandmother's final gamble in a long life of wagering against the odds would hold no new surprises. Unfolding the parchment self-consciously under the scrutiny of the three men whose interest was keener than hers, Lynn burst into laughter. None of the dramatically scrawled notes inside was addressed to her, and all three were written on the same page under the general directive "To be read aloud so that my granddaughter will know she hasn't been forgotten."

The first brief paragraph was addressed to Charles Clayton Trevor and was a pithy comment. "If you've not had the sense to appreciate Trelynn by this time, you'll deserve the devilment she'll cause you. But I'm wagering that despite your pretty Devon looks, you've enough of your father's Cornish blood to know true from false."

In her message to Sir Bevil, Hortensia had been even more admonishing. "Don't spoil this grandson, Bevil; you've not raised your sons capably enough to be an expert. Your oldest is hag-ridden without the gumption to silence the Gordon shrew he married, your second is a lazy incompetent, and Charles Clay needs taming. I want this new lad to be as strong and resilient as his mother. You're not to entertain any thought of resurrecting the old Trelynn title either. I'll wager that the savage new world you're in will mold men who'll make our dying breed of useless aristocrats seem as obsolete as the drafty castles that mutilate the English countryside.''

The letter to Ephraim Penley was more humorously pungent but just as explicit. ''The next time you see my lawyer, John Coleman, remind him that he owes me a hundred pounds. Like all benighted Englishmen, he believed that a bold, bright woman who lacked substantial fortune would never snag a husband at all, much less an elusive, handsome rogue who feels safer in the company of married women. Poor John much prefers spineless females who simper prettily and tend to their embroidery. I doubt our granddaughter will ever waste her time with either such nonsense. 'Tis much more likely the black-haired, impudent minx will have driven more than one idiot man to the violence of declaring her in league with Old Nick himself—a union I've often considered myself whenever masculine stupidity overwhelmed me. Keep watch over her, Ephraim dear, until she's learned to play the game as I have with a gambler's humor instead of anger.''

When Ephraim finished the reading, Lynn was the only one who laughed. She'd been worried about the wrong grandmother! It hadn't been Royce's mother who'd been in league with the devil; it'd been the daring Hortensia who'd defied tradition and taboos all of her headstrong life.

While the two old men were lost somewhere in their long-buried memories of a woman who'd bedeviled both of them with her flamboyant spirit, Clay was concentrating somberly on his own wife. How could he have fallen so completely in love with a dark-haired witch woman that he was jealous of every other man who fell beneath her spell? He knew the reason, of course, when she grinned at him, her upswept eyes gleaming with amusement and her voice rippling with humor. ''If we ever have a daughter, my elusive, handsome rogue, 'twill be your duty to make certain she learns embroidery.''

BY CASEY STUART

ZEBRA BOOKS
KENSINGTON PUBLISHING CORP.

ZEBRA BOOKS

are published by

KENSINGTON PUBLISHING CORP.
475 Park Avenue South
New York, N.Y. 10016

To my husband for his patience, my family for their encouragement, and my friend Cindy for her help.

Virginia, beautiful Virginia
Land of rolling hills and sandy coastline
Land of gentle people and gentler times gone by
Now scarred by the blood of men
Whose martyred bodies fill your soil
Devoted sons called traitors, rebels
But not so—never so
Patriots, brave and true every one
Called to the aid of their homeland
Brother against brother—father against son
While every mother, every wife
Dies a little with each passing day
Caught in the crosswinds of time

Prologue

"The Virginia Confederates, generations ahead of their time, had stumbled onto one of the secrets of ultramodern war. They invented a resistance movement for occupied territory—invented it and then supported it with a great deal of vigor and ingenuity, so that while the Northerners occupied a great deal of Virginia they could hardly be said to have conquered any of it."

Bruce Catton

The Virginia Confederate that Bruce Catton speaks of had many labels; guerrilla, partisan, irregular, ranger, but no matter what he was called, he played a very important role. Throughout the war the guerrillas' movements gave Union officers their greatest embarrassment. The Federals outnumbered the Confederates from the start, but because they used so much manpower to keep the guerrillas out of their hair, they were never able to take advantage of their numbers.

Virginia was the last state to leave the Union, yet because of her geographical location it became the major battleground of the Civil War. No state contributed more to the Confederacy or suffered more. Seventeen thousand sons of Virginia perished.

December 1862

Chapter One

High in the foggy darkness of Cedar Mountain flashed the blue-light signal sending its ominous message of doom to some unsuspecting troops below.

The young Union lieutenant drew deeply on his long, thin cigar as he intercepted the message sent by a Confederate unit on the opposite ridge. The message seemed clear enough, but for some reason he felt uneasy.

His companion watched him silently, wondering what powers his friend had that put him in the right place at the right time. He shivered as he noticed the lieutenant's strange blue eyes glowing in the darkness and remembered rumors going around camp that Marc Riordan was a disciple of the devil. Well, he thought, no matter. Before Marc Riordan had joined the regiment the Rebs had been making a laughing stock of them. Now the tables were turning. Union supply trains were getting through again and Riordan was able to move through the Rebel lines with ease. The men feared yet respected him since he would never ask anyone to do anything he wouldn't do himself. They would follow him anyplace as he rode his big black stallion always at the head of the trouble.

The war was going badly for the North. They had

been turned back at Manassas and then Stonewall Jackson had smashed their attempt to reach Richmond. Jackson's sweep through the Valley had shattered McClellan's plans and the city of Washington feared for its safety. Morale had been terrible in the troops, but since Riordan had joined the New York 5th, the men were gaining back their pride.

"Something wrong, Dave?"

"Sorry, sir, I guess I was daydreaming. What do the signals say?"

"Jubal Early is heading for Culpeper tonight leaving a small group here with very little ammunition to wait for a supply train—a supply train being escorted by Fitzgerald's Raiders!"

"Fitzgerald's Raiders! That train must be mighty damned important to the Rebs."

Marc rubbed his beard in thought. "Early's departure must be a ruse to throw us off. I figure they are trying to get food and ammo here before the snows isolate the troops. Their supplies are probably dangerously low or they wouldn't use a unit like Fitzgerald's. I'm going to enjoy meeting that bastard in battle, Dave. He has caused us trouble long enough."

Dave smiled wryly, remembering the times this group of raiders had eluded them. "You gotta admit, lieutenant, Fitzgerald is a smart one. He's slipped out of our hands more than once."

"Yeah, he's smart all right, but if Slegle would let us fight these guerrillas with their own methods this war might go our way every now and then."

"You don't understand Slegle, lieutenant. All he

12

knows is you got to go by the book or it's not proper war."

"Proper war, hell!" answered Marc Riordan angrily. "Take a deep breath, Dave, smell the stench of death? It has no favorites. It takes young and old, Rebel and Yankee. When it's over what has been accomplished?"

Dave was stunned. This was the first time Riordan had expressed his deep hatred for war and it wasn't in keeping with the man they called the devil.

Dave had joined the army for the glory, but he hadn't found much. Under General Refus Slegle's command the only thing he had been doing was ravaging the fields and homes of the Shenandoah Valley. It made Dave sick to see country as pretty as this part of Virginia being stripped. It must really be hard for Marc Riordan to watch it being destroyed—this had been his home at one time. No wonder he had applied for a transfer. Dave was just thankful Riordan has been with them even for a short time. It was a damned shame Slegle couldn't see what a valuable man he was. The lieutenant and his commander were constantly arguing and if it hadn't been that Marc had an influential family Slegle would probably have had him in prison by now.

A bone-chilling gust of wind whistled through the trees. The horses stamped restlessly, snorting mist from their nostrils. Marc Riordan looked at the campfires dotting the hillside, longing for the warmth of his own.

"Let's get back to camp, Dave. I have a plan that might catch us Morgan Fitzgerald." Marc didn't mentioned the persistent unease he felt about the signal he had intercepted. No matter what the odds, if there was a chance to put the notorious Rebel leader out of commission he would take it.

Quietly through the night they threaded their way around the enemy camps. By scaling a path up the face of a ragged mountain they finally made their way into their own camp.

Slegle was waiting beside his fire for their report. Much to Marc's surprise he agreed to go along with the plan to capture the Rebel supply train. Without taking the time to rest or eat they were on their way with fresh troops.

Topping the mountain range, Riordan spied the train of twenty or more cars. It advanced slowly, as if in another time away from war. He could see several guards riding at the rear of the train and two more with shotguns riding the last car. He signaled to his own men and they fell in behind him single file on a narrow path toward the unsuspecting Rebels. Slowly they rode into the open, playing for time. Dawn was just beginning to meet the morning haze and nothing was distinguishable in the shadows.

The Rebel guards watched the approaching column, never suspecting Yankees would be so brazen as to ride right into them. Each step before the Yankees were recognized would be a great advantage when the charge came. For a few more seconds no one stirred among the Rebs. Then a young soldier on the train recognized the blue uniform.

"Yankees! Yankees!" he shouted frantically.

Riordan's troops let loose, blazing away with their revolvers as they pounced on the enemy. Returning shots from the boxcar and flat bed car were no match for the Yankees on horseback. The train was quickly brought to a halt. The guards were dead and the only remaining force was in the car. Several of the men circled the car firing at the openings until there was silence from within.

Riordan surveyed the scene around him. Several Rebs lay on the ground wounded or dead. One of his own men was dead, lying at the feet of his horse.

Riordan directed Dave to take a few men to check out the train for Fitzgerald while the rest began unloading supplies and weapons. That uneasy feeling still haunted him. Why would Fitzgerald give up so easily? His style was usually to hit and run.

Marc ordered all prisoners removed from the train and prepared to put the torch to it.

Suddenly came un unexpected alarm. One of the lookouts swept in at full speed and reported a heavy column of cavalry coming. "It's Fitzgerald's Raiders, sir. They're coming fast," yelled the young boy, panic showing in his eyes.

Riordan tried vainly to form his men, but there was no chance. They were scattered all over the train foraging for food and weapons. The riders approached two hundred yards off, advancing rapidly. He could see the familiar buckskin-clad figure of Morgan Fitzgerald leading the riders and cursed himself for not having recognized the trap sooner.

He ordered his men to retreat, knowing it would be suicide to try to hold off this charging force. With the heavy firing at their backs they headed for the trees to the left. Riordan whirled and turned on the advancing force, hoping to give his men a chance. He suddenly felt a burning sensation in the fleshy part of his arm. Damn, he'd been hit. The onslaught was overwhelming and he followed his retreating men to the cover of Cedar Mountain.

For the first time since he had been in operation, Riordan felt defeated. "How did I let that bastard outsmart me?" he grumbled bitterly. Three of his men had been injured and two killed and he felt responsible.

Riordan knew he had been set up, but if Slegle knew he'd never give them another chance to fight the raiders on their own terms. He'd learned an expensive lesson this time, but Morgan Fitzgerald wouldn't outsmart him again.

On March 10th Marc Riordan sat at the general's table and read an account of Mosby's capture of General Stoughton. He slammed his fist on the table startling those around him. "Incompetents! The whole United States Army is incompetent!"

"You're talking treason, lieutenant. I would watch what I way," sneered General Slegle.

"Not treason, sir. Just shame. Is the Confederate army the only one with brains in this war? How can we continue to let them make fools of us and not do something about it? First Stuart rides circles around us and now this. Just listen to this account.

'On the dark and rainy night of March 8th, John S. Mosby with a party of twenty-nine men rode into Fairfax at two o'clock in the morning. They had little difficulty seizing the pickets as they approached the village. Mosby went to the headquarters of General Stoughton, climbed the stairs to the second floor bedroom, entered and gave

the general a hefty whack on the rump bringing
the sleeper out of bed in a belligerent state of
mind. Mosby asked the half-asleep general, "Did
you ever hear of John S. Mosby?" "Certainly,"
replied the general. "Have you captured him?"
"No," replied Mosby. "He has captured you." '

"Now you tell me we're not dealing with idiots! This
article even states that Mosby and Fitzgerald had been
spotted in Fairfax several days before this incident.
Damn it, why can't you see that we must do
something?"

"And of course, your idea of using guerrilla warfare
is what you are suggesting."

"Yes, general, we could put a group together in less
than a week. They could be used for reconnaissance
and for hit and run fighting against these partisans.
We have to use more troops and be better organized."

"Forget it, Riordan! We're trying to outlaw this type
of fighting. I certainly will not condone it. Fitzgerald
and Mosby are murdering horsethieves and we'll not
follow suit!"

"You can say what you want, sir, but I say Mosby
and Fitzgerald are brilliant tactical officers. Anyone
who can continually outsmart the whole United States
Army has to be pretty clever. Guerrilla warfare is a
highly effective tactic. They disrupt supply and
communication lines, nullifying our advantage of
having more men and supplies."

The general's teeth clamped down on his cigar.
"Seems to me you're mighty fond of these fellows,
lieutenant. You're lucky your transfer has already

17

gone through or I would consider having you courtmartialed for treason."

"Well, that makes both of us lucky, because I don't think you'd want the country to know what I have to say about you." Marc Riordan left the tent before General Slegle realized what he had said.

"Riordan! Come back here! Damn you! I'll see you punished for insubordination yet!"

Marc Riordan smiled to himself as he headed for his tent. He had planned to lead a raiding party that went out this morning, but Slegle insisted he stay for the staff meeting. Before the men left, Riordan gave them explicit instructions for guarding the train they were using as a trap for the Rebs. If Slegle knew he had given these instructions he would probably hang him, but Marc was sure the train was a target for destruction. If the Rebels could set a simple trap like this and make it work, so could he. Perhaps by nightfall they would have Morgan Fitzgerald behind bars. Then he would concentrate on Mosby.

Strange, he thought, how Fitzgerald and Mosby resemble each other. Both were small in stature, but they sure made up for it in guts. He laughed aloud remembering some of the pranks he and John Mosby had pulled as boys. It was strange thinking of John as his enemy. He'd rather remember the fishing they did together and how John's mom always packed them fried chicken and her specialty, ginger cookies. Those were times never to be forgotten, Marc thought, but now his fervent hope was to put his friend Mosby out of commission before someone killed him. That task sure hadn't proved easy. Mosby was as elusive as water in a stream.

Chapter Two

The Rebel soldier knelt and pressing his ear to the ground felt the vibration of approaching horses. His buckskin-clad companion paced as the rest of the soldiers pried up a section of track of the B & O railroad.

"They're not far off, Morgan. We better clear out."

"How many do you think?"

The soldier listened for a moment. "Forty or fifty, I'd say."

Morgan mounted and shouted to the men. "Set fire to those rails, boys, then let's get out of here."

The ties were stacked with the rails on top and the fire started. Morgan's horse pranced nervously as the blaze crackled. "When you finish, follow the creek bed so they can't trail you. We'll meet at Widow Garret's house."

The young soldier at Morgan's side looked at his sister apprehensively. She had successfully carried off this charade for six months or more, but how long could it last? The Yankees were determined to put a stop to partisan groups and Fitzgerald's Raiders were the target at the moment.

He thought back to a time when his lovely sister wore hoop skirts, had long curls, and had every eligible bachelor in the county at their door. Now she dressed in buckskins and wore her long auburn hair tucked up under a wide brimmed hat. God, will things ever go back to the way they were, he wondered. He watched the alert expression on Morgan's face as she called out instructions to the men who so faithfully followed her every command. "I hear that fellow Riordan has his troops looking for us, Morgan. They say he's a devil and can track anything that moves."

"They're all devils, Michael. Every damned blue-bellied one of them."

"You're right, Morgan, but this one seems very anxious to capture the notorious Morgan Fitzgerald and her band of partisans. Riordan is all the men talk about in camp. You know he captured Harry Gilmor a month or so ago and Lige White was wounded by his troops in Leesburg just last week. I have an uneasy feeling about this Yankee. I'm sure he's going to play a very important role in our lives."

Morgan knew her brother had premonitions, but she tried to make light of this one. "Don't go soft, little brother. This Yankee is no different than the rest. He's just been luckier. Didn't we make him look the fool at Cedar Mountain? I'm sure I put a bullet in him when he pulled that fool stunt of turning back at us."

"It was a brave thing to do, Morgan. He was only trying to give his men a chance to get away."

"I know, Michael. I admire the man for his bravery, too, but he's a Yankee. Stuart is depending on us to put a stop to the rail traffic along the B & O. The Yankees are shipping troops in from Ohio and we are going to bring it to a halt. Mosby is blasting the rail bridge near Point of Rocks and we're responsible for closing this portion."

"I fully understand what we're doing, Morgan and I'm not going soft, as you so bluntly put it. I just think a little caution would be in order."

Morgan realized she had hurt her brother's feelings. "You're right, Michael. We'll lie low for a while after we complete our work here. Didn't I agree that we wouldn't chance ransacking this train, even though we could certainly use the supplies? If Stuart finds out there were food and weapons aboard I am afraid he won't agree with your idea."

"If Jeb realized the danger you're in I'm certain he would agree with me."

Morgan laughed. "You and Jeb are like mother-hens, but I love you both for it."

"Somebody has to think about your safety. You certainly don't."

The eerie sound of a train whistle in the distance startled the big beige horse Morgan sat upon. "Easy girl, you've heard that sound before," she said as she gentled the horse. "The men are finished and on their way, Michael. Let's get to that ridge and watch."

The rumble deepened and the earth began to tremble. In a few moments the train rolled into view, an engine pulling seven cars loaded with supplies and replacements for the Federal troops along the Rappahannock. The locomotive rumbled past the two on the hill. Another screeching blast from the whistle cut through the countryside.

Morgan smiled at her brother. "They won't see the fires below until it's too late."

The train began moving down-grade toward the woods. Morgan continued to watch, fascinated by the

21

roaring giant which would soon be a mass of debris.

Without warning the locomotive swerved sharply and the entire train began to derail, each car going its own way as if in slow motion and finally coming to a halt in jumbled confusion. Morgan stayed watching, motionless, as flames began to rise from the heap of iron. Suddenly a spurt of smoke burst from the trees behind them and like ants, men began pouring out of the underbrush.

"Ride!" she cried, as she spurred her horse to a wild fury. Her brother was just a few lengths behind with the Yankees galloping in hard pursuit. Morgan bent over the neck of her mare, cursing herself for having lingered and placing them in this danger. Bullets whizzed past her as she turned to check on Michael. She saw him slumped against the neck of his horse with the Yankees gathered around him like vultures.

She quickly galloped back, her Colt revolver rapidly firing into the group, killing two Yankees before being subdued by the others.

Struggling angrily against the Yankee who held her arms pinned, she gasped, "Just let me see to my companion. You needn't fear I'll run."

Every man in the group was struck dumb by the sound of her voice. "Good God, we got us a female here, boys!"

Michael moaned and tried to sit up, blood running down the side of his face from a head wound. "Morgan, where are you?"

Morgan yanked away from the soldier and knelt beside her brother. "I'm right here, Michael. Just lie quietly until I get help."

Morgan looked up pleadingly at the soldiers standing around her. "Isn't there a doctor or medic among you?"

"He's not going to need a doctor, lady, just a hole dug," replied one of the soldiers.

"Shut up, private," commanded a young corporal. He turned his attention to Morgan. "It's my duty to take you to Lieutenant Riordan, ma'am. I'm sure the young man will receive help as soon as the rest of my men arrive. Now, please mount up quickly. We're after bigger fish around here."

"I'm sorry, corporal, but I must insist you bring a wagon for my friend."

The men snickered at the demands this red-haired woman had the nerve to make. The corporal looked flustered. "Lady, you're in no position to be insisting on anything. I don't know what you're doing with these Rebs, but I would say you're in serious trouble. Now, I must insist you mount up!"

Morgan stood firm, her green eyes flashing angrily. "You may shoot me on the spot, but I will not move until a wagon is brought for this soldier!"

"Who the hell do you think you are, lady?" the bewildered corporal demanded.

"I am Captain Morgan Fitzgerald and I'm sure your Lieutenant Riordan would prefer to have me alive. Now, do we move my friend my way, or will you shoot me before your lieutenant questions me?"

No one said a word for a moment. "You . . . you're Morgan Fitzgerald?" the young officer stuttered. "The buckskins and matching horse . . . I'll be damned! Morgan Fitzgerald is a woman. Wait till Riordan hears this."

The corporal hurriedly sent for a wagon. When her brother was placed on a stretcher she mounted her horse and rode beside the corporal.

Word had quickly gone through camp that Morgan Fitzgerald had been captured, but not that she was a woman. Everyone gathered as the small group approached.

Lieutenant Marcus Riordan sat at a makeshift table under a big oak tree with his replacement and Lieutenant-General Refus Slegle. After several grueling hours of discussion, the men had not been able to come up with a solution for stopping the Rebel guerrillas who harassed the Federal troops. Neither officer seemed to agree with Riordan's method.

Slegle nervously twirled his handle-bar mustache as he spoke. "The guerrillas are a murdering bunch of horse-thieves, Riordan. I can't understand wanting to lower ourselves to that level. It's no wonder you're being transferred out of this unit."

Riordan angrily stood up. "May I remind you, sir, I asked to be transferred out of this unit. As long as you are in command, the unit will continue to be sitting ducks for every partisan group that comes along."

Slegle's face reddened angrily. "You might be friends with McClellan and have important family connections, but I suggest you watch your mouth, lieutenant. I will tolerate only so much. Besides, you forget the men have captured Morgan Fitzgerald and will bring him here soon. That blows a hole in your theory, doesn't it?"

"I understand Fitzgerald escaped and only returned for a wounded companion."

Before Slegle could reply, a young soldier rushed over announcing that the prisoner had arrived. Slegle and the new lieutenant left to watch the prisoner being escorted into camp, but Marc stayed behind.

Morgan rode tall and proud in her saddle, ignoring jeers from the Yankees. At the moment her only concern was getting medical attention for her brother. She didn't doubt for a minute that she could escape these stupid Yankees when the time was right.

The young corporal dismounted and saluted smartly. "Sir, Corporal Russell reporting with prisoner Morgan Fitzgerald."

Slegle stared at the innocent looking girl sitting on the horse in front of him, her hat hanging down her back exposing her long, auburn hair.

"Corporal, if this is your idea of a joke, it's a very poor one."

Russell flushed. "No, sir, this is no joke. This girl is Morgan Fitzgerald. The wounded soldier brought in with her called her Morgan. Look at the buckskins, the beige horse with the black mane and tail! Why, we caught her red-handed derailing the train."

Slegle was so angry he could hardly speak. "You can't tell me this—this snip of a girl has been running us in circles!"

Morgan saluted and smiled sweetly. "It's wasn't difficult, general. A child could have done the same."

Marc Riordan leaned back against the oak, watching the girl make a fool of Slegle. He smiled appreciatively, but was shocked himself that the notorious Rebel raider was a girl. She couldn't be more than seventeen or eighteen, he thought, yet she had outsmarted him more than once.

Morgan knew she should have kept her mouth shut, but it was too tempting to make this pompous ass who called himself an officer look the fool. While he ranted that she could not be who she claimed, she glanced around the camp, taking quick mental notes of pickets and tents and possible escape routes. Suddenly her eyes locked with the cold blue eyes of a dark-haired lieutenant leaning casually against a tree. Morgan's heart skipped a beat and she found it difficult to look away. He smiled rakishly and nodded and she knew without a doubt he was the one her brother had called the devil. She wondered why he wasn't in on the questioning since he had pursued her for so long.

"Get off that horse, lady," yelled the red-faced general. "We are going to get to the bottom of this."

Morgan gracefully slid out of her saddle and nonchalantly brushed the dust from her buckskins. She straightened and looked Slegle directly in the eye. "May I remind you, sir, that I hold the rank of captain and I expect to be treated as you would any officer held prisoner."

Slegle looked as if he would burst. "Let me tell you something, lady! If you are who you claim to be, you forfeit every right of an officer by being a guerrilla fighter, and I shall take great delight in putting a rope around your pretty neck!"

Morgan inwardly cringed at the venom in his words, but she forced a smile. "If you choose to hang me, sir, prepare yourself for the same fate, for my men are close by." Morgan lied, but she hoped there might be

26

some truth in what she said. She was sure they would be looking for her and Michael by now.

"You are an impudent young lady, whoever you are. Perhaps you could be the murdering Fitzgerald."

Before Morgan could reply, he turned his back on her and walked away. "Lock her up, corporal. I will decide what's to be done with her later."

Marc Riordan watched the girl being led to the barred wagon. The men standing around began shouting obscene remarks, and to Marc's surprise, the color rose in the girl's cheeks. She tilted her chin defiantly and proudly walked past the taunting crowd. Riordan turned to the young soldier who had been standing beside him. "What do you think, Dave? Could she be Morgan Fitzgerald?"

"Damned if I know. I guess anything is possible. She does ride that big beige horse and wear buckskins. And, people talk about how small Fitzgerald is."

Marc ran his hand through his dark wavy hair. "See what you can find out from the wounded man who was brought in with her."

As Dave Gibbs headed for the hospital tent, Marc wondered how the soldier would fare under the new lieutenant. He and Dave had been good friends from the first, probably because they were both loners and respected each other's moods. This new replacement was ambitious and Marc knew the men would have a hard time under him. His thoughts were interrupted by the laughing and jeering around the jail wagon. He hesitated a moment then headed toward the group, suddenly feeling very angry. "Everyone of you, get back to your duties! The next man I see hanging

27

around this wagon is going on report."

"Aw, come on, lieutenant. We're just having a good time," protested one of the men.

"You heard me, stay away from this wagon!"

The men slowly started moving away. Marc turned back to the wagon and his ice blue eyes clashed with smiling green ones.

"Well, Lieutenant Riordan, we finally meet. I must admit I thought it would be under different circumstances. You know, I almost had you at Cedar Mountain."

Marc couldn't help smiling. "So, you really are Morgan Fitzgerald," he said absent-mindedly rubbing his wounded arm.

"I didn't think I would have to convince you."

"I'm surprised though, after following you for the last six months, I thought I knew everything about you."

The green eyes twinkled mischievously. "Obviously not everything, lieutenant."

"No, it seems not," Marc said, noticing the freckles across the bridge of her lovely nose. He fought the urge to reach out and touch her. "Do you need anything?" he quickly asked.

Morgan waved a casual hand toward the straw-strewn wagon. "I have all the comforts of home. What more could I ask for?"

"I won't be here tomorrow, but I will see that Corporal Gibbs checks on you. Just ask him for anything you need."

"I'm curious, lieutenant. The way you have pursued me for the past six months, I thought it was your aim in life to capture me, yet you don't seem to have anything to do with it."

"You're right about it being my aim to capture you. If the guerrilla warfare could be stopped this bloody war would quickly come to an end. As for being in on your capture, I transferred out of this unit effective tomorrow. My replacement is in charge now. Besides, there is very little glory in the fact that you gave yourself up."

"What difference does it make how you got me? I'm out of commission."

"Yes, but are your men out of commission?"

Morgan laughed. "What do you think, lieutenant?"

"I think if you used that pretty head of yours you would realize that you could preserve a few lives."

Morgan watched him walk angrily away. What a strange man, she thought. He certainly didn't seem to be the threat she had expected. Now, that arrogant bastard Slegle, was a different story. She would like to run him through.

Marc met up with Dave as he approached his tent. "Well, she's Morgan Fitzgerald. Doc gave the Reb morphine and he's talking out of his head. The general heard enough to believe her story, particularly when he found out the injured soldier is her brother."

Marc stopped walking. "I'll be damned. That's why she gave herself up."

"Yeah, the corporal said she demanded a wagon brought out for him or they could shoot her on the spot. Spunky little lady, ain't she?"

Marc rubbed his arm again. "You could call it that."

"Her brother mentioned something about Ashby being killed and Morgan taking over his men. What do you think? Could he be talking about Turner Ashby?"

"It's possible. Morgan Fitzgerald wasn't heard of until after Ashby's death."

Dave stopped when they reached the tent. "Why don't you forget about leaving, sir? It's going to be interesting around here for awhile."

"Sorry, Dave, but I can't stomach the way Slegle operates. If I stayed I'd end up doing something to cost me my commission. Besides, General McClellan has offered me a command in his outfit and that will be more to my liking. I'll be working out of the Fairfax area and Mosby will be my objective."

"You'll get him if anyone can. I never saw anyone track like you, Marc. You know, them Rebs and half of your own men think you're a disciple of the devil."

Marc laughed with genuine amusement. "I grew up in this part of Virginia, Dave. I rode and played with Mosby as a boy, even went to the same college. It's no diabolical talent."

"Well, it doesn't hurt to let them think they're facing more than a mere man."

"Maybe not, Dave. Just so it doesn't cause me more trouble than the reputation is worth. Listen, my friend, why don't you come by and have a farewell drink with me this evening?"

Dave slapped him on the back. "Be glad to, lieutenant. I'll even bring the bottle."

Marc entered his tent and found his replacement sitting behind his desk. "Make yourself comfortable, lieutenant," he said sarcastically.

"I didn't see any sense in delaying things, Riordan. I hear you're anxious to be on your way, so you're free to leave anytime."

"You're right, Hawthorne, I am anxious to leave and I'll be on my way in the morning. In the meantime, I suggest you leave. This is still my tent."

Hawthorne nonchalantly stood and brushed off his jacket. "I was leaving anyway. I just came by to tell you General Slegle has decided, after hearing the wounded soldier's story, that the woman held prisoner is Morgan Fitzgerald. He wants an example made of her. Perhaps it will make the rest of those cut-throats think twice."

"What are you talking about, Hawthorne?" Marc asked impatiently.

"The woman is to be hung at sunrise."

Marc was stunned. Smiling green eyes danced across his mind. He quickly masked his feelings. "She's your problem, Hawthorne. I could care less what you choose to do with her."

"Glad you agree, Riordan. Stay around in the morning and enjoy it. I've suggested that we hang her from the big oak on the hill where the Rebels can see our handiwork. When I'm through in this territory they'll wish they never heard of Edward Hawthorne."

"Don't be too anxious to earn your reputation by hanging people. It's liable to backfire on you. The Rebs believe in an eye for an eye."

"You haven't worried about that. I hear you're known as the devil."

Marc laughed. "Only because I have a sixth sense

about this part of the country and they think it's unnatural."

"Well, Lieutenant Riordan, I must see that my things are unpacked properly. We must talk again sometime. Good luck on your new assignment."

"Yeah, same to you," Marc replied absently. When Hawthorne left he collapsed on his bunk feeling very angry and frustrated. He pulled a bottle from his saddle bag and tossed down several swallows. "Damn war! It's bad enough fighting against friends and family, but now we're going to start hanging women." He pulled off his boots and laid back on his bunk. Morgan's freckled face appeared, her green eyes twinkling at him. He dozed off, wondering what it would be like to run his fingers through her long, silky hair.

"Lieutenant, wake up," Dave said shaking Marc roughly. "What kind of a party can we have with you asleep?"

Marc stretched and tried to clear the cobwebs from his brain, reaching for the bottle at his side at the same time.

"You're missing all the excitement, Marc. The men say Slegle is going to turn the prisoner over to them for a little fun and games tonight. The camp is in a real party mood," Dave said watching Marc's face for his reaction.

Marc swung his feet to the floor, suddenly wide awake. "You can't be serious."

"I'm very serious. Slegle is adamant. It doesn't make any difference that he is going to hang the girl, he wants to see her suffer before she dies."

"I know most of the men have been without a woman for too long, but to do this . . . it's outrageous. How do you feel about what they plan, Dave?"

Dave smiled, relieved that Marc hadn't approved of the situation. "Oh, I wouldn't mind having an evening with the young lady, but I sure won't participate in what they're planning. I have a sister her age and I'd kill anyone who touched her."

"I'm glad to hear you say that, Dave." Marc leaned back and took another swig from the bottle. "We have to do something. Will you help me?"

"Of course, Marc. You got a plan?"

"I'll tell Slegle I've decided to leave this evening. I'll say my goodbyes and then disappear, picking up the Rebel's horse on my way out. You give her guards the rest of this liquor. When they're good and drunk, get the key to the wagon and get her out. I'll meet you at the big oak on the hill and take it from there."

"Damn, Marc, we'll be hung with her if this doesn't work."

"It will work, Dave. Just be sure those guards have plenty to drink."

"What if they take her out of the wagon before I get to her?"

"That's a chance we'll have to take. I don't know any other way."

"What will you do with her when you get her away from here?"

"I'll take her to Washington. She will be held in prison there until the war is over. At least she'll have a chance at some life that way."

Dave laughed. "Can't you just see Slegle's face when

he finds out his prisoner has disappeared?"

Marc grinned. "Serves the bastard right."

Chapter Three

The guards needed little encouragement to drink. Most of the outfit was already drunk and anticipating their pleasure with Morgan Fitzgerald so the jail-wagon guards were anxious to join in.

Dave quietly unlocked the wagon and helped Morgan out. Surprisingly, the only hitch to the plan was Morgan herself. She flatly refused to leave without her brother. Dave was forced to tell her that her brother had died several hours before. He regretted the lie when he saw tears spring to her eyes, but after he promised to send the body to her men for burial she readily followed him.

Neither said a word as they crept away from the disorderly group. "Why are you helping me, corporal?" Morgan asked when they were out of hearing.

"Quiet, ma'am. The lieutenant will explain." Morgan could see the outline of the two horses on the hilltop. The lieutenant? Could it possibly be one of her own men? Finally reaching the hilltop, Morgan exclaimed in delight when she recognized her own horse.

"Oh, Gambler, I didn't think I'd ever see you again."

"Be quiet, girl or you'll bring the whole camp out here," a deep voice growled.

Morgan whirled and came face to face with Marc Riordan. "You . . . I don't understand."

"Just mount up," he said, slapping his gloves impatiently against his leg.

Marc and Dave spoke quietly for a moment then Marc mounted his waiting black stallion. Dave slipped away into the darkness as they moved away from the area.

Morgan's mind was actively seeking an answer to this unexpected escape assistance. It certainly wasn't in keeping with his reputation, especially after what he'd said earlier about guerrilla fighters. She shivered when she thought of her brother; how he had known this Yankee would play a part in their lives. Had Michael seen his own death? she wondered.

Recognizing some of the landmarks on the road Morgan knew they were riding east toward Front Royal. She wished he'd slow down so they could talk. After thanking him properly she wanted to get back to Widow Garret's place where she would join her men.

A swirling snow began, quickly covering the hard ground. "Lieutenant, let's stop for a moment," Morgan yelled. "I really appreciate your saving me, but it's time I started circling back. I don't want to get too far from my troops."

Marc pulled his horse to a stop and waited until Morgan was at his side. "Miss Fitzgerald, you are under a misapprehension. I'm taking you to Washington."

Morgan stared in disbelief. "But the corporal said you were freeing me."

"I freed you from being raped and hung. Certainly you didn't think I'd release you to go back to being a nuisance to the United States Army? You'll be detained in Washington until the war is over."

"You Yankee bastard! I should have known better than to think you had a decent bone in your body. Don't you realize I would have preferred to hang rather than rot in prison?"

"It really doesn't matter what you preferred, woman. I saved your neck from a noose and if you can't appreciate that, it's just too bad. Now move!"

Morgan glared at him. "Don't turn your back on me, Yankee. I don't intend to stay with you long."

Marc moved closer to her, his eyes cold with anger. "I said ride, woman!"

Morgan spurred her horse away from him, but Riordan was quickly at her side. He started to warn her again, but relented when he glimpsed tears in her eyes. So, she's not the tough guy she pretends to be, he thought.

The snow got deeper and the temperature continued to drop. The horses were having to struggle every step of the way. Morgan's horse suddenly reared up dropping her unceremoniously on the grond.

Riordan looked down at her, but made no attempt to help. "I heard you were supposed to be quite a horsewoman. I wonder what your men would say if they could see you now?"

Morgan shot him a murderous look and crawled to the mound that had frightened her horse. She brushed the snow away to expose the body of a Rebel soldier. He lay in a pool of frozen blood, his eyes staring skyward. A dark smear marked the trail of a heart piercing bullet.

"I want to bury the soldier," she stated matter of factly.

"We can't. Cover him back with the snow and get on your horse."

Morgan looked at him increduously. "I'm not asking you to lift a finger. I'll do it myself."

"I'm not being callous, woman. The ground is frozen; there's no way we can bury him."

Morgan realized what he said was true, whether she wanted to admit it or not. She said a short prayer and began pushing the snow back over the corpse.

Marc watched through narrowed eyes. He wondered how she could kill so effortlessly and yet worry about a dead soldier she didn't know. Would she have done the same thing if the boy had been a Union soldier?

Morgan took the reins held by Riordan, her green eyes suddenly soft and pleading. "Come on, lieutenant, you have nothing to gain by taking me with you. Traveling will be much easier if you're alone."

Chills tingled up her spine at the look in those ice blue eyes. He didn't need to say anything. She knew he wasn't going to let her go. "I plan to make your life miserable, Yankee."

"I can believe that, *Rebel*."

They traveled in silence for what seemed an eternity. The wind-blown snow soaked Morgan to the skin. She stubbornly gritted her teeth to keep them from chattering. She glanced at the man at her side and silently cursed him for his indifference.

Riordan's horse stumbled, but was quickly brought under control by a few gentle phrases. "We're going to have to find some shelter and give the horses a rest before much longer."

"Anything you say, lieutenant," Morgan drawled sarcastically, overjoyed at the prospect of a rest herself, but not wanting him to know it.

Marc smiled inwardly. "What grit this little hellcat showed. She had to be freezing; he could feel the ice caked in his beard and mustache, yet she still sat proud and arrogant in the saddle.

He hadn't bargained on the weather turning this bad, but there wasn't much he could do about it. When the men found Morgan gone they would need to be as far away as possible. He had hoped to reach Front Royal before they stopped, but at this rate they would be lucky to be there before dawn. He thought of honey-blonde Lucy who would welcome him with open arms. Hopefully she would put up with this spitfire who accompanied him.

Morgan's horse stumbled and went down. She quickly dismounted and pulled the reins over the mare's head, murmuring gently as she examined her forelegs.

"Does she look all right?"

"Yeah, no thanks to you, Yankee."

"Get back on your horse, Rebel!" Marc shouted angrily.

"No, I'll walk for awhile! I'm not going to kill my horse just because you're in a hurry!"

Marc fought to control his anger. He slid off his

horse, took his pistol from the holster and checked it for her benefit.

"Keep that thing handy, because I plan to go first chance I get."

"That's what I figured, my pet, and I sure would hate to put a hole in that cute derriere of yours."

Warm blood rushed to Morgan's face. "You . . . you arrogant bastard."

Marc's laughter rang out as Morgan tried to put her horse between them. "Go ahead and laugh, Yankee. When the tables are turned you won't have much to laugh about!"

"Such threats, my sweet. Do you really think you frighten me?"

"Let's just wait and see!"

Morgan led Gambler, her boots plowing through the snow. Oh how she hated him. She would have been better off a prisoner of that bastard Slegle.

Shortly they approached a deserted farm. Part of the roof had fallen in on the barn, but there was still enough shelter to protect them from the harsh weather. Morgan found it almost cozy. She loved the smell of hay and oiled leather.

Morgan unsaddled her horse and began to rub her down with a cloth she found in the deserted barn.

"I'm glad to see you Rebs take care of your horses," Marc commented as he forked hay.

Morgan turned on him, her hands on her hips. "Listen to me, Yankee. We Rebs raise the best horse flesh in the country and I don't need any blue-bellied Yankee telling me how to treat my animal!"

Marc grabbed her by the arm and swung her

around. "I'm tired of your taking offense at everything I say. This trip is going to be bad enough without fighting you every step of the way—so stop acting like a spoiled child! I was going to say Union soldiers seem to be ignorant in the way of horses, but you didn't let me finish."

Morgan yanked her arm away and began piling straw up into a bed. Curling her body child-like, she rested her head on her arms.

Marc watched her through narrowed eyes for a moment then reached for his saddlebag. When he turned to offer Morgan a piece of dried beef she was asleep. He leaned against the rough wall opposite her, chewing on the salty beef and wondering how a young girl could be so deeply involved in this bloody war, and commissioned an officer at that.

Seeing the involuntary shivering that would surely wake her, he looked around for a covering. Finding nothing, he lay beside her, giving her the benefit of his body's heat. Pneumonia was one thing he didn't want to have to deal with. Besides, he could use a little warmth himself. She stirred slightly, murmuring something incoherent as she snuggled closer in his strong arms.

Marc studied the freckled face and slightly up-turned nose. Her long lashes lay soft against her cheeks playing shadows against her fair skin. He reached out to touch her hair, then pulled his hand back as if afraid of being burned. "Damn stupid kid! What the hell is she doing in the middle of this war? She should be home waiting for some boy to come courting."

Morgan tried to ignore the hand that shook her, but it persisted. "Come on, sleepy head. You've been asleep for two hours. We have to move on."

Morgan sat up stretching and noticed it was pitch black outside. A dusty lantern gave the old barn a cozy glow. "Can't we stay here for the night?" she asked, her voice unconsciously wistful.

"There's a war going on, girl; much as I would like to forget it, I can't."

Morgan wondered at the gentle tone of his voice. She stood up, shaking straw off her still damp buckskins. Her body ached from the long ride in the cold, but she reluctantly saddled her horse as Marc rode out of the barn, impatient to get moving. The snow had let up some but the frosty air had a biting sting to it. Morgan grumbled to herself as she mounted. "Damn stupid Yankees. Don't know when to stay in out of the cold."

"Hurry up, woman. I want to make Front Royal before dawn."

"Why don't you go on, Yankee? I'll see you there." Morgan shouted out to him. She decided against pushing him any further when she heard the grim command telling her to ride.

Shades of pink were just beginning to show in the east as they arrived at a small frame house on the main road through Front Royal. Morgan wearily dismounted and numbly followed Marc to the door. She wondered who would give refuge to a despicable Yankee in this southern town.

Marc's vigorous knocking echoed loudly in the silent street. Finally a small voice was heard from behind the door.

"Open up, Lucy. It's Marc Riordan."

The bolt scraped back hastily, then a small disheveled blonde threw open the door. "Marc, you son of a bitch, where have you been? You told me months ago that you'd be back in a day or so. What am I supposed to do while you're running all over Virginia?"

Marc pushed his way into the dark hallway and secured the bolt. "Do whatever you like, Lucy. I made no promises."

The blonde looked hurt by his callous attitude, but eagerly threw her arms around him. "Oh darling, I'm sorry. It's just that I've missed you. I was afraid something terrible had happened to you."

Marc leaned down and indulgently kissed the full, pouting mouth. "That's better, honey. I need a favor, then you and I will discuss more personal things."

Lucy giggled and snuggled close to him, ignoring the flustered girl standing in the background.

Embarrassed and unable to keep still a moment longer, Morgan blurted, "If you two would like to be alone, I'll gladly leave."

"Stay where you are, Morgan." Marc ordered, then backed it up by grasping her wrist. "I'll need a secure room for my prisoner, Lucy."

"Your prisoner? You're not serious?"

"I'm very serious. Morgan is my prisoner and I'm taking her to Washington."

Lucy eyed the slight figure. "She looks harmless enough. What did she do?"

"Looks are deceiving, my sweet, and I don't care to discuss Army business standing in your hallway. Now what do you say, can you put us up or not?"

Lucy flashed her most beguiling smile. "For you, love, anything. You can put her in the attic bedroom. She'll be safe there."

Marc patted Lucy on the bottom. "I knew I could depend on you, doll."

"I'll see to a warm bath and some hot food for you. I'm sure you want to get out of those wet clothes." Lucy left to wake her maid, leaving Marc and Morgan alone in the gaudy hallway decorated with red velvet furnishings and gold wall paper.

"If you think I'm staying here, you're crazy!"

"Just be glad you'll have a warm bed to sleep in," he said as he shoved her up the stairs ahead of him.

Stubbornly she tried to push her way back down the narrow stairway. "I won't stay in this house of sin!"

"Don't be a hypocrite, Morgan. You've been living with your men, so you're no innocent."

"You yellow-livered, bitch-chaser! You wouldn't know a lady when you saw one. Don't dare compare me with the whores you call women!"

Marc picked Morgan up and flung her over his shoulder. Kicking the door of the attic room open, he roughly dropped her on the bed. He was lighting an oil lamp when she dashed for the open door. A strong arm blocked her way. "You will stay here and keep your mouth shut," he snapped, tired of her protests.

When he turned to leave she pushed her way in front of him again. "Just a minute, Riordan," she demanded.

Marc grinned devilishly. "What's this, my sweet? Can't you stand the thought of being without me?"

Morgan's green eyes flashed. "Don't flatter yourself,

Yankee. I just want you to release me before you start whoring."

"Forget it, *Rebel*. You'll stay in this room until I'm ready to leave."

Morgan opened her mouth, but Marc stopped her. "If you say one more word I swear I'll tie you to the bed for the duration of our stay."

She continued to glare at him, but moved warily away from the door. Marc reached out and touched her face. "That's better, my sweet. I'll see that food and a bath are sent up to you."

Morgan knocked his hand away. "I'll kill you yet, Yankee. Mark my words, you'll regret the day you crossed my path."

Her viperous tone infuriated Marc. He backhanded her, knocking her to the bed. "Don't make threats you can't keep, woman!"

His cold contemptuous tone froze her and she backed away thinking he was going to strike her again, but instead he left her without another word.

Marc entered Lucy's room where she was waiting with a tray of food and a hot, steaming bath. "Come in, darling. Is your prisoner all tucked in?"

Marc ignored the light taunt. "Are you sure she can't get out of that room?"

"Not unless she drops three stories to the ground."

Marc smiled. "I wouldn't put it past her."

"What has she done to be going to prison?" Lucy asked curiously as she helped Marc out of his jacket.

"Unbelievable as it sounds, she's the leader of a band of Rebel soldiers who have been playing hell with our supply trains. When she was captured,

General Slegle ordered her hanged. I wasn't about to hang a woman, Rebel or not. I had my orders for a transfer, so when I left during the night I took her with me."

"My God, Marc! Why risk a promising career to help her? They'll hang you for sure."

"I don't think they'll connect her disappearance with me. She had men waiting in the hills nearby. It'll be assumed they broke her loose. When I get to Washington I'll tell them I captured her on my way there."

"Why is she fighting you when you saved her neck?"

Marc laughed as he lowered himself in the steaming tub. "I don't think she looks at it that way. Come on, doll, no more talk. How about scrubbing my back."

Morgan pressed her nose against the dirty window pane, trying to see outside. She had tried raising the window, but it was stuck fast. Now she could see that there was no ledge or means of escape. Hearing the key turn in the door, she fled back to the bed.

A large black woman peeked into the room as if expecting to see the devil. "Now, chile if you stay on dat bed and don't try to get out, I'll have Jake brin' hot water for yo' tub. It's a long trek down dem stairs and we would jus' as soon forgit it if you is gonna be mean."

Morgan had to laugh at this big woman whose eyes were as large as saucers. "Come in. I promise I'll stay on the bed. After all, I'm quite harmless. What's your name?"

"My name is Kitty, ma'am and the young lieutenant said you was his prisoner and if we lets you go he'll skin us alive."

"That sounds like something he'd say. I guess he and your mistress are laughing about me being here?"

"Oh, no, ma'am. They is too busy . . . well, ain't none of yo' business what they be doing, but they ain't thinking bout you, just be sure of that."

It suddenly infuriated Morgan to be in the same house with Marc Riordan. All she could think of was how she would like to kill him, but she had promised this big, black woman that she wouldn't try to escape and the thought of a warm steaming bath and a hot meal was certainly appealing.

Dressed in the soft, cotton gown Kitty provided, Morgan lay in the big feather bed. She felt very satisfied being clean from head to foot with her stomach full. She couldn't remember the last time she'd slept in anything other than her buckskins. Tears came to her eyes as she pictured her soft bed at home and the elegant surroundings she had taken so much for granted. She wondered if this war would ever be over, and when it was, if she'd recapture that elegant way of life. "You're getting soft, Morgan Fitzgerald! That's what sleeping in a warm bed with a full stomach will do for you! I never laid and cried when I was sleeping on the cold ground with only Gambler to keep me company."

Morgan drifted off into a light, troubled sleep until she heard the key in the lock again. She didn't move as the light from a lamp fell across her face.

Marc Riordan stood silently by the side of the bed looking down at Morgan's serene face. Her deep auburn hair, fanned out on her pillow, gleamed as it caught the light. Lifting a lock, he rubbed it gently between his fingers. Why had he not realized how really beautiful she was — or perhaps he was fighting her for that very reason. Don't be stupid, he told himself. Regardless of her innocent appearance, she has been living with her men.

He cursed himself silently, noticing the bruise at the corner of her mouth. He gently touched it, speaking regretfully to himself as he did.

"If you would just realize I'm doing this for your own good. That lovely neck wasn't meant to be stretched by a rope, little one," he said gently caressing her neck.

Morgan watched him leave the room as silently as he had come. She felt as if she'd been holding her breath forever and let out a deep sigh. She hadn't known what to expect when she saw him standing bare-chested at the side of her bed, but she certainly hadn't expected his tender words or gestures.

"You're a fool, Marc Riordan," she whispered, then drifted into a deep, peaceful sleep.

Chapter Four

Four days passed and still Morgan was a prisoner at Lucy's house of pleasure. She was well provided for, but still felt as if she'd go crazy if she didn't get away from there. She hadn't seen Marc since the night he had stood over her bed. Kitty brought all her meals and Lucy paid an occasional visit to taunt her. At this point, Morgan would have almost welcomed a good fight with Marc.

Lucy informed Morgan that Marc was meeting with his new commanding officer and would probably be gone a few days.

"What's to happen to me if he doesn't return?" Morgan asked.

"Oh, I'm sure he'll be back, dear. In the meantime, I think it's time you earned your keep."

It was nightfall before Marc got back to Front Royal. It hadn't taken him long to convince McClellan to give him time to escort a prisoner to Washington. He had ridden most of the night through Confederate and Union encampments and was glad to be back in Front Royal.

The house on Center Street was already a hive of activity. War seemed to have been prosperous for Lucy and her girls. The little town had changed hands several times, but Lucy's business continued to boom. He was tired and hungry and hoped to be able to avoid being noticed as he climbed the back stairs. He wondered if Morgan had eaten. Perhaps he would join her for a little supper. He was sure she would be going stir-crazy by now. She might even be happy to hear he planned to buy supplies for their trip tomorrow.

Marc came to a sudden stop in front of Morgan's open door. "Jesus Chr . . . Morgan?" He quickly glanced around the room and saw her buckskins still hanging in the corner. He knew if she had escaped she'd have worn them.

Taking the steps three at a time, he came face to face with the startled maid. "Where is she, Kitty?" he asked impatiently.

"I don't . . . she . . . please, sir," she stuttered.

Marc roughly shook her. "Speak up, woman!"

"Miss Lucy made me do it. I told her you would be spitting mad."

"For God's sake, woman, what did you do?"

"Miss Lucy said it were time Miss Morgan done earned her keep." Kitty's eyes were wide with fear as she hesitated before going on. "She done made me dress her up real fancy like."

"Go on, woman!"

"Dat girl gonna be won in a card game," she finally blurted out.

"Christ! Where?"

"I doan know for sure, sir. One of dem rooms at de end of de hall," Kitty cried.

Marc was so angry he would have killed Lucy if he could have gotten his hands on her.

The only sound he heard was coming from one of the rooms to the left of the hall. Pushing the door open, he surveyed the room, his hand casually on his gun. He did a double-take at the woman struggling with a man in the corner of the room. He recognized the deep auburn hair, but that was the only thing familiar. Morgan was dressed in a low cut, gaudy dress that barely covered her breasts and her face was caked with makeup.

Morgan looked up and saw him. A look of relief crossed her face, but instead of going to her, Marc moved to the big round table in the center of the room.

"Do you have room for one more, gentlemen? I understand the lady goes to the winner tonight," he said pouring a glass of whiskey. He looked toward Morgan and made a mock toast.

Morgan's eyes grew large in disbelief. "You bastard! I should have known you had something to do with this." Before she could scream more she was silenced by the cigar-smelling hand of her tormentor.

Marc lit a long, thin cheroot, trying to ignore her black looks. She bit down on the hand that covered her mouth and was quickly released. "Keep your dirty hands off me, you bastard!"

Everyone in the room laughed. "What's Lucy givin' us here? She must want revenge on someone in this room," one of the officers laughed.

Morgan sat quietly on the settee trying to figure some means of escape. She began to sip on the brandy that had been set before her.

Marc pulled one pot in after another. He was exhausted and wished he could just claim Morgan and leave, but he knew no one would take kindly to that.

He had to finish this out.

The man who had been giving Morgan a bad time pushed his chair back and rose. "Deal me out this hand. I need a break."

Marc fought to control his anger as the fellow headed for Morgan.

Morgan opened her eyes and watched him approach. "Stay away from me, creep!"

"Come on, baby. Give old Sam a little kiss. It won't be long before one of us claims you and I want to know what I'm putting my money in for." Pulling Morgan's dress down, he exposed one firm, round breast. His eyes grew large. "By, God, if that ain't incentive." Everyone in the room laughed except Marc.

Morgan struggled to cover herself but Sam was all over her. His mouth covered hers in a sloppy, whiskey-smelling kiss. Suddenly he jerked back in pain. "God damn whore!" he yelled as blood dripped from his lip. He raised his fist and struck Morgan soundly across the face.

Marc jumped to his feet and pinned the man against the wall. "I don't know about the rest of these fellows, but if I win the young lady I don't want her battered and bruised. Now if you're still interested in winning her, I suggest you sit down and play. I'd say this game is just about over."

The men around the table agreed. It was down to Sam and Marc and the last hand was for everything. "Don't you fellows worry," Sam said as he laid down three queens. "I'll share her with you."

Marc laid down three tens and two jacks. "The lady

is mine, gentlemen and I don't care to share her with anyone."

Marc took Morgan by the hand and headed for the door. Sam stepped in front of them blocking the way. "Where did you come from, Mister? Seems mighty strange, you walking in here and winning."

Laying his hand casually on his gun, Marc looked around the room at the other men. "Does anyone else question my winning tonight?"

"The gentleman won fair and square," one of the men said. "Let's not have any trouble. We all wanted the girl, but he won."

Sam backed away, watching the prize disappear. "Damn it, I want that woman and I plan to have her!"

Kitty waited outside the door, anticipating Marc's orders. "Jake is getting a bath ready, sir, and I put food in the room upstairs."

"Thank you, Kitty. Tell your mistress I want to see her," Marc ordered.

Morgan still clung tightly to Marc's hand, but seemed a million miles away. He picked her up at the foot of the stairs and carried her to the room. She looked at him strangely as he laid her upon the bed, suddenly aware of his nearness and the strength he possessed. He had held her so tenderly, so different from the hard, cruel way he had been treating her. "What if you had lost, Yankee?" she asked softly.

He touched the red mark on the side of her face. "What do you think, Rebel?"

"Would you have let that man have me?"

He leaned toward her, his eyes warm with desire. Suddenly he straightened up. "It would have served him right."

Morgan smiled and closed her eyes.

"Oh no you don't," he said pulling her upright. "You look like a whore. Get out of that terrible dress and into the tub. We're going to be traveling in a few hours."

"I will not! I'm tired and I want to sleep."

Marc roughly began to unfasten the red satin dress.

"All right, all right. Get out and I'll bathe."

"I'll be back in fifteen minutes and you'd better be clean and into something decent. I've had a hard day and I don't want any more trouble. Do you understand? I want to get out of this place."

Morgan didn't understand why he suddenly seemed so angry, but she wanted out of this place as much as he did. He acted as if it were her fault she had this terrible dress on. Damn him, if he hadn't brought her here this wouldn't have happened.

Marc leaned against the wall outside Morgan's door. "What in hell is wrong with you, Riordan? You're letting that green-eyed witch get to you. She's your prisoner — nothing more."

They rode out of town before the sun was up. Morgan was tired, yet exhilarated to be on the road again — even if that road headed for Washington. She was sure she'd get away from this Yankee before long.

Marc was in another of his black moods and Morgan wondered why. She had no way of knowing that he had confronted Lucy in a fit of anger. Lucy had been a friend since the war started, but she had betrayed him and he could find no excuse for it. He would never go there again.

Morgan found herself wondering about the man at

her side. She had been speechless when he gave her a cape with the excuse he didn't want her dying on him. She broke the silence. "How far will we travel today?"

"Are you tired already?" he asked impatiently.

"I didn't say I was tired. I just asked you a simple question," she answered defensively.

"We'll try to stop soon. I'm tired myself, after playing all night in a card game I didn't want to be in."

Morgan's face turned red. "If you recall, Yankee—I didn't ask to be there, either."

Marc started laughing. "Touché, Rebel. You always seem to have the last word," Marc said looking back over his shoulder. "I have a feeling we're being followed so I want to travel a little longer."

Morgan turned around, but didn't see anyone. "Have you seen or heard something?"

"No, it's just a feeling and I usually trust my instincts. Your boyfriend wasn't too happy about losing you in that game last night. I wouldn't be surprised if he showed up."

"He wasn't my boyfriend! I hated him almost as much as I hate you!"

"You have a powerful lot of hate in you, little one," Marc said as he rode away.

They topped a hill and spotted a small farmhouse with smoke circling the chimney. "We'll see if we can bed down in their barn. Maybe they have some food they can sell us. It was damned inconvenient to have had to leave Front Royal before we had provisions."

"Seems to me we were there long enough for you to have gotten plenty of provisions—if you hadn't been so busy entertaining all of Lucy's girls."

Marc didn't answer. He swung his horse around and again studied the terrain behind them. He removed a small pistol from his belt and handed it to Morgan. "You go on to the farmhouse and see if we can stay the night. I'm going to circle back and find out who is following us. If you run into any trouble, fire one shot."

Morgan was considering riding in the opposite direction when she heard a scream. She spurred Gambler to a full gallop toward the house. As she approached a woman came from behind the house begging for help. Before Morgan had a chance to find out what was wrong the woman ran back to the river's edge, crying out to a young boy clinging to the ice.

"Please help him," she cried. "I thought the ice was thick enough for him to cross, but he fell through and each time I try to reach him the ice cracks more."

"All right, calm down. You go get blankets and a rope. I'm going to try to crawl to him."

Once the hysterical woman was gone Morgan began planning how she could help the boy. She could tell by the expression on his face he was panic stricken. "You just hang on, honey. I'll have you out of there in a minute."

The boy shifted his weight and the ice cracked again. "Try not to move. Just be real still." Morgan tried to keep her voice steady, but was afraid she wouldn't be able to get to the boy without going through the ice herself. She thought of shooting the gun to summon Riordan, but had heard gunshots in the distance and figured he was having his own problems.

"All right, honey, I'm going to try now. Everything will be fine." Morgan wished she were as confident as she pretended. She didn't know what she was going to do when she reached the boy. He was half in the water with the ice breaking all around him.

She was within a foot of him when she heard the ominous sound of ice cracking. "Don't be frightened, honey. Just hang on." Morgan could hear a horse approaching fast, but didn't dare move to see if it was Marc.

"My God, woman. I can't leave you alone for a minute."

Before Morgan could answer the ice began to give. Reaching out she grabbed the boy by the arms and heaved him away from her.

The next thing she knew she was under water fighting to get air in her lungs. She came within inches under the ice where there was a pocket of air, but she couldn't find the opening. She gave one desperate attempt to break through, but to no avail. Suddenly her limbs seemed very heavy and it didn't seem to matter that she couldn't breathe. She was cold—so cold. Her last thought was how she had outsmarted Marc Riordan. She had cheated him out of seeing her rot in prison.

Marc Riordan knew the Rappahannock was shallow in a lot of places and hoped this was one of them. He plunged his big, black stallion through the ice, breaking it as they went. He could see the shadow of Morgan's body just beneath the surface. As the ice broke, Morgan's body floated to the surface. Marc leaned down and pulled her up and across his saddle.

She was already blue and there was a stiffness to her body that made him fear he was too late. God, he had become fond of this little spitfire. Why had she done such a foolish thing, he wondered. He cursed himself for leaving her alone, but that fool from the poker game had been following them, determined to have Morgan.

Marc slid off his horse and laid Morgan on the ground. He placed his ear to her chest and listened. "There is a faint heart-beat," he informed the woman and boy who waited anxiously. "We've got to get her inside and warm."

The woman, who introduced herself as Mrs. Russell, led the way to her own bed before the fire. Marc began to strip the wet buckskins from Morgan.

"Why don't you let me do that, young man. I know you mean well, but I'm sure she'd feel better if it were done by me."

"It's all right, ma'am, she's my wife." Marc didn't like lying to the woman, but he didn't need her shooting him in the back if she knew Morgan was his prisoner.

"Do you have any whiskey?"

Mrs. Russell smiled. "A bottle my oldest son was saving for when he came home, but I know he would gladly give it up for the woman who saved his brother's life. Not many women would be as brave as she. I will be forever grateful."

Marc looked down on Morgan's pale face. "Morgan is a remarkable woman." And I don't have to lie about that, he thought to himself.

Once Morgan was stripped Marc began to briskly

rub her arms and legs, trying desperately to get the circulation back. He had seen men lose limbs to frostbite during the bitter winter and hoped desperately to prevent that from happening to Morgan. "Come on, babe, wake up," he begged as he forced the bitter whiskey down her throat.

There was no reaction from Morgan. Marc shook her roughly. "Damn it, Morgan, wake up!"

Marc forced more of the liquid down her throat. She choked and tried to push the glass away. "That's it, little one. Come on, fight me."

Morgan slowly opened her eyes, looking around the room. "The boy. Is he . . ."

"You saved him, Morgan. He's fine. Been gathering firewood to get you warm."

"Yes, so cold." Morgan closed her eyes and drifted off into a peaceful sleep. Marc touched her face, relieved the cold clammy feeling was gone. He looked up at Mrs. Russell, standing at the foot of the bed with a worried expression on her face. "I think she'll be all right. I'll let her sleep a little longer then I'll get her on her feet to be sure the circulation has returned."

Marc stood and stretched. He didn't know how long he had been leaning over Morgan, but he was stiff and his back ached.

"You go rest, young man. I'll fix you something to eat."

"I think I had better see to the horses, Mrs. Russell. I completely forgot about them when we came in."

"There is feed in the barn. Just help yourself to whatever you need."

Marc found both horses waiting at the edge of the river. He started to lead them to the barn when he noticed his horse was limping. "Damn, what else is going to happen? Easy boy, let's get you into the barn and see what's wrong."

Marc tethered Morgan's horse and then examined his own. The fetlock joint seemed swollen, but he didn't think it was broken.

"Sorry, old boy, but we didn't have any choice. We had to save that little lady."

As Marc tended his horse he thought about Morgan saving the boy. She had to have known when she heaved him away from her that she would go under, but she had taken the chance anyway. Most people would have saved themselves in a situation like that. She certainly wasn't like any other woman he had ever known.

The young boy Morgan had saved entered the barn and stood silently watching as Marc tended his horse.

"My ma said for me to make sure you found the feed for the horses."

"Thanks, son, but liniment for my horse is what I need most. I'm afraid he's hurt pretty bad."

"That ain't no problem. My ma makes a real special one we use on our stock." He sadly looked around the barn. "Well, we used to have a lot of stock. Them Yankees have taken almost everything now."

"I'm sorry, son. You see if you can get me some of that liniment while I feed the horses."

Marc thought about what the boy said as he fed the animals. He regretted that anyone had to suffer during this blasted war, but the South had done its share of looting. When an army was hungry it didn't matter how they got food. It was the unnecessary burning of towns and crops that he couldn't tolerate and his own army seemed to have a knack for doing it.

The boy was back before Marc finished putting out feed for the two horses. Marc rubbed his horse's leg with the liniment and wrapped cloth pieces around it.

"Where is your father?"

"Killed," the boy answered matter of factly. "Battle of Bull Run. Got two brothers fighting someplace. One's with Lee and the other is with Jubal Early." He looked up from giving the horses water. "Guess they're still alive. Soon as I'm old 'nuff I'm going to join. Gonna kill me a few Yankees."

Marc affectionately ruffled the boy's hair. "Don't be too anxious, son. It's no game of glory—only death and destruction."

Mrs. Russell and her son Billy insisted on sleeping in the loft so Morgan wouldn't have to be moved. Marc stood with his back to the fire, a long, thin cheroot in his mouth, and wondered about this Morgan Fitzgerald who continued to amaze him. She was a real spitfire, yet it wasn't just talk. She had let herself be captured just so she could protect her brother and now she saved this boy without a second thought about her own safety.

He studied her flawless face with its slightly upturned, freckled nose. "How could I have ever mistaken you for a man?"

Morgan began to toss restlessly, mumbling about Yankees coming up the carriage path. Suddenly she sat straight up, screaming for her mother. Marc took

60

her in his arms, trying to calm her fears. "It's all right, little one. It's the whiskey playing tricks."

Morgan looked at Marc, her eyes wide with fear. "Why are they all dead? Everything was so good . . . now they are all dead."

Marc brushed the hair back from her tear-streaked face. "Who are you talking about, Morgan?"

Morgan laid her head against his chest. "Momma, Daddy, Turner, Michael and now me . . . gone . . . all gone."

Marc was still puzzled. "What do you mean, all gone?"

"All dead."

"No, little one, they're not all dead. Michael is alive and so are you. I don't know anything about the others."

Morgan continued to talk incoherently. "Yankees killed Momma and Daddy and now they're trying to kill me."

Marc laid Morgan back on the pillow and lay down next to her. "Go to sleep, Morgan. Dream about pleasant things. Dream about roses and honeysuckle, and a picnic in a field of wildflowers. Have you ever had a picnic in a field of wildflowers, Morgan? Maybe someday we'll do that."

Morgan woke during the night and found herself snuggled in Marc's arms. She gave him a shove nearly knocking him from the bed. "What in hell do you think you are doing in this bed?" she screamed. Marc quickly placed his hand over her mouth. "Now listen to me, woman, and listen good. These are real nice people and they think we're husband and wife. Now,

61

if they find out differently, then I'll be forced to shoot them."

Morgan angrily shoved his hand aside. "God, you are a despicable bastard!"

"Yeah, and you're an ungrateful bitch," he snarled. "I save your life for the second time and all I hear from you is what a bastard I am. The next time you're in trouble I'll just let you get out of it yourself. Besides that, when I want a woman, it won't be a dirty-faced kid in buckskins pretending she's a man!" Marc grumbled as he grabbed a quilt off the bed and threw it on the floor in front of the fire.

Morgan didn't say anything as she watched him trying to get comfortable. He was right, she thought. He had saved her life twice, but then, damnit, she wouldn't have been in trouble if it hadn't been for him. Besides, she thought, he must have some motive for saving her. He probably just wants the glory of bringing Morgan Fitzgerald to prison. She angrily turned her back to him. What had she been doing snuggled against him like that, she wondered. Damn him! Who does he think he is, saying he wouldn't want a woman like her. She had seen what he liked to bed, and to be sure, she would never be that kind of woman.

Morgan woke as the smell of food filled the small room. The place on the floor next to the bed was vacated. Mrs. Russell stood at the wood stove cooking and Billy was setting the table, but there was no sign of Marc.

The boy was quickly at her side when he noticed she was awake. "Did you get warm, Mrs. Riordan? Boy, it

62

took me a long time to get warm. You saved my life. Did you know that? Are you hungry?"

Morgan laughed at the excitement of the young boy. "Yes, I'm finally warm and that food smells delicious." She glanced around the room. "Where is lieutenant . . . where is my husband?" she corrected.

"His horse was hurt when he plunged through the ice to save you. He's real worried about him. He sure is a nice man. He's been talking to that horse like it's a person."

"Billy, you go on and fetch Mr. Riordan. Mrs. Riordan needs a few minutes to get dressed and freshened up before you come back."

Morgan still felt wobbly, but anything was better than the cold she had felt yesterday.

After a few minutes, Billy came running back into the house alone. "Mr. Riordan says he needs to stay with his horse. He'll get something later."

Morgan sat at the table and sipped coffee made from peanuts. "What seems to be wrong with his horse, Billy?"

"Don't rightly know, ma'am. His leg is real swollen and the liniment ma made didn't help none."

Morgan looked concerned. "Mrs. Russell, would you mind if I had my breakfast later. Maybe I can help my husband."

"Of course, child, but don't be out too long. You need to get your strength back slowly."

Marc spoke gently to the big black stallion as he rubbed its leg, unaware that Morgan had entered until she knelt beside him. She felt the fetlock, a worried expression on her face. "Get me a bucket of snow and a bucket of hot water."

Marc looked puzzled. "What do you know about horses?"

"My father raised the best horseflesh in Virginia and he taught my brother and me everything he knew. Now are you going to listen to me?"

"What do you plan to do?"

"The hot and cold compresses should reduce the swelling. I've seen this before and if it isn't treated the swelling could constrict the blood vessels and the horse will have to be destroyed."

Marc left the barn without another word. Returning minutes later he watched Morgan lower the horse's leg into the hot water. The horse snorted and reared nervously.

"Easy, Satan, the lady is only trying to help you."

Morgan looked up, her eyes wide with surprise. "Satan?"

"To be precise, Satan's Thunder."

"It figures you would ride a horse called Satan."

Marc's deep laughter rumbled through the barn. "Do you think I'm the devil?"

Morgan looked embarrassed. "Maybe not literally, but there are a lot of people who think you are."

"So I'm told," Marc said running a finger down the side of Morgan's face. "I'm just a mortal man with feelings like any other man."

"Really, I didn't think you were like anyone else I've ever met," Morgan answered sarcastically.

Marc smiled, ignoring her barbs. "Perhaps I would like to possess your soul," he said as he caressed her hair. "Would you sell me your soul, Morgan?"

The lines of Morgan's jaw grew rigid and she shot him a contemptous look. "Are you so little concerned about your horse, Yankee?"

He smiled suddenly, the quick smile that changed the hard lines of his face completely. "Are you afraid of me, Rebel?"

"It's not fear, Yankee, just hate. I'm surprised you don't know the difference."

"It's hard to tell the difference when hate seems to be the only emotion you feel."

Morgan was becoming angrier by the second. He was the most provoking man she had ever met. "Are you going to stand around talking, or are you going to get me more water?"

"If that wasn't my horse you were tending, I'd put you over my knee and give you a good beating, and I just might do it yet," he snapped. "I suggest you curb your bitchy tongue, woman!"

Morgan started to argue, but forced herself to return her attention to the horse.

Marc smiled at her effort to control her temper. Damned Irish she-wolf, he said to himself as he left to get more water.

Chapter Five

A light snow fell most of the day causing Marc's mood to become even blacker than it was. He hadn't thought traveling in March would have been this arduous.

He and Morgan sat in front of the fire after the Russells had gone to bed, neither saying anything.

Stretching his long legs in front of him, he studied Morgan's face. The fire seemed to make her hair glow as it hung in cascading waves around her shoulders. She wore one of Mrs. Russell's large flannel gowns, but he could still see the outline of her breasts against the material. He felt a tingling in his loins and cursed himself for being so weak, but all he could think of was the velvet smoothness of her skin.

He grabbed a quilt off the bed and placed it around Morgan's shoulders. "Keep yourself covered, woman!"

Morgan looked up puzzled and Marc realized how ridiculous he sounded. His tone softened. "You were near death last night. I don't want you catching cold."

Morgan still didn't say anything.

Marc let a few moments pass before he spoke again. "Thank you for treating my horse."

She glanced toward him then turned back to the fire. "Thank you for saving my life yesterday, even though . . ." Morgan stopped before she finished.

"Even though what? What were you going to say, Morgan?"

"Nothing, just thank you."

Marc laughed. "You were going to say even though it wouldn't have happened if I hadn't brought you here. Am I right? Have you ever thanked me for saving you from being hung?"

Morgan's eyes flashed angrily. "I would rather have hung than rot in prison. I know what happens to women there."

"Do you, now. Tell me, Morgan. Perhaps I've been kept in the dark. Does anything different happen to a southern woman in a Federal prison than it does to a northern woman in a Confederate prison?"

"A southern gentleman would never . . ." she hesitated.

"Go on, Morgan—tell me about this illusion you have that wearing a blue uniform makes a man a devil. You know yourself how foolish it sounds. There are evil men on both sides, Morgan. Believe me, northern women have suffered the same losses southern women have. My mother lost a son in this war. Do you think she suffered any less than your mother when her husband was killed?"

Marc watched tears well up in Morgan's eyes. He wanted to reach out and touch her, but knew she would turn from him. A few silent moments passed. "Morgan, I don't know if you remember, but last night I told you that your brother was still alive."

"Yes, I remember."

"I must say, I'm surprised at your lack of reaction."

"What do you want me to do—thank you?"

"No, I know better than to expect that. Why don't you tell me how you got mixed up in this damned war."

67

Morgan leaned back in the rocking chair and thought for a moment. "Daddy and Jubal went into the war early. Daddy was killed at Bull Run and Momma was never the same after. Michael, my brother, felt he had to avenge Daddy's death so he went off and joined Stuart's Cavalry, leaving Momma and me alone to manage everything. It wasn't long before the Yankees came and made our home their headquarters. They expected us to serve them like hired help. I tried to explain that Momma was sick, but they didn't care. The first night after serving them all day, Momma went in her room and laid down on her bed and just died." Morgan turned and looked at Marc, her eyes filled with tears. "Do you understand? She just died." Morgan wiped the tears from her face with the back of her hand. "I knew I couldn't stay there so I found old Jacob, a black man who had been with my father since he started the farm. He packed enough food for me to get to Richmond, saddled Gambler and sent me on my way. I found Jeb Stuart's wife, Flora, in Richmond and she insisted I stay with her until her husband and his troops returned. I sewed uniforms, patched quilts, made bandages, all the things women are supposed to do, but for me it wasn't enough. Everyone complained about the inconveniences they were suffering. The women didn't have tea for their socials or material to make new dresses. I just couldn't stand the complaining. I didn't see how they could have the nerve when our loved ones were putting their lives on the line. I convinced Mrs. Stuart that it would be all right for me to travel on to meet my brother and her husband. My brother was glad to see me, but I knew I was a burden to him. I could ride and shoot as well as any of the men and begged them to let me ride with them, but they wouldn't hear of it. Finally Turner Ashby, one of my brother's friends, felt sorry for me and told Stuart I could ride with him. I guess it was a kind of joke at first, but I proved I could stand on my own, even though I still felt I was considered more a mascot than anything else."

Morgan rubbed her temples for a moment before going on. "Turner was killed shortly after I joined them. His men loved him and they just seemed to fall apart. It was very sad and Jeb was at a loss as to what to do. They just sat around moping when they were deperately needed. Well, I rallied them, more by chastising them for letting Turner down than anything else, but most of them agreed to follow me. They renamed the outfit Fitzgerald's Raiders." Morgan hesitated. "That's my story, lieutenant. Nothing more."

"Were you Turner Ashby's fiancee?"

Morgan smiled. "No, he was more like a brother. I think he admired my spirit, but there was never anything between us. I admired him because he was the epitome of all southern manhood, a knight in shining armor. He was kind, handsome, and a real gentleman." Morgan suddenly stood up and threw the quilt aside. "I don't know why I am telling you all this. It will just give you something else to use against me when we get to Washington."

Marc grabbed her hand before she moved away. "If you don't want your story known, then it won't be told by me."

"That sounds well and good, until you feel cruel and want to hurt me."

"I don't mean to be cruel, Morgan, but sometimes you push me too far."

"I guess I do. I've been told that by others." Morgan noticed the soft look in Marc's eyes and suddenly realized the pressure of his hand holding hers. "I'm very tired, Marc. I think I'll turn in now."

Reluctantly Marc released her hand and watched her climb beneath the covers like a small child. But, damn it, she wasn't a small child, and he wanted her.

"Good night, Marc."

"Marc looked down at her for a moment then grabbed his pillow and quilt and threw it on the floor.

"Is something wrong, Marc?" Morgan innocently asked.

"Nothing is wrong. Go to sleep, Morgan."

Morgan stared at the ceiling wondering what she had done now. He was the moodiest man she had ever met. One moment he seemed kind and understanding, the next he was a grouch. Suddenly she remembered the night before. "Marc, did you say something about roses and picnics last night?"

"Go to sleep, Morgan."

Morgan laid back and smiled. How strange that he should talk to her of roses and picnics. There certainly was a side to this man she didn't know.

Morgan was enjoying the hospitality of the Russells. She hadn't had a woman to talk to in a long time and was disappointed when Marc announced it was time for them to move on. They said their farewells, loaded down with provisions that Mrs. Russell insisted they take.

They had only been traveling a little while when they heard cannons rumbling in the distance. Marc pulled his horse up and listened. "Funny, for a few days I almost forgot there was a war."

"I know, I felt the same. The Russells were such nice people."

"I think we had better alter our course. I don't want to end up in the middle of that."

"Marc, wait. Let me return to my men."

Marc ignored her plea. "I think we can reach the Potomac before nightfall."

"Why? Just answer me that! Do you really hate me so much you would put me in prison to die? Sometimes I think I understand you, but I can't understand why you hate me so."

Marc listened politely, then smiled, his perfect white teeth gleaming in his bronze face. "I don't hate you, Morgan. Now ride! I want to reach the Potomac before nightfall."

Not if I can help it, she thought viciously. I have to do something before this day is over. I must escape this madman."

Marc smiled to himself. Tonight he would have her, then he would turn her over to the authorities, making sure she got a fair trial. Perhaps when the war was over he could help her get a new start.

Morgan rode silently the rest of the day, planning her strategy for escape. When they stopped for the night she would catch him off guard. She would then knock him unconscious and escape. It was as simple as that. She still had the gun he had given her. She would hit him with that. Hit him—by God, she would shoot him! What was the matter with her? She wasn't thinking straight. He would surely come looking for her. She had to kill him.

"Are you tired, Morgan?" Marc asked as he saw the look of desperation cross her face.

Morgan was startled from her thoughts. "What did you say?"

"I asked if you were tired? I thought maybe you wanted to rest."

"No, I would just as soon get to our destination."

"We're almost to the Potomac. I have a friend who has a cabin not far from here. I'm sure we can stay there."

Oh no, Morgan thought. She had to be alone and carry out her plan. She didn't want to have to deal with two people. "Why don't we just sleep in the open tonight? I feel like I'm getting soft from sleeping in beds."

Marc looked at her suspiciously. "No. We'll stay at the cabin." Marc knew his friend was seldom at the cabin since the war had started. It had been a place they had enjoyed while hunting and fishing along the Potomac River, but tonight he would enjoy it in another way.

Morgan suddenly stopped. She could hear the sound of rushing water. She spurred her horse onward, curious to see the river. She had never been this far north before, but she had heard about this mighty river.

"The cabin is just ahead," Marc shouted. "Don't get too close to the edge. The rocks slide and your horse won't be able to keep his footing."

The sight of the rushing water falling over the rocks was beautiful, yet frightening. There was so much water and all moving so fast.

Morgan quickly fell in behind Marc on the narrow path. Suddenly she saw it. Ahead sat a small log cabin overgrown with weeds and brush.

"It's not like I remember, but it's ours for the night."

Morgan tried not to show her relief that the cabin was unoccupied. Now she would just have Marc to deal with.

Marc shoved the door open and an empty wasp's nest fell from overhead. "Looks like Wes hasn't been here in awhile. I'll clean a place near the fireplace and move the bed there. We can put the bedrolls on top of the mattress so it won't be too dirty."

Morgan didn't bother arguing because she didn't plan to sleep there. She went about cleaning the best she could, but the cabin was in terrible shape. Dirt and cobwebs were everywhere and field mice had ruined the curtains and throw-rugs.

Marc found firewood stacked outside in a shed and built a blazing fire while Morgan took food from the pouch Mrs. Russell had prepared. Then he settled on the bed, his long legs stretched out in front of him. He nibbled on a dry biscuit while Morgan heated some beans.

"This isn't too bad. We have a warm place to stay and food to eat. If there wasn't a war going on I'd enjoy staying here and fishing for awhile. What would you think of that, Morgan?"

She glared at him. "Anything to delay my hanging, Yankee."

Marc threw back his head and laughed.

Morgan turned back to her cooking, but could feel Marc's eyes upon her. Her cheeks grew red under his slow, deliberate gaze. He reached out and touched her hand. "Forget the beans, Morgan. I'm no longer interested in food," he said in a deep seductive voice.

Morgan felt hypnotized as she looked into his blue eyes. "I don't . . . please . . ." she stuttered.

"I want you, Morgan. I have wanted you for a long time. I'm sure you knew that." He pulled her into his arms, kissing her long and passionately. Morgan began to return his kiss, feeling all control slipping as his hand moved up under her shirt and gently caressed her breast.

God, what is the matter with me? she wondered as she continued to enjoy the kiss. This man is a devil and I have to kill him. Morgan suddenly drew back and as she did pulled the gun from her jacket.

Marc's eyes widened at the sight of her kneeling in front of him with the gun he had given her. "Don't be foolish, Morgan. Give me the gun!"

"I'm sorry, Yankee, but I have to kill you. You're my enemy—a devil."

Marc's eyes were still warm with desire. "You don't believe that, Rebel." He smiled, a hint of mockery touching his handsome mouth. "Lie with me—let me love you. Then you can do what you wish."

"Stand up, Yankee. Turn your back to me!"

Marc slowly stood up. He had a sick feeling she wasn't fooling and he knew she was capable of killing. "Are you going to shoot me in the back, Rebel? I wouldn't have thought it of you."

"Just shut up!"

Marc started to turn, but like a cornered animal Morgan struck him with all the strength she possessed. His knees buckled and as he collapsed he mouthed the word, "Why?" Blood began to flow freely from the wound on his head.

Morgan aimed the gun at his heart and closed her eyes. Suddenly she began to cry, not really knowing why. Everything began to come back to her; being taken prisoner, the card game, the icy river. She slowly backed away from the body, then grabbed her cape and ran from the cabin.

Marc shook his head trying to clear the cobwebs. He struggled to one knee, but had to hesitate before standing. He could hear Morgan's horse pounding over the rocks along the river. He dipped his scarf in the pail of water and touched it to his scalp, flinching as the pain shot through him. "You're a fool, Riordan. You knew all along what she was capable of and you still let her get to you." He struggled to pull his cape on and slowly leaned over to pick up his gun. "At least she didn't kill you," he said aloud.

Morgan rode as fast as Gambler would travel. She hadn't gone far when she reined her in, knowing she was lost and would have to wait until morning to continue on. She walked a little way, leading her horse, hoping to find a suitable place to hide while she slept. Stopping and listening, she thought she heard voices and laughter. She tied Gambler to a tree and cautiously approached the area where the sound came from. If it's Yankees, I'll just move on, she thought, but maybe they're Confederate soldiers. Morgan could

75

see the glow from the campfire and around it sat three men dressed in ragged gray uniforms. Morgan felt like crying. Friends—at last she had found her own kind. "Hello. Can you spare a little food?" she asked stepping into the clearing.

Everyone sat as if in shock at seeing this girl in buckskins with long flowing hair.

"Will you lookee here. We musta' done something right to have this bit of fluff dropped in our laps."

Morgan backed up a step when she saw the look in the eyes of the men approaching her. "I am Captain Morgan Fitzgerald and I would appreciate it if you could direct me toward Aldie. I can join my men there."

They all laughed. "You can join us here, you don't need to be traveling nowhere. You're just what we been needing, little lady."

Morgan backed further away, but two of the men were already behind her. She knew she had made a big mistake walking up on them. Hadn't Marc told her there were Rebs as bad as Yankees?

"Where is your commanding officer? I demand to speak with him."

All three laughed again as they circled her. Before she knew what happened one of them grabbed her, pinning her arms behind her.

"We got no officers, missy. We're all equal here and we're all going to share you equal. Ain't that right fellows?"

Morgan's arms arched as she struggled, kicking out frantically. "Now be real still and lets git you out of them duds. What you doing dressed up in Indian skins? Pretty little thing like you should be in silks and satin."

Morgan was suddenly physically and mentally exhausted. She couldn't do a thing to stop them from stripping her. Her limbs were like lead weights.

"Please don't do this. I'm an officer in the Confederate Army. You'll be in a lot of trouble if you do this."

"We're deserters, little lady. We don't answer to nobody."

Morgan felt sick. The fire seemed to blur before her as she felt their hands violating her body.

"Oh God, please help me," Morgan screamed in pure terror.

"Move away from the lady!"

Morgan was abruptly released and dropped to the cold ground. She thought she heard Marc's voice, but it couldn't be. She had killed him.

"Drop your guns!"

Morgan lifted her head and saw him standing on the other side of the fire holding a rifle on her tormentors.

"Can you get up, Morgan?" The split second he looked toward her one of the deserters pulled his gun. The sound of gunfire filled the air for a brief moment. Morgan was afraid to look. There was no way he could survive against the three of them. A hand touched her bare shoulder and gently rolled her over. Marc was kneeling on one knee at her side. She threw herself into his arms sobbing.

"It's all right, Morgan."

Something moving caught Morgan's eye, but before

she could scream one of the deserters fired his pistol at Marc's back. He arched forward, falling against her. Morgan grabbed Marc's gun and screaming hysterically, unloaded it into the soldier. She angrily threw the gun aside and knelt beside Marc. "You'll be all right, Yankee. You have the devil on your side, remember."

Marc reached up and touched her face. "You just killed a Rebel soldier for me, little one."

"I killed a snake. He deserved to die."

Marc gently touched her bare breast. "You're beautiful, Rebel. I wanted to love you, but . . . "

Morgan began to cry. "Damn you, Yankee. What am I going to do now? How the hell am I going to get you on your horse?"

Marc didn't hear her desperate plea as he lapsed into unconsciousness. Morgan struggled with every ounce of strength she had, finally getting him across his saddle. She quickly pulled on her clothes and mounted, glad to leave the scene of death behind.

When they reached the rocky cliffs she dismounted and led the horses, knowing if she stayed on the narrow path it would eventually lead her to the cabin. She thanked God for the full moon giving her a little light in this unfamiliar place. She felt like crying when she finally saw the cabin. Smoke was coming from the chimney and the cabin glowed warmly with the fire that still burned in the fireplace.

Morgan quickly slid off her horse and hurried to Marc's side. "Marc, please listen to me. You must help. I can't carry you."

Marc lifted his head and looked around.

"I'll try to take your weight, but if you can help we'll stand a better chance."

Grimacing in pain, he swung his leg over the pommel of the saddle and slowly slid to the ground. Morgan placed her shoulder under his arm, trying to take most of his weight. They moved a few steps toward the cabin before his weight drove them both to the ground.

"Leave me, Rebel," Marc mumbled.

"Listen to me, Yankee. Somehow we are going to get you into the cabin. You're not going to die and be on my conscience the rest of my life."

"You tried to kill me earlier, why should you care what happens to me now?"

"If I had wanted you dead, you would have been. Now come on, stand up."

Marc managed to get to one knee with Morgan's help. She placed her hand on his back and could feel the warm stickiness seeping through the wool cape. They staggered a few feet to the door, falling heavily against the frame.

"Don't want to hurt you, Morgan," Marc whispered as he leaned against the cabin.

"For God's sake, this isn't the time to be worrying about hurting me. I've got to get you inside. Hang on to me. It's only a little further."

Morgan pushed the door open and they staggered into the small room. A few more painful steps and they were to the bed. "Don't lie down yet. I have to get your clothes off."

Marc smiled through gritted teeth as he lowered himself to the bed. "Now you say that."

"Don't be absurd, Yankee. This is no time for jokes."

"I am afraid you are right, Morgan," Marc said as he keeled over.

Morgan pushed him over onto his stomach. She flinched as she saw the blood covered shirt. "Come on, Morgan. Pull yourself together," she said aloud. She remembered seeing a knife in a case next to Marc's holster. She tried not to move him as she reached under feeling for the knife. Her fingers touched the cold handle and she easily slipped it out of its sheath. Marc moaned and tried to speak. "Save your strength. This is going to be a long night."

Morgan ripped the shirt up the back in one quick movement of the knife. "I hope you have another shirt. I'm not very handy with a needle."

"How are you with a knife?"

Morgan laughed nervously. "Now *that* I can handle."

"Figures," Marc mumbled.

Morgan shuddered as she exposed the wound. It was just under the right shoulder blade and had already turned red and ugly.

"Marc, you know I'm going to have to remove the bullet?"

"Just do it, Morgan!"

Marc turned white, his lips tight with pain as Morgan wiped the blood from the wound. She placed the blade of the knife in the fire then went to get the whiskey from the pack. Thank God, Mrs. Russell had insisted they take the remainder of the bottle with them.

"Marc, can you lean up enough to drink this?"

Grimacing in pain, he raised on one elbow and tipped the bottle up, draining most of the contents before handing it back to Morgan.

"Morgan—don't think this is going to do any good—removing bullet—lost too much blood—can feel it."

"Hush, Yankee, you know me better than that. I'm not going to let my patient die."

Marc smiled and closed his eyes. Morgan touched the tip of the blade to make sure it had cooled enough, then moved the oil lamp as close as possible. "Hold the bars of the bed, Marc."

Marc silently did as she ordered. Morgan cut the flesh quickly. Marc's body stiffened, his knuckles turning white from the grip he held on the bed. She probed for the bullet with the knife, but felt nothing. She had once watched a field doctor remove a bullet from one of her men with ease. Why couldn't she feel it? Suppose it was deeper than she thought. Suppose it had deflected off a bone. Please God, she prayed silently. She placed the knife back in the hot coals, then poured whiskey over her hands. Slowly she probed the wound with her finger until she felt the bullet. Her stomach heaved and she fought being sick.

Marc was unconsicous but beads of sweat stood out on his forehead and ran down his chalk-white face. He still held the brass bed post in a death-like grip.

At last—Morgan had the bullet extracted. She felt faint, but she couldn't give up yet, there was still more to be done. Pouring whiskey over his back, she then took the hot glowing knife and quickly touched it to the skin. Marc screamed out, his body jerking involuntarily. Morgan gagged as the smell of burning flesh assailed her nostrils. She staggered from the bed to the door and fell outside. Kneeling, she breathed deeply of the cool crisp air and fought off the nausea that threatened to overcome her.

After a few minutes she was able to return to the cabin to finish her work. She covered Marc with his cape and began to look around for some way to boil water. She hadn't noticed it before, but the little cabin was fairly well stocked. There were pots in a small cupboard near the fireplace and a chest filled with quilts. The mice had been having a field day with most of them, but they would do to keep Marc warm. She tore one of the quilts into strips, placing them in boiling water. After a few minutes she extracted one and laid it across the wound. She heard Marc's intake of breath and realized he was conscious.

"It's done, Marc. If the wound heals cleanly you'll be fine."

"Remind me to kiss you when I'm on my feet," he said in a whisper.

"I certainly will not. I have repaid my debt to you. There is no need for kissing!"

Marc smiled. "Lie down beside me and rest, Morgan. You must be exhausted."

Morgan didn't argue. She carefully crawled under the quilt beside Marc and drifted off to sleep.

Chapter Six

Morgan was awakened by Marc's incoherent mutterings. She could feel the heat from his body where she lay and she knew he was feverish. She pulled the quilt over him and swung her feet off the side of the bed. Her head ached and she felt stiff all over, but the worst of it was, she didn't know what to do for a fever.

Marc pushed the quilt away and started to get up.

"Hold on, you're in no condition to go anywhere."

"Men are moving up the hill . . . have to get guns in place," he muttered, glassy-eyed.

"It's all right, lieutenant. Your men have everything under control. You just lie down and rest."

"Water . . . need water."

"I'll get you water if you lie back down."

Marc reluctantly lay back and watched her pour a small amount from his canteen. She placed the tin cup to his dry, parched lips and let him drink. "Slowly now, just a little at a time."

Marc touched Morgan's hand as she took the cup away. "Why did you stay, Morgan?" he asked, suddenly coherent.

"I don't really know," she said as she laid a wet cloth on his forehead. "I guess I figured I owed it to you."

"Whatever debt you thought you had is paid. Go

home now, Morgan. Could be trouble if someone discovers the bodies of those deserters or that bastard from the poker game could show up again. That's who was following us before. You must leave, Morgan."

"Stop getting yourself worked up, Marc. We'll be fine."

"Please, Morgan . . ."

"What will you do if I leave, Yankee? You're burning with fever."

"Does it matter to you, Morgan?" Marc asked softly.

"If you have all this strength to be asking dumb questions, then you'd better tell me what to do for your fever, because I don't have the slightest idea."

"Must sweat it out . . . water . . . lots of water." Marc closed his eyes and dozed fitfully.

Morgan stared at him as he slept. She pushed back the damp curls that clung to his forehead. He looked like a little boy, she thought, except that his body was lean and muscular and he had a couple of days growth covering the square, firm jawline. Strange, how that gentle look disappeared when he turned those pale blue eyes on you in anger.

Morgan looked around at the bare cabin. The fire had almost burned down with the wood Marc had brought in and the canteen was about empty. She was going to have to do something about both.

She hauled wood into the cabin after checking on the horses, then took Marc's canteen and a jug and headed for the river. It was cold and gray with the threat of a storm in the air. Morgan shivered as the damp air penetrated her buckskins. She quickened her pace, anxious to get back to the warmth of the cabin. She came to the cliffs above the water and hesitated. She had hoped there would be a stream or some way to get water without climbing down the steep rocks, but she could see there wasn't. She took a deep breath and began the descent.

Morgan hadn't gone more than a few steps when she slipped on the wet rocks and began to slide down the steep cliff. Somehow she managed to grab a jutting rock and hung on for dear life, petrified as she heard the falls rushing beneath her. She carefully swung her leg up and over one of the rocks. She lay there for a moment, too frightened to move. Her fingers and elbows were scraped and bleeding and her head was throbbing from a blow to the forehead, yet the worst of it was she still had to get water.

Carefully Morgan made her way down the sheer cliff, finally reaching the water. She filled the canteen she had been fortunate enough to save when she had fallen and began the slow climb back.

By the time Morgan returned to the cabin she was soaked to the skin. She looked around for something to change into, but the only thing she could find was a man's shirt hanging on a hook behind the door. She stripped out of her buckskins and under garments and hung them by the fire, then slipped into the oversized shirt. She flinched as she touched the lump on her head, cursing herself for having been so careless. She and Marc could have both died.

Marc cursed and tossed on the bed. Morgan tried to calm him but even in sickness he was too strong for her. He looked around, glassy-eyed, then started to get up.

"No, Marc. Please, you'll open that wound again."

"Must get to Christopher . . . he needs me . . . oh, God, why Christopher?"

Morgan gently pushed him back on the bed. "Why don't you tell me about Christopher?"

Marc struggled again to sit up. "You bitch. Don't think I don't know what's going on in your warped mind. All you care about is my name and money. You don't give a damn about Chris or me. But don't worry, I'll keep my word . . . I promised father I'd marry you."

Morgan wondered what hell he was reliving. She took him in her arms and gently tried to soothe him. Suddenly she sensed he was no longer asleep and she quickly pulled away from him.

"Morgan how did you get that cut on your head? What happened to you?"

"It's a long story. I'll tell you about it later. Do you think you could eat something?"

"Please leave here before it's too late. You could be in great danger if the wrong people find you here."

"We'll see this thing through together. I owe you that much, no matter what you say," she said as she covered him.

Marc's hand acccidentally brushed Morgan's bare leg. "Oh God, woman are you trying to drive me crazy?"

Morgan quickly moved away from the bed. "My clothes got wet when I went for water. This was the only thing I could find to put on. Besides, I don't know why my state of dress should concern you."

Morgan dipped out a bowl of broth she had made

from soaking the dried beef in water. She knew it wasn't going to last long and she was going to have to do something about the food situation.

Marc watched Morgan moving around the room. Her long slender legs were fully exposed and he could see the outline of her bare breast beneath the soft cotton shirt. He didn't think he had ever wanted a woman as badly as he did this one. Suddenly it didn't matter how many of her men she had been with.

Morgan sat on the edge of the bed with the bowl of broth. "I think you had better let me feed you. Any movement and you might open that hole again."

Marc didn't answer, but took the bowl from her hands and set it beside the bed.

"What are you doing? You need that to keep your strength up."

Marc pulled her into his arms and kissed her deeply. His lips were hot from the fever and Morgan felt as if she were being branded. His lips parted hers, searching, demanding a response. She melted against him, giving in to the wonderful feelings that consumed her. He gently cupped her breast in his hand. The mere touch of his fingertips stroking her taut nipples sent her into a frenzy. His warm hand traveled downward stroking the soft flesh of her thigh.

Morgan suddenly pulled away, frightened of the feelings he was arousing and not understanding why she didn't want to stop him. She looked into his fever flushed face. "No, Marc, you don't know what you are doing."

"Must . . . need you . . . so lovely."

Morgan managed to escape his grip only because of

his weakened condition. She grabbed his heavy cape and threw it around her shoulders as she left the warmth of the cabin.

"Morgan, come back," Marc pleaded.

Morgan stood outside the door trying to clear her head. What was the matter with her, she wondered. She had been kissed before, but had never experienced the strange sensations Marc's kiss had caused. She hadn't wanted to stop the warm pressure of his hand or to move away from the heat of his body, but she knew she had to. "Oh God, what is wrong with me? He is my enemy—a devil," she sobbed.

Marc opened the door, grimacing in pain from the exertion. "Come back inside, Morgan. I will not touch you again, if my kiss is so repulsive to you."

"Everytime I turn around you are all over me. If you think I am like Lucy, you are mistaken and you'd best remember that!"

"I know you are not like Lucy. She is warm and loving and you're as cold as ice, Morgan. No man will ever be able to get close to you. He'd freeze to death trying." Marc turned his back on her and stumbled back inside.

Morgan gasped when she saw the blood soaked bandage. "Marc, please, lie down. You are bleeding again." She started to help him back to the bed.

"Stay away from me, woman! I don't need your help. Why don't you just get the hell out of here?" Marc said as he collapsed on the bed face down.

"I will, damn you! I was only trying to help you, but you can bleed to death for all I care!"

Marc didn't answer.

"There is still broth over the fire and your canteen has water. You should be able to survive on that."

Marc still did not answer.

"Did you hear me, Yankee?" Morgan yelled angrily.

Morgan finally realized Marc had passed out. "Damn you, Yankee! I should have known you couldn't take care of yourself." She began to gently cut away the wrapping from the wound. "Dear God," she muttered when she saw the yellow festered sore. She remembered her brother having an infection after a nail went through his foot. Her mother had drawn the poison out with hot salt water. She put a little salt in the water over the fire and began tearing the old quilting into bandages.

Marc mumbled incoherently, his mind wandering in delirium as he shouted names that haunted him. How strange, Morgan thought that such a strong, vital man should be so weak and helpless. Surely anyone so strong would not let a fever conquer him, Morgan prayed. Strange, she had believed she could handle any situation. Why did she feel so helpless now?

Marc began shivering violently. Morgan gathered everything she could find to cover him. "Sweat it out, that was what he said," she mumbled. "Well, Marc Riordan, if you think I am going to have your death on my conscience, you're mistaken. You are going to live. I will not let you die!"

Marc alternated between freezing and burning up. His skin was flushed and he sweated profusely, but the fever remained high. Morgan fought to keep him on the bed and covered, exerting every ounce of strength she possessed while Marc begged Christopher to come back and help him. In his jumbled, tortured words he still accused Rachel of being a selfish bitch. Morgan wondered who these people were and what part they had played in Marc's life.

Morgan nodded in a chair next to the bed where Marc lapsed in and out of consciousness. She had sat with him two days and nights, at times nearly having to sit on him to keep him still, but now his skin felt cool and he had not reopened the wound with his thrashing.

Morgan suddenly jumped up from the chair. She thought she heard horses approaching, but she wasn't sure if she had dreamed it or if they really approached. She listened intently for a moment, then took the rifle from the corner and stood waiting, her back against the wall facing the door. Morgan aimed the gun as the door opened.

Marc Riordan opened his eyes and slowly focused on a Rebel officer leaning back in a chair with his feet on the bottom of his bed. He reached for the gun that had been at his side.

"Calm yourself, Lieutenant Riordan. I've no mind to harm you. Your gun is over there on the table."

Marc looked anxiously around the room. "Where is the young lady who was here?"

"Aye, you would be meaning Morgan. She's gone back to Aldie with her men. She nursed you through your sickness then when you passed the crisis she left. I'm Lieutenant Jubal Kelly of Fitzgerald's Raiders."

"What are you doing here?"

"Morgan insisted I stay and make sure you get back

to your lines. I don't really understand why, but I don't question Morgan's orders."

Marc listened to the Irish brogue the big red-headed soldier had and realized Morgan sometimes spoke with the same lilting accent. He tried to sit up, but found he was still weak and light-headed.

"Easy now, boy. Morgan said you were to be staying in bed at least another day. She left some stew from a rabbit one of the boys shot. Made it herself, she did. That's one fine lady."

"Yes she is," Marc answered, suddenly depressed at the thought of never seeing her again. "Have you ridden with her long?" Marc asked as he accepted the bowl of stew.

"Aye, since she took over Turner Ashby's men. I had been with her father til' his death, then with Stuart til' Morgan started riding. The girl had always been special to me so there was no choice but to join her. Turns out she is a better officer than most."

Marc couldn't help but notice the admiration in Kelly's eyes as he spoke of Morgan. He wondered if there was anything between the two of them. Kelly was a bear of a man, yet he wasn't bad looking. His blue eyes twinkled in his red bearded face and his smile showed perfect white teeth.

Jubal watched Marc wolf down the food. "Damn good stew. She's a good cook." Marc said between bites.

"Aye, I have yet to find anything she isn't good at," Kelly laughed.

Marc wondered what he had meant by that. "Sounds like you know her very well."

91

Jubal passed Marc a flask of whiskey. "Aye, I've been knowing Morgan since she was twelve, so I guess I know her better than most."

Marc groaned inwardly. Childhood sweethearts, he thought. Why in hell did she have to leave this big likeable bear behind. Revenge, he thought. Damn her. She figured he would tell me about making love to her and it would drive me crazy. You're already crazy, Marc Riordan. Morgan Fitzgerald didn't have the foggiest notion of how you felt about her.

"Are you all right, Riordan? You looked dazed again."

"Why did Morgan leave you behind?"

Jubal looked puzzled. "I told you, she was wanting me to see you safely to your lines."

"I know that, but why you?"

"She knows I'll follow her orders. I'm afraid some of the men would just as soon see you dead, but I figure she must have good reason not to want you harmed."

Marc didn't say anything, but took another drink of the whiskey and passed the flask back to Jubal. "Why does she wear those damned buckskins?"

"Turner Ashby gave them to her. They were a gift to him from the Choctaw Indians for his bravery. When Morgan started riding with him she wore skirts. Turner thought the skins would suit her better. Fit her like a glove, they did." Jubal laughed. "Who would ever imagine you Yanks would be mistaking her for a man?"

Marc joined in the laughter. "I've wondered how we made that mistake myself."

Jubal passed the flask back to Marc as he talked.

"Aye, what a surprise we had when after our first raid the papers talked about Morgan Fitzgerald . . . how *he* had raided the supply train. Morgan loved it. After that she made certain her long hair was tucked up into her hat." Jubal slapped his hand on his knee. "There was a time it backfired on her though. We were in Fredericksburg after a raid and the boys wanted to celebrate. Morgan thought it would be fun to join us. Only she didn't figure on someone trying to pick her up." Jubal by now could hardly talk for laughing. "One of them pretty little girls at the bar thought Morgan was a handsome young fellow and made a pass. Well, let me tell you, Morgan was fit to be tied. That was the last time she joined us to celebrate."

Marc was trying not to laugh for the pain, but Kelly continued with his story. "Another time Michael, that's Morgan's brother, got into a fracas in Front Royal with a lad from the Mississippi 25th. They were going at it something fierce and Morgan steps in and tries to break it up. Well, this fellow turns on Morgan and damned if she didn't stand up to him. Now don't be getting me wrong, Morgan is a fine lady, just like her glorious mother." Jubal leaned back in his chair with a faraway look in his eyes. "Aye, what a lady that one was. I never met a finer woman in all me days. I was eleven when Sean Fitzgerald wrote to my father that he would give me a good home and teach me to train horses if I wanted to come to America. When I arrived the family took me in like I was one of their own. I went to school with Morgan and Michael, and was introduced to their friends as a family friend instead of a hired hand. I loved those fine people, I did. When Sean died I promised him I would watch over his family, and you best believe I plan to do just that."

"Then why don't you get Morgan out of this damned war before she gets killed?" Marc asked, his speech slurred from the whiskey.

"Aye, I wish I could, but this is what she wants," Jubal replied sadly.

"It doesn't matter what she wants, Jubal. She is going to be hung if she's captured again. If I were you, I'd send her home to stay with relatives or friends."

Jubal laughed. "Would you now? I would have thought being with Morgan for a few days would have shown you the lass is very strong-willed."

Marc laughed. "You win, Jubal. I know only too well how strong-willed she can be."

The two men talked long into the night as if they had known each other for a long time. Marc finally felt exhausted. He lay staring at the ceiling in deep thought. He didn't really understand why, but he had wanted to know everything about Morgan, and Jubal seemed to know all about her. After listening to him extol her virtues he was more convinced than ever that the man was in love with Morgan. He had to admit he liked the big Irishman and he was sure he would never see Morgan again . . . unless she was captured again. God, he hoped not. She would surely be hung the next time. Marc closed his eyes and tried not to think of the green eyes that were sure to haunt him for a long time.

Early on the bitter-cold morning of March 27th, Marc Riordan and Jubal Kelly rode along the ridge overlooking the Federal pickets on duty at Chain Bridge which connected Washington and Virginia. "This is where we part, lieutenant."

"Thank you for everything, Jubal."

"Just following orders. Must say I enjoyed just sitting and talking. This damned war makes men forget the pleasures they used to enjoy."

"When it's over meet me in Washington and I'll buy you a drink."

Jubal laughed. "Will you now? And what makes you think you will still be in Washington? If Morgan has her way, you'll be sitting in some prison."

Marc smiled. "You tell Morgan she had her chance."

"Aye, that I don't understand. Well, I'd best be high-tailing it. Take care of that wound, boy." Jubal saluted and turned his horse south. "God go with you."

"Jubal," Marc shouted. "Take care of your captain."

"Don't you be worrying. All her men love her. We won't be letting anything happen to the girl." Jubal waved and rode off into the morning, unaware of the effect his words had on Marc Riordan.

"All her men? Oh God," Marc groaned. "Why, Morgan? How can you live like that and still look and act so innocent?"

Chapter Seven

Marc Riordan sat in the plush War Department office of General Ambrose Burnside waiting for permission to leave. His shoulder throbbed painfully and he was becoming increasingly more impatient as the general and his assistant spoke in hushed tones as if he weren't in the room.

He had already told his story three times and still there were questions. He wondered how Burnside would have reacted if he had told them the truth; how he helped Morgan Fitzgerald escape from hanging. He knew better. Instead he told them he was wounded while on his way to join his new outfit. A Virginia family had taken him in and treated him. He couldn't remember where they lived or how he later got to Washington. He considered himself lucky not to have been taken prisoner. He saw no reason for them to doubt his story, yet he had been questioned for over three hours.

The assistant hastily left the room and Burnside turned his attention back to Marc. Leaning back in his chair, he puffed slowly on a fat cigar. "Says in your file you didn't join the army until the spring of '62. Why did you wait so long to defend your country?"

"I was in France studying art when the war began."

"Art?" Burnside growled. "I thought you were a lawyer."

"I am a lawyer, sir. I have my law degree from the University of Virginia, but I also consider myself an artist."

"Yes, yes, whatever." Burnside replied impatiently. "I understand you were friends with John Mosby?"

"John and I grew up together. Unfortunately we are fighting on different sides, as are many friends and relatives."

"What is that supposed to mean, lieutenant?"

"I was referring to the fact that President Lincoln's brother-in-law is fighting for the Confederacy and Confederate General Jeb Stuart's father-in-law is a general for the United States Army and his chief of Staff is cousin to our own General George McClellan."

"We are not talking about Lincoln or Stuart, lieutenant. We are taking about you." Burnside answered angrily.

"I wasn't aware my loyalty was being questioned, sir. I was wounded by a Rebel deserter and was fortunate enough to get help. I returned to the Army as soon as I was able. What possible reason could you have for suspecting me of being anything but loyal?"

Before Burnside answered his assistant entered followed by a lieutenant. Marc stood up and affectionately shook hands with the newcomer. "It's good to see you, Wes. I wondered who you were serving under."

"I tried to get in touch with you when you were in Culpeper, but we just missed each other."

"Have your reunion another time, gentlemen. Right now I want some answers. My aide tells me you gentlemen have been friends for a long time.

Lieutenant Lansing, can you give me any reason not to believe Riordan is a southern sympathizer?"

Riordan and Lansing both looked stunned. "Sir, you can't be serious. I have known Lieutenant Riordan and his family most of my life. His father was Senator Willis Riordan of Virginia, one of the most respected Senators Virginia has ever had."

"Exactly, Lieutenant Lansing. His family is an old Virginia family, the lieutenant attended the University of Virginia, he was a boyhood friend of John Mosby and on top of all this, General Slegle informs me Riordan openly criticized U.S. Army methods and procedures. He had also been heard to say he thinks Mosby and Fitzgerald are brilliant strategists and we could learn from them. Yes sir, gentlemen, I think I have every reason to question Lieutenant Riordan's loyalty."

Marc stopped Wes from saying any more. "I would like to have my lawyer present before any more is said."

"That won't be necessary, Lieutenant Riordan," said a voice from the doorway.

Everyone turned as General George B. McClellan stepped into the room. "You're a damned fool, Burnside. Lieutenant Riordan is one of my most trusted officers. He had reported to me just before he was wounded. I don't appreciate his being held and questioned this way."

"Now listen, George, I have this telegram from Slegle . . ."

"I don't give a damn what you have. Slegle is an idiot and we have both known that for years. Now, I would hate to have to make the army look foolish, but if you go against me on this I will have to expose some of Slegle's blunders."

"All right, all right, George. Take your officer and let's forget this incident."

"It's forgotten, Ambrose. Lieutenant Riordan, I want you to spend a week with your family getting your strength back. I'll expect you to be back in camp on the 10th."

"Thank you, sir. I'll be there."

"Good. Give my best to your mother. I've been meaning to stop and see her, but there never seems to be time."

At Marc's insistence, Wes returned with him to the big red brick house on Connecticut Avenue. They were warmly greeted by Marc's mother, Anne and her sister Connie, who was visiting from Harper's Ferry. Marc was treated like a returning war hero and Wes took great delight in teasing him as both women saw to his every need and more.

They enjoyed a scrumptious meal, then relaxed in the drawing room, answering the many questions the two women had.

"I am so glad you will now be with George McClellan, son. He's a good man. I just don't understand why he was relieved as chief of command."

"I'm afraid even McClellan has made some mistakes, Mother. He let Stuart completely circumvent his entire army and did nothing. Lincoln feels his main fault is being overly cautious. The president sent him a wire telling him he was nearer the Confederate capital than Lee; why wasn't he acting? McClellean wired back that his horses were suffering from fatigue. Lincoln wired again, asking what his horses had done since the battle of Antietam that could possibly have fatigued them."

Wes laughed, but Marc's mother looked serious. "If we can't depend on a good man like George, what will we do?"

"Now don't go worrying your pretty head. How could we lose with Wes and I fighting?" Marc said hugging his mother.

"I do wish Rachel could have known you were coming. She's so anxious to officially announce your engagement. When she finds you were here for a week she is going to be very upset."

"I'm sorry, Mother, but I am just not up to entertaining Rachel."

"I can understand that," chimed in Marc's aunt. "I met her while shopping in Baltimore and all she talked about was her wedding. She was furious because she couldn't get French lace for her gown. She just didn't understand what good this war was doing anybody. I am afraid she has a lot of growing up to do before she makes any man a good wife, particularly my nephew."

Marc kissed his aunt on the top of the head. "Don't worry, Aunt Connie, I'm not ready to let her put that ball and chain on me until after the war."

Wes cleared his throat. "I hope you don't mind, Marc, but I paid Rachel a visit when I was last in Baltimore."

"You know I don't mind, Wes. I'm sure Rachel was very happy to see an old friend."

"Yes, she was happy to have company. Poor thing, she seemed so bored living with her married cousin. She talked a lot about the dances and parties we all use to attend in Washington before the war."

"If she would busy herself with volunteer work at the hospital or women's club she wouldn't be so bored," snapped Marc's aunt. "It is a shame her social life is curtailed, but she should think about what southern women are suffering. You know my niece is living in Richmond and working at a hospital. In her last letter she wrote they had to make coffee from chicory or peanuts and hadn't seen sugar or salt since the war began, but she wasn't complaining. All her thoughts were with the many men dying or wounded whom she is taking care of."

"Now, Connie, Rachel can't help the way she is. Her mother died when she was very young and her father spoiled her by giving her everything she wanted."

"Yes, including my favorite nephew."

"Connie! That is quite enough. I think this subject has progressed far enough."

"I am sorry, Anne. I didn't mean to sound so critical. Rachel is a lovely child. I just hope she grows up before Marc marries her."

Marc had become very quiet as everyone discussed the girl he had promised to marry. He kept remembering Morgan's remark about how she couldn't stand being around the women who complained of their hardships while their men fought and died. What an unusual woman she was. Aunt Connie would surely like her spirit, he thought.

Anne Riordan set a tray of brandy and cigars between the two men and excused herself and Connie. "If you need anything, don't hesitate to ring for Brenna."

"We won't need a thing, Mother. Wes and I are going to talk a while then turn in too. It's been a long day."

There was an awkward silence between the two men when they were left alone. Wes refilled their glasses and sat back in the big leather chair studying Marc's face. "Are you going to tell me what really happened, Marc?"

Marc smiled. "I didn't think you believed my story."

"It just seemed like you left out an awful lot."

"I guess you could say I skirted the details, but it is a long story."

"We have enough brandy; lead on."

Marc sipped his brandy and began to talk, explaining how his men had captured the notorious Morgan Fitzgerald and the events that followed, leaving out only the fact that he desired the Rebel.

Wes sat quietly and listened to every word, wondering why his friend's face lit up when he talked of this girl who masqueraded as a man. He finally interrupted. "I wonder why Slegle hasn't reported this. There has been no mention of Fitzgerald being captured or of the escape."

"I was surprised to find that myself. He was furious to find Fitzgerald was a woman. He didn't believe a woman could have made him look so foolish. Perhaps he kept it quiet for that reason."

Wes laughed. "Sounds like something he'd do. With

you on the way to your new command he didn't have anything to worry about. Who would dare question him? If word got out that Morgan Fitzgerald was a woman he could claim it was a mistake."

"Exactly. I seemed to be the only one who believed she was who she claimed."

"What did she look like?" Wes asked.

Marc took out a cheroot, bit the end and struck a sulphur match before speaking. "She has long, wavy auburn hair and the strangest green eyes I've ever seen. Sometimes they are green like grass on a spring morning. When she smiles they sparkle like emeralds. When I first saw her, her face was smudged with dirt, a sprinkling of freckles dotted her nose and cheekbones, giving her a little girl look."

"Damn, I wouldn't mind having a leader like that myself. Can you imagine how nice she'd be to warm your bedroll after fighting all day?"

Marc didn't say anything—he couldn't. He wanted to defend her, yet he was sure some of her men had enjoyed her lovely body. How could it not have happened? Surely the admiration in Jubal's eyes hadn't just been for her ability as a soldier.

"What about the card game? How did you know you would win?"

"I didn't, but if I hadn't, I would have taken her anyway."

"How did they ever force her into that situation?"

Marc laughed. "I wondered about that myself, but she said she dressed like they wanted because she didn't want to get Kitty, the black woman, in trouble. Kitty had been kind to her and apparently Lucy threatened to punish her if Morgan didn't obey."

"Sounds like quite an experience, Marc. I can understand your not telling this story to Burnside, though. Particularly with the look you get in your eyes when you talk about this girl."

Marc looked surprised. "What are you talking about?"

"She must have been quite a woman to put stars in an affirmed woman-hater's eyes."

Marc was getting angrier by the minute. "What in hell are you talking about? What's this woman-hater bit?"

"Have you ever loved a woman, Marc? Now, I'm not talking about enjoying the pleasures of a woman. I know you have quite a reputation for that. I'm talking about love."

Marc didn't say anything for a moment. "No, I suppose I haven't. What difference does it make?"

"I think it would make a hell of a lot of difference to Rachel. She's going to be your wife."

"You know the situation between Rachel and myself. She was engaged to my brother. When he died I promised my father I would take care of her. She doesn't expect any more than that."

"Really? I didn't get that feeling when I visited her last month. All she talked about was you and the wedding plans. What will you do, take her for your wife and keep a mistress on the side?"

Marc nearly knocked the bottle of brandy over as he angrily stood up. "I don't know what's eating at you, Wes, but maybe we had better clear the air. We've been friends for a long time so tell me what ails you."

Wes shook his head. "I'm sorry, Marc. I don't know what's wrong with me."

"Could it be you're in love with Rachel?"

Wes dropped into the chair, his head in his hands. "I am sorry, Marc. I never meant for you to know. It was just seeing you so happy while talking about this Morgan Fitzgerald. I couldn't stand the thought of Rachel being hurt."

Marc put his hand on Wes' shoulder. "Does Rachel know how you feel?"

"No, I've never told her. I was always afraid it would change our relationship. I've tried to be a friend to her, listening to her problems and her plans for a future with you."

"Damn, Wes. I'm the one who's sorry. I've been selfish. I had a feeling a long time ago that you were more than just a little fond of Rachel, but I kept thinking you would make a move to let her know. That's one reason I've been putting off announcing the engagement. For God's sake, tell her before things go any further."

"I can't, Marc. I appreciate your understanding, but I have nothing to offer Rachel. I'm a lieutenant in the army. This is my life. You have everything to offer: money, name, prestige. That's what Rachel wants. Can you imagine her following an army husband to some God-forsaken outpost in the West? Can you imagine her any place but in a city, wearing the latest fashions, giving teas? That's what you can give her, Marc. I love her too much to deprive her of that."

"I don't know what to say, Wes. I promised my

father I would take care of her, but you know I have always felt trapped by that promise. I think you owe it to Rachel to let her know how you feel. Let her make the decision."

"No! I know how Rachel feels. She loves you. She wants to marry the son of the late senator from Virginia. I will not take a chance on her always holding it against me if she gave that up. I'm really tired, Marc. This conversation is getting us nowhere. I'm going to retire."

"All right, Wes. I think I'll have another brandy before I turn in. I'll see you in the morning."

Marc stared into the fire, thinking of the conversation that had just taken place. He knew Wes was right. Rachel didn't care about love. She only wanted what the Riordan name would give her; a respected name, a place in society, money.

Marc thought of Wes' question; had he ever loved a woman. It was strange, but no woman had ever captured his heart. Oh, he found most of them amusing and pleasure-giving, but he had never found one he wanted to spend more than a night or two with.

Suddenly, unbidden, those strange green eyes came to mind. God, he had desired that woman. He was sure if he had just had her once she wouldn't be haunting him now.

He smiled to himself. Funny, when Wes asked what she looked like he left out the important things. He didn't tell him how velvet smooth her skin was, or how her firm, round breasts came to a rosy peak, begging to be kissed, or how her slender waist flowed downward to the softness between her long, slender legs.

Marc suddenly threw his glass of brandy into the fire. "Leave me alone, Morgan. Just leave me alone," he whispered.

Chapter Eight

Morgan sat before the campfire, poking at it aimlessly. Her mood had fluctuated between happiness and despair for the last two days and she didn't know why. The only thing she knew for certain was she was sick of war, of seeing death all around her and of seeing her people starve. "Oh God, why can't things be like they were before?" she said aloud.

Morgan wrapped her arms about her knees, gazing into the flickering fire. Her mind wandered back to when her family had been happy and prosperous. Her father, Sean Fitzgerald, had been one of the fortunate Irishmen to come to America with enough money to buy land. He had been told to see Stuart York, an influential Virginia planter in Spotsylvania County and the two men became good friends. Her father eventually married York's only daughter, Amanda. It had been a marriage of convenience to begin with, but they had fallen deeply in love before the first year had passed. Amanda had taught the big Irishman manners and he had taught her to love life as he did. Then Morgan and her twin brother Michael were born and no family could have been happier. They grew up enjoying the life of prosperous landowners;

traveling, the best schools in Virginia, servants to care for their every need. Morgan had been sought after by every eligible bachelor in the county by the time she was sixteen, but she had been more interested in her horses. Her father had raised the best horse-flesh in Virginia on their Aspen Grove farm, teaching the twins everything he knew about horses. Michael had enjoyed every aspect of the farm, but Morgan devoted every moment to the stock. Her mother would shake her head in disbelief when Morgan would ride by, dressed in her brother's pants, with young Jubal Kelly following close behind. Morgan had perfect manners and could be a lady when necessary, so her mother didn't try to stop her.

In 1860 there was disturbing talk that South Carolina might secede from the Union, but Virginians didn't think it would happen. When it did, Sean Fitzgerald was one of the first to join, thinking it would be quick and glorious. He had been killed at Manassas when the war was still very young.

"Morgan, are you all right?"

Morgan looked up startled. "Jubal, when did you return?"

"Just a little while ago. I have been standing here talking to you for the last few mintues, but you seemed to be in another world."

"I'm sorry, Jubal. I guess I was in another world. I was thinking of home."

"Aye, I go there myself every now and then."

"Do you think we'll ever see Aspen Grove again?" Morgan asked with tears in her eyes.

"Aye, girl, we'll see it again."

"But it will never be the same, Jubal."

"No, nothing will ever be the same," Jubal said thinking how like a little girl she looked at that moment.

Suddenly she straightened up and became the soldier again. "Did you see him safely to his lines?"

"Aye, to Chain Bridge. Then I waited at Point of Rocks for word from Lightner. He said Riordan spent the first day in a hospital; then the last he heard he was being interrogated by General Ambrose Burnside at the War Department."

Morgan laughed. "Maybe they'll think he's a spy and hang him. Wouldn't that be ironic?"

"You wouldn't want that to happen, girl." Jubal answered irritably. "Why did you bother to save his life if you wanted to see him hung? I'm thinking he means more to you than you care to admit."

"Don't be ridiculous, Jubal. He means nothing to me. He saved my life and I repaid him, that's all."

"Then why was I ordered to see him to his lines and to wait 'til I received word he was safe?"

Morgan didn't answer.

"Morgan, did he . . . did he try . . ."

"Did he what, Jubal?" Morgan answered angrily. "Did he make love to me? Is that what you're trying to say? I thought you knew me better than that."

Jubal looked embarrassed. "I'm sorry, girl, but both of you acted so strange."

Morgan stood and stretched. "I'm going to bed now. I'll see you in the morning."

"Aye, Stuart is suppose to be here in the morning. You'd best have a good story for him."

"Damn it, Jubal Kelly! Will you stop picking at me. I don't have anything to hide from Stuart or anyone else. I did the only thing I could do."

Jubal smiled. "Now you're making sense, girl. Just be honest with Stuart and yourself, that's all I ask."

Jubal watched Morgan disappear into the darkness. "Those two certainly had a strange effect on each other."

Morgan sat across the table from General Jeb Stuart, sipping her coffee and trying to avoid his questioning eyes. Their meeting had begun more than an hour ago with her telling her story. He still had not said a word, but continued to tap his fingers on the table. Jubal paced back and forth like a mother-hen behind the dark-haired general he admired so much.

"You, lady, are a fool!" Stuart finally said in a voice low with anger. "That man has plagued us. What possible reason could you have for doctoring him and returning him to his lines?"

"I told you, sir, he saved my life. I owed it to him."

"And what will you do if you meet him on the battlefield?"

"I'll kill him."

Jubal almost choked on his cigar at Morgan's bluntness. Riordan was right, he thought. He should get her away from this damned war. Maybe she was turning into a cold woman.

Stuart's bright blue eyes stared at Morgan as if trying to read her mind. She knew it was best to stay quiet and let him do the talking when he was angry, but sometimes it was very difficult. She tried concentrating on him as he stared at her, studying his face and thinking what a fine looking man he was. His nose was finely chiseled, the kind of nose Napoleon admired in his generals. There was an elegance about him, the way he dressed and carried himself. Some thought him a dandy, but those who knew him knew better. He took great pride in being a soldier and dressed to prove it. He wore gauntlets of white buckskin, a gray cloak lined in scarlet and a soft fawn-colored hat looped up on the right with a gold star and adorned with a curling ostrich feather. In the field his finery was continually plastered with Virginia mud and weathered with dust and rain.

"I want you to ride with me to Chambersburg," he said interrupting her thoughts. "Our aim will be horses and supplies."

"Damn it, Jeb. What is this, some sort of punishment because I didn't kill the man who saved me from hanging?"

"You're not being punished, Morgan. You've put yourself in a position of great danger by embarrassing some very high Union officials. They are out to put a stop to Fitzgerald's Raiders and all other partisan groups. I just want things to calm down a bit. Let Mosby take the heat for a while."

Morgan studied her hands in silence, fighting the tears that threatened to flow. She cursed herself for this weakness. She didn't know what was wrong with her since her return. She seemed on the verge of tears most of the time. I must be tired, she thought.

"Morgan, you know I've never felt very comfortable about your being here. You're a beautiful woman.

111

Why do you insist on risking your life like this? You should be thinking about getting married and raising beautiful children."

"I'm doing what I have to do, Jeb. I could never go back to sewing uniforms or working in a hospital. Surely you can understand that."

"All right, Morgan, but you'll ride with me until I feel it's safe . . ."

Morgan started to protest.

"Or you'll return to Richmond to the safety of some sweet, old lady who'll watch over you."

"When do we leave for Chambersburg?"

Jeb laughed, a deep pleasant sound. "I shall enjoy your company. Now for some good news. Your brother is being released from the hospital in Richmond tomorrow. He'll be joining us soon."

"Oh, Jeb, that's wonderful. Thank you."

"Don't thank me. For some unknown reason a Union corporal guided him back to one of our camps. He was taken to Richmond from there."

Morgan didn't say anything. She looked up at Jubal who gave her a reassuring smile. She knew Marc Riordan had been responsible for her brother's release, which confirmed in her mind her actions. Perhaps he was her enemy, but he had helped her more than once. She just hoped they would never meet on a battlefield.

Spring was late this year and Morgan wondered if she would ever see roses and honeysuckle again. She shook her head angrily. Damn, what made her think of roses and honeysuckle? Hadn't that been what Marc

Riordan had said. Oh, yes, and he said maybe someday they would go for a picnic in a field of wildflowers. He was crazy and so was she. Why couldn't she put him out of her mind? Why did she keep dwelling on things that were said?

Morgan's reverie was broken when she heard Stuart shouting orders. She wrapped the blue wool cape Marc had given her tightly around her as the cold wind bit cruelly. Clouds hung heavy overhead and the skeletons of trees stood out bleakly against the colorless countryside.

Morgan was glancing around when she suddenly noticed the dress of the men around her. "Jubal, have you noticed how most of these men are dressed?"

"Aye, one of the supply trains Mosby took carried overcoats. When one is cold he isn't choosy about the color he wears. Who knows, maybe it will help us get horses and supplies."

Morgan laughed. "For a moment I thought I had dozed off and wandered in among the Yankees."

"Stuart isn't going to let you near Yankees for awhile."

"I know, I feel like a child having her hands smacked."

"Now, girl, he has only your best in mind."

"I know, Jubal, but that doesn't help my pride. Anyway, I guess this trip is a very important one. We certainly need the supplies. I wonder if Jeb has a plan in mind."

"Aye, I'm sure he does. He is familiar with this area. You know he was in command of Carlisle Barracks at one time."

"Perhaps he'll run into some old friends."

Jubal laughed. "None that will help us, to be sure."

The raid went well and within a few days Stuart and his group were enjoying a few quiet days in Winchester. They had rounded up much needed stock and supplies and the teetotaler Stuart wanted to celebrate with an evening of musical entertainment. A dozen or more of Stuart's men were musicians and all seemed to enjoy these interludes. Stuart's servant, Mulatto Bob, played bones and Sam Sweeney of Appomattox, Virginia, played banjo and half a dozen others played fiddles. By midnight Stuart had everyone joining in with his deep, mellow voice leading.

Morgan was enjoying the temporary interruption from war. She listened to Jeb sing "When the Swallows Homeward Fly" and thought of home. Even with Michael alive she still wondered if they would ever get back to Aspen Grove. She had heard a lot of the southern plantations had been destroyed and wondered if her home still stood among the huge oak trees on the North Anna River. She put it out of her mind and listened to Stuart's beautiful voice. What an unusual man, she thought. He loved danger, took fantastic chances, yet here he sat singing a ballad that made grown men cry.

Mosby's capture of General Stoughton at Fairfax and his raids in that area had caused the Union officials a great deal of embarrassment and made him the main topic of conversation. Lewis Gooding, one of his men, told about their standing in the shade of an oak and watching Union General McClellan bid farewell to his staff and officers. He swore McClellan had actually saluted in their direction, which brought a roar of laughter to everyone. Then he told of a time

114

Mosby was breaking in a new horse and how it ran wildly down a hill and unceremoniously dumped him in a creek while a dozen or more spectators watched. He laughed as he described Mosby getting up and nonchalantly brushing himself off before walking out of the creek with his boots sloshing.

Morgan was enjoying the stories, but she felt the need to be alone with her thoughts. She slowly made her way through the crowd of soldiers who had gathered to hear tales of Mosby. As she moved into the darkness she heard footsteps behind her.

"Are you all right, girl?"

"I'm fine, Jubal. I just felt like walking."

"Mind if I join you?"

"Not at all. I'd enjoy your company." Morgan said, moving away from the tent area. "I've enjoyed the music. It's been a nice change. Only Jeb could plan such an evening."

"Aye, he certainly has a talented bunch. Sometimes I think he picks his men for their musical ability instead of their fighting ability."

"Jubal!" Morgan exclaimed, then began laughing. "Oh, Jubal, what would Jeb say if he heard you?"

Jubal laughed. "You wouldn't be telling him now, would you?"

"I really should. He would probably give you some terrible duty and then I wouldn't have to put up with your being a mother-hen over me." Morgan said teasingly.

Jubal looked hurt. "I'm sorry, Morgan. I don't mean to be."

Morgan could tell in the dark that she had hurt her

friend. "Jubal, you know I couldn't do without you. I was only teasing. You have no idea how much you mean to me. You are family, home, everything dear to me. I love you, Jubal."

"Aye, and you're all I have, Morgan . . . You and Michael. You both mean everything to me."

Morgan grabbed his big hand. "Come, we're getting too sentimental. I want to look at the moon and stars and forget war for a few minutes."

Jubal Kelly had his own reasons for wanting the subject changed, but he couldn't say anything. He would never be able to tell her that he was her father's son—her half-brother. He hadn't known it himself until Sean Fitzgerald was dying. It seemed before Sean had left Ireland he had met Briget, his mother. The two of them had been foolish and Jubal was the result. Jubal's own father had never even suspected. No one seemed to think it strange that he looked just like Sean Fitzgerald. He had loved Morgan when he was a boy and had even dreamed that someday he would be prosperous enough to court her, but now . . .

"Look at that, Jubal. You can see Ursa Minor. Do you remember when we were kids and would go up on Duerson mountain to look at the stars? I remember one time you tried to kiss me and I pushed you down the hill."

Jubal laughed. "I remember, you little hellion. I thought you had killed me. I didn't stop rolling 'til I hit bottom."

Morgan teased. "It cured you though. You haven't tried to kiss me since."

Jubal grabbed her in a bear hug and swung her

116

around. "Now why would I be wanting to kiss a dirty-faced girl whom I know can out-ride and out-shoot me?"

"Oh Jubal, it's true," she said pulling out of his grasp. "I've turned into a hard, ugly woman."

"No, no, Morgan. That's not true. You know I was teasing. Every man who has ever seen you thinks you are beautiful."

"But who wants a woman who can out-ride and out-shoot him," Morgan cried. "Even that damned Yankee said he wouldn't want to bed a woman who dressed like a man."

Jubal was at a loss. He pulled Morgan back into his arms and stroked her hair. "This war will be over one day and you'll go back to having every eligible bachelor courting you. Why just tonight I saw that young Lieutenant Jared Law from Fitzhugh Lee's unit mooning over you. Looked to me like you were giving him the cold shoulder."

Morgan wiped her face with the handkerchief Jubal offered. "I don't care for him, Jubal. Have you ever noticed how he is always some place else when a battle takes place, yet he is the one who tells about it, just as if he had been in the middle of it?"

"Aye, unfortunately there are a lot like him, but you won't find them with Stuart or Mosby or yourself. Mosby was just telling me tonight that he is hounded by deserters wanting to join him, but he realizes his band would never survive if he let it become a refuge for men fleeing from the regular army."

Morgan realized Jubal had somehow changed the subject, but it didn't matter. She was sure he would always be there when she needed him. He always had been.

Marc Riordan was commissioned captain by McClellan in early April after repulsing Mosby at Warrenton Junction. Mosby had attacked and surprised the Union guard stationed there and driven them into the buildings. When they refused to surrender he tried smoking them out by burning hay at the lower windows. Riordan, camped nearby, heard the disturbance and caught the Rangers at a disadvantage. The result was one of the worst defeats of Mosby's career. Union General Robert Milroy, bolstered by this turn of events, ordered all Rangers stopped. He wanted Mosby and Fitzgerald captured, dead or alive and while they were at it, they might as well capture White and McNeil. The life of the partisan fighter or better known title, the guerrilla fighter, was more in danger than ever and Marc Riordan was one of the men ordered to stop them.

Marc stood looking down at the valley beneath him while Wes Lansing paced. "This is God's country, Wes. Did you know that? I have traveled all over the world and have never seen anything as beautiful, even with a war going on. Take a deep breath and enjoy the clean crisp air."

"If we don't get out of here we might never take another breath. I heard Mosby was seen in this area this morning. I wouldn't be surprised if Fitzgerald's Raiders are about too."

Marc tried to keep his voice casual. "It seems Morgan is staying close to the West Virginia lines. Rumor has it something big is going to take place and

I'm sure Morgan will be right in the middle."

Marc Riordan was right. A plan had been set in motion to destroy the Cheat River Bridge, a major key to the Union army and Fitzgerald's Raiders were the key to it.

Everything seemed to go against the Confederates as they set their plan in motion. Snow and heavy rains struck in the dying days of winter, pushing streams over their banks and turning little meandering rivulets into angry torrents. Then on top of that the engineer who was to wreck the bridge was taken ill with fever. It wasn't until the 20th of April when Morgan's troops, along with many others, moved into the West Virginia area. Fourteeen out of the first twenty days they had rain and the roads were so deep in mud it took them nine hours to travel two miles.

Finally reaching the bridge, they destroyed one span, 600 feet long, and set fire to 150,000 barrels of oil beneath the rest of the bridge.

Morgan stood on a hillside watching the explosions. The noise was deafening as one barrel after another exploded. The river was soon covered with oil and the flames leaped from boat to boat until for miles it was a river of fire. The sound could be heard for miles, resembling the roar of distant thunder.

Morgan looked at Jubal who stood silently watching the scene. "It's beyond description, wouldn't you say?"

"I have never seen anything like it. I just hope Jones is doing his job on the bridge since we gave him this diversion."

"And what a diversion it is. I understand Imboden has acquired over 3000 head of cattle and some real fine horses. Yes, I would say it has been a good day. I just hope Michael isn't overdoing it. This raid has been hard on even the healthiest man."

"Aye, girl, but I have never seen him happier. I guess when you have come close to death, life seems awfully good, no matter what."

Morgan and her raiders headed back to the Winchester area, confident that they had done a good job on the bridge—but the Cheat River Bridge still towered on its stanchions, ready to move the trains of the B & O railroad, carrying supplies to the Union. The bridge had been repaired immediately. Crews followed close on the heels of the Rebels, throwing up in a matter of hours spans that would have taken a builder months in peacetime.

Shortly after dawn Morgan began preparing her report. She summarized their efforts, reporting that they had set fire to sixteen railroad bridges, 150,000 barrels of oil and a large number of Federal boats, tanks and trains besides demolishing the 600 foot span, putting the Cheat River Bridge out of commission. She was interrrupted by the sound of horses approaching fast. Jubal rushed into her tent announcing General Robert E. Lee's arrival with the general right on his heels.

Morgan had seen the general from a distance, but had never met him personally. He was an impressive looking man with white hair and beard and a presence that commanded respect. Morgan felt she should bow, but then he smiled and reached for her hand.

"Captain Fitzgerald, I have been most anxious to meet you. Stuart speaks very highly of you and your accomplishments."

"Thank you, sir. I am honored that you would come here. Please, won't you sit down?"

"Your accomplishments in the West Virginia area were amazing, but I am afraid I have some unfortunate news. The Cheat River Bridge is repaired and traffic is flowing smoothly again."

"That's impossible. We took out a 600 foot span that would take months to repair."

"Hanse McNeill, who stayed behind to finish at the mills, gave me his report late last night. He said the Federals moved in before you were out of the area and began repairing the span. They had it ready for use in a matter of hours."

Morgan sank dejectedly into her chair. "I don't know what to say, sir. I was convinced the one span was all that was necessary. The engineer backed me on this theory."

"I know, captain, but it's not as bad as it sounds. Of course, we would have been better off with the bridge out, but the supplies that were acquired more than made up for the disappointment. Grumble Jones figures he brought back 3000 head of cattle and 1200 fine horses. You did this with 1,500 men while the enemy with 45,000 men nearby failed to stop you. Believe me, some Union officer will be severely dealt with for letting you get away with this. It was our victory, dear—your victory. Now, *Major* Fitzgerald, I have more important work for you."

Chapter Nine

June is a beautiful time in Virginia, filled with the sweet smell of honeysuckle, lilacs and apple blossoms. Her rolling, rocky hillsides, surrounded by stone-walls and split-rail fences, are covered with dogwood and redbud trees, all pink and white like a fairy-land. It is a time when the young think of romance, a cooling off in the swimming hole, picnics with sweet tasting corn, fried chicken and luscious melons ripe from the garden. But June in 1863 was not a normal time for Virginia; the air was filled with the stench of death and the hillsides were covered with the bodies of men and animals left to the cruel fate of nature. Barns and stables that had once housed thoroughbred horses and prime cattle were now heaps of charcoal dotting the countryside. Yet at this time, the South was still in command. Added to the victories of Bull Run and Cedar Mountain was now Chancellorsville. Unfortunately, there was little cause for celebration, for now added to the ranks of Turner Ashby and the "gallant" Pelham was General "Stonewall" Jackson who died shortly after the Chancellorsville battle. Gloom seemed to hang heavy over the Confederate camps, including the camp of Fitzgerald's Raiders where activity had completely ceased.

Jubal Kelly knelt at the campfire, pouring himself a cup of coffee. He took one drink and poured it onto the fire. "I can be taking most anything but this peanut coffee. What I wouldn't give for a cup of Effie's brewed coffee."

Michael Fitzgerald smiled as he sipped the strange tasting brew. "How about one of her fried chicken dinners. Nobody could fix chicken like her. Do you remember the picnics she'd fix. Oh, God, what apple pies. Nobody in Virginia cooked like Effie."

"Aye, I remember your sweet mother and Effie preparing Sunday supper on the banks of the river. I wish I had thought to tell your mother how much I appreciated her."

"She knew, Jubal. She loved you very much."

"That's kind of you to say, Michael. She was a wonderful woman. Your father was a very lucky man to have had such happiness even for a short while."

"They had nineteen years of happiness, Jubal. If any woman was ever loved, she was. Father absolutely doted on her. I don't think he ever looked at another woman."

"No, Michael, I dinna' imagine he did." Jubal answered uneasily. "I wonder how Morgan is? I dinna' like the idea of her being alone on this assignment."

"She'll be fine, Jubal. Stuart and Mosby are in daily contact with her. Besides, she is probably safer there than here."

"Aye, I suppose you're right. I just hope she doesn't run into that Yankee, Riordan again."

Another plan to capture Mosby had gone awry and an ambush had ended in a massacre when Union soldiers, hiding in the trees, opened fire on their own cavalry. Mosby was not even in the area at the time. It seemed Union Generals and government officials were stung and embarrassed by the enemy degradation this close to the Union capital and they wanted an end put to it.

Captain Marc Riordan was ushered into General Hooker's office and shown to a seat at one end of a long table while General Milroy and General Pleasanton took seats at the other end.

"Son, I'm told you're familiar with guerrilla operations, particularly those of Mosby and Fitzgerald," stated General Hooker.

"Yes, sir, I've made a study of their operations."

"We mean to do something about them, captain. We haven't been able to get a supply train through the Valley for three months. We have a hundred thousand men and eight thousand horses in that area and we have to get food and ammunition to them. We've tried everything, but they always seem to know exactly when our trains are moving and what force is on them. I feel we have a spy in our service, and that's where you come in. We want you to smoke him out; then perhaps capturing Mosby and Fitzgerald will be easier if the spy is in touch with them. General Smyth is in charge of the supply trains working out of Warrenton. I suggest you start there. You'll answer to me and no one else. Go where you have to, do what you have to, but get me those damned guerrillas. Our next move will be Milroy's plan and I must be honest, I don't like it."

"May I ask what that plan is, sir?"

"General Milroy thinks we can bribe Mosby."

Marc laughed. "What makes you think Mosby could be bribed? He's a hero to the Confederacy and the type who loves the admiration of his men and fellow Virginians."

"Every man has his price, captain, including this murdering horse-thief," stated Milroy.

"No offense meant, sir, but I wouldn't want to be the one who offeres him the bribe."

"Enough, gentlemen, Captain Riordan must be on his way. If you'll excuse us, I have some last minute instructions for him."

Marc was glad to be getting away from Washington. He always enjoyed seeing his mother, but the politics of war disgusted him.

After searching a good part of the morning, Marc finally found a small boarding house in the center of Warrenton whose owner reluctantly agreed to let him stay. The small southern town was filled with Federal troops and Marc could understand the hostility of the townspeople. He was sure he'd feel the same if his home were invaded by the enemy, and this particular town had changed hands a dozen or more times already. Fortunately he had been warmly greeted by General Smyth and his staff and had even been persuaded to escort the general's daughter, Belle, to a dance the next evening. Marc had met the young lady in her father's office and wondered why she should need her escorts picked. She was a lovely blonde about twenty, with a full figure she flaunted provocatively. He looked forward to someone who might take his mind off the green eyes which seemed to haunt him night and day. She was in his thoughts even more since he had not heard anything about her or her outfit for more than two months. The last he had heard, she had been involved in the raid in West Virginia. The Union suffered a terrible loss, but things could have been worse if the bridge the Confederates had tried to destroy hadn't been salvaged.

He wondered if she could have been injured. He moaned inwardly as he thought of her lying maimed in some God-forsaken field tent. No, he told himself, her whole unit seems to have disappeared so it doesn't seem likely she was injured. He was sure he would be hearing of her again—she showed up anywhere there was trouble.

God, he could remember the soft, gentle touch of her hands when she had taken care of him during his illness. Then he laughed as he remembered her hitting him over the head with a gun butt. What an unpredictable creature she was! He wondered how he could have any pleasant memories of her.

He cursed himself for letting her occupy his mind again when he had so much to do. He headed to the quarters of the general's aide to see what he could find out about the people who served here. Another supply train was going to be sent to the Valley in three days and he wanted to be sure this one got through.

Marc finished dressing and studied the effect in the mirror. He shook his head in disgust. "This is stupid. Men are out there getting killed and I'm going to a dance," he said aloud, pouring himself a large drink. "I think I hate the politics of war as much as the killing. At least I feel like a man when I'm fighting—instead of a hypocrite."

The owner of the boarding house gruffly announced a young woman waited with a carriage. Marc looked back at the mirror. "What's this world coming to? Women picking up men. She'll probably lead on the dance floor too." He smiled at his reflection. "What's wrong with you, Riordan? You haven't been the same since meeting that Irish witch." He picked up his gloves and headed for the carriage, trying to put all thoughts of the green-eyed Rebel from his mind.

Marc was delighted to find Belle ever lovelier than the day before. He hadn't enjoyed a woman's company in quite a while and was determined to enjoy the evening with this lovely creature.

Belle immediately wrapped her arm in his and began chattering about how awful times were. Thoughts of Morgan flashed through his mind, remembering her saying how she couldn't stand women who stayed home and complained about their inconveniences.

"Captain, are you listening to me?"

"I'm sorry, Belle. Of course, you're right. This war has caused great inconveniences to both sides."

Belle wondered why he sounded so irritable. She sat back and studied his handsome face. The moment he walked into her father's office she knew she had to get to know him better. She had already promised to go to the party with one of her father's aides, but she begged off, telling him that General Hooker insisted Captain Marc Riordan be treated as a very important guest. She smiled to herself. What would she want with some pipsqueak of a lieutenant when she could have this ruggedly handsome man—and have him she would. He was tall and powerfully built, his broad shoulders stretching the material of his uniform. His face was bronzed from the sun, making his eyes an incredible shade of blue.

Marc pondered his situation. This girl suddenly reminded him of Rachel and he wished he hadn't accepted the invitation. God, how he hated women who complained all the time.

The carriage came to a halt in front of a large, white columned mansion, one of the many homes now occupied by Federal officers in Warrenton. The warm, rich patterns of the wood seemed to dance as the crystal chandeliers glowed overhead. He could see a long, curving staircase just off the entrance. Marc listened to the sound of voices and couldn't help but think of how this house had probably once been filled with the happy sounds of children. He wondered where the family was now and again Morgan came to mind as he remembered her telling how Union soldiers had taken over her home.

Music echoed from the elegant ballroom, filling the house with its lilting sound. Marc tried to shake the melancholy mood that threatened to ruin his evening.

"Ah, captain, Belle, there you are. Come, I want to introduce you around," General Smyth said as he took his daughter's arm and moved toward the receiving line.

Marc spent the next half hour trying to be pleasant as he met the many officers and their escorts. He hoped to find something that might give him a lead in his efforts to find a spy, but so far he found nothing.

"Did you hear what happened today?" a young officer asked. "That horse-thief, Mosby rode into town and got a haircut. Sat right in front of two Union officers. When we asked the barber why he didn't say anything, he said he had been cutting Mosby's hair once a month for the last year and nobody told him he should do otherwise."

Belle never released her possessive hold on Marc's arm as they moved from one group to the next. She was by far the loveliest woman there and most of the officers seemed to be quite familiar with her.

"Please, poppa, enough introductions. I want to dance with Captain Riordan. By the way, where is your new lady friend, poppa?"

"She'll be down shortly. She had been out riding this afternoon and lost track of time."

"That's a likely story. I'm sure she just wanted to make one of her spectacular entrances."

"Please, Belle, you have made it quite clear how you feel about her, but I would appreciate it if you wouldn't be rude. I'm very fond of the young lady. Besides, Captain Riordan doesn't want to listen to our family quarrels."

"I am sure Captain Riordan would be appalled to know you were seeing a woman young enough to be your daughter."

Marc took Belle by the arm. "I think it's time we danced. Your father is old enough to take care of himself."

The room suddenly went silent. Marc followed the

stares of everyone in the room to the staircase. His intake of breath was loud enough to be heard, but the figure descending the stairs had the rapt attention of everyone in the room.

There was very little resemblance to the dirty-faced kid in buckskins he remembered, but he knew without a doubt the beautiful woman gracefully descending the marble staircase was none other than Morgan Fitzgerald.

Morgan sensed a strange electricity in the room. She glanced over the crowd and suddenly her eyes locked with the ice-blue eyes she remembered so well. She hesitated, a flicker of fear crossing her lovely face, then quickly composed herself and gave the cluster of men at the foot of the stairs a dazzling smile.

Marc noticed the expression on General Smyth's face as Morgan glided down the stairs, and realized she was the girl Belle had spoken of. Belle tugged at his arm, but he couldn't take his eyes off Morgan. She wore a magnificent shimmering green satin gown that was designed to please men. Her shoulders gleamed like pale satin above the deeply cut bodice. The skirt clung softly to her curves without the traditional hoops most of the women were wearing. Her hair was arranged in soft curls, falling from the crown and caught up with strands of pearls.

"Close your mouth, father," Belle snapped. "You look ridiculous drooling."

Leslie Smyth headed for Morgan, ignoring his daughter's insults. He kissed her hand, then led her back through the men flocked around.

"Captain Marcus Riordan, I want you to meet Morgana York."

Marc swept her a mockingly elegant bow, then slowly kissed her hand, "Morgana, is it? Very unusual name."

"Do you think so, captain? Morgan answered as casually as her nerves would allow.

General Smyth possessively placed his arm around Morgan's bare shoulders. "Morgan is a very unusual woman. One of the few who doesn't get bored with talk of the war. In fact, she insists I tell her everything that goes on," the general stated proudly.

Marc raised an eyebrow as he looked at her flushed face. "You are a very unusual woman," he answered, knowing without a doubt she was the spy he sought.

Belle had been silent as the introductions were made, but couldn't stand all the attention Morgan received. 'I see my dressmaker was able to throw something together for you. The material is quite nice."

"Thank you, Belle. I appreciate your telling me about her. I was very pleased with her work. As a matter of fact, I have asked her to make several things for me."

The general took Morgan's arm. "Excuse us, but Morgana promised me the first dance. You two enjoy yourselves."

Morgan looked into Marc's intense eyes, still waiting for him to expose her, but he said nothing. "It was a pleasure meeting you, captain," she said regaining a little of her composure.

"I hope to have the pleasure of dancing with you this evening," Marc said. "That is, of course, if the general doesn't mind."

"I'm very selfish where Morgana is concerned, but perhaps since you are my guest." The general patted his daughter on the cheek. "Have a good time, dear. I certainly plan to."

Marc watched as Morgan glided into the general's arms. He wondered if the feeling he experienced when he was near her was noticeable to anyone. He had no explanation for it, other than he wanted her more than any woman he had ever met.

"I can't stand that woman! She is so condescending. If she thinks she is going to marry my father, she is mistaken!"

Marc didn't seem to hear anything Belle said. She watched him as his eyes followed the couple on the dance floor. "Quite clever of her to wear green."

"I'm sorry, Belle. What did you say?"

She took his arm possessively. "I was just saying that green is certainly her color. It sets her apart from the crowd, wouldn't you say?"

Marc looked back towards the dance floor where Morgan smiled up at her partner. Belle was right, he thought. She made every other woman seem dull in comparison, including the woman on his arm, who only an hour ago, he thought could help him forget the green-eyed witch on the dance floor. Her auburn hair seemed to glow in the candlelight as she was twirled around the floor.

Belle tugged on Marc's arm and he realized she was still waiting for his reply. "She is lovely, but certainly no lovelier than yourself."

"Why, captain, that's as close as you've come to paying me a compliment. Now when are you going to ask me to dance?"

Marc bowed before her. "Forgive me, lovely lady. May I have this dance?"

Marc listened attentively as Belle pointed out the different couples around them, but he still couldn't keep his eyes off Morgan. He felt his anger rising as she flashed an alluring smile when the general kissed her cheek.

"I can't imagine what she sees in my father. He's almost sixty."

Marc realized Belle knew he was staring at Morgan and her father. "Her type probably is looking for power and money. She's not going to find too many young men with that combination."

"Why, captain, you surprise me," Belle said smugly. "I didn't think you'd be so observant. Of course, I didn't want to say that, but since you did, I'm sure that is exactly why she's interested in him. She is a tramp. She goes with him everyplace, even to his meetings. Can you imagine that? You'd think he'd be embarrassed; instead he asks her opinion on everything."

A young lieutenant tapped Marc on the shoulder and he gladly gave up his talkative partner and headed for the side of the room where he could watch Morgan dancing with a young officer. Leaning against the wall, he lit a long, thin cigar. God, she is beautiful and he had slept next to her and not touched her. Well, if he ever had the opportunity again, he sure as hell wouldn't be so honorable.

Jamming out the cigar, he headed for Morgan. "Do you mind, captain?" he said as he lightly tapped the officer on the shoulder. For a moment the soldier looked as if he were going to refuse, but finally stepped aside. Morgan gracefully moved into his arms. He breathed deep of her scent as they silently moved around the dance floor. Her small figure felt as if it had been made to fit in his arms, he thought.

Morgan looked into his blue eyes, feeling breathless. She realized it was more excitement than fear that made her heart beat so rapidly and cursed herself for having so little control over her feelings.

"Your outfit is certainly an improvement over those damned buckskins," Marc said breaking the silence that prevailed between them.

"Do you think so, captain? I must admit I never thought to see you in your dress uniform. You look very nice."

"I'm sure you didn't expect to see me at all, or you wouldn't have been here; but your little game is finished."

Morgan smiled, her cat-like eyes twinkling. "Why, captain, whatever do you mean?"

"You know very well what I mean, Morgan. You're spying and if they catch you they'll hang you."

"You also have a great deal to lose if they find out who I am, captain. What reason would you give for not exposing me before now? If I recall correctly, your loyalty was questioned after you returned to Washington from our little journey. What would they think this time?"

"I don't plan to expose you here, my sweet, but I do plan to put an end to your trickery. Be sure to say goodby to your general tonight for it will be the last time you see him," Marc said angrily.

"Please keep your voice down, captain. Everyone is looking at us." Morgan stopped dancing and moved off toward an empty room that opened onto the ballroom. She glanced around, then closed the door behind them. "What do you intend to do, captain?"

"I don't know. I just know I would hate to see that lovely neck stretched."

Morgan shivered as he ran a finger down her slender neck, ignoring her protests. "How dare you show up here and threaten me!"

"Dare, my sweet? You forget you're a Rebel spy in the midst of the Union army." He watched her expression change from arrogance to fear. "Be careful, my Irish Rebel, I'm not sure what I'm going to do with you, but if you'll forgive my bluntness, I'm liable to see that pretty neck stretched yet."

Morgan was silent, rooted to the spot. She wanted to claw his eyes out, but knew she was at his mercy at the moment. "Just tell me what you plan to do. I don't intend playing games."

"Is that what you do with your general? Play games?

Morgan's green eyes flashed angrily. "What I do is none of your business, Yankee."

"That's where you're wrong, Morgan. I'm making it my business. I cannot let you go on spying."

The door opened abruptly behind them. "Morgana, I wondered where you had disappeared to."

Morgan moved to the general's side. "I am sorry, Les. The noise and heat had become unbearable and Captain Riordan kindly escorted me in here." She looked at Marc, challenging him to say differently.

"I suggest you return to my daughter, captain. She is looking for you."

135

Marc hesitated a moment, but realized this wasn't the time or the place to say anything. "I was just leaving, sir. Good evening Miss York. It was nice talking to you."

Marc made his way through the crowd looking for Belle. He found her surrounded by young men vying for her attention. "Oh gentlemen, I am sorry, but here is my escort now and I promised him the next dance."

Marc moved Belle onto the dance floor, but his mind was still on Morgan. Something has to be done, he thought. He couldn't let her go on spying.

"I should have stayed among my admirers, captain. You are ignoring me again."

"That's not fair, Belle. I am certainly your most ardent admirer."

Belle smiled. "Really, Marc. I thought you were smitten by that redhead on my father's arm."

Marc glanced over his shoulder and saw Morgan dancing with General Smyth again. "How could I be smitten when I have you, my pet?"

Belle giggled. She had felt neglected all evening by this dashing captain who had caught the eye of every woman in the room, but now he was all hers and she planned to make the most of it. She smiled her most alluring smile as she promised him she was his to do with as he wished.

Marc almost missed a step at her forward declaration. He thought he had a flighty girl on his hands and here she was offering herself for the evening. He wondered how the hell he was going to get out of this without hurting her feeings. He almost laughed aloud when he remembered only an hour ago he was trying to figure a way to get her in bed. Funny how that damned green-eyed witch could take his mind off things. He tried to sound casual as he questioned Belle about Morgan. It seemed she had been introduced to the general as the niece of the Hawthornes, a Warrenton family who had been most receptive to the Union officers. According to Belle, she was staying at the Hawthorne house. He had been sure she was staying with the general since she made her entrance from his quarters.

Marc questioned Belle about any companions who might be in town with Morgan, but she didn't remember seeing her with anyone. She was sure her father was the only companion Morgan had. She had arrived in Warrenton two months ago, claiming her family's home had been destroyed in a fire and the Hawthornes were the only family she had.

Marc rubbed his beard. Two months ago was exactly the time the Union supply trains had started running into trouble.

"Belle, I hate to do this to you, but I must leave immediately. I'll take you home, or perhaps you'd prefer to stay and join your father and his friend."

Belle looked at Marc in disbelief. "But . . . I thought . . ."

"Belle, I'm sure you realize I'm here on a very important mission. Something has broken and I must pursue it. This is very urgent or I wouldn't be leaving you."

Marc felt like a heel as he kissed Belle's pouting mouth and quickly left. He was sure she'd find someone else in a matter of minutes, but he still felt badly. He went to his rooming house and changed, then packed his few belongings and headed for the livery stable. He still wasn't sure what he was going to do, but he knew he had to put some plan in motion, and fast. Morgan wasn't going to hang around and wait for him to arrest her.

As he saddled his horse, he questioned the sleepy-eyed liveryman about the Hawthorne house and found it was located at the edge of town.

Marc was almost to the house when he heard a carriage behind him. Heading Satan off the rode, he watched from a grove of trees as the carriage moved past with Morgan and the general inside. He gritted his teeth as he heard Morgan's seductuve laughter. He followed a short distance behind until they came to a halt in front of a large red brick mansion surrounded by big oak trees. Marc tied his horse to a tree and watched as General Smyth helped Morgan from the coach. He could not hear what was being said, but he could hear Morgan's low seductive laugh. They stopped on the porch and kissed, then instead of the general going inside, he returned to the waiting carriage.

Marc remained in the shadows watching for a lamp to be lit. Suddenly the room over the front porch glowed with a warm light and he could see her shadow move in front of the window. He studied the situation and decided to scale the trellis at the side of the porch and enter from there. When he reached the window he stopped. Morgan paced the room, a worried expression on her face. She jumped as he raised the window and stepped inside.

"Come in, captain. I was sure our conversation wasn't over, but I didn't think you would show up this soon."

"I wasn't about to take a chance on your escaping again. I told you, I cannot let you go on with your spying."

"How do you plan to expose me without exposing yourself?"

"I didn't say I was going to expose you. I said I was going to stop you."

"Leslie won't believe you. I'll tell him you came to my room and made improper advances. When I rejected you, you said you'd accuse me of spying."

"That's very clever, Morgan, but it isn't going to come to that," Marc said moving toward her. Morgan slowly backed away, realizing his intent as his eyes turned a cold blue.

"When I saved your life, I never suspected I'd end up having to take it."

"You can't be serious," she said glancing around for some means of escape.

Marc's hands encircled Morgan's slender throat. "You have caused the death of many men, Morgan, possibly my own brother. I tried to convince you to stop and now I have to stop you."

Morgan could not answer as he increased the pressure on her throat. She began clawing at his hands as blackness engulfed her; all feeling leaving her body. Her knees buckled and she leaned heavily against him. Suddenly he released her. Falling to the floor, she lay gasping for breath. Marc stood over her, his face black with anger. "Damn you, woman! I'm sure you'd haunt me the rest of my life if I killed you. The only way I can stop you is to take you to prison myself."

Morgan whispered in a strained voice. "No, you can't do that. Finish me now! I will not rot in prison." She grabbed his leg as he moved away from her. "Please, I saved your life once. Don't send me to die in prison. Kill me here and now or I'll kill you the first time you turn your back on me."

"I suggest you get into your traveling clothes, Morgan. It's going to be a long, hard trip."

Morgan was too weak and shaken to get up. She rubbed her throat where the red marks of his fingers already appeared.

"Get up, Morgan!"

"I can't."

Marc angrily pulled her to her feet and shoved her toward the bed. "If you're not changed in five minutes I'll do it myself." He stepped toward her, an evil smile touching his mouth. "Perhaps you would enjoy that since your general left you high and dry."

"Stay away from me, you Yankee bastard!" Morgan said hoarsely. Turning her back to him, she began to struggle out of her clothes. She could feel his eyes on her and wished she had a gun in her hand. She grabbed her saddle bag from under the bed and pulled the buckskins from them.

"Wear something besides those damned buckskins!"

"I don't have any other riding clothes, captain, and I don't plan to ride side saddle. Besides, these buckskins are my trademark and if I'm going to hang, I might as well hang in them."

Marc smiled as she pulled the tight fitting leather

breeches up over her shapely legs. The outfit clung snugly to every curve of her body and he wondered again how he could have ever mistaken her for a man. He turned back to the window and lit a cigar.

Morgan took the opportunity to freshen herself. Standing at the dresser, she tried to think of some way to leave a message for anyone who came looking for her. The talc—glancing in the mirror she saw Marc still preoccupied. Quickly spreading the powder over the top of the dresser, she wrote in the dust, Riordan—Washington.

"Hurry up, Morgan."

She stuffed a few belongings into her saddle bags and turned to face him. "My horse is at the livery stable."

"You can ride behind me."

"No! I'll not leave my horse behind for some Yankee to mistreat!"

Marc softened when he remembered her affection for the horse she called Gambler. He agreed to let her take the horse if she promised not to cause him any trouble.

"You seem to forget, Yankee, I'm in enemy territory."

"Just don't you forget it, Morgan," Marc said helping her down the trellis after running his hand over the dresser.

He shoved her toward the woods where his horse was tied.

She turned angrily and faced him. "Is this treatment really necessary?"

"I just want you to remember you have very little control over what happens to you."

Morgan glared at him, her eyes flashing like emeralds. She lifted her chin defiantly. "You'll never have control over me, Yankee."

Marc ignored her as he gave her a hand up behind him. Quietly they slipped through the dark streets of the town to the now empty stable. Marc lit a lantern once they were inside and led her horse out of its stall. Morgan saddled the mare then mounted. Taking a piece of rawhide from his pocket, Marc wrapped it around her wrists, tying them to the pommel of the saddle.

"What's the matter, Yankee, are you afraid of me?"

Marc pulled the rope tighter, causing it to cut into Morgan's wrists. She gasped with the pain. "God, how I wish I had let you die when I had the chance. Don't ever turn your back on me, Yankee!"

"Don't worry, Rebel. I know better," he said as he took the reins from her hands and mounted his horse leading her behind.

"Damn bitch," he mumbled. He was going to have to watch her every move. She was smart all right. It was a good thing he'd seen her writing that message in the talc.

Chapter Ten

Morgan rode sullenly, contemplating how she seemed to be reliving an experience that had taken a tremendous toll on her—an experience that had caused her to do a great deal of soul-searching. She had no way of knowing the man at her side was thinking the same thoughts. He cursed himself for his weakness for her, knowing she would be his downfall one of these days. Even as he had tried to choke the life from her, his thoughts were of possessing her. It had been months since they had been together and his desire for her hadn't diminished in the least. He was sure if he could just make love to her once he could exorcize this spell she had over him.

The eastern sky was a pale pink as the sun began to rise. They had been in the saddle for almost five hours and Morgan was tired and hungry. She studied the surroundings as they rode and realized they were not heading for Washington. "Where are you taking me?"

Marc smiled. "Quite observant, aren't you?"

"I want to know where we're going?" Morgan insisted.

"I'm meeting my mother and some friends at Harpers Ferry and then we'll go on to Washington."

"You have a mother?" Morgan asked sarcastically. "Poor woman. I hate to be a burden to you, captain. It must be nice not to let the war interfere with your social life. Did you know there are men out there suffering and dying who haven't seen their families in years?"

"Shut up, Morgan! I'm tired of listening to you. I'd hate to have to gag that pretty mouth to get a little peace."

"Go ahead and gag me, because it's going to be the only peace you have."

Marc suddenly stopped his horse and listened intently. "We're going to have to take to the woods. I hear troops coming this way and I don't know if they're yours or mine."

"Why don't we just wait and see, captain. I've got nothing to lose."

"Is that right, Rebel? No matter whether they are Rebels or Yankees, they probably haven't had a woman in quite a while. I wonder if you will still be so mouthy when they're finished with you?"

Morgan raised her chin in a gesture of defiance before spurring her horse into the woods as Marc's cruel laughter echoed in her ears. Oh, how she hated him!

Traveling became much harder the further they went into the dense woods. Morgan bit her lip in pain as one after another low-lying limb hit her in the face, but her stubbornness prevented her from crying out.

Marc turned around to check behind them and noticed the welts and bloody scratches on her face. He brought the horses to a stop, took his knife from the top of his boot and quickly sliced through the rawhide that held Morgans hands. "Why didn't you say something?"

"I figured you would only tie me tighter if I complained."

He held his hands up to lift her off the horse, but she slipped down without his aid. "Damn, you are a stubborn woman!" He poured water from his canteen onto his scarf and touched it to the scratches on Morgan's face. She stood perfectly still yet tears welled up in her eyes. "Listen, Morgan, this stubbornness of yours isn't going to make things any easier for you. We are going to be traveling together for quite awhile. I'll try to be more considerate of you if you will stop meeting me head-on at every turn."

Morgan was too tired to argue. She shook her head, but didn't dare look at him for fear he'd see how totally exhausted and defeated she really was.

Marc studied her under the wide-brimmed hat as he wiped the blood from her face. She had her eyes closed, her long lashes lying softly against her face. God, how he wanted to take her in his arms and love her—just once. Raindrops began to pelt the leaves on the trees and before he finished administering to her cuts the rain broke through the shelter of trees, quickly soaking them. "Do you have a poncho?"

Morgan shook her head no. Marc loosened his bedroll and took out his poncho. He slipped it over her head and guided her back to the waiting horses. She did not protest when he helped her mount nor when he took a flask from his inside pocket and offered it to her. She took a deep gulp and shivered. "We'll stop before long and you can rest."

Morgan looked at him puzzled, but said nothing.

The roads quickly became a mire as the rains increased. Marc glanced over his shoulder at Morgan who rode with her head bent over. Damn, he certainly didn't want to break her spirit. That was what he admired most about her. "Are you all right, Morgan?"

She raised her head and looked at him but still said nothing.

"There has to be shelter around here. Just hang on a little longer."

They rode a little further before coming out into a clearing where a small farmhouse stood. Marc stopped the horses in front of house, but Morgan made no attempt to dismount. He held his arms out to her and she reluctantly accepted his help. Morgan leaned on the railing of the porch as Marc knocked at the door. When no one answered he turned the knob, finding the door open.

"Hello, is anyone here?" No one answered.

He led Morgan into the house. "Will you be all right while I look around?"

Morgan numbly dropped on the sofa, but made no move to remove her hat or poncho.

"I'll try to find some firewood. Why don't you get out of those wet things."

Morgan still didn't move. Marc knelt in front of her, taking her cold hands in his. "Come on Rebel, where is that spirit and determination?"

"It's very difficult to keep my spirit when you try to break me at every turn," Morgan spat viciously.

Marc's eyes saddened. "No, Morgan, you're wrong. I have never tried to break you."

"Well, don't delude yourself, Yankee. I will still have my revenge."

"That's more like it, my pet," Marc said patting her on the cheek, "I was afraid that old general had tamed your spirit."

Morgan's eyes flashed agrily. "You bastard . . . you!"

Before she could finish Marc patted her cheek and left grinning. He led the horses around the back of the house to the barn. The place looked as if it had been deserted just recently. There was wood stacked outside the back door and feed stored in the barn. A small smokehouse stood a few feet away. Marc was sure it would be empty, but decided to check anyway. Hanging inside were several slabs of bacon and a ham. He grabbed the ham off the hook and headed for the house whistling.

"Look at this. Ham, and there's bacon too." Marc shouted like a child finding new toys under the Christmas tree.

Morgan struggled to get up. "Where are the people who live here?"

"I don't know. The place seems to be deserted. How lucky can we be. I thought we would be fortunate to find a barn someplace and here we can spend the evening in luxury."

Morgan looked at him strangely for a moment then started looking around. She opened the door to the kitchen and found it stocked with enough staples to cook a good meal. "How do you think this place has escaped the pillages of the armies? I haven't seen a house untouched in this area for years."

"I don't know, but why question fate?" Marc said as he climbed the stairs. "Even the beds are made," he hollered down.

Morgan found it all very strange. No one in these times had the comforts this house seemed to have; a

147

well stocked kitchen, meat in the smokehouse. She shivered. It seemed as if they had been transported to another time . . . or was it as people whispered, the man upstairs really was a devil. She jumped as Marc spoke behind her.

"Can you cook?"

She smiled for the first time. "Better than any Yankee."

"Good. If you'll fix us something to eat I'll bring wood in for the fireplace in the bedroom."

Marc made several trips through the kitchen as he carried the wood up the stairs. When he finished he sat at the table and watched Morgan as she cooked. "If anyone had told me I would be spending the evening with a beautiful Rebel spy, I would have bet them anything I had they were crazy."

Morgan continued to stir the cornmeal. "I wouldn't have thought you the gambling type, captain."

He laughed. "Only on a sure thing and when I have to save a lady's honor."

Morgan blushed. "I haven't forgotten, captain, but I wouldn't have been in that predicament if you hadn't placed me in that house of sin."

"I wasn't trying to start an argument, Morgan. Gambling is a real problem among our soldiers. Is it the same in your army?"

Morgan looked at him suspiciously, then realized he wasn't prying, he was only making conversation. She turned back to her chores. "Yes, orders have been issued forbidding gambling, but it doesn't seem to do any good."

"I guess it's the same all over. We had one fellow

who had a vermin he claimed could beat any other in camp. He would insist they each be put on a plate and the first one to vacate the plate was the winner. Come to find out this fellow was heating his plate so his louse was the quickest to evacuate."

Morgan began to laugh, then suddenly leaned against the table, her body wracked with sobs. Marc jumped to his feet and held her to his chest. "What is it, Morgan? What did I say?"

Morgan pulled away, wiping her face with the apron she wore. "I'm tired. Tired of death and destruction and of meeting you at every turn. I have no hope for my future and here I am laughing with you like a school girl," she said choking back a sob.

Marc knew how to handle her temper, but he wasn't sure how to handle this side of her. He placed his arms around her again. "Let's forget the war while we're here. A day or two of peace surely won't hurt us. What do you say, Rebel?"

Morgan smiled through tear-filled eyes. "You know I'll still have to try to escape the first chance I get."

"Morgan, I promise I won't let anything happen to you if you'll just cooperate."

Morgan pulled away. "Cooperate? What are you talking about? Spell it out, Yankee. What do you mean, cooperate?"

"Calm down, lady. Your Irish temper is showing. All I meant is for you to stop fighting me." Marc walked away and casually sampled the cornbread. "I haven't had good cornbread since I was home a few months ago."

Morgan wasn't quite sure why he had changed the

subject, but she went back to her cooking. "Must be nice to get home as often as you do."

Marc licked his finger after dipping it in the bowl. "If you recall, I had a hole in my back."

Morgan stopped stirring. "You seemed to have recuperated very well."

Marc playfully tweaked her nose. "I had a pretty good doctor. By the way, thanks for leaving Jubal Kelly behind. I enjoyed his company."

"That's funny, because Jubal said the same thing. He said he hoped he never had to face you on the battlefield."

"Hey, no war talk, remember?" Marc said playfully.

Morgan served the ham and beans along with the cornbread. She proudly watched as Marc devoured the contents of his plate. "Do you Yankees have anything like that, captain?"

Marc leaned back in his chair and lit a long, thin cigar. "I don't think I've tasted anything as good since I went to school in Charlottesville."

Morgan's smile faded. "What do you mean, when you went to school in Charlottesville."

"When I went to the law school at the University of Virginia."

Morgan slammed her fist on the table. "How could you fight against your friends? Have you no morals, no loyalty?"

"Morgan, we were going to forget about war, remember?"

Morgan angrily began clearing the dishes away.

"Why are you mad? What difference does it make where I'm from?"

"I just don't understand you. Are you a Virginian?"

"Yes. I was born and raised in Virginia. My father was a senator from Virginia for many years before the war."

Morgan just shook her head. "How could you fight against your homeland?"

Marc stiffened in anger, then visibly forced himself to relax. "I didn't want to fight in this damned war at all. I was in France when the war broke out. My kid brother was a West Point graduate and chose to remain with the army. He was killed at Manassas just as your father was. I didn't feel I had any choice but to return and join the Union. I have answered all your damned questions now and I don't want to talk about anything to do with the war for the rest of the night."

"I'm sorry."

"Yeah, so am I. I sometimes think the ones who died early in the war were the lucky ones."

"Marc, was your brother's name Christopher?"

Marc looked surprised. "How did you know that?"

"When you were delirious you spoke of Christopher and Rachel."

"Enough talk. I have a surprise for you."

"A surprise? What kind of surprise?" Morgan asked.

"How would you like a hot tub bath in front of the fire to ease your tired, aching muscles?"

Morgan closed her eyes as if imagining the hot, steamy water. "Oh, God, that would be wonderful."

"All right, you finish cleaning up here and I'll heat water."

Morgan hummed as she washed the dishes. Perhaps this wasn't going to be so bad, she thought. At least

151

she felt that she understood this Yankee a little better. Anyway, she would escape soon, so a few pleasant days wouldn't hurt anything.

Marc hauled the water to the tub while Morgan rummaged through the house for towels and blankets. She entered the bedroom loaded down with her findings. The tub was filled to the brim with steaming water and the room was warm and glowing with a blazing fire.

Marc bowed before her. "Your bath awaits, madam."

Morgan curtsied. "Thank you, kind sir. Now I truly believe you're the devil. How else could all of this be possible? It's positively wicked to be enjoying such luxuries."

Marc smiled. "Didn't you know the devil makes wickedness attractive so he can corrupt the innocent?"

Morgan's face flushed. "Please, if you would leave now."

Marc smiled and hummed a little tune as he headed for the door. "I'll get some more firewood."

Morgan undressed and slowly lowered herself into the steaming tub. She lathered herself with the soap Marc had left on the chair next to her, then dipped under the water and scrubbed her hair. When she finished scrubbing she laid her head back against the tub and closed her eyes.

"Would you like your back scrubbed?"

Morgan sank under the water, unsuccessfully trying to cover herself. "What do you think you are doing in here? Get out this instant!"

"Surely you don't expect me to let that hot water go

152

to waste. I've been looking forward to a tub bath myself."

Morgan grabbed the towel off the chair and stood up. Marc lifted a dark brow. "It would be more fun with you in there. I happen to enjoy having my back scrubbed."

"You . . . you bastard! I should have known your consideration tonight was for some ulterior motive."

By now Marc stood completely naked, his manhood quite in evidence. Morgan was seething as she pulled a blanket from the bed and wrapped herself in it. She angrily headed for the door, but when she tried the handle it did not budge. She turned back to Marc who smiled as he held up the key. "You didn't think I was going to take a chance on your running away while I bathed or slept, did you?"

Morgan was so infuriated she could hardly speak. "I hate you . . . you Yankee bastard . . ."

"Shut up, Morgan. You're beginning to get on my nerves. Now sit down on that bed while I take my bath or I swear I'll put you over my knee and give you a beating you won't soon forget."

Morgan gritted her teeth, but sat on the bed with her back to him. "I'm going to shoot you the first chance I get, Yankee," she spat viciously.

Marc smiled a crooked smile. "I believe you would, Rebel, I believe you would." He stepped into the tub and lowered himself slowly. Morgan tried to ignore him as she dried her hair. The clock on the mantel ticked loudly, but not nearly as loud as her heart pounded in the silence. She had her back to him, but she could feel his intent gaze on her.

153

Marc lathered his body, humming as he did, then let the soap slip from his hand into the floor. "Would you mind, Rebel?"

"Get it yourself, Yankee," she sneered.

"All right, if you insist," he said, starting to get out of the tub.

"Stay where you are! I'll get it," Morgan said quickly jumping from the bed. "Don't you Yankees have any modesty?" she asked, sending him a withering look.

She handed him the soap, but instead of taking it he grabbed her by the wrist and with the other hand pulled the towel from her. Morgan was too shocked to speak for a moment.

"Damn, you are beautiful, Rebel," he said feeling desire rising in his loins as his eyes lingered on her firm, young breasts. He pulled her into the tub, splashing water all over the room. Wrapping his hand in her hair, he forced her mouth to meet his. Morgan bit down on his lip, drawing blood. "Damn—you little she-wolf!" Again he kissed her forcefully and this time she ceased fighting. Releasing her with one hand, he began to gently caress her. Morgan moaned, trying to push him away, but he held her tightly, savoring her mouth with his tongue. With one motion he lifted her and stepped from the tub. He gently laid her on the bed and began to rub her down with the towel.

"Please leave me alone. This has gone far enough," she begged.

"You are wrong, little one. It hasn't gone nearly far enough. I'm done with patience."

Morgan grabbed for the towel trying to cover herself. "I swear I'll kill you if you touch me, Yankee!"

Marc yanked the towel away. "I'm tired of your threats, Morgan. Let's see if you're worth all the trouble you've caused me."

Morgan choked back tears as Marc held her firmly beneath him. "Relax, little one, I'm not going to hurt you. My God, you travel with that band of cutthroats and give yourself to old men for their secrets. Why deny me your favors? Let me show you what a real man is like."

"Of all the arrogant, egotistical . . . you certainly have an inflated ego, Yankee."

"Do I, Rebel?" he questioned, the corner of his mouth lifting in a wicked grin. "We'll see."

Morgan kicked and flailed in a panic. "Wait, wait, listen to me. My men have never violated me. They know better than to ever think about it and I picked that old man so he wouldn't bother me. I have never . . ."

"Come now, Rebel, do you really expect me to believe that?"

"How dare you! Listen to me, Yankee. I out-rank you and I expect to be treated accordingly," Morgan desperately blurted out.

"I don't give a damn what your rank is or who you slept with to get it. Lie still before you get hurt."

Morgan kicked out at him, barely missing his manhood. "You'll have to kill me before I let you touch me."

"I don't think so, little one," he said covering her mouth with his.

She struggled beneath him until suddenly a warmth seem to spread through her. Oh God, what was happening to her, she wondered. Why did she want to give in to the warm pressure of his hands and body? She struggled to regain some control over her trembling body, but he held her firm.

"You are so beautiful, Morgan. Your skin is like velvet," he moaned, running his tongue over one nipple. "I've wanted you since the first time I laid eyes on you."

"Please don't do this. I beg you, let me up. It isn't fair. You are taking advantage of one weaker than you. Where is your honor?"

Marc whispered, his breath warm against her neck. "I never claimed to be fair or honorable where you're concerned, little one. Stop fighting me now. Let's both enjoy this night."

His lips moved over her body doing things she never imagined. Her senses rebelled against her mind. She gripped his hand, moaning with desire.

"That's better, my sweet. Why shouldn't we enjoy each other while we're together?"

His voice broke the spell Morgan was under and again she struggled. "Damn, you are a wildcat. Stop struggling before you get hurt." "I've waited a long time for this moment. You possess me, Morgan and I'll never be rid of you till this is done." Wherever he touched Morgan a flame seemed to streak along her nerves. His tongue left a burning trail down her neck and across one taut nipple, lingering a long moment before moving to the other. Gently he positioned himself between her legs. "Spread your legs for me, Morgan." She silently obeyed, no longer capable of protest. Slowly he began to penetrate, but again she panicked, begging him to release her. Marc was past understanding. Morgan screamed in pain as he plunged forward. He stopped abruptly, but remained inside of her. "My God, Morgan . . . I thought . . ."

"You thought I was a whore," she sobbed. "I told you the truth, but you wouldn't listen. All you could think of was behaving like an animal, not caring how much you hurt me. Oh my God, what am I going to do?"

Marc kissed the tears that ran down her cheeks. "I'm sorry, little one, but what's done is done." He kissed her mouth, tasting the salt of her tears, then slowly began to move in and out of her, his tongue tracing patterns on her lips all the while.

"No, no," she moaned softly.

"It won't hurt again. I promise you, little one. Relax, let me teach you to be a woman."

Somewhere in the back of her mind a demon urged her on. She was on the edge of something she had to know more about. Without thinking, she placed her arms around his neck and moved with him. She had the feeling they were being lifted higher and higher and nothing could stop them. "Oh, Marc, Marc . . . it's . . ."

"Yes, little one, I know," he answered, his voice low and raspy.

Morgan's whole body trembled under his onslaught. Her nails dug into his muscled flesh as her body took over from her mind. She had never imagined it possible to feel this way. She hated this man, yet she wanted him. She twisted her legs around his, anticipating, savoring every driving thrust of his hard body. Every inch of her felt the intenseness of the moment. She heard her own voice, begging for release, as she reached peak after peak of emotion.

They lay exhausted for a long time before Marc spoke. "I'm sorry, Morgan," he whispered against her neck. "I never imagined you were still a virgin."

Morgan was too tired to answer, but continued to lie contentedly with his flesh still a part of her. Marc could tell she was bewildered as he stroked her hair tenderly. "Sleep for a while, my sweet. Tomorrow we face the world again."

Morgan slept restlessly, dreaming of being whisked away on a big black stallion by a man whose eyes could see into her soul. Then a soft voice and a comforting hand stayed the dream. She clung to him, frightened, her arms clasped tightly around his neck. Marc stroked her hair, feeling her tenseness disappear. His hand moved over her body, feeling the curves, feeling her ardor rising. Slowly, patiently, he made love to her, savoring her surrender, tutoring her until she met his passion with a new found confidence.

The rest of the night he lay holding her, studying her beautiful face. What was it about this girl that seemed to have a hold on him? This auburn-haired, green-eyed waif who caused him more trouble than all the other Rebels put together. Yet here he lay holding her in his arms after making love to her. He pushed her long hair away from her face and traced her high cheekbone with his finger. Would he be able to take her to prison? Perhaps he could convince her to stay with his mother for the duration of the war. He wondered what Rachel would think. He ran his finger over Morgan's lips. "What the hell do I care what any of them think. She needs my help and I'm going to give it to her."

Chapter Eleven

Morgan's eyes opened as the bright sunlight streamed in through the windows. For a brief moment she thought she had been dreaming, but then felt the warm body against hers. Marc's arms encircled her tightly, one leg possessively holding her down. As the memory of the night's lovemaking came to her she could feel her skin flush warmly at the thought of what had taken place—and she had enjoyed it. Strange, she thought, she felt relaxed, almost contented, for the first time since the war began. The tenseness she had come to accept was gone. Turning her head, she looked at Marc and found him studying her. She shoved his arm away.

"Are you determined to crush the breath out of me?"

His blue eyes narrowed as he studied her boldly. "God, you are a changeable creature."

"If you think you can treat me like one of your whores, you are mistaken." Morgan blushed as she spoke because she really knew very little about whores, and she was beginning to realize she knew very little about herself. As she protested, she was enjoying the closeness of the man who still held her. It was an oddly exhilarating feeling to have his warm skin touching hers. She forced herself to look into his face and found his eyes as warm as a summer sky.

He buried his face in her hair, his lips warm against her ear. "You are like no woman I have ever met, my sweet, and I promise no to treat you like one of my whores."

Morgan pulled back angrily before realizing he was teasing. He returned her gaze with a twinkle in his blue eyes. "I know you feel embarrassed, little one, but don't be. Every man and woman goes through this. It will be easier the next time."

"There will be no next time. You have robberd me of my virginity and no man will ever want me now, but that doesn't mean I will continue to wallow in sin with you."

"Don't be naive, Morgan. You're no different today than you were yesterday," Marc said as he swung his feet off the bed and slipped into his pants. He felt guilty enough without her acting like a martyr. He'd always made it a point to stay away from virgins and he certainly wouldn't have gone as far with this one if he'd known. He looked at Morgan curled up in a ball with the sheet pulled to her chin. Who was he kidding? He'd have done the same thing even if he'd known. Hadn't he been hoping all along it was possible?

Neither said much as they ate biscuits and ham for breakfast. Morgan couldn't understand Marc acting as if nothing unusual had happened. She felt as if her whole world had changed, yet here she sat, cozily eating breakfast with him. I ought to kill him, she thought. He's ruined my life and now he'll pack me off to prison without another thought. God, how did I let this happen?

Morgan watched Marc as he ate. He must possess some power to be able to get me to act like I did. Well, he'll not use those powers on me again.

"What's the matter, Morgan? You're very quiet."

"You know very well what is the matter. You could be a little sensitive to my feelings."

"The devil take your feelings! Why can't you be honest. We both found pleasure in our lovemaking and that's all that matters."

"That might be all that matters to you, but it isn't to me," Morgan said stung to anger. "All my dreams are shattered."

"I'm sorry you feel that way, Morgan," Marc said trying to put his arm around her. "What are your dreams, little one?"

"A home, children, happiness and above all peace."

"Peace doesn't always bring happiness."

"I know, but unless there is peace I don't see how you could find happiness."

"Perhaps you're right. I certainly haven't seen much happiness lately."

"Do you have dreams, Marc?"

"All men dream, or life would be unbearable. My dreams of late have been of a green-eyed girl whom I would like to possess," he said with a smile.

Morgan sat on the edge of the bed trying to think with some logic and reason. Marc realized she was confused and decided it best to give her a chance to sort out her feelings. "I'm going out to check on the horses and get some more wood. Will you be all right for a little while?"

"I'll be fine," she said, anxious to be alone with her thoughts.

Standing at the window, she watched the rain while Marc went for the wood. She had been relieved when they decided not to travel, but now wondered if she trusted herself to stay here another night with this Yankee, but then she had to put off getting to Washington for as long as she could.

Suddenly something drew her attention to the woods at the right of the house. Pressing her nose against the glass, she strained to see. Soldiers—Confederate soldiers. Her chance to escape. She struggled to raise the window. She had to catch their attention before they were out of sight. She frantically beat on the sides of the window trying to loosen it. "Open, damn you, open!" Looking around for something to break the window, she spotted the fireplace poker. She raised it and suddenly found herself reeling across the room, the poker flying in the opposite direction. She couldn't breathe, pain filling her lungs. Marc's angry face loomed above her, his voice droning as if in the distance.

"I should have known better than to think last night meant anything to you."

Morgan struggled to speak. "The only thing it meant to me was, you ruined me. No man will ever want me. You took away my virginity—not my loyalty to the Confederacy."

"Stop being so dramatic, Morgan." Marc raised up to peer out the window. As he relaxed his hold, Morgan began to scream. He clasped one hand tightly over her mouth. "Damn you, Morgan, don't make me do something I'll regret!" Morgan continued to struggle frantically. "I'm sorry, Morgan. You forced me to do this," he said clipping her across the chin, knocking her unconscious. He angrily dropped her on the bed. "You little hellcat! I told you one of these days you would push me too far. Here I was feeling guilty about last night. I should have my head examined."

Waking later, Morgan found herself gagged and tied. She'd been stripped of her clothes, her hands tied behind her. Her jaw felt as if it were broken and she was freezing. He's gone too far this time, she thought. She listened for any sound that would give her a clue as to where he was. She had to get loose and away from him. She struggled to sit up, but was on the edge of the high, four-poster bed and realized she'd probably break something if she fell while trussed up. Brilliant, Morgan. Fall off the bed and break your neck. That will solve all your problems. She tried to slide off on her back, but with her hands tied behind her, the pain was excruciating. Damn, what am I going to do? Where is that Yankee bastard? Why did he have to truss me up this way? Morgan lay back on the bed, frustrated. The sun had gone down and it would be dark before long. Could he have gone to see where the soldiers were? Oh God, what if he's been captured. I'll surely die here. Frantically she struggled, working her way off the bed. She lay stunned, crying in pain. Pull yourself together, Morgan. You've been through worse than this. She rolled toward the door, but could do nothing once she got there. Darkness swiftly consumed the room.

Morgan shivered, panic rising. Oh, God, am I going to die like this? Why? Why has he done this to me? Surely last night meant something to him. You're a fool, Morgan Fitzgerald. He's a Yankee—your enemy—he takes any woman he wants without a thought.

She kicked the door in anger. Suddenly she heard a door open and close. She stopped struggling and listened. God, let it be someone to release me, she prayed. She listened to the footsteps coming closer, then they stopped. The gag choked back her screams. Suppose it were Yankees. What would they do to her? That could be worse than having Marc come back.

The door opened a few inches before pushing against something. Marc raised the lamp to see what held the door. "Morgan? What the hell?" He set the lamp on the table and quickly untied her. When she was free she threw her arms around his neck, forgetting her anger or that he had done this to her. Marc took out his flask and forced her to drink, then lifted her to the bed and gently covered her. He quickly built up the fire that had died out, then returned to rub her arms, slowly reviving her circulation. He insisted she drink more of the fiery liquid that worked instantly to warm her whole body.

Morgan studied Marc's face as he administered to her, and wondered if she would ever know this man who now seemed so gentle. She started to sit up, but fell back, her head spinning from the liquor.

"I'm sorry, Morgan. I was very angry when I left you. I thought last night was special to you and then you tried to turn me over to your soldiers. All I could think about was making you suffer. Then while I was out I realized I would have done the same thing if I had been held prisoner."

His blue eyes narrowed as he studied her boldly. "God, you are a changeable creature."

"If you think you can treat me like one of your whores, you are mistaken." Morgan blushed as she spoke because she really knew very little about whores, and she was beginning to realize she knew very little about herself. As she protested, she was enjoying the closeness of the man who still held her. It was an oddly exhilarating feeling to have his warm skin touching hers. She forced herself to look into his face and found his eyes as warm as a summer sky.

He buried his face in her hair, his lips warm against her ear. "You are like no woman I have ever met, my sweet, and I promise not to treat you like one of my whores."

Morgan pulled back angrily before realizing he was teasing. He returned her gaze with a twinkle in his blue eyes. "I know you feel embarrassed, little one, but don't be. Every man and woman goes through this. It will be easier the next time."

"There will be no next time. You have robbed me of my virginity and no man will ever want me now, but that doesn't mean I will continue to wallow in sin with you."

Morgan felt warm and flushed. She turned her face away, embarrassed because she wanted Marc to take her in his arms and make love to her. She hated herself for these feelings, but he had awakened new feelings and sensations in her and the nearness of him made her very much aware of those feelings now.

"My legs, Marc, I can't move my legs," she lied, her speech slurred from the lack of food and the large gulps of whiskey.

Marc gently removed the covers, exposing her nudity. Trying to ignore the warmth he felt in his loins, he rubbed her legs. She moaned, but not from the pain as he thought.

"Oh, Morgan, I am so sorry. I guess I forgot you were a woman. I never meant to be so rough with you."

Morgan stared into his blue eyes. "Don't ever forget I am a woman, Marc," she said moving his hands upward.

"Morgan, Morgan," he whispered against her neck as he moved his body over hers. "You're all woman, my Rebel, and I'm sure your body will haunt me 'till my dying day."

"Love me, Marc, love me and make this world go away."

Marc cut off her words with his mouth. His tongue parted her lips, seeking, searing, then moved from her bruised mouth to her taut nipples and down over her stomach, teasing, exploring, burning every place his lips touched.

"Oh God," she moaned incoherently, straining against him, aching for relief from the pulsing in her veins. He gently moved up and on her, slowly, teasingly, then finally driving his hard maleness into her until the violent storm reached its peak and both lay exhausted clinging to each other.

"Rebel, Rebel, you're mine and I'll never let you go," he whispered against her neck.

Morgan could not answer as the world seemed to be exploding around her.

Marc relaxed his hold, enabling her to breathe normally again. He gently pushed her hair away from her face. "You've bewitched me, Rebel. I've never known a woman like you. I'd be a fool to let you go."

Morgan traced patterns on his chest, but said nothing.

"Do you still think I'm a devil?" he asked nibbling at her ear.

"I'm sure of it," Morgan answered lightly.

"Then you must have been sent from heaven to change my wicked ways," Marc whispered as he buried his face in her auburn hair.

Morgan pushed against his shoulders. "Please, Marc. If I don't get some food I won't be good for anything. I'm starved."

"So am I, little one, but for your body."

"I won't have the strength."

"Um . . . perhaps you're right. We want to keep up our strength. You lie right here and I'll get some ham and biscuits. Will that suit you?"

"Deliciously," Morgan mumbled as she stretched contentedly.

Marc dressed and headed for the door. Suddenly he stopped and turned back to the bed. "Morgan . . ."

She smiled. "I'll be right here, Marc."

Morgan thought about the circumstances she found herself in. She had hated this man earlier, then like a whore she gave herself to him. What had come over her? Here she lay, waiting for him to return—anxiously waiting. What were these strange feelings she

167

felt when he touched her. She had heard of men lusting after women, but were women supposed to lust after men? She sat up. "What is wrong with you, Morgan? Get out of this place while you have the chance. He still plans to take you to prison. Forget him. He is your enemy and a dangerous one — he knows your weaknesses." Morgan searched the room for her clothes but found nothing. Suddenly the door opened and Marc stood there with a tray of food.

He looked at her suspiciously. "Are you looking for something, Morgan?"

"I just wondered where my clothes were."

"They are in the kitchen," he said setting the tray down. "You'd better get back in bed before you catch cold."

Reluctantly she climbed back under the covers. "I thought you trusted me."

"Should I, Morgan?"

She looked him straight in the eyes. "No," she whispered softly.

Marc smiled. "I think I would have been disappointed if you had said yes." He set the tray on her lap and began to butter a biscuit for her. "That was Mosby and some of his men going through here today. I think we had better move on in the morning."

"How do you know it was Mosby?"

"I followed them for awhile and heard them discussing their plans. We seem to be in the middle of their battlelines and I would just as soon get away from here before all hell breaks loose."

"Marc, let me go home."

"If I thought you would go home, I would, but you

168

and I both know better, so there's no sense discussing it."

"How can you make love to me like you do and then talk about taking me to prison?"

"I said there is no sense discussing this, Morgan."

The next day dawned clear, the sun rising like a red ball of fire over the mountains, shining on the fields, filtering through the forests. Marc set a leisurely pace, more like a Sunday ride than taking his prisoner to jail.

After riding a good part of the day Marc stopped and dismounted. Morgan sat atop her horse looking out over the golden fields covered with wildflowers and the sparkling stream that cascaded over the rocks. Marc put his hands to her waist and lifted her off before she had a chance to protest.

"This looks like the perfect place."

"The perfect place for what?" Morgan asked curiously.

"For a picnic, my sweet."

Morgan laughed. "You can't be serious."

"I'm very serious. I brought along some food from the farmhouse and we're going to have a picnic. Now pick a good spot while I get the saddlebags."

Morgan felt like a young girl again. How could this be possible? She had been involved with war so long she forgot the pleasantries of a picnic along a cool stream. God, how it brought back memories of better days. Her mother used to love to have Sunday-supper along the North Anna River where the family would play games and then dance the evening away.

Marc noticed that Morgan was a thousand miles away. "What's the matter with you, girl? Haven't you ever been on a picnic before?"

"Not in a long, long time," Morgan answered sadly.

"Well, you probably don't remember, but I told you once that we would have a picnic in a field of wildflowers and I always try to keep my promises."

"I remember," Morgan said thinking about the night he had comforted her when nightmares invaded her sleep.

Marc grinned, his white teeth flashing against his bronze skin. "I didn't think you heard a thing I said that night. Come, we're wasting precious time." Marc led the way to a grove of trees near the stream and spread his saddle blanket.

Morgan twirled about like a child delighted with finding a fairyland. "It's so beautiful. I could stay here forever, hidden away from the rest of the world."

Marc dropped to the ground, stretching his long legs in front of him. "Enjoy it, my sweet," he said with a grand sweep of his arm. "Consider it yours for as long as you like."

Morgan dropped to her knees, suddenly feeling very depressed. She slowly began to take the food out of the saddlebag.

"What's wrong, Morgan? A minute ago you were so happy."

"I suddenly remembered men are dying all around us. It just doesn't seem right that we should be enjoying ourselves this way."

"These are bitter times, Morgan. Everyone must die sooner or later. Would you have wanted to die never having tasted the fruits of life? Enjoy everything you can while you can. It's the only way to live in these times. I've had three bullets in me," he said touching her face. "One of which was yours, and each time I found I valued life a little more—mine and my enemy's."

"But, you said you were fighting for the Union to avenge your brother's death. How can you do that and value your enemy's life?"

"I was looking for revenge until I realized life is like a candle burning in the wind; it can be snuffed out at any time. I wanted to enjoy life—not spend it seeking revenge."

"You are very eloquent, sir, but I recall you're known as the devil. This doesn't sound like the devil's way of thinking."

Marc pulled Morgan into his arms and rolled her under him. "Ah, my sweet, didn't you know anyone who looks the devil straight in the eye comes out a better person for it?"

Morgan recognized the look in Marc's ice blue eyes. She felt hypnotized, unable to look away, while he studied her appreciatively. "I would like to see you in a peach satin gown and a diamond tiara."

"I have little need for diamonds where I am going."

"True, diamonds would be dull in comparison to your beauty," Marc said, ignoring her reference to prison.

Marc reached out and touched her face. Suddenly the world seemed to fade away. The sound of the babbling stream and the birds in the trees above them could no longer be heard by either of them.

"I've always had a fondness for green eyes," he said as he began to unlace her buckskins.

Morgan felt a slow consuming blaze and lost all will to protest — all will to stop his hands as he slowly undressed her. Her nerves tingled with waves of desire as his warm breath lingered teasingly against her eyelids, her hair and then her mouth, whispering sweet words before hungrily finding her tongue with his own. He was bringing her to life with a deliberate slowness that threatened to drive her crazy. She felt as if she were being consumed; becoming a part of this man, and both were caught in an undercurrent, forgetting the war and death that surrounded them, forgetting everything but assuagement.

Afterwards they lay in each other's arms with the summer sun warming their bodies. Marc leaned up on his elbow, looking down into Morgan's face. She opened her eyes and met his warm smile.

"How quickly you learn, little one."

Morgan blushed and turned away. "Please don't."

"It's hard to believe you have never let a man explore your loveliness."

"You must know I haven't," Morgan said surprised at his bluntness.

Lifting a lock of her hair, he rubbed it between his fingers then rolled onto his back and studied a bird flying overhead. He knew it was stupid of him to still be questioning her, when he knew he was the first man she had ever been with. Yet he still found it difficult to believe she could have camped with her men and no one had touched her.

Morgan studied his face. She wanted to reach out

and touch him, but held back. The heavy fringe of black lashes shadowed his eyes and she wasn't sure if he was awake.

Marc smiled, placing the palm of her hand to his mouth. "Don't be afraid to show your feelings. There's nothing wrong with a woman touching a man."

Morgan still could not bring herself to touch him. Instead she rolled onto her back and watched the hawk soaring overhead. "Do you realize we have not had our picnic yet?"

"It doesn't matter. I think we'll spend the night here. It's too late to move on and then have to find another place to bed down."

"It will feel good to sleep under the stars again."

"Do you enjoy this life, Morgan?"

"Some aspects of it. It has certainly made a better person of me. I was very naive before the war."

"In what way?"

"I was very spoiled. I would never have considered wearing a dress more than once or twice, I had servants to take care of my every need, I was surrounded by love and happiness and thought the whole world was the same. Now I know what it is like to be cold and hungry and I'll never go back to living like I once did. I'll be more anxious to share with those less fortunate."

"I guess there are a few who'll come out of this war better people, but you'll be among the minority."

"I hope you're wrong," Morgan said sadly.

"I hope so too, little one. I sincerely hope so. Now, tell me, do you really enjoy sleeping under the stars?"

Morgan giggled. "On a warm, summer night. Not on a cold, snowy night."

"And here I thought you were an unusual woman," Marc teased.

"I never claimed to be unusual."

"I know you didn't, but you are. I've never known anyone quite like you." Marc rolled over on top of Morgan, looking down into her smoldering green eyes. "I feel like loving you again."

"You're insatiable."

"And you have bewitched me."

Morgan's eyes twinkled. "What a combination we make. The devil and a sorceress."

Marc silenced her words with his mouth. "Marc, please—we can't lie here and make love all day."

Marc's warm kiss traveled down her neck. "I don't know why not," Marc said as thunder sounded in the distance. He looked down into her eyes. "Do you hear that, Morgan? That was the thunder, the lightning is yet to come." With that he engulfed her in the warm flow of his love again. She entwined her fingers in his dark, wavy hair and let him lift her to heaven.

The sun was setting before Marc stirred at Morgan's side. For the last hour she studied his ruggedly handsome face while he slept like a small boy exhausted from play. She had traced the firm line of his jaw and the hard lines of his mouth that softened when he laughed. God, why couldn't she sort out her feelings for this man?

Suddenly Marc smiled and reached for her hand. Morgan's cheeks flamed. "I thought—I mean—you were asleep."

"Don't be embarrassed. Our lovemaking is a natural thing, Morgan. As natural as breathing. Now how about our picnic?"

Chapter Twelve

Two weary riders arrived in Harpers Ferry shortly after dark. Morgan slumped over the saddle of her horse exhausted from the steady hours of traveling, every bone in her body aching.

Marc slid off his horse and came to her side. "Morgan, we're here."

She raised her head, staring glassy-eyed at their surroundings. Marc lifted her from the saddle. "Can you walk?"

"Of course I can walk. I'm no weak-kneed female."

Marc grinned as she leaned heavily against him. "We'll get you some food and a hot bath and then you can sleep for as long as you like.'"

"It's going to be hard getting used to the hard ground again."

"Morgan, there is not going to be any more sleeping in camps."

"Oh yes, I forgot. It's going to be the cold, damp cell of a Federal prison," she answered sarcastically.

She'd see him in hell before she would beg him to release her again. It was very apparent that what had happened between them meant nothing to him.

A young child opened the door of the frame house and stood for a long moment before excitedly calling out. "Aunt Connie, come quick. It's Captain Riordan and an Indian."

Marc chuckled. "I told you those damned buckskins

were ridiculous."

"They serve me very well, captain. You'd be much better off wearing them instead of the blue of the devil you wear."

They entered the entrance hall of the small but elegantly furnished house where several people gathered in the hallway. Everyone began talking at the same time while Marc tried to answer their questions.

"Well, it's about time you got here," said a voice from the doorway.

Everyone parted to let a fragile looking blonde through. "I really thought you would be here sooner. What in the world have you dragged in here?" she asked noticing Morgan for the first time.

Morgan blushed with embarrassment as everyone made her the center of attention without actually speaking to her. Marc tightened his grip on her hand for moral support.

"It's good to see you too, Rachel," he answered sarcastically.

The girl turned her cheek for him to kiss. "I'm sorry if I don't sound happy to see you, but your aunt gave a party for us last night and I had hoped we would announce our engagement there."

Morgan suddenly seemed to come to life. "Your fiancee?" she laughed.

Rachel looked down her nose at Morgan. "What is so funny about that?"

Marc shot Morgan a threatening look. "I don't think you'd see the humor," she answered caustically, biting back the retort she felt.

176

"This is Morgan Fitzgerald. She's my prisoner and I'm taking her to Washington. Morgan, this is Rachel Todd and my aunt . . ."

Rachel cut him off before he could finish. "Really, Marc, it isn't necessary to introduce your prisoner or to even have her in this house. Couldn't one of your men have escorted her to Washington? My goodness, doesn't rank mean anything anymore? My father would never have lowered himself to such menial jobs."

Marc ignored her barbs and turned to kiss his aunt. "Hello, Aunt Connie. It's good to see your sweet face again. Where is mother?"

"She didn't make the trip, Marc. She is well, but with the roads so bad . . ."

"I'm glad she used good judgement. The weather has been terrible. It has taken us three more days than it should have to get here from Warrenton. I'm afraid Morgan is exhausted. Could you see to it that she gets some food and a warm bath. She'll need a room close to mine."

The woman smiled warmly. "Of course," she said holding her hand out to Morgan. "Why don't you come with me, dear. I'll show you to your room."

Morgan was still staring at the blonde when she realized Marc's aunt was speaking to her. So this was the Rachel Marc had spoken of in his delirium. How could she be his fiancee when he had spoken of her with such hate. She followed Connie up the stairs, but could still hear Rachel raking Marc over the coals. Morgan felt as if her blood were boiling. Damn him! She'd kill him yet—if Rachel didn't do it first. She smiled to herself. Serves him right. That woman will make his life miserable.

Huddled in a blanket, Morgan listened to Marc's Aunt Connie talk as she prepared the bath. She poured a scent into the water and laid soap and a towel next to the brass tub. "All ready, dear. If you need anything just ring that bell. Our staff is small now, but we live very comfortably. Marc will be in the room next door."

"Why are you being so kind to me? Don't you understand, I'm Captain Riordan's prisoner?"

Connie smiled, an all-knowing smile. "I know my nephew, Morgan. I have a feeling he has found a real woman in you and if it gets him to see what Rachel Todd is like, then I'll do everything in my power to encourage it."

Morgan felt embarrassed. "I wish I could help you, but in my opinion, he deserves whatever he gets."

"Perhaps you're right, my dear. Come take your bath before the water cools. I'll have a tray sent up to you later."

After thoroughly scrubbing Morgan laid her head back against the tub, trying to sort out her feelings. What was it about Marc that kept her in a constant state of turmoil? Everytime she thought she hated him he would do something kind and gentle and she would submit to his charm, giving her body without another thought. God, just thinking about him gave her a warm, flushed feeling.

Angrily stepping from the tub, she began vigorously rubbing her skin. Tears ran down her face as she realized the inevitable. She loved Marc Riordan.

"Damn you, Marc Riordan! Damn you to hell!"

"You're lovely when you're angry, Morgan, but what did I do to deserve this tirade?"

Morgan turned, startled by his voice. "What are you doing here? How long have you been standing there?"

"Long enough for my ears to burn. Why the anger, Morgan?"

"Just leave me alone. Go back to your fiancee before she comes looking for you."

"I'm not leaving until I know why you're angry."

"I'll tell you why, damn it. I don't know how you could make love to me when you had a fiancee waiting for you. I hate you for putting me in this situation and for taking advantage of people who care for you."

"Do you care for me, Morgan?"

Morgan angrily wrapped a blanket around her. "Don't be ridiculous, Yankee. Get out of here before I scream for your fiancee."

Moving toward her, Marc placed his hands on her bare shoulders. "Morgan, the past few days have been very special for me. Please believe that."

"I wouldn't believe anything you said, Marc Riordan. Now get out before I make a scene."

"I just came to see if you were ready to eat."

"No. I would rather go to bed."

Marc grinned wickedly. "So would I."

Morgan's eyes widened in disbelief. "What kind of man are you?" she asked angrily.

Marc opened the door to leave. "A very confused one," he answered seriously. "Morgan, don't fall in love with me."

"Don't flatter yourself, Yankee. The only thing I feel for you is hate."

They spent two days with Marc's aunt. Morgan found her kindness and company a blessing since Rachel chose to make her life miserable. Rachel had decided it was improper for her fiance to be traveling over the countryside with another woman, prisoner or not, so she decided to accompany them to Washington. Marc did everything he could to change her mind, but she wouldn't bend.

Morgan smiled when Connie leaned over and whispered. "I'm afraid my good fortune will be your misfortune. I hope you're strong enough to handle it."

Marc tried to convince Rachel it would be too hard on her. "You know we will be traveling on horseback, Rachel. There will be no carriage or bed to sleep in at night. We will do the best we can to find a barn or stable, but that will be the most we'll find."

"If she can do it, so can I," answered Rachel, sneering at Morgan.

Marc laughed. "You will have to go a long way if you think you can keep up with Morgan. There's probably no better horseman in the Confederate Army."

"Well, if I wanted to be known as one of the boys, I'm sure I could. I prefer being a lady."

Morgan's face reddened. She knew Marc meant to be kind, yet it sounded so ridiculous—the best horseman in the Confederate Army. My God, was that the way he sees me, she wondered. No wonder he'd stayed away from her the last two days.

Connie squeezed Morgan's hand. "Marc's mother could ride and shoot with the best of them. She loved to hunt with her husband. He would always brag about her to his friends. She even helped win many a campaign by traveling with him."

Morgan fought to control her tears. "Excuse me, I think I will put my things in order." She turned to Rachel. "I will leave your dress on the bed, Miss Todd. Thank you for lending it to me."

Rachel turned to Marc's aunt while Morgan was still within hearing. "You can burn it! I certainly wouldn't wear it again."

"You have no reason to feel that way. Morgan has never done anything to you," Connie replied.

"She's a tramp. How am I supposed to feel having her under the same roof?"

"Morgan is not a tramp, Rachel," Marc answered exasperated. "Her only crime is being a spy for the Confederate Army, and I might add, a damned good one. She's a woman with a lot of spirit and a fierce loyalty to her country. You could take lessons from her on that count."

"How dare you talk to me like that! I'm your fiancee and here you're belittling me for not being like her."

"That's not what I'm doing, Rachel. I only meant she does not deserve your contempt."

Connie smiled to herself as she picked up the teacups. She bit her tongue to keep from saying—wait until you see the two of them together, my dear nephew—you'll really see the difference then.

Morgan descended the steps dressed in her

buckskins and found Marc arguing with Rachel, who was dressed in a brown velvet riding outfit with a cocky feathered hat.

Marc drew in his breath as he spotted Morgan.

"Will you look at this, Aunt Connie. One dressed like an Indian and the other dressed to meet the Queen of England. Would you say we look like a traveling carnival?"

Connie smiled. "I'd say Rachel will leave most of her belongings on the ride to Washington or end up walking after her horse collapses from all the weight."

"I'm not going to Washington without decent clothes. There will surely be parties and balls to attend while we're there," Rachel pouted. "And I spent a lot of time and money picking out this wardrobe."

Marc kissed his aunt goodby, promising to give his mother the letter she pressed in his hand. "You take care of yourself and come to Washington first chance you get."

When he turned back, Morgan was already mounted, but Rachel waited beside her horse for Marc to lift her into her side-saddle. "Are you sure you want to make this trip, Rachel?" he asked once more, hoping she might have changed her mind.

"Of course, my dear. It's going to be great fun."

Morgan's laughter echoed in Marc's ears as she spurred her horse around.

"Shouldn't she be tied or something?"

Marc just shook his head. "Let's move out. We're wasting precious time."

They had only ridden a few hours when Rachel

begged them to stop for a rest. Marc insisted they go a little further or they wouldn't make Washington the next day.

Rachel rode another fifteen minutes without complaining, then abruptly stopped. "I cannot go another foot."

"If we stop now you're going to get rid of that junk you're carrying."

Morgan leaned against a tree, chewing on a piece of dried meat and watching Marc check the overloaded horse's legs.

"I should never have gone along with this hair-brained idea of yours, Rachel. One woman is bad enough, but two! God, deliver me from all females. What did I do to deserve this?" Marc asked looking skyward.

Morgan smiled to herself. Three hours out of Harpers Ferry and he was already begging for mercy. This was going to be a delightful trip.

"All right, mount up. We've got to get moving."

Morgan could tell Rachel was suffering, but she did so in silence while they traveled for more than four hours before stopping again.

As Morgan dismounted, Gambler reared her front feet, pawing the air. Morgan collapsed on the ground gripping her leg as her horse continued to paw the air dangerously close. A gunshot echoed through the woods as Marc shot the rattlesnake at Gambler's feet and quickly brought the horse under control.

He knelt, examining Morgan's leg. "Where did it get you?"

"The pain is just above the ankle. Gambler must

have seen it as I dismounted, but I couldn't move fast enough to get away."

Marc struggled to pull Morgan's moccasin from her foot. "Damn, Morgan, if you'd wear boots instead of these flimsy moccasins, this wouldn't have happened."

"I don't have access to fancy boots like you, captain. I'm lucky not to be barefoot like most of my army."

"I'm sorry, Morgan. Lie back and let me see to this," he said, gently examining her leg. "I'm going to have to make an incision and suck the poison out."

"Oh no," gasped Rachel who stood watching. "That could kill you if you swallowed any of it. Don't take the chance. She'll probably die in prison anyway."

"Shut up, Rachel! Morgan has saved my life more than once and I don't intend to let her die."

Morgan smiled. "I've tried to take it once or twice too, Yankee. Besides, I'm not sure you would be doing me a favor. It would be a blessing to be away from this hell on earth."

"Don't talk like that, Rebel. No matter how bad it gets, peace will come sooner or later. Hold on now, I'm going to make the incision."

"No, Marc, please don't do it," Rachel begged. "I'm going to be sick."

"For God's sake, Rachel, go someplace and sit down. You'd think I was going to cut you."

"How can you be so insensitive, Marc Riordan. I was just concerned for you," Rachel said before storming off.

"You better watch her, Yankee or she'll have your sons wearing lace on their underwear," Morgan said, a devilish twinkle in her eyes.

Marc laughed. "Shut up, you little fool, before I cut your leg off."

Morgan bit down on her lip as he cut into her leg. "Well, at least we know you have red blood in your veins, Rebel."

"What a disappointment for you. I'm sure you thought it was ice water. I believe you told me that one time."

Morgan watched as he sucked the poison and spit. She could feel herself slipping away as he repeated the process.

"Marc . . . I think it's too late . . . I feel . . ."

Marc felt her pulse and when satisfied she was all right he poured whiskey over her leg, then took a deep swallow and rinsed his mouth.

"Come on, little spitfire, wake up," he said forcing a small amount of the whiskey down Morgan's throat.

Morgan sputtered and choked before opening her eyes.

Marc smiled at her. "You didn't really think I was going to let you leave this world, did you, little one?"

"No, I'm sure you'd rather see me rot in prison."

Marc's face turned black with anger. "We're going to have to get moving, Morgan. We need to find a doctor as soon as possible."

Morgan realized how ungrateful she sounded. "Marc, I'm sorry, I know you think I should be grateful, but if you had only left me in Warrenton, this wouldn't have happened."

"No, if I had left you there you would have been the cause of many men dying."

"That's where you're wrong, Marc Riordan. If I

could have gotten my information to Stuart, more of *my* men would have been saved."

Marc pulled her roughly to her feet and swung her over his shoulder.

"You're hurting me. Put me down!"

"Shut up, Morgan."

"Marc . . . please," she begged as everything began to spin again. Marc shifted her to lie cradled in his arms with her head against his chest. Her eyes fluttered once before she fainted.

"Damn it, Morgan. What is it about you that makes me lose all reason!" Marc said cursing himself for being so rough with her. Damn, she was infuriating. He had never dealt with a woman like her before, and she stirred him much more than he wanted to admit. He knew he should have already turned her over to the authorities, but he couldn't do it. He had to try to convince her to stay out of the war. She was a very dangerous spy. He'd once been told she was one of Lee's favorites and he could understand why. She certainly didn't have any trouble getting General Smyth to confide in her.

"Mount up, Rachel. Morgan is going to need a doctor as soon as possible," Marc said as he lifted her into the saddle in front of him.

"Can't she ride on her own horse? I don't really . . ."

"Shut up, Rachel. I'm in no mood to listen to what you want or don't want."

Marc wrapped a blanket over Morgan and started off at the fastest pace he thought Morgan could handle. He decided to stick to the main roads, hoping they wouldn't meet the enemy. It worried him that she remained unconscious and he wondered if she could be in shock. Gently he pushed her hair away from her face and she opened her eyes.

"Try not to move. That poison is pumping through your system and we don't want it to travel any faster."

"Rachel isn't going to like your holding me like this, but I must admit it's very comfortable."

"You little devil. Here I am worried that you're dying and you want to tease me."

Morgan snuggled closer. "I think I could learn to like it here."

"Well for God's sake, be still or you'll have Rachel's wrath down on me again."

"I didn't think you were afraid of anything, Yankee."

"Only of women with acid tongues, Rebel, and I happen to be traveling with two of them."

"Maybe it's God's way of punishing you."

"Morgan, Morgan, what am I going to do with you? Why can't you always be as loving and sweet as you were at the farmhouse?"

Tears came to Morgan's eyes. "I thought I meant something to you then, but you didn't bother to tell me you had a fiancee. You were too busy taking my virginity and not caring a damn what I felt."

"You're wrong, Morgan. I care a great deal for you."

"Oh sure, I kept you from being bored."

"Do you enjoy making my life miserable, Morgan?"

"Is that what I'm doing, Marc?"

"It's what you have been doing since the first day I met you."

Morgan turned her head away so he couldn't see the hurt in her eyes. "You haven't exactly been a shining light in my life either, Captain Riordan."

"Jesus, Morgan, give me a break."

"I think I can ride my own horse now. We would both be happier that way." Morgan began to struggle and Marc quickly brought his horse to a halt. Rachel pulled up beside them.

"Well, I see she has made a remarkable recovery."

"I told you she was tough."

Morgan looked at him, her eyes flashing angrily. "Oh, you . . ."

Morgan angrily limped to her horse. Marc shook his head. No one else would be stomping around after being snakebit, but she was too stubborn to give in. God, what a woman. She'd make any man proud to know her.

At Point of Rocks they found a doctor, but he was too drunk to administer to Morgan. It seemed he had been on the battlefield for the last thirteen days treating the wounded and his wife said he was trying to forget those he couldn't help. She promised by morning he would be fine, but Marc couldn't wait until morning. Morgan's coloring had turned an ashen gray and her eyes were glazed.

"I know there are good doctors in Washington. Do you think you can go on?"

"I think so, but I'm so tired."

"I know, Morgan. I would stay here for the night, but I really think we should get to a doctor. You'll ride with me now where you can sleep."

Morgan gave no resistance as he gently lifted her

188

from her saddle and placed her on his horse. He mounted behind, wrapping his blanket around her. She closed her eyes and drifted off into oblivion, unaware of Rachel's outrage.

It was long after dark when they reached the outskirts of Washington. Morgan's leg was throbbing with pain and her head was splitting. Marc looked down at her and knew she was suffering. Her coloring was still a pallid gray and her eyes had dark circles around them. "It will only be a few more minutes, Morgan. Just hold on."

She didn't answer him but was thankful it wasn't much further. She wondered if she would be able to get medical help in prison. Funny, it didn't seem to make any difference now. She was probably going to die, so going to prison didn't seem so terrible.

They went through several check-points without any problems, only a few strange looks. Marc stopped the horses in front of a large red brick house with an iron fence surrounding it. He helped Rachel off her horse then came back to Morgan. Placing his hands at her waist, he lifted her from the horse. She looked at him through pain-filled eyes.

"I can't move my leg, Marc."

"I've heard that before, Morgan," he said trying to keep his voice light.

She tried to smile. "I remember," she said gasping in pain when he shifted her weight.

Wes Lansing rushed down the steps of the house to help. Rachel had been fine until he appeared, but now pretended to be faint. He grabbed her under the arm and helped her up the stairs following Marc.

189

"Welcome home, Marc. You always did know how to make an entrance."

"Thanks, Wes. I'm glad you're here. I'm going to need your help. Morgan was bitten by a snake and is going to need a doctor."

Marc kissed his mother while still holding Morgan, "I'm going to put her in my room, Mom. I'll use my studio while I'm here."

Wes settled Rachel in a chair and grabbed his jacket. "I'll be back as soon as I find a doctor."

"Wes, wait," Marc said looking back over his shoulder as he climbed the stairs. "Try to find a civilian doctor."

"I understand, Marc. I'll do the best I can."

Marc's mother helped Rachel to the guest room before coming back to help her son. She leaned over Morgan, feeling her forehead. "She is feverish, son."

Marc looked concerned. "I thought I had gotten all the poison out, but the leg is really swollen."

"You look really tired, Marc. Why don't you rest for a while and let me help your friend get comfortable."

Morgan had not spoken, but her eyes followed Marc. He knelt beside the bed and took her hand in his. "You're in good hands now. Don't worry about a thing."

Morgan grimmaced in pain as Anne helped her out of the buckskins. Every move made her head spin and her stomach sick. "I'm sorry, dear. I wish there were some other way. Perhaps we could cut them off."

"No, please. I'll be all right. Go ahead . . . pull them off." Morgan gritted her teeth as the tight-fitting pants were pulled over her swollen leg.

"I think those pants might have been cutting off your circulation. The bite doesn't look infected. Lie right here while I get you a nightgown."

"Thank you, Mrs. Riordan. Thank you for letting me come here. I won't impose on your hospitality long."

"Now, dear, don't start worrying about imposing. Marc's friends are always welcome here. I miss having a house full of his guests since this war began."

"Mrs. Riordan, I'm not actually a friend. I'm your son's prisoner. He is delivering me to the Federal prison."

Anne Riordan didn't say anything for a moment. When she finally spoke she did so as she was leaving the room. "I know my son, Morgan, and I don't think he'd deliver you to that hideous place."

Morgan laid her head back on the pillow and wondered if anyone really knew Marc Riordan. She certainly didn't.

Marc met his mother in the hallway. "I'd like to talk to you, Mom."

"I should think so. That young lady is under the impression you're delivering her to prison."

Marc frowned. "I know and that is where she should be going, but I hoped you might be able to help me."

"Come, talk to me while I get some things from my room."

Anne Riordan gathered clothes for Morgan as Marc explained about her spying activities. She smiled as he told some of her exploits and how she had ended up saving his life.

"She certainly has spirit. Quite rare these days," Anne said.

"She is fiercely loyal to the Confederacy. Lee's armies rely heavily on her information and that's why I brought her here. I had hoped she could stay with you when I return to my men."

"What makes you think she'll stay here?"

"She is terrified of going to prison. She has said she'd rather die. I think if she has a choice of going to prison or staying here, she'll pick the latter."

"How does Rachel feel about all this?"

"She doesn't know yet."

Anne looked at her son for a moment before speaking. "What is your relationship with Morgan, son?"

"I told you, she saved my life."

"Marc . . ."

"I don't know, Mom. I only know every other woman seems dull in comparison."

"Even Rachel?"

"Especially Rachel."

"I know your father took advantage of you at a crucial time, but you did give your word to marry Rachel and take care of her."

"I'll marry her, Mother. I don't see I have any choice unless Wes decides to tell her how he feels and he doesn't seem inclined to do so."

"I don't understand, Marc."

"Wes is in love with Rachel. He has been for years, but he feels he has nothing to offer her."

"Well, until he does, I suggest you stay away from Morgan. You'll only end up hurting her if you don't. Besides, it's very improper for you to be in her room."

Marc didn't say anything. Could he really stay away

from her, he wondered, or would he continue to tempt fate and cause everyone concerned a lot of grief.

By the time Wes returned with the doctor, Morgan's fever raged. Anne insisted Marc leave the room, but he refused. He couldn't desert her now, not after she kept him alive when he was near death.

The doctor carefully examined Morgan's leg. "Your quick thinking saved her life, captain. You did a nice job. I'll give her something to bring the fever under control, but she'll have to be watched very carefully for a few days. She is to be kept in bed for at least two days after the fever is completely gone. Don't let her overdo it when she is up and about. Follow my orders and she'll be fine in no time."

Everyone left the room but Marc, who ignored his mother's frown as she escorted the doctor out. He laid a cold compress on Morgan's forehead. She opened her fever-glazed eyes.

"I want to go home," she mumbled.

"You are home, Morgan. Sleep and I'll take care of you."

Chapter Thirteen

Morgan opened her eyes and stared at her unfamiliar surroundings. She was lying in a massive, four-poster, canopied bed in a room dark with muted shades of greens and browns. It was a masculine room and for her life she couldn't remember where she was or how she got there. She felt weak and lightheaded, but the burning heat that she thought would consume her was gone.

"Oh good, you're awake," said Anne Riordan from the side of the bed. "Are you feeling better, dear?"

Slowly the memory of the trip to Washington as Marc's prisoner and the snake bite came back to her. This was his home and his bed.

Anne Riordan placed her hand on Morgan's brow. "The fever is down. That's good."

Morgan's mouth was dry and parched, but she managed to speak. "How long have I been sick?"

"Two days, which really isn't too bad. The doctor thought you might be feverish longer than that," she said sponging Morgan's face.

"Where is Marc? I thought I heard his voice."

Anne straightened the blankets around Morgan, trying to avoid her questioning eyes. "No, he hasn't been here," she lied, hoping to prevent Morgan from getting hurt. "He and his fiancee have been visiting friends and making plans for their wedding for the last two days. They haven't seen much of each other in months, so they had a lot to do in just a short time."

Morgan was confused. She was sure Marc had been with her. She remembered his holding her hand, giving her water, but surely she must be mistaken if his mother said he hadn't been there. Why should he have been there? He was with his fiancee in his own home and he wouldn't have time for her now. He was probably anxious for her to be well so he could deliver her to prison, but she planned to make her escape before that happened.

Marc stood outside Morgan's door listening. He was about to enter when he heard his mother telling Morgan that he had not been there. He was torn between rushing in and telling her that he had been with her every night since they arrived or going along with his mother. He knew Morgan would be hurt if he continued seeing her. He was sure she was in love with him and he had finally admitted to himself that he loved her, but it was hopeless. He was bound by honor and must stay away from her.

Morgan spent the next two days being entertained by Anne Riordan. She pretended not to notice Marc's obvious absence. She had to think of escape; nothing else should matter, yet she found herself listening for his footsteps outside her door. She had been awakened by a sound during the night and when she opened her eyes she was sure she had seen him leaving her room, but she couldn't understand why he only came when she was asleep.

After three days without fever, Anne felt Morgan could use a change of scenery. She helped her down the stairs and into the lovely garden at the back of the house. Morgan settled herself on a bench with a book of Lord Byron's poetry she had found on her breakfast tray. When she tired of reading she strolled through the rose garden that Anne so lovingly tended. She should feel at peace here, she thought, yet she didn't. She felt as if her insides were churning. Reading Byron's poems only made her feel lonelier. Somehow she had to get away from this place—from Marc Riordan. She must find a way to get word to Jubal.

Turning to leave, she saw Marc standing at a window at the top of the house. Morgan's mouth was suddenly hot and dry and she felt lightheaded. He was here, yet he had not offered his help on her first day out. Why—why, she wondered. He smiled and waved, but then another figure appeared at his side. Morgan felt as if the earth were suddenly upside down as Rachel possessively took hold of Marc's arm. He was no longer smiling, but their eyes held. Oh God, why did she hurt so? Get hold of yourself, Morgan Fitzgerald, she told herself. She straightened her shoulders, determined not to let him hurt her again. She would escape this place soon and never think of him again.

She headed for the house, but before she reached the door Anne Riordan stopped her. "Please sit for a moment more. I wish to speak to you."

Morgan sat down on the wrought iron bench, wishing she were in her room so she could release the flood of tears that threatened to break lose.

Anne took her hand. "Marc and I have been talking about your situation. We both agreed that it would be best for you to stay here for awhile."

Morgan's eyes widened in shock. "No. I cannot," she blurted out. "I thank you for your kindness, but I cannot stay here."

"Morgan, listen to me. You are not being fair to Marc. Surely you can see if you refuse this offer he has to take you to prison. You know he cannot release you. The last thing he wants to do is break your spirit. Don't take away his pride by forcing him into a situation he can do nothing about. I'm afraid he would never get over it. You have done all you can for your country. You can't fight this war by yourself."

Morgan shook her head unable to speak as tears flowed down her face. Anne tried to comfort her, placing an arm around her trembling shoulders. "Agree to stay with me and I won't ask you to promise anymore than to keep an old lady company for a while."

Morgan hesitated before speaking. Her mind was a jumble of confusion, yet she knew she couldn't refuse Anne's offer. "Thank you, Mrs. Riordan. I would enjoy visiting with you."

Anne Riordan kissed Morgan on the cheek. "You must call me Anne. We are going to be great friends. I can just feel it in my bones."

"I think so too, Anne. It has been a long time since I had a female friend."

"Now, dear, you must return to your room and rest. We promised Dr. Gillespie we wouldn't let you overdo and I would like for you to join the family for dinner this evening."

Morgan was shocked at the suggestion. "Oh, no,

Anne. I don't think that would be wise. I am still Marc's prisoner."

"You are no longer a prisoner, Morgan. You are my guest and cannot stay cooped up in your room. I insist you join us for dinner."

"Does Marc know you are asking me?"

"Of course, dear. When you get to your room you'll find something he picked up for you just today."

Morgan felt as if a weight had been lifted from her heart. He had thought about her enough to get her something. Maybe he did care. She could hardly wait to get to the room.

Spread out on her bed was a pale, peach satin gown with matching slippers and soft delicate undergarments. Morgan held the gown up to her, twirling around the room in delight. "He had said he wanted to see me in a peach satin gown. He remembered." Suddenly the smile disappeared from her face. "You're being a fool, Morgan Fitzgerald. The man is a Yankee officer with a fiancee. You are nothing more than his prisoner." She collapsed on the bed, the gown crumpled in her arms. He never said he loved you, only that he wanted you. Why are you kidding yourself? But an inner voice persisted—why the peach satin gown—it could have been anything else.

Anne Riordan stood at her bedroom window staring out over the rose garden. She twisted her handkerchief nervously between her fingers. Her son was the only thing she had left in this world and it was tearing her apart to see him suffer as he was. She knew without a doubt he was in love with Morgan, yet how could she condone the match? She was fond of the girl herself, but what about Rachel? She had never had to fend for herself. At least Morgan was strong and independent.

She kept seeing the portrait of Morgan that Marc had apparently painted while recuperating from his wound. She was sure he had not meant for anyone to see it, but she had gone to tell him Morgan had agreed to stay and found him staring at it. When she questioned him about it, he became very evasive and she realized he had been drinking.

She wiped a tear from her cheek. It just wasn't like him to drink this way. Were his black moods from the drinking or from his self-imposed deprivation? She had a very uneasy feeling things were not going to be very pleasant for awhile. She just wished Marc hadn't insisted on Morgan joining them before he left. Rachel wasn't going to like it, particularly when she saw the dress Marc had spent the whole morning picking out.

Anne frowned as she saw Wes and Rachel walking below in the garden. Those two are alone too often. Why doesn't Marc object to their relationship? she wondered. "Oh, Willard, why did you have to interfere in Marc's life? It is complicated enough, without trying to live up to your standards."

Brenna, the Riordan's young Scottish maid, helped Morgan from her warm bath. "You look to be feeling better, ma'am."

"I do, Brenna. It's amazing how soaking in a warm tub can relax you."

"I wouldna' know, ma'am. I dinna' often ha' the leisure with Miss Todd around."

"To be honest, Brenna, neither do I. This is the first time I have stayed in a house longer than a couple of nights since I became involved in this war."

Brenna looked puzzled. "Tis a strange life for one so young and pretty. I dinna' think I could do it."

"You could if everyone you loved had been killed or had died because of this war. My brother and I are the only ones left in the family. I also have a very dear friend who is like a brother to me. He's a big Irishman who watches over me like a mother-hen. They both mean everything to me."

"You are lucky to ha' someone to watch over you."

Morgan saw the fleeting look of sadness in Brenna's violet eyes and wondered what this lovely, dark haired girl had been through in her young life. "Have you been with the Riordans long, Brenna?"

"Aye, near four years. the Riordans ha' been very good to me."

Morgan stopped drying her hair and turned to face Brenna. "Then you knew Christopher Riordan?"

"Aye, I knew him. He was a fine young man, but I always preferred Marcus."

"Why, Brenna? Were they very different?"

"Aye, very," Brenna said as she began to brush Morgan's auburn hair. "Christopher was always very serious, more settled than Marcus. He planned to follow his father in politics, to marry Miss Todd and settle down with a family. But Marcus, ah he was a devil."

Morgan's eyes widened in surprise. "A devil? What do you mean?"

"That one enjoyed life, he did. A scoundrel, he

was. A way with women no man should ha'. He could look at you wi' those blue eyes and your heart was his forever."

"He forces himself on women," Morgan accused angrily.

Brenna looked surprised. "D' you think he needs to force himself on any woman?"

Morgan thought of his smile, the laughter curving his hard mouth and his cold blue eyes softening into the blue of the sky. "No, I don't imagine he would have to force any woman."

"I would I had him to call my own, and thought once a long time ago I could."

Morgan looked into the soft, violet eyes filled with tears. "You are in love with him?" she asked sympathetically.

"Marcus was very kind to me. Mayhap I knew nothing of life, but I mistook his kindness for more than it was. I came here very young from Scotland and had dreams of marriage and living like a grand lady. I thought Marcus was my knight in shining armor, but Rachel Todd and others like her were quick to let me know I was only a servant girl and best know my place. Miss Todd takes great delight in making me look the fool in front of Marcus."

"I'm sorry, Brenna," Morgan said, her heart going out to the young girl. She knew exactly how it felt to be hopelessly in love with Marc Riordan. No matter how hard she tried to convince herself, the feelings she had when she thought of him proved otherwise.

Brenna picked up the delicate undergarments and held them to her. "I've no' seen the likes of these. Tis almost sinful," she giggled.

"I'm sure I will feel quite sinful wearing them," Morgan said, blushing as she thought of Marc knowing what she wore against her skin.

Morgan's curiosity was piqued and she wanted to know more about the Riordans. "Brenna, how did Marc become Rachel's intended?"

"Tis a long story," she answered as if dispensing with the subject, but instead continued on. "I think Marcus was the one she wanted all along. I came upon Rachel and Marcus in the sitting room shortly after she and Christopher announced their engagement. She was telling Marcus she loved him and if he would just say the word she would forget Christopher. Marcus was furious. I thought he would strike her. Well, along with his problems with Rachel, his father was constantly at him. I think Senator Riordan felt Marcus was wasting his life pursuing art. He had a law degree and the senator felt he should accept an offer Rachel's father made to make Marcus a junior partner. Marcus told his family he had to live his life as he saw fit and immediately left for Paris to study painting. Shortly after he left, the war broke out. Christopher was killed in one of the first battles and Douglas Todd died of a heart attack. Mrs. Riordan wrote to Marcus telling him of his brother's death and that his own father was very ill. Marcus arrived in time to hear his father's last words, telling him it was now his responsibility to take care of the family and Rachel. Marcus gave his word he would. The only reason Marcus and Miss Todd have not married before now is the war. Marcus has said he dinna' want to get married and then ha' to leave. I believe he is just finding excuses. Rachel dinna' like it, but I think she is afraid to push Marcus too far."

"I would not think Marc the kind of man who would do anything against his will."

"He felt guilty that Christopher died. Somehow he takes the blame. He is no longer the fun-loving artist, the scoundrel everyone loved. Poor man seems to ha' the weight of the world on his young shoulders. He seems deeply depressed to me, more so this trip than ever before. He is drinking ever so much. His mother sees it, but she is torn between seeing him happy and having him honor his father's dying wishes."

"Thank you for telling me all this, Brenna. I think I understand him a little better."

"He is a very fine man, but I ha' heard tell he has the temper of the devil if he is crossed."

"Yes, I believe that," Morgan said thinking of her experiences with Marc.

Morgan descended the long, curved staircase with Anne Riordan. She could hear Rachel's high-pitched voice and suddenly wished she hadn't accepted Anne's invitation. Forcing her chin high, she walked into the room. Her first sight was of Marc's dark head bent to Rachel's blonde one as she said something that amused him. Morgan had the urge to turn and run, but Anne held her arm.

"Morgan, I believe you have met everyone," Anne said, trying to break the awkward silence.

Wes Lansing moved toward Morgan. "This couldn't possibly be the young ragamuffin brought in here a week ago! Why you're absolutely beautiful."

"Thank you, Lieutenant Lansing. You are most kind."

Rachel turned her back to Morgan, blocking Marc's view and speaking loud enough for everyone to hear. "I will not tolerate that woman's presence here. She is a spy and a murderer. You should not expose your mother and me to her."

Anne squeezed Morgan's hand as Rachel's voice carried across the room. Marc stepped around Rachel and took Morgan's hand, bringing it slowly to his lips. "You look lovely, Morgan. I'm glad to see you're feeling better."

"Thank you, Marc. How could I not get better with the kind attention I have received?"

Marc turned Morgan around as he inspected her gown. "I knew it was made for you," he said in a low voice.

Morgan blushed. "Thank you for thinking of it."

"I'm just sorry I couldn't give you the diamonds, but that brooch you have on looks beautiful with the dress."

"Thank you. It belonged to my mother. It is one of the few things I keep with me."

Marc raised his glass. "Here's to your mother and the legacy of beauty she left behind."

Morgan found it difficult to breathe. She wasn't used to playing games and looked toward the door with thoughts of escape. Why did he always make her so uncomfortable? she wondered.

Wes stepped forward, handing Morgan a glass of sherry. "I don't know why I couldn't have found someone like you when I was in Front Royal. All I saw were dirty, bearded soldiers. You always did have the luck, Marc."

Rachel joined the group and possessively grasped Marc's arm. "Where did you get that gown? I thought you said you left your things behind."

"I did, Miss Todd. This was a gift.'

"From whom?" Rachel asked indignantly.

"I had them ordered for her," Anne Riordan said. "I knew she was going to need something when she felt better. The buckskins would not do for dinner."

Marc wondered why his mother was lying for him, but she kept her eyes averted to Morgan.

"I don't know why anyone would ever choose to wear those horrid buckskins anyway." Rachel said.

"It is much easier to ride a horse with pants on, Miss Todd. I spent days at a time in the saddle so they were very practical. Besides, a very dear friend gave them to me."

Rachel fluttered her fan in front of her face. "Why would a woman choose to fight—particularly for the South. It is just terrible how southerners keep slaves in chains and all."

"Miss Todd," Morgan said, trying to keep her composure. "I suggest you look around you before condemning southerners. Take a good look at your women and children dying in your mills and factories every day. My family had slaves, but we loved them. They were given their freedom, but chose to stay with us. As far as I know, they are still taking care of my home with all the pride my family would. As I was told so eloquently, by one of your union officers; there is good and bad on both sides."

"I had been told secessionists always had an answer for slavery," Rachel said disdainfully. "By the end of the war you will all know your place."

"Morgan, my mother tells me she thinks she knew your mother and father," Marc interjected.

Anne Riordan was quick to pick up on his attempt to change the subject. "Yes, dear. Marc tells me your father was a Fitzgerald from Spotsylvania County. My husband and I did quite a bit of traveling in that area and we became acquainted with a Sean and Amanda Fitzgerald while in Charlottesville."

Tears welled up in Morgan's eyes. "They were my parents," she said, but found it impossible to say more. She felt Marc's warm hand squeezing hers, as if to reassure her.

"They were lovely people, Morgan. I can now see the resemblance. Did you know your father was one of my husband's supporters?"

"Willard Riordan," Morgan said to herself as the recollection came to her. "I had not connected the name, but yes, I do recall his talking about Senator Riordan. He had the highest regard for him."

"Isn't it a small world," Wes said laughing. "It's possible that your family could have arranged for your marriage to Marc instead of Rachel's father."

Marc glared at his friend and Wes quickly left to refill his glass. "You must excuse my friend's rudeness, Morgan. I expected it of Rachel, but not of Wes."

"Why should it be any different? I am an intruder here."

"You are my guest," Marc insisted.

"Of course, how foolish of me to have forgotten.

And how will you explain my presence to your friends? Do you think Miss Todd is going to keep my identity a secret? Don't you see, Marc, this isn't going to work."

"Look at the alternatives, Morgan. I'd say it's the only solution."

"Darling, if you can tear yourself away from your prisoner, I'd like another drink," Rachel said locking her arm in Marc's.

Marc looked irritated, but said nothing. "Would you like another one, Morgan?"

"No thank you," Morgan answered, wishing Marc would not leave her alone with his fiancee. Green eyes met blue as the two women appraised each other.

"What is this game you are playing, Miss Fitzgerald?"

"I don't know what you're talking about, Miss Todd."

"I saw the way you wrapped Marc's aunt around your little finger and now his mother. If you think for one moment you're going to interfere with my plans to marry Marc, you are mistaken."

Before Morgan could say anything, Brenna announced dinner. Anne Riordan, who had been standing nearby, looked toward heaven and gave thanks for Brenna's timely arrival. She just didn't know how long she could take this tension. It seemed to hang in the air. She wasn't sure what Rachel and Morgan had said to each other, but she could see the hatred in their eyes.

Wes was quick to take Morgan's arm, leading her into the dining room. Marc picked up his brandy bottle and followed his mother and Rachel. There was an awkward silence as Brenna began serving.

Marc sat at the head of the table with Rachel and Morgan on each side. Morgan could feel his eyes on her, but she kept hers averted and tried to pretend interest in what Wes Lansing said. When she did look Marc's way, she met his intense brooding gaze and silence.

Wes possessively took Morgan's hand. "Tell me, beautiful Morgan, why do you have such a fierce loyalty for the south when you're obviously Irish?"

Morgan attempted to remove her hand, but Wes held it trapped. "My father came to America many years ago. My mother was a third generation Virginian. I think that should answer your question."

Morgan sipped her wine, trying to avoid Marc's cold eyes as he watched Wes holding her hand.

"You must attend General Pleasanton's party with me tomorrow night, Morgan. I'm tired of tagging along with Marc and Rachel."

"And how will you introduce her, Wesley?" Rachel asked snidely. "I don't think General Pleasanton will be overly thrilled at having the notorious Morgan Fitzgerald as a guest in his home."

"He won't have to know who she is. How about it, Morgan? Will you go with me?"

Before Morgan could answer, Rachel was on her feet. "This is absolutely ridiculous! That woman will make a fool of you, Marc. Please put a stop to this foolishness before it goes any further."

"Thank you for your invitation, Wesley," Morgan said, "but I do not wish to attend any party given by your General Pleasanton. I will let Rachel play the fool in my place. Now, please, Lieutenant Lansing, if you don't mind, I would like my hand back so I can finish my dinner."

"For God's sake, Wesley, how can you pretend such admiration for this tramp? You know what she is! She's been living with her men," Rachel sneered.

Morgan slammed her glass down on the table. "I am quite tired of your insinuations, Miss Todd. You know absolutely nothing about me or my past. I can assure you my family probably would not have considered associating with the likes of you. You are rude, spoiled and obviously poorly bred, and if you dare to make any further reference to my reputation, I shall be forced to show you what I learned while fighting for my country—and living with my men."

Rachel looked flustered. "Well, I would say it is quite obvious that you are well enough to be taken to prison before you hurt someone in this family."

Marc finally spoke, sounding as if he were bored with the whole affair. "Morgan will not be going to prison. She is going to be a guest of my mother's for awhile."

Rachel's eyes widened in disbelief. "You can't be serious. You are going to let this murdering spy stay in your home among your loved ones?"

"I think I made myself quite clear," Marc said pouring another brandy. "And you Wesley, will keep your hands off Morgan."

Morgan stood to leave. "I'm sorry to have caused this trouble, Anne. I think it would ease the situation if I take my meals alone from now on. I would just as soon be on my way, but I am afraid my fate lies in your son's hands. Perhaps you can convince him to let me return to my home."

"You'll do no such thing, Morgan," Marc stated angrily. "You are a guest in this house. Just as you are, Rachel, and if I hear you insult Morgan again, I'll be forced to ask you to leave."

"Well, I have never been so insulted," Rachel said rising from her chair. "When you decide to apologize, you will find me in my room."

"My only apology will be to Morgan."

"Then perhaps it is time I leave," Rachel said as she stormed from the room.

Wes looked imploringly to Marc. "Surely you will stop her, Marc. For God's sake, apologize. She is your fiancee."

"She created this problem. Let her cool off for awhile."

"If you don't mind, I'd like to go to her. She was very upset."

"Do whatever you like, Wes."

Anne hugged Morgan before excusing herself, leaving an uncomfortable silence between the two. Marc poured two glasses of brandy, handing one to Morgan. "Drink this. Sometimes it helps ease problems."

Morgan turned on him angrily, tears streaming down her face. "What did you hope to accomplish by bringing me here? Was humiliation to be part of my punishment?"

"If you will just stop and think, you'll realize what I've done is for your own good. You forget I planned to—never mind, that's not important. Just remember you are better off here."

"I remember only too well the feel of your hands on my throat, captain, but I still find it difficult to see this favor you are doing me. If you want to do us both a favor, let me go back to my friends."

Marc stared at Morgan for a long moment, his eyes deepening with desire. "I can't, Morgan," he answered almost in a whisper. "I too remember the feel of my hands on your throat—and your body," he said running a finger over the smooth, silky skin of her neck.

Morgan slapped his hand away. "I will not be the cheap tramp I've been accused of being!"

"No one is suggesting you are a tramp or should act like one. I just thought maybe we could work something out, Morgan. This situation is not impossible."

"I don't know what you're talking about."

"Stop acting so damned innocent, Morgan. You desire me as much as I desire you. What I'm saying is, I could take care of you. Give you a home. I could be with you every chance I got."

Morgan's green eyes blazed angrily. "You despicable, arrogant bastard. You're offering to set me up as your mistress. How could you ever think I would agree to such an arrangement? I hate you, Marc Riordan. Oh, God, how I hate you!" Morgan cried as she ran from the room.

Anne entered the room after passing Morgan in the hall. "Is everything all right, Marc?"

"Women! What did I do to deserve this?"

"You know very well what you did."

"Now what is that supposed to mean, Mother?"

211

"It means you're treading on thin ice and someone is going to get hurt. I don't want it to be Morgan."

"My, my, she already has a champion in her corner. You certainly took an instant liking to her."

"And you didn't?" Anne asked.

Marc studied the brandy in his glass, swirling it around before answering. "Do you have any suggestions as to how I can keep from hurting either of them? I feel I owe them both more than I can ever live up to."

"I know you promised your father you would marry Rachel, but it certainly wouldn't be fair to marry her loving someone else. Besides, it seems to me Wesley is most anxious to pick up the pieces, whichever one it might be."

"Yes, I've noticed. You know, something we're both overlooking is the fact that Morgan is a Confederate spy."

"Then why do you feel you owe her anything?"

Marc smiled and patted his mother on the cheek. "It's not something I care to discuss with my mother."

Anne Riordan smiled as her son left the room. "So, Morgan was innocent when they met. I wonder if Rachel can say the same thing."

Morgan sought the refuge of her room only to find more of Marc's handiwork. Lying across her bed were two more dresses of pastel colors. She angrily threw them on the floor then sank to her knees holding the delicate garments to her breast. "What are you trying to do to me, Marc Riordan?"

Morgan jumped as Brenna entered carrying a tray with a teapot.

"I was thinking you would be needing some tea for your nerves. Climb into bed and I will serve you there."

Morgan let Brenna unfasten her dress, then climbed into bed wearing only her delicate undergarments.

"It was a big mistake to think I would be welcome downstairs. I should never have left this room," Morgan said between sips of tea.

"You were welcome by all but Miss Todd. I wouldna' say you did too bad."

"I'm so keyed up, Brenna. I wish I could ride someplace. That always helped calm my nerves."

"You will be calm enough before long," Brenna said picking up the gowns from the floor.

"What do you mean, Brenna?"

"Marcus was concerned about you and decided it was best if he put something in your tea to help you sleep."

"No!" Morgan shouted as she jumped from the bed. "Oh, God, he's poisoned me," she said grabbing the bedpost to steady herself.

"Dinna' be ridiculous. You will feel fine in the morning. Now get back in bed before you hurt yourself. The drug works very quickly."

Morgan was already too weak to protest. She fell back on the bed, the room spinning around her. "Please, Brenna, don't leave me alone. He plans to kill me. I know he has poisoned me."

"You are being foolish. Marcus was just concerned that you were upset. I will stay right here with you 'til you fall to sleep," she said as she covered Morgan.

"I knew it would come to this. He's an evil man, Brenna. I tried to tell you," Morgan said drifting off to sleep.

Marc sat moodily staring into the flames of the fireplace in his study. Swirling the brandy in his glass, he thought of the two women upstairs; one his fiancee and the other the woman he desired above all others.

He laughed aloud, a harsh, cruel sound as he thought of his best friend consoling his fiancee. What a cruel twist of fate; he was in love with a Rebel spy and his friend was in love with another man's fiancee. It was hopeless for both of them, he thought, downing the last of the brandy in his glass. He stared into the empty glass, thinking of Morgan's sweet kisses and the velvet feel of her skin. Suddenly he felt an uncontrollable anger surge through him. Why was he sitting here when he wanted her? Damn the auburn-haired, green-eyed witch. He was going to have her this night.

"Would ye be wanting another bottle of brandy, sir?"

"No thank you, Brenna. I've had enough."

"Aye, I should say so."

"Are you sermoning me, Brenna?" Marc asked with a grin.

Brenna blushed with embarrassment. "I'm sorry, sir, it's just I've not seen you drink so much."

"I know, Brenna, and it hasn't solved my problems."

Brenna stood behind Marc's chair, massaging his shoulders. "Why don't you come to my room tonight and let me help you forget your problems. You are so tense."

"Ah, Brenna," Marc said taking her hand. "You are sweet, but that will not solve my problems. It would only add to them."

Brenna looked hurt. "I would welcome you to my bed. Rachel will never ha' to know. You must know I care for you."

"And I care for you, Brenna. That is why I will not ruin your life. You deserve a man who will give you his undivided attention and I would never be able to do that."

"My offer stands. If you dinna wish to accept it, I can do nothing else."

"When the right man comes along you'll be glad I didn't accept your offer—and the right man will come along, Brenna. Now tell me, is Morgan asleep?"

"Aye, she is asleep, but she was sure you had poisoned her."

Marc looked surprised. "She knew I put the sleeping potion in her drink?"

"Aye, I saw no reason to lie to her."

"No, of course not. So, she thought I poisoned her," he mused.

Brenna watched the expression on Marc's face and realized Rachel was not the one she should have been worrying about. Marc was obviously in love with Morgan.

"I will be turning in now, sir. Do you need anything else?"

"Thank you, Brenna, I'm fine. You sleep well."

"Aye, and you."

Marc entered Morgan's room and stood silently beside her bed. The light from the lamp reflected a golden glow over her sleeping form attired only in the thin, delicate shift he had so carefully picked out. He expelled his breath as his passion rose and he fought to control his desire for her. The sweet smell of her hair tantalized him as he lifted a lock, rubbing it between his fingers. He bent down and kissed her slightly parted lips.

"Do you really think I would let poison pass those honey lips?" he whispered. Morgan turned her head to the side, softly murmuring in her sleep. Marc gently kissed her again. "I have a fierce desire for your lovely body, but I cannot take you like this. Sleep well, my love."

Chapter Fourteen

Morgan woke the next morning totally disoriented. The memory of the night before slowly came back to her and she felt anger rising again. If she didn't care for Anne she would kill Marc Riordan without a second thought. The nerve of the man offering to put her up as his mistress. Well, all she hoped was Rachel Todd was as frigid as an iceberg and Marc would find himself impotent. "Ha!" she said aloud. "That would serve the egotistical bastard right!"

A sudden harsh knock startled Morgan. Brenna entered with a tray, but did not look at Morgan.

"Good morning, Brenna."

"Morning, ma'am," she answered without looking up.

"Thank you for breakfast. Won't you sit and have a bite with me?"

"I have more important things to do, ma'am. You forget I'm but a servant here."

Morgan couldn't understand the girl's change in attitude. She liked Brenna and thought they had become friends. "Is something wrong?"

"Aye, I feel I ha' been taken for a fool."

"Not by me, Brenna."

"Aye, by you. You must forgive me, ma'am, but I find it difficult to be pleasant to someone who lies to people who try to show only kindness."

"What makes you say that?" Morgan asked puzzled.

"Had I known you and Marcus were lovers I would not ha' been so free with my talk."

"That's not true! I hate him!"

"Do you now? Strange the look I saw in your eyes last night was not hate."

"No, no. You're wrong. I hate him," Morgan insisted. Brenna didn't say anything. "Oh Brenna, I'm sorry. I am very confused. How could I have told you what my feelings are when I don't know myself?"

Brenna sat on the side of the bed, taking Morgan's hand in hers. "I know you would be better for Marc than that money-hungry bitch. She will only make his life miserable."

"He only wants me for his mistress, Brenna. He cares nothing for me."

"I think you are wrong, lass. I saw the look in his

eyes last night when he spoke of you. I even offered to ease his troubles, but he turned me away because you were on his mind."

Morgan saw the hurt in Brenna's eyes, but couldn't help feeling relieved that Marc hadn't taken advantage of the girl. "I'm sorry, Brenna. I don't want to love him. Most of the time I want to kill him. That's why I have to get away from here. I don't want to hurt Anne Riordan. I was hoping maybe you could get a message to a friend for me."

Brenna thought for a moment. "Marcus leaves soon. We'll talk about it then."

Morgan lay across her bed welcoming the soft, summer breeze that drifted through her window. She was confident Brenna would help her escape if for no other reason than to be rid of her.

Her thoughts turned drowsily to Marc. What would he do when he discovered she had escaped? Well, it didn't make any difference. She would be long gone before he knew.

Images of their lovemaking came to her memory. Dark, brooding eyes came to mind and then his words, whispered in her ear after their passion had ebbed. I'll never let you go, Morgan. You are mine. Morgan shook her head, trying to clear her thoughts. If you hate him so, why can't you dismiss him from your thoughts? Morgan angrily swung her feet off the bed and went to the window.

"Oh, Marc, if you had only offered more. How could you think I would ever agree to be your mistress while Rachel was your wife?"

She pressed her fingertips to her temples to ease the throbbing. How good it would feel to ride across an open field with the wind in her face. Oh God, who are you kidding, she asked herself. Nothing has changed. This grim, bloody war continues. The Yankees are blazing a path of death and destruction across your beloved Virginia. What are you going back to that you should feel so elated?

There was a light tap on the door and for a moment Morgan thought it might be Marc. Instead Anne Riordan asked if she might come in. "Of course Anne. It is always nice to have your company."

"Did you sleep well last night?"

."Marc saw to it that I had a sleeping draft so I slept very well."

"That was considerate of him. I knew you were upset and I worried about you."

"My skin is thicker than you think, Anne. Rachel's barbed remarks don't bother me," she lied.

"Rachel has been spoiled all her life, Morgan. You must try to overlook her childish behavior. But, I am not here to make excuses for Rachel. I am here on Wesley's behalf. He entreats me to ask you again to join him for the party tonight."

"I cannot, Anne. Surely you can understand that. I am a prisoner here. My countrymen are fighting and dying for a cause I fiercely believe in. I will not socialize with my enemy as if there weren't a war going on."

Anne affectionately squeezed Morgan's hand. "You are a remarkable woman, Morgan. I now understand why Connie wrote about you in such glowing terms. I am flattered to say she thought you were much like me when I was young and politicking with my husband across the Commonwealth of Virginia."

"Is that when you met my mother and father?"

"Oh no, child, it was much later than that. Willard was already a Senator when we met them. It was at a rally in Charlottesville. I remember how lovely your mother was. She reminded me of a delicate Dresden doll."

"Her delicate looks were deceiving, Anne. She was a very strong woman—at least until my father died." Tears welled up in Morgan's eyes as she thought about the way her mother had willed herself to die. Her mother had been such a vital woman. She had loved her husband and children more than life and it showed in everything she did.

"Morgan, I am sorry to have brought up such sad memories."

"Oh no, Anne. They're not sad. I was just remembering the love my mother had for her family."

"Do you have brothers and sisters, Morgan?"

"Only a brother. A twin and a . . ."

"A what, dear?" Anne asked puzzled at Morgan's flustered state.

"Nothing. I was just going to say my brother rode with me until I went to Warrenton on my last mission. I guess he's been very worried about me."

"Perhaps I could get Marc to send word to him that you are well, but being detained for awhile."

"Do you think he would?" Morgan asked anxiously. "That would ease my mind a great deal."

"I will talk to him right away. Now I had better get back to Wesley and tell him he will have to go alone tonight."

"Please thank him for me," Morgan said absent-mindedly as Anne left the room. She had not wanted to tell Anne that she didn't like Wesley Lansing. She had seen the looks that passed between him and Rachel and it made her angry that he pretended to be a dear friend. He reminded her of Jared Law who rode with Fitzhugh; so arrogant, and always flirting and trying to impress all the females around. She much preferred someone like Marc; the strong silent type, yet women seemed to be drawn to him without his doing a thing.

Morgan thought of the look in his dark, brooding eyes last night at the dinner table. He had seemed so upset when Wesley had flirted with her. Damn him, what did he want from her anyway?

The day dragged out interminably, a matter Morgan would usually have eased by riding swiftly across the Virginia countryside. Here in her opulent prison she could only pace the confines of her room, not wanting to chance seeing Marc again. She plopped herself down on the bed and let her thoughts drift back in time, remembering an occasion when Jubal had pledged to always be there to help if she needed him. She had teased him because he never went swimming with her and Michael. In an attempt to prove his bravery, he jumped into the swift moving North Anna River and nearly drowned before Morgan pulled him to the shore. Afterwards, he sheepishly admitted he had never learned to swim and was too embarrassed to let anyone know. She had set out immediately to teach him and within the week he was out-swimming Michael, who never knew what had taken place. That was when Jubal swore his loyalty to

221

her. Morgan fought the tears that welled up in her eyes. "Oh, Jubal, where are you?"

Jubal Kelly was at that moment in Stuart's camp in Aldie, Virginia, exchanging details with Jeb on their frustrated search for Morgan. He had gone into the town of Warrenton as an Irish merchant so no one suspected a thing when he asked questions. He learned that Morgana York as she was known in union circles, had mysteriously disappeared after a party given by General Smyth. The Hawthornes, who were Rebel sympathizers and knew Morgan's work, had no idea what had happened to her. She had said goodnight to them when she came home from the party and that was the last time they had seen her. There was no clue to be found in her room.

Jubal had a gut feeling that Marc Riordan had something to do with Morgan's disappearance, but he wasn't sure how or why.

Jeb had made contact with everyone he knew who had knowledge of prisons and there was no mention of Morgan Fitzgerald being taken prisoner. He was sure the newspapers would have carried elaborate details of her capture, but there was nothing.

Jubal finally convinced Stuart to let him travel to Washington, still masquerading as an Irish merchant, and try to find the Riordan's residence, but he would not agree to let Michael accompany him. It made sense the Union might believe Jubal Kelly with his Irish brogue, but they might be very suspicious of a young man with a southern accent accompanying him. Michael relented, for Morgan's sake. He would bide his time riding scout with John Mosby as close to the Washington area as possible, hoping for some information on his sister.

Marc Riordan returned from General Hooker's with his new orders. He was now going to lead his own unit into the Loudoun County area to try to flush out the partisans who concentrated on the city of Washington and its surrounding area. The head of the partisans was none other than John Singleton Mosby, his friend and adversary. Marc had been relieved that Hooker had not pursued the issue of why he had not brought a prisoner back to Washington. Hooker had accepted the fact that Marc had discovered the spy and killed him. Union officers were so relieved that the trains were moving freely again they would probably have accepted any method of dealing with the spy.

Marc looked forward to this new challenge, yet the thought of leaving Morgan was disturbing to him. He would like to tell her how he felt, but she would never understand. He'd just stay away from her and perhaps one of these days he would forget her and be able to lead a normal life again.

He poured himself a large brandy and raised it toward Morgan's room. "To you, green eyes, and to a normal life," he said before downing the fiery liquid, knowing his life would never be normal again.

Anne tapped lightly on the door of the study and entered. "I heard you come in and hoped we could talk for a moment."

"Of course, Mother. I'm sorry I have been so distant and irritable lately."

"I understand the turmoil you're going through,

son. I wish there were something I could do to help you."

"I'll be leaving tomorrow. I think that will be best for all concerned. If I'm away from here maybe I can get my mind off . . . off my problems."

"You mean off Morgan?"

Marc turned his back to his mother and stared out the window. "Yes, I suppose I mean off Morgan."

"Running away isn't going to solve your problems."

"If I hadn't been such a failure to my father I wouldn't have felt it necessary to give him my word to marry Rachel."

Anne looked stunned. "That's not true, Marcus. You were never a disappointment."

"Oh, Mother, you know how he felt about me. He didn't want me to pursue art. He was terribly disappointed when I refused Todd's offer to join his law firm. Then when I chose to travel to Europe instead of settling down here, I thought he was going to disown me. He said I was a carouser, a rogue and would never amount to anything. How could I let him down now, when it is the only time I promised him I'd do what he asked?"

"If he had known Rachel, he would never have asked such a thing or if he had known how you felt about this girl . . ."

"No, Mother!" he said harshly, then regretted his tone. "I'm sorry. I know you mean well, but father gave his word to Douglas Todd that Christopher would marry his daughter. Since Chris was killed he felt he had to keep his word by marrying his other son to Rachel. It was the most important thing on his mind when he was dying. I will not deny him that wish now. My only hope had been Wesley and he tells me Rachel laughed at him when he tried to tell her how he felt."

"He has no backbone. I knew all along he would be weak when it came to speaking up. He would rather flirt and play the cavalier."

"Don't be too hard on him, Mother. He truly loves Rachel, but knows only too well what she wants out of life."

Marc hugged his mother when he noticed the worried expression on her face. "You stop worrying about me. As soon as I get back in the field I'll forget about Morgan."

Anne Riordan knew better. If only her husband had realized what he was doing when he asked Marc for his word. Without knowing it, he had ruined their son's life. Rachel would never make him happy. She had already insisted he give up his art and that alone would slowly kill him.

Marc poured himself another brandy after his mother left. Funny, he thought, this stuff doesn't seem to dull the pain anymore. Why had he been fool enough to fall in love with this Rebel termagant. She wasn't worth all this pain. How could he let himself be so weak. He should have delivered her to prison the moment they arrived in Washington instead of playing all these games. There hadn't been any reason for him to take her to Harpers Ferry. He had only wanted her with him, but he hadn't counted on falling in love with her.

Marc was not in the mood for his next intruder and

his eyes clearly showed the irritation as Rachel entered the room.

"I have been waiting to speak with you all morning."

"You knew I had a meeting with General Hooker this morning."

"Well, I'm not happy with the arrangements for tonight and I had hoped you would speak to Wes. He insists on asking that girl upstairs to attend the party."

Marc poured another drink and swallowed it before speaking. "Morgan will not be attending the party tonight. She has chosen to stay here."

"Well, I am relieved to hear that. It would certainly have been in poor taste to take a Rebel spy to General Hooker's party."

"You're right there," Marc said in a slurred voice. "Knowing Morgan, she would have had him spilling secrets within the hour."

Rachel turned to leave but stopped at the door. "I do hope you will be sober tonight. It just disgusts me to see you drinking this way."

Marc lifted his glass in a mock toast. "I certainly don't want to embarrass you, my dear. I shall do my best not to be disgusting," he said sarcastically, enjoying the effect it had on his fiancee.

"You must remember your position, Marc. You have a name and reputation to uphold," she said over her shoulder as she left the room.

Marc glared at the closed door. "To hell with name and reputation!"

Anne entered Morgan's room just before the group

was ready to leave. She turned before Morgan for her approval.

"You look absolutely beautiful. I feel sorry for all the young girls who think they will be the belle of the ball."

"Well, I certainly wouldn't be if you were there," Anne said.

Morgan hugged the little woman. "Thank you, Anne. You are too kind. You'd better hurry now or they'll leave without you."

Morgan listened for the door to close as the group left, then she dropped on the bed and stared at the ceiling. "Well, Morgan, what are you going to do, lie here and feel sorry for yourself?" She picked up a book of Byron's poems and flipped through the pages. She found herself wondering if Marc enjoyed poetry. Surely an artist would enjoy . . . She suddenly sat up. This was her opportunity to see his work.

Morgan slipped into a satin robe which Anne had given her and hobbled to the door. The staircase leading to the attic was at the end of the hall. She lit a lamp and slowly began her climb up the narrow stairs. She was astounded when she reached the top. The roof of the room was a skylight and the stars shone brightly overhead. The window overlooking the garden was large and uncovered to let in the light. A perfect room for an artist, she thought. There was a large feather-bed in the corner of the room and a big overstuffed chair off to the side. She was amazed how warm and inviting a little hideaway like this could be.

She studied the oil paintings strewn around the room. There were seascapes, mountain scenes, sketches of war life; all so beautiful and so realistic. He has a real talent, she thought. What a shame if it is wasted.

Morgan turned and saw a covered easel. This must be what he is working on, she thought. She lifted the cover and gasped as she revealed a painting of her sitting atop Gambler. For a moment she couldn't move. Why would he have painted her—and in her buckskins? She felt as if she were looking into a mirror it was so realistic. Her hair cascaded around her shoulders and the green of her eyes seemed almost to glow.

She sat for a long time studying the painting. Perhaps his eye for beauty was why she had always felt he could see into her soul. Hadn't she heard someplace that an artist could see the inner person?

She stood and stretched. "Well, Marc Riordan, I hope you pursue this God-given talent and don't let a selfish woman ruin your life."

Morgan picked up the lamp and descended the stairs, feeling more confused and bewildered than ever. She just wasn't ready to go back to her room so she headed down the stairs thinking to find a book to occupy her boredom.

Lamps had been lit throughout the house so Morgan wandered through the deserted rooms. She entered the library and noticed the piano. She wondered how she had missed it before, but then she was fending off Rachel the last time she had been in this room.

She sat down and ran a light finger over the keys, forgetting all about the book she had come for. She ran through Chopin's Prelude in E minor, enjoying the beautiful tone of the fine instrument. She couldn't help but think of home and the many hours she had sat before her piano practicing when she would rather have been out riding with Michael and Jubal. Her mother had always told her she was good enough to one day go to Washington and play for the president. Well, she thought, I am in Washington even if it isn't to play for the president.

She began to softly play one of Beethoven's Sonatas, letting its haunting melody take her home.

Marc opened the door and paused when he heard the lilting melody coming from the library. No one had played the piano since Christopher and it left him stunned for a few moments when he heard the familiar sound of music filling the house. When he reached the library door he was shocked to see Morgan playing. Her eyes were closed as she skillfully played the difficult chords.

Marc was amazed at the talent she possessed. Surely she hadn't touched a piano in years yet it sounded as if she had never been away from it. He could not bring himself to break the spell she was under so he stood, transfixed, listening to the beautiful sounds. Suddenly she slammed her fists on the keys and began to cry. Marc was hesitant to intrude, but he knew he couldn't leave her like this.

"Eyes as lovely as yours shouldn't be clouded with tears."

Morgan jumped at the sound of his voice. She wiped her face, trying to hide the tears. "What are you doing here? Surely the party isn't over."

Marc sat on the bench beside her. "No, it isn't over. I came home because I was concerned about my prisoner."

"You needn't have been. I told your mother I would stay for awhile."

"I know, but it made a good excuse," he answered very seriously.

"If Rachel believed that, she is a fool."

Marc laughed. "Rachel was too busy being the belle of the ball to care whether I stayed or not. Besides, Wesley will take care of her."

"Doesn't it bother you that he shows such obvious attention to your fiancee?"

"No, it only bothers me when he is attentive to you."

Morgan's face warmed with a flush that rose to her cheeks. "Please, don't play games with me, Marc."

"I have never played games with you, Morgan."

Morgan turned back to the piano, suddenly unable to look at him. "Would you like to hear another piece? I am really out of practice, but your piano is magnificent."

Marc smiled at her attempt to change the subject. "The piano was Christopher's. He played, but not as well as you, and yes, I would love to hear you play again."

Morgan began to play Chopin's Polonaise. "This was one of my mother's favorite pieces."

Marc watched her face as she became engrossed in the music. It was all he could do to keep his hands off her. He had known it would be a mistake to come back, but he had to be with her again before leaving.

He had tried all week to stay away from her, but the desire to feel her body next to his was more than he could bear.

Morgan finished playing and slowly turned to face him. She recognized the look in his eyes and began to move away, but he grabbed her hand.

"Don't go, Morgan," he pleaded.

"Please go back to the party. I can't think straight when you are so near."

"It's too late, Morgan. You and I both know that. These past few weeks have been hell knowing you were so near, yet I couldn't touch you."

He pulled her to him and gently kissed her. "You belong to me, Morgan, why can't you see the inevitable?"

Morgan sighed, leaning against him. Don't fight it, she told herself. This moment is all that matters. This is what you have been wanting.

Marc lifted her into his arms and carried her to his studio in the attic.

"This is wrong, Marc."

"How could it be wrong? You need love as much as I do. Why can't you admit it?"

"What you are offering is not love."

Marc stared into her eyes. "It's as close as I have ever come, Morgan. All I know is you're in my every thought, my every breath. When I'm with you I feel as if I could move mountains, conquer armies."

Marc gently laid her on the bed. Her robe fell away, exposing the creaminess of her breast. Marc stood mesmerized as the moon shone brightly through the skylight illuminating her in its brightness. Slowly he slipped the robe from her. She did nothing to stop him as his eyes locked with hers, rendering her incapable of movement. When she was naked he stood and quickly undressed. Never before had he felt the intensity of the moment. Women had always been a release to him; a release from pent-up tension and fury, but this woman possessed him. He lived and breathed for her, for the feel of her moving beneath him.

Her body was warm against him as he lay beside her, kissing her deeply, feeling her soft, yielding lips trembling against his. She closed her eyes as he brushed her taut nipples with his tongue, letting her body take over from her mind, leaving her powerless against this man who could seduce her by his touch. She was helpless as his lips explored her body. She ran her hand over his back and felt the muscles ripple under her fingers. He was like the Greek gods she had read about when growing up; a bronzed skin, beautiful god who women idolized, and he was hers for this night.

"You are so beautiful, Morgan. So beautiful and desireable. I want to love you, every inch of you," he whispered, his voice hoarse with desire.

Her pulse quickened, her breathing became rapid as he positioned himself between her legs. "Tell me you need me, love. Tell me," he demanded, plunging deep inside of her, but remaining motionless. Morgan clung to him like a drowning person. Liquid fire seemed to be spreading through her veins.

"I need you, Marc . . . I want you . . . I want you," she cried, her voice breathless as he slowly moved inside of her. She matched his rhythm with a shameless abandon, driving him past the forced patience he had tried to contain. His long-denied hunger for her body surged through him as Morgan cried out for release of her pent-up emotions. Together they climbed the highest peak, and slowly, very slowly returned to reality.

They lay exhausted, Marc's flesh still a part of her. "Every night I have lain here and imagined what it would be like to make love to you under the moon and stars," he whispered against her neck.

"And how was it?" she asked, no longer embarrassed by their intimacy.

"Better than my wildest dreams. I only regret we wasted so many nights."

"We will have others."

Marc leaned up on one elbow and looked down into her face. "I must return to my outfit tomorrow. Wes and I will be leaving early in the morning. I don't know when I will get back."

"Oh Marc, for a moment I almost forgot this terrible war. When will it be over?"

"I don't know, love. Soon I hope," he said kissing her tenderly. "Will you wait here for me, Morgan?"

"We are both forgetting Rachel."

"I will work something out. Just say you love me and will wait here."

"I love you, yet I know I shouldn't. You are my enemy."

"A love that risks nothing is worth nothing, my sweet."

"You know I will wait for you."

"Perhaps I won't be away too long."

"Do you know where you're being sent?"

"Into Loudoun County, but let's not talk about that now."

Morgan laughed. "Do you still think of me as a spy, my love?"

Marc smacked her soundly on the bottom. "You little devil. Life with you will never be dull," he said pulling her back into his arms. "Morning is just an hour or two away, love. You'd better sleep for a little while because I'm going to make love to you before dawn."

Marc had avoided telling Morgan that his mission was to stop Mosby. There wasn't any need for her to know. He already felt a little like a traitor without her adding guilt to his problems. John Mosby and he had been friends a long time ago. Marc thought of Mosby in younger years and remembered his tendency to fight. He was frail and slender yet there was something hardy and virile in his nature. He never hesitated to take on someone twice his size. His name was now known all over the nation as well as Virginia. He was a synonym in the South for brave deeds and daring escapades; a byword in the North for fear and hatred. His colorful figure in gray cape, lined in scarlet and gray plumed hat made him easily identifiable. He would lead his men into the jaws of death one moment and talk of birds and books and poetry the next.

Mosby and Fitzgerald had both been of untold value to the Confederacy in keeping a watch on enemy movements and giving reconnaissance reports. Intelligence brought in by them figured in several of the major campaigns. Mosby's elusiveness was a matter of constant worry to the North and now Marc was given the job of capturing the man who was considered a godly figure by some, and a damned nuisance by others. Although the Union forces were not aware of it, he had already put Morgan Fitzgerald out of commission—for good, he hoped.

Marc looked down at the sleeping figure wrapped in his arms. How could he have ever thought this warm, passionate girl was his enemy? He should have known the first time she smiled at him his life would never be the same. He would be finished with one night affairs that meant nothing; with women who were more interested in his money and name than him. Life meant something to him now . . . somehow he had to make her a permanent part of it.

Marc spent much of the night either making love to Morgan or just watching her sleep beside him. Now he could see the pink light of dawn through the skylight and for the first time in his life he wished the new day would never dawn.

Morgan was still cradled in his arms, her body warm and flushed from their lovemaking of moments earlier. "Darling, it's dawning a new day," he whispered against her ear.

Morgan turned her face toward him, her eyes pleading. "Don't leave me, Marc. I have a terrible feeling something is going to happen and we'll never be together again."

"You are wrong, darling. I'll never let that happen. You are my reason for living. My life had no meaning until I met you. I don't plan to ever let you go, darling. We've been fighting the inevitable; caught in a crosswind, but we were meant to be together. Our paths have crossed too often."

Morgan didn't understand her uneasy feeling, but she knew Marc would never understand this inner-sight she and her brother had. He kissed her tenderly and she knew he must be right—he had to be. They were meant to be together.

"You lie there while I get dressed. I want you in my sight as long as possible."

"You know I must get back to my room before everyone is up and about."

"I know, but we still have a little time. Maybe I can get Brenna to fix us some breakfast before everyone is up."

"I'll fix it. We don't need to wake Brenna," Morgan said as she swung her feet from the bed, carefully keeping the sheet around her.

Marc knelt in front of her, taking her hands in his. "Morgan, we probably won't be alone again once we leave this room."

"I know, darling, but this night has been ours and we'll not let the sun part us again."

Marc's blue eyes locked with Morgan's green and their love glowed in unspoken words as he held her possessively.

Chapter Fifteen

Morgan paced her room listening to the sounds coming from below as Marc said goodbye to his family. She ached with the pain of his leaving, wondering if she would ever see him again. Suddenly she raced to the door. She had to see him once more, if only from a distance.

He was standing at the door with Anne, Rachel and Wesley. He was leaving her—leaving to fight against her family and friends. She wanted to call out—to beg him not to go. Tears burned her eyes as she tried to hold back the flow. Suddenly Marc turned and looked toward the landing. Their eyes met and for a moment everyone and everything else in the room faded. Morgan felt a renewed strength. Somehow they would be together again.

Marc climbed the steps toward her, their eyes still locked, oblivious to everyone else in the room. He clasped his hand over hers on the railing. "Wait for me, Morgan," he asked softly.

"You know I will."

"I'll keep thoughts of last night to help me get through the next few weeks."

Morgan clutched the railing, her knuckles white from her deathlike grip. She fought the urge to throw herself into his arms—to throw all caution to the wind and let the world know she loved this man who was supposed to be her enemy. But she didn't. Instead looking deep into his eyes, she saw his love and knew she would have to be satisfied with that for now.

"I love you, Marc."

"And I you, little one. When I return I'll prove it to you over and over."

The moment was interrupted by Anne's voice reminding Marc of the time.

"Oh, Morgan, how I want to take you in my arms, but it would only cause you trouble once I am gone."

"I know, darling. You must go now. Please take care of yourself," she whispered.

He took a step forward and put his hand under her chin. Lifting her tear-stained face, he studied it, as if trying to memorize her features. "Take care of yourself, green eyes. I'll be back soon."

Turning, he quickly descended the stairs. Morgan did not stay to watch him leave. Insted she fled to the safety of her room where she could let the tears flow openly; not only for Marc, but for all those who had left her in one way or another.

She finally cried herself to sleep, hoping the arms of Morpheus would ease the desperate feeling of loneliness that swept over her.

Morgan was awakened by the sound of someone fumbling with her door. She sat up, staring in surprise as Rachel entered her room.

"I think it is time we had a private talk, Miss Fitzgerald."

"Of course, Miss Todd. What do you want to talk about?"

"Let's not play games. I know what you're up to and you will not get away with it."

"I have no idea what you are talking about."

Rachel nervously tapped the fan she held. "I happen to know you spent the night in the arms of my fiance last night. Now I know you probably forced yourself on Marc and being the gentleman that he is, he didn't turn you away. All men have these desires of the flesh, but you will get no further with him. He is going to be my husband. I will have his name, his money and his children."

Morgan was appalled. "What an odd way you have of expressing your love, Miss Todd. Does his name and money really mean so much to you?"

"I have waited a long time to have Marc Riordan," Rachel answered angrily. "You will not interfere in my plans. You will pack and leave immediately."

"I am afraid I have already interfered in your plans. You see, I love Marc for the compassionate man he is, and I will wait here for his return."

"You will regret that decision, Miss Fitzgerald. You will regret ever having interfered in my life. I am going to marry Marc and you'll have nothing. Don't say I didn't warn you," Rachel said, a strange, evil look in her dull, colorless eyes.

"Don't threaten me, Miss Todd. I have dealt with my enemy far too long to be frightened by a woman scorned."

Rachel's evil laughter sent chills up Morgan's spine. "You're a fool, woman. You deal with love and compassion. I deal with hate and vengeance. Mark my word, I will triumph in the end."

Morgan only stared at the frail, nondescript woman who seemed to have been transformed into something evil.

Rachel headed for the door then turned and smiled. "Don't say I didn't warn you, my dear."

Morgan was stunned. She had greatly misjudged Rachel Todd. She thought her a witless, money-hungry woman, but she was much more than that. It was obvious she wouldn't stop at anything to get what she wanted.

"Well, Miss Todd, you're going to have your hands full getting rid of me."

Morgan suddenly felt a new determination. She was not going to stay in this room feeling sorry for herself. The Riordans had a beautiful garden she could enjoy, a music room and a library full of works of the masters. She would take advantage of these opportunities and try to pass the time constructively until Marc returned. Also she would pursue her friendship with Brenna. It would be nice to have someone her own age to talk with. She was sure she was going to need all the friends she could get with Rachel around trying to make life miserable.

Morgan wandered around the house for a little while until she found herself in the kitchen sitting on a stool watching Brenna and the cook going over the menus for the week. They were both so absorbed in what they were doing, neither paid any attention to Morgan as she nibbled on an apple.

Brenna looked up as she heard the crunching of the fresh apple. "I'm sorry, ma'am. I dinna' see you come in. Can I get you something?"

"No, Brenna, I was just bored and hoped I might be able to help. Perhaps I could set the table or something."

"Oh no, ma'am. You are a guest here. Mrs. Riordan wouldna' like it a bit if she found you working."

"You know, Brenna, being inactive could drive me crazy. Now would you want to be responsible for that?"

Brenna laughed. "Go on with you. You'll ha' me crying in a minute. Take that basket and pick some flowers for the table. I dinna' think Mrs. Riordan would object to that. Here, let me tie this apron on you."

Morgan glanced about the colorful garden at the roses so lovingly cared for. She closed her eyes and listened to the sounds of the insects. It was so beautiful here, so removed from the sounds of guns and cannons.

A few blocks from the Riordan house things weren't so peaceful for the Hooker household. Lincoln had begged General Hooker to keep at Lee and not be trapped at the Rappahannock River, like an ox jumped half over a fence and liable to be torn by dogs front and rear, without a fair chance to gore one way or kick the other. Then he questioned the general about being in Washington when he was supposed to be on duty. Hooker had stood all he could. He messaged Hallack that he requested to be relieved of his position. Within the hour the request was granted and General George C. Meade, a quiet, courteous officer had been named his successor. Meade lacked personal magnetism, but he possessed one idea that would affect Marc Riordan. He believed in irregular warfare, as the South did, and would give Marc the opportunity to use it.

Mosby, in all his glory with the broad arena between Washington and the Rappahannock as a field for his daily activities, was taking on new strength and expanding his reputation.

The guerrillas were relentless in their drive to worry the Union now occupying most of northern Virginia. Federal camps were raided almost nightly, some Union units disappearing without a trace. Other officers complained they had lost all contact with Washington because of lines being cut by the guerrillas. The countryside in which these men operated was ideal. The people resented the Northern invasion and made sure the guerrillas were fed and well protected. They were able to move about the countryside without fear, coming to the outskirts of Washington where they rounded up prisoners, destroyed telegraph lines and terrorized unguarded parts of Fairfax County.

Marc Riordan, now promoted to the rank of Major, was determined to quiet the Rebels and with the backing of General Meade he could do it his way. Ignoring the protests of the officer in charge of the Union stables in Alexandria, he confiscated one-hundred prize sturdy mounts to dangle before Mosby. He was sure the temptation would be too great for the partisan leader to ignore. Fifty men escorted the horses while Marc and fifty more men stayed in thewoods. Near Gooding's Tavern, on the Little River Turnpike, the wily partisan leader took the bait. There in the dust and heat of late afternoon the Rebels circled the small group of Union soldiers and their valuable stock. Even with the fifty horsemen coming out of the woods, the Rebels nearly routed the Union plan. The soldiers who had been with the horses panicked, and instead of joining the fight ran for cover, ignoring Marc's orders to rejoin the men. Suddenly the fighting eased and Marc turned in the saddle to see why. He saw Mosby reeling in his saddle stunned, then he rode out of the combat area with blood pouring from his side and thigh. The fight was over. The Rangers followed their wounded leader into the woods.

Word of John Mosby's injury spread rapidly. Newspapers positively announced Mosby's death, even to the details. Rejoicing was universal in the Union ranks, but Marc Riordan had considerable doubt that his long-time adversary was dead, and although he could not voice his thoughts to anyone, he hoped he wasn't.

Several days later Morgan sat in the darkness of her room with the Washington Star newspaper crushed in her lap. The tears had now dried on her face, but she still felt the painful knot in her stomach that had threatened to make her sick as she read the account of Mosby's death. She choked back a sob as she thought of the man she loved killing her dear friend. She imagined services being conducted with her brother, Jubal and Jeb around an open grave in a tree-shaded glen and Mosby's blanket-wrapped body being lowered into the ground.

Morgan lay staring at the ceiling. Could she hate Marc for doing what he felt was his duty? She was being foolish. It probably wasn't even his bullet that had killed her friend, just because the papers said it was Major Marc Riordan's crack outfit which had finally run the infamous guerrilla leader down.

"Major Marc Riordan," she mused. "I wonder when that happened?"

Morgan, wearing a garden apron and carrying a trowel, walked through Anne Riordan's small garden enjoying the peace and quiet it offered. She had spent the morning listening to Rachel's nasty remarks until she could not stand another minute. It had been like this for four days now and Morgan wondered how long she could stand being confined in the same house with Rachel Todd. She could tell the tension was wearing on Anne and wished there were some way she could do something to ease the situation.

She bent to cut a long, yellow rose and suddenly the peace was shattered by Rachel's caustic voice.

"Well, Miss Fitzgerald, I see you've made yourself quite at home. You certainly didn't waste any time, did you?"

"I don't believe in wasting time, Miss Todd. There is not enough of it to suit me now."

"Then why do you waste your time waiting around here for *my* fiance to return? Are you really so anxious to attend my wedding?"

"I have no choice in the matter, Miss Todd. I gave Marc my word I would not leave here," Morgan answered as she continued cutting flowers.

"Well, perhaps we could keep you on as help. Anne could always use another hand. That girl Brenna is worthless in my opinion."

Morgan stopped what she was doing and stared at Rachel in disbelief. "My dear Miss Todd, I don't need

244

your charity and Brenna does not deserve your disparaging remarks. I think the Riordan family would be a lot better off if you found some way to help instead of imposing the way you do."

Brenna appeared at the back door, interrupting the conversation. She could feel the tension hanging in the air between the two women. "Excuse me, Miss Fitzgerald, but there is a gentlemen to see you in the library."

"No doubt one of your Rebel friends," Rachel remarked sarcastically.

"No doubt," Morgan said over her shoulder as she left the garden. She was curious herself to see who would be visiting her here. She wondered if Jubal could have found her after all this time. She opened the door of the library and was stunned to find a young soldier in a blue uniform waiting for her.

"Miss Morgana York?" he asked.

It took Morgan a moment before realizing Marc would not have taken the chance of using her real name if he had sent this messenger.

"Yes, I am Morgana York."

"I have a message for you from Major Riordan. He insisted I give it to you when you were alone."

"Thank you, private. You have done your job well. Can I get you a glass of lemonade?"

The boy blushed. "Thank you, ma'am, but I must get back. We had word Stuart was in the area and I don't want to miss the fight."

Morgan forced a smile as she saw the soldier to the door, yet she felt sick to her stomach as she thought of her dear friend being in danger.

Morgan hurried up the stairs, hoping to reach the

privacy of Marc's studio before meeting anyone who might question her about the messenger. She stood at the window staring out over the garden, the unopened note still clutched tightly in her hand. Slowly she opened it and began to read.

My darling,

All is well here. I hope the same for you. I can't begin to tell you how many times our last night comes to mind. It has been my salvation. Strange, I'm experiencing a loneliness I never imagined possible. That never bothered me until I knew how it could be having someone like you. I often summon your lovely face to my memory and I can feel your velvet skin next to mine—your sensuous lips touching mine. You see, my darling, you have truly woven a spell over me. You mean everything to me. You are in my every thought night and day.

I hope you won't ever get tired of hearing me saying these things because I plan to tell you how I feel every day of my life. I just wish I could be there to tell you in person.

I hope you are not too restless, but it certainly eases my mind to know you are safe and away from danger. Don't feel you have to stay in the house all the time, but please, be careful.

I must get back to my duties now. I will try to get another note off to you soon. If you will have one ready when the private comes, he will bring it back to me. By the way, John has been seen in Lynchburg. I know his parents live there so I guess he is recuperating with the help of some loving care.

I love you, darling. Take care of yourself for me.

Marc

Morgan hugged the letter to her breast, tears of joy flowing down her cheeks. "Oh, Marc, I love you."

Anne Riordan had no objection to Morgan leaving the house as long as she took the family driver and Brenna with her for protection.

Morgan was glad for Brenna's bright, gay company and quickly forgot Rachel as the carriage pulled onto Pennsylvania Avenue. The city was teeming with troops. Everywhere there was confusion, with soldiers sleeping on doorsteps, prostitutes on every street corner, and gamblers setting up their games on the sidewalks. It was a madhouse, Morgan thought.

"It looks as though the whole city is drunk," Morgan said as she stared out the window of the carriage.

"Soldiers are looking for fun when they return from the war area. You canna' blame them for that."

"No, I suppose not," Morgan said thinking of her own company of men and the sacrifices they made for their country.

Suddenly the carriage came to a halt as a fight broke out in the middle of the street. Morgan stuck her head out the carriage window to see what was happening, but her attention was drawn to the magnificent building they were stopped before.

"Brenna, what is this building?" she asked, still not taking her eyes from it.

"It is the Willard Hotel. Would you like to go inside for a lemonade?"

"You're reading my mind, Brenna. I must see everything," she said as she stepped from the carriage.

Brenna asked the driver to wait and then hurried to catch up with Morgan who stood in the lobby of the beautiful hotel taking everything in. She was completely unaware of the attention she drew by her beauty. She wore a pale green, batiste dress that Marc had given her and the effect with her auburn hair and green eyes was breathtaking.

"It is quite impressive, isn't it, Brenna? My mother and father used to stay here and I always thought someday I would too, but I guess I'll have to be content to have a glass of lemonade in the dining room."

They followed the maitre d'hotel to a table and ordered lemonade and biscuits. Morgan looked around the room, imagining how it was when her parents stayed there. She quickly looked away when she noticed a young major smiling at her. He was sitting with a stern-looking gentleman who nervously tapped his fingers on the table. Morgan watched as the major whispered something to his companion and then both men rose and headed toward them.

"Be very careful what you say, Brenna. I think we are about to have company."

"Aye, dinna' worry. I am use to handling the likes of them," she said watching the approaching men.

"Ladies, we could not help but notice you were without escorts and wondered if we might join you?"

"We choose to be without escorts, major," Morgan said in as clipped an accent as possible.

"Surely you would not deny us the honor of your company for just a few minutes. Let me introduce myself. I am Major Wayne Gill and this is Lafayette Baker, head of the Federal Secret Service."

Morgan wondered if her face showed her shock as she was introduced to the one man in Washington she had hoped never to meet. This was the man who had imprisoned thousands of men and women he accused of spying or being traitors to their country. He was sly, scheming and clever. He would stop at nothing to achieve his evil fame and was given an open hand to do as he wished. Morgan was sure her face showed the fear she felt as Baker openly studied her.

"Where do you ladies come from?" Baker asked.

"I am personal maid to the wife of the late Senator Riordan and this is her niece from Harpers Ferry," Brenna quickly answered.

The major took one of the empty seats at the table and Baker followed.

"It is dangerous for young ladies to be wandering the city unescorted. There is very little discipline among the troops while they are here."

"Thank you for your warning, major, but our driver is waiting just outside the door," Morgan answered.

"I know a lady of your gentle upbringing must be appalled at the sights you see in the city. Perhaps you would let me call upon you and escort you on your next outing," asked the major. "I could show you the more pleasant areas of the city."

"I don't think so, major. My aunt is very set in her ways and will not let me see anyone she does not select herself," Morgan answered trying to keep her voice calm as she felt Baker's shifty eyes studying her.

"You don't sound like you're from the Harpers Ferry area," Baker said.

"You are very observant," Morgan smiled. "My family was from southern Virginia before the war, but because of our loyalty to the Union, we moved to Harpers Ferry."

Baker said nothing, but Morgan noticed the suspicious squint of his steely eyes. She had the urge to run, but she knew she was being ridiculous. This man was only a Yankee. She had lived among them, spied on them; why should this one be any different. But this did not assuage the ominous feeling she felt as she tried to sip her lemonade.

Baker studied Morgan openly as he puffed on a foul-smelling cigar. "You're afraid of me. Why?" he asked bluntly.

Morgan tried to control her voice as she looked him straight in the eye. "I'm afraid of all strangers who push themselves on innocent, unchaperoned ladies. Now, gentlemen, if you will excuse us. It is time my companion and I returned home."

Brenna took the cue and quickly rose, following Morgan as she all but ran through the lobby to the waiting carriage.

Once they were inside the carriage and on their way, Morgan took a deep breath and collapsed back against the seat. "Oh, Brenna, could you tell how frightened I was?"

"Why were you so afraid of that man? Baker wasn't it?"

"Yes, Lafayette Baker. Detective, expert at interrogation, Rebel hater. He has ways of reducing anyone he questions to a state of confusion. A year ago an acquaintance of mine, Antonia Ford of Fairfax, was thrown into prison by this man. She was a beautiful, intelligent young lady and her only crime was giving some information to Mosby about a worthless general staying in Fairfax. From what I hear, she is being starved to death in prison for this minor crime. Can you imagine what he would do to me?" Morgan asked, shaking as she thought of her close call.

As they neared the house Morgan's attention was

drawn to a big man dressed in a gray suit and dapper hat standing across from the Riordans' house. She stepped from the carriage and slowly mounted the steps, looking back over her shoulder at the figure standing in the shadows of the trees. Suddenly she let out a shriek of delight and ran toward the approaching figure.

"Jubal, Jubal! Is it really you?"

Jubal Kelly lifted her in his arms and twirled her around, both oblivious to the fact that they were standing in the middle of the street.

"Are you all right, girl? We've all been so worried about you."

Morgan, laughing and crying at the same time, touched his face affectionately. "I am fine, Jubal and so glad to see you. Come inside and tell me what you're doing here."

Jubal noticed the violet-eyed girl waiting on the steps for them. Morgan smiled as she noticed the way they looked at each other.

"Jubal, this is my dear friend, Brenna."

Brenna curtsied, shyly lowering her dark lashes. "Tis nice to meet you, sir."

Jubal looked pleasantly surprised. "You're from Scotland?"

"Aye, Edinburgh."

"We must talk later. I have friends in Edinburgh."

"I will look forward to that, sir. Now I will be getting Mrs. Riordan. She will want to know a friend of Morgan's is here."

Jubal looked confused. "Are you sure Mrs. Riordan won't be calling the Federals?"

"No, we're safe here. Please, Jubal, come inside. We have so much to talk about."

Anne Riordan graciously welcomed Jubal and then

left them to talk privately. Morgan explained everything that had happened, including how she and Marc had fallen in love and how she promised him she'd stay.

Jubal didn't say anything for a few minutes after Morgan finished her story.

"Jubal, please don't be disappointed. I think my time was up to help the war effort. Every time I turned around I was being captured. Can't you see they were on to me?"

"Oh, I'm not disappointed for a minute that you're out of danger. I just wish I knew more about Marc Riordan."

"He is a good man, Jubal. He is a Virginian and only chose the Union because his brother died fighting for it. He had the opportunity to raise himself in the eyes of his superiors by turning me in, but he didn't. This war can't go on forever. Marc says we'll work things out. Please believe me, Jubal. This is what I want."

Anne and Brenna entered carrying trays loaded down with cheeses, fruits and other goodies. "I know you haven't had much to eat where you've been, so please help yourself, young man. Then you must stay with us until you are ready to return to your outfit."

"Thank you, ma'am, but I have already taken a small room not far from here."

"Then you must at least stay and have dinner with us. We would all like to hear the latest news."

"The cook is frying chicken," Brenna said smiling bashfully at Jubal.

Jubal looked at Morgan. "Please, Jubal, stay. We have so much to talk about," Morgan begged.

Jubal threw up his hands in defeat. "How could any man in his right mind refuse three such lovely ladies?

Especially any Irishman."

"Ah, Jubal, I knew the Irish blarney would reappear sooner or later. I haven't heard it since the war started."

Jubal became very serious. "There hasn't been much opportunity. There isn't much to laugh about lately."

"Are things going badly, Jubal?" Morgan asked fearfully.

Jubal glanced around the room cautiously.

"It's all right, Jubal. It won't go past this room. Anne and Brenna are friends."

"Let's just say they're not going as well as they had. I guess times have gotten hard for all. Did you hear about Mosby getting shot?"

Morgan tried to stay composed. "He is all right, isn't he?"

"Aye, he is in Lynchburg recuperating at his folk's place. He had a close call, but I hear he will be back before long."

"Are Michael and Jeb all right?"

"Aye, as mean as ever. Michael has been riding with one of Mosby's units, trying to hear some word of you. Jeb is grouchy as an old bear. You know he feels responsible for you. He will be glad to know that you are all right, but I'm afraid he will be furious when I don't bring you back with me."

Morgan quickly changed the subject. "You should have been with Brenna and me today," Morgan said as Brenna poured the tea. "We came face to face with the infamous Lafayette Baker. I was so frightened I could hardly speak."

Jubal looked concerned. "Did he suspect who you were?"

"No, I don't think so, but he certainly asked a lot of

questions. I hope you don't mind, Anne, but we told him I was your niece."

"That is fine, dear. As a matter of fact, I have a niece, but she is serving as a nurse in Richmond."

"I wonder if Baker knew that?" Morgan said thoughtfully. "He questioned my accent. That could mean trouble."

Rachel Todd stood outside the half-closed door listening to everything that was being said. Her eyes gleamed over her own cleverness. All her problems were solved. She would tell Lafayette Baker about Morgan Fitzgerald and her Rebel visitor if Morgan did not agree to leave. "You little tramp. I told you I would win and you have given me the tool with which to do it."

Chapter Sixteen

Rachel stood before the mirror in her room and smiled as she took in her appearance. She touched the silvery-blonde coiffure she had spent hours perfecting. "You're a fool, Morgan Fitzgerald, if you think you could take Marc from me. I am beautiful, a woman of quality. I could have any man I wanted. You are plain and cheap and when I finish with your reputation, no man will want you."

Morgan was delighted to hear that Rachel planned to take her meal in her room. She had dreaded Jubal seeing her having to put up with Rachel's contemptible remarks. She knew he would never understand the situation.

Anne had quickly noticed the looks that passed between Brenna and Jubal and had insisted Brenna join them. Morgan and Jubal were sitting in the library when Brenna entered. She was dressed in a deep lavender, muslin gown, setting off her violet eyes and black hair in a startling effect. Morgan heard Jubal's intake of breath when he saw her.

"My word, lass, you are a beauty," he said unashamedly.

Brenna curtsied. "Thank you, sir. You are too kind."

Morgan watched her big friend ogling this little black-haired girl. She thought how perfect they were for each other. Both so kind and gentle-hearted.

"Brenna McIntyre," Jubal was saying, his tongue lingering over the words. "What a lovely name."

Brenna's face turned pink. "You do have the gift of blarney, sir. I ha' been warned to beware of Irishmen with such a gift."

Jubal laughed. "It was certainly no Irishman who warned you, lass."

Jubal Kelly spent the evening entertaining the three women who listened to his stories and laughed at his jokes. He hadn't had such a rapt audience in a long time and he was taking full advantage of it.

Morgan smiled as she watched Jubal trying to impress Brenna. Her violet eyes lit up with laughter as he told them about Morgan pushing him down a mountainside when he had tried to kiss her.

When the evening was over, Jubal thanked Anne for her hospitality then turned to Brenna. "I will be coming back to check on Morgan. I hope you will allow me to call on you."

"I would like that, Jubal. I shall look forward to your next visit."

Morgan and Jubal were left alone as he prepared to leave. "Are you sure you won't be going with me, girl?"

"If I did then you wouldn't have an excuse to visit Brenna," Morgan teased.

"I think I would find my way back even if you weren't here. Maybe I have found someone who can take my mind off you, little one."

"Jubal, please, don't say things like that."

"You know I have always loved you, Morgan. Even if it did have to be as a brother. I am happy that you found someone. I hope you will be very happy with him."

Morgan's eyes brimmed with tears. "I love you too, Jubal and I promise you, I'll try to be very happy. You just take care of yourself and stop worrying about me. You can see I have good friends here."

"Just stay away from Lafayette Baker."

Morgan laughed. "I will, Jubal. Give my love to Michael and Jeb. Tell them I'm sorry if I let them down."

"They will be glad to know you are safe. If I know Jeb, he'll be coming into Washington just to check on you."

"Oh, Jubal, don't let him do that. He's too well known," Morgan exclaimed, before realizing Jubal was teasing her.

Jubal laughed. "I'll try to get back in a month or so. You take care."

Morgan kissed him on the cheek then watched him cross the street. It was strange watching him leave. Here she had hoped he would come and take her away and now she had chosen to stay of her own accord.

Morgan slowly climbed the stairs, thinking about what Jubal had said about loving her. Strange, at one time she had thought Jubal might be the man she would marry.

"Well, Miss Fitzgerald, did you see your lover off?" Rachel asked sarcastically from the top of the stairs.

"Don't push me, Rachel. I'm becoming very short of patience where you're concerned."

"Well, we can remedy that, Miss Fitzgerald."

"What is that suppose to mean?" Morgan asked impatiently.

"We have a mutual friend who is very interested in you," Rachel answered smugly.

"And who might that be?" Morgan asked, bored with the whole conversation.

"Lafayette Baker," Rachel answered smiling like a cat about to devour a mouse.

"I'm too tired to play games, Miss Todd. You will excuse me, I'm going to turn in."

"If you think going to prison is playing games, you are very naive, and I doubt that."

Morgan looked into Rachel's evil face and knew she wasn't one to be taken lightly. "What are you leading up to, Miss Todd?"

"It is quite simple. You will be leaving here in the morning. I will be gracious and give you your choice of going back to where you came from or being picked up by Lafayette. It really doesn't matter to me as long as you are out of my life."

"Don't you think Marc is going to be a little upset when he finds out you forced me to leave?"

"Marc is going to think you left of your own accord, Miss Fitzgerald. When he finds out you were entertaining your Rebel friends here, he won't have any reason to doubt it. Besides, think how upset he would be if his mother were arrested for giving refuge to a Confederate spy."

"You've thought of everything, haven't you?" Morgan asked, defeated.

"I told you once, you were no match for me. When I set my mind to having something, I usually get it."

Morgan walked past Rachel to the door of her room, then angrily turned and faced her. "Don't count on it this time, Miss Todd. I will leave because I care for Anne Riordan, but I'm not going to let you have Marc. He loves me and will not believe the lies you tell."

"We'll see who has Marc in the end, Miss Fitzgerald."

Morgan stood just inside her door for a long moment. She didn't doubt for a moment that Rachel would turn her or Anne Riordan over to the authorities to have her own way. She just had to stay calm and figure the best way to handle this situation. First she would send word to Jubal that she would be leaving with him, then she would see Anne and explain to her why she was leaving. Perhaps it would be best to go back to Aspen Grove. Marc would surely understand her waiting there. "Oh God, please let him understand," Morgan said aloud.

Morgan headed for Anne's room after talking with Brenna. The girl had begged her not to leave, sure that Rachel was bluffing, but Morgan knew better. When she told Brenna of Rachel's threat to Anne she agreed it was probably best for Morgan to wait for Marc in Virginia. She even insisted on taking the message to Jubal herself.

Morgan knocked softly at Anne's door and entered.

"I need to talk to you for a moment, Anne."

"Of course, dear. Come sit down."

Morgan sat on the edge of the bed and explained what had taken place between her and Rachel. Anne was stunned that it had come to this.

"I'm not afraid of her threats, Morgan. You just stay here. I have plenty of friends in high places who would help you."

"I can't take that chance, Anne. If you'll just explain to Marc what has happened, everything will be all right."

"Of course, Morgan," Anne said still concerned. "Where will you go?"

"I'll go home to Aspen Grove and wait there for Marc, unless the fighting is centered in that area."

"I'm so sorry this happened, Morgan."

"It's not your fault, Anne. It has just made me more determined than ever not to let Rachel marry Marc. I think your husband would have agreed it would be a terrible mistake."

"Men are strange when it comes to their pride. I think because Willard gave his word Christopher would marry Rachel, he felt he could keep that word by pledging Marc when Chris died. I knew at the time it was wrong."

"Well, there is nothing for you to worry about now. Marc and I will work this out before long." Morgan leaned over and kissed Anne on the cheek. "You've been very kind to me and I'll never forget it."

"It's been easy being kind to you, Morgan. You're like the daughter I always wanted."

"Well, maybe when I come back we can take care of that. In the meantime, you take care of yourself."

Morgan rose to leave then turned back to the bed. "Anne, be very careful around Rachel. I'm afraid she is a very sick woman."

"Don't you worry about me, child. You just take care of yourself."

Morgan packed a few belongings, but left the dresses Marc had given her hanging in the closet. She glanced once around the room before leaving, but instead of going down the stairs, she headed for the attic where she tucked one of Marc's small paintings into her saddlebag. By the time she reached the back door Jubal was waiting there with her saddled horse. He didn't ask any questions as he gave her a hand up.

"Aren't you going to say anything, Jubal?"

"Don't need to. Brenna explained everything. She told me to tell you goodbye. She couldn't do it."

Morgan looked toward the little room at the back of the house and saw Brenna's figure silhouetted by candlelight. Morgan waved, not knowing if Brenna could see her.

"We'll need the luck of the Irish to get out of this place tonight," Jubal said glumly as he threw her saddlebag on her horse.

"Well, my big friend, we should certainly have that between the two of us."

Jubal laughed and mounted his horse. "May we get to Virginia before the devil knows we're gone."

If anyone had heard the two riders laughing as they rode down the street they would never have believed they were two Confederate soldiers trying to escape the Union city of Washington.

Anne spent the entire morning in her room trying to avoid Rachel. She didn't want to come right out and throw the girl out, but she did hope she would go back to her cousin when she realized she was not welcome. By late afternoon Anne decided it was useless trying to avoid a confrontation with her. They would have to have it out sooner or later. She opened her bedroom door and started for Rachel's room but her attention was drawn downstairs. She stood at the landing and listened to Rachel screaming orders at Brenna.

"Rachel, I would like to speak to you. Please come up here now!"

Brenna turned and fled from the room leaving Rachel alone with Anne.

"I really wish you wouldn't interfere when I am reprimanding the servants, Anne. That girl is intolerable. I wouldn't keep her for a minute," Rachel said as she climbed the stairs.

"That girl is not my servant, Rachel, nor is she yours. She is paid to work for me, to be my companion and I'm very happy with her. But, that is not why I want to talk to you. I know all about your threats to Morgan and believe me, Marc is not going to be happy when I tell him."

Rachel faced Anne at the top of the steps. "I thought you were smarter than that, Anne. Couldn't you see she was using your home for her spy headquarters? When I exposed her she left. That's all there was to it."

"I know better than that, Rachel and so will Marc. I think it would be best if you packed and returned to your cousin in Baltimore."

Anne turned to walk away but Rachel grabbed her by the arm and swung her around. "You are as stupid as she was. I tried to warn her I wouldn't let anything interfere with my plans to marry Marc. I am certainly not going to let a stupid old woman interfere."

"Get out of my house, Rachel."

Rachel suddenly shoved Anne, knocking her off balance. Anne clutched the railing, trying desperately to regain her balance. She looked at Rachel, for help, but Rachel only smiled.

"My house, old woman," she said as she shoved Anne the rest of the way down the long, winding stairs.

The next morning dawned with the household still up. Brenna sat at the kitchen table feeling completely drained. It had been a long, terrible day. First Morgan had been forced to leave and then Anne had taken a terrible fall down the stairs. She was still unconscious and there wasn't anything that could be done for her. The doctor wasn't sure she would live.

Rachel had cried and carried on, but Brenna was sure it was all an act. She had left them only a few minutes before Anne had fallen, but she couldn't prove anything so she didn't dare make any accusations. The best thing for her to do now was to try to help Anne the best way she could. She would send a wire to Anne's sister in Harpers Ferry asking her to come as soon as possible. That would probably help Anne more than anything she could think of. That and Marc being with her, but surely Rachel would send for him.

Rachel stood at the foot of Anne's bed watching the doctor examine her again. He finally looked toward Rachel and shook his head in a hopeless gesture. "It doesn't look good, Miss Todd. There must be brain damage, but there is no way of knowing nor anything to do for it if there is. The only thing you can do is try to keep her comfortable. I'd have Brenna move in here with her. That way she can be watched at all times."

"I'd rather not do that, doctor. I don't trust that girl. It's possible she might have had something to do with Anne's fall. She was very friendly with the girl I told you pushed Anne."

Dr. Whitlock shook his head. "I find it so hard to believe that anyone would harm Anne Riordan. She has never done an unkind thing in her life. And Brenna, why that girl has been like a daughter to Anne."

"Are you doubting my story, Dr. Whitlock?"

"No, no, of course not. It's just that I have known Brenna since she was fourteen. She has been with the Riordans for four years and I don't think she would hurt Anne Riordan."

"I am mistress of this house now Dr. Whitlock, and I will decide who can be trusted, and I might add I'll also decide what doctor is to see Anne Riordan."

"You may be right, Miss Todd, but I might remind you that Marcus will not take it kindly if he finds you have interfered with any chance Anne has to live."

Rachel knew Dr. Whitlock was a long-time family friend and wasn't going to be put off by someone who wasn't actually a member of the family. She decided it best to handle him a little differently. She took out her handkerchief and dabbed at her eyes. "If you think Brenna would be of any help to Anne, then of course I'll have her move in here. It's just that I am so worried for Anne. This has been a very trying experience for me. I had no idea that wicked girl would do anything so horrible. Now I've been left in complete charge and it's such a responsibility."

Dr. Whitlock wasn't fooled by Rachel's sudden change, but he couldn't figure what part she played in Anne's accident. He didn't believe for a minute that the girl he had treated for snakebite would push anyone down the stairs and he was certain Brenna would never do anything to hurt Anne Riordan. As a matter of fact, he would bet his life on it. "I think it would be best if I spoke with Brenna to explain what to expect from the patient."

"Of course, Dr. Whitlock. I'll get her for you this minute."

Rachel left the room in a quandary. She didn't want Brenna around to help Anne and she couldn't let this doctor talk to the girl.

"Damn, why didn't that old woman die when she fell," Rachel said angrily. It crossed her mind to smother the woman, but she was afraid someone would become suspicious if she didn't die from the fall. Brenna she could deal with, but this nosy doctor was another story. He had asked far too many questions.

Rachel stood in the doorway of Brenna's room wondering where the girl was. She hurried to the kitchen and angrily questioned the cook about her whereabouts.

"I'm sorry, ma'am. I don't know where Brenna was going. She just said she had to go out for a while. Is there something I can get for you?"

Rachel didn't answer as she was too busy scheming to hear anyone. She realized this was perfect. The doctor wouldn't be able to talk with Brenna today and hopefully Anne would die during the night. She smiled as she headed back to Anne Riordan's bedroom.

Brenna reread the telegram before giving it back to the telegraph operator. She didn't want to frighten

Connie, but she wanted her to know it was urgent that she come at once.

Doctor Whitlock reluctantly left without speaking to Brenna. His suspicions were even more aroused as Rachel hurried him out the door to his waiting carriage.

Brenna entered the house through the back door unaware anyone knew she had been out. She quietly slipped into her room and began to remove her shawl and bonnet.

"You may as well leave them on, girl."

Brenna jumped as Rachel spoke from a chair in the corner of the little room.

"What are you doing in my room?"

"I will ask the questions. You can begin by telling me where you have been."

"I went for a walk, but I dinna' see why that should be any of your business."

"Were you meeting with one of your Rebel friends?" Rachel asked smugly.

Brenna untied the ribbons of her bonnet and slowly removed her hat, trying all the while to stay calm. "You know I ha' no Rebel friends except Miss Fitzgerald."

"Well, that's not what Lafayette Baker thinks. He has instructed me to terminate your employment here. He doesn't think it looks good for a senator's wife to have a traitor in her employ."

"I'm not a traitor," Brenna answered angrily.

"Perhaps not, my dear, but you must go anyway."

"Where will I go?" Brenna asked, tears filling her eyes.

"You should have thought of that before associating with that Rebel bitch. Just get packed and leave before nightfall if you don't want to be arrested. Lafayette Baker is coming late this evening and I would rather not have a scene," Rachel said, her voice cold as ice.

"You will be sorry for doing this when Marcus gets home."

"Now why should Marcus care anything about what happens to a worthless servant girl?" Rachel asked maliciously.

"Because he has compassion for people. Besides, when he finds out what you did to his mother and Miss Fitzgerald you'll probably be thrown out on your ear."

Rachel's eyes blazed with anger. "Get out before I change my mind and have Lafayette arrest you."

"I will leave after I see Mrs. Riordan," Brenna said, feeling a bit of confidence return.

"She won't know you, but if you want to take a chance on being caught here, go right ahead."

Brenna stood at Anne's bedside wishing desperately that the helpless woman would open her eyes and set everything straight. She took her hand in hers. "Oh, Mrs. Riordan, I do so hate to leave you at a time like this, but I ha' no say in the matter. I do so want that evil woman out of your house, but you need to be well so we can do it together."

Brenna leaned over and kissed Anne on the cheek then hurried down the stairs. She grabbed her one and only valise and without a backward glance left the Riordan house. She had no idea where she was going or what she would do, but she had to get away quickly in case Rachel was telling the truth about Lafayette Baker, which she doubted.

Brenna walked to the end of the block then stopped, trying to decide where to go. She noticed the Riordans' carriage coming down the street. "She goes too far. Damn that woman. If she thinks to follow me she is mistaken."

Brenna picked up her valise, lifted her skirt and took off running as fast as her feet would carry her. Her heart was beating rapidly when she finally slowed down several blocks away. She struggled to catch her breath, unable to take another step even though she could hear the carriage approaching. She ducked back into the doorway behind her, hoping to go unnoticed.

"Brenna, where are you?" a familiar voice called.

Brenna stood motionless for a moment, then she slowly peeked around the corner of the wall. "Adam? What are you doing here?"

"I thought you might be needing some help. Was I wrong?"

Brenna climbed up on the carriage seat with the Riordan's elderly coachman. "You weren't wrong, Adam. I guess you know Miss Todd dismissed me."

"She's a bad one, Brenna, but we all know that. When Mrs. Riordan gets well, she'll have you come back."

"I dinna' think she'll get well, Adam. I've wired her sister to come as soon as possible."

"Why don't I take you to Harpers Ferry to give Miss Connie the message in person. It would be much kinder and then you can stay at her home until this mess is cleared up."

Brenna's eyes widened. "Adam, that's a wonderful idea, but how can you just leave to take me there? It would be days before you got back. You will surely be dismissed when Miss Todd finds out what you have done."

"I've been with the Riordans too long to worry about being dismissed. Besides, I'll be returning with Mrs. Riordan's sister who will surely give me her protection."

"I dinna' know what to say, Adam. It is so kind of you to do this. I dinna' know what I was going to do before you came along. I was not sure I had any friends."

"Sure you do, girl. You have me."

Connie Lancaster listened in stunned silence to Brenna's story, a shocked expression on her face as the incredible details poured forth between Brenna's sobs.

Adam sat awkwardly, his hat in hand, nodding his head in agreement with what Brenna was saying.

"How terrible! How could she turn you out that way? And when Anne needs you the most. You poor child, you will stay right here and take care of my house while Adam and I return to Washington. I will see what Doctor Whitlock has to say about Anne's condition and I'll put a stop, once and for all, to Rachel's tyrannical ways."

Chapter Seventeen

Marc pounded on the door, wondering why Brenna or some other member of the staff wasn't answering. After a few minutes he heard Rachel's voice asking who was there.

"Damn it, Rachel, open the door. It's me," he shouted.

"Rachel opened the door and flew into Marc's arms sobbing hysterically.

Marc shook her angrily. "What's wrong with you, woman. I can't understand a thing you're saying."

"That terrible woman you left here tried to kill your mother," Rachel blurted out between exaggerated sobs.

Marc pushed her away from him. "What are you talking about?"

"Your Rebel friend shoved your mother down the stairs when your mother found out she was letting her friends use this house for their spy headquarters."

"You're lying!"

"Think what you will, but your mother has not regained consciousness since Morgan pushed her down the stairs."

With long strides Marc took the steps three at a time. He threw open the door to his mother's room and rushed to her bedside. When he saw the death-like pallor to her skin he knew Rachel was telling the truth. Anne was near death.

"Mother," he whispered softly. "Can you hear me?" Anne did not answer.

"Do you believe me now?" Rachel asked from the doorway.

"Has Doctor Whitlock seen her?"

"He's been here every day, but he says there's no change."

Marc sank into the chair next to the bed. "Tell me what happened?"

Rachel tried to conceal her pleasure. "Soon after you left, Rebel soldiers began showing up here. One of them was named Kelly. I believe he was the leader; the one that slept with your so-called prisoner. There were so many of them I couldn't keep count."

Marc clenched his fist, feeling as if his blood were boiling. "Go on."

"Your mother begged her to stop her spying activities. I begged her, but she threatened both of us. She was vicious, Marc. I tried to tell you it was dangerous to leave her in your home, but you wouldn't listen." Rachel said as she began to cry. "It was so terrible. Your mother couldn't put up with it any longer. She finally confronted Morgan, told her to leave. That's when she pushed your mother down the stairs. Then she packed and left with the one she called Kelly."

An anguished moan escaped Marc's lips. Rachel fell to her knees and laid her head on Marc's lap. "I've been so frightened, darling. I prayed you would come home. It has been such a terrible ordeal for me. I was so afraid she would come back and kill me."

Marc looked down at the girl at his feet. He had wronged her terribly, placing her and his mother in this situation. He owed her a great deal for staying with his mother when she could have escaped. He placed his hand on her head. "Everything will be all right now, Rachel. I'll take care of everything."

Rachel smiled to herself. "I knew you would, darling."

Marc spent the rest of the night sitting next to Anne's bed. His mind was in a turmoil as he thought about Rachel's story. How could he have been such a fool, he asked himself over and over. He had played right into her hands, leaving her free to do just what she wanted—spy. What a poor judge of character he was. His mother was lying on her deathbed because of him.

"If she dies, I'll find you and kill you, Morgan. I swear it."

Marc dozed fitfully as dreams of Morgan riding her big beige horse through fields of wildflowers came unbidden. Suddenly he was facing her, looking into her green, flashing eyes. Then he pulled his gun and aimed it at her, and all the while she smiled. He pulled the trigger, heard the explosion and when the smoke cleared away he saw her covered with blood. Slowly she began to fall backward, her hand reached out to him as he watched everything happen in slow motion. He screamed her name, waking himself as he did.

He sat for a moment trembling. It had seemed so real, so vivid. He looked down at his mother and realized her eyes were open and staring at him. "Mother, can you hear me?"

Anne did not answer. Marc rushed to the door and

called for Rachel. She entered the room moments later and stood in the doorway.

"Is she dead?" she asked, trying to make her voice sound concerned.

"No, no, she isn't dead. She has opened her eyes. Send Brenna or someone to get Doctor Whitlock."

Rachel was stunned to silence, waiting for the woman on the bed to say something.

"Rachel, what are you waiting for?" Marc asked impatiently.

"Brenna is no longer here. Only the cook remains."

Marc looked puzzled, but he was too concerned about his mother to ask questions now. "Well, for God's sake, send the cook."

Rachel took one more look at the woman on the bed and hurried from the room. She stood for a moment at the top of the stairs. "I should have killed her," she said to herself. "She is going to ruin everything. I'll have to get rid of her."

Doctor Whitlock sat at Anne's side examining her. "This is some improvement, Marc, but not much. She isn't able to move or speak and I'm not even sure she can hear us."

Rachel gave a sigh of relief as she heard the doctor's diagnosis. If she couldn't move or speak she wasn't a threat, but if she showed any signs of improving she would have to get rid of her.

"You will need a qualified nurse to stay with her. I had hoped Brenna would, but your Miss Todd tells me that Brenna left and she doesn't know where she went."

"Yes, I don't understand that. Brenna has been with us for years and loved my mother. It's strange her leaving at a time like this. Was there some problem?" he asked, turning to where Rachel had been standing. "Where in hell did she disappear to?"

"There have been a lot of strange things going on here, Marc. I would be very careful whom I trust."

"Are you talking about Rachel?"

"I'd rather not make any trouble for you and your fiancee. Just be careful. I'll be back tomorrow, hopefully with a nurse who can stay here. Unfortunately this damned war has taken most of the good ones."

Rachel waited in the library for Marc with brandy and a tray of food. She was determined to win his trust. She had to bind their relationship before anything was said to ruin her plans.

Marc let the doctor out then headed back up the stairs.

"Marc, wait. I've prepared some food for you. Anne will be all right until later."

"I don't know. I don't like leaving her."

"Surely you could use some nourishment. You won't do your mother or yourself any good if you don't eat."

"I guess you're right. Now that you mention it, I'm famished," he said as he came back down the stairs. "I haven't eaten since yesterday."

Rachel led him to a big leather chair before the fire. "You just sit right here while I fix you a drink."

Marc leaned his head back against the chair and closed his eyes. Damn, he was tired. So much had happened since he left here three weeks ago. His outfit had captured several partisan units and the North was finally coming out on top of this damned war. Lee's troops were going hungry and when winter came they would really be in trouble. Again Morgan came to mind. Would he have to fight her? Was his dream a premonition?

"Here you are, darling. This will make you feel better."

Rachel stood behind Marc's chair massaging his shoulders as he sipped his drink. "You feel so tense, darling. What can I do to help you relax?"

"I'll be fine when this whole mess is cleared up. Why don't you sit down and tell me what happened to Brenna."

Rachel slid into his lap. "Now, darling, I don't want to talk about her tonight. I want you to think only of me."

"That's going to be difficult until I have some answers."

Rachel pouted, "I want you to love me, Marc. You don't know how much I have needed you these past few weeks. I realize now that it is foolish for us to wait until we are married. I need you now, darling."

Marc laughed bitterly and pushed her off his lap. "Are you telling me that you've never slept with Wesley?"

"Marc, how could you think such a thing."

"It's very easy to prove, Rachel. I'll know if you're a virgin the minute I take you."

"And was your Rebel friend a virgin?" Morgan asked angrily.

Marc started to retort, but bit back his words. "I'm going upstairs to Anne. I had thought things would be different between us, but I can see they haven't changed. When you decide to tell me just what happened to Brenna I'll be upstairs."

Rachel suddenly threw herself in his arms, clinging to his neck. "Please, please don't go. I'm sorry, I should never have mentioned Morgan. I know how she betrayed you. It's only because I love you, darling. It hurt me terribly when she kept telling me how you made love to her, giving me all the details of being with you in your studio."

Marc's eyes widened in disbelief. "You're lying!"

"Oh, darling, don't you see what she did to you? She took your love so she could escape. She nearly killed your mother, she corrupted Brenna and I'm afraid she has ruined your love for me." Rachel began to cry. "I didn't want to tell you, but Brenna followed her when she left. I tried to stop the girl, but she wouldn't listen. Now you hate me. I have loved you all my life and she has taken your love from me," she sobbed.

Marc listened to her hysterical weeping, cursing himself for taking out his hate for Morgan on her. Why should he doubt what she said? It was Morgan who had lied and tricked him.

Rachel pulled his head down to hers. "Love me, Marc, hold me."

He found her lips as her fingers dug into his shoulders. She parted her mouth and expertly returned his kiss, then moved away and slowly began to unbutton her dress. "I'll make you forget Morgan."

The mention of Morgan's name turned him cold. "Stop, Rachel. This isn't the time or the place."

Rachel held out her hand to him. "Don't turn from me, darling. I'll be patient. I know you need time to put her out of your mind."

"Damn it, Rachel, just stop talking about her," he

growled through gritted teeth.

"How can I," she cried. "She taunted me day and night about her affair with you. Don't you understand, it's eating at me. I need desperately for you to prove your love for me. All I can think of is her in your arms. Show me you love me, Marc. Please . . ."

Marc forced himself to take her in his arms. He didn't love her, yet she didn't deserve his scorn. He forced himself to kiss her again, gently at first, then his thoughts went to Morgan and his kiss turned brutal. Rachel struggled against him, surprised at his attack.

"You wanted this, Rachel. You begged for it," he said pushing her backwards on the settee.

"Not here, Marc . . . upstairs," she murmured against his mouth.

"Now, Rachel. Here and now, " he said forcing her backwards and taking her without another word.

Marc stood in the center of the room pouring himself another brandy. He turned back to Rachel lying on the settee. "Did you really think you could fool me," he said contemptuously.

"Marc, I can explain."

"Don't! It doesn't matter. I expected as much. I saw the way you and Wes looked at each other."

"Why do you think you can sleep with every tramp who comes your way and it's perfectly all right? Well, I'll tell you something. I wasn't about to sit around while you played your little games. Sure, I slept with Wes, but I've had others too. All men desire me, Marc. All except you. Your brother was my first. He took my virginity, against my will, I might add, but he loved me, desired me."

"You lying bitch. You're all alike. Get out of my sight!"

Rachel straightened her dress and headed for the door. "You'll be back for more, darling. Don't forget, you don't have your Rebel bitch any more," she said closing the door behind her.

Marc picked up the brandy bottle and headed for his mother's room. She opened her eyes as he came near the bed. "It's all right Mother. I'm going to sit here with you for awhile. Doctor Whitlock says you're improving and before long you'll be good as new."

Anne's eyes followed Marc, but she didn't say anything. She finally closed her eyes as he settled in the chair next to the bed. He took another gulp of the brandy, trying to wipe out the episode downstairs. How could he possibly have thought making love to Rachel would erase his memory of Morgan. He wouldn't be able to put her out of his mind until he killed her.

Morgan sat in Stuart's tent while Jeb discussed her predicament with Jubal, but her mind was elsewhere. They had gotten as far as Culpeper only to find the Spotsylvania area was overrun by Yankees. There was no way to reach her home on the North Anne river. She had told Anne she would await at Aspen Grove, but now she was going to have to change her plans.

Morgan looked across the table at her friends and for the first time realized how tired Jeb looked. He had aged years in the few short months since she had seen him. How selfish she was. Here she was worrying about her problems and Jeb had been going through hell. He had sacrificed so much for what he believed in—and suffered so much. She had been with him when he received word his daughter was dying.

No one had really known what it had taken for him to stay in the midst of battle instead of going to his "la Petite's" side, as he called his little daughter. He sent word to his wife that he must leave his daughter in the hands of God: his duty to his country required him to stay. When word came that his little girl had died, he secluded himself in his tent. She had wanted to go to him, but Jubal insisted Jeb needed time to be alone; no one could help or comfort him until he was ready. She could see him, his head bowed on his arms, his wide shoulders shaking miserably. She suffered with him that night, yet could do nothing for him. She had never known a man who loved his family more or one whose sense of duty burned with a clearer flame . . . and duty came first, always. His heartbreak was unofficial; he had to keep on soldiering—fighting against destiny. Probably no other man believed as passionately in the cause of Southern independence as he did. He had said many times he did not wish to survive his country's liberties.

"Well, what do you think, girl?"

Morgan looked startled. "I'm sorry, Jubal, what were you saying?"

"I said, Jeb and I think you should stay here. It's not safe for you to go off alone since you don't know when, or if, your friend will come for you. Besides, Michael is on his way back here to see you. He would be very disappointed if he missed you."

Morgan thought for a moment. She didn't really have much choice. When she got right down to it, she didn't have any place to go, yet she knew Jeb didn't approve of her relationship with Marc and she was putting him on the spot by staying.

"Jeb, be honest with me. How do you feel about my staying?"

"I want you to be safe, but I'm strictly against your interest in this Yankee."

"I didn't choose to fall in love with a Yankee, Jeb. It just happened."

"Look at Jubal here," Jeb said patting the big Irishman on the back. "A finer man you'll not find."

Jubal's face turned red as Morgan laughed. "Jubal and I grew up together. He's like a brother to me."

"Well how about Von Borcke. He'll be up and about before long. Every unmarried girl in Virginia would like to have him for a husband."

"Stop it, Jeb. Stop trying to play matchmaker. It's too late. I love Marc Riordan, Yankee or not."

"Suit yourself, Morgan, but don't say I didn't warn you," Jeb said as he angrily left the tent.

"He's being selfish and unreasonable," Morgan said, hurt to tears.

"Do you think so, girl? I don't," Jubal answered in a tone of voice he had never before used with Morgan. "Did you so quickly forget what he has been through? Every day he faces tremendous odds against him — of men, horses and arms. He has to show a happy face and lead his men to battle as if they were going to a foxhunt. His problems are too serious to treat seriously. If his men ever stopped to contemplate the odds against them it would be all over. Any other man would have been driven to drink, but not Jeb. He drinks deep of life: he loves fine horses, beautiful women, gallant men and the rich splendor of the seasons in Virginia. With his enthusiasm, he is able to keep all those around him intoxicated with his gusto for life, yet you have the nerve to sit there and tell me he is selfish and unreasonable!"

Morgan said nothing as she stared at Jubal, her eyes wide with surprise at his outburst. She had never seen him like this. She watched him bite off the end of a long, thin cigar and spit it angrily on the ground. "I can tell you're not finished, Jubal. Go on."

"Aye, there's more."

"Well, don't stop now. Let's finish this so I can be furious with the two of you."

"Maybe, but you know Jeb, if there is the slightest chance of trouble he won't leave. I dinna' know what else to do for him. He canna' continue to carry the weight of the world on his shoulders. He's exhausted, dead on his feet, yet he still tries to show a happy face and goes on with his duties as if everything were fine. Right now he is trying to figure a way to keep Meade from crossing the Rapidan."

"I'll talk to him, Jubal. Maybe I can convince him that Flora needs him for a few days."

Morgan sat alone in the tent thinking about what Jubal had said. She had known things weren't going well for the Confederacy, but she had no idea the outlook was so bleak. Strange, when she had become involved in the war she didn't think the South stood a chance, yet they won battle after battle. Now the lack of food, ammunition and supplies was going to be their worst enemy. The North would not defeat them; circumstances would.

» » »

Jeb Stuart stood on the banks of the Rappahannock looking beyond at the mist-shrouded peaks of the Blue Ridge mountains. Morgan hesitated in the shadows before going forward.

"It's a beautiful evening. I haven't seen a prettier sunset in a long time."

"You'll find none like it any place else," Jeb said very seriously. "I've always felt Virginia was God's favorite part of His country, yet he seems to have turned his back on us."

"That's strange, my father used to say this was God's country. I think he loved Virginia as much as you, Jeb."

"It's probably the Irish blood in us. I guess Virginia is the closest thing to the green hills of Ireland."

"Are you forgetting your Scotch blood?"

"With the name Stuart?" he laughed.

"The devil take ye if ye forget your background, Jamie Stuart," Morgan said in her best Scottish burr.

"And what would a fine Irish colleen be knowing about my Scottish background," Jeb retorted in an Irish brogue.

"Oh, Jeb, it's good to hear you laugh. I was afraid you were angry with me."

"How could I stay mad with you, Morgan? We've been through an awful lot together and I should know you're not going to desert your country. I don't think this war is going to last much longer so you'll be free to love whomever you like."

"That doesn't sound like your blessing, my friend."

"I'm sorry, Morgan. I can't give that and you know it. I'll not speak to my own father-in-law because he's a Yankee, so you can hardly expect me to welcome your beau with open arms."

"I understand that, Jeb. All I ask is that you try to understand my predicament."

Jeb tenderly touched the side of Morgan's face. "You remind me of Flora when your eyes sparkle like that."

"Are you changing the subject, Jeb?"

"Aye, my fair colleen. Let us speak of things that don't weigh heavy on my mind."

"All right, my friend. Why don't you start by telling me how Flora is."

Jeb looked back toward the river. "She is as well as can be expected. It was very hard on her losing our daughter, and my not being there made it even harder. I was able to get to Lynchburg for two days right after little Flora died, but that wasn't much comfort to her. She was very quiet and withdrawn. She's back in Richmond now, staying with the Prices. I think she'll be better off there."

"Jeb, why don't you go visit her for a few days? It would do you both good. Meade doesn't look like he is going to make a move for a while and if he does there are enough troops here to turn him back."

"The thought has been on my mind day and night. I would really like to see her and Jimmy."

"Then it's decided. We'll have a songfest tonight and tomorrow you'll be on your way to Richmond."

Sweeney tuned his banjo as everyone gathered around the campfire in anticipation of the night's entertainment.

Morgan sat before the fire listening to John Esten Cooke answering questions about von Borcke's condition. There was laughter all around as he told how once there was a report that von Borcke had been killed after the Battle of Chancellorsville. Virginia Governor John Letcher requested General Lee to have the Prussian's body forwarded to Richmond for cermonial burial by the state. Lee's answer was short and to the point; "Can't spare it; it's in pursuit of Stoneman." Everyone cheered when Cooke told them von Borcke had robbed the grim reaper again. He was recuperating nicely and rumor had it, had fallen in love with his doctor's daughter.

Jeb stood in the shadows with Jubal watching the activities. "Look at Jared Law trying to impress Morgan. She could have any man she wanted and she had to fall in love with a Yankee."

"Marc Riordan is a fine man, Jeb. The type of man you would admire if he were in your army."

"I still have hopes Michael can make her see the light. That is, if he gets through. I heard John Mosby's unit was last seen in Middleburg and the Feds have covered the countryside between here and there."

"I didn't think there was a Yankee alive who could keep Mosby from his destination," Jubal kidded.

"Perhaps you're right. I've known him to get through in tighter spots. I'm going to be leaving for Richmond in the morning. If you haven't heard from him by the day after tomorrow, send George Smyth out to see if he can get word of them. I wish Farley were still alive. He'd get through to them. God, Jubal, do you realize how many good men we've lost?"

"Aye, Jeb, but we have to look forward, not backward."

"You're right, Jubal. All those men gave their lives

for a cause they fiercely believed in and we can't let them down by giving up."

"Speaking of giving up, it looks like Jared has given up where Morgan is concerned. He just left the fireside in a fury."

"I'm not surprised, Jubal. I'm afraid Morgan's forgotten how to use her charm on a man."

"No, Jeb, she hasn't forgotten. She just doesn't care for Jared Law, and neither do I."

"Would you perhaps be jealous, my big friend?"

"I just want what is best for her, even if it happens to be a Yankee."

Jeb looked surprised. "You love her that much?"

"Aye, but not in the way you think, Jeb. Morgan is my sister, but she dinna' know."

"My God, man! I've know you both all these years and never imagined. And Michael, does he know?"

"No. I've not had the opportunity or inclination to tell him. I dinna' know myself until Sean Fitzgerald was shot at Bull Run. He told me just before he died. He had never bothered to tell anyone so I dinna' feel I should announce it to the world."

"Sean Fitzgerald was a very wealthy man."

"I'm not interested in his wealth. The Fitzgeralds always made me feel like one of the family. I'll make my own fortune someday."

"I don't doubt that for a minute. I'm proud to know a man like you, Jubal. Proud to call you my friend."

Jubal felt an overwhelming emotion for this man he admired above all others. "That means more to me than I can tell you, sir."

"What is this, sir? We are friends, Jubal. Friends until our dying day."

Jeb looked back toward the campfire where Morgan was sitting by herself. "You're going to have to watch her very carefully, Jubal. I think she has lost her spirit for this war. I'm afraid she'll be hurt if she is forced back into battle."

Sweeney's banjo began to pick out the notes of "Dixie" in a slow, melancholy strain. Suddenly Morgan's clear voice joined in and a hush fell over everyone as she sang the words that aroused passion and inspired courage and devotion in the Southern people.

Jeb smiled to himself. "I've worried needlessly, my friend. She hasn't lost her spirit."

Chapter Eighteen

Marc woke with a splitting pain in his head. He wondered for a moment why he was sleeping in the library when the sun was high, then saw the empty bottle lying on the floor. His head throbbed terribly and his stomach churned as he struggled from the chair and stumbled across the room. He stood for a moment holding tight to the table for support. "I've got to get hold of myself."

As he said the words, he remembered his aunt saying the same thing last night when they had gotten into an argument; one of the many since she had arrived. For some reason she had questioned Rachel over and over about Anne's accident. He didn't know why, but she insinuated she didn't believe Rachel.

Then she turned on him, telling him he was becoming totally useless sitting around and getting drunk, that he wasn't doing himself, the Army, or anyone else any good.

Marc rubbed his head, trying to ease the pain. God, why couldn't he put Morgan out of his mind. Five days he had been blind drunk and still she haunted his memory. "How did she ever get such a hold on me?" he said aloud. "What a cold, spiteful bitch she turned out to be. How could she profess words of love and then do this? I'll never trust another woman," he swore under his breath.

He reached out and with a shaking hand poured another drink, but his thoughts were interrupted by a knock at the door.

Connie entered the room, quickly closing the door behind her. "Marc, Wesley Lansing is here to see you. I sent for Rachel to entertain him until you get cleaned up. I didn't think you would want one of your men to see you in this condition."

"You're going to straighten me out in spite of myself, aren't you, Aunt Connie?"

"You're my favorite nephew and I can't stand seeing you like this," she said as she cleared the bottles and dirty glasses away. "There just isn't any sense in it. Your mother is showing some improvement. When she can speak we'll find out exactly what happened the night she fell."

"You don't believe Rachel's story, do you?"

"No, frankly I don't. I told you Brenna insisted that Morgan was forced to leave before your mother fell. I have no reason to doubt her. I have known her a lot longer than I've known Rachel."

"Morgan is not the kind of person to be forced to do anything against her will and certainly not by Rachel. I think she had us all fooled."

"Well, I don't know about that, but she just didn't seem like the kind of person to hurt anyone."

"Enough, Aunt Connie," Marc said holding his head in his hands. "I don't want to hear her name mentioned again. I'm going to get cleaned up as you suggested. Tell Wes I will be with him shortly. I have been most anxious to talk with him."

Connie watched her nephew weaving as he left the room. "That girl means more to him than any of us imagined."

Marc bathed and changed into clean clothes, but the pain in his head still persisted. The whole time he was dressing he kept thinking about what his aunt had said. Was it possible that Rachel had lied about Morgan? She had lied about other things, why not this. If she had, it was possible that Morgan was hiding someplace. Perhaps she had tried to get a message to him, but he had been too drunk lately to know if one came. Rachel certainly wouldn't let it get through to him if it had.

"Sweet Jesus," he said as the idea became clearer. Why hadn't he realized before that Rachel could be lying? Why had he been so quick to believe without looking into the situation. There was a possibility that Morgan hadn't betrayed him. If only his mother could communicate in some way, but she hadn't been able to. Not even to blinking her eyes when they asked her questions.

Marc made his way to the sitting room where Wes waited with Rachel. Connie was coming out the door when he reached it. "I made coffee for you. You'll feel better after you have some."

"Stop worrying about me, Connie. I'm going to be fine," he said as he affectionately hugged his aunt.

"I knew you would, Marc. I just didn't know how long it would take."

Marc entered the room and found Wes with his arms around Rachel. "I hope I'm not interrupting anything," he said sarcastically.

"Now come on, Marc," Wes laughed awkwardly. "I was only greeting an old friend."

"Rachel, would you mind leaving us alone. Wes and I have things to discuss."

"Really, Marc, where are your manners?" Rachel asked indignantly.

"I have no manners where you're concerned, Rachel. Now leave."

Marc turned back to Wes as Rachel reluctantly left the room. "Did you come with a message or just to bed my fiancee?"

Wes's face turned red as he attempted to find words. "What's the matter with you, Marc?"

"You know damned well what the matter is. I didn't mind you flirting with my fiancee, but I had no idea how far you had gone."

"Listen, Marc, I hadn't touched Rachel until Morgan came into the picture. I swear it. Then the only time I ever made love to her was the night after we all had dinner and the argument took place. I shouldn't have to be defending myself anyway. I never lied to you about my feelings for Rachel. I just never meant for it to go that far. Please believe me. Your friendship means a great deal to me."

Marc realized he was being unfair. He had even encouraged Wes to pursue Rachel and now he was accusing him because he had. He had known Wes stayed with Rachel that night, but it hadn't mattered to him at the time.

"It doesn't matter, Wes," he said, defeated. "Everything has just gotten out of hand. I guess I'm just looking for someone to blame."

"I can understand that if what Rachel told me is true."

"And what did fair Rachel tell you," Marc said feeling his anger rise again.

"Just that Morgan pushed your mother down the stairs when she was discovered spying. Is it true?"

"Your guess is as good as mine."

"I saw her the day before yesterday. Just as plain as day. She wasn't much further away than you are."

Marc's eyes widened in surprise. "Are you talking about Morgan?"

"Damned right. I came to tell you the unit has been moved to Brandy Station. We were trying to move across the Rappahannock but were forced back. I was leading a charge when I saw her. Big as life, she sat on that big beige horse, her red hair flying in the wind. I could hear her shouting orders to her men as the battle raged. She sure wasn't trying to conceal her identity."

Marc felt as if an iron band squeezed his heart. Less than an hour ago he had thought Rachel had lied, but now, proof she hadn't. Morgan was back in action. No longer hiding her identity. "Bitch!" Marc said angrily slamming his fist on the table. "Damned traitoress bitch."

"I don't understand, Marc. You knew all about this. Rachel told me you knew," Wes said confused.

"You've just confirmed her story. I still had some doubt, but no longer," he said as a cold rage consumed him. "She will pay for this. She will pay dearly."

"Calm down, my friend," Wes said as he poured them both a drink. "No woman is worth such anguish."

"You're right about that. Certainly not that Rebel bitch."

Marc lay awake, staring blankly at the ceiling, his mind in a turmoil as he thought of the events of the last month. It didn't seem possible he could love and hate a woman so passionately in so short a period of time. She must laugh every time she thinks of how she made a fool out of him, he thought. "Damn her, he said slamming his fist on the bed. "And the last thing she said was 'I love you'."

He swung his feet off the bed and poured himself another drink from the decanter on the bedside table. The liquor jolted through his veins, but it didn't seem to have the effect he wanted; the forgetfulness. Unbidden, her image crept into his mind; he could feel her soft, velvet legs against him, smell the faint perfumed scent of her auburn hair. "Don't do this to me, woman. You will not possess me," he said aloud as he felt the heat rising in his loins. "I can feel you reaching out to me, but I won't let you torment me."

Morgan lay in the darkness of her tent thinking of the last night she spent in Marc's arms. She could almost feel his warm lips against her throat and the mere memory sent her pulse racing. He was a mortal like all others; he felt anger, boredom, indifference; he loved and hated as other men, yet he was so different. He was the one she loved more than life itself. She remembered his face, the easy, sardonic smile, his long lashed blue eyes and the way they glowed with desire. "Oh Marc, Marc, how I miss you. Why haven't I heard from you?"

Morgan's deepest fear crept to mind again. She had been involved in a skirmish yesterday. Nothing of any consequence, but she kept wondering, what if she had been killed. Marc would never know that she had tried to wait for him at Aspen Grove, but had been forced to stay where she was because Union forces occupied the area, nor would he understand her being involved in the war again, but when the Union troops had tried to move across the Rappahannock it had become necessary. She was the one who had insisted Jeb go visit his family so she couldn't stand by and watch the blue troops move on them. Suddenly she had been involved. It had seemed so natural.

"Damn, why couldn't he understand? I don't question his loyalty to the Union." She shook her head. Why should I feel the need to defend myself to him. Anyway, Jeb would probably be back tomorrow. Then she could make some decision as to what she would do. She certainly couldn't stay here with her friends and not fight if the need arose. For that matter, could she just leave for some safe harbor when her friends needed her?

"Oh, my love, you certainly have complicated my life," she said closing her eyes and hoping sleep would come this night. She had felt so poorly since leaving Washington.

Jubal read Lee's latest report, just delivered by messenger, by the candlelight in his tent. He was stunned as he read that they had lost 30,000 men at Gettysburg and the Union estimated the same. Sixty thousand men struck down in their prime, he thought. The next paragraph was as devastating to him. The chance of foreign intervention was gone. If they had won the battle at Gettysburg they would have received help, but the European countries they had counted on decided to stay neutral. Jubal wiped his hand across his eyes. For some reason his vision was blurred, but he would never admit tears welled in his eyes. He knew the South was lost. How could any sensible man not realize it. It was only a matter of time and Jeb had known it for weeks, but he would never admit it. He would never show discouragement. Jubal remembered a conversation with Jeb about a river they had tried to cross and were driven back time after time until they finally gave one last effort and made it. Jeb had said, "Well, if we hadn't been able to get across the river there would have been just one thing left to do . . ." Jubal had replied, "You mean surrender on as good terms as possible?" "No," said Stuart. "To die game."

He is always ready to die game, Jubal thought, and the Federals realized it. That was why he is so successful. A smart person will get out of the way of the person who is perfectly ready to die. He had seen it time and time again. Jeb charging in front of his men, his scarlet-lined cape flying behind him, sword raised against his enemy. He was a symbol, a gonfalon who led the elite of the Confederacy and he would continue to lead them, no matter what the odds were against them.

Jubal placed the report on the table and blew out the candle. He sat in the darkness, drawing deeply on his cigar and wondered what he was going to do about the other bit of information the scout delivered. Well, there wasn't much he could do about it tonight. Tomorrow he would face Morgan.

In the early hours of the morning Morgan sat with her back against a pine tree, watching the sun making its spectacular entrance. The day dawned so fresh and new she couldn't help but feel better. The aroma of pine needles gave the air a pungent, clean smell, reminding her of many pleasant days as a child riding through the pine forest near her home. She closed her eyes and thought of the bayberry and wild roses that grew in the woods and she could almost smell them.

"You're up mighty early, girl, or have you been asleep at all?" Jubal asked as he sat down next to her.

"I've slept a little, Jubal. I don't know why, but I've not been sleeping well. I guess I have too much on my mind. Sitting here watching the new day dawn makes me feel fresh and new again."

"Aye, I guess we all have a lot on our minds. It looks like the Union forces are building up on the other side of the river. Just last night one of the scouts reported a large troop movement coming from Washington."

"Lee is joining us from the Valley so we should be able to hold them back."

"Aye, we should be able to hold them, but it's going to be a bloody battle," Jubal said his face sober.

"When will it all end, Jubal? I can remember Poppa talking about the war lasting for a few months. We've been at this for almost four years now."

"I don't know, Morgan, but it looks like we're going to go through another winter."

Morgan suddenly felt nauseated. She wasn't sure if it was the thought of the war going on or the lack of sleep. She rose, brushing the pine needles from her clothes. "I'm going back to my tent and lie down for awhile. I think my lack of sleep has caught up with me."

Jubal noticed Morgan's ashen color and was sure it wasn't lack of sleep. He wondered if his prediction of the war going on alarmed her. He considered putting off telling her his news, but decided it best she know. "Morgan, I'll walk you to your tent. I have something I wish to speak of."

Morgan looked at Jubal's serious face. "I don't like the sound of that."

"I wish I dinna' have to tell you this, but Marc Riordan is the officer bringing troops to back up Meade."

Morgan's face lit up. "Don't you see, Jubal, that is perfect. I'll be able to get a message to him and explain what I'm doing here."

"I dinna' think you see, Morgan. What will you do after you get a message to him? Join his side and fight against us or stay here and fight against him?"

Morgan's nausea was becoming worse and she fought against being sick. "You know I'll not fight against my own people, Jubal. How could you suggest such a thing?"

"Will you fight against Marc Riordan? Tis a sad affair, girl, but God knows, it's going to come to one or the other."

Morgan put her hands to her head. "Oh God, what am I going to do? How did I ever get into such a mess? Jubal, I've got to lie down," Morgan said as she broke out in a cold sweat. "I'm sorry, I can't talk about this now."

Jubal watched Morgan hurry off to her tent. "God, she can't take much more," he said looking heavenly. "I wish you could see fit to easing up on her."

Colonel Marc Riordan sat atop his big black horse and watched the men form their units. They had spent the night outside Warrenton and would be at the Rappahannock by evening. He breathed deep of the fresh morning air, glad to be active again.

His mother had shown some improvement, but still could not write or speak. Connie had insisted Anne would do better if he wasn't there hanging over her day and night. He had to admit he was glad to get back to his unit. He hoped it would take his mind off of Morgan. He was still having dreams of killing her, yet he would always wake from them desiring her.

Marc turned in the saddle as he heard the pounding of hoofbeats coming behind him.

"Custer was just attacked by Mosby," Wes shouted. "They took half of his force prisoner. He's so angry he wants to take on every guerrilla and suspected disloyal person between the Potomac and Richmond. He's ordered out scouting parties to shoot anyone that is armed or resembles a guerrilla. If someone doesn't calm him down a lot of innocent people are going to be killed."

"Where did it happen?"

"Not more than five miles from here. Custer says Mosby somehow learned their countersign and then using it, relieved every picket before dashing in in force. Custer himself was not in camp at the time or he would have been taken prisoner for sure."

"Lucky for him he wasn't there. Mosby would have loved to make him look like a fool. If George is smart, he'll forget revenge before Mosby eats him alive."

"I thought you wanted Mosby captured?" Wes said, surprised at the admiration Marc obviously had for the Rebel leader.

"I do want him captured, but Mosby is too smart for Custer. He'll make him look like a fool just as he has done so many others, including myself. I have to see that these men are delivered to Meade. Then I hope to pursue Mosby myself."

"And Fitzgerald?" Wes asked.

"And Fitzgerald. Now let's get these men moving. I want to get to the Rappahannock before this war is over. Send word to George that he is needed on the Rappahannock and will have to forget pursuing Mosby for now."

Wes rode up and down the line issuing orders to the men. The line began slowly moving out as Marc sat atop his black stallion and watched. Wes rode back and stopped beside him.

"I sure am glad I don't have to mess with foot soldiers very often."

"That's funny you should say that. I was just thinking the same thing. I think the only reason they prompted me was to make sure I would take this outfit to their destination."

As the slow moving line approached Remington they could hear gun fire in the woods to their right. Marc ordered the troops stopped and sent out a scout to find out what was going on. He broke out his canteen and waited for word to come back.

"Some of the men are low on water, Marc. I thought I would see if we can use the well of that farmhouse over there."

"Check with the people first, Wes. We're not too welcome in this area."

"Right, I'll go ask myself. How could they refuse so gallant an officer."

Marc laughed as Wes headed for the little house off the side of the road. It was run down, as most were now days, and seemed deserted except for a cow that had somehow escaped slaughter. It reminded him of the Russells' place where Morgan had saved the boy. Damn, what was he doing thinking about her again?

"Marc, I think you better come over here," Wes shouted from the doorway.

Marc entered the dark room and looked around. There in the corner were two kids huddled together, their eyes wide with fright. "Where's your mom and dad, son?" Marc asked the young boy.

The little boy's eyes watched the two men, but he stayed huddled in the corner with his arms tight around his sister, neither saying a word.

"We're not going to hurt you, son. Why don't you tell me where your folks are. Maybe we can help you. You and your sister look hungry," Marc said taking some dried beef from his pouch. "Here, try this. It's not too bad."

The little boy cautiously came forward and accepted the beef. He broke it in two and gave his sister half.

"Now, son, why don't you tell me where your folks are?"

"Me and my sister are alone, mister. Poppa died when the war started and a couple of Yankees hurt my maw real bad and she died awhile back."

"How did they hurt her?"

The boy took another chew on the beef and looked anxiously at his sister. "Don't rightly know, 'cept they had her on the bed and she didn't want to be. When they left there was blood all over her. I tried to take care of her best I knew how, but she died that night. Me and sis buried her out back under the big oak tree."

"I'm sorry, son. I know that was hard on you. Do you remember anything about the men that were here? Can you tell me what rank they were or anything that might help me find them?"

The boy thought for a moment. "One of them was called Burly. He was the mean one. The other man kept telling him not to hurt my maw. Burly rode a big red colored horse with white stockings. I figure when I get big enough I'll find him and make him pay for hurting my maw."

Marc looked at Wes. Both men knew who Burly was. He rode with Lavine and had a reputation for meanness. "You're not going to have to, son. I know who this Burly is. He's going to go to prison for a long time when I'm through with him."

"But, you're a Yankee too."

"All Yankees aren't bad, son. Just as all Confederates aren't good. Now sit down here and listen to me. I know a lady in Washington who has a nice big house and would love to have you and your sister stay with her. What do you say?"

"Thank you, sir, but my Paw always told me this was my land and I should take care of it."

"I know, son, but for now with the war going on, you can't do anything with it. When the war is over you can come back here and farm it."

"Some Yankee will claim it if I leave. Me and Jeannie can take care of ourselves."

"All right, son. Wes, see if we have some spare food and blankets to leave."

Marc left a young private to help the kids chop wood and get their place in order. The soldier promised to join his outfit as soon as possible, but Marc wondered if he would ever see him again. Morale was terrible in this group. The worst he had seen in a long time. Most of them had fought at Gettysburg and had been convalescing in hospitals until they had been assigned to this march. They were still sick in spirit and body. Marc had been appalled when he saw what he was ordered to deliver to General Meade for reinforcements, but he had been unable to convince anyone that these men were not fit for service yet. Meade needed them to force his way across the Rappahannock. He had already been repelled twice and was determined he would make it the next time. Marc looked around him and wondered if he would be able to do it with this sorry looking bunch.

"Colonel Riordan," Wes said riding up behind

Marc. "This is Colonel Horace Sargent of the First Massachusetts Cavalry. He thinks he has a way to eliminate the Rebel raiders."

"Really, Colonel?" Marc said trying to surpress a smile. "And what might that be?"

"A policy of extermination, Colonel Riordan. Every house and every tree burned. The people here all have sons and brothers in gray. The raiders have friends in every house. If we destroy their hiding places they will have to stay in the open. Then we'll have them."

"And what about the innocent people? Do we kill them or just leave them homeless to starve to death?"

"Those people, Colonel, are farmers today and soldiers tomorrow. They are acquainted with every woodpath, every grove of trees, every place possible for a man to hide. I can clear this country with fire and sword, and no mortal can do it any other way."

"If I'm not mistaken, Colonel, that same method was used by Attila the Hun and I hope and pray we have come a way from the barbarians that used it."

"I was told you were anxious to rid this area of these guerrilla fighters. That person must have been mistaken," Sargent said sarcastically.

"No, they weren't mistaken. I just don't think it's necessary to kill thousands to get to a few."

"You've only dealt with Mosby and Fitzgerald, Colonel. When you get to the Rappahannock you'll have Gilmore, McNeill and White added to the growing list of irregulars. They will heckle you, steal your supplies, cut your communications and make you feel like a full-fledged idiot. When you're tired of it, send word to me and I'll start clearing them out."

"Colonel, I'm sure you have duties to attend to, just

as I have. I suggest you get back to them. This conversation is over."

The officer spurred his horse around and galloped across the field without another word.

"He and Custer would get along famously," Wes said as he watched the officer leave.

"Let's hope the two of them don't get together. Unfortunately, he's right about these farmers being guerrillas. I've thought that all along."

"Why didn't you tell him you have already had dealings with Gilmore and White?"

"There wasn't any need. Come on, we got to get this rag-tag outfit moving."

Daylight was opening rapidly in the east when Train Number One rolled around a curve near Brandy Station. Within 300 yards of the station a rider hailed it to a stop. As it slowed, a lone passenger scurried from one of the cars unnoticed. A waiting horseman emerged from a grove of trees leading a riderless horse.

"I'm mighty glad to see you, Jubal, but how did you know I'd be on that train?"

"Well, I'll tell you, General. We intercepted a message being sent to General Meade last night. It seemed some yellow toad in Richmond saw you board the train and decided to inform the good General. He's waiting in force for you just ahead. I decided to flag the train, hoping you would leave it when you realized it was stopping."

"Good work, my friend. That was a close call. How are things at the camp?" Jeb asked as he mounted his horse.

"Nothing much has changed. The Union forces tried one time to move forward, but Morgan took charge and drove them back."

"Ah, that's good to hear. I've been worried about that girl."

"Aye, we've all been worried about her. How was Flora and little Jemmie?"

"Flora was much better. Almost like her old self. Of course, Jemmie was as feisty as ever. He asked about his Uncle Jubal."

"He's quite a boy, Jeb. You're a very lucky man to have such a fine family."

"I know, Jubal. I thank God for them everyday. I just hope to keep them safe. Richmond is a terribly depressing place to be now. The whole city looks like one big hospital, with dead and wounded everyplace. I never thought to see anything like it. The people are all doing God's work, but they're as tired in mind and body as we on the battlefield."

It wasn't long before the two riders looked down over the camps from a hillside. Activity in both camps was just beginning. The smell of coffee and fried bacon drifted up to them from the Union camp.

"Do they ever run out of food?" Jeb asked angrily.

"Not as long as they have the Orange and Alexandria Railroad to bring them supplies."

"Do you think Morgan is up to doing a job for me?" Jeb asked as his brain worked out a plan.

"I would say so after seeing her in action a few days ago. "What's your plan?"

"We'll stop that damned train from bringing supplies and put these Yankees on equal footing. When we get to camp, send a scout to see when the next train is due," Jeb said smiling smugly. "Morgan will put a crimp in Meade's plans, then we will see how these Yankees fight on an empty stomach."

Chapter Nineteen

Robert E. Lee, sitting on his horse, Traveller watched his line of men filing down the hillside toward Stuart's camp. Lee, the attacker, must now turn his thoughts to the hard business of defense. He must keep the enemy from crossing the Rappahannock.

Stuart had only been in camp a few hours when word came of Lee's approach. He immediately ordered his officers to stand their troops at attention to honor their leader. When this was done, Lee and Stuart sat at a make-shift table with a map between them, staff and couriers looking on. Lee quickly agreed to Stuart's plan for Fitzgerald's Raiders to harass the supply trains and for Mosby to keep up his hit and run tactics on the outskirts of Warrenton.

When the meeting was over, Lee had a few Sharp's carbines that had been procured at Gettysburg and gave them as gifts to the officers, including Morgan.

"Young lady, I thought you would be married to one of my officers by now," Lee said with a twinkle in his blue eyes.

"No, General, you keep your officers too busy for them to do any courting. Maybe when the war is over."

A brief look of sadness crossed Lee's face. "Yes, when this war is over maybe we can get back to the pleasantries of life; like a tall, cool glass of lemonade while you sit in a porch swing with your loved one. Isn't it funny how such a little thing means so much to you when you can no longer enjoy it? I don't know how many evenings I spent sitting in a swing with my wife and never realized anything would ever change our way of life."

"I guess we were all that way, sir. Even when the war was evident we still believed nothing would change. When I think about it now, I realize how foolish we were. Nothing can ever be the same, no matter the outcome."

"You are very wise for your years, Morgan, but I guess years of war experience are bound to make you so. Just don't forget how to be the Virginia belle you once were. I expect to see you in your best finery when this war is over."

"We will have a victory ball, sir, and I will save you the first dance."

"I shall remember that, Morgan."

Morgan instructed Jubal to pick the men that were to assist in stopping the next supply train. She wanted to keep the unit small so they would be inconspicuous. They moved out of camp shortly after dark, staying to the hills overlooking the tracks. The evening air was pleasant and Morgan's spirit was high as they undertook this dangerous assignment. For miles in every direction, Union sentinels were stationed along the rails, but none of these precautions would stop her.

They picked a spot just south of Warrenton Junction and set up their own surveillance. There were about a dozen Federal guards in the area. Some slept, some nodded, some sat around the campfire playing cards. While the cards were being dealt, the Rebels stole along the ridge, their hands on their animals' muzzles, and set up for their attack on the unsuspecting Yankees.

Morgan whispered orders to her men, each waiting for the signal to attack. Suddenly she gave the command and the cool night's silence was split by a blood-curdling Rebel yell, the symbolic scream that sent Yankees running in the opposite direction. Confusion paralyzed them; most were captured before they had a chance to pull a gun.

Morgan ordered the men stripped from their uniforms and tied up in a pine grove. The shrill sound of the train whistle sounded around the bend as the Rebels changed into the blue uniforms.

"Everybody take your places. You know what to do. Tom, get that card game started. Jubal come with me. We'll need a lantern."

Jubal and three other men began prying up ties and placing horseshoes over the rails just beyond the campfire. They could feel the vibrations of the train approaching as they hurried about their assignments.

The train rattled through the darkness, hissing steam as it went. It was made up of a locomotive, an Adams Express Company car and nine well-loaded freight cars.

The engineer yawned as he looked out into the darkness. The night was clear and there was a tang of the harvest season in the air, but the farmers had lost their fields and stock to warmongers so there would be no harvest this season. He could see the flickering of a campfire up ahead as they rounded a bend in the tracks.

The engine blasted forth a whistle and rumbled on spraying sparks everywhere. They passed a group of guards playing cards and the engineer waved. Suddenly there was a great commotion; cars jammed violently against each other. There was an explosion and loud hissing and then the staccato bark of gunfire as blue uniformed men boarded the train taking charge.

"What's the matter with you fools? Don't you know this is your own supply train?" shouted the irate engineer.

Morgan didn't answer as she bruskly gave orders to take what they could and fire everything else."

"You're guerrillas," the engineer said in amazement. "You're not Union soldiers at all. You're Rebels."

Morgan smiled. "You're a very intelligent man. Now I suggest if you want to stay alive to enjoy that intelligence you will start walking from where you came. You can give Lincoln the regards of Morgan Fitzgerald and tell him we appreciate the supplies."

The engineer took off down the tracks, only looking back once as his train went up in flames after being soaked in pitch.

All the Raiders gathered on the ridge with their plunder and watched the train burn. They had stopped the train at 1:40 am; it was nearly 3:00 am when they departed.

The dawn was beginning to light the sky as they

approached the Rappahannock. Morgan sent all but Jubal ahead while she stayed on the ridge overlooking the Federal camp.

"Why are we stopping, Morgan?"

"That's Marc's camp down there."

"How do you know that?"

"I just know it," Morgan laughed. No supernatural powers, Jubal. I recognize his horse. See the black stallion? It's larger than most, she said handing him her spy glass. "I'm going down there, Jubal."

"You're out of your mind, girl. I will not allow it! You just robbed and destroyed their supply train. Surely word has already reached them and you want to just waltz in and see your lover. I gave you credit for being smarter than that."

Tears welled up in Morgan's eyes. "I've got to get word to him, Jubal."

Jubal saw the desperation in her eyes and his heart went out to her. He didn't say anything for a moment. "I'll go down under a flag of truce and ask Marc to come here and speak with you."

"Oh, Jubal, what would I do without you?"

"You would probably get yourself killed," Jubal said taking a white scarf from his pocket. "You stay right here until I come back. If there is any trouble, you take off and fast."

"No, wait," Morgan said realizing the danger she was putting her friend in. "I'm being selfish. I am placing you in a great deal of danger and I can't do it."

"Just stay here, Morgan. I want to get this thing over with."

Jubal rode down the hill to the guard on duty. They

talked for a few moments and then Jubal moved back about fifty yards and waited. A few minutes later Morgan saw Marc walking to the spot where Jubal waited. Her heart skipped a beat as she watched him talking with Jubal. Minutes that seemed like hours passed, but they still talked. Morgan was sure they were arguing, but why? She couldn't stand it any longer. Spurring Gambler, she headed down the hill toward the men.

"Stay on your horse, Morgan!" Jubal yelled as Morgan approached.

Morgan looked from one to the other before seeing the cold, hard look in Marc's eyes.

"What's the matter, Morgan, did you need a new man in your bed tonight?" Marc asked sarcastically. "Well, I remember your body well, my sweet, but the idea of bedding such a traitoress, lying bitch just leaves me cold. I'm sure Jubal would be glad to oblige you."

"What are you talking about?" Morgan asked fighting tears at his harsh words.

"I'm saying I would rather bed the lowliest whore than you, Morgan. The thought of touching you makes me sick. You're a cold, ruthless, calculating bitch!"

Jubal stepped forward, his fist clenched in anger. "Don't, Jubal. He isn't worth it." She faced Marc again. "You will regret . . ."

"The only thing I regret is not having killed you before you had a chance to soil the people I love."

Morgan could take no more. She cocked her rifle and aimed it at Marc, but was blinded by the tears in her eyes. "You and Rachel deserve each other," she said vehemently. "I hope you both rot in hell!" She yanked the reins of her horse, causing her to rear and paw the air dangerously close to Marc, then turned and galloped away.

"By all that's holy, what is the matter with you? What did she do to deserve that?"

"You know damned well what she did. I ought to kill the two of you . . . and if my mother doesn't get well, I swear I will."

"I think you better explain, Yankee, because I'm losing patience with these riddles."

"I'm talking about Morgan shoving my mother down the steps and leaving her to die."

"That's a damn lie. Your mother saw the two of us off the night we left Washington. Who in hell told you that?"

"I expected you to lie for her. I'm well aware you are her lover."

"I should kill you for that, Yankee, but I'm not going to waste my energy. You're not worth it. I'll tell you something, I do love Morgan, but I have more respect for her than to tarnish her — to use her like you did. Morgan had never been touched by anyone until you came along. She loved you . . . at least she did until a few minutes ago."

Jubal mounted his horse and looked down on Marc. "I've been hoping something would change her mind about you. It won't take her long to forget all about you, but I'll tell you something, Yankee, I hope her lovely face haunts you 'til your dying day."

Jubal rode after Morgan as fast as his horse would carry him. She had been willing to give up everything for Riordan and he wondered how this was going to affect her.

"Hold up, Morgan!" he shouted trying to catch up to her as she raced wildly across the hills. He finally got within reach and grabbed the reins of her horse. "What are you trying to do, kill yourself?" he asked angrily.

Morgan slumped over the saddle sobbing hysterically. "Oh, Jubal, how could he talk to me that way? I thought he loved me."

"Morgan, listen to me," Jubal said helping her from Gambler. "He is under the impression that you shoved his mother down the steps. It sounds to me like your friend Rachel has been up to her old tricks."

"It doesn't matter. If he cared for me like he said, he would not have believed anything she said. I hate him! Oh God, how I hate him, Jubal," she sobbed.

"I know, Morgan," he said holding her in his arms. "I know."

Marc felt as if he were being torn apart. Jubal's words hammered in his brain. His mother had seen them off . . . Jubal had never touched Morgan. Was it possible?

"Rachel," he said aloud. "I'm going to get the truth out of you if I have to kill you."

"What was that all about?" Wes asked as he came up from behind.

"That was Morgan and Jubal. I accused her of being a traitoress whore and she threatened to kill me."

"I know it's going to be hard on you, Marc, but you're better off without her. Rachel will be a good wife for you."

"Funny, that's what Morgan said. She said we

310

deserved each other."

"That's just an angry woman talking."

"A woman that I think I've wronged, Wes. Jubal says it is all lies. He says my mother saw them off. I think Rachel lied about everything."

Wes didn't say anything.

"You know she hated Morgan. Would she have gone so far as to blame her for my mother's fall?"

"I really don't know, Marc. She loves you and I would guess she'd do anything she felt she had to to keep you. Sometimes I think Rachel is a very sick woman in her obsession over you. At times she thrives on my attention, my flattery; she tells me she loves me, yet when there is mention of you and another woman, she swears she will never give you up. The night we were together I thought I had convinced her to be my wife. Then I made the mistake of mentioning Morgan and it was as if I had set a time bomb under her. All she could think of the rest of the night was getting rid of Morgan. I love her, Marc, but I'm not sure she isn't very sick."

Marc looked at his friend's anguished face and felt guilty for burdening him with his problems. Wes was hopelessly in love, just as he was.

Marc ran his fingers through his hair. "Why hadn't I seen this before? I've ruined any chance I had with Morgan. I should have given her the opportunity to explain, but I was too anxious to hurt her. She'll never forgive me for the things I said."

"Marc, you're not being realistic. What chance could you possibly have to find happiness with Morgan? You're a Union officer. She's a notorious guerrilla fighter for the Confederacy. My God, man, you're not thinking straight if you think you could overcome those obstacles. On top of all that, you know the train that was destroyed this morning?"

"Yeah, what about it?" Marc answered irritably.

"If you hadn't been so preoccupied you would have noticed Morgan and Jubal carried sacks taken from that train. Don't you see, it was her raiders that destroyed our train."

"Damn this war. When will it ever be over?"

"I don't know, Marc, but even if it were soon, it still wouldn't work for you and Morgan. If the Union is victorious, and I believe we will be, Morgan will not be given parole as other Rebels. She's a partisan fighter and it has long been said they would be dealt with severely. She will probably hang, Marc."

"No! I won't let anything happen to her. I'll get her away from this blasted war. I'll take her to the Bahamas or Europe."

"Come on, Marc, you're not thinking clearly. Are you going to disgrace your father and mother's good name for a woman with a reputation like she has?"

"What do you mean with a reputation like she has?" Marc said, his face white with anger.

"I just meant her being a guerrilla fighter. For God's sake, don't get mad with me. I'm just trying to help you. Nothing could make me happier than to see you marry the woman and leave Rachel for me, but I'm your friend and I can't stand seeing you ruin your life."

"My life is ruined if I can't have Morgan. Even while I professed my hate for her, I wanted her. She possesses me and will until my dying day."

"I can see there is no sense talking to you about

Morgan. Well, there is no sense worrying about it. We don't even know if we'll still be on this earth tomorrow."

The next two evenings Marc rode to the brow of the hill overlooking the Rebel camp and waited—hoping Morgan would see him and come. When dark came he would ride dejectedly back to his camp and spend a sleepless night thinking about her. He felt as if he were losing his sanity. He found himself praying he could hate her as much as he loved her—for ease from his desire for her, but still the driving need for her persisted. He thought of letting himself be captured so he could see her and explain, but what if he went through all that and didn't see her?

Meade had issued orders to prepare for a renewed attack. He had been furious when he found out the Raiders had gotten to their supply train and not only taken their food supply, but had made such shambles of the tracks that it would be days before supplies would reach them. Meade felt if they didn't attack now, they would be fighting on empty stomachs and he didn't want that. He felt men lost their reason when they were hungry. With the new troops Marc had brought into camp, they would outnumber the Rebs two to one so there shouldn't be any problem pushing them back to the Rapidan and from there to Richmond.

Marc tossed and turned reliving the dream he had of killing Morgan. He broke out in a cold sweat as he saw her covered with blood and falling from her horse.

He finally left his tent and saddled Satan. He rode into the woods, listening to the sounds of the wildlife. Soon the silence would be broken by gunfire and the screams of men in agony.

"Oh, Morgan, if I could only whisk you away in the night. We would leave this hell and find our own paradise."

Morgan was out riding by herself when she saw the lone-rider whom everyone had been talking about. She knew it was Marc as soon as she saw him silhouetted in the moonlight atop Satan's Thunder. She wondered why he appeared each night, waiting on top of the ridge as if he were meeting someone. The men in camp had wanted to capture him, but Stuart felt it might be a trap. That was all she needed; he a prisoner in her camp—reminding her, taunting her.

Morgan tied Gambler to a tree by the river's edge and began to walk. She listened to the night sounds and remembered how the sound of the whippoorwill had lulled her to sleep as a child. The night air was sweet with the smell of pine and hemlock and it somehow soothed the hurt she felt. She still couldn't believe Marc had said such hateful things to her. For two nights she had lain in bed going over what he had said. Was she a cold, ruthless bitch? Is that what this war had done to her? She didn't think so; she still had compassion, and she could still love. That was more than she could say for him. Why, why did he say those things?

Suddenly tears flowed down her face. "The touch of me didn't always make you sick, Marc Riordan," she sobbed.

Morgan sat by herself for over an hour trying to sort out things. Her life was going to have to change now. Her plans to be with Marc would never take place. She looked to the hill and he was gone.

"Out of my life—out of my mind," she said. "He was just someone who passed through my life. There will be someone else to fill the void—the dull ache. In a few years I won't ever remember his name—the name of the father of my child."

The light of dawn began to filter through the trees as a light mist fell. A gray, shroud-like fog rolled off the river giving everything an ominous look.

Marc watched as the howitzers were lined up facing the Rebel camp and everything was readied for this new attack. He could see activity in the Confederate camp as he looked through his spyglass. Suddenly he felt a chill to the bone, yet the morning was pleasantly mild.

The Confederates knew the time had come. They realized the Federals had been bringing troops in faster than they could fortify their position. They would not be able to prevent the passage of the river by this renewed Federal force.

All the top officers were there; Lee, Early, Ewell, Stuart, Rodes, but they all agreed the only thing they could do was to hold off the enemy long enough for the troops to take position behind the Ford. If that didn't work, they would have to retreat to Culpeper.

Marc hoped for some delay—some change in plan, but the order was given by Meade and all hell broke loose. Federal forces began swarming across the river; some swimming, some wading and others taking to the pontoon bridge while the big guns fired over their heads into the Confederates trying to hold the river.

Marc's cavalry unit stayed behind the gunners, giving orders as the troops advanced across the river. The Rebel guns were firing directly into the advancing troops and keeping them from retreating was the cavalry's job until all were across the river.

Two of the big guns near Marc were hit by a shell that scattered debris, knocking Marc off his horse. He struggled to calm Satan and remount, his face bloody and streaked with gunpowder. Men were running all around him. "Get back to your guns!" he shouted. "You want to push them to Richmond, don't you?"

Most of the men headed back to the guns while Marc rode up and down the lines shouting encouragement. "Load up and get those guns firing!" he shouted as shells dropped around him

The guns were loaded and firing, vomiting a death load of grape that dropped Rebs in their tracks. After several hours Marc was confident the guns were in good hands and rushed to join his cavalry who were fighting in the trees to their left. The clash of steel echoed over the hillside as blue fought gray.

A shrill whistle split the air, then a deafening explosion. A rider and horse hit the ground with a thud as the horse was decapitated by the shell only a few feet from Marc. He shouted encouragement to the troops around him to hold their position as the hail of bullets and whistling cartridges fell around them. Suddenly a big cavalryman clashed with him and struck him across the shoulder with his saber, almost knocking Marc from his horse. He pulled his revolver and as he straightened up in the saddle shot the Reb in the stomach. He was promptly leaped upon from behind and was pulled to the ground. He fought hand to hand with the Reb, getting the best of him until he heard Morgan's voice shouting orders to her men as she rode well ahead of them into the fray of battle.

A bullet ripped through Marc's sleeve as he stood immobilized watching Morgan in the midst of the battle. A young soldier in blue handed him a gun.

"Get hold of yourself, sir."

Morgan's spirited horse pawed the air as she clashed steel with her enemy. Their eyes met for a split second, then suddenly the whole world seemed to go still as Marc heard an explosion and saw Morgan grab her stomach and sway. A strangled cry stuck in his throat as he watched her fall over backward, her hand reaching out to him.

He turned on the soldier who had fired the shot. The boy, seeing the crazed look in Marc's eyes, got off a wild shot that caught him in the temple. Marc fell to his knees, blood pouring from the wound. He struggled to crawl to where Morgan lay, but one of his own men fighting with a Rebel cavalryman trampled him beneath the hoofs of his horse.

Marc, barely able to raise his head, called out to Morgan. He could see Jubal carrying her lifeless, bloody body from the field. "If not here, Morgan, then in eternity," he said laying his head on the cold, blood-soaked ground.

Chapter Twenty

Marc didn't know how long he had been unconscious, but the sounds of the battle had faded as the fighting moved across the river. He painfully raised his head and looked around. Death and devastation were everywhere. The groans and cries of the wounded were mingled with the prayers of others who prepared to die.

Marc dragged himself to a young Rebel officer who begged for water. There was a canteen at the soldier's side, but his arm had been blown off. Marc opened the canteen, grimacing in pain at the exertion, and held it to the soldier's mouth. "Drink slowly, Reb. There will be help soon, but you need to ration your water."

"The only help I need is from my Maker, Yank. I'm not going any place."

Marc looked at the boy's arm and knew he was bleeding to death. "Is there anything I can do to make you comfortable?" he asked as he fought to remain conscious himself.

The soldier smiled weakly. "Looks to me like you need help yourself, Yank," he said as Marc's strength ebbed and he fell over.

"Where are you hurt?"

"My head, but I think I got some broken ribs too."

"If you're still alive when help comes, tell them I'm Bobby Lane from Fitzgerald's Raiders and to please send my body to my unit or my home in Front Royal. Will you do that, Yank?"

"You ride with Morgan?" Marc asked, straining to lean up on one elbow.

"How do you know Morgan?"

"She saved my life once," Marc said remembering a time when she doctored him in a little cabin on the Potomac. God, how long ago that seemed.

"I wish you could have returned the favor today. I saw her struck down just before I fell." As the soldier spoke tears rolled down his face. "I never knew another woman like her. She was the bravest, most compassionate woman I ever met. It will be worth dying if I see her in heaven."

Marc couldn't reply. He didn't have the strength to do more than summon Morgan's face to his memory. He weakly smiled as he remembered her green eyes twinkling when they had lain in the grass on the river's bank. How beautiful she had been after their lovemaking.

"Was her brother here today?" Marc asked weakly.

There was no reply from the Rebel soldier.

Marc rolled onto his side and closed the boy's eyes.

He tried to block out the sounds around him when suddenly he realized someone was moving among them. He listened intently to the murmuring voices, but he was too weak to raise his head.

"Here he is," someone shouted.

Marc opened his eyes and tried to focus on the soldier standing above him. He thought he saw Wes, but he must be dreaming.

"Easy, men, lift him gently." Wes said as Marc was placed on a stretcher.

"You're going to be fine, Marc. We'll get you to the field hospital and take care of those wounds."

Marc grabbed his friend's hand, struggling to speak. "That Rebel . . . send body to Jubal Kelly . . . Fitzgerald's Raiders."

"I don't understand, Marc. Why?"

"I promised . . . if I lived longer."

"All right, I'll take care of it. You lie back and let these men take you to the hospital. I'll be there shortly."

Marc was too weak to protest.

Marc opened his eyes and listened to the sounds around him. He saw the tent over his head, but he could swear he was still on the battlefield. The cries and moans of those around him hadn't changed. Men were screaming, begging to be put out of their misery. He forced himself to sit up and look around. He didn't know what was worse, the bloody, gory scene on the battlefield or this. A doctor was sawing off a soldier's leg while others were lined up waiting for the same.

"They will get to us soon, sir," stated a young lieutenant. There are others who are in worse shape than we are. Me, I just got a hole in my foot."

"I don't think I belong here," Marc said looking around at the dying men. "These doctors don't need to be wasting their time on me."

"You'd better wait, sir, you look like you've lost a lot of blood."

Marc didn't have the strength to leave anyway, so

he lay back on the stretcher to wait.

"We sure pushed them Rebs back. I hear they are holed up in Culpeper now."

"Yeah, I guess we did," Marc answered, not really interested in talking.

"I bet Robert E. Lee was unhappy today. I saw him sitting on that big gray horse looking all proud and defiant. I hear he don't like to lose."

"Does anyone?" Marc answered.

"They're going to have to be unhappy a lot, cause we're going to whip their tails off," the lieutenant said as Wes walked up. "Isn't that right, major? These Rebs don't stand a chance against us now."

"You're right, lieutenant. You just hurry and get that leg fixed so you can get back out there." Wes said before turning his attention to Marc.

"Are you all right, Marc?"

"I'd like to get out of here. Doc Webster can look after me. It's nothing serious."

"If you could see yourself you wouldn't say that."

"Did you know we killed that murdering Morgan Fitzgerald," the lieutenant butted in. "Yes, sir, Jimmy Long shot her right off her horse. I can tell you, she deserved to die. She was a ruthless killer. I just don't know how a woman could be so heartless."

Marc's face turned white with anger. "You son of a . . ."

"Lieutenant," Wes interrupted. "I don't think this is the time or place to be discussing this. None of these injured men want to hear talk of death and war right now."

"I don't know why they wouldn't want to hear about that horsethief being killed. It will make them feel better. I got her horse. Yes sir, wait 'til the boys see that animal. Beautiful beige with a black mane and tail."

"I've got to get out of here, Wes," Marc said struggling to get up. "If I don't I'm going to kill the bastard."

"All right, Marc, let me help you before you hurt yourself," he said, knowing that Marc would somehow find the strength to kill this stupid lieutenant if he didn't get him out of there.

"Hey, where you going, colonel? You'd better stay and get yourself treated."

"It's all right, lieutenant. We've got our own doctor at camp," Wes said over his shoulder.

Doc Webster, as the boys called him, had spent a few years in medical school, but had never graduated. When the war broke out he decided to join the cavalry for a little adventure. From the first time he had set a broken leg to now, the men depended on him for everything. He often protested that he wasn't a doctor, but it didn't matter to the men. He had been able to cure all their ills so they had complete faith in him.

He leaned over Marc, feeling the rib area where he complained of pain. "The head wound isn't too serious, but you have a lot of broken ribs. How in hell did you get your ribs broken?"

"A horse trampled me when I was down."

"Well, you're going to have to stay quiet and let them heal or you could have some real serious problems. I've seen ribs puncture right through the skin. Really messy when it happens. I'm going to bind them tight and see if that helps. Might be a bit uncomfortable, but you can live with that. Let's just hope there is no internal bleeding. If there is, you'll need more than my help."

"How long before I can ride?"

"It's going to be a while, colonel. What's your hurry?"

"I don't like being confined."

"That's exactly why I want you to stay with some friends of mine who live near here."

"That isn't necessary, Doc. I'll be fine right here."

"Come on, Marc, you know damned well you're not going to be able to lie here in this tent with all the activity going on. Doc is right, you'll be much better off staying with his friends."

"Are your friends Union sympathizers?" Marc asked.

"They're just good people, colonel. I knew them in Maryland before the war. They won't care if you're Union or Confederate. If you're hurt they'll take care of you. They have a lovely daughter . . ."

"I'm not interested in anyone's daughter," Marc interrupted angrily. "I'm not going anywhere. Just leave me alone. I don't need anyone's help to get well."

Doc Webster looked to Wes for some explanation.

"Doc, why don't you and I step outside and let Marc rest. I know he must be tired."

"Wait, Wes. Did you do what I asked? Did you get the horse from that soldier?"

"I got it, Marc. It cost you a pretty penny, but I got it."

When the two men got outside the tent Wes began to explain about Morgan. "I know you won't understand—her being a Rebel and all, but he saw a different side of her than we did. He truly loved her and he's miserable. Unfortunately, I think the worst is yet to come. I don't think the full realization of her death has hit him yet."

"All the more reason for him to be away from here in a different atmosphere. I'd send him home, but he'd never make the journey without those ribs coming through the skin. Judge Bryan and his family are fine people. They will understand his problem and help him."

Marc was carefully moved to the judge's house, a home that had been a beautiful example of southern architecture before the war, but like most was now run down. Doc Webester had given Marc morphine to ease his pain so he wasn't aware of the judge and his wife gathered in the foyer as he was carried in or of the sad-eyed young woman watching from the landing at the top of the stairs.

They placed him in a room on the south side of the house that opened onto a veranda. Doc made sure he was settled and then went to the library to join the family. He accepted a brandy from Judge Bryan before speaking.

"Does Katie know yet?"

"Yes, she knows. As we suspected, she didn't take it very well."

"I still think this will help her and hopefully, it will also help Colonel Riordan."

"She claims she won't lift a finger to help him. She says he could be the Yankee who killed her husband."

"You know that isn't true, judge. John was killed in West Virginia. That has never been our territory."

"We know that, Captain Webster, but she isn't thinking straight. I just hope she doesn't do anything to harm him," said Mrs. Bryan.

"Please, Mrs. Bryan, stop worrying. Katie is a kind, loving woman. She is just mixed up right now and I think if she sees another human suffering, someone who needs her help, it won't matter to her that he is a Yankee."

"And what if you're wrong, son? What if she kills your friend in his sleep? You know she has sworn to kill every Yankee that comes in her sight. Are you going to be responsible for that?" the judge asked.

Doc Webster didn't say anything for a moment. "Judge, I think you know that I love Katie. I had hoped to be the one to marry her, but when you moved to Virginia and she met John, I knew my plight was hopeless. I have a chance again, but now she is living in her own dark world, and if I don't help her she is only going to retreat further and further into the darkness. This is my only chance."

"We understand, son. I guess we agree if there is any chance this can bring her out of this depression, it's worth it."

Katie Bryan wandered aimlessly through the house wondering what she was going to do about the Yankee who was in her house. She hugged herself, mumbling as she went through the rooms. "I'll get rid of him, John. Tonight I'll go to his room and do it."

Doc decided to look in on Marc before leaving. His patient was coming out from under the effects of the morphine, but his skin was hot and flushed.

"So cold . . . more blankets," Marc mumbled

through chattering teeth.

"Damn, you've gotten feverish. I hadn't planned on that, my friend. I guess I'll be staying with you after all."

"Where are we?" Marc asked looking around him.

"This is Judge Bryan's house in Brandy Station. You remember, we talked about your recuperating here."

"Why is it so cold?" he asked, grimacing in pain as he was wracked with a coughing spasm.

Doc mixed a concoction of morphine and quinine, hoping to keep Marc comfortable until the fever passed. Above all else, he had to keep him from moving around. "Drink this, Marc."

Marc pushed the glass away. "Don't want any more drugs . . . need to know what is going on."

"You have to drink it, Marc. You need all the rest you can get and this will help the fever. I'll be staying right here with you."

Marc reluctantly drank the mixture. "Why are we at Brandy Station?" he asked, his eyes glassy with fever.

Doc chose his words carefully, explaining how they pushed the Rebs back to Culpeper, but trying to avoid bringing up anything that would remind Marc of Morgan Fitzgerald.

"Terrible fight . . ." he said before closing his eyes.

"They are all terrible, colonel. If this is a civil war, I hope never to see an uncivil one."

Doc didn't bother to light a lamp as the moon was shining brightly and lit the room enough for him to see his patient. He settled in a chair in the corner of the room and dozed while Marc rested peacefully.

A short time later he was startled out of a sound

sleep by Marc's blood-chilling scream. Marc was sitting straight up in bed, his face stark white even in the dark.

"I killed her . . . Oh my God, I killed her," he moaned.

Doc rushed to his side, struggling to hold him on the bed. "You didn't kill her, Marc."

"The gun was smoking in my hands . . . she was covered with blood . . . Morgan, Morgan, I saw it in my dreams. Why didn't I heed the warning?"

"Marc, lie back! You're going to hurt yourself."

The bedroom door opened and Katie stood silhouetted by the lamp she held in her hand.

Doc started to tell her to leave, but he realized this was the opportunity he had been waiting for.

"What's the matter with him?" she asked.

"Besides being shot, he saw the woman he loved killed today. One of his own men killed her," he said watching for some expression on her face.

"He's a Yankee," she said bitterly.

"Yes, he chose to fight for the Union. That doesn't make him any different. He loved this woman as much as you loved John, but he is not going to hate all his friends because one soldier killed her."

"Morgan, Morgan," Marc moaned. "I loved you . . . didn't mean to kill you."

Katie watched Marc for a moment then turned to leave. As she did, Doc saw the light gleam off the knife she held in her hand. "He is a Yankee," she said again.

"He is a man, Katie! A man who needs your help. Are you going to turn your back on all mankind because one man killed your husband? If so, Katie, I pity you, because your life is going to be miserable."

The young woman didn't say anything. She left the room, quietly closing the door behind her.

"Damn! That did a whole lot of good."

Doc spent most of the night trying to keep Marc quiet. He was delirious until almost dawn when the quinine finally eased the fever. When Doc felt Marc was sleeping peacefully he settled once again in the corner.

He was dozing fitfully when something disturbed his sleep. He tried to ignore it, but he suddenly realized a lamp had been dimly lit and someone was in the room. He moved cautiously from the chair toward the bed where Katie sat looking down on Marc. She raised her hand and Doc started to grab it, but saw she had a cloth in it that she gently laid on Marc's forehead.

Doc backed slowly away from the bed, but continued to watch from the shadows as Katie gently sponged Marc all over. When she was finished she picked up the basin and cloth and left the room.

Doc let out a sigh of relief. He felt Marc's head and was relieved to find it cool. "You have an angel of mercy, my friend, but what you don't realize is you just might be her savior."

Chapter Twenty-one

With the help of morphine, Marc slept around the clock. Doc felt the longer he was kept quiet the better chance the ribs had of healing.

Katie waited until late evening before venturing to the patient's room carrying a wash-basin and towel. She had decided she would continue to bathe this stranger as long as he was drugged, but she wouldn't help him once he was conscious.

She stood motionless at the side of the bed, thinking about the woman who was killed. She had been very lucky to have had love from a man like Marc Riordan. Katie suddenly felt flushed all over as she stood looking down at his strong, muscular body. He exuded power even lying helpless from the wounds which had struck him down.

Carefully she sat on the edge of the bed. Dipping the cloth in the warm soapy water, she slowly ran it over Marc's broad shoulders and chest, then pulled the sheet down below the bandages and taking care not to apply any pressure, washed the skin below the bandages.

"Morgan?" Marc asked incoherently.

"My name is Katie, not Morgan," she answered irritably.

"Marc tried to focus on the girl sitting on the side of the bed, but everything was blurred. "Who are you?"

"I told you. My name is Katie. Katie Rogers."

"Where is Doc?" he mumbled.

"If you mean Gene, he went to camp to pick up a

few things. He didn't think you would be awake for a while."

Marc tried to sit up but the room began to spin. "Tell Doc . . . no more . . . no more drugs," he said feeling as if his mouth were filled with cotton.

"Doesn't it help you forget?" she asked sympathetically.

"No. Nothing eases this pain I have."

"Is your pain from your wounds or because the woman you loved was killed?" she asked pityingly.

Marc's eyes widened in surprise. "How do you know about that?"

"You talked a lot while you were delirious. Also, Gene told me you saw her killed."

Marc closed his eyes as Morgan's image came to mind. "I'd like to be alone. Please leave, I don't need your help."

"I should have known better than to expect anything but rudeness from a Yankee," Katie said picking up the wash-basin and storming from the room.

Marc struggled to sit up, grimacing in pain as he did. He swung his feet off the bed, then sat hugging his ribs before he could move again. He finally summoned the strength to stand. Slowly he made his way to the armoire and began searching through it for his belongings. When he found nothing there he began to pull everything from the chest that stood in corner.

"What are you doing out of bed?" Doc asked from the doorway.

"Where are my clothes and guns?"

"Downstairs. Now get back in bed, colonel," he answered impatiently.

"I want my things brought up here," Marc retorted

as he staggered back to the bed.

"You're not going any place, so why should you need them?"

"You seem to forget I'm your commanding officer, captain. You don't question my reasons."

"And you forget that you and Major Lansing begged me to take care of you. I tried to convince you to stay at that field hospital, but you wouldn't listen. Now you think I'm going to just let you walk out of here and do yourself harm. Well, you're wrong, colonel. You put yourself in my care and I intend to see that you're well before you leave, in spite of yourself!"

"All right, Doc," Marc answered defeated. "You win. I'm too tired to argue. We just need to get a few things straight. First, I don't want any more drugs. Second, I want my belongings in this room. Believe me, I'm not trying to escape your good medical attention. I just want them with me. Third, I would just as soon not have that girl bathing me."

"I'm the doctor and I feel you need the drugs a little longer. You wouldn't be able to sleep if you didn't take them. I'll limit them to the nights and see how you do with that. I'll send your belongings up if I have your word you won't try to get dressed until I say it's all right."

"You got my word, Doc. Now how about the girl?"

Doc paced back and forth at the foot of Marc's bed. "There is something I need to explain," Doc said sheepishly. "Katie's husband rode with Harry Gilmore and was killed about three months ago in the hills of Western Virginia. They had only been married a few months before it happened and Katie has been in a deep depression ever since. She would sit and cry for hours, rocking herself back and forth like a little

331

child. Her family was afraid she was going crazy. When you came to me and needed help, I thought of Katie and hoped her taking care of you might help. She needed to know that someone besides herself was suffering from losing a loved one."

"Just what is your interest in this girl?" Marc asked.

Doc dropped into a chair facing Marc. "You're very observant, my friend. I've been in love with Katie since I was a young boy. I always dreamed she would be my wife, but then her family moved to Virginia where she met John Rogers. Unfortunately for me, they fell in love at first sight. I never had a chance to tell her how I felt. I don't really know what will happen now. All I can hope for is to get her back to the beautiful, happy girl I once knew. Right now she thinks she hates anyone who wears a blue uniform and I guess that includes me. I think she actually contemplated killing you at one point."

"My God, are you serious?"

"Afraid so. But don't worry, I'm sure she doesn't feel that way any longer. The fact that she helped you is a step in the right direction."

"Do you really think she . . ."

"What were you going to ask, colonel?"

"I started to ask if you really thought she could kill me, but then I remembered I could have killed one of my own men for killing the woman I loved. I would have too, if he hadn't fired a shot at me first. God, every time I think of it my stomach feels all knotted up. The sight of her reaching out to me as she fell from that horse will stay with me the rest of my life."

"Try not to think about it, Marc."

"Her memory is all I have, doc."

"You will only make yourself miserable if you keep dwelling on it."

"You would understand if you had met her. She was so beautiful. I remember the first time I saw her. She rode into camp so proud, her green eyes flashing defiantly. Our eyes met and for a moment I found it hard to breathe. She had this smudge of dirt across the bridge of her nose . . ." Marc suddenly became silent.

Doc stood up to leave, knowing Marc preferred to be alone with his thoughts. "Marc, will you help my Katie?"

"I don't know if I can, Doc. You know I'd do anything I could to help, but my mental state is not conducive to helping anyone with a problem like this."

"All you have to do is let her continue taking care of you. Surely that's not so bad. Katie is a very beautiful woman."

Marc ran his hand through his hair. "Doc, I'm going to be out of here in a few days, but until then I'll go along with this scheme of yours."

"You won't regret it, colonel. I promise you, I'll be forever in your debt."

"Listen, my friend, I'll never be able to repay you for saving my life, so don't talk to me about being in my debt."

"Well let's just say we're even. Your life for Katie's."

"I hope you're not being over-confident. We don't know that this will help her."

"It will, colonel. I think your being here has already helped."

Katie lay staring at the ceiling of her room, a feeling of great yearning engulfing her as she thought of Marc Riordan's strong, muscular body. Johnny had taught her the ways of pleasuring a man and of being pleasured and then he had gone, leaving her alone and miserable. Her breath caught as she heard Marc scream out.

Katie slipped out of her bed and headed for Marc's room, hesitating as he became silent again. She quietly opened the door and slipped into the room. She watched from the foot of his bed as he tossed and turned in his drug-induced sleep and wondered what she could do to ease him. She placed her hand on his brow to make sure he wasn't feverish.

"Morgan, my darling Morgan," he said pulling her down beside him.

Katie started to pull away, but she didn't—she couldn't. She was on fire, her breathing rapid and irregular. This man needed her as she needed him. Why should she leave him? She slipped the flimsy shift down over her shoulders and snuggled against his warm muscular body.

Marc moaned with pleasure as she ran her hand over his chest and down over his stomach. All doubts and scruples were gone from her mind as his hands found her ready. He mounted her gently, still whispering Morgan's name against her neck. Their tongues entwined as his strong arms enfolded her slender body. He forgot the pain in his ribs as he felt the surge begin in the pit of his stomach.

"Oh yes . . . yes," she whispered as he called out Morgan's name.

Katie lay contentedly at Marc's side as he slept deeply. She studied his profile, thinking how handsome he was even with the newly acquired scar at his temple. He was such a ruggedly attractive man, where her Johnny had been handsome in a boyish way.

Marc became restless and she decided it best to leave before anyone came in and found her there. Slowly she eased out from under the covers, trying not to disturb him.

"Please don't go, Morgan."

"Don't call me Morgan," she pleaded unable to bear the thought of his thinking he made love to someone other than herself.

Marc opened his eyes and stared at Katie. A desperate animal sound escaped his lips. "Oh God, let me be dreaming."

"You're not dreaming. I came to your room because you were crying out in your sleep. It just happened."

"What kind of an animal am I? While I'm mourning for the only woman I'll ever love, I rape another."

"Colonel, if it is any consolation, I needed you as much as you obviously needed me. It's not as though I was a virgin. It certainly wasn't rape."

"It wouldn't have mattered. You could have been a virgin for all I knew and still I violated you. You are the woman my friend loves. Oh God, what a thing to do to him."

Katie's eyes widened in shock. "What are you talking about?"

"Doc . . . he has been in love with you since you were children. He had hoped to make you his wife."

"No. You're wrong. He has never shown in any way that he cared for me. He has always been a friend, but . . ."

"I don't know about that, but I think you'd better

get out of here before he finds you. He doesn't have to know, but if he should find out, tell him it was rape. That I attacked you."

Katie backed away from the bed then turned and ran from the room. She stood in the hallway leaning her head against the door. This was just too much to believe. Gene had always been a good friend. Nothing more. What Marc Riordan said couldn't be true.

Her thoughts were suddenly interrupted by the sound of something crashing to the floor. She listened for a moment and heard Marc stumbling around the room. Slowly she opened the door and saw him sitting on the edge of the bed, a silver revolver in his hands. She threw the door open and faced him, her hands on her hips.

"Are you going to blow your brains out, colonel?" she asked forcing her voice to sound indifferent.

"Are you afraid I'll deprive you of the pleasure? I understand you wanted to kill me."

"Yes, I wanted to at one time, but then Gene made me realize you had never done anything to me."

"You can't say that now."

"You're a very strange man, Colonel Riordan. I'm not upset or feeling guilty by what happened. It was enjoyable and it's over. Perhaps you had planned to practice celibacy the rest of your life."

Suddenly Marc leaned back holding his sides, his deep laughter filling the room. "You are a very unusual woman, Katie Rogers. You have a way of making a person see things clearly. You're right, it happened and it was enjoyable. I loved Morgan and I'll mourn her for a long time, but she enjoyed life and helped me to enjoy it and I will remember her in that way forever."

"As long as you remember her she will always live for you. You can't live in the shadow of what could have been . . ." Katie stopped, realizing what she had just said.

"Katie, what's the matter?"

"I just realized I have been doing that very thing. Seeing you with that gun made me realize life is very precious." Tears began to flow down Katie's cheeks.

"Are you all right, Katie?"

"Is what you said about Gene loving me true?"

"Every word. He loves you very much."

Katie smiled. "Then I'll be all right."

Marc prepared to leave Judge Bryan's house. Doc felt he was well enough to go home for a few days rest and then return to his outfit. Funny, he thought, he had mixed feelings about that prospect. He wondered if every battle would remind him of Morgan. God, he wished this war would come to an end.

Doc entered the room in an unusually happy mood, humming as he adjusted the bandages on Marc's chest.

"Are you going to tell me what you're so happy about or just continue to look like the cat that swallowed the canary?"

Doc smiled mischievously. "Just between you and me, things are finally falling into place for Katie and me. She said she would be honored if I continued to visit her. She even kissed me before I left, and I don't mean a brotherly kiss. I just can't believe it, colonel. I've loved her for so long."

"I'm happy for you, doc. I wish you all the happiness in the world."

"Thanks, colonel. I hope someday you'll find someone to fill the void in your life."

"I'll be fine as long as I stay busy. I had the best for a short time and most people can't ever say that."

The trip from Brandy Station seemed endlessly long and boring. Wes insisted on a slower pace than Marc felt necessary, but he couldn't convince his friend that he was able to travel faster. The only saving fact was the weather. The day was crisp and clear, the sky a brilliant blue with white puffy clouds. The mountains were alive with color, every ridge and hollow clearly outlined with the gold and crimson of the turning trees.

Marc thought how strange, even though men war and kill, leaving the land devastated, every season arrives undaunted, bringing with it a breath of hope.

It was just the kind of day Morgan would have loved. How he would love to have her riding at his side now, her green eyes twinkling mischievously at him. God, why had they wasted so much time fighting? That day they had picnicked in the field of wildflowers had been so perfect. She had smelled of lavender and her hair had been so silky to the touch. He smiled. Strange, how at a time of death and sadness, it was the little things that seemed most vivid in his memory. He would always remember her lying next to him, her long, wavy hair fanned about her head and her eyes glowing warmly with desire.

Marc suddenly reined Satan in. "Hold up, Wes! I can hear a group of horsemen approaching."

"They should be our own, Marc. There hasn't been any Confederate activity between Warrenton and Washington for a couple of weeks."

"I'd feel better . . ." Marc didn't get to finish his sentence as the riders spotted them. "Damn, it's a group of Irregulars! Don't do anything, Wes. We're sitting ducks here."

The leader of the Rebel group held up his hand and those following stopped. He advanced alone, his spirited horse prancing sideways.

"I think we might be in luck, Wes. Just let me do the talking."

Wes threw Marc a questioning look, but said nothing.

"Hello, John. It's been a long time."

"I'll be damned. I thought I recognized you, Marc. How's it going with you?" the rider said leaning across his horse to shake hands.

"Not too bad. How are your folks?"

"Fine, fine. I was there not too long ago recuperating from a slight wound."

"Ah, yes, I believe I heard something about that," Marc said with a twinkle in his eye.

Mosby laughed. "I'm sure you did. I wouldn't be surprised if you hadn't put that bullet in me."

"Now, John, would I do that to an old friend?" Marc asked laughing.

"Perhaps to an old friend who is now your enemy," Mosby retorted.

"John, I'd like you to meet a good friend of mine, Wes Lansing. Wes, this is John Mosby."

Wes leaned over the head of his horse and shook

hands with the gutsy leader he had faced so many times in battle.

"Where are you headed, Marc?"

"It's my turn to go home for a little recuperation. I was wounded at Brandy Station a few days ago."

"I'm sorry to hear it, Marc. I heard that was a terrible battle. I hope your recuperation will be fast. I must say goodby now. Stuart waits for me up ahead. You take care of yourself, old friend. When this war is over we'll have to go back to that fishing hole you found for us on the Shenandoah. I think of it often."

"So do I, John. Those were good times."

Mosby's horse pranced nervously, appearing too big and spirited for the slight rider, but was held in total control. "Be careful around Aldie. I still have a few men in that area," he shouted as he rode back to his men.

The two officers watched them gallop away, leaving only a cloud of dust behind. "I'll be damned. Who would ever believe that?" Wes said, his eyes wide in amazement. "I'll tell you, my friend, traveling with you is never dull."

Marc laughed. "We were lucky that was Mosby and not one of the other partisan groups or this would really have been an interesting trip."

Marc stood at his studio window looking down on the small garden where only a few months ago he had watched Morgan picking flowers.

He had been home three days and was close to going insane from the loneliness that threatened to overwhelm him. Everywhere he looked there were reminders of Morgan; the painting of her, the dresses

340

he had carefully chosen, her horse in the stable, the big feather bed where he had professed his undying love for her. Undying love—until he had let Rachel's treachery blind him and turn him into a fool. No, he couldn't entirely blame Rachel. He should have believed in Morgan. He still didn't know what had happened the night his mother had fallen. Rachel swore she only told him what she believed happened; that she had found his mother at the foot of the stairs and Morgan had mysteriously disappeared.

What did it matter now, he thought. His mother was showing some improvement and perhaps one day would be able to shed some light on the mystery. At least Rachel had accepted his decision to call off their marriage. He had prepared himself for one of her scenes, but was relieved that she had agreed to return to her cousin. Wes had volunteered to take her there, so maybe he would be able to court her without feeling he was betraying their friendship.

Marc turned back to the painting on the easel and studied Morgan's face. "I knew the first time you rode into my camp you would have a tremendous effect on my life. If I had only realized my whole life was involved around you. Oh, Morgan, why did we waste so much time? If only I had it to do over again, I'd never let you out of my sight," he said, placing his hand on the painting. "I didn't do you justice, my love. Your inner beauty doesn't show on my canvas. If only I had taken you away before the battle . . . If only I had died with you on that battlefield . . . if only."

"Marc, may I come in?" Connie asked.

"Of course, Aunt Connie," Marc answered trying

quickly to compose himself.

"You and I haven't had a chance to talk alone and I thought perhaps . . ."

Marc hugged his aunt. "You know me too well. Somehow you're always there when I'm at my lowest."

"Morgan would be most unhappy if she thought you were mourning her this way. She was of Irish descent and they believe in celebrating going to a better place."

"I know, Connie, it's just the way we parted. You wouldn't believe the things I said to her. Now that I think of it, I can't believe it. I hurt her terribly, yet just before . . . just before she was shot, she turned those soft, green eyes on me and I saw her love was still there."

"Then why do you dwell on this? She is away from this hell on earth we have made for ourselves and she will always be remembered by those who knew and loved her."

"I know, but I keep thinking, if only she had stayed here she would still be alive. Damn it, why did she leave, Connie?"

Connie looked away toward the window. "I think only Rachel could have answered that question."

"I asked her and she swore she didn't know why."

"And of course you believed her?"

"Connie . . . you know something you're not telling me."

"No, Marc, you're wrong. I've been telling you for months. There is nothing Rachel wouldn't do or say to get her way. I was afraid to turn my back on her for fear if she knew Brenna had told me the truth she would shove me down a flight of stairs. I don't believe for a minute that we have heard the last of Rachel."

"What truth? For God's sake, Connie, what are you talking about?"

"I tried to tell you once before, but you wouldn't listen. You were too preoccupied with drinking and feeling sorry for yourself . . ."

"Connie," Marc growled.

"Brenna was forced to leave here by Rachel, because she was Morgan's friend and knew Morgan had also been forced to leave. I firmly believe that Rachel pushed your mother down the stairs when your mother confronted her with these facts."

"I can't believe it," Marc said pacing the room.

"You believed Morgan could do it."

"If this is true, she is the cause of Morgan's death," he whispered as he absorbed this latest development. "I'll kill her . . ." he growled, his face black with anger.

"No! Listen to me, Marc. Rachel is gone from here. Nothing you do will bring Morgan back. Rachel will have to live with what she did for the rest of her life and I don't think she'll find any peace in that."

"I don't know if I can let her go unpunished," he said, his voice filled with anguish.

"She will not go unpunished, Marc. Believe me, sooner or later her sins will catch up with her. Come now, let us visit with your mother for a while. She seems so much better since you arrived. She will be very disappointed when you leave to rejoin your men tomorrow."

"I know, but I must return. Stuart has intensified his activities along the railroad and Mosby has most of the Union troops riding around in confusion. I'm going to teach my old friend that Yankees can bushwack too."

Chapter Twenty-two

The doctor's voice droned on and on as Morgan patiently listened to the same lecture she had endured since Jubal had carried her to this farmhouse two weeks ago. She had been sure it was the end for her. She remembered hearing the concerned voices around her, but couldn't see anyone. She had existed in a dark, foreboding world for over a week.

"All I can say is you're a mighty lucky young lady. If that bullet had been a few inches down, you and your baby would both be dead."

Morgan glanced anxiously around the room. "Please, Doctor Lane, you've told me that over and over and I've asked you not to say anything about the baby. I don't want anyone to know yet."

"Don't know how you expect to keep it secret much longer. I figure you're three months or more now."

"It's just that friends are concerned enough. They don't need to know about the baby until I'm better."

Dr. Lane didn't reply as he changed her bandage. When he finished he looked at Morgan and shook his head. "Damndest thing I've ever seen—a woman soldier," he sneered. "Women were made for having babies, not fighting wars."

"Well, see how capable I am—I'm doing both,"

Morgan answered sarcastically.

Morgan was grateful to the old doctor for saving her life, but she was really losing her patience with his sermons and was greatly relieved when Michael stuck his head in the door.

"Don't you agree, she's too mean to die?"

"You know her better than I do, son," the doctor answered without a trace of humor.

Michael looked at his sister and both stifled their laughter. "Did the wound look better today?" he asked trying to be serious.

"Better than yesterday. Leastwise, there's no infection. She'll be able to move about before too long."

Michael sat on the side of Morgan's bed holding her hand. "We're very grateful, doctor. No one gave her a chance of pulling through."

"Your sister is a mighty strong woman. Mighty strong and mighty lucky."

Michael looked at his sister's pale face and dark-circled eyes and wondered if she was really doing as well as the doctor said. "If you're through, doctor, I'll walk out with you. It looks like the patient is going to fall asleep with our visiting." He leaned over and kissed Morgan on the forehead. "I'll be back later."

Michael quietly closed the door behind them. "What's the matter with her, doctor? You keep telling us the wound is greatly improved. Why isn't she looking any better? Those dark circles around her eyes get worse every day."

The doctor busied himself putting his medical bag in order before replying. "Where are your parents, son?"

Michael's face paled. "My parents? Oh God she's not getting better . . . she's going to die."

"No, no, that's not why I asked. I just thought she would be better off with her parents right now."

"Damn! You scared the wits out of me, doctor. I'm afraid Morgan will have to do without the benefit of parents. Ours died several years ago."

"I'm sorry, son. Then you're her only relative?"

"What the hell is this all about, doctor? Is my sister all right or not?" Michael asked becoming irritated at the doctor's evasiveness.

"Calm down, young man. Your sister is recuperating from her wound very nicely, but there is another problem."

"Well for God's sake, tell me what it is. I can't stand your beating around the bush!"

The doctor fumbled with his glasses, trying to find the right words. "Your sister is . . . well, she's with child."

At first Michael felt relief that Morgan wasn't dying, but then he thought of her condition and his relief turned to anger. "Are you sure about this?"

"Of course I'm sure. She's almost four months."

"Four months," he said under his breath. "That bastard Yankee! I'll kill him . . . I'll kill the bastard!"

"Son, I don't know what you're talking about, but I think your main concern now should be for your sister. She is very weak from the wound and that is going to make it difficult for her for awhile. She'll need plenty of rest, fresh air and good food. That's why I was hoping your parents were nearby and could take care of her. I'm just not sure she's strong enough to carry this child."

"I'll see that she gets rest, doctor. She has plenty of friends who are very concerned for her and will help me."

"I'll be back tomorrow to look in on her. She's not going to be very happy when she learns I told you about the baby."

"It's all right, doctor. I'll handle my sister. I appreciate your confiding in me."

When the doctor left Michael collapsed in a chair wondering what they were going to do. His despair turned to anger as he thought of the Yankee who had violated his sister. It had to have been rape. Morgan would never let anyone close to her, but why hadn't she told him? He would have killed the bastard! He thought of his premonition. He had seen Riordan deeply involved in their lives. Was this what his dream had meant?

"Would you look what I have," Jubal shouted as he charged into the room. "The old man we helped sent a hog for us. 'Tis enough meat to last until Morgan is able to travel. The saints are watching over us, Michael me boy."

"You think so, Jubal? I'd say they have deserted us completely."

"What are you saying, boy?" he asked, noticing for the first time the look of despair in Michael's eyes. "Is Morgan all right?" he asked almost in a whisper.

Seething with anger, Michael was barely able to speak. "That bastard! That Yankee bastard! He ruined her, Jubal. Her life is ruined. I promised to protect her and look what has happened."

Jubal grabbed Michael by the shirt, shaking him violently. "What in hell are you talking about? Tell me what's wrong with her?"

"She is pregnant! She's going to have that Yankee's baby," Michael shouted.

Jubal shoved Michael away from him. "For God's sake, boy, I thought she was dying. Don't be scaring me like that."

"You don't think this is serious?" Michael asked, not believing Jubal's reaction.

"Of course it's serious, but you are carrying on like a baby yourself. Marc Riordan is an honorable man. He'll do the right thing by Morgan."

"The honorable thing! We don't even know if he's alive. You said yourself you saw him shot. Besides, we don't want her with that Yankee!"

"You're forgetting that *Yankee* saved you from spending the war in prison and saved Morgan from hanging."

Michael collapsed into a chair, his head between his hands. "What about Jared Law? He's been spending a lot of time with Morgan since she returned."

"It's better that come to a halt!" Jubal sneered. "He's no good. Everyone knows he's a gambler and always needs money. He would just love to get his hands on Morgan's inheritance."

"I have to agree with you there. I personally can't stand the man, but what is Jeb going to say about Morgan and this Yankee?"

Jubal had been wondering the same thing, but hadn't said it. "He'll not be happy, but he'll want what is best for Morgan."

Jubal sat on the bed facing Morgan as she picked at

her food while Michael paced the room sipping from a cup of coffee.

"I'm just not very hungry, Jubal. It's wonderful that you were able to get such food, but I just can't eat."

"You're going to need to eat . . . for you and the baby."

Michael dropped the cup he held to his mouth, letting it crash to the floor.

Morgan looked at Jubal as if he had struck her. "How did you know?"

"When would you be planning to tell us, girl?"

"I was going to when the time was right. Besides, this is my problem, not yours."

Jubal took her hand in his. "This won't be a problem if you just use your head."

"What is that supposed to mean?"

"Just that we'll send word to Riordan that you are expecting his child."

Morgan looked from Jubal to her brother in disbelief. "No! Absolutely not! How could you think I would allow you to send word to that bastard," she asked, tears welling up in her eyes.

"He is the father?" Jubal asked wondering at Morgan's reaction.

"Of course he is the father," Morgan answered angrily. "But, you're forgetting the way he talked to me at Brandy Station. I went there to tell him of the child, but now he will never know of it."

"It's not right to deprive the man of a child, girl. He has a right to know."

"No, no," Morgan began to sob. "I will not have him forced to marry me because I carry a child. I can't do that. You must see I can't," she cried.

"Aye, girl, I can see that. Calm yourself now. We'll work something out."

"What will we do, Jubal?" Michael asked. "She will be ruined if she tried to raise a child without a father. He will be a bastard."

"Shut up, Michael! You're only upsetting your sister. She needs you to act like a man."

"Please, both of you, just give me time to think and work things out. I don't want everyone arguing about this. I need the two of you."

Michael's face suddenly lit up. "Jubal! Jubal, you can marry Morgan."

"No! I cannot!" Jubal exclaimed.

Michael's expression changed to anger. "What in hell is wrong with you? You've been in love with Morgan all your life."

Jubal looked at Morgan, his eyes begging for understanding. "I cannot, Morgan," he whispered.

"What kind of a fool are you?" Michael persisted. "You're as bad as the Yankee who did this. I've always thought of you as a brother, but you won't even help us at a time like this."

"Stop it, Michael! Stop it right now. You should know Jubal has good reason for not marrying me."

"What reason? What possible reason when I know he loves you."

Morgan took Jubal's big hand in hers. "He is our brother."

The silence was deafening as Michael stared at the two of them. "You're lying! I don't know why, but you're lying. Father would never have . . ."

"Michael, your father did not cheat on your mother," Jubal interrupted seeing the hurt on his friend's face. "Your father met my mother before he left Ireland. He didn't know anything about me until he came back to Ireland on a trip. At that time he had already married your mother."

"Morgan can believe this cock-and-bull story if she wants, but not me. I know father would have told me if it were true," Michael shouted as he stormed from the room.

Jubal started to go after him, but Morgan stopped him. "Give him time to think this out, Jubal. This had to be quite a shock to him."

"Aye, I never meant for either of you to know."

"I suspected a long time ago, Jubal. You confirmed my suspicions when you came back after Daddy was killed. I knew he must have said more to you when he was dying than to take care of us. You were suddenly so different, so aloof. Besides, I always thought it strange that you looked so much like Daddy."

"Aye, you're right, girl. He told me I was his son and how it came to be. At first I was angry, but then I realized how good he had been to my mother and me. I'd still be a potato farmer in Ireland if it hadn't been for him. He educated me and treated me like one of his own. He even sent my mother a yearly sum of money from the day he found out about me 'till his dying day."

It broke Morgan's heart seeing the pain in Jubal's eyes. "I'm sorry father didn't tell us when we were children, Jubal."

"It was right he didn't. You can accept it now, but you might not have then. Michael can't accept it even now," he said as his eyes filled with tears.

"He will when he has time to think," Morgan said

351

touching his face. "He will be as happy as I am to acknowledge your birthright."

"I want nothing, Morgan! What your father left is yours and Michael's. I will make my own way when this war is over."

"Michael and I need you, Jubal. We have always depended on you. Please don't think you have to go away."

"What you need is a husband and a father for your babe. I canna' be that, but Marc Riordan can. He will take care of you, Morgan."

Morgan's eyes flashed angrily. "How can you bring that up again? I will not listen to it. I tell you I will not marry the man. He wants no part of me, nor I him. Jared Law has asked me to marry him and perhaps I will."

"Sweet Jesus, Morgan, you canna' be serious. Did that wound dull your brain? He's no good and you know it. How many times have you told me you dinna' like the man?"

"Things change, Jubal. He knows I am with child, but he still wants to marry me. He can't be so bad if he would accept this child as his own."

"Hah! He wants your money, girl. He cares little if he has to take another man's bastard to get it."

Morgan turned away, trying to hide her hurt. "It is time you leave, Jubal. There is no sense in our discussing this. I have made up my mind. I will marry Jared Law."

"Aye, go ahead and you will regret that decision 'till your dying day."

Jubal's relationship with Michael was strained the

first week after discovering they were brothers, but Michael seemed to be accepting it as time went on. Jubal wondered if the common dislike they felt for Jared Law had anything to do with things improving between them. It seemed the quicker Morgan recovered, the pushier Jared became about setting their wedding date. No matter how often Morgan insisted she knew what she was doing, Jubal was sure she wished for a miracle to save her from her own decision.

Jubal whipped the horses to a faster pace as he remembered Stuart waiting for him. Jeb had insisted Morgan be moved to a house away from the fighting and had granted him and Michael leave to stay with her until her wedding took place in two weeks.

Jubal gritted his teeth in anger as he thought of Morgan marrying the slick-talking gambler. He still had a good mind to go for Riordan. The man should at least have the opportunity to decide if he wanted his child. Morgan wasn't being fair. "Damn it, she's just not thinking straight!" Jubal said aloud as he whipped the team of horses to breakneck speed.

Stuart's cavalry and Jared Law, who insisted on joining them, escorted the wagon carrying Morgan to a palatial country home overlooking the winding Rapidan River. It was a well secluded spot and one of the few left untouched since the beginning of the war.

With Michael's assistance, Morgan walked to the house from the carriage. She was greeted by the Winfields, who were overwhelmed to have been chosen by the famous Jeb Stuart to host his friend.

Morgan was exhausted and didn't argue when Michael suggested she retire and take her evening meal in bed. She said a tearful goodbye to Stuart and Jared Law before being shown to a beautiful suite of rooms with a long balcony overlooking the river.

Morgan undressed and sat on the edge of the bed. She suddenly felt overwhelmed by her predicament, giving in to the tears she had been holding back for so long; tears for Marc, for her child and for herself.

Jeb Stuart and his men enjoyed a light meal before preparing to depart. Jubal was talking with Jeb while he saddled his horse when Jared Law interrupted.

"I don't really see the need for Captain Kelly to stay here, General Stuart. Surely these fine people are able to take care of Miss Fitzgerald."

Stuart's expression blackened. "Do you question my judgment, *Lieutenant* Law?"

"Of course not, sir, " Jared stuttered. "I was just thinking of the support we need."

"You let me worry about that, lieutenant!" Stuart said turning his back on the man and shaking hands with Kelly. "Take care of her, Jubal. I'll try to swing by here in a week or so."

Stuart mounted and waved his men forward, but Jared Law lagged behind. "Don't think I don't know what's going on, Kelly."

"And what might that be meaning, lieutenant?"

"I know you had hoped to marry Miss Fitzgerald, but she chose me. If you think your hanging around here is going to change her mind, you're mistaken."

"Aye, you're right about one thing, Law. I plan to change her mind while she's here. Because you'll have to kill me before I let you lay a hand on her."

354

"You're a little late, captain, since Morgan carries my child."

"You lying bastard! I know whose child Morgan carries and it isn't yours," Jubal said as he moved menacingly toward Law. "I'm going to kill you with my bare hands and have done with it."

Jared Law backed away, his face white with fear as Kelly towered over him. Suddenly he broke into a run, heading for his waiting horse. He leaped into the saddle and galloped a few feet away. "We haven't finished, Kelly. I'll be back."

"Get out of here while you still can, you sniveling coward!"

Michael joined Jubal as he watched Jared Law disappear in a cloud of dust. "What was that all about? I could hear the two of you from the house."

"Perhaps I overstepped my bounds, but I told Jared Law that the only way he was going to marry Morgan was over my dead body."

Michael let out a long whistle. "Morgan is not going to like it. She is planning to have a wedding in two weeks."

"Aye, she'll have a wedding, but it won't be to Jared Law."

Michael's eyes widened. "What are you saying, Jubal?"

"I'm saying the father of that babe deserves to know about it. I'm going to find Marc Riordan."

Chapter Twenty-three

Jubal Kelly spent a week traveling the Federal lines trying to learn something of Marc Riordan's where-abouts. Dressed in his merchant's garb he was able to move from one camp to another without raising suspicion. By the time he reached Manassas he was beginning to have a sinking feeling he wouldn't find Riordan in time to stop Morgan's wedding.

At Cub Run, in the last light of day, he came upon a group of Federal soldiers roasting a plump chicken over their fire.

"Could you be sparing a cup of coffee, lads?"

"Sure, dismount and pull up a rock. We got plenty to spare."

"That's mighty generous of you. I've come a long way since my last meal," Kelly said as he tied his horse to a limb.

The soldier who had offered the food handed Jubal a tin cup filled with steaming coffee. "What's a finely dressed gent like you doing riding around in the middle of the battle lines."

"I'm looking for a friend. An officer named Marc Riordan."

The soldier stopped drinking and looked across his cup at Jubal. "Now why would you be looking for Colonel Riordan?"

"Ah, you know him?"

"Yeah, I know him."

"Would you be knowing where I can find him?"

"Maybe," the soldier said still studying Kelly suspiciously. "What's your name, Irishman?"

"Kelly, Jubal Kelly."

The soldier stuck out his hand. "I'm Doc Webster. Sit down and have a bite to eat while you tell me why you're looking for Marc Riordan."

Jubal chewed on a hunk of chicken as he told the soldier how a good friend of Riordan's was very sick and wanted to see him and how he had been going from camp to camp trying to get some information on Riordan's whereabouts—that for a time he thought Riordan might be dead.

The soldier sat and listened without saying a word until Jubal had finished. "What's this friend's name, Kelly?"

"I'm not sure Riordan would be wanting me to say."

"It couldn't possibly be Morgan Fitzgerald?"

Jubal was stunned for a moment. He glanced around to see who might be listening, but their companions were busy playing cards.

Jubal nervously touched his gun, wondering if he was going to have to fight his way out of this camp. "Why would you be thinking this friend was Morgan Fitzgerald?"

Doc Webster smiled. "Well, my friend, you stumbled onto one of Riordan's units. I was with him at Brandy Station when he thought he saw her killed. He told me the whole story, including the fact that a big Irishman was her companion. Now I figure if you were a merchant, you wouldn't know anyone that Riordan knew. If you were a Union soldier you would have gone through other channels to find him. My guess is that you're one of Morgan Fitzgerald's officers and she's still alive."

"Why don't we let Colonel Riordan decide my position here," Jubal stated nervously. "If you'll just tell me where I can find him he can straighten this whole thing out."

Webster rubbed his chin in thought. "Colonel Riordan was seriously injured at Brandy Station. He's been in Washington recuperating for the last two weeks."

Jubal felt as if he had been struck. There was no way to get to Washington and back in time to stop Morgan's wedding.

"Don't look so glum, Irishman. We're here to meet Colonel Riordan. He's due before morning."

"I'm mighty glad to hear that. I'm afraid my friend's time is running out."

"It's that bad?"

"Aye, it's that bad."

Jubal and Doc sat around the campfire discussing the battle at Brandy Station, each amazed that they had fought so viciously against each other and were now sharing a bottle of whiskey like old friends.

Into the night and early morning the two men talked. The sky was a pale pink when the picket announced riders approaching.

Marc Riordan and two other soldiers rode into the camp area and dismounted. Riordan was engrossed in greeting his men when he spotted Jubal. He looked from Webster to Jubal saying nothing for a moment.

"My God, man! What are you doing here?" he said shaking hands with the Irishman.

"I'll leave you two alone," Doc said. "Let me know

if I can be of any help."

Marc looked at Jubal for some explanation. "What's going on, Jubal? How did you manage to ride into this camp without being taken prisoner?"

"It's a long story, colonel. I'll explain everything."

Marc slapped him on the back. "Well, no matter, I'm glad to see you. I had planned to try to find you . . . to find out where . . . where Morgan is buried," he said trying to control his shaky voice.

Jubal looked stunned. "Buried? It would take more than a Yankee to put that lady in the ground!"

Marc grabbed Jubal by the front of his jacket and shoved him against a tree. "If this is your idea of a joke, it's a very poor one!"

"Easy, Riordan. I'm telling you, Morgan is alive. She was badly wounded, but she is recuperating at a hideaway on the Rapidan River."

Marc released his hold on Jubal and slumped to the ground by the fire. He stared off into the distance, unable to say anything for a long time. When he finally looked up at Jubal he struggled to speak. "I saw her shot . . . all this time I thought she was dead."

"Aye, I'm sorry you had to go through that. We dinna' think she was going to make it for awhile, but she is on the mend now. Except for . . ."

"What is it, Jubal? What's wrong?"

"I wish there were an easy way to be telling you, but . . . Morgan is expecting your child."

"My God! A child," Marc said his face lighting up. "I'll be damned, Jubal. I'm going to be a father! That's wonderful. How long will it take us to get to her? I don't want to keep her waiting."

"Riordan, there is something I need to explain."

"Can't it wait, Jubal? I've got to explain to my men why I'm leaving again."

"No, Riordan, we need to talk now," he said handing Marc the bottle of whiskey he had shared with Doc.

"I have a feeling I'm going to need this from the tone of your voice. Start talking, Jubal. You have my undivided attention."

"Morgan does not know I'm here. To be honest, she insisted you not be told about the babe."

"Not be told about my own child?" Marc asked in disbelief.

"Aye, tis a sad affair, but you must remember your last encounter with Morgan was anything but friendly. She was there to tell you about the babe, but you verbally attacked her before she could say a word."

"God, that day will haunt me for the rest of my life. If I could take those words back, I would, Jubal. I'll just have to convince Morgan I'm sorry. Surely since she's pregnant with my child she'll be understanding."

"Aye, but there's a little more to it, lad. Morgan is marrying Jared Law day after tomorrow."

"Marrying?' Marc asked stunned. "Who in hell is Jared Law?"

"He's a lieutenant with Fitzhugh's Cavalry. He's also a lying, money-hungry coward."

"I don't give a damn what he is! What I want to know is why is Morgan marrying him?"

"I dinna' know, lad. I guess she thinks she needs a father for the babe."

"The baby has a father!" Marc answered angrily. "This is incredible! What could she possibly be thinking about. I'll break her damned neck!"

Morgan pressed her face against the glass of the window and watched the rain beat relentlessly on the balcony. Another omen, she thought. The weather had been beautiful until today; her wedding day. Added to that, Jubal had gone off on what he said was a mission and had not returned for her wedding. She knew he disliked Jared, but she didn't think he would desert her at at time like this.

She walked back to the bed and picked up the dress Jeb had sent by messenger. The note read that he just happened to be at a dressmaker's shop in Frederick, Maryland and spotted it, knowing right away it was meant for Morgan.

She threw the dress back on the bed. It was hypocritical, she thought. What am I doing wearing white when I am carrying a child? Not even the child of the man I am marrying!

Michael slowly climbed the stairs, feeling as though his feet were made of lead. He dreaded the next few hours. If there were only some way to stop things, but how? Jubal had gone off to find Riordan and hadn't been heard from since. Jared Law had been here since last night and had already asked to borrow money from him so he could buy his bride a wedding gift. His very presence made Michael's blood boil. He had the nerve to insist on seeing Morgan when he arrived and afterward Michael had heard her crying herself to sleep. How could she possibly pretend to want to go through with this farce?

He lightly knocked on the door and entered to find Morgan tearful again. "For God's sake, Morgan," he said taking her in his arms. "Why are you going through with this?"

Morgan pulled away from her brother's embrace. "That's a foolish question for you to ask," she countered harshly. "You were the one who said my child would be a bastard without a father."

Immediately Morgan regretted her harsh words. "Oh, Michael, I'm so sorry. Now I'm lashing out at you. I have no one but myself to blame for the predicament I'm in."

"I know you regret your decision to marry Jared. Tell him before it's too late."

"It's already too late, Michael. I have accepted Jared's proposal and I plan to go through with the marriage. I don't really think he'll stay around long to care for a wife and baby. He's just not the type, but at least he'll give my baby a name. I've sworn to him that no one will every know the child is not his."

"The price is too high, Morgan. There must be another way."

"It's high, my dear brother, but I am the one who has to pay it. Now, please leave. I must start getting dressed. I don't want to keep Jared waiting."

Michael left her room, shocked at the coldness of her attitude. He just couldn't let her go through with this. Jubal had said the marriage would take place over his dead body. He shuddered, wondering if Jubal had been killed or taken prisoner while trying to find Riordan. Damn, this was his brother he was thinking about and if Jubal had been so violently opposed to their sister's marriage then it was now up to him to stop it. He would have to challenge Jared Law to a duel. He stopped in his tracks. Would Morgan ever forgive him? No matter, it was a chance he would have to take. He wondered how fast a gun Jared Law was as he walked toward the stables where Jared was saddling his horse.

"Where are you heading, Law? It's only a couple of hours until the wedding."

"I guess I'm just a little nervous. I thought I'd take a ride to calm my nerves."

"Good idea. I'll ride with you."

The two men rode through the woods until they came to a clearing along the river. Michael pulled up alongside of Jared.

"Get off your horse, Law!"

"What in hell is this all about?" Jared asked seeing Michael's gun pointing at him.

"I'm willing to give you a fighting chance, but if you choose not to get off your horse, I'll shoot you where you sit."

Jared dismounted, never taking his eyes off Michael. "You're a fool, Fitzgerald. I was willing to marry that tramp of a sister of yours to give her bastard a name, but you can forget that now."

Michael laughed. "You still don't get the meaning of this situation, do you, Law? You're even stupider than I thought."

Michael climbed down from his horse and shoved Jared forward. "Start walking, fool. When I count to ten, turn and shoot."

"No, no, Fitzgerald. Just let me get on my horse and I'll ride away. I swear it. I'm not very good with a gun . . . I don't stand a chance. You've got no reason to shoot me."

Michael was trying to decide what to do when he heard riders coming up fast behind them.

"I knew I could count on my little brother to handle things while I was gone," Jubal shouted.

"You took your damn good time getting back here, Jubal. I was going to have to kill him to stop the wedding," Michael answered, a smile spreading across his face.

"Aye, it took longer than I figured to find this fellow," Jubal said, looking toward Marc. "Michael, I want you to shake hands with Marc Riordan. He's to be our brother-in-law."

Michael looked at the rider dressed in jeans, a blue fringed shirt and western style hat and could see why his sister had been attracted to the man. His brilliant blue eyes smiled warmly as he held out his hand to Michael.

"I'm glad you're here, Riordan. I didn't relish the idea of killing this snake, but I didn't know what else to do."

"I know how to get rid of him," Jubal said smiling, motioning Michael and Marc away from the silent Jared Law.

"Okay Jubal, tell me how to get rid of this joker without bringing the Confederate army down around me?"

Jubal laughed. "Aye, I'll tell you," he said pulling a leather pouch from around his waist. "Money is the answer. What better way to sour Morgan on him than if she finds out he accepted money to leave."

"Your idea has possibilities, Jubal, but Morgan is my woman and I'll take care of whatever Law requires to be cooperative."

Jubal slapped Marc on the back. "I knew I dinna' misjudge you, Yankee. Morgan is going to be lucky to have you for her husband."

"Let's hope Morgan will think so."

Jubal showed Marc to Morgan's bedroom door and then left. Marc quietly opened the door and found Morgan on the balcony already dressed in her wedding gown. He watched her unnoticed as she stared off into the distance.

God, he had forgotten how beautiful she was. Perhaps a little pale, but that only seemed to exaggerate the brightness of her eyes. He smiled as he noticed the slight roundness of her stomach.

She suddenly turned and faced him, letting the perfume bottle she held in her hands crash to the floor.

"Hello, Morgan."

"What are you doing here?" she asked, barely able to speak.

"I've come to take you away with me."

"You're crazy, Marc Riordan. Haven't you heard, this is my wedding day?" she said turning her back to him.

Marc grabbed her by the shoulders and turned her to him. "How can you stand there with my child growing inside of you and talk about marrying another man?"

"Would you prefer I raise it in disgrace, without a name?"

"My child will carry only my name, Morgan," he answered, his tone softening as he noticed the tears in her eyes.

"And how do you propose that, sir?"

"I believe it is the custom for a woman to take her husband's name."

"You can't be serious?"

"I'm very serious, Morgan. I will not have you marrying anyone else carrying my child. We will be married and you'll go back to Washington to wait for me."

Morgan laughed bitterly. "Your fiancee would just love that. Besides, it's a little late for this show of honor. Too much has happened between us. I certainly wouldn't want to soil your family any more than I already have."

Marc reached out and pulled her to him. "You are carrying my child Morgan. That's the only thing that is important. The child will need both of us. This war has made us do and say things we didn't mean. Now we have a chance to make some good come from it."

"What about love?" she asked angrily. "We wouldn't be doing this child any favor by bringing him into a family without love. Jared Law wants to marry me knowing that I carry another man's child. That is love, Marc. Not the kind of love I could expect from you—who bedded me while you were engaged to another."

"You're not being fair, Morgan. That just happened, and afterward I intended to marry you."

Morgan couldn't bear the closeness of him any longer. She kept reminding herself he was only there for the child, not for her. But God, every time she looked into those blue eyes she was tempted to give in. He was so handsome. Even the new scar at his temple gave him a dimension of mystery. Oh damn, why did she want to reach out and run her fingers through his curly black hair. Remember his words, Morgan. He called you a whore—the lowliest whore.

She forced herself to walk away from him, but he followed her, so close she could feel his warm breath on her shoulder.

"Go away. If you pretend to care anything for this child, give it a chance to have some happiness."

"You can't make me believe you love this man," he said kissing the back of her neck. "Look at me and tell me you love him."

Morgan turned and angrily shoved him away. "Why don't you just get yourself a whore and save us both a lot of trouble?"

Marc struggled to control his anger. He had known it wasn't going to be easy, but she was really pushing him to the limit. "I didn't want a whore, Morgan. I wanted you," he said running his thumb along her jawline.

"Strange, the last time we met I didn't get that impression," she retorted sarcastically.

"Morgan, Morgan, what do I have to say to make you forgive me? I made a terrible mistake not believing in you. I'm sorry."

"It matters little whether I forgive you or not. Jared loves me and I have promised to marry him."

Marc grabbed her by the shoulders, forcing her to face him. "Tell me his touch brings you alive. Tell me his kisses awaken a fire in you, turning you into a wild, passionate woman. You love me and I will never let you marry another. I'll see you in hell before I'd let you marry that bastard!"

The cold, hard finality of Marc's voice sent shivers down her spine, but her stubbornness persisted.

"I hate everything you stand for. Our child wouldn't stand a chance with the differences between us. Now go. I have made my decision."

Marc tightened his grip on Morgan's shoulders, unwillingly bruising her fair skin. "You have no decision to make, Morgan. Jared Law eagerly accepted my money and has left you, and if that doesn't convince you that I'm serious, I have also instructed my men to hold Jubal Kelly until they hear from me. If they don't get word by nightfall, he'll be hung."

Morgan backed away, her eyes wide in disbelief. "Oh God, how I hate you!"

"The feeling is mutual, my dear. Now finish getting dressed. You are to be downstairs for the ceremony at the appointed time. If you give even the slightest hint this wasn't your idea, your friend will die.'

Marc turned to leave, but Morgan grabbed his arm. "Please, Marc, this will never work. Your family and friends will never accept me. If you want to see the child that will be fine. I'll even let him know that you are his father."

"That's very decent of you, Morgan, but not necessary. I will be with him to tell him myself. Now finish getting ready. I don't want to be kept waiting."

"Damn you to hell, Marc Riordan! I'll go with you, but you'll regret the day you forced your will on me," Morgan screamed as she picked up a vase and threw it as Marc ducked out the door.

Marc stormed into the room where Jubal and Michael waited and poured himself a stiff drink before sinking into a chair. "Bitch," he swore under his breath.

"What happened?" Jubal asked.

"I went to her, heart in hand, but she wanted my head on a platter!"

Jubal roared with laughter. "Our girl hasn't let this affair dull her. She's still full of spunk."

"You can call it spunk if you want. I call it damn, stubborn pride!"

"Did you tell her you loved her, lad?"

"I don't know. She put me on the defensive right away. I don't remember what I said."

"She is going to marry you?" Michael asked with a worried look on his face.

"Yes, but I had to use our last plan. She thinks my men are holding Jubal and will hang him if she doesn't go through with the marriage."

"Damn, I had hoped it wouldn't come to that," Michael said slamming his fist on the table.

"When we are on our way to Washington, I'll tell her the truth."

"I wouldna' like to be in your shoes, lad," Jubal said laughing. "Dinna' turn your back on her."

"I've always known better than to do that, Jubal. But, I figure anything worth having is worth fighting for."

Chapter Twenty-four

Marcus Leigh Riordan and Morgana Lacey Fitzgerald were married in the library at the Winfield house with a small group of Morgan's friends in attendance. All present thought it was a fairy-tale wedding. What could be more romantic than the bride's true love showing up to stop her from marrying someone else.

The day had started out cold and dreary, but as Michael led his sister up the aisle, the sun appeared, bathing everything in its warm, golden glow.

Morgan had spoken her vows softly and mechanically, looking only at the minister while Marc had spoken out for all to hear and looked only at his beautiful, tear-dimmed bride.

Jubal had watched the ceremony from an alcove off the library where he was sure he wouldn't be seen. He was glad he wasn't in view, because he wouldn't have wanted anyone to see how much this wedding affected him. He just hoped and prayed pride would not keep Morgan from admitting her love for Marc.

He watched from an upstairs window as the couple prepared to leave. He held his breath as Jeb Stuart spoke to the couple with a scowl on his bearded face, but then he turned and moved away from the carriage. Jeb had been strongly against Morgan's marriage to Riordan, but knowing how Michael and Jubal felt, he finally agreed to go along with their plan. His only words to Riordan were that if he ever did anything to make Morgan unhappy he would personally hunt him down and kill him. Riordan hadn't said anything for a moment and then his only comment was that he liked the general.

Jubal watched as Michael kissed his sister and said a few words to Riordan. She didn't wave or look back as the carriage slowly pulled away from the front of the house.

Neither said a word as the small black carriage with the black stallion tied behind careened over the muddy ground. They traveled empty back roads, past deserted farms and empty fields. Occasionally Marc would ask her if she was all right, but was rewarded with brief, noncommittal answers.

The air became colder as the sun disappeared behind the mountains. Morgan wore a forest green velvet cape over a beige wool dress, but she was still cold. She fought to control the shivers as she cast a sidewise glance at Marc and wondered why he looked so solemn.

"Are you cold, Morgan?" he asked without looking at her.

"A little."

"We'll stop for a few minutes. I have some brandy in the back that might help."

Marc brought the horse to a stop and jumped down. He held his hands up to lift Morgan from her seat, but she made no effort to get down.

"This would be a good time for you to stretch your legs, Morgan. I'll get a blanket for you while you do." Morgan's face was outlined by the soft hood of her cape and he could see the indecision as she tried to decide what to do. He fought the urge to take her in his arms and kiss her, giving her something to really be confused about, but he didn't.

She reluctantly accepted his assistance and walked off to the woods while he untied their bags. She had to admit it felt good to be walking for a few minutes. She had already become stiff and they had only been traveling for a few hours. She wondered briefly where they would stay the night, but quickly put that unpleasant thought from her mind.

"Are you all right?" Marc called from the carriage.

"Of course I'm all right. I'm not some helpless woman."

"Of course, how could I have forgotten?" he answered sarcastically.

He held out his hand to assist her into the carriage but she ignored it and clumsily climbed in, not noticing the smile on her husband's face as he tucked the blanket around her legs.

They traveled for a few more hours before a word was spoken between them. Marc knew she was terribly uncomfortable and he knew he was going to have to be more considerate of her needs. She had been shifting back and forth on the seat for the last hour, but had not said a word.

"We'll be stopping soon, Morgan. I don't want you to get too tired."

"How considerate of you. I suppose we'll be staying the night in a run-down barn or stable." she replied sarcastically.

"As much as those memories are dear to me, no, my pet, I've made other arrangements for your comfort. I have some friends nearby who are expecting us."

Morgan's head snapped around. "You are very sure of yourself."

"Of course, my love. I knew you would never refuse my proposal."

"No, not when you were holding Jubal prisoner."

"Jubal has never been held prisoner, Morgan. I only told you that to make you agree to the marriage."

Morgan was too angry for words. She had had a feeling he had lied to her, but then when Jubal hadn't returned, she assumed it was the truth. She stared off to the side of the road, seriously considering throwing herself off the carriage. No, you'd only hurt yourself and the baby, she told herself.

They rode on in silence until they pulled onto a tree-lined drive.

"I hope this isn't another of your whore-houses," she said.

"These are my friends, Morgan. They took care of me when I was wounded and I expect you to treat them decently."

Morgan said nothing as the carriage pulled up in front of the large house and stopped. A soldier rushed out to meet them, leaving a young blonde to follow behind. Morgan couldn't take her eyes off the girl, wondering what her relationship was to Marc as he kissed her affectionately. He seemed to suddenly remember her sitting in the carriage and pulled the girl back with him.

"Doc, Katie, this is my wife, Morgan. Morgan these are my dear friends who brought me through a very bad time."

Morgan barely had time to nod before the soldier had her out of the carriage and on her way into the house. She glanced back over her shoulder to see the girl standing with Marc as he took their bags off the carriage.

"Was the trip very hard on you, Morgan? I know Marc was concerned he wouldn't be able to get a carriage to travel in. I'm glad to see he did. I was concerned about his traveling too long on horseback, but he would have been furious if I had suggested he wasn't well enough to travel."

"I didn't realize his injuries were that serious. I noticed the scar on his head, but . . . ."

"That sounds like Marc. He would just as soon no one knew about his problems. That scar on his head was minor. He was trampled by a horse which broke most of his ribs on the left side. It was touch and go there for a while and all the time the poor fellow thought you were dead."

"What's this, Doc? Are you boring my wife to death?" Marc asked from the doorway.

Doc laughed. "I hope not, Marc. At least she hasn't told me to shut up."

Marc helped Morgan off with her cape revealing the plain beige traveling dress she had chosen to wear. He had wondered why she tried to hide her lovely figure, but then smiled as he realized she was probably trying to discourage his attention.

"I know you must be tired, Mrs. Riordan. Would you like to wash up before having tea?"

Morgan followed Katie out while Doc poured brandy for them.

"Did you have any problems, Marc?"

"Not with the groom. For two hundred dollars he took off like a scared rabbit. Morgan was a different story. I had to tell her I was holding Jubal and if she didn't go through with the marriage he would be hung."

"My God, she really is stubborn."

"Irish pride, my friend. Don't ever get mixed up with an Irish Rebel. By the way I met General Jeb Stuart. He's quite a commanding figure."

"You don't mean he knew who you were and went along with this whole thing?"

"Well, he threatened me with my life if he ever heard I mistreated Morgan, but yes, he went along with it. I have to admit, for all his gruffness, I liked him. I believe he meant what he said. He would probably hunt me down if I ever mistreated Morgan, but I respect him for that. I know he is only concerned for her well-being."

"Isn't it strange. You sound as if you liked the man and he's your sworn enemy. I felt the same way about Jubal Kelly."

"Ah, Jubal. He's one in a million. I wish I had a whole regiment like him. Now tell me, what do you think of my bride?"

"She's a beauty, Marc. You're going to have a time keeping the wolves from your door."

"Just as long as I can keep the authorities from my door."

Doc looked surprised. "Surely no one would suspect your wife to be Morgan Fitzgerald, the Rebel guerrilla."

"I know a few people who would gladly turn her in. The only thing stopping them are my threats."

"Well, things are starting to go our way, so maybe this war will be over soon."

"I wonder if my war will ever be over," Marc mumbled to himself.

"Here we are, gentlemen," Katie said as the two women entered. "I trust you were able to entertain yourselves while we were away."

"It was terrible while you were gone, Katie my sweet," Doc kidded, hugging her affectionately.

"Oh, Gene, you are such a tease, but don't stop. I've missed your flattery these past few weeks."

Morgan watched her husband join in the jesting and felt embarrassed at being an outsider. Marc quickly sensed the awkwardness for her and moved to her side. "Are you all right, Morgan?"

"I'm very tired. If I could just . . ."

"Oh, Mrs. Riordan, how thoughtless of me. Of course you would like to lie down for a while. If you would like, I'll have your meal sent up later."

"Please don't go to any trouble. I'm not really hungry."

"Morgan and I will both take our meal in our room if it isn't too much trouble," Marc interjected.

Morgan couldn't help but notice the disappointed look in Katie's eyes. "Oh course; I'm just not thinking, Marc. This is your wedding night. Of course I'll have your meals sent up. You have the same room you had when you were here before. The one right next to mine. I hope that will be satisfactory."

Morgan didn't miss the reference to Marc's room being next to Katie's, but she was more concerned with the fact that she was expected to share a room with him. Before she had a chance to protest he had her by the arm leading her up the stairs.

"What do you think you're doing?" she asked

376

pulling away from him.

"Don't cause a scene, Morgan. We're husband and wife and are expected to share a room."

"I agreed to this farce of a marriage, but said nothing about sharing a room with you."

Marc turned her face up to his. "I remember a time you didn't mind sharing a room with me."

Morgan angrily pulled away. "That was before I knew what you were really like!"

"All right, Morgan. I won't force my company on you. I hope you sleep well."

Morgan was amazed that he gave up so easily —amazed, but relieved. She wondered if he would always be as easily handled.

Morgan woke to the morning's light streaming across her bed. She stretched lazily, before realizing she was not alone in the room. Marc stood at the window looking out, unaware she was awake.

She watched him unobserved as he stared off into the distance. His legs were slightly apart and his tall frame and wide shoulders blocked most of the sunlight. She felt her heart skip a beat and cursed herself for not being able to control her feelings where he was concerned. He didn't care anything for her, only the child. They had once professed words of love, but then he had accused her of . . . forget it, Morgan. Don't dwell on it. It's not important.

Marc turned and realized she was awake. "Good morning, Mrs. Riordan. Are you well this morning?"

"Quite well. What time is it?"

"Almost ten."

"I had no idea it was so late. You should have awakened me."

"I thought you must need the rest. We can leave for Washington in the morning."

The thought of another day's leisure before traveling was very appealing to Morgan, but she didn't want Marc to know it. Last night was the first good night's sleep she'd had since being wounded.

"I brought you some tea and rolls. Are you hungry?"

"A little," she answered, wondering why he was being so thoughtful.

Marc carried the tray to the bed and sat facing her. He slowly spread jam on a roll and poured her tea.

"Why are you doing this?"

"Why am I doing what?"

"You know very well what I am talking about. Just why the sudden kindness? You don't care anything for me. All you care about is the child."

"That's not true, Morgan. My feelings toward you haven't changed at all. You forget, I wasn't the one about to marry another person."

"No, you were already engaged!"

"Damn it, Morgan," he said moving away from the bed. "Are we going to do anything but fight?"

"Not if I can help it, Marc Riordan. You took me away from my loved ones by pretending to hold Jubal prisoner, and I will never forgive you. I will take great delight in making you miserable!"

Marc stared down at her, his eyes flashing with anger. "Two can play at that game, my pet."

Morgan watched Mark leave before taking a bite of the roll he had jellied. She felt very smug, but only for a moment. Suddenly she lost her appetite and pushed the tray away. Was this what she wanted—to make him miserable? Tears flowed freely down her cheeks.

"Damn! Why can't I hate him?" she sobbed.

Marc stormed into the room where Katie and Doc sat and poured a large drink.

"It's a little early to be drinking, my friend. How about a cup of tea?"

"No! I need a drink!"

"You knew it wouldn't be easy, Marc. Just give it a little more time."

"That's all I've done since I met her. When is the fighting and bitterness going to stop? I don't want this child to think his mother and father hate each other."

"Come on now, Marc. Things will be better before long."

"I don't think so, Doc. I really don't think so," he said staring into the glass of dark liquid. "I'm going for a ride. I'll be back later."

"Marc, be careful!" Doc yelled as Marc left the room. "There are still gray troops around here."

Gene started up the stairs. "I'm going to talk to her, Katie. Maybe I can convince her she's being very foolish."

"No, Gene, you'll only make things worse. She must have reason to be so bitter. Perhaps she'd like to have a woman to talk to."

Morgan was watching Marc gallop off down the drive when Katie knocked at the door. "I thought you might like to get out for a breath of air, Mrs. Riordan. We have a garden out back that used to be quite lovely before the war. Mother would love it if she thought someone still enjoyed it."

Morgan wanted to be angry with this woman who seemed so familiar and at ease with her husband, but she found it difficult since she had only shown her kindness.

"Thank you. I think I would find that very pleasant."

"You might need your cape. It is quite cold today. At least the weather slows down the fighting."

Katie led Morgan down the stairs and through a corridor leading to double doors that opened out onto a terrace. Katie breathed deeply as they stepped out. "My husband used to say this was his favorite time of the year."

"Your husband! I didn't realize you were married."

"I'm widowed, Mrs. Riordan. My husband was killed during a skirmish in Western Virginia. He rode with Harry Gilmore."

"I know the outfit well. They are brave, fierce fighters."

"I suppose. I'm afraid I'm still bitter. We were only married a few weeks when it happened. I have been in sorry shape ever since."

"I know how you feel. I've lost both mother and father to this war."

"You're very lucky to have Marc. If it hadn't been for him, I'd probably be in an insane asylum or have killed myself by now."

Morgan faced Katie, a bewildered expression on her face. "I don't understand?"

"Gene knew how I was taking my husband's death. When Marc was wounded he brought him here, hoping I would be able to help and in doing so, it would help me. Marc thought you had been killed and he was going to take his own life . . ."

"No! I don't believe you," Morgan said backing away.

"It's very true, Mrs. Riordan. I have no reason to lie to you. I never saw a man love a woman the way he loves you. Gene kept him drugged, trying to ease the memory of you, but it didn't work. He had terrible dreams of seeing you shot. Then on the third day he was here, I walked in on him and there he sat with that silver revolver in his hand. It was at that moment I realized how precious life is. I talked him out of killing himself. I made him see you wouldn't have wanted that and while I talked, I realized I wanted to go on living too. So you see, we saved each other."

"I didn't know," Morgan whispered. "If what you say is true, why did he tell me he couldn't stand to touch me?"

"We all say things in anger we don't mean. Have you given him a chance to explain?"

"Yes . . . I don't know."

"You are a very lucky woman to have a man like Marc Riordan. I don't mind telling you I'd give anything to have him."

Morgan sat in her room staring out the window. She didn't know how long she had been there, but the sun was beginning to disappear behind the mountains. She had gone over and over what Katie had said. Was there a chance for her and Marc to find the happiness they had once briefly known. Had she been the one keeping them apart?

"No! Damn it, he was the one who had said those horrible things." She leaned back against the chair and stared down the path where Marc had disappeared. "Oh Morgan, what are you going to do? Are you going to be a shrew and drive him to another woman? Could you live with yourself knowing he is sleeping with other women, bringing them to life like . . ."

Morgan leaped to her feet. "I'll be damned if I'm going to let him make a fool of me. I'm his wife and I expect to be treated as such."

Morgan began throwing things out of her bag until she came to a deep copper dress of velvet. She held it up to her, smoothing the wrinkles as she studied it in the mirror. "Well, Jared, when you gave this to me, I'm sure you never expected it to be worn for another man, but . . ."

Morgan brushed her hair vigorously and pinned it on top of her head with soft tendrils hanging around her face and neck. Then, adorned in her low-cut dress she descended the stairs and entered the room where Katie and Gene sat with her mother and father.

Katie's father quickly came to his feet and greeted Morgan at the door. "You must be feeling better, my dear."

"Yes, thank you. I'm feeling much better," she said glancing around the room. "Has my husband not returned?"

Katie smiled knowingly. "He'll be back soon, Mrs. Riordan. Would you like a glass of sherry while we wait? We'll be having dinner shortly."

Morgan accepted the sherry, hoping it would help calm her nerves. She wasn't sure what she was going to do yet, but she knew she wasn't going to let her husband go. She had seen the rapport between Marc and Katie and didn't think it would take much for him to go to her. And, hadn't Katie said she'd give anything to have him? Well, at least she was honest.

Marc did not return for dinner. The meal passed in embarrassed silence and Morgan wished she had never come out of her room.

"I understand you will be traveling on to Washington in the morning, Mrs. Riordan," Judge Bryan said breaking the conspicuous silence.

"If my husband returns," Morgan answered. "If he doesn't, I'll be returning to my home."

"Marc is probably at our camp, Morgan. The men aren't far from here and he's been concerned about them. If he's not back soon I'll ride out."

"Thank you, Gene, but I'm sure he would be furious if he thought we were checking on him. If you would excuse me, I'll think I'll turn in. I'm not very good company tonight."

Katie looked across the table at Gene, wondering where Marc could have gone. Gene saw her look and shrugged his shoulders. "Damn poor timing for a ride."

Morgan paced the room like a caged animal. Where had he gone? Had he left her to fend for herself? No, surely not. He wanted this child or he wouldn't have gone to all the trouble of getting her back. Morgan clutched the post of the bed. What if he had been captured or killed? She jumped as she heard the sound of a horse advancing. She ran to the window and strained to see the rider. It was dark, but she could make out the obvious form of Satan's Thunder.

Morgan blew out the candle and struggled out of her clothes, throwing them in a heap on the floor. She slipped into a gossamer sheer gown that touched her skin like a breeze, then slipped into bed to wait. The room was dark except for the moonlight shining across the bed. She waited to hear his footsteps, shivering as the cool breeze stirred the curtains, casting eerie shadows on the walls.

Where was he? It had been over an hour since she heard him return. Why now did he choose to stay away from her?

She slipped off the bed and opened the door a crack. There was only silence in the big house and she wondered if Marc could have already gone to his room. As she stepped into the hall she realized she didn't know where he was staying. She knew the room next to hers was Katie's and the room at the end of the hall was . . .

Katie's door suddenly opened, throwing a stream of light into the hallway. Morgan quickly stepped back into her bedroom, but did not close the door. She felt sick as she heard Marc's voice and then saw his figure step into the hall. The candle light from the room played off his bare torso as he stood in the door laughing at something the person in the room had said.

"I'll be back in a minute. I just want to get another bottle," he whispered.

Morgan closed her door and stood leaning against it.

"Fool!" she said aloud, slamming her fist against the door. "How could you have believed that story? Marc Riordan never loved you and he certainly would never take his life for you!"

Tears ran down Morgan's face. He was only interested in the child and she was going to spend the rest of her life tolerating his indiscretions. "Oh God, why is this happening to me?"

Chapter Twenty-five

Morgan waited impatiently in the carriage while Marc spoke with Gene and Katie. She had eaten in her room and said a brief goodbye to the Bryan family before leaving, but she still had not spoken to Marc. He looked at her quizzically every now and then, but otherwise ignored her.

Katie came toward the carriage and Morgan wished she would just leave her alone. Her sweetness was disgusting under the circumstances.

"It was very nice meeting you, Mrs. Riordan. I'm sorry things didn't work out for you last night."

"Oh, but you're wrong, Mrs. Rogers. Things worked out just fine. My husband has chosen his way of life and I will have mine."

Katie's eyes widened in surprise, but before she had a chance to question Morgan, Marc was at her side.

"Well, Katie my love, you take care of yourself. I'm sure I'll be back by here before long."

"I'll look forward to that, Marc. You take care of yourself and your lovely bride."

Marc had a dark scowl on his face as they rode off. Morgan could tell he was furious, but she ignored him, studying the countryside as they rode. Finally he burst out angrily.

"Do you mind telling me why you were so rude to my friends this morning?"

"The only rudeness I saw was your actions, my dear husband," she answered nonchalantly.

"What in hell is that supposed to mean?" he asked angrily.

Morgan turned to face him, her eyes flashing furiously. "I don't like having your conquests flaunted in front of my face. If you choose to take other women, at least do it when I'm not in the same house!"

Marc grabbed her wrist angrily, barely able to control his rage. "You don't know what you're talking about," he said between gritted teeth.

"It doesn't matter," Morgan said trying to pull away from his grip.

"You have the nerve to accuse me of having an affair with my friend's girl and then you say it doesn't matter."

"I saw you coming out of her room with only your pants on. I believe you were going for another bottle, or so you said."

"What were you doing, Morgan, spying on me?"

"You overestimate your importance, Yankee."

"Really, my dear? Then how is it you know my exact words," he asked with amused insolence.

"I was . . . it doesn't matter how I know, but I certainly wasn't spying!"

Marc smiled, but said nothing. This was the first indication Morgan had shown that she still cared for him. Katie had said she thought he would see a difference, but then Morgan had been the same shrew.

He stopped the carriage when they came to a tree-lined creek and jumped down. "We'll rest here for a while. Katie packed some cheese and wine for us and I suddenly have a tremendous appetite."

Morgan reluctantly held her arms out as he offered to assist her from the carriage. He placed his hand around her waist, holding her much longer then necessary, then lowered his mouth to hers and gently kissed her. She returned the kiss for a brief moment then suddenly turned her head aside.

"What an unpredictable termagant you are. One minute you're throwing a jealous tantrum and the next you're as cold as ice."

"I was never throwing a jealous tantrum!"

"I'm going to tell you something, Morgan. I don't feel I owe you an explanation and I'll never give you another, but Gene and I shared Katie's room because it was the largest. Katie stayed downstairs in the room next to her parents."

Morgan was speechless. She had never considered the possibility that Katie hadn't been in the room. "How do I know you're telling the truth?" she said before thinking.

"You have no way of knowing, my dear wife, but don't judge others by the way you lie."

"How dare you! I don't lie!"

"Really? It seems to me you are lying to yourself when you pretend you don't care for me."

"I don't care for you. My life has been nothing but heartache since I met you."

"You're not remembering the good times, Morgan."

"How many good times were there, Marc? You could count them on one hand. One moment you would tell me you loved me, the next you were telling me that bedding the lowliest whore was better than making love to me—that the thought of touching me made you sick!"

"Oh God, Morgan, don't you know those words were said in anger. Surely you must see that."

"And you must see that my hurt has grown and festered and will not be easy to assuage."

Marc put his hands on her shoulders and pulled her close. "There, you have said it. It won't be easy, but it's not impossible."

"No! You're reading things I didn't say. This is an impossible situation. Nothing you can say or do will ease the hurt you have caused me. Jared offered me a life of ease. He would not have kept me in constant turmoil. He would not have made demands on me."

"Jared Law was a weak, crawling coward. He would not have made you feel like a woman or loved you like I do."

"No . . ." Morgan cried, holding her hands to her temples. She couldn't give in to him. He would only hurt her again. "I won't believe what you say. He was willing to overlook the fact that I carried another man's child to save my reputation. Where were you when I needed you?"

"You know damned well where I was. I thought you were dead."

"Did you bother to inquire? If you loved me like you say, I would certainly think you would have checked. I think the only reason you are here now is because of the child."

"The child is mine. I will not have another man claim it," Marc said losing his patience. He tightened his grip on her shoulders without thinking. "You are my wife and I won't tolerate having that bastard's name mentioned again! Do you understand me?" he asked shaking her.

"Yes, I understand," Morgan said trying to pull away as he dug his fingers into her shoulders. "Why must you always hurt me?" she asked, fighting the tears that threatened. "I agreed to this marriage to give my child a name, but I would rather raise it alone before putting up with your cruelty."

Marc's eyes did not leave her face, his hands still bruising her shoulders, but when he spoke again his voice was void of all anger. "I don't mean to hurt you, Morgan, but you always push me to the brink."

Suddenly Morgan gave way to tears, all the frustrations and tensions that had been building up for the past couple of months coming to the surface.

Marc pulled her into his arms. "Morgan, I'm sorry. Please forgive me."

"No, no, I don't want your sympathy," she cried as she tried to pull away. "I hate you, Marc Riordan. I hate you!"

Marc stroked her hair. "There's a very thin line between love and hate, Morgan."

"Don't you see, I can't go on like this . . . I'm being torn apart . . . you're always hurting me . . . I can't, I can't," she sobbed.

"Morgan, calm down. I promise you I won't hurt you again. Just listen to me. You can have your own room, whatever you want. Stay at my home until the child is born and then you can decide what you want to do. I swear I won't make any demands on you. I won't touch you, if that's what you want."

Morgan choked back a sob. She looked up at him, her eyes wide and glistening with tears. "Do you really mean that?"

"I swear to you, Morgan. Let's stop this fighting. It's not doing you or the baby any good. We want our child to be happy."

Morgan laid her head against his chest as he continued to stroke her hair. "When this trip is over we're going to have to start taking better care of you. You're not eating properly and you'll need lots of rest and fresh air."

"I'm getting plenty of fresh air," she said still shuddering with sobs.

Marc chuckled at her attempted humor. "I know you are, little one. Come, sit down on the bank and we'll have a bite to eat." Marc led her to an area covered with leaves and pine needles. He spread the food out before her then set about cutting her bread and cheese.

"I'm sorry about the way I acted to Katie, but I thought . . ."

"I know, Morgan," Marc said sitting down beside her. "I'll see Doc in a few days and explain."

Morgan made no move to stop Marc as he took her hand and began examining it. She felt flustered at his closeness. "You were very lucky to have had Doc with you when you were wounded."

Marc ran a finger over her palm. "Yes, I know. Do you remember that day?"

"Vividly," she answered almost in a whisper. "That was the worst battle I had been in. I remember after twenty hours in the saddle thinking I couldn't go on, yet somehow I did. It was as if everything was in a fog."

"Do you remember seeing me?"

Morgan looked away toward the creek before

answering. "Yes, in the pine grove. Your face was the last thing I remembered seeing."

Marc took her chin and gently forced her to look at him. "I lived in hell thinking you were dead, Morgan. For days all I saw was you falling from your horse, covered with blood."

"The bullet deflected off a rib, otherwise I would be dead. Jubal said I was in a coma for over a week. I don't really remember. When I came to all I felt was anger because we had been driven back. I felt a tremendous guilt because I felt if Jubal and several others hadn't stopped fighting to take me from the field they might have continued to hold."

"It's easy to win battles with hindsight, Morgan, but I don't really believe a half a dozen men could have made a difference at that point."

"Maybe not and I guess there's no sense thinking about it. It's done," Morgan said taking another bite of cheese. "This is very good cheese. We haven't been able to get any for a long time."

"I sent this to Katie's family after they helped me."

"I just don't know how you Yankees are able to go right on enjoying everything as if there wasn't a war."

Marc laughed. "I think it will be over soon, Morgan, and then everyone can get back to enjoying life."

"Perhaps it will be over soon, but things won't ever be the same for the South."

Marc cut Morgan's words off with his hand as he pushed her backward on the bank.

She kicked and struggled, finally biting his hand before he released her. "Damn you, what kind of maniac are you? One moment . . ."

391

"Be quiet, Morgan. Troops are just across the creek."

Morgan sat up and strained to see. He was right, Union troops were filing into the pines just across the creek.

"They're your troops. Why are you worried?"

"Listen to me, Morgan, they wouldn't care if I were General Grant if they've been without a woman for a while."

"My God, I don't understand you Yankees! I never have that trouble from Confederate soldiers."

"Did you ever stop to think that might be because you have Jubal and your other officers at your side most of the time?"

"Well, what do you propose we do? They're sure to hear the carriage if we try to ride away?"

Marc thought for a moment. Damn, he wished he knew who the commanding officer was, but he couldn't chance getting any closer.

"Marc, I could ride with you on Satan," Morgan whispered.

"No, I can't do that. Besides carrying my child, you are still recuperating from your wound."

Marc listened as the group across the creek became louder, but he still couldn't see any sign of an officer.

Then he heard it, the last voice he wanted to hear; General Rufus Slegle. The man who nearly had a rope around Morgan's neck and would be delighted to still accomplish that feat.

"All right, Morgan, we're going to have to ride Satan."

"It's that pompous ass of a general who tried to hang me, isn't it?"

"It's him all right and he would love to hang the two of us so we've got to get the hell out of here."

Marc stuffed what little food they had in his saddle bags, lifted Morgan into the saddle and slowly led Satan away. They had no more than left the camp behind when they ran right into droves of Federal troops. They stayed off the road, stopping to watch as the steady stream of Federal troops filed by.

Morgan choked back a cough as guns rumbled by kicking up clouds of dust. "Where do you think they are heading?"

"Eventually Richmond, if they're lucky."

"Oh God," Morgan moaned thinking of her brothers and friends and the battle they were in for. "Doesn't it bother you that you have friends who are going to be facing this horde of men?"

"It bothers me very much, Morgan, but there isn't much I can do about it. I chose to fight for the Union because I believed in it just as you believe in the Confederacy, but I have never felt a young man's death justified what was gained."

"Wouldn't it be wonderful if we could just say, enough! Everybody go home and resume your life. But that will never happen. I'm afraid the South is going to lose and will be made to suffer for a long, long time. Men like Sheridan, Custer and Sherman won't be happy until they break her."

Marc knew exactly what Morgan meant. These men had the reputation of destroying everything that stood in their way; divide, destroy and defeat was their method.

"I had a run-in with Custer about a year ago," Morgan continued. "I watched the bastard casually eat his dinner as he hung four of my companions. He forced me to watch, assuming I was a girl friend of one of the men. Well, I watched him hang four good men, then as I rode away I told him who I was and someday I would repay him for his injustice. I can tell you he choked on his dinner that night. My only regret was I didn't have a gun so I could have shot him through the head. Two of those men were John Mosby's men, but the other two were totally innocent. We tried to tell him that, but he wouldn't listen. They had only been trading clothes for fruit."

"I'm sorry, Morgan. I'm sorry for the evil men on both sides do, but most of all I'm sorry you ever became involved in this damned war. If the armies could be made of men like your General Lee and the Union's General McClellan things would be better. They would sit down and sensibly work things out."

As Marc spoke Morgan realized her feelings for him hadn't changed at all. It wasn't just the passion he could arouse in her, it was his sensitivity. He didn't like the killing and destroying any more than she did.

"Look, Marc," Morgan said pointing to the rear of the long column. "What is that cloud of dust bearing down on them?"

"That, my dear Rebel, is your countryman, John Mosby chasing and terrorizing Yankees."

Morgan laughed. "Nothing is too big for him. He probably has no more than a hundred men harassing thousands. Would you look at him turning those wagons off. The soldiers don't know what's going on and he's stealing them blind. By the time they get to Richmond they probably will only have half of their force."

"We'd better get away from here before my conscience gets the best of me and I report what's going on," Marc said.

Morgan studied him for a long moment, wondering if she would ever really know the man. He could pursue his enemy with a vengeance, yet now he was going to overlook Mosby's flagrant abuse of the Union army.

Marc smiled a warm, devastating smile as Morgan stared at him. "Is there something wrong, Morgan?"

"No, no of course not."

Marc headed Satan in the direction of Middleburg, confident that on horseback they could reach the little town before dark. The route they had taken most of the day was through heavy underbrush and rough terrain, but Morgan rode uncomplaining. The countryside was beautiful except for the scars of war. The leaves were shades of gold and red and the air smelled pure and clean. She couldn't help but relax against Marc as they rode on through forests of white birch and gnarled aspens. At times they could hear troops off in the distance, but most of the time she was able to put the war out of her mind. She thought of fall days before the war when she would take her father and the boys cider as they worked in the fields shucking corn. Oh how she had loved those fields with the endless bundles of stalks ready for the winter. She closed her eyes and let the fluid motion of the horse lull her as she dreamed about days gone by. When she shifted her position Marc tightened his arms around her. Strange how comfortable she felt in his arms. Here she was placidly traveling with him to Washington to live among her enemy. Why? She hadn't really believed he would have hurt Jubal. When she had turned around and found him in her room she had wanted to throw herself in his arms. Why had she lied about her feelings. The last thing she wanted was to marry Jared Law and he had saved her from that . . . but what about Rachel? Could they overcome the obstacles that stood between them and make this marriage work?

Marc reined in the horse as they approached the outskirts of town.

"What's wrong?" Morgan asked looking around.

"Confederate troops are all over the place. I don't know whether to chance riding into town or not."

"Are you afraid I'll scream for help?"

"Morgan," he said, his voice tinged with irritation. "You're my wife, not a prisoner."

"It's the same," she answered bitingly, then wished she hadn't said it.

"I agree. I've always felt marriage was the end of an individual's freedom, but then we must pay for our folly," Marc said with a twinkle in his eye that Morgan didn't see.

Morgan jerked around, nearly falling from the horse. "How dare you! Folly? Is that what you call it? You didn't have to marry me, Marc Riordan. I could take care of this baby!"

"I know you could, little one, but who would take care of you?"

"Oh you—"

"Morgan, let's not fight now. We have other problems at hand. I know a little inn in town where we could get a hot meal and a good night's sleep, but I want your word if anyone recognizes you, you don't tip your hand that I'm a Union officer."

"Of course, Marc," Morgan answered sweetly.

"I've got a feeling you'd love to see me hang," Marc mumbled as he urged Satan toward the little town of Middleburg.

Marc led Morgan into the crowded room of Confederate officers in Chin's Ordinary. He tried unsuccessfully to block her from view, but several Confederate officers greeted her warmly as he signed the register.

"Hello, Larkin, how are you?"

"I'm fine, pretty lady, but how about yourself? I heard you took a bullet at Brandy Station."

"I did, but thanks to some good friends and a wise old doctor I'm still here."

The officer looked around. "Are you alone, Morgan? Where's that old bear, Jubal Kelly?"

"Jubal is keeping my men together. I'm here with my husband. He's arranging for a room for the night."

"Do I know the lucky man?"

"I don't think so. He's from down around Charlottesville."

Larkin studied Marc as he talked to the inn keeper. "Funny, he doesn't look familiar. Can't imagine why I haven't see him before."

Marc wondered what Morgan was up to as he walked toward her and the Confederate officer. "We have a room, Morgan. Are you ready to go up?"

"Yes, dear, but first I'd like you to meet an old friend. This is Larkin McClenna. Larkin, my husband, Marc . . . Marc Winchester," she stuttered.

"Winchester," the soldier said still trying to place

Marc. "Your name isn't familiar."

"That doesn't surprise me. There are an awful lot of soldiers in this war. If you'll excuse us, it's been a long journey and my wife needs her rest."

"Of course," McClenna said surprised at Marc's abruptness. "Morgan, it's been nice talking to you. I'm glad to see you're as lovely as ever."

Marc led Morgan through the crowd toward the stairs before being stopped by a buxom woman carrying a tray of ale.

"Morgan, sweetie, I haven't seen you in a while. Where's Jubal . . . " Her words faded off as she saw Marc.

"Liz, why don't you send a pitcher of ale up for my wife and me," Marc said flashing a disarming smile.

"Marc . . . I don't understand . . . what's going on?" she asked nervously looking between the two.

"Everything is fine, Liz. We'll talk when you bring the ale."

Marc practically shoved Morgan up the stairs as she tried to ask him questions. When they got to the room he gently pushed her inside and closed the door behind them.

She turned, her hand on her hips and glared at him. "Do you mind telling me what that was all about? How did you know Liz? My God, is she a spy?"

"Damn it, Morgan, just slow down. I've been here often dressed as a civilian. Any spying that was done was by me. Liz found out who I was, but she agreed not to turn me in."

There was a knock at the door and Liz entered carrying a tray of ale and cheese. She set the tray on the table with her back to Marc, then turned pointing a small derringer at him.

"What are you doing with him, Morgan? He's a Union officer."

"I know, Liz. He's also my husband. There isn't any need for the gun. We just need a place to rest before going on to Washington."

"But how? I don't understand. You're both high ranking officers—on opposite sides."

"Before I answer your questions, Liz, I have a few of my own. Like how you know a Yankee officer so well?"

Liz quickly realized the implication of Morgan's words. "I didn't do any spying, Morgan. I swear it. We were just friends and had a little fun. There wasn't any harm in that."

Morgan shot Marc a look of disgust. "It figures."

Marc gave the girl a pat on the bottom and walked her to the door, talking softly out of Morgan's hearing. Liz smiled at him as he put a coin in her hand and quickly left.

"She's agreed not to say anything," he said as he came back into the room.

"My God, have you bedded every woman between Washington and Richmond?" Morgan asked incredulously.

Marc laughed. "Not quite, but I'm not through trying."

"You . . . you're despicable!" Morgan spat.

"And you're jealous, my lovely wife."

"Don't flatter yourself. I feel nothing for you. I just hate having every woman I meet tell me about her little escapades with you. I'm surprised your folly, as you so crudely put it, hasn't forced you into marriage before this."

"Perhaps there was never love before." Marc's voice was teasing, but the look in his blue eyes made Morgan quickly turn away.

"You take me for a fool, Marc Riordan."

"You're only a fool if you don't believe me."

Morgan moved away to the window. He was too close; she couldn't think properly. "Do you tell everyone you bed that you love them?"

"You're the only one, Morgan."

"I'm flattered. Now do you mind telling me where you plan to sleep tonight," she asked trying to change the subject.

"Whoa, lady. I might not be sharing a bed with you, but I'm sure as hell sharing a room with you. I'll sleep in the chair, and you madam may have that large, soft, comfortable featherbed."

A knock at the door again brought Liz into the room pushing a cart of steaming food. "I did the best I could, Marc. There's some roast beef and corn pudding and a small bit of bread. I hope that will do," she said looking to Marc for approval.

"You are wonderful as usual, Liz," Marc said picking up a lid from the roast beef. "Ah, it smells delicious."

"Here's a little surprise for you. One of your favorites," Liz said lifting a lid exposing two large pieces of apple pie covered with cheese.

"You outdid yourself, Liz. This is a feast fit for a king."

Liz smiled and curtsied. "And for my queen, I have ordered a bath of steaming water."

"That will be wonderful," Morgan said before realizing she was sharing this room with Marc. "But, I think I'll just retire after eating. I am really exhausted."

"Send the water up, Liz. If Morgan doesn't use it I will," Marc said realizing Morgan's predicament.

Marc pulled the chair out for Morgan and she cautiously accepted it. He then poured her mug full of ale and took the chair opposite her.

"Would you like me to serve you, Marc?" Morgan asked feeling awkward at their closeness.

"Please," he said handing her the plate. "Do you know this is the first meal we have had alone since we were married."

Morgan felt the heat rising in her face. She was well aware of that fact. She was starving yet she found it difficult to think about the food before her. Her eyes kept going to his handsome tanned face and his chest where his shirt had been unlaced at the neck.

She tried to think of something to say, something to break the silence. "I haven't had roast beef since . . . in a long time."

"You were going to say when, Morgan."

"Aye, I was going to say when Jeb Stuart's men gave a victory party after the battle at Fredericksburg, but I don't want to think about war."

"Then we'll not talk about war. It's strange, how every now and then you lapse into the Irish brogue."

"Not so strange when my father and Jubal both came from the old country."

He smiled, the swift smile which changed the hard lines of his face so completely. "Jubal tells me you accepted him as a brother without hesitation."

"He has always been like a brother, so why should blood change anything?"

"You're a very wise woman, Morgan."

"Wise, but foolish," she said boldly, then wished she hadn't said it.

Marc did not speak for a long moment, but his eyes were steady on her. "Do you so regret carrying my child, Morgan?" he finally asked.

She struggled to keep her voice steady. "No, I've not regretted that for a moment."

"I'll try never to cause you regret, Morgan. You'll have security, and perhaps one day, if you choose, you'll find happiness being my wife."

Morgan could think of nothing to say. She didn't dare look at him. If he so much as held out his hand she would give herself to him willingly. What was the matter with her. Why was she so weak where he was concerned. How could a few sweet words send her blood boiling and her heart racing?

"Eat before your food gets cold," she said for lack of anything else.

She didn't see the smile that touched Marc's mouth as he studied her across the table. He took a bite of the beef, suddenly famished, and washed it down with ale. "I have a gift for you when we get to Washington."

"You needn't give me gifts, Marc. It is enough that you have to take care of me."

"Yes, you're going to be a terrible burden," he said with a twinkle in his eye. "I can see you're going to eat me out of house and home."

Morgan couldn't help smiling, her eyes going a warm green. Suddenly she was hungry and she attacked the food on her plate.

Marc finished and pushed his plate away, then

poured them both more ale. He swung one foot over the arm of the chair and idly leaned back to watch her eat. She devoured the food then washed it down with the ale. "I can't remember when I had such a meal," she said wiping her mouth on the napkin. She protested as Marc filled her mug for the third time.

"You don't have to go any place tonight. Drink up and relax. Liz should be back with water for your bath before long."

Morgan's eyes widened. "I cannot."

Marc laughed. "Such modesty, my sweet. Don't worry, you may enjoy your bath in privacy. I'll be out for a little while. It will probably be late before I return."

Morgan was glad for her privacy while she soaked in the warm, scented water, but she couldn't help wonder where Marc was spending the evenig. The old man who delivered the water told her Liz was off for the evening and it didn't take her long to put two and two together. She didn't know why, but she felt angry beyond words. She couldn't believe he could be so charming to her one moment and then slip off to spend the night with another. She dried herself briskly and then filled her mug with ale. She knew a miserable loneliness and fought to hold back the tears.

"Damn him! Damn him! He pushes me beyond endurance!"

Morgan opened her eyes as the door slowly creaked open. She had lain awake for hours imagining Marc in the arms of the barmaid. Then much to her surprise, Liz had come to her room with a bottle of sherry to see if she needed anything while Marc played cards. She didn't know why, but she felt as if the weight of the world had been lifted from her shoulders. She had felt absolutely giddy, until the room began to spin and she had to fight to control her stomach. Now she watched him release his gun belt and remove his shirt. Then he sat next to the bed and lit a cigar. As the first whiff reached her she moaned.

Marc quickly stubbed the cigar out and moved to sit on the side of the bed. "I'm sorry, Morgan. I thought you were asleep. Are you all right?"

Morgan hiccuped before answering. "Things just keep spinning . . ."

Marc laughed. "Did you finish that ale after I left?"

"I think so. Then Liz brought some sherry."

"God help me, now I have a tipsy wife on my hands," Marc teased.

"Don't be angry. I'm just not used to drinking. Oh, Marc, I feel so badly."

"I know, little one. I've been there a time or two myself. Just lie real still and I'll get a cold cloth for your head."

Morgan stared after him, wondering at the tenderness in his voice. Strange, he had seemed so agitated before going downstairs.

Marc came back and laid the cool cloth on her forehead. "Does that feel better?"

"A little," she moaned. "Did you do well at cards?"

"I always do well at cards," he answered smugly.

"What conceit," she mumbled before closing her eyes.

Marc moved away to the chair he had chosen for his bed. He removed his boots and tried to get comfortable. The chair squeaked as he positioned his large frame.

Morgan giggled as he cursed. "This bed is very large. Why don't you lie on top of the covers."

Well, it's better than sleeping in the chair, Marc thought to himself. He had been a fool to have given his word not to touch her. The little hell-cat was surely going to drive him crazy this night.

Chapter Twenty-six

Dawn was slow in coming for Marc Riordan. Morgan slept restlessly, often tossing a bare leg across his already tense body. Several times he considered making love to her, but common sense told him she would never forgive him. He had given his word.

When she woke he was pacing the room fully dressed. "Is something wrong, Marc?"

"It's time to be up," he answered impatiently. "I'd like to be on the road before it's dark again."

Morgan wondered what had put him in such a foul mood. He had been so kind and gentle to her when she had felt bad.

"Would you mind leaving long enough for me to dress, Marc," Morgan asked shyly.

"For God's sake, woman, I'm your husband and I'm not going to spend the rest of my life leaving the room when you dress!"

Morgan sat up and boldly let the sheet drop. She knew he was right, but he didn't have to be so nasty about it. She tried to stand straight and proud, ignoring the look on his face.

"Oh God," he moaned as he stormed from the room.

Whatever is the matter with him, Morgan wondered. His moods change like quicksilver.

Marc stood in the hallway trying to compose himself. He was thinking the woman was surely going to drive him crazy when voices from downstairs interrupted his thoughts.

"Sho, I kin lead you to dat Yankee, ifen you gimma de money you done promised."

"You will get paid nicely, my friend. Just lead us to him."

Morgan was in the middle of dressing when Marc moved, panther-like back inside the room. He whirled and motioned Morgan to his side as he listened at the door.

"Someone tipped the Rebs that I'm here," he said as he cracked the door. He could hear footsteps, a lot of footsteps and quickly closed it.

"I've got to get out of here, Morgan. I'll have to leave you."

"No, I'll go with you."

"Morgan, there isn't time. I'll meet you at Sutter's Ford. I'll leave you Satan."

"But how will you . . ."

Someone spoke in a whisper outside the door. Marc dashed for the window, his footsteps silent and quick as a cat. As he lowered himself from the window the door of the room crashed open and three Confederate soldiers rushed in with guns pointing.

Morgan modestly held the sheet up in front of her. "Do you mind telling me what's going on, soldier?"

"Sorry, ma'am, but the captain says there is a

Yankee in here."

"You tell your captain this is the room of Morgan Fitzgerald of Fitzgerald's Raiders and if he thinks I have a Yankee hidden in my room to get up here and make the charges himself! Or if he prefers we can take this matter up with General Stuart."

"Oh damn," one soldier exclaimed as he recognized Morgan. "We were only following orders, ma'am. The captain must have misunderstood. Someone told him the big black stallion in the stables belonged to a Union officer named Riordan."

"It did at one time, soldier, but the horse now belongs to me. Spoils of war, as they say."

Two of the soldiers had already disappeared from the room and the third backed out apologizing.

Morgan knew it wouldn't be long before more questions were asked about her companion of last night. She had to move fast. She donned her buckskins, packed a few possessions and climbed from the window as Marc had done earlier. She just hoped Satan wasn't being guarded.

A heavy mist hung over everything enabling Morgan to reach the stable unseen. Satan was in a back stall, towering like an immense shadow in the mist-shrouded stable. At the sound of her footsteps he snorted nervously. Morgan rubbed the silken black nose gently as she moved into the stall.

"I'm going to ride you, Satan. Easy now," she said as the horse stomped nervously about. "Satan, if we are to help Marc you have to let me mount you. Calm down," she said trying to be patient. Satan stood calmly as she threw a saddle on him. "Good boy," she mumbled.

Morgan led the horse from the stable into the cold, misty morning. When she was out of sight of the inn she mounted and rode in the direction of Sutter's Ford. The wind brought tears to her eyes as she spurred Satan on, feeling free for the first time in a long while. Thoughts of turning the horse back to Culpeper flashed across her mind briefly, but she continued on her way to the ford.

The trail stretched before her without a turn so she let Satan have his way, flying past the mist covered forests. She came upon the ford quite suddenly and had to use all her strength to bring the stallion under control. A light rain began to fall as she sat motionless waiting for Marc to show himself. Finally she dismounted and led the horse to the safety of the woods. Where could he be, she wondered. He had a half hour start on her. Maybe he didn't get away. Oh God, maybe he had been killed . . .

"Morgan, over here," Marc shouted from the other side of the ford. "Ride Satan across. It's not too deep."

Morgan wanted to shout for joy when she saw him. She suddenly felt vibrant and alive as she urged the great horse into the water.

Marc's face was inscrutable as she approached him. He grabbed the reins of Satan while she threw a leg over the saddle and slid to the ground. Suddenly he picked her up and twirled her around.

"I can't tell you how relieved I am to see you! I was afraid you would get on Satan and head back to Culpeper."

"Was it me or your horse you were worried about?" she teased.

Marc held her away from him, looking over her

outfit. "Well, if I'd known you were going to show up wearing those damned buckskins I'd probably have given you Satan and been on my way." He gave her a bear hug and a brotherly kiss as her face showed her bewilderment. "I'm only teasing, Morgan. Did you have any trouble? I heard them enter as I dropped to the ground."

"Fortunately one of the soldiers recognized me and believed my story. I made my escape before my captain showed up to ask any more questions about my husband's disappearance."

"Good girl. I'm glad you're on my side."

Morgan's eyes widened. She stared at him for a moment before speaking. "I'm not on your side, Marc Riordan. You're my husband and the father of my child, but I am a loyal member of the Confederate States of America. Nothing will change that."

Marc smiled and touched her face. He loved her because of her arrogance and pride. Oh yes, she was lovely to look at, to be sure, with a smile that was too rare, but could melt his heart in a moment. But, her courage, that was what he loved most about her, what he had searched for in a woman all his life. "I wouldn't have you change for anything in the world, Morgan."

Morgan could feel her face getting warm. "Are we going to stand here in the rain until the troops find us or shall we ride on and end this miserable trip?"

Marc swung into the saddle and lifted her so easily she might have weighed nothing. She sat in the saddle before him, held secure by his arms as he turned the horse toward the road and gave him his way. For hours they rode, often taking to the woods to avoid

Federal and Confederate troops. Morgan's buckskins were damp and cold against her skin and she fought to control the shivering which engulfed her each time the wind blew more rain in her face.

They stopped only once to eat some dried beef and biscuits and to stretch their legs. "Why is it when we travel together the weather always seems to be terrible?" she asked.

Marc smoothed a damp curl away from her face. "Do you think it's an omen?" he teased. "Don't worry, you're not traveling in the company of the devil."

"That's debatable, especially while you're wearing that uniform."

"I changed because I thought we stood a better chance getting through the pickets."

An eerie mist rolled over the countryside covering everything in a ghostly blanket as the two weary riders slowly made their way into the city of Washington. Morgan welcomed the sight of the house as they rode down the muddy street, but her body felt cramped and she wasn't sure she would be able to move when they stopped. She gently slid from the saddle as Marc tied Satan to the post. Every inch of her protested and her knees buckled as her feet touched the ground. She made no protest as Marc gathered her in his arms.

Adam, the handyman opened the door and greeted Marc warmly. "What can I do for you, sir? Can I get you food, warm water, just tell me."

Marc looked down into Morgan's face. "What do you say, little one? Are you hungry?"

"Sleep," she moaned, "just sleep."

"We'll be fine until morning, Adam. Just let Connie know we're here."

Marc slowly took the stairs, making no attempt to hide his own strain. "I hope we make it," he teased. "You're suddenly very heavy. We're liable to both go sprawling any minute."

"I've put my life in your hands, Yankee and you best see me to the safety of a bed," she answered laying her head against his chest.

Marc pushed the door to his room open and gently laid Morgan on the bed. She moaned as she straightened her legs.

"I never want to see another horse."

"We'll see about that," he said pouring her a glass of brandy from his side table. "Here drink this. It will help you sleep."

"I need nothing to help me sleep," she said taking the glass, "only to ease the aches."

"Do you want me to send Connie in to help you undress?"

"No, I'll be fine. Just pull my boots off."

Marc gently removed her boots then stood looking down at her for a long moment before kissing her tenderly on the mouth. Morgan did not stir until she realized he had moved away from her.

"Marc, where are you going?"

"To sleep in my studio, Morgan. I'll see you at breakfast."

Morgan felt a desolate loneliness in the dark room. Damn, why couldn't she have swallowed her pride and asked him to stay? She had to make this more than a marriage because of the child. Tomorrow she would face up to her feelings—and to Rachel Todd.

Morgan stretched like a cat as the morning sun fell

across her face. She took a deep breath and could smell the delicious aroma of coffee and bacon wafting up to her from the kitchen below. She smiled as she thought of Marc carrying her up the stairs and of their lighthearted banter.

Suddenly she sat straight up in bed. Rachel . . . was Marc downstairs having breakfast with Rachel at this very moment? What was she doing lying here? She had to look very special today. Today was the day Marc Riordan was going to be glad he had married her.

Morgan filled the wash bowl with cold water and scrubbed until her skin glowed, then she vigorously brushed her hair, letting it fall in deep waves around her shoulders. She opened the armoire and smiled as she found the beautiful dresses Marc had given her still in his closet. She chose a yellow-gold morning dress, humming to herself as she buzzed about the room. She was pleased with the effect as she studied herself in the mirror, smoothing each fold of the gown.

Marc knocked gently and stuck his head in the door. "Good morning, sleepy-head."

Morgan smiled at the sound of his voice. She turned to greet him, but froze as she saw him standing there in his uniform.

Marc studied her appreciatively. 'You look lovely, Morgan. I'm glad I had a chance to see you before I left. My memories of you always seem to be in buckskins."

"Where are you going?" she asked barely above a whisper.

"I'm afraid I've been neglecting my duties. I must get back to my men."

"So soon?" she asked bewildered.

Marc turned and looked out the window. He wanted to tell her he never wanted to leave her, that he died a little each time he did; he wanted to take her in his arms and smother her with his love, but he kept reminding himself of his promise never to force her to his will. If she ever came to him again, it would be of her own accord.

"Will you miss me a little, Morgan?"

Morgan did not answer. Her mind was in a turmoil. "Marc, what about Rachel?"

"Rachel?" he asked surprised. "Rachel has been gone for months. I sent her away when I thought you had been killed."

Morgan wanted to shout for joy. She and Marc could pursue their relationship without Rachel's interference. She had a thousand things to talk over with him, but he anxiously paced the floor.

"Can't you stay for breakfast?" she asked.

Marc kissed her on the cheek in the same brotherly fashion as before. "I had mine hours ago, love. Connie is waiting for you to join her downstairs. Come, walk your husband to the door."

Morgan couldn't think of anything to say. She numbly followed his lead down the stairs. Did he really feel she was a weight around his neck? At last she managed to find her voice. "Marc, we need to talk."

"Morgan, don't worry about a thing. Your finances have been taken care of. Connie will explain everything to you."

"Morgan," Connie exclaimed from the doorway. "How good to see you," she said hugging Morgan.

"You certainly gave us all a scare. We had you dead and buried for a while."

"It's nice to be here, Connie," Morgan said forcing a smile. "I've been most anxious about Mrs. Riordan."

"Well, you'll do her a world of good, I can tell you that. When you're finished saying goodbye to your wandering husband we'll have breakfast and I'll fill you in on everything."

Morgan turned to face Marc and was surprised at the tender way he looked at her.

"I hope to get back here in a month or so, Morgan. I've instructed Connie to see that you have everything you need." He leaned down and kissed her on the lips, a quick, light kiss, but enough to send her blood racing.

A month, she kept thinking. She would be fat and ugly in a month. "Please, Marc," she stammered.

"Please what, love?" he asked hopefully.

"Please take care of yourself," she said lowering her eyes to the floor.

"You too, Morgan," he said as he walked away from her. He mounted Satan at the hitching post and looked back once more. "Take a walk to the stables after breakfast. You'll find a surprise."

Before she could say anything he had galloped off down the muddy road. "Oh, Marc, why can't I tell you how I feel?"

Marc spurred Satan at break-neck speed, before realizing the horse was lathered and panting. He dismounted and led him to a stream. "I'm sorry, boy, I shouldn't be taking my frustrations out on you." He sat on the bank of the creek and tried to comprehend what he was feeling. He had given Morgan his word not to touch her, not to make demands on her, but to keep his word, he knew he was going to have to stay away from her. He leaned back against a tree and remembered the touch of her warm lips. She had seemed so warm and willing this morning. He thought of her smile and those green eyes twinkling at him beneath dark lashes. He clenched his fist as his stomach knotted. "Morgan, Morgan," he moaned.

Morgan visited with Marc's mother most of the morning. She had been unprepared for the condition of her friend and swore to herself that somehow she'd try to make the woman's life a little more bearable. Anne's eyes followed her and she accepted the food offered, but there was no movement in her body. Connie had said her eyes had filled with tears when Marc was there, but Morgan doubted Anne knew what was going on around her.

While Anne napped Morgan walked out into the garden, where a few months before flowers had bloomed. Suddenly she remembered the stables. She looked around for Adam, but when she didn't find him, she decided to go on in. The stables were dark, except for the stall windows left open. She felt her way around, careful to hold her delicate yellow skirts up.

"What surprise could he possibly have in here?" she asked herself aloud.

The horse at the far end of the stables snorted and stamped about nervously. Morgan strained her eyes in the darkness. "It can't be," she whispered. Forgetting her skirts she shrieked and ran toward the stall. "Gambler, Gambler," she cried. "How can it be? Oh

Marc, you're wonderful," she said hugging the horse's neck.

"Colonel Riordan said you would be happy to see your horse. It's a pity he's not here to get a little of that gratitude."

"Oh Adam, isn't he wonderful? How did he ever get her here? She was lost during a battle."

"I know, ma'am. When the colonel was in the hospital he overheard a young officer talking about having your horse. The colonel made arrangements to buy her and had her sent back here. When he thought you were dead he used to come out here and talk to her, as if he were talking to you. I can't tell you how happy we are that things have worked out for you and the colonel, ma'am. None of us cared much for Miss Todd."

"Thank you, Adam. I just hope I don't go crazy waiting for Marc to return. It's going to be at least a month."

"You'll have lots to keep you busy, ma'am, with the baby and all."

"You're right, Adam. Mrs. Riordan needs therapy, and I'd like to exercise Gambler before I get too big . . . and of course, I'd like to make one of the rooms over into a nursery. Do you think anyone would mind, Adam?"

Adam smiled warmly at her exuberance. "No ma'am, I think anything you wanted to do would be all right with the family."

The first two weeks flew by for Morgan. She had been too busy with Anne to think much about her loneliness. Anne was making a remarkable recovery since Morgan arrived. It was as if Morgan had breathed life into her; she could sit up with help and was learning to feed herself. Morgan worked tirelessly over her, massaging muscles back to life, grooming her and always talking about the future. The doctor called it a miracle, but Connie felt Morgan's condition gave Anne a will to live.

Brenna had returned to the Riordan household and she and Morgan spent hours talking about everything they had been through. Morgan had filled her in on everything about Jubal and both women glowed as they talked about the men they cared for. The household seemed to come alive as Morgan's condition became more evident and plans were in progress for the nursery.

The third week Morgan received an unexpected visitor while Connie and Brenna were out shopping. She had been working strenuously on Anne's therapy when the doorbell rang. She headed for the door, her sleeves rolled up and her hair in disarray and came face to face with Rachel Todd in her Sunday best.

"My, my, don't we look domestic. Does Marc have you scrubbing floors?"

"What do you want, Miss Todd?"

"Why, darling, I just came to offer my congratulations, and to tell you that Wesley and I are to be married soon," she said pushing her way past Morgan. "Dear Wesley tells me you trapped Marc into marrying you. That was very clever of you, my dear. I should have thought of that. Oh, don't worry, I don't hate you for breaking up my engagement. No, on the contrary, I'm grateful. I don't think I could stand being left at home to raise Marc's brats while he beds every woman he meets." Rachel smiled at the effect her words had on Morgan. "Oh you poor dear. You didn't know. Wesley tells me Marc keeps a mistress in every town. He does have an insatiable appetite. I remember a few delightful times myself, but that's all in the past. Unless of course he is looking for company while he's in town. Who could resist a man like Marc. You certainly couldn't blame me for welcoming him back with open arms. It would only be fair and I'm sure Wes wouldn't object."

"Are you quite through, Miss Todd? I haven't time to play your nasty little games. Anne needs my help after her so-called accident."

"Oh yes, how is the poor woman? I understand she is paralyzed and cannot speak. Such a shame."

"Oh Rachel, haven't you heard? She is greatly improved. She is up and about and learning to speak again. It won't be long before she can tell us what happened that fateful night."

Rachel's face paled as Morgan spoke. "That's just wonderful," she said pulling her gloves on. "I know Marc must be happy. Well, I must go now. You should take care of yourself, dear. You have aged ten years since I saw you last."

"Goodbye, Rachel. Don't bother to come back."

"Oh, I won't, dear. I'm sure Marc will be looking me up when he is tired of his dowdy wife."

Morgan slammed the door and slowly climbed the stairs. She wanted to lock herself in her room and cry. She felt drained of strength and spirit. Suddenly she tilted her chin arrogantly. "Oh no, Miss Todd. I will not doubt my husband again. I know your evil ways and I won't be tricked into making a mistake again."

For all Morgan's show of confidence the next few

months took a terrible toll on her. Marc had said he would be back in a month and now two months had passed. The Christmas holidays had come and gone, but the family had decided to wait for Marc's return before doing any celebrating. Now she just prayed they would have something to celebrate. She was spending too many sleepless nights imagining him in the arms of someone else; someone still thin and beautiful.

Chapter Twenty-seven

As the snows melted, General Lee advanced with his gray troops and pushed U.S. General Meade back from Culpeper. Meade's cavalry, headed by Marc Riordan, had been so rudely hustled by Stuart's cavalry that the Federal commander was completely in the dark as to his adversary's position and plan.

In the foggy darkness of morning, Marc Riordan pushed his unit toward the Rappahannock where the Orange Railroad crossed. His plan was to ascertain if General Lee had fallen back after his victory and if Meade could advance once again. As they neared Brandy Station the fog began to lift and what looked like Stuart's entire cavalry could be seen crossing the river.

Marc ordered his men to prepare to fight when the hillside to their left roared with cannon aimed at them. They quickly retreated to the shelter of the woods where Marc kept his men firing, determined to hold off until reinforcements arrived. Stuart's men charged time and time again, but the troop of Federals somehow held. Marc couldn't help but admire the Southern cavalry leader in front of his men, shouting orders, oblivious to the dangers around him.

Night was beginning to fall and suddenly Stuart pulled his men to the hillside overlooking the woods. Marc hoped it wasn't the calm before the storm. He took the opportunity to rest against a rock, having a sip of water while those around him followed his example. Closing his eyes for a moment, Morgan's face came to his mind.

"Colonel Riordan, camp fires have been lit along two miles of that hillside. There's got to be thousands of them blasted Rebs up there," one of his men stated.

"Give orders to break out the food and rest, corporal. It's going to be a long night."

Marc was studying the hillside, wondering if all the fires were a ruse when suddenly the night was filled with the sound of a band playing Dixie. He smiled to himself. Everything Morgan had told him about Stuart was true; the man was a master in every situation. If he could believe the campfires on the hillside, Stuart's troops were now reinforced by thousands of soldiers, all waiting to descend on them in the morning. Was it a ruse, he wondered. Something told him it wasn't.

Through the thick underbrush no glimmer of firelight could be seen so the Federals ventured to kindle a fire. Marc was warming his hands over the open fire while discussing strategy with his officers when Stuart and three of his men appeared out of the shadows. Everyone stood dumbfounded that three horseback riders could have ridden up on them. The only sound breaking the silence was the click of a gun.

"Hold your fire," Marc ordered.

"Good evening, colonel," Stuart said smiling. "May we talk for a moment?"

Marc thought how Stuart seemed to be enjoying the situation. He had one knee thrown carelessly over the pommel of his saddle as he coolly looked over the enemy camp.

"Don't do anything foolish," Marc said to one of his officers who stood with his hand on his gun. "Stuart is an honorable man."

The two cavalry leaders walked out of the range of hearing while the stunned soldiers just watched.

"I promised a crazy Irishman and his brother that if I ran into you I'd find out how their lovely sister fared."

Marc was stunned for a moment then his laughter echoed through the woods. "You rode into the camp of your enemy to ask about my wife? Now I know why you win most of your battles. I don't believe you fear anything."

Stuart put his arm around Marc's shoulder and walked further away from the campfire. "We all fear something, lad. I guess my biggest fear is seeing Virginia destroyed. She is what I love most, what I would lay my life down for. But enough. How is the fair Morgan?"

"It's been three months since I've seen her, but at that time she was well. As a matter of fact, she saved my hide in Middleburg by covering for me while I dropped out a window."

Stuart laughed. "She'll never change. You're a very lucky man, Riordan. There are not many like her."

"I know that, sir. That's one of the reasons I love her."

Stuart smiled. "I didn't think your sense of duty was the only reason you married her."

"I love her more than life itself. I just hope I have the chance to tell her that."

Stuart studied Marc for a moment. "Get your men out of here tonight."

Marc didn't think he had heard right. "What did you say?" he asked confused.

"If you want to see your wife again you'd better get out of here tonight. Lee plans to come down on you at dawn and you won't stand a chance. He's ten to one against your unit. All of his forces are merged right here to repel Meade and you just happen to be in the way."

"Why are you telling me this?"

"I don't want Morgan to be widowed before she has a chance to have a husband. Besides, I like you, Marc. I like you enough to offer you a command in my army. Walk away from here and join me."

"I'm honored, sir, but you must know that I won't desert my men. I believe in the cause for which I fight."

Stuart smiled, but sadness touched his eyes. "I would have been disappointed if you had said anything else; but still, think on what I have said."

"I will put it to my men. It will have to be up to them."

"I can understand your feelings, but what can you do with so few against Lee's army?"

"I'm surprised you ask that, general. I'll do the same thing you would. Fight for all I'm worth and give Meade a chance to fortify his position."

"And die game," Stuart said almost in a whisper.

"And die game," Marc repeated.

Stuart placed the soft, fawn colored hat with the curling ostrich feather back on his handsome head and moved toward his horse. Everyone stood as if hypnotized, watching the cavalier who had already become a legend mount and adjust his sword.

"Good evening, gentlemen," he said saluting. "And good luck."

After long hours of deliberation Marc told his men of their chances. Everyone to the last chose to stand and fight. They knew the odds, but also knew Meade would have a chance to push forward if their unit could detain Lee's army.

Marc cleaned his gun before the fire as did most of the men. The situation was desperate, but everyone talked and kidded as if it were an ordinary night before a battle. The sounds of the band playing and the Confederates partying drifted down to them.

"They sound like they are enjoying themselves," Doc said of the Confederates.

"I'm sure a good deal of it is for our benefit."

"Marc, may I make a suggestion? Why don't you let the men write to their loved ones. Billy Gober can ride out of here tonight and deliver them to Washington. The boy is too young to make the decision we made tonight."

"You're right, Doc. I just hadn't thought about it. I'm afraid I haven't thought about anything except Morgan."

"My God, man, you're no exception. I haven't thought of anything except Katie. If we don't get out of this I would at least like her to know I was thinking about her."

"Make the suggestion, Doc. I'll explain to Billy what an important mission he is being sent on."

Jubal Kelly was watching the Federals moving toward the mountains when word reached him that Stuart had a Federal cavalry unit trapped near the Rappahannock. Word quickly spread that Stuart had gone into the camp of the Union officer they called the devil and had returned without an explanation. Jubal realized immediately that Marc Riordan was the man trapped. After talking it over with the men who made up Fitzgerald's Raiders, they agreed they had to stop the slaughter that would surely take place.

They were two hours away from the Rappahannock and it was going to take an all-out ride to get there in time to put a plan in motion.

A gust of wind whistled through the pines, whipping the fire to a bright glow. Marc studied the blank pages of paper, trying to find the right words to tell Morgan how much he loved her. He finally began to write.

My darling Morgan,

I am sitting by a glowing campfire surrounded by my men. It is a warm, friendly atmosphere, which is surprising since there is a cold, damp fog spreading its veil over us. I can hear the sound of a night-bird in the distance and the merriment of the Rebels nearby. We are surrounded by Rebels, Morgan. To be specific, we are trapped by Lee's army on the hill overlooking our camp and Stuart's cavalry surrounds us. We were trying to ascertain where Lee's forces were and rode right into their trap. It doesn't look good. Stuart rode into my camp this evening and we spoke for quite a while. How I admire the man. He's the last of the gallant, shining knights and he wants so badly to save Virginia.

He offered me the opportunity to flee in the darkness, Morgan. My men and I discussed this at length tonight. They chose to stand and fight. Please understand this, my darling. Before I met you I might have taken the opportunity to save myself, but the thought of disgracing you prevented me from doing anything so cowardly.

We're trapped in a world filled with trouble, Morgan, but perhaps someday our child will have the opportunity to live in peace. That's why I'm fighting, darling; for you and our child.

Oh God, what do I say, Morgan, when I don't know if I'll ever see you again? How can I convince you of my love? How do I write all the things I should have said to you — all the things I tried to say. Why did I waste so much precious time? There are so many pictures I wanted to paint. Thoughts of you fill my mind. In you I see the beauty of a sunset, in your eyes the green of a pine forest, the sparkle of the moon on the water. I could go on and on, Morgan. You are so beautiful, so spirited. What pictures I could paint of you, but I guess I'll have to be satisfied to keep them locked in my mind.

I've loved you from the first day I laid eyes on you, darling. The happiest day of my life was spent making love to you by the river's edge. Do you remember that day, where a cool stream fed our thirst and the warm sun touched our bodies? I know that must have been where our child was conceived—conceived in love, my darling. The very remembrance of it stirs my senses, Morgan. I have known heaven—what more could I ask?

I'm sorry I was not able to be with my mother more during the days of her illness. Please love her for me. Give her a grandchild to help pass her days. Whatever happens I want you to be happy, Morgan. Do whatever you must. If it means returning to your home, remarrying, whatever; I understand. I love you, my darling. You have made my life worthwhile. You are my sun, my moon, my every breath. Believe in my love, darling. Let it help you through the times to come. Yours will get me through the morning.

Your loving husband,
Marc

The Union soldiers who bedded down in the pine grove that night would never have believed the discussion going on in the enemy camp.

"Holy Mary, we canna' go against Morgan's husband. She would never forgive us," Jubal exclaimed.

"What am I supposed to do, Jubal? Lee has given his orders. I've given Riordan every opportunity to move his men out, but he chooses to fight," Stuart answered.

Jubal paced the floor, chewing on his cigar. "They dinna' stand a chance. It will be slaughter."

"We could try to capture them before daylight," Michael stated matter-of-factly.

Jeb Stuart and Jubal Kelly stared at the young man. "Take them prisoner? Is it possible, Jubal? Do you think it could be done?" Jeb asked, a glimmer of hope in his eyes.

"It's the only chance we have. By God, little brother, you're a genius. It's so simple. Why didn't we think of it before?"

"Hold on, Jubal," Stuart said. "It's not all that simple. You're going to have to get past their pickets and I'm sure Marc Riordan is not going to let his gaurd down just because the odds are against him. If just one person gives a warning you'll have no choice but to fight."

It was decided that Fitzgerald's Raiders would be the only outfit to carry out the plan. Stuart felt the less men involved the better chance they had to surprise the Federals.

A little past three in the morning fifty men led by Jubal Kelly and Michael Fitzgerald moved in the direction of the pines. Much of the distance they crawled on their stomachs, hugging the ground, hoping they wouldn't be seen. In the distance the eerie howl of a wolf broke the silence. Pickets were barely visible by light of the campfire as most of the men slept. Jubal gave the prearranged signal and one by one each man moved off toward a picket, silently capturing them. When that was done, and the camp lay unguarded, they formed a circle around the encampment, Jubal fired one shot bringing everyone awake.

"Sorry to be waking you this way, but you're now prisoners of the Confederate Army."

Marc Riordan said nothing as his men were searched and marched off toward the Confederate camp. When it was over, one hundred and thirty-five men had been taken prisoner, including four officers. Missing was little Billy Gober who had ridden out earlier for Washington carrying the letters which had been so painstakingly written.

Marc's hands had been tied behind him, but when he was taken before Jubal they were released.

"Strange, I thought you would be the kind of man to give your enemy a fair chance—to leave a man with some pride," Marc said angrily. "Not sneak up on him in the night, like a thief."

"I'm giving you a chance to see your child, lad. I think that's more important than pride."

Jubal caught sight of one of his men going through Marc's belongings. "Leave Colonel Riordan's belongings," he ordered. "I'll take them."

Marc looked disgusted. "Perhaps you'd like the clothes off my back or maybe my boots?"

"Shut up, Riordan," Jubal sneered. "I've no intention of keeping your belongings." Jubal glanced back over his shoulder as the last of the prisoners were led away. Michael was heading in their direction, a big grin on his face.

"Good to see you alive and well, Riordan. I was afraid we were going to lose a sister over this touchy situation."

Marc looked from one to the other. "What in hell are you talking about?"

"Stuart told us you didn't stand a chance once Lee's

army began to move this way," said Michael. "We had orders to clear you out. Well, last night we came up with the brilliant idea of taking you prisoner so we wouldn't have to kill you. Can you imagine how Morgan would have reacted if we had killed the father of her baby?"

"Can you imagine how she'll react having a coward for a husband?" Marc answered angrily.

"Dinna' be a fool, lad. There is no such thing as death with honor—just death. You had no chance against us and we were not about to tell Morgan we had to kill you. If you know what it's like to feel Morgan's wrath, you'd be knowing why we did it this way. We canna' give you any supplies, but we can at least give you back your guns and horse. Take the road to the east and you'll come out at . . ."

"Hold on a minute. Excuse me for being so slow, but I just realized what you two are up to. Thanks, but no thanks."

"Now listen, Riordan, we're giving you a chance to get the hell out of here," Michael said angrily. "We risked a great deal with this fool plan, all to save your neck and now you tell us you want to go to prison?"

"I can't let my men be taken off to prison while I ride merrily on my way. I'm their commanding officer and if being with them can help in any way, then that's where I'll be."

"For God's sake, man, you don't know . . ."

"Enough, Michael," Jubal said. "Marc has made his decision. We'll just have to alter our plans. Marc, we'll do what we can for you. I'm sure an exchange can be made so you shouldn't have to spend too much time in Richmond. In the meantime, I'll see that your horse and belongings get back to Washington."

"I know you both were thinking of Morgan and someday I'll probably thank you for what you did, but I also know that every day I spend in prison I'm going to wish I could get my hands on the two of you."

"Maybe, lad, but I think when you have time to think on it you'll be glad you're alive. Prison is better than dead. This way you have a chance to hold the fair Morgan again."

Chapter Twenty-eight

Time is most often a fleeting thing, but to Marc Riordan time seemed to be standing still. He had been chained to the wall of a small, damp room in Libby Prison for more than three weeks. The building, which had once been a tobacco warehouse, now crawled with rats and every bug known to man. There was no sanitation, little medical attention, and with the South having trouble getting supplies for their own hungry soldiers, there was very little food.

Marc was given one meal a day consisting of a poor grade of meat chopped up in a meal made by grinding corn and corn cobs together. Water was sparingly given twice a day. All these hardships he was able to endure, but what bothered him the most was the isolation. He had no way of knowing if his men were all right or if any arrangements were being made to exchange them. He had quickly learned if anyone showed himself at a window or tried to question a guard he could expect a beating or worse. He had tried to bribe a guard to at least tell him how his men fared, but the suggestion met with a rifle butt to his head. He thought if he could just get together with a couple of his men perhaps they could plan an escape. Alone he could do nothing.

He was lying on his back on the board that was his bed when he heard the iron bolt on the door being shoved back. It wasn't time for his meal and he hadn't been allowed any exercise so he waited apprehensively for an order.

"Get yourself together, Yankee. You have a visitor in Captain Duerson's office."

"Who is it?" Marc asked.

"How the hell should I know. I was just told to get you. If you're going to be picky about who your visitors are, you can stay here."

Marc struggled to stand up. He had been trying to exercise in the confines of the small cell, but his muscles were getting weak and he feared it wouldn't be long before he lost all his strength.

The guard unlocked the chain that held him to the wall, but not the ones at his ankles. He shuffled down the long hallway, trying to get a glance at some of the other prisoners, but Confederate guards were the only men visible. When he slowed his pace his escort roughly shoved him forward.

They entered a different part of the warehouse where offices had been set up in the five story building. It was like a different world. No longer could he smell the sewage and garbage that reeked in the prison area or hear the moans and cries of injured and starving men.

"Jesus, Mary and Joseph!" Jubal swore as Marc was shoved into the room. "This man is an officer. Ye canna' be treating him like an animal."

"You know the charges against this man as well as I, major," the captain answered defensively.

"We'll discuss his crimes later, captain. I want to talk to the colonel alone."

"I'm sorry, sir, I cannot allow that."

Jubal's eyes flashed angrily. "Listen to me, you young pup, my orders come from General Jeb Stuart. I suggest you obey them or you'll be digging ditches on the outskirts of town with the others who were foolish enough to question his orders."

"Well, I suppose there is no harm since the guards are just outside the door," the captain mumbled, quickly realizing his mistake.

Marc hadn't said a word since entering the room. He was glad to see anyone who could give him some news of what was going on, but he couldn't help remember Jubal was responsible for his being there.

"Did you come to gloat?"

"You know better, Riordan. I've been trying to see you for weeks, but until I had Stuart's orders it was hopeless."

"Well you see me. Now what?"

"Listen to me, Riordan. You were the one who chose to come to this hell-hole. I'll take some of the blame for your predicament, but not all. Now do you want to be fighting me while we have these few minutes or do you want to hear what I have to say?"

"Do you know anything of Morgan?"

"No. We dinna' know any way to get word to her. She must be sick with worry not knowing whether you're alive or not."

"I wrote to her the night before we were captured, but I don't know if she ever received the letter. If she did, I'm sure she assumes I'm dead."

"Damn, I was afraid of that," Jubal answered as he paced the floor unaware that Marc struggled to stay on his feet. "I wish we had known. My God, man are you all right?" he asked noticing the sweat beaded on Marc's forehead as he swayed on his feet. "Here, sit down. You're as pale as a ghost." Jubal removed a flask from his inside pocket and held it to Marc's mouth. "Drink slowly," he ordered.

The liquid burned all the way down, but Marc felt better immediately.

"I'm sorry, lad, I know this hasn't been easy on you. I'll try to see that things are a little better. Maybe I can arrange for those chains to be removed."

"Where are my men?" Marc asked.

"The South doesn't have much food as you know, but perhaps I can have your portion increased."

Marc looked up suspiciously. "Jubal, you didn't answer my question. Where are my men?"

Jubal leaned back against the table and rubbed his shaggy beard. "They've been exchanged."

"Good God, man, that is wonderful. I don't know why you would hesitate to tell me news like that. How about me? Is there any talk of my exchange?"

"There will be no exchange, lad."

"No exchange? I don't understand. I know there are

high ranking Confederate officers being held in Washington. Why wouldn't an exchange be made?"

Marc knew the answer before Jubal had a chance to reply. "They think I'm a spy, don't they?"

"Aye, lad, I'm afraid they do. If I had any idea it would come to this . . ." Jubal said, his voice rough with emotion.

Marc didn't speak for a moment as the facts sank in. "Am I to have a trial?"

"Aye, three days from now. I have an appointment to see one of the generals who will preside. I dinna' know if it will help, but it canna' hurt."

"I appreciate your trying to help, Jubal, but I don't think there is anything you can do."

"If only Morgan were here," Jubal said thinking out loud.

"No! I don't want Morgan to be told about this. She already thinks I am dead, so let's leave it at that. My God, in her condition she can't take much more."

"Easy, lad, I was just thinking out loud. There is a great lack of comunication between Richmond and Washington, so it would probably be impossible anyway."

Marc suddenly felt so tired; so defeated. The night before the battle he had prepared himself for never seeing Morgan again, then he had been taken prisoner and the only thing keeping him going was the thought of seeing her. He pictured her eyes, green and glowing with desire, her mouth yielding to his kisses, her body soft against his. He ached to feel her, to see her, but now that hope was dashed again. He would never see her—never hold her, never hold his child. He turned away from Jubal as tears filled his eyes.

"Dinna' give up hope, lad. By all that's holy, I'll do what I can to help you."

For two days and nights Morgan had sat numbly in her darkened room trying to make some sense out of the letter from Marc. Death wasn't new to her, yet it never seemed any easier to accept. Her first reaction was always the same; she was defeated—she couldn't go on living. Then anger took over and she found herself being driven by a desire to strike back, but at whom she didn't know.

She stood at the window staring out into the darkness. Oh God, he can't be dead. He is too vibrant, too much a fighter. She leaned her forehead against the cold glass of the window, tears running unchecked down her face. Had it really been three years since she had been caught up in the great rebellion; the fight for the South's freedom? She remembered so well her father coming home from a trip to Richmond, eager and excited to serve his country after hearing John Daniel speak on a street corner. His speech had inspired many and brought fear into the hearts of others.

"The great event of all our lives has at last come to pass. A war of gigantic proportions, infinite consequences, and infinite duration is upon us, and will affect the interests and happiness of every man, woman and child, lofty or humble, in this country called Virginia. We cannot shun it. We cannot alleviate it. We cannot stop it. We have nothing left but to fight our way through these troubles."

"Nothing left but to fight our way through these troubles," Morgan said aloud. "You always said you admired my stubbornness and my pride, Marc. Well, maybe it will help carry me through this."

"Morgan," Brenna said as she entered the room with a tray of food. "Oh sweet, you've been crying again. You've got to be thinking of the babe."

Morgan attempted a smile. "I know, Brenna and I will soon, but there are a few things I have to take care of first. I want to know how Marc died and where his body is. The government cannot just tell you a man has been killed and leave it at that."

"Oh, ma'am, leave it be. This just canna' be good for you."

"Brenna, don't you understand? Maybe Marc isn't dead. I've got to have some proof?"

As Morgan quickly learned, getting anyone in Washington to listen to the plight of an irate woman who thought her husband had been killed was next to impossible. The capital was flooded with wives and families trying to learn the whereabouts of someone dear to them.

Morgan was returning home from one of her many frustrating trips when she spotted a rider cautiously making his way toward the Riordan house.

Her breath caught in her throat as she recognized her brother. Her eyes slowly moved from him to the big black stallion he led—Satan's Thunder.

Michael had anticipated his visit being a shock to Morgan, but he had never expected her to collapse in the street. He knelt beside the bed as Brenna laid cold compresses on Morgan's head.

Morgan slowly opened her eyes. "Morgan, dear, sweet Morgan, are you all right? I never meant to startle you so."

Morgan clutched her brother's hand. "Is Marc dead?" she whispered.

"No, sweet, but things are not good with him."

Morgan's eyes widened in shock. "He is alive?"

"Marc is being held as a spy in Libby Prison. He has already been tried and condemned to hang."

Morgan clutched Michael's hand, but said nothing.

"I am sorry to be so blunt, Morgan, but I have no time for putting things gently. According to Marc you already think he is dead. He confided to Jubal he sent you a letter the night before he was captured implying it was his end. He insisted you not be told any different, feeling it would be easier on you to continue to assume he died that night. Jubal and I discussed his request at length and decided we couldn't just let him die if there were the slightest chance we could help. Jubal remembered that you had been friends with General Worthington and his family and thought perhaps they could help. If that doesn't work, then perhaps your friendship with President Davis's wife could help. Jubal suggests you send wires to both."

Morgan swung her feet off the bed. "Brenna, pack a few warm things for me. I'll need traveling clothes."

"Now wait a minute, Morgan. you're not going anywhere," Michael said pushing his sister back on the bed.

"I cannot chance telegrams getting there, Michael. I must talk to these people in person. Please don't argue with me. We're wasting precious time."

"Morgan, you cannot seriously be thinking of riding a horse in your condition," Connie interrupted.

"Don't you all see that I must do this. Marc's life is in danger. I have to help."

"I have a better idea," Connie said knowing that Morgan would somehow have her way. "I have a friend who has been using his ship for exchanging prisoners. I talked with him just today and he is leaving for one of his trips tomorrow. I'll send a message to see if you can be discreetly transported to Richmond. It will take a little longer, but you'll be more comfortable and there will be less chance of being stopped. I'm told very few people are being allowed to travel through the countryside."

Morgan looked anxiously at her brother. "What do you think, Michael?"

"I think Jubal will probably kill me. He instructed me to have you send a wire and here we are planning a boat trip."

Morgan kissed her brother on the cheek. "I'll make him understand, Michael."

"You'll not be going without me," Brenna insisted. "You will need a woman with you."

"This trip could be very dangerous, Brenna. I can't place you in that situation."

"Ha! I ha' known nothing but danger since you arrived, and I rather like it," she smiled. "Besides, it may give me a chance to see Jubal again."

Morgan fluffed her pillow and tried again to get comfortable. She sighed and stared at the ceiling. She knew she needed her rest before the long trip ahead, but sleep just would not come. Suddenly she bolted upright as someone banged on the front door. She jumped from the bed and pressed her ear to the door. She could hear voices down the stairs; angry voices. She gasped in shock as her door was suddenly shoved open against her.

"Shhh, it's me, Morgan," Michael whispered. "Get your cape. We've got to get out of here."

"Who is it, Michael?"

"Lafayette Baker and some of his henchmen."

"Oh God . . ."

"There is no time to talk, Morgan. I know it's dangerous, in your condition, but I'm going to have to lower you out the window."

Morgan was gently lowered to the yard where Brenna waited. Then Michael dropped silently to the ground beside her.

"We can't chance making our move yet. We'll hide in the shadows until his carriage leaves, then we'll head for the docks."

"But what about Connie and Anne? They won't know what happened."

"I'm sure they'll surmise what happened, but we can try to send word once we reach the ship."

"They come this way," Brenna whispered.

"Into the shadows, both of you. I'll be just across the yard in the doorway of the stables."

Morgan held her breath as one of the men passed by close enough to touch. He stopped in front of her and began talking with one of the other men who searched the garden.

"Do you think Baker's informant was wrong?"

"If she was lying, she'll regret it. Baker does not like to be made the fool."

Another man joined the group. "Someone was recently sleeping in the bedroom just above us. Are you sure you didn't see anyone?"

"No sir, nothing out here. Miss Todd said the woman was pregnant, so she couldn't have dropped from the window without hurting herself."

Morgan was trembling with anger. So Rachel Todd was the informant. Somehow it didn't surprise her. She only wondered why she had waited so long to turn her in.

As the men moved toward the front of the house, Brenna moved from her hiding place and joined Morgan.

"Did you hear that?"

"I heard, Brenna. I just hope Anne and Connie aren't in any danger from that man."

"Are you ladies all right?" Michael whispered as he joined them.

"What do we do now, Michael? Baker knows someone was in the bedroom so he's sure to keep looking."

"You and Brenna stay put. I'm going to see what's going on out front."

Michael hid in the shrubs listening to the man called Baker talking with a woman who waited in the carriage. Baker was telling her to go home, that their work was going to keep them for awhile. As the carriage moved slowly away from the house, Michael leaped aboard, quickly subduing the driver without the passenger knowing it. The carriage slowly turned the corner and doubled back toward the Riordan stables where it stopped.

"Driver, is there something wrong?" a voice called out from inside.

The door of the carriage opened and Morgan climbed in with a gun aimed at Rachel. "If you make the slightest sound I'll kill you without a second thought."

Rachel cowered in the corner as Brenna climbed in beside her. The carriage slowly began moving down the street toward the center of town.

"Tie her hands with her scarf, Brenna."

"You're not going to get away with this. Lafayette Baker will find you and hang you."

"If he does, you won't be around to see it."

"What do you mean by that?" Rachel asked, her eyes widening with fear. "Surely you don't mean to . . ."

"Kill you, my dear Rachel?" Morgan asked, enjoying having the upper hand.

The carriage came to a stop and Michael opened the door. "Is she tied up?"

"Yes, what now?"

"We'll leave her here in the park. If we are to reach the Virginia border tonight, we have to get moving."

Morgan looked up surprised, but quickly realized what Michael was up to. He pulled Rachel from the carriage and dragged her off into the darkness.

Morgan and Brenna slipped aboard the small ship, appropriately named *Hope*, while Michael got rid of the carriage. Two hours later the Confederate prisoners were loaded, oblivious to the passengers traveling below. It was a cold, rainy morning, the wind off the water chilling to the bone as the ship began its journey down the Potomac River toward the Chesapeake Bay. They moved swiftly down the Potomac as the ship's sails filled with the wind.

The sound of canvas flapping and waves lapping at the hull did nothing to help Morgan's jangled nerves. She sat stiffly on the bunk, her cloak wrapped tightly around her. She wished she had opted for the more familiar method of traveling—her horse. She wondered at Connie's knowledge of comfort as she shivered violently from the damp cold that seeped into the little cabin. She started to lie down, but the damp, cold feel of the bunk changed her mind. She kept reminding herself that nothing mattered but getting to Marc. Keep your mind off the pitching of the ship, she told herself. She looked across the cabin at Brenna sitting silent and grim.

"I wonder if Connie has ever been on a ship," Brenna asked innocently.

Both women began to laugh.

Chapter Twenty-nine

Michael stood on the deck surveying the night activity around the harbor. Instead of being allowed to proceed up the James River to Richmond, the ship had been detained at Fort Monroe. Michael's natural instinct as a scout did not fail him. He managed to learn that Union troops were preparing to move on the city of Richmond with the intent of releasing prisoners held at Libby and Belle Island. The captain had been in favor of continuing their trip, not anxious to be burdened with a shipload of cold, hungry Rebels, but authorities seemed unclear about their instructions.

A light snow fell, adding to the discomfort of the prisoners huddled together. Michael gritted his teeth, thinking of the inhumanities man inflicted upon his own kind. The captain had informed him that these men could have been exchanged back in the fall before the bitter winter set in, but officials in Washington refused to make any exchange at that time. The South had asked for a prompt and fair exchange of prisoners and the Union agreed, but they only kept their agreement as long as the preponderance of captures rested with the South. When the fortunes of war transferred this balance to the Union, Washington authorities refused further exchange.

Michael pulled his cape closer as the wind whipped

across the deck. All but one lantern had been extinguished, casting ghostly shadows. Somewhere from across the water drifted the eerie, sad sound of a flute. Michael shivered, thinking of facing Morgan who waited below for some word. She had been near hysterics when first learning the ship was being delayed. Marc's life depended on their getting to Richmond and here they helplessly waited at Fort Monroe for someone to give them a go-ahead.

"Good evening, Mr. Fitzgerald. I thought perhaps I'd find you out here."

"Evening, Captain London. Have you any word yet?"

"We can proceed at dawn."

Michael grasped the man by the shoulder, pumping his hand at the same time. "By God, that's wonderful. My sister will certainly be relieved."

"It isn't going to be easy. I'm not even sure we'll make it as far as Richmond, but we'll give it one hell of a try."

Morgan looked up expecting the same negative response until she saw the expression on Michael's face.

"We move at dawn, my dear sister."

Morgan clasped her hands in prayer. "Oh God, don't let us be too late."

"The captain isn't sure we'll get as far as Richmond, but we'll face that when the time comes."

"Michael, do be sitting awhile," Brenna insisted. "You look to be near freezing. The nice captain was kind enough to provide us with some tea."

Michael removed his cape and took the straight-back chair offered. There was barely room for the three of them in the same cabin, but the crowded condition helped make it a little warmer. He studied Morgan's face while sipping the tea. Her face was ashen, stark against her dark hair, and her green eyes held a worried, desolate expression. Michael covered her hand with his.

"Are you all right, Morgan?"

Morgan smiled weakly through tears. "I feel so helpless, Michael. Captain London told us about the move on Richmond. I can't help but worry for Jubal and Jeb. If they have any idea what's happening, they'll be right in the middle of it."

Michael brushed a tear from Morgan's face. "They've faced much worse, Morgan. You're tired and have been under a great strain, so things seem worse than they are. We have no way of knowing if the Union will even get to Richmond. They've tried before and failed."

"What will happen to Marc if they are successful this time? Oh, Michael, what will we do?"

Michael took her in his arms, not sure what to say. She had always been so strong—much stronger than he. He had depended on her from the beginning, but now she needed him. Somehow he would get her through this. It was time for him to be her strength.

When the time came to weigh anchor a heavy fog obscured everything around them. The *Hope* moved up the James River at a snail's pace, the first mate standing at the helm, a pair of field glasses never leaving his eyes. Hour after grueling hour they moved at this pace. Where there had been the sound of conversation between the prisoners before, there was only silence now. The tension seemed to hang as heavy as the fog. Suddenly the rays of sunlight broke through and a cheer went up from the crew and prisoners.

"Broad landing, starboard," shouted the first mate.

"We haven't done too badly," the captain said to Michael who had been standing silently beside him since they left Fort Monroe. "If the weather stays clear you should see Richmond tomorrow."

"That's good to hear, captain. I know everyone on board appreciates your efforts to get us there. You took a real chance starting this morning before the fog lifted."

"I don't like to see anyone suffer, son. These men should have been exchanged long ago. I'm afraid a good many of them will have pneumonia after this trip. I don't recall ever seeing so many sick ones."

"How long have you been making this run, captain?"

"Since '62. I'm a peaceful man, so when this war started I decided I could help both sides by using my ship to exchange prisoners. I can tell you, I'll be damned glad when this stinking war is over. I can hardly stand to look at these poor souls any more. It seems to get worse all the time."

Michael relaxed his vigil and watched the scenery as they sailed up the narrows of the James. What was once a fertile countryside was now barren wasteland. Acres of stumps showed where once stood good timber; houses were reduced to ashes and others vandalized beyond use. When will it all end, Michael wondered. Suddenly a vision began to form in his mind—they were running—people were running all around them. Then it changed. Jubal was in an open field, blood covering his shirt. Then it was gone—gone as quickly as it had come. Michael felt shaken. He knew well enough to take these premonitions seriously. Too many had come to pass. He tried to compose himself as he headed for Morgan's cabin. He couldn't let her know he had had one of his visions.

The rest of the trip passed uneventfully until the ship reached Harrison Landing, two hours below Richmond. Smoke could be seen rising above the trees in the distance.

"Looks like the blue boys are just ahead of us. I think it might be wise if we unloaded these prisoners here. I'm sure no one in Richmond is thinking about exchanging prisoners with the Yankees knocking at their door. I'll try to get up the river a little further, but I can't promise to get into Richmond."

"I understand that, Captain London. I'll tell my sister and her companion to prepare for a quick departure, if necessary."

A light snow began to fall as the exchange prisoners were hurried off the ship. Even those who earlier seemed disabled now walked off on their own, eager to be with friends and loved ones. The rumble of guns could be heard in the distance and Michael wondered if he wasn't making a mistake taking Morgan into the city. It was obvious Richmond was being invaded.

"That's the last of them, Mr. Fitzgerald," Captain London said as he joined Michael at the rail. "God willing, they'll all make it home."

"Aye, captain, God willing we'll all make it home soon."

The ship made it as far as the tobacco warehouses at the edge of the city. Michael quickly led Morgan and Brenna off the ship and through the crowds. Artillery barked away in the distance, blended with the sound of the bell on Capitol Square summoning men to the defense of the city. Refugees filled the street, wagons loaded with women, children and furniture.

Michael grabbed the arm of a young boy dashing by. "What's happening, son?"

"Yankee cavalry have ridden inside our lines of defense," the boy yelled before darting away.

The thunder of artillery echoed with reverberation that seemed to shake the very ground they stood on. Everywhere there was panic. Rumors were running rampant as to what was actually happening. Every step they took was blocked by people heading in the opposite direction.

"It's just a little further," Michael yelled above the noise.

When they reached the prison they found the gate unguarded. The three slipped into the prison yard unnoticed.

"Where is everybody, Michael?" Morgan asked bewildered.

"They have probably taken all available men to defend the city," Michael lied, knowing full well they wouldn't leave the prison unguarded.

Inside the building was the same; deserted. Michael

led the way to the office where he and Jubal had met with Marc several times. Morgan reluctantly agreed to wait while Michael went to find out what was going on.

He wandered through the corridors toward the cells. Something strange was going on. There wasn't a guard to be found, but the prisoners were still confined in their cells. He strained to see in the darkness, wishing he knew what cell Marc was in. The stench was nauseating and the moans and cries unnerving. Damn, how could they let this place get this bad, he wondered.

"You got any water, mister?" a voice asked from the darkness. "Nobody has given us any water since yesterday."

Michael found the guard's room where buckets of water sat. He rummaged through the guard's desk and found the cell keys then carried two buckets back to where the prisoner had spoken to him. He dipped the cup in the water and handed it to the prisoner.

"What's your name, soldier?"

"Jones, Captain Luke Jones of the 29th Michigan Cavalry."

"Do you have any idea where everyone is?"

"I heard one of the guards saying something about Union soldiers coming to break us out. A few minutes later they all disappeared. I've heard a lot of activity coming from below. Must be a basement or something."

"How about Colonel Riordan? Do you know who he is?"

"Sure, he's the ranking officer here."

"Do you know which cell he's in?"

"He isn't in a cell. They took him out this morning and didn't bring him back. I figure they must have hung him."

Michael tried to control his voice. "What makes you think they hung him this morning?"

"I know he was condemned to hang. I figure when they take a man out and don't bring him back, something must have happened to him. I'd say he is the lucky one. He's finally out of this hell-hole."

Michael hesitated a moment then unlocked the door of the cell. "I'm going to have to trust you to pass water around, Jones. If I find a guard I'll have him bring food."

"Who are you?" Jones asked puzzled.

"Captain Michael Fitzgerald of Fitzgerald Raiders, but that's not for general information. I'd just as soon you kept that to yourself."

"I'll be damned. We've faced each other many times. Is it true you're led by a woman?"

Michael laughed. "Where did you hear a fool story like that?"

"I didn't think it was possible. I've seen you in action too many times and no woman could be that smart."

"No, there are not too many who could."

Michael continued his search of the prison. He could hear a digging sound and followed it to the basement. He slowly opened the door and stared in amazement as he saw a dozen or more men shoveling a mound of dirt more than six feet high in the center of the room.

One of the men spotted him immediately. "What are you doing here, mister?"

"I'm looking for one of my officers. Jubal Kelly. He's been spending a lot of time here lately."

"Yeah, I saw him this morning, but I don't know where he is now."

"Was there a hanging this morning?" Michael asked apprehensively.

"No, we ain't had any hangings in a long while."

Michael breathed a sigh of relief. Was it possible Marc had escaped? If so, he'd better get the women and get the hell of out of there before someone got suspicious. He started to leave, but his curiosity got the best of him.

"What are you men doing?"

"We just buried enough powder to blow the prison sky-high if the Feds get here," the guard answered proudly.

"Let's hope for everybody's sake they don't."

Michael headed back to the office where the women waited. Everything was running through his head. Did that guard really know what he was talking about? Surely if there had been a hanging everyone would know about it. Maybe with the threat of Yankees breaking into the prison they moved Marc to a safer place. Damn, that must be it. He was the highest ranking officer here and the only one condemned to hang. Why couldn't anything be simple. They couldn't stay around here to find out where he was. Those damned fools downstairs were liable to blow up the prison at the drop of a hat.

Michael burst into the room and grabbed Morgan

by the hand. "Come on, ladies, we've got to get out of here."

"What's going on, Michael? Where is Marc? Is he all right?"

"I don't know, Morgan. He doesn't seem to be here."

Morgan's face paled. "Oh no . . ."

"There has been no hanging, Morgan. Now come on. This place could go up any minute."

"Go up? What are you talking about?"

"They have booby-trapped the whole building. If the Federals get this far the whole place will go up."

The trip across town to General Worthington's was a waste of time. The house was boarded up and looked as if it had been deserted for quite a while.

Morgan stood motionless, staring at the empty house that loomed before her. Michael spoke to her, but he seemed so far away. Suddenly her legs wouldn't hold her and she sank limply to the ground.

"Morgan . . . Are you all right?" Michael asked kneeling over her. "I knew this was a mistake. You should be thinking about this baby instead of running all over the country. Damn it, we're going home, Morgan. There is nothing we can do for Marc. You'll just have to hope Jubal has been able to help him."

Morgan was too tired and desolate to argue. She knew she was endangering the baby. Michael was right. She should be taking better care of herself. She couldn't bear to lose Marc and his child.

Morgan sat on the back of a wagon, every bump sending pain through her tired, sore body. Somehow Michael had convinced this merchant to let them ride.

Otherwise, she didn't know how they would have attempted this trip home. She watched the ragged, dejected men, women and children trudging along the roadside, all fleeing from their homes with everything they could carry. A pain shot up her spine as they hit another hole in the road.

Oh God, what was she doing bringing a child into this troubled world. Poor little thing, what chance did it have when everyone was consumed with hate.

"It won't be long before we're home," Michael assured Morgan as he noticed her paleness. "I know you must be starved, but if you can just hang on for a little while."

"I'm not hungry, Michael. Please don't worry about me."

"When we get to Aspen Grove, I'll fix something to pique your appetite. You must think of the babe," Brenna said squeezing Morgan's hand.

"Thank you, Brenna. I just hope Aspen Grove is still standing. There doesn't seem to be much that hasn't been destroyed."

Michael had been hoping the same thing. Everywhere along the route lay the devastation caused by war. Fields and workshops abandoned, farms neglected, houses burned. What would they do if Aspen Grove had been destroyed. No, he couldn't think of that now.

Darkness fell quickly on this dreary evening. The merchant agreed to keep traveling if Michael took over the reins while he slept for awhile. He passed around a loaf of bread and a cask of bitter tasting wine, but to the travelers who hadn't eaten since leaving the ship, it was a feast. Even Morgan gnawed hungrily on the hard bread.

The wagon moved on in the darkness, bouncing over every hole in the road. Morgan lay perfectly still, her eyes closed against the pain. She tried to concentrate on the rhythmic sound of the creaking wheels that seemed to fill the night, hoping to dull her mind to everything.

The sky in the east began to brighten as the wagon neared the North Anna River. Michael held his breath as they rounded a bend in the road. He should be able to see his home just ahead . . . if it was still standing.

"Morgan, wake up Morgan. There she is, beautiful as ever."

There across the river stood the big white house completely circled by balconies on both upper and lower floors.

Morgan stared at the house, tears filling her eyes. She didn't think she'd ever see it again, but there it was, as impressive as it had been in the days of her childhood. The only difference was the fields were bare, the stables empty and the people gone.

The wagon crossed the wooden bridge over the river and turned into the long driveway lined with gigantic oak trees.

"Tis beautiful, Morgan. The most beautiful I ha' ever seen."

"My father designed and helped build it, Brenna. He and my mother put a lot of love into it," Morgan said between gritted teeth as another pain came and went.

The wagon stopped in front of the darkened house.

Morgan closed her eyes for a moment and imagined her mother and father rushing out to greet them.

Michael's concerned voice brought her back to the present. "We're home, Morgan. It's a little different homecoming than either of us have dreamed about, but we're home."

Suddenly a deep voice broke the dawn's silence.

"I got dis here gun aimed right at yo' back so you best git back in dat wagon and git moving!"

"Jacob, you old bear. If you shoot me you'll have a hell of a lot of explaining to do to Effie."

The old colored man hobbled forward and hugged Michael. "Bless yo' soul, boy, I never thought I'd see you again. Wait 'til Mama sees you."

Michael turned to help Morgan off the wagon. She started to slide down, but grimaced in pain.

"Jacob, is the house open? I need to get Morgan to a bed."

"It will be in a minute. I got de keys right here," the old man said slowly climbing the stairs. "Mama will have to make beds. Things have been covered a long time."

A sudden hot rush of fluid between her legs made Morgan cry out. "No, no, it's too soon. It can't be happening now."

Michael gently picked her up. "Everything will be all right, Morgan. Just thank God we made it home."

Morgan was in constant pain throughout the day and long into the night. Several times she blessedly lost consciousness, her only respite from the pain since leaving Richmond. Effie and Brenna did everything possible to make her comfortable, but nothing seemed to help.

Michael paced the room, feeling every pain as Morgan screamed out, twisting and turning on the blood-soaked bed. He cursed himself for letting her talk him into this trip. If only she had stayed in Washington everything would be all right. "She can't go on like this much longer. She's been in labor over thirty hours."

"De baby jus not right," Effie answered, a worried expression wrinkling her brow as she examined Morgan for some change. "De head should be at de opening, but it ain't."

"Breech," Michael whispered to himself as he remembered delivering several breeched foals. He had lost one of his finest mares when her foal was breeched. It tore her so badly she bled to death before anything could be done for her. Another time he and Jubal had successfully turned a foal before its birth and both mother and baby had made it fine.

Michael rolled up his sleeves and scrubbed his hands in the bucket of water Effie had been using. He knelt next to the bed, pushing Morgan's perspiration soaked hair away from her face.

"I'm going to try to turn the baby, Morgan. It's going to be very painful, but it's the only chance you have."

Morgan opened her eyes and stared blankly at her brother. "Dear, sweet, Michael . . . please take care of my baby . . . I'm so sorry . . . oh God, help me," she screamed as another pain wracked her body.

Michael knelt beside the bed. He separated her

thighs, probing as gently as possible. There—he could feel the baby's shoulder.

"Easy, Morgan, don't push yet," he said as he attempted to shift the baby's position.

Morgan's whole body twisted, her screams echoing through the house.

"Push now, Morgan . . . that's it . . just a little longer . . . push . . . it's almost over," Michael said guiding the baby's head, then shoulders. "It's a boy, Morgan. You have a son," he said proudly as he cut the cord and handed the screaming baby to Effie.

Morgan grabbed Michael's hand as another pain ripped through her. "No, please no more," she begged.

"That's it, Morgan. It's over," he said tenderly kissing her on the cheek.

Morgan closed her eyes, oblivious to Brenna's gentle hands washing her. "I have a son," she mumbled.

Chapter Thirty

Morgan held the baby to her breast, studying his small but perfect features. His hair was brown with reddish tints like hers, but his eyes were the same startling blue as his father's.

Brenna sat next to the bed sewing a tiny nightgown for the baby. "If the wee bairn continues to eat like that he'll be big before you know it."

Morgan smiled down as a little fist clutched and unclutched her finger. "He does seem to always be hungry, but he is so small."

"Aye, and well he should be. He was a month early coming into this world."

"Do you think he will be all right, Brenna?"

"He will be fine. His lungs are strong, he eats well and he is content. All the bairn needs is a name."

"Yes, I know. I will name him soon."

Brenna knew Morgan was waiting for some word of Marc, but it had been over a week and still nothing. Michael had been fishing one day and met a soldier traveling back to Culpeper from Richmond. The soldier told him that Richmond had turned the Yankees back and all was back to normal in the city, but he knew nothing about Jubal or Marc, nor had he heard anything of a hanging.

Brenna shivered as she thought of Michael's premonition of Jubal covered with blood. She had felt so sorry for him when he had confided to her. She knew he was torn between staying to protect Morgan and leaving to find out what happened to Jubal and Marc, but there was nothing she could do or say to help him.

"Brenna, I want to get up for a while today."

"You best talk to Effie about that," Brenna said breaking the thread between her teeth and holding up the tiny gown.

"Oh Brenna, it's precious, but I do believe you're trying to avoid the subject. I'm tired of lying here. I feel much stronger and I am anxious to see how the place looks."

"I know you are bored, Morgan, but you lost a lot of blood and it takes time to get your strength back. You just canna' overdo. Besides, Effie and Jacob have been working all week to get everything in order. I'm sure she'll not let you out of bed until she has everything just right."

With a sigh of resignation Morgan settled back in the bed while Brenna dressed the baby in his new gown.

"There, wee bairn, ye will be as warm as a bug in a rug now."

"You and Effie are spoiling him."

"I dinna' know much about little ones, but Effie seems to be an expert and she says a baby canna' have too much love."

"And well she should know. She raised seven of her own besides Michael and myself and filled us all with love. Oh Brenna, if only you had seen this place before. It was such a happy place."

"It will be happy again. You will fill it with your children."

Brenna realized her mistake immediately. She had been so careful to avoid any reference to Marc.

Morgan's eyes filled with tears. "There will be no other children. I must face the fact that Marc is dead."

"Dinna' say that, Morgan. Michael wants to go to Richmond to try to find out what happened, but he is afraid to leave us."

"I know he means well, but he can't stay here forever. We should be all right with Jacob. Besides, we are off the main roads so we shouldn't have any uninvited guests. Just to be safe, it might be a good idea to teach you to shoot."

"God's love," Brenna exclaimed, her eyes wide with fright. "I canna'."

"You cannot what?" Effie asked as she entered the room carrying a tray. "Doan you let Miss Morgan talk you into letting her outta dat bed."

"You know her very well, Effie. That is precisely what she has been suggesting."

"Bless de Lawd, child, you gots to get your strength back first. Hows you 'spect to be all beautiful again with dem dark circles around your eyes?"

"All right, all right, you win as usual. I'll stay here and die from boredom. Where is that brother of mine? He promised to play chess this afternoon."

"He done gone to visit de colonel's wife. He caught some nice fish dis morning and thought she might like to come to dinner."

Morgan was suddenly alert and bright eyed. "The

colonel's wife? What colonel, Effie?"

"Why Colonel Stuart, of course. Yassah, Mrs. Stuart been spending lotta time with the Fontaines since she had dat new little girl baby."

"Why didn't Michael tell me? He knows Flora and I are friends."

"I spose he knew you would want to be over dere."

"Well now you can be sure I am going to get up. If Flora is coming to dinner I want to greet her properly."

"I knows you real good, Missy. Dats why I pressed you a dress dis morning. But de only way I is gone to let you outta dat bed is for you to eat your soup and take a nap."

"Good heavens, Effie, you're treating me like a child."

"Yessah, and I can still puts you over my knee too," she said with a twinkle in her eyes.

Morgan grinned. "I know you would too. I remember a few times I felt that hand on my bottom."

"You turned into a lady too, didn't you?"

"That's debatable to some," Morgan answered thinking of what she had been through lately.

Michael returned alone that evening, his mood sullen and disagreeable.

Effie served dinner in the dining room to the silent trio, looking from one to the other for some explanation.

"Was Flora well?" Morgan asked, trying to break the gloomy silence.

"Yes, she seemed well."

"And the baby?" she persisted.

"A girl. She named her Virginia Pelham Stuart for John."

"Who is John?" Brenna asked.

"John was one of Jeb's officers," Morgan explained. "A brave gallant soldier who earned the admiration of all who knew him. Unfortunately he was killed at Kelly's Ford near the Rappahannock."

Michael poured another glass of Jacob's corn liquor and downed it.

"Has she seen Jeb recently?" Morgan asked, determined to get her brother to talk.

"He was there for a few minutes this morning."

"This morning?" Morgan asked astounded. "For God's sake, Michael, what is going on? Why did his visit put you in such a foul mood?"

Michael twirled the empty glass in his hand before answering.

"I spoke with George McClellan while Jeb visited with Flora. They had just returned from another battle at Wilderness. It seems the Union army has a new Commander-in-Chief named Grant and a new cavalry leader named Sheridan. George says they are a different breed of soldier; determined and ruthless. Word is, Sheridan has 13,000 cavalry, all with fine mounts and brand new Spencer repeating carbines. Somehow they were turned back at Wilderness, but the casualties were high, including General Longstreet. Sheridan has regrouped and is now heading this way, burning and looting as he comes. Jeb is heading for Hanover Junction and then on to Yellow Tavern where he will take a stand with his 3,000 men and try to turn back more than 13,000 before they reach Richmond."

Morgan didn't say anything for a few minutes. Now she understood why her brother's mood was so sullen. She knew he wanted to be with Jeb. "Jeb needs every man he can get, Michael. You should be with him."

"I cannot leave you. I explained our situation to Jeb and he understood. He sends you his love and said he wished he could see you and your son, but circumstances prevent him from doing what he wishes."

"Michael, I beg you to go. We will be safe here. I would never forgive myself, nor would you, if you stay here."

"It's out of the question, Morgan. Jacob has corn and potatoes that need planting and he can't do it by himself."

"I can help Jacob," Morgan insisted.

"And I can help," Brenna added. "I know nothing about planting, but I'd as soon learn that as shoot a gun."

"You see, Michael, we'll be usut fine."

"What's this about shooting a gun?" Michael asked as he realized what Brenna had said.

"It's nothing for you to be concerned about. I told Brenna that I'd teach her to shoot, that's all. My God, Michael, surely you must know I can take care of myself."

"A few months ago I would have staked my life on it, but things have changed."

"And if the Yankees decide to come here, will you be able to stop them?" Morgan asked.

"I guess I couldn't," Michael said with a gesture of defeat.

"Oh, Michael, I didn't mean to hurt you," Morgan said clasping her brother's hand. "My son and I would be dead if it weren't for you. I'll never forget your strength when I needed it."

Michael took her in his arms and stroked her hair. "What went wrong, Morgan. We had such high hopes. Now we're all that is left of our family and we are broke and near starving. The way of life we once knew is gone forever. We're fighting a battle we can't possibly win."

"Don't talk like that, Michael. We must not give up. Go with Jeb and help him. Everything will work out. I just know it."

"All right, Morgan. I'll leave in the morning. I just hope we don't regret this."

The next few weeks passed uneventfully as Morgan tried to fill her days so she wouldn't dwell on the loneliness. She and Brenna worked side by side in the fields with Jacob. She would be forever grateful to the old man. If he hadn't harvested potatoes and corn from each previous crop there wouldn't be any hope for food in the months to come. Even so, she worried about her son. She was breast feeding him now, but when her milk dried up she didn't know what she would do. Anything on four legs was a scarcity nowadays.

Brenna's lessons in firing a gun were going amazingly well. To Morgan's surprise the girl was quite apt at marksmanship. Even Effie, grumbling and complaining, was learning to load and shoot a gun.

The evenings were the worst for Morgan. After

dinner she would spend time alone with her son, then to avoid going to her room alone she would walk in the fields or down to the river where she had played as a child. She found nothing eased her pain. The baby, looking more like Marc every day, was a constant reminder of the man she loved. She had always considered herself such a strong person, but the desolation she now felt frightened her. If it weren't for the child she wasn't sure she would be able to go on.

Morgan leaned down and picked a small wildflower blooming by the river's edge. Was Michael right, she wondered. Was the way of life they had known gone forever? Would the once-rich soil of Virginia ever be fertile again?

Suddenly she crushed the flower in her hand. Tears flowed down her cheeks as she look toward heaven. "Why, God? Why?"

The sun was going down as Morgan placed the last of the potato eyes in the ground. She stood up, her hands on her aching back and stretched. She was bone tired, but satisfied at what the three of them had accomplished.

"That's it, dear ones. Now if our seeds will just grow."

"They will, Missy. God gonna shine down and make things grow. He knows you a good person," Jacob said, wiping his brow with a dirty cloth he pulled from his pocket.

"Do you think so, Jacob. Sometimes I . . . Oh my God!" Morgan exclaimed looking past the old man. "There is smoke coming from beyond the trees. That has to be Prospect Hill."

"Yessah, dats the only place over dere."

Suddenly the figure of a young black girl emerged from the woods.

"Dats Peggy, the Smith's kitchen girl," Jacob said as he rushed toward the girl.

"Jacob, Jacob, Yankees are here," the girl screamed as she caught sight of the old man. "They is coming this way. We gotta hide."

"How many were there?" Morgan asked.

"Oh ma'am, I doan rightly know. I was jus so scared I ran," the girl sobbed. "They was talking bout digging up graves. Can you imagine?" she asked wide-eyed.

"That doesn't sound like regular army. Perhaps they are deserters. Think, girl. It's important that I know how many men were there."

"Please, missy," Jacob begged holding the frightened girl. "Peggy doan know how to count."

"I do so," the girl insisted. Miss Smith taught me to count."

"Well then think, Peggy. How many horses rode up to the house? Was it five, ten, more? Think child!"

The girl's pride was now in question. She looked back toward the woods. "Was no more then ten. I'm sure of it. Weren't no more than ten."

"Good girl. Go on in to Effie. Tell her what is happening and help her close the shutters on the lower floor. Jacob, I want all the guns taken to the bedroom at the front of the house. We'll be able to see anyone approaching from there."

Jacob hurried off to do as Morgan instructed, leaving Morgan and Brenna still standing in the field.

"You are going to fight them," Brenna said as it

466

dawned on her what Morgan was planning.

"Aye, my friend. To be precise, we are going to fight them. Come, we'd better hurry to the house before they catch us standing in this field chatting."

Brenna ran beside Morgan, but continued protesting. "This is ridiculous, Morgan. How can two women and an old man hold off the Union army?"

"You heard the girl, Brenna. She said there were less than ten. They are probably deserters. We stand a much better chance defending ourselves than to let them in. Have you any idea what they would do to you and me?"

Brenna stopped dead in her tracks. "Oh, my God," she whispered. "Can we stop them, Morgan? Do you really think we can?"

"We're not going to do it standing here. Hurry now, get upstairs while I make sure everything is secure."

With Effie, Peggy and the baby safely hidden in an attic room, Morgan joined Brenna and Jacob in the front bedroom. Brenna was already kneeling at the window, her gun aimed toward the courtyard below them. She had a good view of the road leading to the front of the house.

"Any sign of them?" Morgan asked as she blew out the lamp.

"Nothing, thank God. Is it possible they won't come?"

"Possible, but unlikely."

The room seemed intolerably hot to Morgan. Beads of perspiration stood out on her forehead. The sun was beginning to set, the western sky turning a strange purple against the glow of fires being set by the intruders.

"Damn them," she whispered under her breath.

"What did you say, Morgan?" Brenna asked nervously.

Suddenly Morgan held up her hand for silence. "I hear them. They're heading this way. Don't do anything until they are just below us. When I start shooting you do the same. Brenna, aim very carefully. Remember it's our life or theirs."

The riders appeared in the lane, slowly approaching the house. Morgan counted seven of them.

"Don't make a sound," she whispered as she felt Brenna trembling next to her.

Peering through the shutters she could see they were a shabby looking bunch. She was sure they were deserters. "Get ready," she whispered. She held the rifle Lee had given her and carefully aimed. "Now!" she ordered.

Gun fire split the silence as all three began shooting. Two of the riders instantly fell while the others scrambled for cover. The shooting ceased while Brenna and Jacob reloaded. One of the men ran toward the house, but Morgan picked him off before he reached the porch.

"Three down, four to go," she said confidently.

"You're going to pay for this, whoever you are," one of the men shouted. "Marvin, we're going to burn them out. Henry, go around back and make sure no one gets out."

The man who had taken cover in the barn made a dash for the house, but Morgan got off two shots, dropping him in his tracks.

"Keep shooting, Brenna. There are only three of them now."

Suddenly the courtyard lit up with flames from the burning barn. Morgan stood frozen, a horrified look on her face.

"Morgan, they are going to burn us out. What are we going to do?" Brenna asked.

"Jacob, get Effie and the baby and try to get them out the back to safety. We'll keep them busy until you're out."

"Morgan, two more riders are approaching," Brenna warned. "We'd best get out of here too."

"I can't just let them burn Aspen Grove, Brenna. This is my heritage, my son's heritage. It's all I have left."

Morgan raised her gun, carefully aiming it at the two approaching riders. Then slowly she lowered it, watching in amazement as the men opened fire on the intruders. She turned from the window, leaning against the wall for support, all color draining from her face.

"Morgan, what is it? You look as if you've seen a ghost."

"He is alive, Brenna. Marc is alive. He and Jubal are the riders."

The bedroom door suddenly flew open and Marc's large frame filled the doorway. Morgan stood frozen, unable to say anything.

"Are you all right, Morgan?"

"Yes," she somehow managed to answer.

"We've got to get the fires out before the wind shifts," he stated before leaving as quickly as he had come.

Morgan numbly followed him to the courtyard, her

mind reeling. She reacted by sheer instinct as Jacob passed her a bucket of water. Marc and Jubal were trying to beat out the fires while the rest of them hauled water from the well.

Marc tried to concentrate on putting out the fires, but his mind reeled with the thought of Morgan losing the child. He wanted to take her in his arms, to comfort her, but the look in her eyes was unreadable. He couldn't take his eyes off her. God, she was beautiful as the breeze blew her hair in swirls around her face.

Morgan looked up and found Marc watching her, but he still hadn't said anything. She remembered his letter, professing his love.

The roof of the barn collapsed with a loud roar and everyone moved on to the next building. Morgan was exhausted, leaning heavily against the fence as the last of the fires was brought under control. She looked around her at the charred ruins where the barn her father had built once stood.

"Hello, lass. How goes it with you?"

Morgan threw her arms around Jubal's neck, unable to say anything for a long moment.

"I didn't know what had happened to you, Jubal. I was afraid . . ."

"Aye, I know, girl. We had to move fast when the Union army got near Richmond. We thought you were in Washington so that is where we headed. Then on the way back I was wounded and we had to hole up just outside of Fairfax."

"Wounded? Oh, Jubal, are you all right?"

"Aye, thanks to your husband. He removed a bullet from my side."

Morgan looked past Jubal to where Marc worked vigorously to remove burning boards from the stable.

"Where is Michael, little one? I thought he would be with you."

"He was until a few weeks ago. Jeb was through and needed every man he could get. I insisted he go."

Jubal didn't say anything for a moment. "Morgan . . . Jeb is dead. He was wounded at Yellow Tavern and died a few days later in Richmond."

Morgan's knees felt weak. Jeb Stuart couldn't be dead. He was too strong, too vital. He was the hope of the South. She choked back a sob, shaking her head back and forth.

Jubal shook her gently. "Listen to me, girl. Jeb would not be wanting you to mourn him. He lived life to the fullest and he died leading a cavalry charge. Remember him with fond memories, but don't dwell on him. Thanks to him, your husband is alive and he is the one who needs you now. Go on into the house and compose yourself. We'll be through here in a short while and he'll be wanting to talk to you."

Morgan numbly obeyed. She was filled with conflicting emotions. She would always remember the plumed cavalier who counseled her with words of wisdom when she had so desperately needed someone after her parents were dead. And Flora. Poor, dear Flora. She would have to see her tomorrow, but Jubal was right. Marc was alive and her thoughts should be of him tonight. They had a great deal to talk over.

"Everything is secure," Marc's voice sounded behind her.

They faced each other across the room, the silence deafening between them.

Marc wanted to take her in his arms, but hesitated, afraid she would turn from him again. His mind reeled with the nearness of her; did he dare reach out and touch her?

Morgan stared at the man she had reluctantly married. He was thinner, paler, yet his eyes were still strong and vital, holding hers magnetically.

"Morgan, I'm sorry about Jeb. I only met him a few times, but I greatly admired him."

"He was a rare man. I will miss him sorely."

"Jubal tells me Michael was with him."

"Yes, I hope he is all right."

"I'm sure he is. You'll probably be hearing from him soon."

"And you, Marc. Are you well?"

"I had a bout with pneumonia while in prison, but I'll be as good as new before long."

"I'm sorry," she answered awkwardly. What are we doing standing here talking like total strangers, she wondered. Why doesn't he take me in his arms.

"Morgan," he started, then hesitated. "Did you lose the baby?" he blurted out.

Morgan fought to control her anger. So, they were back to the same old thing. He was only here for the child. She was a fool to have believed he meant what he said in the letter.

"You are free of any obligations you felt, Marcus," she said turning away so he couldn't see the hurt in

472

her eyes. "I will have Jacob prepare a room for you," she said heading for the stairs.

"No! We will talk now, Morgan," he said grabbing her by the wrist. "We have already wasted too much time."

"You are hurting me, Marc."

Marc dropped her wrist. "You are the most exasperating woman I have ever known. I certainly didn't expect our reunion to be like this."

"Nor did I," she answered. "I don't have the time nor the inclination to play any more of your games."

"If you think all we've been doing is playing games, then one of us is a fool. I did not marry you because of the child. I love you. I've always loved you. Only your arrogance and stubborn pride have kept us apart this long. Why can't you admit how you feel? Why is it always I telling you how I feel?"

Marc threw up his hands in defeat. "Damn it, I'm sorry I made this trip. I should have known you wouldn't change. My aunt had been under some misguided impression that you had left Washington to help me. I should have known it was only your way to get back to your precious home."

Morgan placed her fingers on his lips, silencing his angry words.

"You are right, Marc. I am a stubborn, foolish woman, but I did journey to Richmond to help you. When we arrived the Union army was on the outskirts of town and you were gone. My only hope was that Jubal had somehow saved you from hanging. I tried not to let myself think of anything else."

"Are you saying you care, Morgan?" Marc asked hesitantly.

"Yes, Marc, I care. I love you."

"Jesus, woman," he said pulling her into his arms. "That didn't take long to drag out of you."

"I'm sorry, Marc, but I had to know if you were only here for your son."

"My son?" he asked disbelieving.

"Yes, darling, we have a beautiful son. I will take you to him in just a moment, but we need to talk. There is still so much between us."

Marc looked down at her, his blue eyes penetrating to her very soul. "I'll not let a war interfere in our lives again."

"It's more than that, Marc. I can never go back to Washington. Rachel exposed me to the authorities. If I set foot in the city I'd be thrown into prison, or worse."

"Rachel is dead," he stated matter of factly. "So is Wes."

"Oh, Marc, how?" she asked, quickly forgetting the bitterness between Rachel and herself.

"Apparently Wes caught her cheating on him. It wasn't anything new. She had become a whore, but he would never have admitted it. He truly loved her, Morgan. Somehow he persuaded her to marry him. He came to the house while I was there and wanted me to celebrate with him. We had a few drinks before he left to see her. According to the authorities he walked in on her in bed with one of Lafayette Baker's agents. He beat the fellow to within an inch of his life, but for some reason let him go. He then killed Rachel and took his own life. They found her in his arms the next morning."

"How could he have done it? If he loved her, how could he kill her?" Morgan asked bewildered.

"Love sometimes does strange things to people, Morgan. I can understand how he felt. My love for you is that intense."

Morgan laid her head against Marc's chest. "What a price we have paid for our pride and stubbornness. Three years we have wasted."

"Yes, but we have a lifetime ahead of us, Morgan. The war is close to an end . . ."

Morgan started to protest.

"Don't say anything, Morgan. You and I are both out of it. We will stay here until it is over, then we'll decide what we want to do. Virginia will need people like us to rebuild her; to rebuild her for the next generation and generations to come. Speaking of generations, am I going to see my son?"

"Oh, darling, come, Brenna is with him."

"Wait, Morgan," Marc said pulling her back into his arms. "Are you sure you love me?"

"I've never been more sure of anything in my life."

His hands closed on her shoulders and for the first time since their wedding his lips met hers in a long, leisurely kiss.

"How old is this child of ours?" he asked, in his eyes.

"Old enough, my darling."

"Woman, you are one of a kind," he whispered huskily as he picked her up and headed for the stairs.

"And don't you ever forget it, my dear husband."

Epilogue

Sean Michael Riordan giggled and kicked as his father held him high above his head. Morgan's eyes were filled with love as she watched her husband and son playing on the floor at her feet.

They had been fortunate these past few years. War in the Valley had taken on a savage tone before finally coming to an end. Her homeland, once a fertile, virgin land was now desolate, trampled by the hoofs of cavalry and the feet of men. The Shenandoah Valley had been destroyed, Fredericksburg and Richmond lay in ashes, homes and farms were charred skeletons of a time and era gone forever. The so-called Reconstruction was doing more harm than good and left most people on both sides with a very bitter taste. Morgan thanked God they had been able to harvest two good crops and things looked brighter after a very lean year.

She smiled as she thought of Jubal and the lovely daughter Brenna had borne him. They were living in the carriage house on the west end of the estate until Jubal could build them a permanent home on the property their father had left him. At the present Marc and Jubal were spending every waking hour trying to restock the stables that had once been the best in the county. They had already promised Gambler's first foal to the governor of Pennsylvania when he stopped on a visit through the state.

Michael was living in Washington, taking care of Anne Riordan's house while she stayed at Aspen Grove. Under Marc's influence and guidance he was studying law and hoped to go into politics. Virginia had been a proud land of hope and promise and she needed good, honest men to help her rise out of the ashes.

Morgan gasped and touched her stomach as the child she carried moved inside her. Marc sat Sean on the floor and came to stand before her. He leaned over, kissing her tenderly.

"I love you, Rebel," he whispered against her neck. "This time I will be with you when our child is born."

"And all those to come?" Morgan asked as she wrapped her arms around his neck.

"And all those to come," he answered, his eyes filled with love.

Yes, Morgan thought, she had been very fortunate. Somehow in this time of war and destruction she had found a love that would last her a lifetime.

ZEBRA BESTSELLERS

FOUR SISTERS (1048, $3.75)
by James Fritzhand
From the ghettos of Moscow to the glamor and glitter of the Winter Palace, four elegant beauties are torn between love and sorrow, danger and desire—but will forever be bound together as FOUR SISTERS.

BYGONES (1030, $3.75)
by Frank Wilkinson
Once the extraordinary Gwyneth set eyes on the handsome aristocrat Benjamin Whisten, she was determined to foster the illicit love affair that would shape three generations—and win a remarkable woman an unforgettable dynasty!

A TIME FOR ROSES (946, $3.50)
by Agatha Della Anastasi
A family saga of riveting power and passion! Fiery Magdalena places her marriage vows above all else—until her husband wants her to make an impossible choice. She has always loved and honored—but now she can't obey!

THE VAN ALENS (1000, $3.50)
by Samuel A. Schreiner, Jr.
The lovely, determined Van Alen women were as exciting and passionate as the century in which they lived. And through these years of America's most exciting times, they created a dynasty of love and lust!

THE LION'S WAY (900, $3.75)
by Lewis Orde
An all-consuming saga that spans four generations in the life of troubled and talented David, who struggles to rise above his immigrant heritage and rise to a world of glamour, fame and success!

A WOMAN OF THE DAWN (1066, $3.75)
by Antonia Van-Loon
From the excitement and joy of the turn-of-the-century, to the tragedy and triumph of World War I, beautiful Tracy Sullivan created a mighty empire—and cherished a secret love!

Available wherever paperbacks are sold, or order direct from the Publisher. Send cover price plus 50¢ per copy for mailing and handling to Zebra Books, 475 Park Avenue South, New York, N.Y. 10016. DO NOT SEND CASH.

READ THESE PAGE-TURNING ROMANCES!

LEATHER AND LACE
by Dorothy Dixon

#1: THE LAVENDER BLOSSOM   (1029, $2.50)
Lavender Younger galloped across the Wild West under the black banner of Quantrill. And as the outlaw beauty robbed men of their riches, she robbed them of their hearts!

#2: THE TREMBLING HEART   (1035, $2.50)
Wherever Jesse James rode, Zerelda rode at his side. And from the sleet of winter to the radiance of fall, she nursed his wounds—and risked her life to be loved by the most reckless outlaw of the west!

#3: THE BELLE OF THE RIO GRANDE   (1059, $2.50)
Belle Star blazed her way through the wild frontier with two ambitions: to win the heart of handsome Cole Younger, the only man who could satisfy her fiery passion—and to be known as the west's most luscious outlaw!

#4: FLAME OF THE WEST   (1091, $2.50)
She was the toast of the New York stage, a spy during the Civil War, and the belle of the Barbary Coast. And her passionate untamed spirit made her the unforgettable legend known as the FLAME OF THE WEST!

Available wherever paperbacks are sold, or order direct from the Publisher. Send cover price plus 50¢ per copy for mailing and handling to Zebra Books, 475 Park Avenue South, New York, N.Y. 10016. DO NOT SEND CASH.